Materials Engineering in the Arctic

Proceedings of an International Conference
St. Jovite, Quebec, Canada
September 27 - October 1, 1976

Edited by

M. B. IVES, Conference Chairman

AMERICAN SOCIETY FOR METALS
Metals Park, Ohio 44073

First printing, May 1977

Library of Congress Cataloging in Publication Data
Main entry under title:
Materials engineering in the Arctic.
Sponsored by the Canadian Council of ASM.
Includes index.
1. Materials at low temperatures — Congresses.
2. Civil engineering — Arctic regions — Congresses.
I. Ives, Michael Brian, 1934- II. American Society for Metals. Canadian Council.
TA407.M36 620.1'1'0911 77-4214

PRINTED IN THE UNITED STATES OF AMERICA

FOREWORD

The acceptable and economic utilization of Arctic resources represents one of the major engineering challenges of the next decade. This is a challenge which demands an interplay between research and experience, vision and pragmatism. Clearly, of major importance to the future of engineering in the Arctic is the provision and utilization of materials in the broadest sense. This should include the provision of new structural materials, the utilization of wastes and the provision of adequate and ecologically acceptable systems of transportation and urban development.

This volume records the proceedings of a week-long conference devoted to the development of engineering materials for use in an Arctic environment. The Canadian Council of the American Society for Metals chose a non-urban setting in Quebec, Canada to provide a milieu appropriate to a week of scheduled and unscheduled informal debate, argument and scientific criticism in an attempt to develop a consensus on the state-of-the-art of materials performance in Arctic environments.

This volume comprises 38 scientific and engineering papers covering those subjects which appear to be currently the most in need of detailed attention by materials engineers. The papers are accompanied by a summary of the oral discussions which took place at the conclusion of each paper presented at the Conference. In addition, session chairmen have provided critical introductions and summaries of the sessions in order to provide the reader with an assessment of the significance of each subject covered.

More than 100 research scientists, engineers, designers and those with records of achievement and experience in the Arctic took part in the Conference, representing materials specifiers, producers and users. Some indication of their week-long activities is provided by the montage of photographs at the front of this volume. Eight countries are represented by the contributors to the Conference.

The calibre of the Conference was due completely to those colleagues who contributed to the development of the programme, who critically refereed all the papers submitted, who acted as session chairmen and who generally advised a Conference Chairman largely ignorant of the Conference topic. The Programme Advisory Committee comprised:

J.D. BOYD, CANMET
D. BURNS, University of Waterloo
E.I. CAREFOOT, Associated Engineering Services
J.F. CLAYTON, Gulf Oil Canada
P. CHOLLET, Noranda Research
W.L. DANIELS, Canadian Arctic Gas Study
J.D. EMBURY, McMaster University
R.K. FEILDEN, Associated Engineering Services
G.T. HAHN, Battelle Columbus Laboratories
E.C. HAMRE, Interprovincial Steel and Pipe
J.E. HOOD, Steel Company of Canada
F.E. KING, Canadian National Railways
J.D. MAKARCHUK, Union Carbide Canada
V.P. MILO, Shell Canada
A.B. ROTHWELL, Noranda Research
F.S. SOMERVILLE, Canadian Arctic Gas Study
W.M. WILLIAMS, McGill University

Special thanks are due to David Embury, who contributed in many ways from the conception of the Conference topic to the reading of the final proofs, but who was unable to attend the Conference.

The cooperation of each and every author and their understanding acceptance of the many strokes of the editor's blue pencil is also recognized. The papers have, as far as possible, been prepared in a standard format, and the inclusion of SI unit equivalents recognizes the pressing need for a unified system within the international engineering community.

The personal thanks and appreciation for the time and effort provided by the Organizing Committee and Conference Staff is gratefully acknowledged: to John D. Makarchuk (Union Carbide Canada) who served as Vice-Chairman of the Conference; to Victor G. Behal (Dominion Foundries and Steel) who kept the Treasury and served as hotel liaison during the Conference; to Pierre Chollet (Noranda Research) who coordinated the recording of discussion sessions, generally assisted the editor of the Proceedings Volume and organized an exhibition of topical movies during the Conference week; to Heike Soeder (McMaster University) whose unstinting and faultless service as projectionist was appreciated by all; to David Hodgson (McMaster University) for the graphics and lay-out of this volume, and to Marilyn Foster, for stenographic services at the Conference and for the unenviable job of typing this entire volume, a heartfelt thank you.

The financial support of the following organizations is recognized: Dominion Foundries and Steel Limited; Noranda Mines Limited; The Steel Company of Canada, and McMaster University (Department of Metallurgy and Materials Science, and Institute for Materials Research). The Canadian Council of the American Society for Metals and the ASM Publications Department are also gratefully recognized for their support of the Conference and the publication of this Volume.

M.B. IVES
McMaster University
January, 1977

Excerpt from CONFERENCE BANQUET ADDRESS

A. Hurlich
President, American Society for Metals
1976-77

Back in the 1930's the Belgians built welded steel bridges and several broke apart with resulting casualties. The fractures were brittle and these failures initiated major research programs on the brittle fracture of welded bridges. So we learned our lesson on bridges and finally learned how to select materials and design welded bridges that wouldn't collapse. Then during the 1940's and World War II we built the welded "Liberty" ships, and of approximately 5000 built, 500 had to put into port with major hull fractures and about 50 broke up on the high seas with total loss of cargo and many casualties. In fact, the Soviets accused the United States of deliberate sabotage since some of these ships had been turned over to them.

Because of this epidemic of brittle ship fractures, we instituted the Ship Fracture Research Committee, which, I believe, is still in existence. This problem was solved by improvements in ship steel specifications and in ship design practice.

Later, in the 1950's we started building rocket motor cases. And again, premature and brittle fractures plagued the rocket motor case industry. New research committees were invoked to handle this problem. Then, a few years later we started building high performance supersonic fighter and bomber aircraft; and more brittle fractures occurred. More research committees were organized, and we became more sophisticated in handling brittle fracture problems. Linear fracture mechanics analysis came into its own.

However, through all this, it was the same brittle fracture problem again and again. The unfortunate thing is that there is little technology transfer from industry to industry, from product to product. We have to learn the lesson painfully and expensively each time - in bridges, in ships, in rocket motor cases, in aircraft, etc.

I started working at the Watertown Arsenal shortly before the United States became involved in the shooting phase of World War II. Soon after getting into the war, we started supplying the Soviets with tanks and guns. Shortly thereafter we received reports of excessively brittle behavior of ordnance equipment when it was used in cold weather. As a consequence the Army Ordnance Corps initiated a cold weather test program. A large number of tanks, guns, other tracked vehicles, armor plate, and ammunition was procured. Half were tested at Aberdeen Proving Ground, Maryland during the fall of 1942, at temperatures in the range of 50° to 80°F (10 to 23°C). The other half were sent to Camp Shiloh, Canada, halfway between Winnipeg and Brandon, Manitoba and were tested at temperatures down to -50°F (-46°C) during the period from December 1942 to February 1943. The vehicles and guns were operated on frozen ground and armor-piercing ammunition was fired at both tanks and flat armor plates.

The material tested at Aberdeen generally behaved very satisfactorily, although there were a few cases of brittle cracking of armor under ballistic attack. The story at Shiloh was different and horrible - tank hulls and turrents broke up when hit with armor piercing shells, gun trails fractures when artillery was fired on frozen ground, hand tools fractures when used, etc.

The pieces were all brought back to Watertown Arsenal and we started dissecting the corpses to find out what could be done to correct the situation. As a result, armor and gun material specifications were quickly changed. What had happened was that under war emergency conditions we had reduced the strategic alloy content of armor and gun steel to such a low level that we did not get through-hardening of the steels. While we had changed from oil to water quenching to improve the response to heat treatment, we had also reduced the permissable alloy content too drastically and we had to go to somewhat higher alloy steels. At about this time, the high hardenability achieved by small additions of boron was starting to be recognized and used commercially. We did resort to boron treated alloy steels for armor.

At this same time, the British, while even more strapped for chromium, nickel and molybdenum than the Americans, still oil quenched their armor and guns in the belief that water quenching causes excessive cracking. So we shipped them alloys for their inefficient heat treating practices while we denied these alloy levels to our own industry.

By 1944, we introduced the V-notch Charpy impact test as an inspection test requirement for armor and gun tubes. Prior to this we had used a fracture test for several years. This test involved breaking a notched section of the material under a drop-weight mechanism, and observing the fracture for a ductile, or what we called a crystalline, fracture. As we became smarter, we recognized that the crystalline-appearing fracture was caused by the flat, transgranular cleavage fracture associated with embrittlement.

The imposition of the V-notch Charpy test unleashed a considerable uproar from the steel producing industry. They said the test was non-reproducible, unreliable, and that nobody understood what it meant anyway, and it was going to greatly increase the cost of our ordnance equipment. The notched bar impact test has an interesting history. Monsieur Charpy worked for the French army during World War I, and Mr. Izod for the British. Both became involved in research on the brittle fracture of machine gun barrels and other military equipment and found that a notched or saw-cut bar when gripped in a vise and hit with a hammer seemed to correlate with the brittle fracture characteristics of the equipment. Some bars broke readily with little energy input and had shiny fractures. When this happened, the gun barrels also showed a tendency to break prematurely, often into many fragments. Other bars bent considerably before breaking, had to be hit several times with considerable energy and showed a tearing type of fracture. The gun barrels from which they came were good ones that behaved as they were intended.

Thus came into being the V-notch Charpy and Izod impact tests. Between the wars we seemed to have forgotten their significance.

But to go back to the industry reaction, we rounded up a team of people at Watertown Arsenal to visit the armor and gun producing industry to sell them on the merits of the notched bar impact test. First, we took a heat of good quality armor steel, divided it into four groups and heat treated each to a different hardness level. We then machined a large number of V-notch Charpy impact test specimens, and in the process developed machining techniques, notching tools and gang grinding methods to produce a large number of specimens simultaneously and at low cost. These then became our standard bars - one large group was at the approximately 10 ft lbf impact level, another at 25 ft lbf, the third at about 35-40 ft lbf and the fourth at about 60 ft lbf. Each company was given sets of five replicate specimens with coded numbers, told to test them and send us the results.

Replicate specimens when tested at Watertown Arsenal showed variations generally less than 1 ft lbf from high to low within a group. Some of the steel companies' laboratories showed results scattered all over the map. We then sent our teams to visit these laboratories, and, as we expected, we found impact test machines with worn out bearings, with rusty and virtually frozen bearings, machines tilted at an angle, or sitting on a warped wooden floor, or other improper conditions of maintenance or operation. These laboratories were not necessarily sloppy - their tensile test machines were in proper calibration and their people were sincere and capable. It was just that many people were totally unfamiliar with the effects of the above conditions on test results. Many companies had impact test machines that had been installed a decade or two before that were rarely used and never kept in proper operating condition.

After the testing machines were brought up to snuff the complaints about the non-reproducibility of the Charpy impact test faded away and people became believers. As far as I have been able to learn, all material purchased to the armor and gun specifications that incorporated V-notch Charpy impact test requirements behaved well in service.

However, like all good things, it didn't last. By the time the Vietnamese War came along 10 to 15 years later, many of the army ordnance designers and metallurgists had retired. Their successors designed the long range powerful 175 mm cannon and heat treated them to a yield strength of 180 ksi (1240 MPa). Even tempered martensite is not particularly tough at this strength level, and if you encounter a moderate degree of temper embrittlement or a metallurgical defect that would not be particularly serious at a lower strength level, it could be catastrophic at this high strength level. Some of these guns blew up in action, causing casualties and poor morale among gun crews. Well, the problem was solved by backing off in strength level and applying autofrettage to maintain the high performance level of the gun barrels. Autofrettage involves internal pressurization of the gun tube to produce a slight amount of plastic deformation and leave the bore of the gun under compression.

The moral of my story is, are we ever going to learn something that will remain learned, or must each generation repeat the errors of its fathers?

Your hosts
DOFASCO
noranda · stelco

GREY ROCKS INN, ST. JOVITE - SEPTEMBER 27 to OCTOBER 1, 1976

CONFERENCE PARTICIPANTS

E. P. ANTONIADES
Chevron Research
Richmond, California, USA

G. L. ARCHER
The Welding Institute
Cambridge, England

P. E. BEDFORD-JONES
The Steel Company of Canada
Welland, Ontario, Canada

V. G. BEHAL
Dominion Foundries and Steel
Hamilton, Ontario, Canada

B. E. BOARDMAN
Deere and Company
Moline, Illinois, USA

M. BODERIOU
Vallourec
France

F. G. BOURDILLON
Usinor
Dunkerque, France

J. D. BOYD
Canmet,
Ottawa, Ontario, Canada

P. BOUSSEL
Climax Molybdenum Company
Ann Arbor, Michigan, USA

J. P. BOUVARD
Usinor
Longwy, France

J. BRODER
Canadian Liquid Air
Montreal, Quebec, Canada

J. R. BRODERICK
Imperial Oil
Calgary, Alberta, Canada

W. H. BROKENSHIRE
Inco
Toronto, Ontario, Canada

D. J. BURNS
University of Waterloo
Waterloo, Ontario, Canada

D. S. BURNS
Cameron Iron Works
Houston, Texas, USA

M. CAIRE
Vallourec
France

E. I. CAREFOOT
Assoc. Engineering Services
Edmonton, Alberta, Canada

H. E. CHANDLER
American Society for Metals
Metals Park, Ohio, USA

D. L. CHEEVER
John Deere Dubuque Works
Dubuque, Iowa, USA

P. CHOLLET
Noranda Research Centre
Pointe-Claire, Quebec, Canada

J. F. CLAYTON
Gulf Oil Canada
Sheridan Park, Ontario, Canada

J. CONVEY
Ottawa, Ontario, Canada

R. J. COOKE
National Energy Board
Ottawa, Ontario, Canada

J. N. CORDEA
Armco Steel Corporation
Middletown, Ohio, USA

H. C. COTTON
British Petroleum
London, England

V. F. CROWLEY
The Shawinigan Engineering Co.
Montreal, Quebec, Canada

R. P. CULBERTSON
Brown & Root
Houston, Texas, USA

R. G. DEEKS
Procor
Oakville, Ontario, Canada

O. B. DRAGANIUK
Syncrude Canada
Edmonton, Alberta, Canada

W. M. DROPE
Northern Engineering Services
Calgary, Alberta, Canada

S. W. A. DUNCAN
Gov't. Northwest Territories
Yellowknife, N.W.T., Canada

T. M. EVEN
Canadian Arctic Gas Study
Calgary, Alberta, Canada

D. FLECKENSTEIN
Union Carbide Metals Division
Niagara Falls, N.Y., USA

B. FRUCK
Imperial Oil
Calgary, Alberta, Canada

D. R. GALLIART
Deere & Company
Moline, Illinois, USA

J. L. GERLITZ
Shell Canada
Calgary, Alberta, Canada

P. G. GLOCKNER
University of Calgary
Calgary, Alberta, Canada

A. G. GLOVER
Canadian Welding Development Inst.
Toronto, Ontario, Canada

T. GLYNN
Taylor Forge
Chicago, Illinois, USA

B. A. GRAVILLE
Dominion Bridge
Montreal, Quebec, Canada

G. T. HAHN
Battelle Columbus Laboratories
Columbus, Ohio, USA

E. C. HAMRE
Interprovincial Steel and Pipe
Regina, Saskatchewan, Canada

B. HAWBOLT
University of British Columbia
Vancouver, B.C., Canada

D. R. HAY
Ecole Polytechnique
Montreal, Quebec, Canada

J. E. HOOD
Steel Company of Canada
Hamilton, Ontario, Canada

C. P. HOOGENSEN
R. M. Hardy & Associates
Calgary, Alberta, Canada

A. HURLICH
General Dynamics
San Diego, California, USA

J. F. HUITT
Taylor Forge
Hamilton, Ontario, Canada

A. G. IMGRAM
Gulf Research & Development
Pittsburgh, Pennsylvania, USA

A. ISMAIL
Montreal Engineering
Montreal, Quebec, Canada

M. B. IVES
McMaster University
Hamilton, Ontario, Canada

W. JACKSON
National Energy Board
Ottawa, Ontario, Canada

D. JAMES
Indian Affairs & Northern Devt.
Ottawa, Ontario, Canada

F. S. JEGLIC
Canmet,
Ottawa, Ontario, Canada

G. JOHNSTON
Polar Gas Project
Toronto, Ontario, Canada

J. T. JUSTICE
Trans Canada Pipelines
Toronto, Ontario, Canada

J. G. KAUFMAN
Alcoa Laboratories
Alcoa Centre, Pennsylvania, USA

D. KENNY
Dominion Foundries and Steel
Hamilton, Ontario, Canada

F. E. KING
Canadian National Railways
Montreal, Quebec, Canada

E. KRANZ
Mannesmannrohren-Werke
Mulheim, W. Germany

M. R. KRISHNADEV
Université Laval
Quebec, Canada

T. KUNITAKE
Sumitomo Metal Industries
Amagasaki, Japan

B. LADANYI
Ecole Polytechnique
Montreal, Quebec, Canada

M. LECA
Vallourec
France

P. C. LICHTENBERGER
R. M. Hardy & Associates
Calgary, Alberta, Canada

M. L. LaFRANCE
Usinor
Dunkerque, France

L. LUYCKX
Remacor
W. Pittsburgh, Pennsylvania, USA

J. D. MAKARCHUK
Union Carbide Canada
Don Mills, Ontario, Canada

L. MALIK
Dominion Bridge
Montreal, Quebec, Canada

H. MATSUBARA
Nippon Kokan K.K.
Fukuyama, Japan

R. G. MAUGHAN
Montreal, Quebec, Canada

W. A. MAXEY
Battelle Columbus Laboratories
Columbus, Ohio, USA

J. T. McGRATH
Canadian Welding Development Inst.
Toronto, Ontario, Canada

J. L. MIHELICH
Climax Molybdenum
Ann Arbor, Michigan, USA

Y. NAKAMURA
Nippon Kokan K.K.
Yokohama, Japan

I. C. G. OGLE
Canmet,
Ottawa, Ontario, Canada

D. M. PARK
Canadian Arctic Gas
Calgary, Alberta, Canada

C. A. PARRINI
Italsider MTP
Taranto, Italy

K. R. PERUN
Brown & Root
San Francisco, California, USA

P. A. PETERS
Mannesmannrohren-Werke
Mulheim, W. Germany

V. RENAUD
Cameron Iron Works of Canada
Calgary, Alberta, Canada

A. RIUTTA
Algoma Steel
Sault Ste. Marie, Ontario, Canada

J. ROCKEL
Armco Steel
Middletown, Ohio, USA

M. D. RONEY
Canadian Institute of Guided Ground Transport
Kingston, Ontario, Canada

A. B. ROTHWELL
Noranda Research Centre
Pointe Claire, Quebec, Canada

J. E. RYMES
J. E. Rymes Engineering
Calgary, Alberta, Canada

A. SAGE
Highveld Steel and Vanadium
London, England

C. M. SARGENT
University of Saskatchewan
Saskatoon, Saskatchewan, Canada

H. SCHWARTZBART
Rockwell International
Pittsburgh, Pennsylvania, USA

E. SHELTON
Alberta Gas Trunk Line
Calgary, Alberta, Canada

A. K. SHOEMAKER
U. S. Steel Research
Monroeville, Pennsylvania, USA

W. H. C. SIMMONDS
National Research Council
Ottawa, Ontario, Canada

P. R. SLIMMON
Bethlehem Steel
Bethlehem, Pennsylvania, USA

T. C. SLIMMON
Northern Engineering Services
Calgary, Alberta, Canada

J. H. SMITH
Interprovincial Steel and Pipe
Regina, Saskatchewan, Canada

D. C. SNYDER
Alberta Gas Trunk Line
Calgary, Alberta, Canada

F. S. SOMERVILLE
Canadian Arctic Gas Study
Calgary, Alberta, Canada

K. N. STREET
R. M. Hardy & Associates
Burnaby, B.C., Canada

J. P. TRALMER
Shell Oil
Houston, Texas, USA

W. J. TRENT
Chemetron - Tube Turns
Louisville, Kentucky, USA

G. M. TUTTLE
Gulf Oil Canada
Calgary, Alberta, Canada

G. D. UTTRACHI
Union Carbide Linde Division
Ashtabula, Ohio, USA

O. VOSIKOVSKY
Canmet,
Ottawa, Ontario, Canada

A. H. VROOM
Sulphur Innovations
Calgary, Alberta, Canada

J. M. E. WALLBRIDGE
Foothills Pipe Lines
Calgary, Alberta, Canada

B. D. WARR
Hawker Siddeley Canada
Montreal, Quebec, Canada

A. L. WEISHAR
Canadian Bechtel
Toronto, Ontario, Canada

T. WILLIAMS
Guelph Engineering
Guelph, Ontario, Canada

W. G. WILSON
Molybdenum Corporation
Pittsburgh, Pennsylvania, USA

W. WINSOR
Memorial University
St. John's, Newfoundland, Canada

N. YURIOKA
Nippon Steel
Kanagawa, Japan

CONTENTS

MATERIALS ENGINEERING

IN THE ARCTIC

INTRODUCTION

M.B. Ives

All engineers are involved with some kind of useful structure. For most engineers this means monitoring the particular structure of interest from a design conception until it becomes an object useful for man's needs. The materials engineer, however, seems to consider his useful object to be that appropriate arrangement of grains, phases and imperfections which will provide a material with just the right value of some physically measurable property. The metallurgist, ceramist and polymer chemist seem quite content to let other engineers select their man-made marvels for a useful place in society. Is such aloofness a virtue or a vice? Can the materials engineer be like the shopkeeper who cares little for what happens to a purchase once it gets home?

The introductory session of the Conference was devised to provide some background for materials engineers whose products may ultimately find themselves utilized in an Arctic environment. The papers of this session allow us to tap the minds of a former director of a Canadian government laboratory concerned with energy, mines and resources, an engineer whose passion for reading and public libraries has taught him much about the history of man in the Arctic, a sociologist concerned with man in lonely places, and an engineer who has actually done some engineering in the Arctic. These papers, along with a paper on the Arctic climate which will lead off the transportation session later in the Conference should provide us with a back-drop in front of which the materials engineer must learn to play.

THE RESOURCES OF THE CANADIAN ARCTIC

John Convey
Ottawa, Ontario
Canada

As a country, Canada has for many years treated its North more or less as a frozen asset, a barren land covered with snow and ice during most of the year. However what is in some circles viewed as a useless land, a sleeping giant, has in recent years completely changed, both in appearance and the scope of human activity.

THE CANADIAN NORTH

Northern Canada is a vast territory of approximately 2 x 10^6 miles^2 (5 x 10^6 km^2) extending through every time zone from the Atlantic to the Pacific Oceans. From the Yukon border to the West, mountain ranges extend north from the Rockies to the Bering Sea. Just inside the mountains is the mighty Mackenzie River, one of Canada's most historic and important rivers. The prairie-like watershed of the river is actually an extension of the southern plains. Towards the east comes the Precambrian Shield, Canada's most dominant geological feature. This vast area which forms a large portion of the territories is marked along its western and southern edges by a series of great lakes such as Great Bear Lake and Great Slave Lake. Covered with a multitude of lakes and muskeg areas, the Shield is the location of many mineral resources. From this Shield, an almost saucer-like area slopes down to Hudson Bay and to the north. The true barrens are found here with no trees, but still the ever-present lakes, marshes and muskegs. To the north, extending within five hundred miles of the North Pole, are the Arctic Islands. These too are as varied as they are numerous. Some are flat and are covered with lakes, others have mountains which to the north and east rise to great heights, often covered with ice and providing a fiord-like coastline opposite Greenland. Viewed from the air between Ellesmere Island and the vast edge of Greenland, the eastern edge of Canada looks like a row of sharp teeth with cavities filled with ice (1).

The general impression of Northern Canada as an empty barren land is correct in one sense. For the most part the climate is very cold and the land is inhospitable. The sparse population is, as a rule, found in pockets along the coasts or along the Mackenzie River, the location dictated by shelter and the concentration of game or food. In general, the Indians are found in the west where the trees are. The Eskimos, or Inuits as they are now referred to, live to the north and east above the treeline.

The cold climate has been a factor in the history and development of the Canadian North. It is not just the cold though, for as the winter season takes over, so does the dark season. The long days and the long nights influence human behaviour as much as that of animals and plants. There are times during winter when one feels that all one wants to do is to keep alive. With a strong wind lowering the chill factor to more than -100°F (-75°C) it is too much to expect to get much real work out of the people.

In the area to the north of Churchill there are no hills and no mountains to slow down the cold winds. It is from this area that a great part of Canada inherits much of its winter climate.

RESOURCES

One of the first resources exploited in Northern Canada was fur, in particular the beaver pelt. This resource was sought hundreds of years ago and that search with the consequent development and expansion of the Hudson's Bay Company has served to put a permanent imprint on the history of the Canadian North.

While game and furs may not now be so important as a resource, it must not be written off, particularly since it is a renewable asset. It is of interest to note that while game and fur-bearing animals are becoming scarce around the settlements that are increasing in population, there has been a resurgence of these animals around many abandoned settlements.

Economic pressure from the east and the south has pushed this northern frontier of Canada further and further back. There is no doubt that this pressure or penetration has played a dominant role in the Canadian national purpose. While in earlier times the reason for the expansion may have been items such as furs and surface minerals, in the last five years the emphasis has been placed on energy resources, oil and gas.

Within the space of a decade, Northern Canada has become very much an awakened giant. It is not all due to exploration and the search for mineral resources, but that search has greatly contributed to the fever of activity found in the North. It has helped to agitate the local inhabitants, some of whom can be described as anxious, some even belligerent.

Minerals

With the major part of Canada's northland still to be geologically explored and mapped in detail, one cannot say with any certainty what resources the area holds, or in what quantities. Each year there are new mineral deposits found and oil and gas discoveries are becoming more frequent. However, one can assume that Canada has a very valuable storehouse of riches in the North. Asbestos, gold, silver, copper, lead, zinc and nickel are known to exist in certain areas, with gold being produced from two mines at Yellowknife. Enlargement of these gold producing operations through explorations and the sinking of new shafts by the Con mines is well advanced.

Large deposits of iron ore are found in Labrador and Northern Quebec and along the mountains forming the southern boundary between the Yukon and the Northwest Territories as well as in the Milne Inlet area towards the north end of Baffin Island. At Strathcona Sound efforts are underway to extract copper and lead. A few miles from Arctic Bay, the Strathcona Sound project has enjoyed the attention of government planners who are trying to work out arrangements with the developers which will protect the ecology and yet permit economic mining.

Mineral exploration has been active at Hope Lake near Coppermine, where Samuel Hearne in 1770-71 made his historic search for copper. Near the Nahanni is a heavy mineral development and further north from this area tungsten is being extracted. At Pine Point Cominco has developed and operated a large lead-zinc deposit for many years. This mining operation is on a scale large enough to necessitate the construction of a railway to bring the ore to market.

Associated with the exploration and mining development of minerals in the northern or permafrost areas of Canada, there are many problems to which only partial solutions have been found. Permafrost seems to impose several difficulties and few benefits on mining activities. A recent literature survey of these problem areas has been completed by Caron (2). The Northern Miner published a summary (3) of two feasibility studies relative to a southern and northern mining operation, with the conclusion that a 1.7% copper grade is required in a large Arctic open pit orebody to obtain the same profit as a 0.67% grade in the south.

Table 1

Copper ore production costs for two surface mines

Costs/Profitability	Southern	Arctic
Mining cost/ton	$0.93(dollars)	$3.96(dollars)
Milling Cost	0.72	0.82
Smelting and refining	1.61	1.61
Transport to smelter	0.10	1.14
Capital repayment	1.15	2.83
Total costs/ton	4.51	10.36
Net ore value	5.69	5.69
	1.18	loss(4.67)

A comparison of mining costs for a southern and an Arctic copper mining operation is given in Table 1.

Although the validity of these mining data are open to question by somè experts, they indicate that surface mining costs in the Arctic are considerably more increased than are milling costs. Energy as a northern cost is four times higher than in the south. Capital costs would be 2.5 times higher for the Arctic.

Despite the efforts to compensate for them, winter conditions in northern surface mining lead to shortening of equipment component life and increased maintenance and production costs due to metal failure. This is evident in the occurrence of brittle failure of steel members of loading equipment, such as power shovels and front-end loaders which are subject to severe impact and abrasion, and also the failure of steel and transportation equipment at low temperatures.

Oversize in the explosive fragmentation of cold rock results in increased costs of blasting. Wet drilling in permafrost makes extensive use of calcium chloride solutions which must have a freezing point depressed below that of the rock temperature. This brine solution presents varying degrees of difficulties to recirculation through the works in underground mining. It also has a corrosive effect on underground equipment, with consequent high maintenance costs. Its use adds up to $10/ft ($33/m) of mining development advance.

On the positive side, underground mining in permafrost could employ a mixture of ice and waste/tailings for stope support, and consequently help in alleviating the problem of tailings disposal.

More effective and economical methods of transport, storing and handling of frozen ores and concentrates are needed at northern mining sites.

Gas and Oil

It may be reasonably asserted that no single topic has stimulated more interest, aroused more controversy, involved more research, and presented more political and financial problems than the much-publicized discoveries of large reserves of gas and oil in the Canadian North. In view of the energy situation that exists in the world today, these non-renewable resources are a factor of considerable importance to the Canadian economy and every effort must be made by government and industry to ensure their efficient utilization.

The magnitude of the Northern gas and oil reservoirs remains to be proven, and millions of dollars are being spent annually on exploratory drilling for this purpose. Estimates, however, range as high as 30 billion barrels of oil and over 200 x 10^{12} ft^3 (6 x 10^{12} m^3) of gas from the Northwest Territories alone, much of it in the Mackenzie Delta. These figures do not take into account the potential of the Canadian Arctic Islands, where substantial gas discoveries have already been reported on Melville, King Christian and Ellef Ringnes Islands. The challenge is how these essential energy resources can be most effectively developed and transported to the ever-increasing markets in the South, bearing in mind the remoteness of the reservoirs, the environmental extremes, the nature of the terrain and the relatively fragile Arctic ecology.

In order to meet the challenge of the finding, developing and transport of Northern oil and gas, millions of dollars have been devoted to research and feasibility studies by the gas and oil industry. The Government of Canada, likewise, has been fully aware of its responsibilities and has been actively engaged in acquiring the data necessary to enable the establishment of optimum policies and guidelines relative to oil and gas development in the North. Numerous methods of transportation by sea, by air and by land have been examined, some in theory and some in practice. For transportation by sea there are the super-tankers of which one version, the icebreaking tanker "Manhattan", aroused considerable interest in 1969 by its exploits in the Northwest Passage. An additional possibility is the use of a fleet of nuclear-powered submarine tankers, each carrying nearly two million barrels of oil. For transportation by air there are two possibilities, large resource-carrying aircraft and dirigibles, both of which would require some years to develop. Finally, for transportation by land, there is the long-established pipeline method and various suggestions involving the use of rails: standard railways with tank cars or applications of monorail principles. It must be remembered that natural gas can be transported in the liquefied state. Some of these proposals may capture the imagination, but the overriding criteria must be those of economics and practicability. In the light of the discoveries both in Canada and in Alaska, there seems little doubt that there will be a need for natural gas, and probably oil pipelines from the Arctic coast down the Mackenzie River Valley to southern markets. Subsequently, one or more lines will probably be required to handle the discoveries in the Arctic Islands. Alternative routes are to hook-up with the proposed Mackenzie Valley pipeline, such as the proposed 1600 mile (2600 km) gas line from Prudhoe Bay to Western Canada (4).

Although no specific decisions have been made to date, it is realistic to assume that the first proposal will be a gas pipeline down the Mackenzie Valley. The pipe will be 48 in. (1220 mm) diameter to accommodate a flow of 4×10^9 ft^3 (1×10^8 m^3) of gas per day. For the tentatively designated route, the length of the line would be of the order of 1500 miles (2400 km). This does not include the section from Prudhoe Bay to the Mackenzie Valley. More than a million tons of special steel will be required for the complete installation and the financial investment will be of the order of $814 billion, with a probable start-up in 1981.

For comparison purposes and to assist in appreciating the size of the undertaking, the investment will far exceed the combined cost of the St. Lawrence Seaway, the Aswan Dam and the Churchill Falls, Labrador, hydro-electric project.

The Mackenzie Valley line proposed by Canadian Arctic Gas Study Ltd. needs proven reserves of 25 to 30×10^{12} ft^3 (7 to 8×10^{11} m^3) of gas. This amount could already be developed along the combined Alaskan-Canadian south shore of the Beaufort Sea from Prudhoe Bay to the Mackenzie Delta, but a joint venture here appears doubtful.

Over one-half of the threshold reserves of 20×10^{12} ft^3 (6×10^{11} m^3) for a line from the Arctic Islands to southwestern Canada has been found. An immediate objective is to prove up the remaining threshold volume, but the longer aim is to evaluate the entire oil and gas potential of the Islands and to make these reserves available. This accelerated exploration program is dependent upon an improved political and economic climate. Associated with such an exploration program one must recognize that a 10,000 ft (3,000 m) Arctic well costs between $2.5 and $4.5 million. Exploration costs in the Arctic are about 10 times higher than in the southern producing areas. More than $20 billion will be needed over the next ten years to maintain a desirable degree of activity in the Arctic, (5). However, the drilling program in the Mackenzie Delta has a success ratio of approximately one discovery per 4.5 holes, compared to an industry ratio in Alberta over the last ten years of one in 8 holes.

As regards the actual installation of the pipelines, they may be fully buried in the conventional manner, at ground level protected by an earthen or gravel berm, or supported above the ground. The method of installation adopted will depend to some extent upon the particular resource being transported. In all likelihood, a line which transports refrigerated gas at -10°F (-23°C) to 20°F (-7°C) will be largely in the ground, whereas any line which will transport oil at about 140°F (60°C) will be on or above ground. Whatever the circumstances, the first 1000 mile (1600 km) of pipe, essentially north of the 60th parallel will have to meet what may be termed Arctic specifications. The integrity of the pipelines is of paramount importance from both economic and ecological considerations, the latter being particularly applicable to the oil line. High strength pipe with sound mill welds and good field weldability and, above all, exceptional fracture toughness will be required. Furthermore, the extent and degree of non-destructive testing and inspection are significant factors.

To put the proposed Mackenzie Valley Pipeline in perspective, it should be pointed out that pipeline construction in Canada is running at some 5000 to 6000 mile (8000 to 10,000 km) per year. About 1000 mile (1600 km) of this is "big-inch" pipe, i.e. 18 in. (460 mm) or more in diameter. The major pipeline companies have substantial mileage forecasts of expansion of existing big-inch systems for several years ahead. On this basis, construction of a Mackenzie Valley line over a two-year period will represent an increase of about 75% for a 1500 mile (2400 km) line to link to existing transmission systems in Alberta.

A further factor is that the line will be larger in diameter than any existing North American gas line. Most of the line will also be substantially thicker than any previously constructed line, i.e. 0.72 in. (18 mm). There will be minor portions with a thickness in the range of 1.125 in. (29 mm) to 1.5 in. (38 mm). A 48 in. (1220 mm) pipe with a 0.72 in. (18 mm) wall weighs some 365 lb per lineal foot (540 kg/m). Single pieces of pipe in 40 ft (12 m) lengths will weigh 7.3 ton. It is more likely that the standard pipe length will be about 60 ft (18 m) and such pieces will weigh some 11 ton. An increase in magnitude of this order obviously has implications for every stage from steel production and pipe manufacture, through shipping, field handling, ditching, welding, etc.

In addition to the increase in scale contemplated for the Mackenzie Valley gas line, there is the concomitant requirement for an increase in quality, since the line must meet standards of integrity higher than previously required. This demand for maximum integrity is not primarily because failure may cause loss of life or destruction of valuable property, since the line will be located in remote areas for most of its length and gas is non-polluting, except for the localized destruction attendant on burning at the failure site. Rather, integrity is required because of the economic cost consequent to a failure which may occur in a remote area in difficult terrain during a three-day blizzard or white-out. The economic costs will derive from penalties due to interruption in delivery and the direct cost of repairing the line and/or equipment. As a result, the increased quality requirements must cover all aspects from skelp properties through in-plant pipe testing and inspection, restrictive requirements in shipping and field handling, stringent field welding, inspection and testing.

Probably the toughest construction job in Canadian history will have to be performed under the worst climatic conditions in Canada. Most construction north of the permafrost line will be carried out in winter. This means construction crews will be subjected to cold, wind and darkness to a degree rarely experienced. The pipeline construction industry has successfully met the challenge of construction in northern British Columbia and the southern fringe of the Yukon and the Northwest Territories where the climatic extremes are very nearly as severe as those encountered further north. It is generally true that it is no colder in the Arctic, only colder longer. However, it is not quite that easy for it is also windier and it is darker much longer. Indeed, a significant fraction of the winter construction season is in total darkness in the high Arctic. Countering the effect of darkness, cold and isolation on the work performance of the crews may be the toughest challenge facing the project. The effects of such factors on crew performance has implications for every activity associated with the pipeline. If morale declines, equipment will be used with less care. Equipment subjected to stress will be prone to overloading and thus to a higher incidence of failure if not robustly designed and carefully fabricated. Inspection staff will be hard pressed to maintain that degree of alertness necessary to pursue their job efficiently.

Human Resources

The human resource of northern Canada is mostly Indian and Inuit. Their number is not great relative to the population in southern Canada. However, the fact that these people already in the North look upon it as their home and have always been accustomed to the northern climate makes them a valuable asset. The number of southern Canadians locating in the North is increasing yearly, but it can be assumed that a large proportion of them will not become permanent. The native people are the ones who will form the bedrock of the population in the years ahead.

An assessment of the economic and sociological impact of the Mackenzie Valley pipeline has indicated that the number of long-term jobs anticipated from the pipeline and associated oil and gas development will be far greater in number than it will be possible to meet from the available labour force of the region. The real challenge is one of ensuring that through adequate training and other programs, the indigenous population is given full opportunity to exploit the job potential of northern development. It will take time and understanding to develop the human resources.

ENVIRONMENT

Extraction of resources, whether renewable or non-renewable, cannot properly be considered without assessing possible damage to the environment. Arctic resources exist in an area that is in a delicate state of ecological balance, the disturbance of which could lead to irreversible environmental damage, with consequent detrimental effects for the inhabitants and the wildlife of the North. The next decade will undoubtedly witness a marked upsurge in industrial activity associated with Arctic resources in spite of the difficulties imposed by the lack of easy accessibility and by the severe climatic conditions. It is therefore of manifest importance that such activity should proceed in an orderly and responsible manner with a maximum of safety, a minimum risk of pollution and the optimum utilization of materials. With careful planning based upon good information, man-altered and material ecosystems can exist in harmony. However, resource development must be considered from a total system point of view. As an example, Syncrude Canada Ltd., in the development of the Northern McMurray tarsands resource, has carried out a comprehensive program of surveillance of the effects of their tarsand technology and the careful application of that technology to prevent any accidental damage to the environment. A review has been completed (6) on the characteristics of available engineering metals and alloys with respect to service in Arctic and subarctic environments. Gas pipeline research in the Arctic Environment is under study by Gas Arctic at Prudhoe Bay, Alaska; Norman Wells, Northwest Territories; and Nordegg, Alberta.

Over vast areas of the Canadian North, the land is underlain with permafrost, extending even as far south as Yellowknife. It is where the permafrost occurs in tundra, muskeg or moisture-laden soils that complex environmental problems are found. Large portions of the Arctic are tundra, where the ground surface is covered by a thin mat of lichens, mosses and other vegetation adapted to the Arctic climate. This organic mat serves as insulation, limiting the transmission of solar heat through the permafrost. If this insulating layer is disturbed, as by a bulldozer cutting a road, the equilibrium of the active layer of soil just beneath the tundra is upset by additional melting during the following summer. Evaporation or run-off of the additional water can then occur, permanently altering the composition of the surface layer. Having lost some of the moisture, the soil slumps, creating gullies and new ponds. In succeeding summers, melting progresses deeper, in a process called thermal erosion. Even if the thermal erosion is arrested in a comparatively short time, the existence of even a small trench represents a new condition in which the upper profile of the active layer of soil has been lowered. The conditions which made a certain thickness of soil active before the disturbance reassert themselves, and so the upper surface of the permafrost is pushed downward. This is called permafrost regression.

Permafrost in high moisture-content soils that lose their stability and strength on melting is referred to as detrimental permafrost. Muskeg, a humus soil, contains so much moisture that when the water is not frozen, the whole mixture behaves like a liquid rather than a solid. Disturbance of muskeg areas leads to water loss, slumping and a chain reaction similar to that described above.

To protect permafrost where gas is moved by pipeline the gas will be transported through the northern regions at temperatures between 10°F (-12°C) and 20°F (-7°C). Compressors will be installed at stations at approximately 40 mile (65 km) intervals to keep the gas chilled and flowing through the pipeline. The laying of the pipeline is expected to be engineered during the winter months to further reduce any permafrost damage.

Pipeline transportation of oil at 140°F (60°C) will be above or on the ground dependent upon whether the area is covered by muskeg or rock. The oil pipeline must be of a high quality both from the economic and ecological viewpoints. Unlike natural gas, oil spillage in an Arctic environment could create environmental damage that would be difficult to repair.

It is impossible to move and process minerals without disturbing to some degree the environment itself. Mining operations in Canada affect only 310,000 acre (53,000 hectare) or 0.006 of the total landmass, with permafrost mining accounting for only a fraction of this figure. The proposed Mackenzie gas-line and its related facilities, throughout Alaska, the Yukon and the Northwest Territories will affect less than 50 $mile^2$ (130 km^2) out of an area of some 2×10^6 $mile^2$ (5×10^6 km^2), (7). However, mining produces various forms of wastelands, such as scars from strip and open-pit mining, tailings embankments and other mine waste piles, and there is a very obvious lack of information referring to land reclamation of permafrost mine sites. This lack of experience and of basic information is being alleviated, for the permafrost areas, by the growing research bearing on vegetation, both natural and rehabilitated, of sites disturbed by human activities in general. The findings of such programs will provide a basis for solving rehabilitation, revegetation and the stabilization of mine waste embankments at permafrost mining sites (8,9). The work done in relation to pipelines has yielded a large amount of practical knowledge (10). However, there is an apparent urgent need for more research and field testing to be done in order to minimize empiricism in revegetating and stabilizing mining waste embankments in the permafrost areas.

CONCLUSION

As yet the full extent of Canada's northern resources are unknown, but they are known to be valuable and not too readily accessible. The untold resource wealth must become an essential part of Canada's national purpose. However, its development must be handled in a manner best calculated to help Canada and in particular its northern people with the least possible permanent damage to the environment.

REFERENCES

1. W. G. Morrow, Journal of Natural Resource Management and Interdisciplinary Studies, University of Manitoba, 1976, vol. 1, (1), pp. 2-11.
2. V. Caron, "Summary of a Literature Survey bearing on Mineral Exploration in Permafrost Areas of Canada", 1976, CANMET, Ottawa.
3. H. A. Mackenzie, Northern Miner, May 31, 1973.
4. Oil and Gas J., 1976, April 19, p. 38.
5. J. E. F. DeWiel, Northern Miner, Nov. 1975.
6. "Metals and Alloys for Arctic Use". Report 75-21-R. CANMET, Ottawa, January 1976.
7. W. P. Wilder, Canadian Arctic Gas Study, Ltd.
8. G. Berube, et al., "Mine Waste Containment and Water Quality in a Northern Environment", Dept. of Indian Affairs and Northern Development, Ottawa, 1972.
9. A. R. Walsh, C.I.M. Bulletin, Sept. 1975, pp. 91-96.
10. L. C. Bliss, Report No. 73-74 for Task Force on Northern Oil Development, 1973, Dept. of Indian Affairs and Northern Development, Ottawa, 1973.

DISCUSSION

J. M. Wallbridge (Foothills Pipe Lines): Because this is an overview paper, I feel that it should be pointed out that there are at least three alternatives to the Arctic Gas proposal to bring gas from Alaska and the Mackenzie Delta to southern markets. These are the El Paso, Maple Leaf and Alcan Projects. Each of these involve substantial differences in pipe size, construction techniques and other design features from those presented in this paper.

J. Convey: I appreciate the remarks of Mr. Wallbridge reminding us of the other proposed pipelines for the transport of gas from the Arctic area to the southern market. I have used the proposed Mackenzie Valley pipeline as an example to illustrate the dimension and associated problems inherent in its possible construction. I hope that my remarks will be extended with details from those concerned with the other proposed pipelines, during this conference.

M. B. Ives (McMaster University): What are the long-term prospects for any mineral delivery system? What will they be used for if, or when, the resources for which they were originally developed are exhausted? Are the resources in fact likely to be limited?

J. Convey: Past experience in mineral prospecting combined with the positive results from gas prospects of today, suggests that investment in the future Arctic gas developments are well merited. As I mentioned, mineral evaluation of reserves within the Arctic are in a very early stage of exploration, but results to date are very encouraging with regard to long term future. It is possible that someday oil from this remote area may be transported in gaseous form.

M. B. Ives: Are we talking of a resource that can be tapped for 5 years, 10 years, 20 years?

J. Convey: I would say a minimum of 10 years.

A BRIEF HISTORY OF MATERIALS ENGINEERING IN THE CANADIAN ARCTIC

C. M. Sargent
Department of Mechanical Engineering
University of Saskatchewan
Saskatoon, Saskatchewan
Canada

Man has inhabited the Canadian Arctic for several thousand years. Until comparatively recently, the materials available for food (acquisition and preparation), shelter and clothing, and transportation had to be provided locally. Driftwood, an uncertain source, provided the only wood available, and other construction materials such as antler, walrus tusk, and bones of animals were widely used. Animal skins were used for clothing and tents, with sinew for thread. The properties of snow and ice, abundant in winter, were well understood, and these materials were widely utilised, including, of course, the well known snow-house.

During the early period of contact with European explorers and whalers, the local inhabitants were provided with an uncertain, irregular supply of iron and copper as well as wood, as several expeditions abandoned stores. Later, contact with whaling stations led to trading, first by exchange of labour for goods, later with regular traders, by exchange of furs. The introduction of the rifle produced a profound change in lifestyle, not the least of which was the dependence on trapping which resulted.

INTRODUCTION

This paper should be regarded as a journalistic rather than a scholarly endeavour. It attempts to describe the materials technology of the Eskimo prior to the arrival of the European. The prehistory of the Eskimo is not traced and the remarks on lifestyles and artefacts apply mainly to the Central Eskimo who lived along the Arctic coastline of Canada and the Arctic archipelago to the northwest of Hudson Bay. Their dependence was on sea-mammal hunting and on caribou during the annual migration. The environment is a harsh one, temperature averaging around -30°F (-34°C) in winter and below 50°F (10°C) in summer. As Kemp (1) points out, there are two requirements for survival in such conditions: firstly, "an adequate caloric intake in terms of food", and secondly, "maintenance of a suitable microclimate in terms of shelter and clothing". For both these requirements only a limited number of materials were available and these had to be used with great ingenuity.

THE ARCTIC

Whereas everyone is agreed that "the Arctic" is a region surrounding the North pole, and that it is a cold region, the limitations of that region are not clearly established.

The Arctic Circle (the circle of latitude 66 1/2° N) defines a region within which there is at least one day when the sun never sets, and at least one when the sun never rises. However, this is not a climatological boundary and the present definitions are based on climate or on some manifestation of climate.

Koppes suggested that the Arctic regions are those for which the average temperature of the warmest month is below 50°F (10°C). (In this case the boundary coincides closely with the tree line. This is the definition which will be followed here). Arctic Canada would then be described by the area north of a line from the Mackenzie Valley to York Factory, and northern Quebec.

Other definitions include the southerly limit of continuous permafrost, the tree line, and Nordenskjold's limit of "those regions in which the average temperature of the warmest month plus one-tenth of the mean temperature of the coldest month is 51.4°F". (quoted by ref. 2).

The U. S. Army defined the Arctic Operations Area as that area in which a temperature of -40°F (-40°C) may be expected, an area incidentally which includes Saskatoon!

MATERIALS OF ESKIMO TECHNOLOGY

The materials available to the (pre-European) Eskimo were limited. Driftwood was available to certain areas, and in places close to the tree line, or to isolated pockets of trees, some timber was obtainable. Otherwise, bones of animals provided the only other source of solid construction material, apart from ice and snow. The skins of animals and birds provided the only "fabric" and as such were used for clothing, bedding, tents, etc., as well as "cordage" for lashings and fastenings. Certain minerals were utilized, e.g. soapstone for making seal-oil lamps and cooking vessels. Pyrite was used for fire lighting.

The materials technology was extremely elementary. Very little processing of the materials was attempted. Wood and bone were bent after soaking and heating into required shapes. Skins were scraped and defatted and, if required, the hair was removed by scraping and soaking. However, there was no appreciable amount of tanning. This did, of course, mean that the skins were edible and available to supplement the food supply in times of emergency.

Joining and fastening techniques were important. The Eskimo women perfected the sewing of waterproof seams on sealskin boots. Since the supply of wood was uncertain, joining of pieces into the required form was necessary. This was accomplished by lashing, riveting, and by glueing with a glue made from seal's blood (3). Gordon (4) has pointed out that "in pure strength, the lashings, sewings, and bindings used by primitive peoples are more efficient than metal fastenings" (of wood).

SHELTER

The snow-house is probably the best known of all Eskimo engineering achievements. Wide usage was confined to the Central regions. Stefansson (5) points out that this structure is the only dome to be built without scaffolding. Although for fuel economy the size was kept quite small (10 to 12 ft, or 3 to 4 m), some very large igloos were built (e.g. "The Christmas Igloo", The Beaver, Winter, 1956, describes a giant igloo 18 ft (5.5 m) tall) for ceremonial uses. Snow blocks about 18 x 36 x 6 in. (46 x 910 x 150 mm) are cut from snow of suitable compaction. The first layer is placed in a circle and then trimmed with the snow knife to form a ramp. It is the formation of this ramp which is the key to the stability during construction (6). The snow-house is then built by continuing to add blocks until the dome is complete. Snow is shovelled onto the walls to provide the requisite amount of insulation. Inside is a large sleeping bench at the original snow level and entrance is made below this level to provide a "cold-trap". Ventilation is achieved by punching a hole in the top. A "window" may be provided by inserting a panel of fresh-water ice, either "natural" or "cast" in a sealskin (7).

Koppes (8) is reported by Elsner and Pruitt (9) to have estimated that the metabolic heat produced by four occupants is sufficient to sustain a temperature difference of 50 deg F (28 deg C) in an 11 ft (3.4 m) diameter, 9 in. (230 mm) wall thickness domed snow shelter. Since an oil lamp is capable of burning about 4 oz (120 ml) of seal oil per hour (1), thus providing about 1000 kcal/h (4200 kJ/h), the internal temperature may easily be maintained at around the melting point of ice. For short periods, temperatures may be maintained at higher than the melting point of ice, the resulting water being "blotted" by the snow. Ultimately, however, the snow-house would start to creep under such conditions. Stefansson (5) describes how under such circumstances it is possible to "shave" the walls of the snow-house to reduce the internal temperatures, snow being piled on again when the external temperature falls. Some groups increased the allowable internal temperature by lining the snow-house with skins (7).

The Caribou Eskimo did not have the use of seal oil lamps for heating and, therefore, lived in unheated snow-houses (10), cooking outside even in the depth of winter. Elsner and Pruitt (9) have shown, however, that even an unheated snow-house may be maintained at a higher temperature than the external air, since it is essentially an "insulated air pocket warmed by heat derived from the heat reservoir of the earth". They performed several measurements under various conditions, and we may quote as an example the case of a snow-house containing two occupants overnight, when the outside air temperature was -55°F (-48°C), the inside temperature was measured at 19°F (-7°C).

In 1970, during the voyage of the S. S. Manhattan, Richard L. Handy, a civil engineer, observed the building of an igloo by residents on Pond Inlet on Baffin Island (11). He observed that the snow-house was not a hemisphere, as has frequently been stated, but a catenoid of revolution and that the height to diameter ratio was near the optimum for such a shape. The catenoid shape for a shell structure has the advantage that the stresses are everywhere compressive, and that the bending moments are zero everywhere within the shell. Thus, under creep conditions, the sides should not buckle, whereas for a hemispherical dome the tensile ring stresses around the base causes bulging by creep until the top falls in. Handy points out (11) that, for the snow-house, "the design process constitutes an evolutionary optimization for design of domed masonry structures, matched but hardly surpassed by modern scientific engineering".

In areas where the winter food supply was assured locally, more permanent structures were built, consisting of a semi-underground, sod-insulated structure with a low entrance as a cold trap. Spanning the roof in earlier times were whale rib bones or driftwood, with skins draped over. Brushwood or grass could be piled on as insulation, and then covered by skins. Boas (7) points out that "this kind of hut is very warm, light and comfortable". The light came from a window sewn from seal intestines, which is waterproof and translucent. A modern descendant of such a hut is described by Kemp (1) "a low wood-frame tent some 20 feet long, 15 feet wide and 7 feet high ... covered with canvas, old mailbags and animal skins and were insulated with a 10-inch layer of dry shrubs". This "quagmag" was heated by three stone lamps which burned 250 oz (7.4 l) in a day maintaining an average temperature of about 56°F (13°C) when the highest external temperature was -30°F (-34°C). An approximate calculation suggests a thermal resistance ("R" value) of around 10 ft^2h °F/Btu (1.8 m K/W) for such construction.

In summer, tents were generally used with sealskin covering a pole structure of driftwood or bone.

FOOD AND FUEL

Bows, spears and harpoons were among the various projectiles used in hunting.

The construction of the bow represented a considerable problem. Even if driftwood were available, the properties of the wood would not be ideal for bow-making. Often antler had to be resorted to but this had the disadvantage of being weak in tension. A composite bow was often made using many pieces of antler joined together with a backing of stretched and plaited sinew to carry the tensile load. Pope (12), quoted by Van Buren (13), tested one Eskimo bow and found it to have a "pull" of 80 lbf (360 N) and a range of 180 yd (165 m). It is unlikely that this range is meaningful since the accuracy of the bow depends upon accurate reproducibility of arrow manufacture (14). Van Buren (13) summarizes work on North American Indian hunting practices and points out that shooting ranges were in fact quite small, about 10 to 20 yd (9 to 18 m). [The buffalo were shot from a range of 18 to 24 in. (460 to 610 mm)]. Eskimos used the bow for hunting caribou, seal and musk-ox. The caribou were shot (10) from distances less than 20 yd (18 m), seal from considerably less than this. The spring hunting of seal involved stalking the seal as it slept on the ice edge (Stefansson (5) provides a good description) and a wounded seal could easily slip into the water*. The range therefore had to be sufficiently small that a hunter could dash forward and capture the prey. Musk-ox form a defensive circle to protect the young of the herd -- dogs are used to promote this reaction (7) -- and could be approached to within a few yards before shooting (or stabbing with a spear).

Arrows were made from wood, feathered at the butt. The heads were of bone, copper or iron. The use of iron predates the arrival of Europeans in the region, the sources apparently being meteoritic iron in north-western Greenland, and Norse iron from the Greenland settlements, fully 400 years before Hudson's discovery of his bay (15). Eskimos enthusiastically adopted iron in preference to local materials and utilized abandoned supplies of explorers whenever available. Foxe journeyed to Hudson Bay in 1631 and found iron implements (16). Recently Meyer (17) has suggested that Jens Munk or Thomas Button had unwittingly supplied the material. Stefansson (5) described how the "Investigator" abandoned by McClure in the mid-nineteenth century became a "veritable treasure house" for Eskimos of the region, who removed all the soft wood and the iron except for those too heavy for working by the Eskimos. Interestingly, Stefansson accounts for the extinction of the musk-ox on Banks Island as being due to hunting by the Eskimos who came to exploit the resources of the ship. (Living from abandoned European stores has continued until recent times. Crowe (18) describes how fishermen in Fort Chimo, Quebec, used aviation gasoline abandoned in 1949, to power outboard motors until 1963!)

Harpoons were constructed with a unique detachable head, which was attached to a sealskin thong. By attaching the thong to the centre rather than the end of the head, a "toggle" effect was achieved whereby the head became firmly embedded in the flesh of the prey. Seals, walrus and whales were hunted using various weights of harpoon.

Although much food was eaten raw, cooking was known, often using a soapstone vessel suspended over a soapstone lamp. The use of this blubber-fueled lamp provided heat and light during the winter months. The fat from a 100 lb (45 kg) seal provides about 640 oz (18.6 l) of oil (1). Stefansson (5) observed that his "party of three men and six dogs need about two seals per week", and the provision of a large cache of seal during the early winter is obviously important in governing the conditions of life during the winter.

* Kemp (1) estimates about 60% of the kill is lost, and Stefansson (5) has similar figures.

The Caribou Eskimos never learned the use of the seal-oil lamp and used caribou fat as illumination. Cooking (and melting snow and ice) was done outside over fires of heather and brushwood gathered from beneath the snow (10).

TRANSPORTATION

The reliance on hunting for supplying the material needs of the society resulted in a limitation on the size of a band and the necessity to travel to the best hunting grounds for a particular quarry. The fall hunt for caribou to provide skins for clothing was conducted at favourable sites along the caribou migration route. Winter seal hunting was carried out on the sea ice at breathing-holes. Later, journeys to obtain trade goods were undertaken, which for an isolated group could be extensive. (Mowat (19) describes journeys of two to three hundred miles by the Caribou Eskimo, from the Barren Grounds to Churchill, Manitoba, and Brochet on Reindeer Lake in Northern Manitoba).

Winter travel used the dog-sled. The form of the sled was rather like a long ladder with the runners upturned at the front. The length depended upon the materials available and the nature of terrain. For those privileged to have a source of driftwood, wooden runners were used, but the bones of whales were also used. Boas (7) describes sleds made from ice. An intriguing composite material was made by soaking sealskins (from the summer tent-skins) and then rolling them up, sometimes around frozen fish, and allowing to freeze. This assembly is edible and could be fed to the dogs in spring. Crossbars for the sled were made from wood, bone or antler and were lashed on with rawhide. The shoeing in later years was made of steel, but was formerly of whalebone, if available. In order to reduce friction*, the runners were coated with ice, but a frozen mud substrate was first applied to allow the ice to stick. In order to repair this substrate, clay or pulverized moss of the required properties had to be carried, but in modern times, porridge or custard (10) has been said to be a good substitute. The mud must be planed smooth and then water applied and wiped on with a strip of polar bear skin. For emergency repair on the trail, urine was used for this purpose.

CLOTHING

Caribou skin, taken from caribou killed in the fall, provided the best winter clothing. Seven caribou skins were required for an adult suit of clothes, the dried sinew of the caribou being used for thread. The trousers and jackets were loose and contained no buttons. Standard dress was a suit of "underwear" with the fur side inside and "outerwear" with the fur side outside. This allowed a good combination of mobility plus insulation plus ventilation, essential for Arctic conditions (21). The clothing was extremely lightweight (7 lb/3 kg), and the insulation value has been quoted as equivalent to 7-12 Clo units (22). (A Clo unit is the amount of insulation necessary to maintain a mean skin temperature

* Stefansson (5) points out that at "fifty or sixty below the grains of sand ... act upon the steel shoeing of the sledges somewhat as grains of sand would on a beach". Bowden and Tabor (2) show that, indeed, the friction of skis on cold snow is very similar to that observed on sand.

of 92°F (33°C) with a metabolism of 50 kcal/m^2h (14 W/m^2) in a room heated at 70°F (21°C) in which the humidity is less than 50%. This amount of insulation is roughly equivalent to a business suit and is equal to a thermal resistance of 0.18 m^2 h deg C/kcal, or 0.88 ft^2 h deg F/Btu, (or 5.0 m^2 K/W).

CONCLUSIONS

The picture often presented of primitive man huddled in skins surviving only because of his ability to endure tremendous discomfort is clearly false. Many early explorers, in fact, perished because of their inability to adopt the lifestyle of the indigenous population. Extended expeditions suffered from scurvy until they learned to eat the local food prepared in the local manner (23). Some explorers had quite strange ideas on diet: Back, for instance, carried abundant supplies of "cocoa and macaroni, than which few things are better suited to such undertakings" (24). Hall (25) was one of the first to adopt Eskimo clothing and to travel using dogs and "igloos" for shelter -- albeit accompanied by an Eskimo couple to provide the knowhow. Stefansson (5) waxed enthusiastically about the Eskimo way of life, confounding his critics by entitling his chronicle of the Canadian Arctic Expedition of 1913-1918 "The Friendly Arctic". Since he travelled for five years over the polar seas and through the islands (discovering several in the process), living "off the land" and remained in excellent health, his testimony must be credited.

Early coexistence of "European" and Eskimo inhabitants of the Arctic thus resulted in a trading, not only of goods, but also of lifestyles. The Eskimos' knowledge of the properties of metals led them to eagerly seek needles and knives in particular. It was the introduction of the rifle which resulted in a permanent reliance by the Eskimo on trading. For now, ammunition must be acquired, and gradually a reliance on trapping the fox developed. The fox had never been an important animal in Eskimo hunting. Its skin was occasionally used for decoration, but was often used for "rags". The fox does not possess sufficient fat to maintain an adequate diet. (Caribou and seal provided not only skins but meat, fat, bone, antler, etc.). Also the Eskimo was now at the mercy of the fluctuations both of the fox supply and of the price of skins.

REFERENCES

1. W. B. Kemp, Sci. American, 1971, vol. 224, p. 104.
2. J. E. Sater, A. G. Ronhovde and L. C. Van Allen, "Arctic Environment and Resources", 1971, The Arctic Institute of North America, Washington, D. C.
3. A. Balikci, "The Netsitik Eskimo", 1971, The Natural History Press, Garden City, N.Y.
4. J. E. Gordon, "The New Science of Strong Materials". 1968. Penguin Books Ltd., Harmondworth, England
5. V. Stefansson, "The Friendly Arctic", 1944, MacMillan, New York.
6. "Northern Survival", 1966. Department of Indian Affairs and Northern Development, Ottawa.
7. F. Boas, "The Central Eskimo", 1964, University of Nebraska Press, Lincoln, Nebraska.
8. W. F. Koppes, "Characteristics of snow-houses and their practicality as a form of temporary shelter". A report to the sub-committee on shelter and clothing, 1948, Committee on Sanitary Engineering and Environment, Nat. Res. Council, Washington.
9. R. W. Elsner and W. O. Pruitt, Arctic, 1959, vol. 12, p. 20.
10. K. Birket-Smith, "Eskimos", 1971, Crown Publishers, N. Y.
11. R. L. Handy, Arctic, 1973, vol. 26, p. 276.
12. S. T. Pope, "A Study of Bows and Arrows", University of California Publications, 1923, vol. 13, (9), Berkeley, California.
13. G. E. Van Buren, "Arrowheads and Projectile Points", Arrowhead Publishing Co., 1974, Garden Grove, Californnia.
14. P. E. Klopsteg, Am. J. Phys., 1943, vol. 11, p. 175.
15. A. P. McCartney and D. J. Mack, American Antiquity, 1973, vol. 38, p. 328.
16. "The Voyage of Captain Luke Foxe and Captain Thomas James", Vol. II, The Hakluyt Society, London (1894). (Quoted by reference 17)
17. D. Meyer, "Eskimos of Hudson Bay, 1619-1820", Na'pao, 1976, no. 6, p. 41.
18. K. J. Crowe, "A History of the Original Peoples of Northern Canada", 1974, McGill-Queens University Press, Montreal.
19. F. Mowat, "The Desperate People", 1975, McClelland and Stewart, Toronto.
20. F. P. Bowden and D. Tabor, "The Friction and Lubrication of Solids", 1964, Oxford.
21. L. Fourt and N. R. S. Hollies, "Clothing: Comfort and Function", 1970, Marcel Dekker and Co., New York.
22. S. E. Sater, "The Arctic Basin", 1963, Tidewater Publishing Corp., Centreville, Maryland.
23. V. Stefansson, "Unsolved Mysteries of the Arctic", 1939, MacMillan, New York.
24. G. Back, "Narrative of the Arctic Land Expedition", 1970, M. G. Hurtig, Ltd., Edmonton.
25. C. F. Hall, "Life with the Esquimaux", 1970, Charles E. Tuttle Co., Rutland, Vt.

ARCTIC ENGINEERING THROUGH HUMAN EYES

W. H. C. Simmonds
National Research Council of Canada
Ottawa, Canada

Technology and engineering are likely to be best used to the extent that specifications for projects include the human, social, cultural and environmental aspects with the technical, economic and financial factors.

This paper discusses the effects of the labor shortages and turnover in the north, in the light of the four sources of human stress--isolation, unfamiliarity, lack of stimulation, and loss of normal relationships. It suggests ways of diminishing such stresses, which can best be achieved by looking at projects through the eyes of those concerned and by adapting technology to people.

INTRODUCTION

Under what conditions can technology and engineering be maximized?

Well-engineered projects are technically sound, economic, and safe. Today we increasingly require that new technology and engineering be compatible with the environment, and that the interests of the human beings and groups involved be taken further into account. Under southern conditions, there is no difficulty in doing this, so long as all the requirements are genuinely included in the project and specifications at an early enough date (1); but in Canada's mid-north and far-north, the situation is more difficult. Conditions are adverse; it is difficult for human beings to operate with the same efficiency as in easier climates; personal problems increase; turnover rates are high, leading to high costs. Large projects disrupt small communities; the ratio of southerners to northerners may (usually does) change abruptly, leading to further long-term social problems; and the supply of labour may diminish in the eighties.

There are, therefore, increasing reasons for looking at the relationship of technology and people in the North(2). The purpose of this paper is to present two principles to act as guides in this complex field. These are:

1. Adapt technology <u>to</u> people.
2. Learn to examine projects <u>through the eyes</u> of those involved.

The concern of this conference is materials engineering under Arctic conditions. The above two principles can be used to enable new technology and engineering to be put in place and successfully operated under the adverse conditions of the North and in the face of greater competition for the supply of labour.

THE COMING LABOUR SHORTAGE

Demographers are warning us of possible shortages of labour in the mid-eighties, which is roughly one research time frame away. In round figures the number of entrants to the Canadian labour force is expected to fall from 240,000 persons per year on average at the present time to 150,000 persons per year in the mid-eighties, as shown in Figure 1. Where before we had three entrants we are likely only to have a more highly educated two (3), assuming current levels of immigration to continue (4). In the U.S. the same drop is forecast but only from four entrants to three.

The drop-off in entrants to the labour force in the eighties is relatively sharp, but its effects on competition for labour for mines, smelters, forest operations, etc. on remote sites is likely to be much more dramatic, since unlike Denmark, Canada does not grant any tax concessions for working in the mid- or far-north. It may be wise therefore to look at mine requirements in terms of technologies and people, technologies which require southerners, technologies which northerners can master and maintain, technologies which do not require unnecessary people but which also foster and require competence among those who control them; and further, working conditions which are compatible with northern ways of living or for southerners who can adapt to the north (5).

There is a case here for some sensible and pragmatic foresight, which is likely to prove close to the first principle of adapting technology to people.

ADAPT TECHNOLOGY TO PEOPLE

For three-quarters of a century we have been adapting people to technology. The thrust

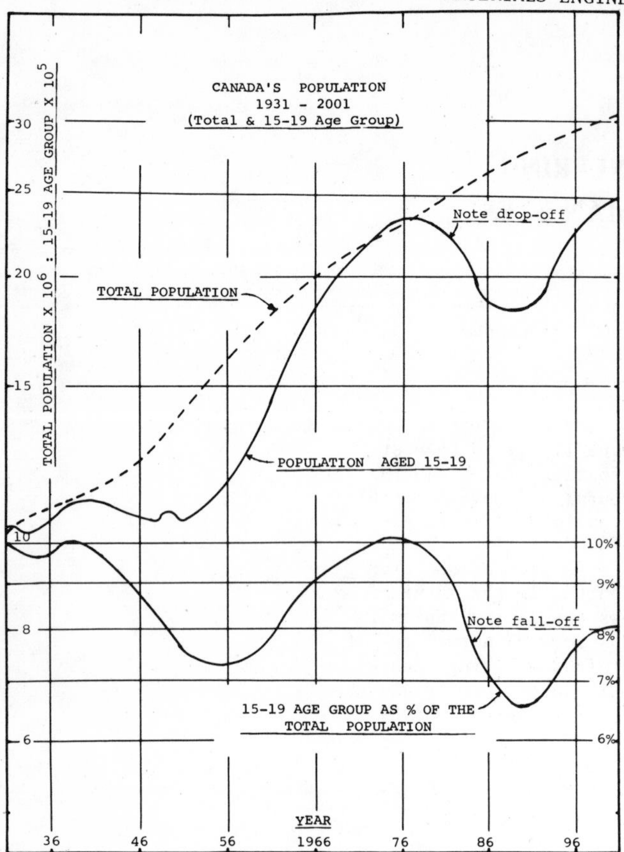

Figure 1: Canada Population Statistics

of Taylorism and automation was simple (6); the more closely men behaved like machines, the greater their efficiency and productivity would become. Charlie Chaplin pilloried this concept in his film, "Modern Times"; automation reached its <u>reductio ad absurdum</u> when workers refused to work in the most completely automated auto plant in the world at Lordstown, Ohio.

What went wrong? Put in a nutshell, it was the increasing absurdity of earning higher and higher real incomes by work which required less and less human contribution, thanks to the technologies of automation and the economics of scale. This has led to the demand for work which needs and requires human intervention and contribution, in which technology aids and assists people instead of dominating them. We are thus reaching the point where the diminishing gains in increasing scale of operations can begin to be offset, or even overtaken, by gains in human productivity. The critical point is the mental switch from thinking that "here is the technical solution and people had better accept/ like it" to the opposite pole of "here are people and how can we enable them and us to win by means of appropriate technologies?"

The emphasis has thus begun to shift from scale and the rigidity of technology to a renewed interest in different kinds of technology and their flexibility.

This is not new. Machine tools were once highly specialized for specific, and sometimes single, duties. Today, the multi-purpose, tape-controlled machine is common, and if there are problems, they lie in a lack of ability to fully exploit the capabilities of such machines. Thus, to increase productivity, improve performance, and lower costs, the human being ranks high as the best bet to bring these about in the seventies and eighties. But do we know how to do this? And the answer at the moment is: "sometimes"!

QOWL, etc.

There are many names for it - job satisfaction, work improvement, quality of working life (QOWL), making work more satisfying, humanness-in-living (HIL), etc. (7,8). In the U.K., as an example, the Work Research Unit was recently set up as a tripartite body composed of the U.K. Dept. of Employment, the Confederation of British Industry, and the Trades Union Congress. This unit has summarized all the cases where attempts have been made to "humanize" work. They found success in some cases but not in others, but what was more curious, that where there was success in one unit or part of a company, it did not necessarily spread elsewhere in the same unit or company (9). We are thus at the point where we know that work can be conducted in quite different ways, that the change from one kind of working to another is tricky, and that we do not yet know the criteria for success.

THROUGH HUMAN EYES

What then can engineers, scientists and technologists do about it, if anything?

Fortunately, there is one simple test which designers can make in regard to the human situations in projects, that is, to examine them through the eyes of those involved. Such an exercise forces management to look at, not just <u>what</u> is being done, but <u>how</u> it is being done.

Consider, for example, arriving at work. If this is done by being collected by the company bus, it may be cheap but the human being arrives at work as an isolate at a time and in a way set by someone else and over which he has no control. If he drives his own car, at least he arrives under his own volition, i.e. as a person in his own right. If he arrives in the town (community-owned) bus or shares a car-pool, he arrives as a member of a group, no longer as an isolate. Thus, there are profound psychological differences even in such a simple example as that of getting to work. These are exacerbated as conditions become more adverse. And the psychological frame of mind with which a person starts a day colors his/her productivity, safety, quality of work, responsiveness, responsibility, etc., and in due course helps to build up the determination to get out and never return, or to stay and make a go of it.

The key to the individual's reaction in this case is his perception of the situation and how it relates to himself, or to his "sense-of-being" (10). When a proposal or change is put to a person, his/her reaction to it can be judged, not so much by what is said, as by the body-language response. If the proposal enhances someone's sense-of-being by making them feel more of a person, by reinforcing their humanness, by recognizing them and their contribution, it shows; conversely, a proposal which does the opposite may be accepted in words but the body-language reveals the impact of being treated as disposable, unimportant, convenient, etc.; the diminishment of one's sense-of-being. To discover what these reactions are likely to be, it is only necessary to step into the shoes of the person or group concerned, look at the proposal through their eyes and record whether one's sense-of-being is affected positively or negatively. In many cases it may then only require a change in how the project is carried out to convert a negative reaction to a neutral or positive one. No one can win every battle, but designers can seek a net overall gain and, in particular, to identify the crucial points in their projects from the human point of view. Hindsight suggests that this has not always been done in the past.

But we have ignored the north in this part of the argument. What additional effect does that have?

THE STRESS OF THE NORTH

The three stresses which a southerner experiences in the North have been identified (11) as:

(i) the felt isolation;
(ii) the unfamiliarity, and
(iii) the lack of stimulation.

Each of these is highly negative for most southerners, i.e. they reduce or lower their sense-of-being. These effects have been studied most thoroughly by the National Aeronautics and Space Administration (NASA) in the U.S. (12), since the dangers of psychological breakdown due to prolonged stress in the confined quarters of a spacecraft on deep space missions are known to be very real. The main findings can be very briefly summarized as follows:

(a) psychological factors are, in general, more important than physiological factors;
(b) emotional stability, social compatibility with, and leadership within the group are essential;
(c) work is preferable to "spare time"; it should be sufficiently challenging to reduce monotony and boredom, but must not exceed the maximum level of capability under the actual Arctic (or spacecraft) conditions when allowance is made for possible deterioration in performance or for emergencies;
(d) a person's normal roles of husband/wife, father/mother, parent, counsellor, amuser, confidant, participant in community, sports, hobbies or other affairs, etc., should be maintained to the extent possible;
(e) for some people, knowledge of the aims and objectives of the project and its progress is valuable.

The above findings suggest that we should add a fourth item to the list of negative factors to working in the far north, namely:

(iv) loss, or diminution, of normal relationships. With the increase and improvement in telecommunications in the North, the ability to maintain contact with relatives, friends, families and girl or boy friends should be improved.

A DIFFERENT APPROACH

The remarks made earlier suggest a new approach to the question of increasing the stability of workforces in the North, by designing from the inside outwards, i.e.: looking at the problem from the point of view of those involved, or looking through their eyes.

When this is done, a number of new possibilities begin to emerge, or, in different language, the priorities change.

a) Sell Experience, not work

In 1958 the Prime Minister of Canada revealed that among Canadians there was a great latent interest in the North, but few could get there, or afford to do so. It is thus possible to sell x months in the mid- or far-North as an essential lifetime experience for all Canadians. Come and see it, find out what your own country is really like, work part of the time to earn money and pass some of the time, but look around, do what you would like to do and make the most of your stay in the North. The author has called this "charter-work"(13).

Not all youngsters wish to sign contracts for several years in the North; if companies aim for a longer employment period than workers really want, the contract basis is false and turnover costs and labour shortages will surely rise. In its 1974 Annual Report, the Mining Association of Canada speculated that, in 1974, total labor turnover and shortages could cost the industry $350 million; this includes $50 million for the hiring and training of new employees plus an 8% reduction in the output of the industry attributed to labor shortages. A more realistic balance between the interests of both parties offers the chance of an increase in the time spent in the North per person and lower turnover rates. If accommodation to the interests of workers will become inevitable, why wait until then?

b) Arrive in groups!

In their report to the National Design Council's study on Design Excellence, the University of Calgary study team emphasized the value of people arriving in the North as groups, rather than as isolates (14,15).

If you can, recruit friends, or groups from the same neighbourhood or similar backgrounds; if possible, let them meet in a party before taking off in the Boeing 737 so that they arrive on a first-name basis; see that they are welcomed by "similars" and, obviously, that appropriate accommodation is available.

c) Girls can work too!

The most effective way to keep a young man in the North is still a girl, but the under 30 sex ratio is very unsatisfactory in most mining communities (16). Companies have been discovering that girls can handle heavy equipment; more women are now willing to work in a wider range of industries; and servomechanisms are making this more possible.

d) Reinforce identities

The excision of normal social roles hurts. Suddenly one is no longer a husband or father; men and women become concerned about their girl or boy friends elsewhere. The effects of cutting normal social ties appear to be underestimated. The NASA work (12), for example, does not emphasize the importance of maintaining these social roles in deep space flights. There appear to be opportunities here (17).

e) Freight-equalize culture

This is a more controversial area. There are obvious reasons for "freight-equalizing" the FM radio culture in the same way as electric power and the telephone. Cable networks seems to be essential for the coming electronic age of the eighties. The present penalties in living outside the range of FM radio stations in cities encourages more urbanization, which many people believe to be unnecessary and highly expensive. On this basis cable FM transmission should follow telephone or satellite communications into the North at incremental cost, to help to reduce the feeling of isolation and separation from the known.

This view is opposed by those who wish to enjoy the North as it is, without juke boxes, garbage, and noisy internal combustion engines.

But, there appears to be room for both points of view in any but the very smallest settlement (14).

f) Knit the community together

The design of northern communities on conventional North American lines makes little sense. At least some parts of a community should be designed to bring people in close proximity by means of townhouses or apartments. Safdie has outlined how this could be done in his proposal for Frobisher Bay (18). The subject of community design and its effects is not followed up here, but continues to receive attention.

It will be clear from the above that work schedules represent the balance between the opposing driving forces of the desire for money versus the four negative stresses - isolation, unfamiliarity, lack of stimulation and cut-off from normal social roles.

By reducing these stresses, work schedules could be lengthened or the average length of stay in the North increased. However, an upper limit is set by the monotony of the surroundings and repetitiveness of most work, especially during the period of winter darkness (19). The Russians, for example, pay up to 2 1/2 times Moscow rates and transport workers from a city as large as Norilsk (70°N) to Yalta for a break during the period of total darkness. For regular work in the Canadian Arctic, work schedules may vary from 18 days on, 10 off, for drilling, to 21 on, 7 off, during the winter to 14 on, 14 off, during the summer. Work schedules on a one-shot basis are tougher, e.g. 6 months every four years for the Canadian Armed Forces at Alert; 12 weeks on, 1 week off, for the Alaska pipeline currently being constructed.

At the present time, schedules have been arrived at from experience. The way may now be open to a more careful enumeration of the different factors which affect them, with more satisfactory results for all.

CONCLUSION

This paper has emphasized the integral part which human beings and the conditions under which they work, play in the development of materials engineering in the Arctic.

It is encouraging to report that such an attitude is being built into new mining ventures in the North, such as the Strathcona Sound project on Baffin Island (20). This represents a serious attempt to integrate technical, industrial, economic, and social objectives within a thought-out set of northern policies (21,22). 60 per cent of the workforce, for example, will be Inuit, but in a manner which takes into account their traditional lifestyle and the expected life of the mine. Agreement has been obtained from customers of the mine, financiers, the producing company and government, with government holding an 18% equity interest in the company in return for the infrastructure provided. The future will show how well the results will match the intentions; the important point at this stage is that this wider approach and planning has begun.

The complexity of Northern projects and of policies for the North is not to be underestimated (23); but it still appears to be a sound bet that policies and specifications which include the human, the social, the cultural, and the environmental, may well prove to be the lowest cost solutions in the long run; and one reason will be that meeting specifications which include the human, the social, the cultural, the technical, the economic, and the environmental will require the most advanced technology and engineering.

REFERENCES

1. W. H. C. Simmonds, Chem. in Can., 1974, vol. 26 (11) pp. 21-24.
2. J. A. MacMillan, J. R. Tulloch, D. O'Brien and M. A. Ahmad, "Determinants of Labor Turnover in Canadian Mining Communities', Report #19, Series 2, Center for Settlement Studies, Univ. of Manitoba 1974; J. M. Cram, Cdn. J. Behavioural Science, 1972, vol. 4 (2) pp. 135-145; "Manpower Requirements of the Canadian Mineral Industry", C.I.M.M., 1967.
3. F. W. Doyle, Dept. Industry, Trade & Commerce, Ottawa, private communication; L. O. Stone, "Canadian population trends and public policy through the '80s", Inst. for Res. on Public Policy, McGill-Queen's University Press, 1976.
4. F. W. Kelly: "Population growth and urban problems", Science Council of Canada, Perceptions 1975, pp. 20-23.
5. R. M. Gray: CIM Bulletin, 1975, vol. 68 (759) pp. 57-64.
6. F. W. Taylor: "Principles of Scientific Management", Harper, 1911.
7. N. A. B. Wilson: "On the Quality of Working Life", H.M.S.O., London, 1973; Labour Canada, "Measuring the Quality of Working Life", Information Canada 1973.
8. W. H. C. Simmonds, The Business Quarterly, 1973, vol. 38 (2) pp. 32-37.
9. S. Cameron et al: "Improving Satisfaction at Work by Job Redesign", Work Research Unit, Report #1, May 1974.
10. W. H. C. Simmonds: Tech. Fore. & Social Change, 1974, vol. 6, pp. 267-276.
11. L. Zrudlo: in Proceedings of Conference on Building in Northern Communities, Arctic Institute of North America, 1974, pp. 118-126.
12. S. P. Vinograd: "Studies of Social Group Dynamics Under Isolated Conditions", NASA Contractor Report CR-2496, 1974.
13. W. H. C. Simmonds: "Design Criteria for the City of Athabaska", National Design Council Project, N.R.C. Ottawa, 1974.
14. "Human Aspirations and Design Excellence", School of Social Welfare, University of Calgary, 1975.
15. "Design Excellence - A National Objective", National Design Council, Ottawa, 1975.
16. J. Lajzerowicz et al., "Mining Communities in Canada", Dept. of Energy, Mines & Resources, 1974.
17. J. H. Kunkel: "Behaviour, Social Problems and Change", Prentice-Hall, 1975.
18. M. Safdie: "The Replacement Staff Housing for Frobisher Bay", National Design Council, Ottawa, 1974.
19. J. F. Schindler: Pipeline & Gas J.1974 (7), pp. 42-58.
20. A. B. Yates: CIM Bulletin, 1975, vol. 68 pp. 71-78.
21. "Canada's North 1970/1980", Dept. of Indian & Northern Affairs, Ottawa, 1972.
22. A. R. Walsh: CIM Bulletin 1975, vol. 68, pp. 91-96.
23. R. F. Keith et al., Science Council of Canada Background Study No. 34, Ottawa, 1976.

DISCUSSION

E. I. Carefoot (Associated Engineering Services): This paper is of direct interest to me, as I am faced continually with the problem of fielding and maintaining a group, although the number may be relatively small, of technically oriented employees well beyond the Arctic Circle. On reading the abstract, I thought I would be presented with some new and interesting adaptations of technology to the northern working force. As I read it, the paper concerns itself with psychological ways and means to, in effect, "keep the worker happy in the North". From an engineer's point of view, there seems to be little information contained on how engineering and new technology can best be used to enhance working conditions.

W. H. C. Simmonds: This is a very large request. A start has been made in improving the quality of working life in manufacturing industry. The situation in the resource industries is wide open, and information needs to be generated in these industries as well.

E. I. Carefoot: An excellent thought brought out for technology by the author is the communication media. I suggest that with modern technology of satellite communication, direct voice communication could be made available to the northern worker at a nominal cost, or perhaps free. This would certainly go a long way to dispel the feeling of isolation and keep the worker in touch with family and friends.

W. H. C. Simmonds: Agreed, surely this was one of the reasons for launching a Canadian satellite.

E. I. Carefoot: Before we really solve the northern labor force problems we have to eliminate the disparity of wages and benefits of southern import and northern resident. The import generally has a big brother who picks up the tab for transportation, periodic rotation flights to southern homes, subsidizes him with northern allowances and provides him with free or very low-cost room and board. The resident worker gets none of these benefits. If in fact the resident worker received anywhere near comparable compensation, we would attract many more people on a permanent basis at a lower cost. As it now exists, it is a disadvantage to be a northern resident worker, and a "fast buck" situation for the southern imported worker. The author suggests that Canada does not grant a tax concession for working in the far north. There is an indirect subsidy to a group of workers who are provided with subsidized housing and holiday benefits, which the income tax people ignore. The subsidy is unfortunately limited to a select group, not to the prevale miner, technician, tradesman, etc. This is the group that needs the assistance.

W. H. C. Simmonds: Agreed. It would appear to be in the interests of the Mining Association of Canada to set out the comparative tax, "hidden" subsidies, and impact of equality legislation of northern and southern mining situations, especially in the light of the reduction in the number of entrants to the labour force in the 1980's.

D. G. Snyder (Alberta Gas Trunk Line): Did you research the Alyeska project in developing your theories or did they come about as a result of that project?

W. H. C. Simmonds: The thesis was originally developed in relation to Alcan's turnover problems and through the National Design Council's design exercise for a new community in the tarsands area of Alberta. The Alyeska and other projects were checked to the extent that information about them could be obtained. There is also a parallel with studies of human experiences of remoteness in space programs.

J. F. Clayton (Gulf Oil Canada): I would like to add to the comments on the subject of orientation. I feel groups should undergo a form of orientation before going into the Arctic which should stress the positive aspects of Arctic life and what recreational activities there are available, e.g. cross country skiing, fishing, etc.

B. Fruck (Imperial Oil): I have noted that our society tends to classify people by socio-economic factors such as for example, "trades people". I was pleased to see Mr. Simmonds avoid oversimplifying the human subsystem of Arctic projects. Two basic needs have been defined for human beings -- stimulus hunger and structure hunger. Although stimulus hunger was identified in the talk, both of these needs exist in various degrees in all people. I also accept Korda's classification, although broad and general, of people into two other groups, those who are time-oriented and those who are goal-oriented. My own experience suggests that stimulus hunger is the stronger in goal-oriented people and structure hunger is the stronger of the two in time-oriented people. My limited observations of camps in remotely located areas also suggests that the majority of workers tend to be more time-oriented than goal-oriented. My fear in soliciting employees by advertising for "experience" instead of "workers" is that we attract the type of person with a stronger degree of stimulus-hunger. Although human beings are adaptable even in extremely trying situations, they do so with neurotic side-effects. I believe that people with a greater degree of structure hunger fare best in a closed environment. Attracting the right type of person is of course imperative to the success of any venture.

V. G. Behal (Dominion Foundries and Steel): In every discussion concerning the development of Canadian Arctic resources, after the need for billions of dollars for investment and the vast tonnages of materials, the subject turns to the huge numbers of skilled personnel required in the realization of any of the projects. There seems little doubt that the funds and material can be found, but unless immediate steps are taken to provide the technical training, the personnel required will not be available when needed, as even at present there is a great and steady demand in Canadian industry for people possessing these very skills, without any additional vast requirements.

For many years, many young people desiring an excellent education at the government's expense were able to attain their goal by studying at institutions such as the Royal Military College in Kingston, where the condition of such an arrangement was that upon completion of their studies they would serve a certain term in the Armed Forces to pay for their education.

More recently, the Canadian government has financially supported many refugees allowed to enter Canada as landed immigrants, to enable them to participate in government-sponsored courses in language and trades, while being supported by the government. To the best of my knowledge, this policy has paid off handsomely as most of these newcomers are now not only self-supporting, but well earning, tax paying citizens, contributing to the economy rather than being a burden upon it.

My proposal is to combine these schemes through the efforts of the Departments of Labour, Industry and Commerce, Health and Welfare and others and provide technical training to the many unemployed young Canadians now on welfare, or any young Canadian wishing to be trained at government's expense, while receiving a living allowance, in skills such as welding, nondestructive testing, etc., providing they agree to serve in the Arctic for a period to be determined, to repay the investment made in them. Upon completion of this tour of duty, many would no doubt remain in the north, while those returning south would have little trouble finding well-paying jobs, compared to their chances at their present state of education. Technical groups, such as the Canadian Welding Development Institute and the Canadian Society for NDT Foundation, are ready to provide the necessary education and certification to meet requirements. Thus, at a relatively small cost of investment, we could turn a liability into a most valuable asset, by utilizing the potential of the presently unused and sorely needed natural resources, viz., manpower.

SPECIAL PROBLEMS OF CONSTRUCTION IN THE ARCTIC

A. L. Weishar
Canadian Bechtel Ltd.
Toronto, Ontario
Canada

The Arctic environment imposes problems and restraints upon the construction of an enterprise which result in relatively high costs. A number of these factors, and some of the techniques which must be employed to reduce costs and maintain a competitive position are discussed.

The engineer, constructor and materials scientist are challenged to develop the techniques and materials which will assure the success of such an enterprise.

INTRODUCTION

Many of the problems of constructing a project in the Arctic are similar in nature to those encountered in other areas remote from the industrialized parts of the world. Such problems, to name but a few, include: Engineering design to satisfy local conditions; logistics of supply to the job site; availability of construction skills; housing and sustenance of the work force; communications amongst the various project control centres. However, the unique nature of the Arctic severely compounds these problems and introduces additional ones which must be overcome if a project is to be brought to a successful conclusion.

If we disregard projects sponsored by government agencies to provide services to the sparse population, and those undertaken for military purposes, most projects are undertaken to satisfy the needs of the growing world population for energy and mineral resources, either in terms of meeting increased consumption requirements or replacing those depleting materials sources located closer to civilization. Most of these resources are known to be available elsewhere in the world, so that the decision to proceed with the development of a project in the hostile environment of the Arctic will be based on the comparative economics of constructing and operating an enterprise there, versus constructing and operating that enterprise in more friendly environments. In other words, Arctic projects compete for their existence with the rest of the world on the basis of cost -- the one problem which outweighs all others. The task of the materials scientist, the design engineer and the constructor is to so design the facilities and carry out a total construction programme that the objectives of the enterprise will be achieved economically while overcoming the unique problems and complications posed by the Arctic environment.

Some of the main characteristics of the Arctic which present special problems to constructing a project are: the area is sparsely populated; it is severely cold, and the Arctic darkness envelopes the area for weeks, even months; there is permafrost and ice; the Arctic ecology is extremely delicate; there are few towns with a developed infrastructure such as town utilities, schools, warehousing facilities, etc.; there are only very limited conventional road and rail transportation facilities; indigenous materials of construction are scarce, non-existent in some areas; fresh water is scarce in some areas.

Conditions vary throughout the Arctic regions, so that a problem which exists at one location, may be non-existent or minimal at another. Furthermore, the nature of the particular project will determine whether the most severe problems are people-oriented, requiring solutions based on human engineering, or technically-oriented, requiring solutions based on materials development, design development or construction technique. Because of the variety of projects and conditions which may be encountered, construction problems in the Arctic will be dealt with in this paper more in the context of executing a total design/construct effort than in the examination of specific problems in detail.

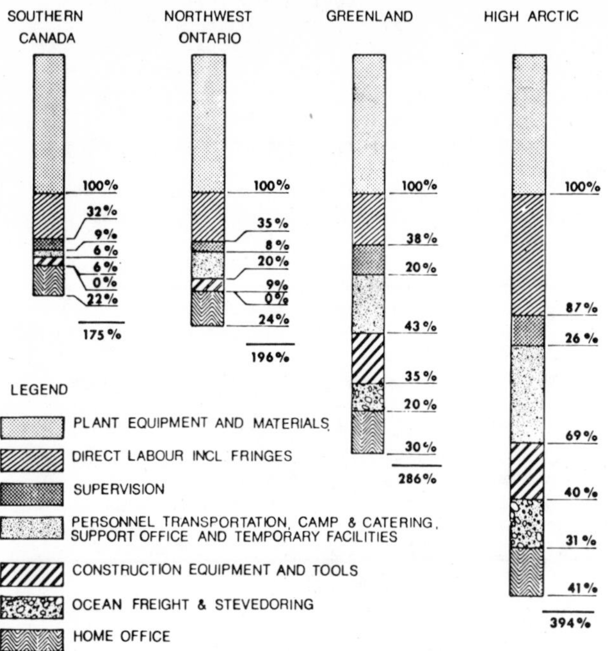

Figure 1: Comparison of cost components of projects

COST

An indication of the magnitude of the one problem which outweighs all others is shown on Figure 1, which illustrates the impact of the Arctic on the capital cost of comparable metallurgical projects, using the purchased cost of equipment, structures and bulk materials as the base, equal to 100%. Major cost effects appear in direct labour cost, as well as in the indirect costs such as personnel transportation, camp and catering, temporary facilities, support offices, construction equipment and tools, and ocean freight. (It should be noted that the effect on the direct labour element in Greenland is not as severe as in the Canadian High Arctic, largely because of the favourable personal tax treatment given Danish workers who complete a specified contract period in Greenland.)

Some explanation of this buildup of costs is indicated in the discussion which follows.

AVAILABILITY OF SKILLS

The Arctic areas are so sparsely populated that, even when every effort is made to employ the local population on a construction project, it is necessary to import the vast majority of supervisory personnel, skilled craftsmen, and labourers from the south. Today skilled construction craftsmen are highly paid and usually in short supply in the more southerly regions. How to attract them to the north is a major problem. The usual way is to offer high wages, by guaranteeing extended work weeks, plus the opportunity for substantial amounts of additional overtime at premium rates, along with free room and board, and paid travel between home and jobsite at frequent intervals, eg. 8 weeks at jobsite, 2 weeks home. Campsites must be provided for these people with comfortable living quarters, cooking, dining, laundry, first aid and recreational facilities, water supply and waste disposal systems. Operating a camp requires additional personnel, who must also be housed and fed, as well as storage facilities for the multitude of items needed by the people during their stay in camp. As an example, in spite of the Greenex project being located at the base of the Greenland ice cap, it was still necessary to provide a large freezer and controlled temperature storage facility for perishable food supplies.

The nett effect is that direct wage cost of a man working in the Arctic is high, and there are also the costs of personnel transportation, travel and sick time, housing and catering, the essential support in the way of temporary facilities, freight, and the tools and equipment required to maintain worker productivity. As shown in Figure 1, these additional costs far exceed the direct cost of wages.

Table 1 gives a recent cost comparison which illustrates the buildup of costs per direct productive man-hour in a developed location (e.g. Toronto/Montreal), versus a northern project. Clearly the labour cost differential must be reduced if northern projects are to be competitive. This can be done by reducing the numbers of directly productive tradesmen required at the job site and reducing, where possible, the level of skills required. A reduction of numbers of direct tradesmen will have a multiplier effect through reducing the support costs. Lowering the level of skills required will reduce the direct wage rates and the competitive pressures for the higher skills, at the same time presenting greater scope for the constructor to train and employ the local population. It is the higher skills such as specialty welders and electricians which are traditionally in short supply, whereas construction carpenters and masonry workers are not.

COLD, DARKNESS, ISOLATION

The extended period of cold, Arctic darkness and storms through the winter months, makes it impossible to carry on many construction operations and slows down others. Erection of structures is hazardous. Operating a concrete batching plant is difficult with frozen aggregates, water freezing problems etc., while concrete pouring operations must be completely sheltered and heated. Servicing the project by fixed wing aircraft or helicopter may be impossible for substantial periods of time due to weather or darkness. Even so, a limited amount of work can continue outdoors in good weather under artificial light, and certainly work can continue efficiently inside buildings

Table 1: : Comparison of direct manual labour costs

ITEM	DOLLARS PER DIRECT MANUAL MANHOUR	
	REMOTE LOCATION	DEVELOPED LOCATION
BASE WAGE	8.00	8.00
O'TIME PREMIUM	3.07	0.20
FRINGES & PAYROLL ADDITIVES	2.38	1.95
DIRECT LABOUR TRANSPORTATION	1.34	0.30
DIRECT LABOUR TRAVEL & SICK TIME	0.41	0
DIRECT LABOUR CAMP & CATERING	3.23	0
SUPERVISION	4.28	1.30
TEMPORARY CONSTRUCTION FACILITIES	4.45	1.27
TOOLS, FUELS, CONSTR. EQUIPMENT	11.45	4.97
TOTAL	38.61	17.99

in a lighted and heated environment.

Another problem created by the lengthy period of darkness is the lowering of work force morale. This is compounded by the sense of isolation from the outside world, and the fear of disaster in the event of failure of the life-supporting heating, water and power systems. These problems are met by providing work schedules which keep people busy, (it is better to work than to do nothing), by providing indoor recreation facilities for use during the off hours, by maintaining radio/ telephone communication with the outside world, showing movies once or twice a week, by ensuring that there is adequate back-up emergency life support systems and that employees know that these back-ups exist, and by providing stand-by helicopter or aircraft at the camp site to evacuate seriously ill or injured personnel.

These problems and restraints to normal construction practice dictate that if project costs are to be minimized, the constructor must develop and employ a sequence of activities which will be radically different from that which would be employed in a Southern climate, and which will tend to compress the period of peak activity into those relatively few months of extended daylight and "warm" weather. This sequence has the disadvantage of necessitating a higher peak work force and aggravating the labour supply and accommodation problems.

PERMAFROST

We now have sufficient practical experience in dealing with permafrost that insofar as design and construction is concerned, most technical problems have been solved, and it is usually only a matter of selecting the appropriate technique. In itself, permafrost is a rather lengthy topic, but it is worth mentioning here that when dealing with permafrost in soil, one should take all necessary measures to prevent the permafrost beneath the active layer from melting. If by good fortune the project site location permits, structures should be laid out so that all structures and major equipment are founded on rock. In Greenland, every effort is currently being made to construct even individual dwelling houses on rock, to avoid future maintenance problems. When dealing with permafrost in rock, one problem is preventing the concrete from freezing before it has set and gained strength. In an industrial plant founded on rock, insulation may have to be laid beneath the ground floor to prevent freezing of water on the floor as well as to reduce heat loss to the ground. The cost impact of permafrost may or may not be significant, depending on the particular project circumstances.

Ice in the Arctic is at one time a blessing, at another time a curse. Travel is greatly facilitated across the ice when the nearby terrain is rough. In building the Alaska pipeline, rivers were crossed during the freeze-up by ice bridges until such time as permanent bridges were built. On the other hand it is the ice which prevents sea access to most of the regions. Enormous ice pressures and movement of icebergs make the design of dock facilities tricky and costly. Innovative ideas are needed to solve these problems. For example, in Greenland we were able to cantilever a berthing facility out from the steep rocky shore, thus avoiding the ice pressure problem and other costly types of construction.

MATERIALS OF CONSTRUCTION, WATER, ELECTRICITY

Indigenous materials of construction such as wood, concrete aggregates, selected backfill materials, even fresh water, are all relatively scarce and poorly distributed throughout the Arctic. Removal of these materials may in some instances be harmful ecologically. However, such materials are essential to construction so that the project site location should be selected with such sources in mind, if extraordinary costs are to be avoided.

Concrete aggregates may be manufactured by a quarrying, crushing and screening operation. This is costly, but if the resulting excavation can serve a useful purpose in the final constructed facility, the costs are minimized. Generally speaking, all other materials of construction have to be imported, contributing to the high freight costs involved in Arctic work.

With the exception of the few areas where electric power supplies have already been developed, projects must include power generating facilities. This is another addition to costs not faced by many southern projects. Where the need to generate power coincides with the lack of fresh water, the essential supplies of water can be obtained by desalination of sea water, utilizing waste heat from the generators.

LOGISTICS

The problem of bringing all the skills, materials, and services to the construction site in the correct quantities at the right time is the real key to success in carrying out a project in the Arctic. It requires meticulous planning and scheduling of all of the elements of the operation, starting with the design phase and carrying through to job completion. Access through the Arctic seas by the less costly modes of transportation, ship or barge, is limited to a few months or even a few weeks per year depending on locality, so that for practical economic reasons alone, the bulk of equipment, materials, food stuffs, etc. must be delivered during this time and stockpiled or warehoused for use during the closed shipping season. To achieve the most economical operation of the project, only personnel, perishable materials such as fresh fruit and vegetables, mail and emergency supplies should be brought in by air. The designer must recognize that there are "no hardware stores around the corner", so that every nail, nut and bolt, electrical coupling, fuse, flashlight battery, must be ordered and may be just as critical as the turbine, the crane, or the ball mill. The equipment must be ordered with the engineer specifying the degree of assembly or sub-assembly that is to take place in the manufacturer's shop, bearing in mind the manner of shipment, the lifting capacity of the ship's gear or the ship off-loading equipment, the lifting capacity at the site, and in emergency the size of door openings of the helicopter.

The engineering must be carried out in the sequence which will permit early delivery to the ships of those items which must be constructed or installed first in order that the construction programme can be continued during the closed shipping season, and in order to minimize the amount of temporary construction facilities required. If the project has to generate its own electric power, then the generators should be delivered as early as possible so that permanent power can be available during the closed season. The structural steel, roofing materials and siding for the various buildings should be delivered in time so that the buildings can be erected and enclosed to permit a high level of construction activity to be maintained during the closed season. When one considered that delivery times of nine to fifteen months are not uncommon for some items of process equipment, it can be seen that accurate major decisions are required early in the design phases of the project. Schedules are won or lost in the crucial early phases, and when the schedule is lost, it is not lost by a few days or weeks, but by a complete shipping season. This may mean a financial disaster to the enterprise. It is these detailed planning operations, and extra design office efforts which cause the additional home office costs, but which really pay off in reducing the cost impact of the other factors. Incidentally, some of the best construction weather occurs in the period immediately before the shipping lanes are open. To take advantage of this period, all of the materials and equipment required for use at that time must be shipped in the previous year. This in itself ties up capital, imposing higher interest costs on the project.

To repeat, the objective of all this exercise is to minimize cost. If the outdoor construction is organized to take place during the long warmer days, it is more efficient. If the structures are enclosed so that equipment installation, wiring, piping and so on can be done during the winter months, then the work load can be levelled out, the peak number of tradesmen required is reduced, the schedule may be shortened and the campsite with all its associated costs can be reduced.

THE CHALLENGE

What does all this mean to the engineer, the constructor, the materials scientist?

Few of the resources of the North have been developed. The big push is now on in North America with the oil and gas developments, so major challenges face us.

The design engineer who usually lives with all the comforts and conveniences of the South, must be more acutely aware of the actual conditions prevailing in the Arctic, especially at the specific construction site. Into his design he must incorporate innovations, simplicity, energy conservation and ease of site erection. He and the constructor must work closely together to develop the designs and techniques which will minimize site labour requirements. Some of the techniques which are, or can be employed include modularization, pre-assembly to the maximum possible extent consistent with shipping restraints, use of simple reliable components easily assembled and serviced by semi-skilled personnel, use of snap-joint type designs to speed up field assembly and recognize that workers wear bulky gloves and clothing. An alternative technique, the ultimate in preassembly, is to construct complete facilities in the South, on a barge or ship configuration, and float them to the permanent location where they are beached or otherwise fixed in position.

Engineer, client and constructor must collaborate closely on the development of carefully detailed programmes and schedules, and adhere to them, all with the objective of reducing the total and peak site labour requirements.

The materials scientist must devote his attention to develop the materials which meet the technical need of the engineer and constructor but equally important, which can be worked with by people having the lower levels of skills. New materials are required. For example, can an inexpensive cementitious material be found to replace Portland cement, which will have a freezing point of, say, -20°C, or even -40°C, be lightweight, and less sensitive to the gradations of aggregates? This one item would allow us to reduce freight costs, extend the construction season, and increase the usable indigenous construction material resources. There are many other needs, such as steels less subject to embrittlement but readily weldable in colder weather using simple techniques, building materials which are fire proof, light-weight and impact resistant, better insulating materials, and so forth. Many such materials exist but do they meet the criteria of "fool-proof" workability, ease of installation and durability under the Arctic conditions?

The challenge is there for all of us, owner, engineer, materials scientist, constructor.

DISCUSSION

J. E. Rymes (Rymes Engineering): While Mr. Weishar has presented an overview of construction problems, he should have really emphasized three major points which are not readily understood. These are: 1) design experience; 2) criticality of scheduling; 3) assessment of project. Only experienced design people with extensive Arctic background should be assigned. Scheduling is critical - a missed schedule usually results in a calendar year's delay. Projects (fixed or mobile) must be examined from the point of view of the North. The design, planning etc. must reflect this assessment. Most Arctic errors are "southern made".

A. Weishar: I concur. However, for the amount of design work to be done for forthcoming Arctic projects, there just are not enough design people with "extensive Arctic background". I refer to the engineer with his calculator, and the designer on the drafting board. This emphasizes the need to provide experienced project leadership as well as the need to disseminate accumulated experience via conferences such as this one, and in technical publications. As for project assessment, this is another aspect of the problem of variety of conditions, and variety of projects. Each project, and each project site location must be tackled on its own "merits". Just as in the south, there are no "standard" projects.

J. F. Clayton (Gulf Oil Canada): Is the Clivus system of sewage treatment being used in the Arctic and if not, why not? It meets all the requirements for Arctic use, as it needs no water, no power, has no moving parts and produces no odour.

E. I. Carefoot (Associated Engineering Services): The Clivus system is used for human waste disposal by toilet in difficult climates where water supply and waste disposal is difficult. The system was developed in Sweden and has been in use for quite a number of years. Specifically, it is not in general Arctic use but has real potential. Similar low-water or no-water systems include propane toilets, electrical incineration, etc. e.g. "Humus".

Waste disposal will still have to consider "grey" waters, as the above systems will easily flood out. "Grey" waters are of such origin as wash water, kitchen sink drain, shower, etc. which do not have the same pathogenic bacteria implications and are less environmentally harmful.

A. Ismail (Montreal Engineering): Regarding logistics, what experience is there of movement of heavy equipment between the islands of the Arctic archipelago either by barge or over the thick sea ice which may vary between 5 ft and 10 ft thickness?

V. F. Crowley (Shawinigan Engineering): The majority of materials for Prudhoe Bay, especially modular items and heavy equipment were transported by barges in convoy from Seattle about July 1st each year to arrive on the North Slope during early August. The system has been very effective, except in 1975 when an ice pack prevented a number of barges from reaching shore.

NEW MATERIALS FOR THE ARCTIC

INTRODUCTION

E. I. Carefoot

The engineer of today is faced with a bewildering variety of materials which he must use in his work. The simple conception of steel held by a past generation has been complicated by considerations of grain size, hardenability and heat-treatment and the main varieties of alloy steels have multiplied the materials that are available. The plain portland cement of a few years ago has been split into several specialized varieties. The old white lead and linseed oil have been supplemented by new products that refuse to fall into older classifications. Light alloys and plastics have provided entirely new types of materials. The boiler plant seems to demand the ministrations of a dietitian rather than a brawny stoker.

These advances have been due to intensive research on the part of consumers and producers alike. The structure of our knowledge is still far from complete, but the foundations are sufficiently visible to permit a survey of properties as a function of internal structure.

This session will be quite varied, with discussion on materials of relatively new origin. A fairly new development in construction materials is the sulphur-based materials being researched to utilize the large quantity of sulphur that is produced as a by-product of the gas processing industry.

Several features of the products being developed are showing real promise for Arctic use. From the materials point of view, it is unfortunate that the gas being discovered in the Canadian Arctic is basically a sweet or non-sulfur bearing gas. From the construction material point of view the new products would have a real economic advantage had they been surplus in the Arctic. The gas producers and processors would likely not share this same view.

We will also hear some new and interesting concepts on the use of an age-old material - ice, which the north produces in a plentiful supply.

FIBER COMPOSITE MATERIALS IN AN ARCTIC ENVIRONMENT

K. N. Street
R. M. Hardy and Assoc. Ltd.
4052 Graveley Street
Burnaby, B.C. V5C 3T6
CANADA

As a general class of materials, so-called fiber composites or multiphase materials wherein one of the phases takes on a fibrous form, are not new to the Arctic environment. For many centuries, polar peoples have made good use of those few natural fiber composites available to them, such as bone and sometimes wood. Laminated structures were likewise adapted for various weapons. Moss impregnated ice blocks were found to exhibit superior crack arrest characteristics. Such properties as light weight, durability, strength and fracture toughness were thus the selection criteria for these early materials engineers.

Modern day materials engineering has the good fortune to possess a vast number of composite structures which can be incorporated into many applications demanding special or unique properties. The basic principles describing the behaviour of such composites remain little changed from those of the natural composites. However due to the relative rapidity and the wide scale of present-day Arctic development programmes, the materials selection criteria will undoubtedly be much more severe than those of the polar hunters.

Examination of the general behaviour of composites may lead to enlightened discussion on new applications where these multiphase structural materials could provide ingenious and innovative solutions which are both cost-effective and ecologically acceptable.

INTRODUCTION

For historical reasons alone, it would appear justifiable to introduce fiber composites or fiber reinforced materials to any conference on materials engineering in the Arctic. It is well known that the early inhabitants of the Arctic made good use of such materials as bone and wood, both spectacular examples of natural fiber composites (1-4). The materials selection was, of course, rather limited but certain types of bone and wood must have performed better in some applications than in others (5). Also the importance of the orientation from which the tool or utensil was cut or ground out of the bone or wood must have been discovered by trial and error. The durability of the item would have been found to vary, depending upon whether it was left outdoors at all times or subjected to temperature cycling by bringing indoors, or being dunked repeatedly in water. Finally, all things being equal, the lighter composite must have taken preference over a heavier one as lengthy journeys were a basic necessity in the struggle for life.

The laminated bow made from various types of bone which were bound together to form a multi-layered stiff and effective weapon shows that the art and science of laminated structures was also discovered early by the Arctic people (6).

Whereas the weapon, household utensil and transportation industry may have involved some materials engineering, the housing industry evolved very little from the snow house of the winter to the hide or skin and stone shelter of the summer. One important discovery was the introduction of moss into ice. As the ancient Egyptians found that straw and hair reinforced their mud walls and prevented them from cracking and crumbling, the early Polar people, by chance or by intuition, discovered that moss tended to produce a more crack-resistant ice, and probably a slower melting material. Ice also tends to have very directional properties. Moss additions would result in a more isotropic material and the ice grain size would likely be much smaller, leading to improved properties in the matrix material itself. The production of such an advanced construction material would require some prior planning and hence was probably only done in the permanent base camps.

A similar housing material, but less of a fiber composite, was stone-filled earth which was apparently used by the Lapps (5). The composite must have shown improved crack propagation resistance, reduced spalling tendencies, reduced sensitivity to temperature cycling, increased mechanical shock resistance and perhaps more favourable shrinkage characteristics.

MATERIALS SELECTION CRITERIA

The uniqueness of materials engineering in the Arctic as compared to elsewhere in North America can be equated to three principal factors: viz. environment, geographic remoteness, and sparce population.

Those characteristics of the environment of concern to materials engineers include a number of extremes: high winds, very low and moderately high temperatures, freeze-thaw cycles in certain regions, large snow and ice loadings, very unstable geological conditions, and a strong environmental political lobby. The latter, amongst other things, produces a greater importance on failure prevention or fail-safe design, particularly where potential wide-spread damage is concerned. Strong and stiff materials at low temperatures which are resistant to thermal fatigue and freeze-thaw cracking are required. Toughness and a low propensity for brittle failure will rank high on the list of property requirements.

The geographic remoteness places a premium on availability of materials, weight and transportation economics. High specific properties (i.e. strength/unit weight) are important and considerable incentive exists for utilizing locally available resources. Consequently, a look at the past from a materials standpoint, no matter how simplistic the materials or applications may have been, could well provide engineers and designers with innovative solutions to modern-day problems.

Kelly (7) has recently compared the energy costs of most types of engineering materials, which are shown in Table 1. It is evident that the high volume construction materials such as cement, concrete and plaster place relatively small demands on energy. Likewise, the production of ice by man is relatively cheap, and nature could be called upon to reduce energy requirement even further.

A sparce population will mean that all types of skilled labour will not be readily available. Costly penalties will result if distant population centers are the prime source of service and maintenance personnel. The modern idea of "if it breaks, ring up a local service man" will generally not be appropriate in the Arctic. Thus, ease of repair must be considered an important materials selection criterion.

It would be hypocritical not to accept the premise that mistakes are going to be made at a higher rate than in climates where extensive service experience has been gained. Mistakes need not imply disasters, only poor durability, inability to service any higher than necessary costs will likely characterize many materials selected for Arctic applications.

Table 1

Energy Costs for Various Engineering Materials (after ref. 7)

Material	GJ/t	Density (10^3 kg/m^3)	GJ/m^3
Sand & Gravel	0.1	2.6	0.26
Ice	1.0	1.0	1.0
Gypsum Plaster	1.21	2.32	2.8
Portland Cement	7.0	2.2	15.4
Glass	8.8	2.5	22.0
Steel, Finished	47.5	7.9	376.
Primary Copper	61.	8.9	543.
PVC	81.9	1.4	115.
Aluminum	327.	2.7	884.

DESIGNING FOR ARCTIC ENVIRONMENTS

Coupled directly to the above materials selection criteria are the problems of designing structures to less than precise requirements. Designers do not know exactly what combined service conditions exist in the Arctic. Due to the fact that fiber composites have the intrinsic advantage of being "tailor-made", a thorough knowledge of both the physical and mechanical requirements of the structure is important. In addition, fiber composites are a new breed of material and classical design principles are no longer sufficient or even valid.

For the wide variety of fiber composites that are available, the scarcity of performance records in Arctic environments poses a major problem to designers. The limitation in attempting to design structural elements utilizing laboratory test data, (primarily short term data only) is that such data rarely include the combined effects of the severe Arctic service conditions. Nevertheless, small scale laboratory or field testing is a necessary first step and can produce large scale savings in both money and time.

Tobiasson (8) has suggested that the high initial cost of instrumenting structures in order to monitor their performance in the Arctic may well be balanced by a substantial reduction in final life-cycle costs, if latent problems can be pinpointed early. Major repairs at a later date are expensive, due not only to increased labour costs but to the tendency to over-react when failures occur.

PRINCIPLES OF FIBER REINFORCEMENT

This discussion will be confined to simple basic unidirectional or bidirectional fiber reinforcement systems. Several reviews of composite behaviour provide (9-12) further details to the discussion herein.

Tensile and Flexural Strength

In applications where tensile or bending strength is a primary design requirement, high-strength fibers are aligned in a matrix material parallel to the major stress axes. The upper and lower limits to tensile strength of a unidirection array can be calculated from the formulations:

upper limit: (law of mixtures)

$$\sigma_c = \sigma_f^* V_f + \sigma_m V_m$$

lower limit: (bundle theory)

$$\sigma_c = \gamma \sigma_f^* V_f$$

where σ_c = composite tensile strength parallel to the fibers; σ_f^* = average fiber strength; σ_m = matrix stress at the average fiber failure strain; V_m and V_f = volume fraction of matrix and fiber respectively; and γ = efficiency or bundle factor (generally of the order of 0.7).

The strength falls off sharply with orientation of the fibers from the stressing direction. As many high strength fibers are also of low density, high specific strengths are obtainable which are superior to light alloys and steels.

Young's Modulus

In the longitudinal direction, Young's modulus,

E_c, of a unidirectional array is given by another mixtures law:

$$E_c = E_f V_f + E_m V_m$$

where f, m and c denote fiber, matrix and composite as before. Once again, high specific values are obtainable, much higher than those characteristic of many monolithic materials.

Breaking Strain

For continuous brittle fiber composites of sufficiently large volume fraction of fibers, the composite fails when stressed parallel to the unidirectional fibers at a strain approximately equal to that of the fibers. In general, this is of the order 0.5 to 1%.

Fracture Toughness

Many workers have more or less concluded that classical fracture mechanics methods of testing and analyses can be applied to a wide variety of fiber composites. Anisotropic theory is however needed in place of isotropic theory.

Toughness is a property that can be controlled by varying the adhesion between the fibers and matrix, the dimensions of the fibers and the fibers and matrix themselves.

Stress intensity factors, K_c, have been determined for a wide number of systems, using the well known formulation,

$$K_c = Y\sigma\sqrt{a}$$

where σ = stress, a = half crack length for a center-notched specimen and Y = anisotropic specimen geometry factor. In many cases, high K_c values go together with high yield strengths, an anomaly when compared to metals.

In brittle-matrix composites, such as ice and concrete, fibers serve to block crack propagation. This is shown schematically in Figure 1. The fibers will continue to bridge the cracks provided their breaking strain is greatly superior to that of the matrix. The end result is that the matrix cracks on a microscale in a number of locations, but the overall structural integrity of the material is not lost.

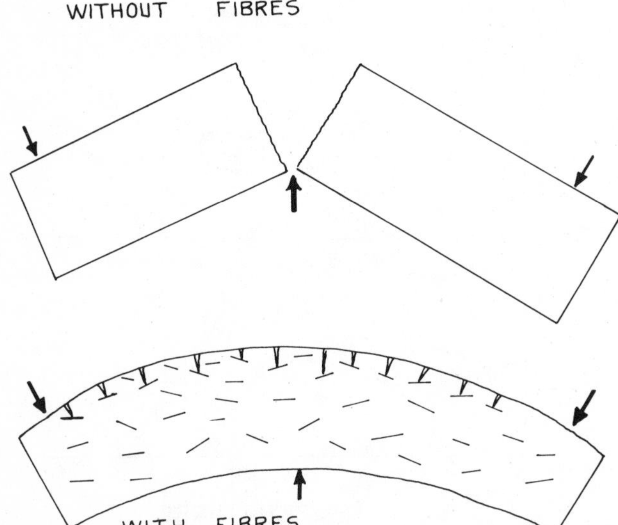

Figure 1: Schematic illustration of the crack-arresting characteristics of a fiber reinforced brittle material

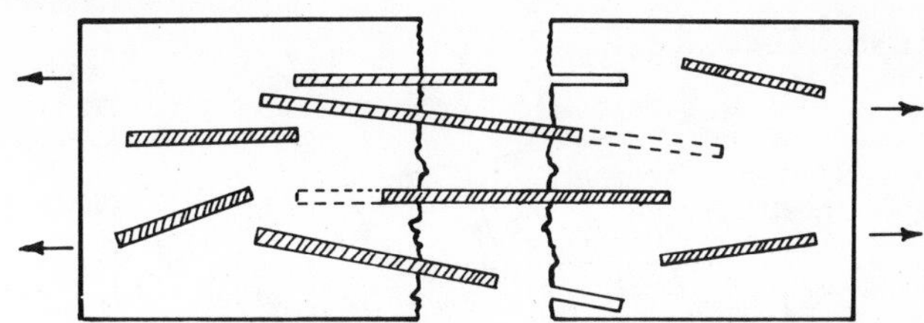

Figure 2: Schematic illustration of the energy absorbing mechanism of fiber pullout during fracture of a composite material

Impact Strength

The adhesion between fibers and matrix can also be controlled to produce a wide range of impact strengths. No simple formulations exist for predicting impact strength, although various energy absorbing mechanisms have been recognized. Fiber pullout, Figure 2, absorbs energy through the frictional forces between fibers and matrix and is a prominant mechanism in both brittle and ductile matrix composites.

Creep Strength

Creep-resistant fibers can be utilized to produce creep-resistant matrices or composites. An outstanding example is reinforced ice.

Fatigue Strength

A low crack propagation rate can be obtained by designing a composite microstructure to give crack deflection or crack arrest at fiber-matrix interfaces. Cracks are thus rendered harmless relative to the principal axes of stress.

Thermal Expansion

The formulations are well developed for calculating thermal expansion coefficients. For cross-ply composites, the unique possibility of a zero expansion or contraction material exists for certain fiber orientations. A noteworthy feature to be considered at the design stage is that thermal fatigue can take place during relatively small temperature cycles, due simply to the difference in expansion coefficients of the fibers and matrix. Given the characteristics of the constituents, the behaviour of the composite can be calculated for various temperature extremes.

FIBER REINFORCED PLASTICS (FRP)

Phillips (13) has stated that all the experiments by all the experts have shown that fiber reinforced plastics get stronger and stiffer as the temperature is decreased. Of particular note, though, is the fact that the elongation at failure remains uniformly low, about 1%, at all temperatures below the glass transition temperature of the plastic matrix.

Kasen (14,15) has gathered together in several recent excellent reviews specific low temperature data for FRP. Figure 3 shows the general increase in ultimate strength found for uniaxial filament-wound (UFW), biaxial filament-wound (BFW) of 0/90° orientation and woven-cloth lay-ups. The data for the UFW composites refers to the principal axis parallel to the fibers, whereas the BFW and cloth systems were tested parallel to one of the major principal axes.

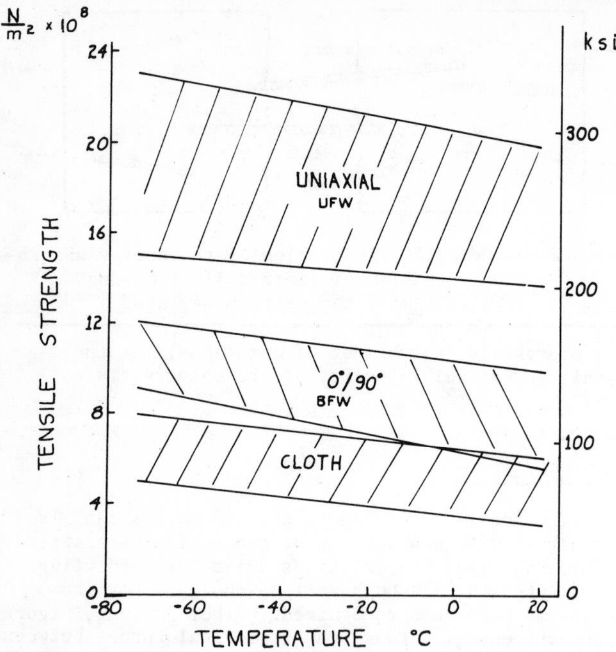

Figure 3: Ultimate tensile strength of glass fiber epoxy composites as a function of temperature (after ref. 15)

Similarly, the temperature dependence of the initial elastic modulus is depicted in Figure 4. It appears that in only one case, curve No. 2 for a woven-cloth composite, the elastic modulus decreases with decreasing temperature.

Thermal expansion and contraction data are of interest for many low temperature applications. Figure 5 shows that the contraction varies widely with orientation relative to the fiber axes. Of the three types of composite shown, the smallest contraction occurs parallel to the fibers and the greatest orthogonal to the fibers in a uniaxial composite.

Thermal conductivity is apparently extremely difficult to measure accurately in glass fiber composites. The results in Figure 6 show a significant decrease in conductivity in a direction parallel to

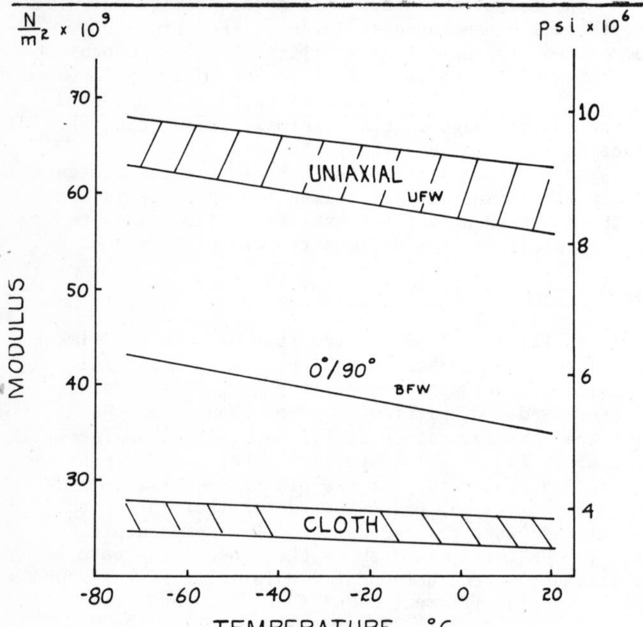

Figure 4: Primary tensile modulus of glass fiber epoxy composites as a function of temperature (after ref. 15)

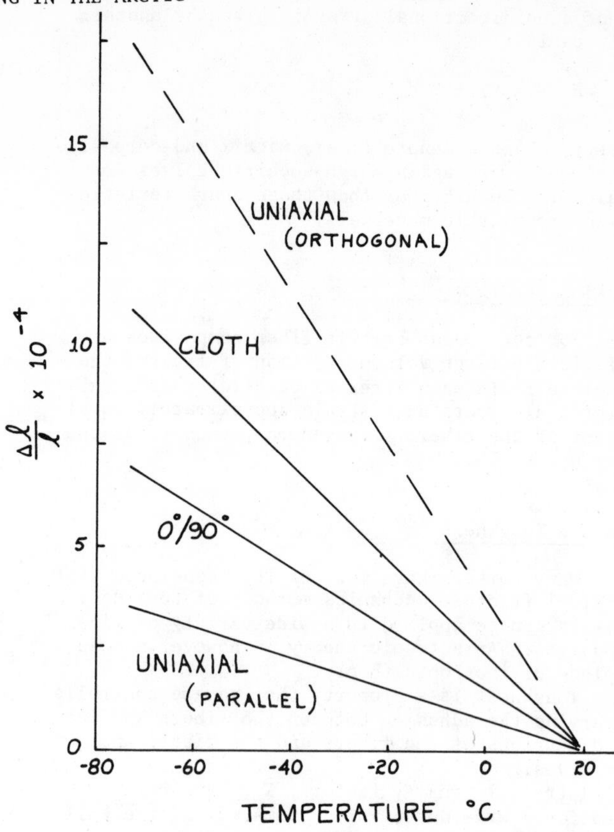

Figure 5: Thermal contraction of glass fiber-epoxy composites as a function of temperature (after ref. 15)

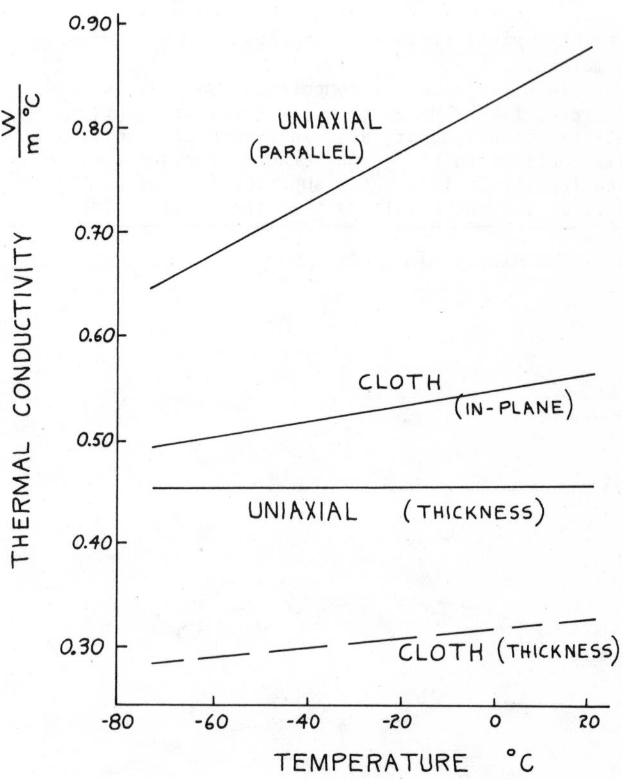

Figure 6: Thermal conductivities of glass fiber-epoxy composites as a function of temperature (after ref. 15)

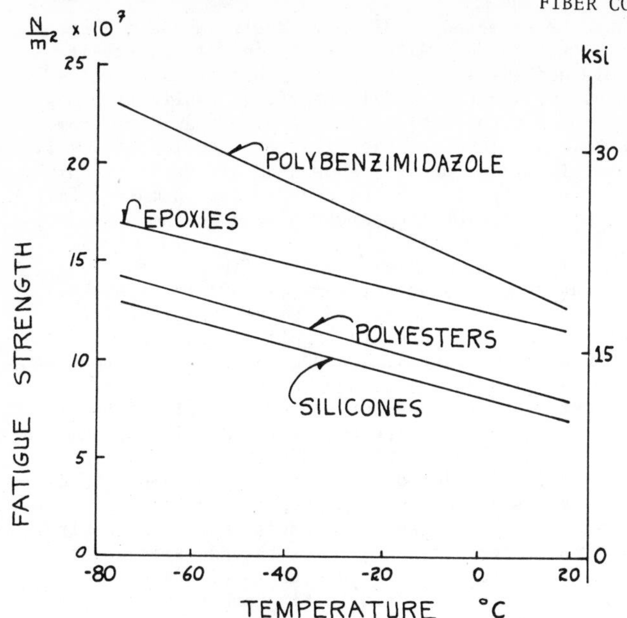

Figure 7: Fatigue strength at 10^6 Hz of glass fiber-epoxy composites as a function of temperature (after ref. 15)

the fibers in a uniaxial composite but very little decrease in a cloth composite, over the temperature range 300 K to 200 K (30°C to -70°C). Conductivity has been found to be significantly affected by the ambient atmosphere. Thus, different service behavour would be expected under Arctic conditions.

Glass-fiber composites also show very favourable fatigue strength at low temperatures. The results for a number of composites of varying matrix are shown in Figure 7. In all cases, the tensile fatigue strength increases with decrease in temperature.

Little change in impact strength with decrease in temperature is also a characteristic of several fiber reinforced plastics (Table 2).

Given the above properties of FRP, a number of applications in Arctic environments have been realized or considered. The fracture toughness characteristics could be utilized to produce leak-before-break structures which would be favourable for line-pipe applications. About 5 years ago, the idea of an 8 ft (2.5 m) diameter FRP pipeline operating at 900 psi (6.2 MPa) pressure was suggested for use in

Table 2

Tensile, Flexural and Impact Strengths of Several Commercial Reinforced Plastics (Ref. 25)

Material	Tensile Strength ksi (MPa)	Flexural Strength ksi(MPa)	Impact Strength ft.lbf/in notch (J/mm notch)
glass-phenolic (FM-4030-190)			
Room temperature	8.8(61)	20.4(141)	20.4(1.09)
-20°F (-30°C)	10.0(69)	22.6(156)	22.5(1.20)
-40°F (-40°C)	9.0(62)	22.4(154)	26.3(1.40)
chopped cotten-phenolic (FM-3510)			
Room temperature	6.8(47)	13.8(95)	2.1(0.11)
-20°F (-30°C)	7.6(52)	13.9(96)	1.5(0.08)
-40°F (-40°C)	7.2(50)	13.7(94)	1.5(0.08)
nylon-phenolic (FM-1303)			
Room temperature	9.2(63)	12.4(85)	0.51(0.03)
-60°F (-50°C)	8.5(59)	13.0(90)	0.48(0.03)

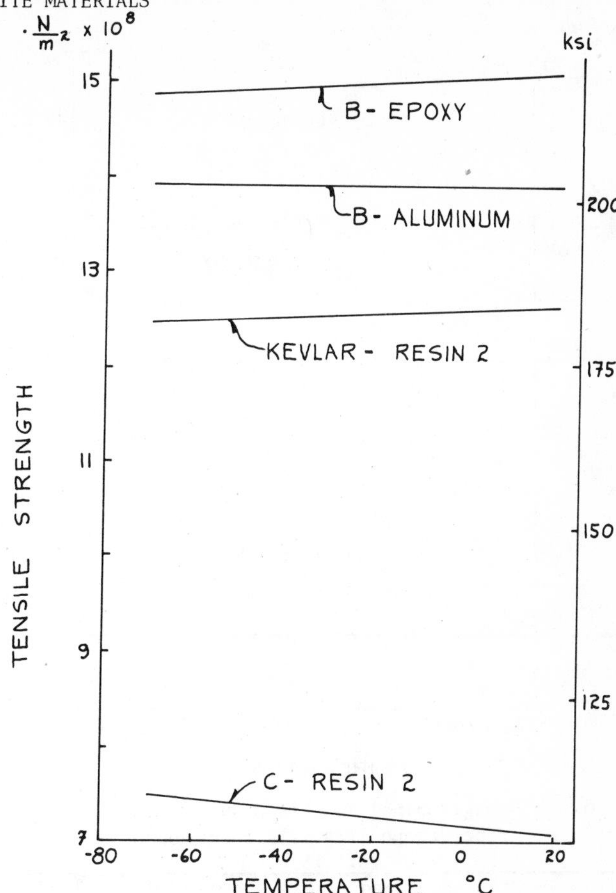

Figure 8: Longitudinal ultimate tensile strength of advanced fiber composites as a function of temperature (after ref. 15)

the North Slope projects (16). It was estimated that the material costs were about equal for steel and composite but the latter had the attractive features of corrosion resistance, insulation and on-site fabrication. Continuing the argument here, the toughness of FRP pipe joints can be made superior to that of the pipe itself, overcoming any joining problems. Also, no longitudinal seam welds would be present in a composite pipe.

The low density of FRP, 1.7 g/cm^3, or about 2/3 that of aluminum, would result in lower transportation costs, overall ease of handling and lower settling rates in soil over long periods of time. Acoustic emission techniques could provide an NDT assessment of the entire pipe, including joints. In-service inspection could concentrate on leak detection and hence simplify major failure prevention detection methods being considered for steel pipe. Repairs could also be carried out with less skilled manpower than is required of more conventional materials.

ADVANCED FIBER COMPOSITES

Fiber reinforced materials based on such fibers as graphite,boron and "Kevlar" (or PRD-49) are generally reserved for special applications where the high cost of the fiber can be justified on a cost-effective basis. Due to their unique and exciting properties, it is worthwhile including them in this review of potential materials for Arctic environments.

The temperature dependence of longitudinal ultimate tensile strengths and moduli for several types of unidirectional composites are depicted in Figures 8 and 9, after Kasen (15,17). The strength values of 200 to 220 ksi (1400 to 1500 MPa) for boron

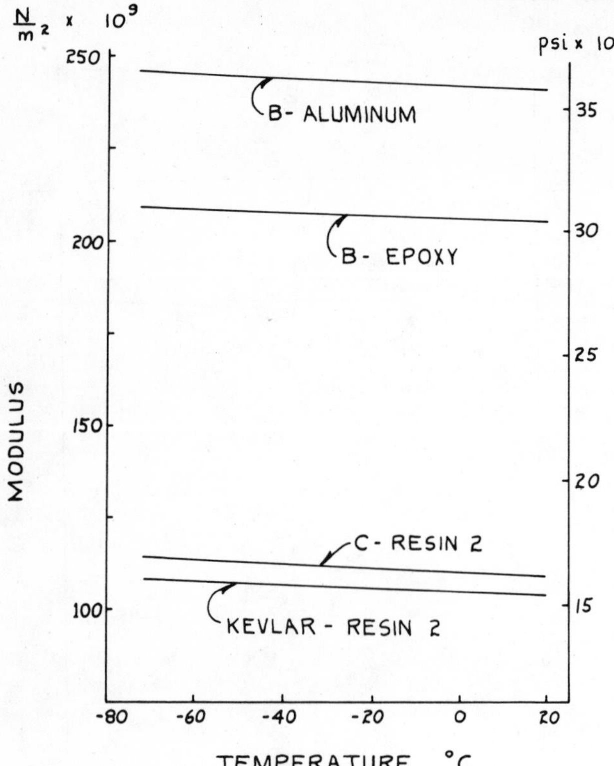

Figure 9: Longitudinal Young's modulus of advanced fiber composites as a function of temperature (after ref. 15)

fibers in both epoxy and aluminum are notable. The elastic moduli of these two composites are also notable, being equal to or greater than that of steel. Furthermore, the densities of boron-epoxy and boron-aluminum are only 1.8 and 2.6 g/cm^3, making their specific strengths and moduli even more attractive.

As is the case for glass-fiber reinforced plastics, the advanced composites display, in general, an increase in strength and modulus with decreasing temperature.

The thermal expansion/contraction characteristics of the materials are widely different and depend on the composite system. Boron-epoxy and boron-aluminum contract with decreasing temperature. However, the Kevlar material expands on cooling and the graphite fiber materials shows excellent dimensional stability over a wide temperature range (Figure 10).

A novel application of an advanced composite presently undergoing tests in Denmark for use in Greenland is a 3-cup anemometer of carbon fiber-epoxy (18). This composite cup is more attractive than either glass-reinforced plastics, PVC plastic or aluminum because the stiffness per unit weight is much higher. Stiffness gives stability and accuracy and the lightness means high sensitivity to wind speed variations. Tests up to wind speeds of 80 m/s have been carried out with no deficiencies revealed. Ordinary PVC anemometers disintegrate at about 35 m/s.

CONCRETE AND CEMENT COMPOSITES

A new composite which is generating considerable interest in the construction field is chopped steel wire reinforced cement and concrete. It consists of approximately 1 to 2 vol% steel wires about 1 in. (25 mm) long, mixed randomly throughout the concrete or cement. The mixture possesses superior flexural strength and toughness, mainly due to the fibers preventing the formation of large singular fracture paths (7). In an Arctic environment such material would be expected to display vastly improved freeze/thaw resistance. Although the high Arctic itself would not likely see a large number of such cycles, except adjacent to tidal waters, an application might be found in the sub-Arctic. Freeze-thaw data from a U.S. Department of Highways test section of 2 vol% steel fiber in concrete showed no damage to the highway pavement after 300 cycles, compared to complete failure of conventional concrete placed on the same day, after 240 cycles (19).

The more familiar asbestos fiber cement has already seen substantial service in cold climates. It is reported to be in wide usage in Norway for roofing, siding and piping applications. However temperature cycling around 0°C has proven to be the most damaging (5), although the precise nature of the deterioration was not specified. Elsewhere it has been found that freeze-thaw cycles induce delamination within the layered structure of the material (8). This is related to the method of manufacture of asbestos-cement which consists of depositing successive layers of asbestos-cement slurry on an air suction screen until the final thickness is achieved.

Fiber reinforced concrete is at present being studied in a major field testing program under the combined sponsorship of several Scandinavian countries (5). The applications being studied are road pavements and slope stabilization. The possiblity of fiber concrete storage tankers in the Arctic has not been discussed in the literature but may warrant some consideration. Likewise breakwater or marine docking facilities where tidal induced freeze-thaw cycling would be extremely damaging to ordinary concrete, may provide another potential area of application. Railway ties, airport runways and erosion-sensitive structures could well be subjects for future consideration.

FIBER REINFORCED ICE

Ice as a load bearing material has already received considerable scientific attention dating back to the 1940's. The most adventuresome idea originated in

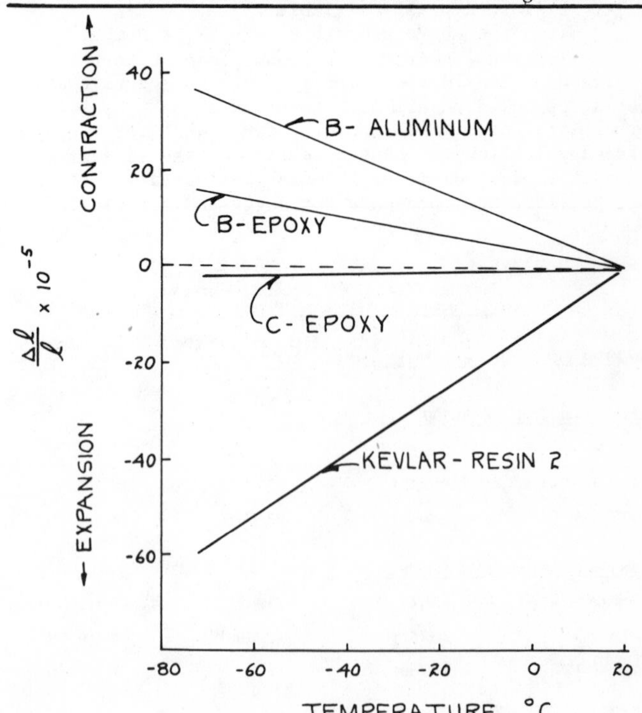

Figure 10: Longitudinal thermal expansion and contraction of advanced fiber composites as a function of temperature (after ref. 15)

Table 3

Modulus of Rupture of Wood-reinforced Ice at -17°C as a Function of Percentage of Wood Pulp

Wood Pulp Vol %	Modulus of Rupture (mean) at -17°C, kgf/cm² (MPa)
0	22.5 (2.21)
1	22.8 (2.24)
2	32.0 (3.14)
4	50.0 (4.90)
6	51.0 (5.00)
7	61.5 (6.03)
8	53.7 (5.27)
14	66.7 (6.54)

Great Britain. It was to construct a fleet of aircraft carriers for use during the Second World War. Unfortunately, pure ice was found to possess a very low and unpredictable flexural strength. However, when a small quantity of wood pulp was added, the mechanical properties of the "composite ice" were greatly improved. The material was named "Pykrete" after the originator, Pyke, of the iceberg ship, but it was actually discovered at the Brooklyn Polytechnic Institute.

The modulus of rupture of Pykrete at -17°C was found (20) to increase rapidly as the percentage of wood pulp was increased, up to approximately 4 vol%, after which it increased more slowly, (Table 3). At 4 vol% pulp the flexural strength is twice that of pure ice. The tensile and compressive strengths of ice were similarly improved, as indicated in Table 4.

Another significant result was the decreased scatter of strength values of the reinforced ice. Pure ice was found to break in flexion in the range of 5 to 35 kgf/cm² (490 to 3400 kPa), whereas reinforced ice exhibited strengths which varied by only ±25%. This reduction in brittleness enabled reinforced ice to be machined in a lathe.

The enhanced impact and shock resistance of reinforced ice is demonstrated by projectile penetration depths, (Table 5). The addition of 14 vol% wood pulp reduced the penetration at -7°C by 50% over pure ice. On a weight-for-weight basis, the reinforced ice was as good as concrete.

As in the case of pure ice, reinforced ice creeps, but the creep rate depends not only on stress, temperature and reinforcement, but also on the type of wood. Scotch pine-reinforced ice stressed to 7 kgf/cm² (690 kPa) in compression displayed a steady-state creep rate of 1%/a. Canadian spruce-reinforced ice displayed negligible creep under the same stress.

An estimate of the effects of several important parameters on the creep of reinforced ice can be obtained from the relationships developed by Kelly and Street (21). For aligned rigid fibers within a creeping matrix, the composite strength, σ_c is given by:

$$\sigma_c = \delta \sigma_{mo} (\ell/d)^{(m+1)/m} (\dot{\varepsilon}_c/\dot{\varepsilon}_{mo})^{1/m} V_f + \sigma_{mo} (\dot{\varepsilon}_c/\dot{\varepsilon}_{mo})^{1/m} (1-V_f)$$

where δ, σ_{mo} and $\dot{\varepsilon}_{mo}$ are constants, m the stress sensitivity of the pure matrix and 1/d the fiber aspect ratio. Ice has a value of $m \simeq 3$ and hence the creep strength increases as $(1/d)^{4/3}$. The theory assumes that the basic characteristics of the ice in the composite are unchanged from those of pure ice. This is not likely to be the case and hence the formulation would tend to predict a lower limit to the strength as the grain size of the matrix in the composite would likely be smaller than in the unreinforced ice material.

The case of much longer or continuous fibers is also interesting. If a perfect bond between fibers and matrix could be achieved (no slipping or shearing) then very low creep rates indeed should be achieved if the fibers themselves deform only elastically (22).

Several modern day applications for reinforced ice have been considered. Runways in Arctic countries were mentioned in 1947 (20) and the idea is attractive today. Assuming that temporary runways will be needed for relatively heavy transport during the construction stages of major projects, reinforced ice would be an ecologically favourable choice as it would melt and disappear in the spring, leaving no permanently damaged or altered terrain.

Another idea has been to make off-shore storage tanks or basins for oil in reinforced ice. One of the problems mentioned by Kelly (23) is that the thermal conductivity of ice is small, making it difficult to prevent melting at the water interface without bringing a refrigerant very close to the surface.

Some companies have been carrying out off-shore drilling in the Arctic Islands utilizing "floating ice platforms" (24). The platforms consist of natural ocean ice which is artificially thickened to approximately 16 ft (5 m) in depth. However no mention has been made of introducing fibers to reduce the creep of the ice under the weight of the drilling rigs.

Reinforced ice as a structural material represents one of the most challenging yet potentially attractive Arctic materials. One must assume that it has a place already reserved in the evolution of new materials that man will "engineer" in the development of the Arctic regions of the earth over the centuries to come.

Table 4

Tensile and Compressive Strengths of Pure Ice and Ice + 14 vol % Scotch pine wood pulp, at -14°C

Mean Strength at -14°C	Ice kg/cm² (MPa)	Ice & 14vol% Wood Pulp kg/cm² (MPa)
Tensile	11.6(1.14)	49.2(4.82)
Compressive	43.6(4.28)	77.3(7.58)

Table 5

Penetration Depths of a .303 Rifle Bullet in Various Materials

Material	Penetration (Depth mm)
Concrete	70
Brickwork	152
Ice + 14% wood pulp (-7°C)	165
Pure Ice (-7°C)	356
Soft wood	635

CONCLUSIONS

Examination of the general behaviour of a number of fiber reinforced materials leads to the conclusion that potential application of these materials in an Arctic-like environment warrants further study.

The possiblity exists for enhanced fracture

toughness and crack arrest properties in several common brittle-matrix materials such as cement, concrete and ice. High specific strengths and stiffnesses are also available from many reinforced plastics and metals.

The relatively well-developed state-of-the-art of basic fiber composite behaviour is a feature favourable for their inclusion as useful and innovative engineering materials.

Acknowledgements

Particular thanks are extended to those many people who corresponded in detail with the author, especially J. Sovik, L. Phillips, A. Kelly, H. Lilholt and R. Sager.

References

1. W. Bonfield, Composites, 1971, vol. 2, p. 173.
2. K. Piekarski, ASM Tech. Rep. 1963, T9-2.2.
3. J. M. Dinwoodie, Composites, 1971, vol. 2, p. 170.
4. G. S. Cooper, J. Young, Report No. 16, Project 7, National Physical Laboratory, Teddington, 1969.
5. J. H. Sovik, SINTEF, Trondheim, Norway, 1976, private communication.
6. D. Fishlock, The New Materials, Basic Books Inc. N.Y.,1967.
7. A. Kelly, Rilem Conference Proceedings, London, 1975.
8. W. Tobiasson, in Cold Regions Engineering, 1971, vol. 2, U. Alaska.
9. A. Kelly, G. J. Davies, Metall. Rev., 1965, vol. 10, p. 1.
10. G. A. Cooper, Rev. Phys. in Tech. 1971, vol. 2, p. 49.
11. A. Kelly, Strong Solids, 1973, Clarendon Press, Oxford.
12. D. K. Hale, N. P. L. Report IMS 27, 1975.
13. L. N. Phillips, R.A.E. Farnborough, U.K., 1976, private communication.
14. M.B. Kasen, Cryogenics, 1975, vol. 15, p. 327.
15. M. B. Kasen, ASTM STP 580, 1975, p. 586.
16. Editorial, Composites, 1971, vol. 2, p. 134.
17. M. B. Kasen, Cryogenics, 1975, vol. 15, p. 701.
18. H. Lilholt, RISO, Denmark, 1976, private communication.
19. D. R. Lankard, Composites, 1972, vol. 3, p. 65.
20. M. F. Perutz, J. Glaciology, 1947, vol. 1, p. 51.
21. A. Kelly, K. N. Street, Proc. Roy. Soc. London, 1972, vol. A328, p. 267.
22. K. N. Street, in Properties of Fibre Composites, 1971, IPC.
23. A. Kelly, 1976, private communication.
24. Vancouver Sun, January 23, 1976, p. 23.
25. Fiberite Corporation, Minnesota, 1976, private communication.

DISCUSSION

C. S. Sargent (University of Saskatchewan): Is it possible that the introduction of newer and more sophisticated materials in Arctic construction will prolong the dependence on skilled transient labour from southern Canada?

K. N. Street: In my opinion, no. Many of the materials would be utilized in structures fabricated in the south only. The high specific properties would allow more efficient design and lower transportation costs. Repair of many composites is in fact a very simple task. Highly skilled welders etc. would not be required. The construction material composites based on ice, concrete, etc. do not require highly skilled labour to install and are equally simple to repair. The early inhabitants of the Arctic have had, in fact, many years experience in fabricating, designing, and repairing composite materials.

W. G. Wilson (Molycorp): What are the variations in properties about the values shown in your tables for such materials as ice and ice with reinforcing fibres?

K. N. Street: The tabular values are shown as average values. The pure ice values were reported to vary widely (i.e. approximately ± 75%). This was considered as being too difficult to handle from a design standpoint. However, the wood-fiber reinforced ice produced much less scatter in strength values, i.e. ± 25%, which was more acceptable to designers. The reinforced material would then be machined also.

F. S. Jeglic (CANMET): Composite materials have been used in linepipe manufacture. What are the prospects for using composite material linepipes in Arctic environment?

K. N. Street: The last reference to the use of fiber reinforced materials for linepipe applications in the Arctic appears to have been made in 1970-71. I have posed this same question to a number of people recently but no additional work seems to have been done. Two problems have been mentioned -- the joint problem and the problem of lack of materials. The question would seem to warrant an up-date study.

W. M. Drope (Northern Engineering Services): I believe that composite pipelines are not being pursued due to the tremendous challenge of efficient (safe) and economical joining. A mixture of water, snow and sawdust was used to repair potholes in the Canadian Arctic Gas Inuvik Test Snow Road -- the mixture was referred to in a final report as "Snowcrete".

K. N. Street: I cannot see why a joining problem should exist, assuming a coupling device would be the most logical method to adopt. In my opinion, such a joining technique would be much less troublesome to install than perhaps welding. Thank you very much. "Snowcrete" - I like it!

B. Hawbolt (University of British Columbia): Halpin published a paper in 1973 comparing the economics of steel vs epoxy-glass composite for North Slope pipe applications. The composite alternative, although economically viable at that time, was too difficult to join and bend in the field installations. A current reassessment of the economics of the epoxy base would also be favourable for the steel alternative.

K. N. Street: Thank you, Bruce, for the precise reference I referred to. I believe a "Composite Materials Committee" in Canada reviewed this idea also in the past. Perhaps some interest in secondary applications or distribution lines will take place in future. The attractive low temperature properties of reinforced plastics cannot be ignored.

SOME PROPERTIES OF REINFORCED ICE

R. G. Stanley and P. G. Glockner
Department of Civil Engineering
The University of Calgary
Calgary, Alberta T2N 1N4
Canada

Spun glass fibre yarn was used to produce reinforced ice specimens which were tested to determine its bond-creep behaviour in ice and its effect on the tensile-creep properties of ice. On the basis of these tests it is concluded that the yarn, if appropriately anchored, may be a suitable reinforcement for ice, and that the tensile properties of ice are enhanced by such reinforcement.

INTRODUCTION

The need for providing temporary enclosures in cold regions led to a research project recently completed at the University of Calgary. The prime objective was to establish the feasibility of a proposed construction technique whereby a cable-stabilized inflatable is sprayed with water to create a reinforced ice dome (1). Selection of a suitable reinforcing material and its effect on mechanical properties of ice became a secondary research objective.

Properties of plain ice are well known to investigators in this field (2-6). On the other hand, although some studies have been carried out on properties of reinforced ice (7-10), types of suitable reinforcement and methods of optimizing its effect have not been investigated fully. In this project, the bond strength of glass fibre yarn embedded in ice and the tensile and shear strength of the composite were studied.

DETAILS OF THE EXPERIMENT

After considering several alternatives, spun glass fibre yarn of 0.9 mm (approx.) diameter was selected as reinforcing material. The bond characteristics of this yarn and its effect on the tensile behaviour of ice were observed under short and long duration loading conditions. In addition, the shear strength of this reinforced material was studied under short term loads.

All specimens were cast in specially machined steel molds and were frozen in a 12 ft^3 (0.34 m^3) deep freeze chamber at -15°C. Test conditions for each phase of this work are described in detail below.

Pull-out tests, with different lengths of yarn embedded in 25 mm x 25 mm cross- section ice prisms, were carried out in a Hounsfield extensometer to determine the bond characteristics of this reinforcement when subjected to short-term loading conditions. The effects of such yarn on the tensile and shear strength of ice was also studied under short duration loads. Details of this aspect of the programme were presented earlier, (1).

Based on the results of these tests, bond specimens with an embedment length of 25 mm were subjected to dead loading to study the bond-creep behaviour of the yarn in ice. A frame (Figure 1) was designed to allow loading of the yarn with dead weights while producing a continuous output of deflection of the yarn. The specimen, 1, complete with end blocks, was placed on the top plate, 2, with the yarn passing vertically down through a hole in the plate and load beam, 3, to which it was clamped by means of a thumbscrew, 4. The load beam, pivoted at one end, 5, was loaded at the midpoint with a weight hanger, 6, to produce deflection of the free end which was observed by means of an L.V.D.T., 7. A lever, 8, allowed the beam to be supported until the desired instant of loading.

The tests were conducted in a Tenney Ten*, a 0.28 m^3 environmental chamber maintained at -15°C.

* Model TTRC, Temperature and humidity controlled test chamber, from Tenney Engineering Inc., Union, New Jersey, U.S.A.

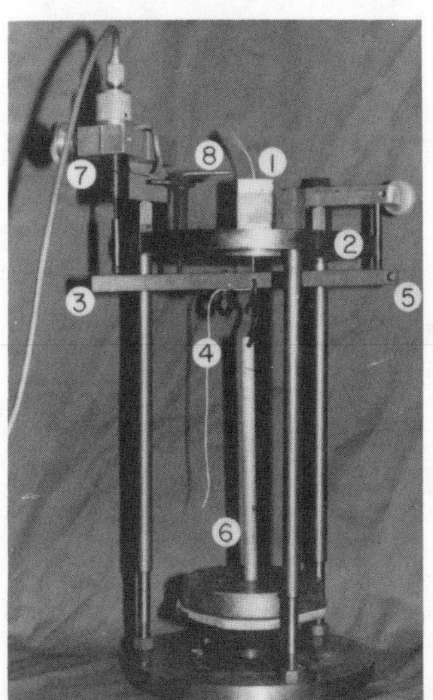

Figure 1: Bond Creep Frame

Table 1

Details of Bond Specimens used in Creep Tests

Specimen No.	Embedment Length (mm)	P_{ult} (avg) (N)	Dead Load (N)	Dead Load (% of P_{ult})	Time to Failure (min)
BC1, BC2	25	126	78.4	63.2	219,187
BC3	25	126	68.6	54.4	258
BC4, BC5	25	126	58.8	46.7	1479, 1435
BC6	25	126	53.9	42.8	2343
BC7, BC8	25	126	49.0	38.9	8898, 8957

The temperature inside the chamber was continuously monitored using a copper-constantan thermocouple connected to a Hewlett-Packard strip chart recorder through a reference bath. The peak-to-peak fluctuation during stable conditions was approximately 0.2 deg C. The humidity inside the chamber was very low, so that it was necessary to enclose the specimen in a Perspex box to reduce sublimation.

A specimen, frozen in a metal mold placed in a deep freeze, was carried to the test chamber in a pre-cooled insulated box and quickly installed in the loading frame with no load applied to the yarn. After one hour, the temperature of the specimen was again stable at -15°C and the load was applied by releasing the retaining lever. The electrical output from the L.V.D.T. was plotted on a strip chart recorder. Eight specimens were tested with loads varying from 78.4 N to 49.0 N (Table 1).

To study the effect of yarn on the tensile creep behaviour of ice, a steel frame to support the tension specimens when subjected to a hanging dead load, was placed inside the deep freeze. The thermostat of the deep freeze was adjusted until an average temperature of -15°C was obtained, with the operation of the compressor producing regular fluctuation between -14°C and -16°C within a period of approximately twenty minutes.

The specimen was suspended from a threaded steel rod equipped with a turn buckle (Figure 2) to raise the load off the base plate, thus applying the load smoothly, causing minimum temperature deviation. The elongation of the specimen between the two steel pins was observed using two L.V.D.T.'s, the separate outputs of which were plotted on a

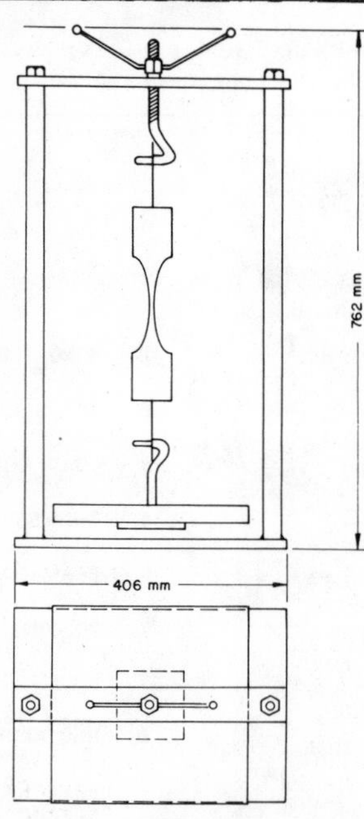

Figure 2: Dead-Load Tension Frame

Table 2

Details of Tensile Creep Specimens

Specimen No.	Lengths of Yarn	Avg. Nominal Failure Stress (MPa)	Nominal Stress from Dead Load (MPa)
TC4, TC5, TC6	2	2.33	1.70
TC7, TC8, TC9	0	1.82	1.70
TC10	4	2.33	1.70
TC11, TC12	0	1.82	1.36
TC13, TC14	2	2.33	1.36
TC15, TC16	4	2.33	1.36
TC17, TC18	0	1.82	1.02
TC1, TC19	2	2.33	1.02
TC20	4	2.33	1.02
TC21, TC22	0	1.82	0.68

2-channel strip chart recorder. Sublimation of the specimen was, in general, negligible if a bucket of crushed ice was left in the chamber. Table 2 shows the number of lengths of reinforcement and the dead loads for the specimens tested.

TEST RESULTS AND DISCUSSION

Results from the short load-duration tests were given in (1). Some of the results from the bond-creep experiments are presented in Figures 3 and 4. Selected tensile-creep curves from this study are given in Figures 5 - 8. Full details of this work have been described by Stanley, (11).

In the long load-duration bond tests, the deflection of the load beam indicated that the yarn exhibited definite three stage creep behaviour with decelerating primary, constant secondary, and accelerating tertiary creep, leading to failure for all loads applied to the specimens. From the data, deflection was plotted as a function of the

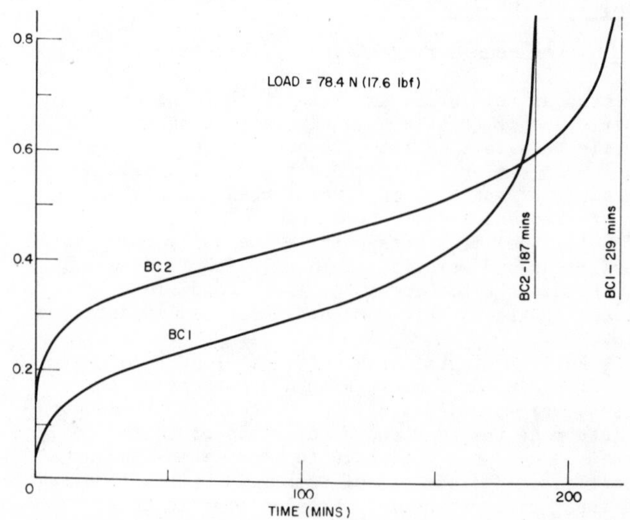

Figure 3: Deflection - Time Curves for Bond Specimens BC1 and BC2

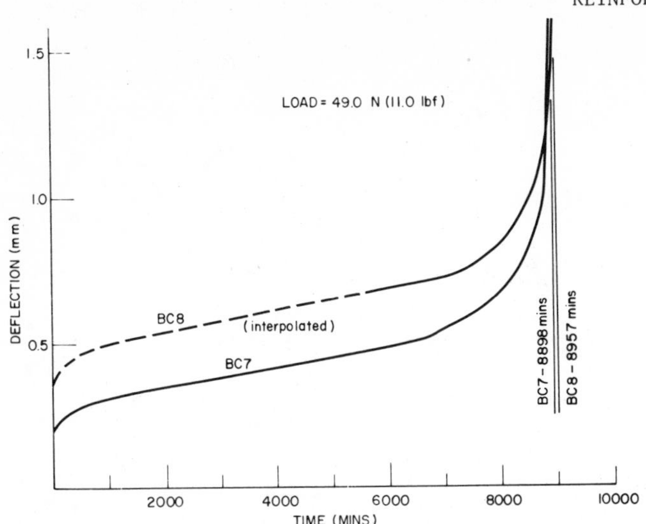

Figure 4: Deflection - Time Curves for Bond Specimens BC7 and BC8

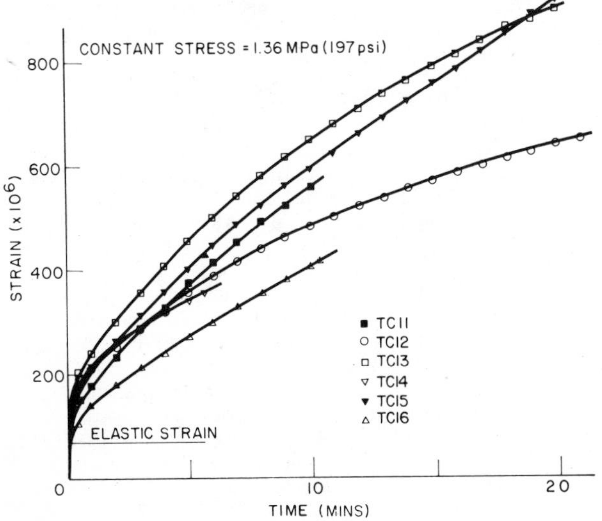

Figure 5: Creep Deformations of Tensile Specimens at Constant Stress of 1.36 MPa

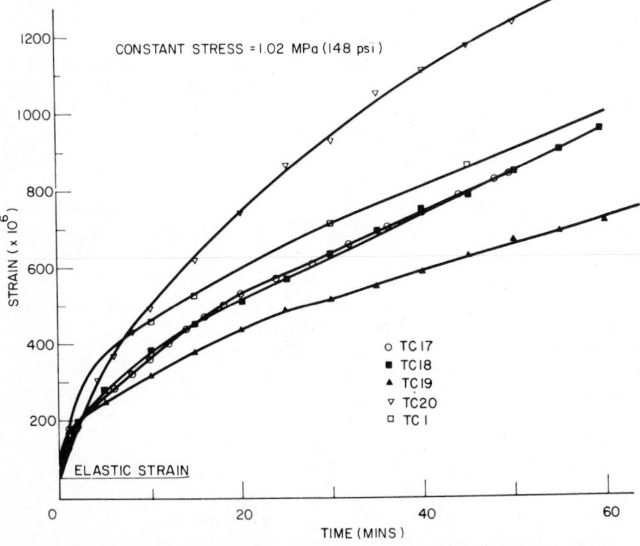

Figure 6: Creep Deformations of Tensile Specimens at Constant Stress of 1.02 MPa

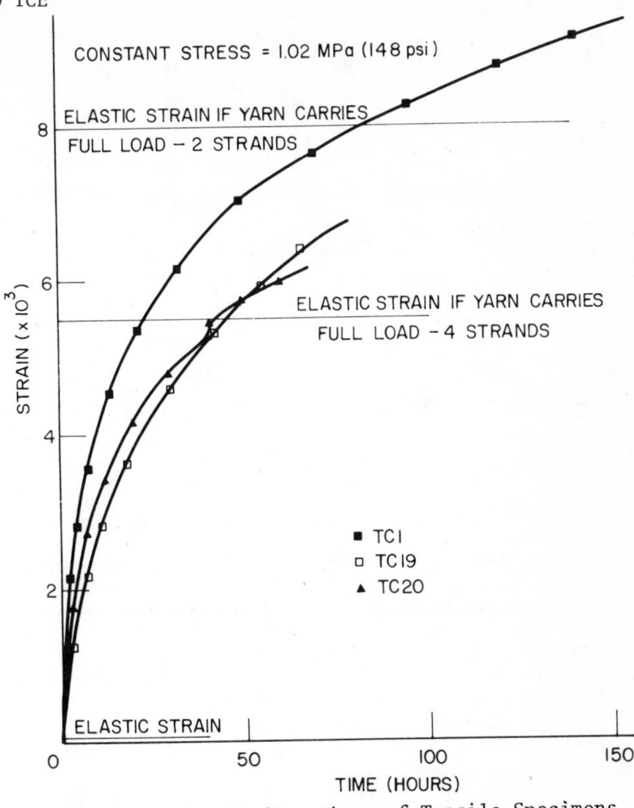

Figure 7: Creep Deformations of Tensile Specimens at Constant Stress of 1.02 MPa

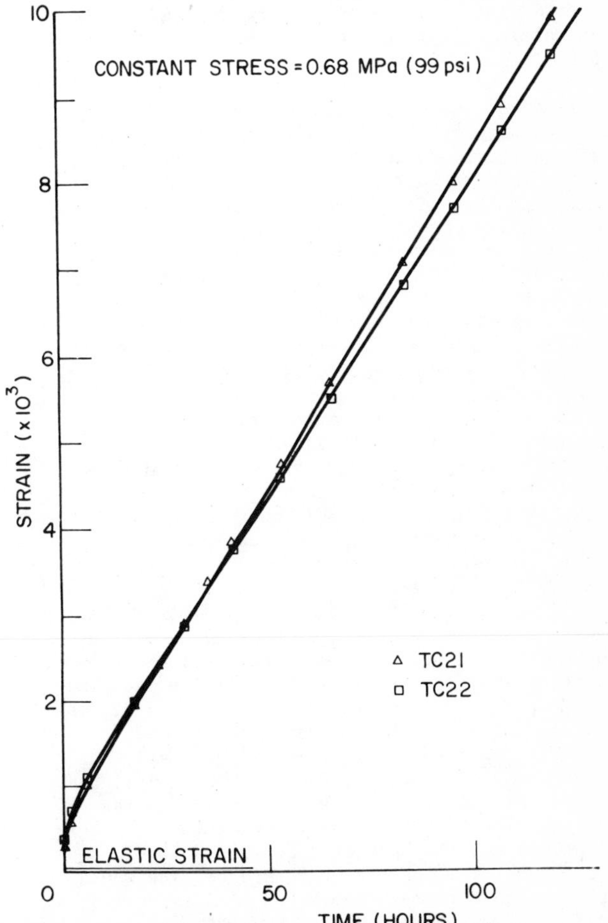

Figure 8: Creep Deformations of Tensile Specimens at Constant Stress of 0.68 MPa

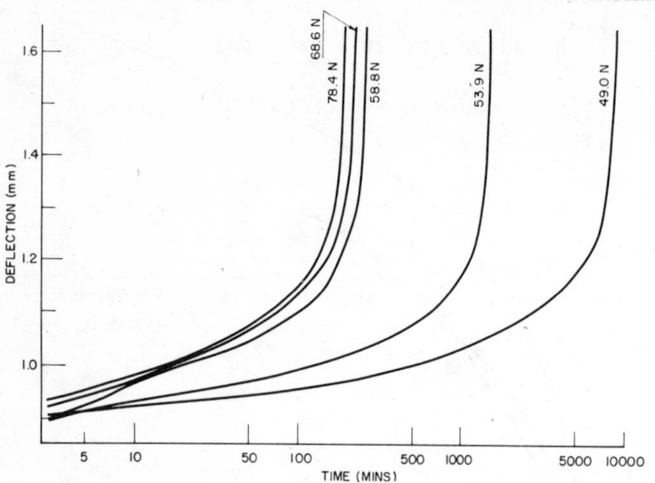

Figure 9: Comparison of Deflection - Time Curves from Bond Tests

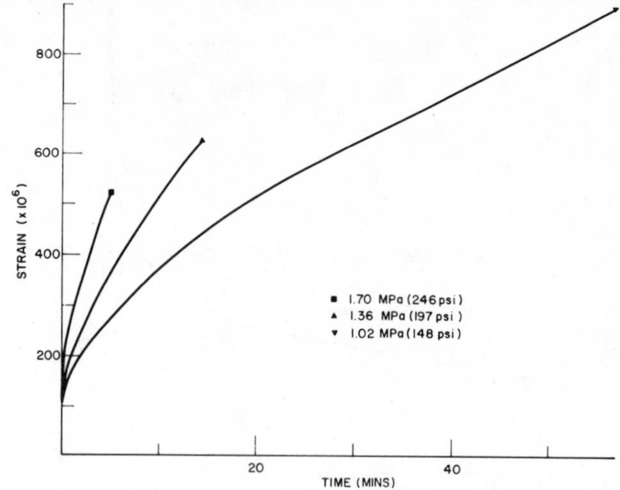

Figure 10: Average Creep Curves for Tensile Rupture at Constant Stress

log(time) (Figure 9) for each load. Accurate definition of the origins of the original creep curves was not possible since a small variable amount of beam deflection occurred at the instant of loading due to slip of the yarn. Therefore, comparison was based on the value of intercept made on the vertical deflection axis by the extrapolated straight line of secondary creep, this value being approximately 1 mm for all cases.

For pairs of specimens at equal loads (BC-1 and 2, BC-4 and 5, BC-7 and 8), the times to failure were very similar. In particular, the difference in test duration for specimens BC-7 and 8 was approximately 60 min, out of a total of approximately 150 h. Despite this observation, there is no evidence for a reasonable relationship between the load and any observable features of the bond-creep behaviour, including the time to failure. Based on the tests reported here, one concludes that as load increases, the time to failure and duration of secondary creep both decrease, while the secondary creep rate increases.

The results show that all loads down to 39% of the ultimate bond strength (observed in short load-duration tests) caused eventual bond failure, suggesting that special anchorage of the ends of a length of yarn in ice would be required if the yarn was to carry useful long-term loads.

In the long load-duration tension tests, all the specimens subjected to stresses greater than 1.02 MPa crept to failure. Most of the curves show that failure occurred towards the end of a decelerating creep stage, as suggested by Gold (5), with a relatively large range of failure times and average strains. The yarn does not appear to have any effect on the creep rupture strength at these high stresses.

A stress of 1.02 MPa produced similar creep behaviour in the early stages of loading with no apparent effect of the yarn on the ice. However, the reinforced specimens did not fail as the plain specimens did, but continued to creep at a decreasing rate until the experiments were stopped.

The plain specimens also did not fail when the stress was reduced to 0.68 MPa, and continued to creep at a constant rate until the load was removed. There may have been, therefore, a critical stress for the specimens between 0.68 MPa and 1.02 MPa below which the un-reinforced ice would not creep to failure. The value of this stress for S2, columnar-grained ice, has been reported as 0.55 MPa or less (5).

If the strain in the yarn of the reinforced specimens was the same as the failure strains in the plain ice subjected to a tensile stress of 1.02 MPa, the total force on the yarn must have been very low, less than approximately 12 N (1). This requires a stress in the ice of at least 0.98 MPa. It is unlikely that a critical stress, as described above, would be such an exact property of ice that the consistency of results, observed in these tests, would be attained. It is more probable that the yarn strengthens the ice, inasmuch as it inhibits propagation of potentially destructive cracks.

The curves of Figure 10 show the typical strain-time behaviour of the specimens creeping to failure at stresses of 1.70 MPa, 1.36 MPa and 1.02 MPa , and were obtained by averaging the initial portions of the relevant curves to the time of the earliest failure, and interpolating to the average of the failure strains and times. It can be seen that as stress increases, the time to failure, creep strain at failure and minimum creep rate (minimum slope of the curve) all decrease.

CONCLUSIONS

Although the short-term bond between ice and spun glass fibre yarn was observed to be adequate (1), the long term behaviour of the bond is not good, creep failure having been observed at relatively low stresses. In applications of this yarn to structures where such long-term loads would be encountered, the yarn would require adequate anchorage.

The yarn was observed to enhance the tensile-strength of ice in both short- and long-term loading situations. If long-term tensile stresses in an ice dome reinforced with this yarn were kept below 1.0 MPa, tensile creep rupture might be avoided.

The effectiveness of the yarn, which exhibits high flexibility at low strain levels might be considerably improved by pretensioning the yarn prior to embedment.

Acknowledgments

The results presented here were obtained in the course of research sponsored by the National Research Council of Canada, and the Defence Research Board of Canada.

REFERENCES

1. R. G. Stanley and P. G. Glockner, Proceedings 3rd International Conference on Port & Ocean Engineering under Arctic Conditions, (in press).
2. L. W. Gold, Tech. Paper No. 256, Div. Bldg., Res. , N.R.C. Canada, 1967.
3. L. W. Gold, Tech. Paper No. 369, Div. Bldg., Res., N.R.C. Canada, 1972.
4. Inland Waters Branch, Rept. Series No. 17, Canada, 1971.
5. L. W. Gold, Tech. Paper No. 283, Div. Bldg. Res., N.R.C. Canada, 1966.
6. A. S. Kraus, Res. Paper No. 176, Div. Bldg. Res., N.R.C. Canada, 1963.
7. R. L. Coble and W. D. Kingery, Proceedings, "Ice and Snow", Kingery (Ed.), M.I.T. Press, 1963.
8. B. Michel, M. Drovin, L. M. Lefebvre, P. Rosenberg, and R. Murray, Can. Geotech. J., 1974, vol 11, p. 599.
9. L. W. Gold, Can. Geotech. J., 1971,vol. 8, p. 170.
10. W. D. Kingery, D. W. Klick, J. E. Dykins, et al., U. S. Naval Civ. Eng. Lab., Tech. Rept. R189, 1962.
11. R. G. Stanley, M.Sc. Thesis, The University of Calgary, 1975.

DISCUSSION

J. L. Gerlitz (Shell Canada): Have you looked at the relationship between temperature and creep properties for the reinforced material?

P. G. Glockner: No, not on our reinforced ice -- but I agree that this is an extremely important aspect of our project and we are planning on investigating these problems. It should be mentioned that a lot of research work has been done on creep properties of plain ice.

J. E. Rymes (Rymes Engineering Co.): What was the utilization of water for the experimental domes -- this would be critical for applications in the Arctic.

P. G. Glockner: The amounts of water and time required for the erection of such domes depends on the thickness of the dome, the prevailing environmental condition (temperature and wind), on the spraying equipment and the appropriate setting of the nozzle, as well as on the experience of the personnel involved in the erection procedure. We found that with experience we became much more efficient in building up the design thickness of ice, in terms of using less and less water for each successive dome. Also, the time required for the last dome we built was substantially less than that required for the second dome, even taking into account the difference in thickness.

R. J. Cooke (National Energy Board): Could you comment on the effect and variability of very low ambient temperatures on the feasibility of applying water to form a large scale dome in the Arctic?

P. G. Glockner: The appropriate environmental conditions (temperature, wind,sunlight, etc.)have to be established or,alternatively, the size of water stream used will depend on such conditions as well as on the size of the structure to be erected. Of course, there are environmental conditions which could prohibit the efficient use of this proposed erection procedure.

F. S. Jeglic (CANMET): What is the effect of the interior temperature on the structural integrity of an ice dome?

P. G. Glockner: I believe that inside temperatures would be kept relatively high, i.e. just slightly below freezing, especially if outside temperatures are quite low, since under such conditions, the temperature on the inside surface of the ice will be substantially lower than the air temperature in the dome -- unless you had a very high velocity air flow and air circulation along the inside surface of the dome, which I believe is not very likely in the type of structures for which these ice domes are intended.

M. B. Ives (McMaster University): Sargent made the point this morning that the best igloo shape to avoid high stresses etc. is the catenoid. Your use of a spherical cap suggests you might not have the best shape to start with.

P. G. Glockner: The question of optimum shape is very intimately related to the loading condition to which the structure is subjected. If the dome were subjected to nothing else but dead load, perhaps it would be worthwhile to start thinking about such problems. However, the dome will be subjected to unsymmetric snow loads, wind loads, etc., and therefore we will have to design for some bending. Also, if one wanted to eliminate circumferential reinforcing, one would have to be very careful in providing just exactly the right kind of support conditions which would provide the reactions necessary for a state of membrane stress. For practical uses, one would not guarantee that the reactions will be exactly the right kind so as to avoid bending effects near the boundary. One of the main reasons for including reinforcement is to take care of temperature effects during erection and to prevent formation of temperature/ erection cracking. Finally, if you keep the height/span ratio of your spherical dome low enough, i.e. keep the angle of the tangent at the lower boundary shallow enough, you will have a purely compressive state of stress in the dome in both the meridional and circumferential directions. Also, I believe it is easier to make a spherical inflatable than some other geometric shape.

P. R. Slimmon (Bethlehem Steel): Is there a design stress level where creep properties will not be a problem for long term service? Is there really any problem in making your inflatable to a shape that should be structurally more efficient than a hemisphere?

P. G. Glockner: More work (research and experience with prototypes) is required to establish safe design stress levels for bond, tensile and flexural stresses and compression and shear stress levels. Only then can we start using reinforced ice as a structural material in the sense that I have suggested here.

B. Ladanyi (Ecole Polytechnique): There is an old saying that "one should not throw stones in a glass house". Is this valid also for an ice house? Or, in other words, how resistant is your reinforced ice dome to impact?

P. G. Glockner We have not done any tests on concentrated or distributed impact loading. Clearly, given a sufficiently large blow by some steel hammer or sharp equipment, we could fracture these types of structures locally. However, since they are reinforced, local fracture would likely remain localized and could easily be repaired.

K. N. Street (R. M. Hardy and Assoc.): I would like to point out that the fiber composite literature contains at the present time most of the basic mechanistic information required to explain your results, in both the static tensile tests and the continuous fiber creep tests (see for example "Properties of Fibre Composites", Proceedings of NPL Conference IPC Science and Technology, 1971). Your creep problem appears to be one of fiber - ice adhesion and hence attention should be concentrated on enhancing this adhesion under conditions of creep. Randomly oriented fibers sprayed onto your dome along with your water may offer some attractive lubrication advantages.

G. M. Tuttle (Gulf Oil Canada): I do not see the applicability of constructing ice houses in the Arctic for the following reasons:

a. Water cost. The cost of water for drilling rig use is about 15¢/lb, which would make a large structure very expensive.

b. Hazard. The obvious problem of collapse with warming, either inside or outside.

c. Usefulness. The shelter would only be good for temporary winter storage of a product stored at sub-freezing temperatures.

d. Awkwardness. One would have to transport the inflatable which would be extremely heavy for large structures. One would also need air compressors to inflate the apparatus, and an anchoring system for the base.

e. Alternative. Why not just leave the inflatable inflated? One would not even need an air lock if one would use an internal liner, such as in the inflatable used at the Calgary Tennis Club during the winter, 1975/76.

In summary, the work that is being done at the University of Calgary could be very useful, but I fail to see its direct usefulness in the Arctic.

P. G. Glockner: As I tried to point out, the proposed erection procedure is limited to sites where water (sea or fresh) is available. One could try to melt snow but that would put the cost up. Several other thoughts come to mind: for example, blowing snow (powdered) onto the inflatable and provided the surface of the inflatable is warm due to higher inside temperatures, the inner layer of the snow would melt and form an ice layer. This would be very inexpensive. The main merit of the proposed structure is the fact that it attempts to use a material which is available on site.

The structures are proposed as temporary or intermediary enclosures. For winter storage of equipment and/or material we don't have the problem of safety. In the case of domes for ice-rinks and skating arenas, one would have to establish the safe life span and safe environmental conditions (ie. outside temperature vs inside temperature). When analysis and experiments predict possible failure, use would be discontinued. Short periods of "chinook-like" winds would not present any serious problems, especially during the "dark" period, since night temperatures still go down to well below freezing. Structures are safe when properly designed and used under the conditions for which they are intended.

c. I have already answered the usefulness question. I disagree, of course. I happen to think these structures will serve a very useful purpose for the people in the Arctic.

d. Awkward? No. Another main advantage of the proposed structures is the relatively low weight of the materials (inflatable and reinforcing cables made of fibreglass) which need to be shipped in. I am assuming that there are facilities available at the site to pump water and air. Otherwise you could take such equipment along on the plane - the pumping equipment does not have to be too large. Anchoring cables are also required to anchor the inflatable - here again we are talking about materials which are relatively light and/or represent a relatively small load for one of the larger planes flying into the North.

e. No. As I mentioned, inflatables have been tried by the Defense Research Board as temporary enclosures for the north some 10-20 years ago. Without some stiffening structure, they are not stable in the high winds of the north. If you go to substantial stiffening, liners, etc., you defeat the purpose of this proposal, because you are again increasing the quantity, bulk, and weight of the materials that have to be shipped into the north.

SULPHUR CONCRETE
A NEW MATERIAL FOR ARCTIC CONSTRUCTION

A. H. Vroom
Sulphur Innovations Ltd.
3015 58th Avenue S.E.
Calgary, Alberta, T2C 0B4
Canada

A strong, durable sulphur concrete has recently been developed which appears attractive for many applications in Arctic construction. It contains no portland cement and develops strength immediately on cooling from the molten state. It consequently does not have the customary freezing problems associated with cold weather concreting. It offers high strength, high corrosion resistance, low thermal conductivity, and requires no water in the mix. The availability of surplus sulphur in Northern Alberta and British Columbia should also provide some economic incentive for considering its use, particularly in the Northwest Territories and Alaska.

INTRODUCTION

Sulphur has been considered as a possible cementing agent for different aggregates for more than a century, with patents dating back to 1859. In 1900, McKay (1) obtained a patent for sulphur compositions suitable for pavements, conduits, roofing, etc. The successful use of a sulphur/sand mortar in pouring joints for a sewer conveying acid waste from a pulp mill was described in 1920 (2). In 1924, Kobbe (3) reported on the acid-resistant properties of cements and concretes prepared from sulphur-coke compositions.

Duecker (4,5) studied sulphur-aggregate compositions in the 1930's and reported on their potential use for construction and repair of acid tanks, flooring and corrosion-resistant pipe. He was perhaps the first to demonstrate that fluctuating temperatures had a deleterious effect on the strength of many sulphur compositions but that the addition of a "plasticizer" such as an olefine polysulphide, e.g. Thiokol*, would significantly improve the durability.

Many subsequent investigators have examined plasticizers for sulphur but with limited success. Some of these chemicals have been too expensive for use in general construction materials and some impart a particularly objectionable odour to the resulting product. Dicyclopentadiene (DCPD) has been observed to impart some stabilization or plasticization to a number of different sulphur systems (6-9) but it does not appear to have been recognized by some experimenters that DCPD vapour exhibits considerable toxicity (10). In the Soviet Union, the maximum permissable concentration in a working environment has been set at 1 mg/m^3 (0.185 ppm).

Another significant contribution to sulphur concrete technology has been made by Crow et al (11) but they did not use plasticizing additives and did not report on the durability of their specimens.

Since 1969, there has been an increasing surplus of by-product sulphur as a result of pollution abatement programs in many countries of the world. Canada is the largest involuntary producer of sulphur, principally from sour gas processing and currently has sulphur stockpiles totalling approximately 20 million ton. Canada's rapidly increasing sulphur surplus has provided incentives to develop new large volume uses for sulphur (12,13).

Investigations conducted by the author (7) in 1972-3 laid the groundwork for new inexpensive methods of producing durable sulphur concrete. About the same time, some preliminary tests were carried out at McGill University (14) and the University of Calgary (15) to gain some experience in the design, construction and testing of structural members made with sulphur concrete. An intensive research and development program over the last 3 years by Sulphur Innovations Ltd., has resulted in the development of a variety of sulphur concretes which have now been proven through laboratory and field evaluation to be attractive construction materials for many applications and particularly for use in the Arctic.

CHARACTERISTICS OF SULFURCRETE

"Sulfurcrete" is a term which has been adopted to describe the sulphur concretes developed by Sulphur Innovations Ltd. The name has been registered as a trademark in Canada and the U.S.A. Patents are pending in these countries and many others.

The major distinction between Sulfurcrete and conventional hydraulic concretes lies in the composition of the cement paste. In portland cement concrete, the cement-water paste sets and hardens through a complex of hydration reactions whose rates are strongly influenced by ambient conditions and additives.

In Sulfurcrete, the paste consists of liquid sulphur, a viscosity-increasing or stiffening agent and a proprietary, stabilizing additive. The setting or hardening of Sulfurcrete is purely a physical phenomenon dependent solely on the rates of phase change of the sulphur.

Elemental sulphur in the solid state possesses

* Thiokol Chemical Corp., New Jersey, U.S.A.

a pale yellow colour, easily masked by darker or more intense colours of added materials. Thus Sulfurcrete in its usual formulations is barely distinguishable from portland cement concrete in appearance. Due to a somewhat higher density of the Sulfurcrete paste, the density of Sulfurcrete is 3 to 6% higher than that of portland cement concrete utilizing the same aggregates. While some compounds of sulphur possess vile odours, elemental sulphur has a very faint but non-repulsive odour. The sulphur odour in Sulfurcrete is barely detectible and, where desirable, can be eliminated completely by a coat of sealer or paint.

Virtually all aggregates usable in portland cement concrete can also be incorporated in Sulfurcrete. On the other hand, Sulfurcrete can be made with certain low grade aggregates which are unsuitable for portland cement concrete. Aggregates containing significant amounts of organic matter and silt may also be used successfully.

Elemental sulphur contracts in volume by 7.9% on cooling from the melt (115°C) to its stable (orthorhombic) crystalline state. For a molten Sulfurcrete mix containing 17 vol% sulphur, this contraction would be 1.3% of the total mix volume. Most of the shrinkage occurs in the vertical dimension such that lateral and bottom form dimensions are reproduced very closely. Because the setting and hardening of the sulphur cement is a physical process and not an irreversible chemical process, pouring can be carried out over a wide range of temperature conditions without concern for damage to the mix. For example, Sulfurcrete blocks 20 in. x 20 in. x 10 in. thick have been poured outdoors at -34°C without difficulty,and directly on an ice surface.

The shrinkage of sulphur cements from the plastic/molten state to the solid/hardened state is quite distinct from the thermal expansion of the hardened state. Sulphur cement paste has a linear coefficient of expansion of 1.0×10^{-5}/deg C between 20 and 60°C compared with portland cement pastes with linear coefficients of $(1.1 - 2.0) \times 10^{-5}$/deg C.

Because of the excellent insulating properties of elemental sulphur, Sulfurcretes have thermal conductivities in the range 3 - 6 BTU in./$ft^2h°F$ (0.4 to 0.9 W/m K) compared with 6 - 9 BTU in./$ft^2h°F$(0.9 to 1.3 W/m K) for normal concretes. Furthermore, Sulfurcrete is essentially inert to chemical attack by acids or aqueous salt solutions in contrast with concrete which is corroded by these environments.

Mechanical Properties

The strength of Sulfurcrete, like that of portland cement (p.c.) concrete, is influenced by the strength and surface texture of the aggregate and by the mix design. On the other hand, the ultimate strength of p.c. concrete can also be adversely affected by many factors, such as quality of water* used, age of mix before pouring, temperature during curing, evaporation or freezing of moisture content during curing, presence of moisture content during curing, presence of admixtures to accelerate curing, etc. Sulfurcrete strengths are not affected by such factors.

Table 1 compares qualitatively a typical Sulfurcrete with a 5 ksi (34 MPa) portland cement concrete. Table 2 lists examples of physical test data of Sulfurcrete made from different aggregates.

Compressive strengths of most field-poured concrete lies in the range of 2 - 5 ksi (14 - 34 MPa). Using similar aggregates, Sulfurcrete will have compressive strengths in the range of 4 to 10 ksi (30 to 70 MPa).

Flexural strength of Sulfurcrete, determined by three-point loading, is generally in the order of 1.3 to 1.4 ksi (9 to 10 MPa) with normal graded aggregates and 0.65 to 1.0 ksi (4.5 to 6.9 MPa) with lightweight aggregates (expanded clay and shale.) Tensile strength of Sulfurcrete, determined by the splitting tensile test using 4 in. (100 mm) x 8 in. (200 mm) cylinders, is generally 0.55 to 0.675 ksi (3.8 to 4.7 MPa) with normal aggregates and 0.325 to 0.400 ksi (2.2 to 2.8 MPa) with lightweight aggregates.

Creep behaviour of Sulfurcrete, measured under 1 ksi (7 MPa) compressive load at ambient laboratory temperature, appears to approximate that of portland cement concrete (12). After 7 months, the creep rate of a typical Sulfurcrete was observed to average 7.5×10^{-12}/s at 1 ksi (7 MPa) with an initial elastic strain of 1.74×10^{-4}. There is some indication that the extent of creep and elastic strain is roughly proportional to the sulphur content of the Sulfurcrete, e.g., specimens made with fine sand as the sole aggregate and twice the normal sulphur content showed approximately twice as much creep and initial elastic strain.

The stress-strain curve of Sulfurcrete under compressive loading is essentially linear up to the point of failure, indicating perfectly elastic behaviour and a somewhat higher degree of brittleness than p.c.concrete. Incorporating a small amount (less than 1 wt%) of chopped glass fibres in the mix alters the shape of the curve so that it resembles more closely a typical concrete stress-strain curve. The presence of glass fibres increases impact resistance (toughness), tensile and flexural strength. The effect of glass fibre reinforcement on some physical properties of sulphur cement paste and a Sulfurcrete mortar mix are illustrated in Table 3 and Figure 1.

Table 1

Properties of Sulfurcrete

Property	Comparison with 5ksi P.C. Concrete	Testing Laboratory*
Compressive Strength	Greater	1
Flexural Strength	Greater	1
Splitting Tensile Strength	Greater	2
Impact Strength	Slightly Less	4
Modulus of Elasticity and Poisson's ratio in compression	Greater	2
Compressive Creep	Less	2
Bond Strength to Reinforcing Steel	Greater	2
Coefficient of Linear Expansion	Equivalent	2
Water Tightness	Greater	2
Thermal Conductivity	Less	3
Durability under Thermal Cycling	Equivalent	4
Abrasion Resistance	Equivalent	2
Weathering Resistance	Equivalent	4
Corrosion Resistance	Much Greater	4
Fire Resistance	Much Less	4

* 1 - EBA Engineering Consultants Ltd., Calgary
2 - R. M. Hardy and Associates Ltd., Calgary
3 - Ontario Research Foundation
4 - Sulphur Innovations Ltd., Calgary

* Presence of silt or humic acids may be detrimental and salt may cause corrosion of prestressing strands.

Table 2

Representative Sulfurcrete Test Data with Different Aggregates

	Aggregate			
	Graded Gravel (3/4in. Max.)	Athabasca Oil Tailings Sand	Expanded Clay (1/4 in. Max.)	Expanded Shale (3/4 in. Max.)
Density, lb/ft^3 (kg/m^3)	152.7 (2446)	142.2 (2278)	111.6 (1788)	107.2 (1717)
Compressive Strength(ksi)	9.43	6.76	8.27	5.29
Splitting Tensile Strength psi(kPa)[1]	650 (4480)	340 (2340)	---	430 (2960)
Flexural Strength[2] psi (kPa)	1340 (9240)	---	920 (6340)	660 (4550)
Elastic Modulus psi x 10^6	6.1	3.86	---	---
Poisson's Ratio[3]	0.226	0.140	---	---
Linear Coefficient of Expansion (x 10^{-6}/deg C)	8.6	14.5	---	8.8
Abrasion Resistance[4] (% of weight loss)	1.4	1.6	---	0.82

[1] Measured on 4 in. x 8 in. test cylinders

[2] The modulus of rupture measured using 3 1/2 x 3 1/2 x 15 in. test bars by the third point loading method

[3] Measured using 6 in. x 12 in. test cylinders

[4] The abrasion test consisted of carrying a 4 in x 8 in. test cylinder together with 18-1 7/8 in. steel balls through 500 revolutions of a Los Angeles abrasion apparatus with the drum blades removed. The results are to be compared with a 0.62% weight loss of 5,000 psi portland cement concrete specimens

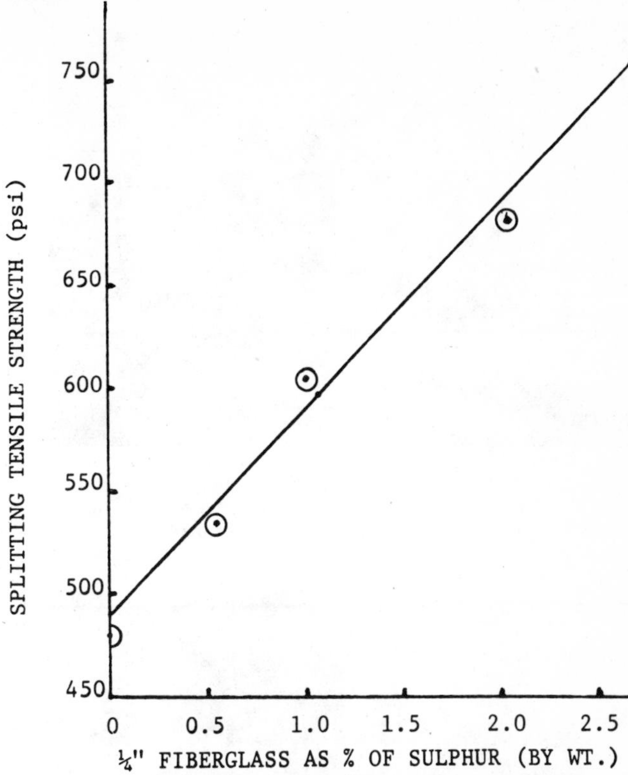

Figure 1: Effect of added glass fibre on the tensile strength of a concrete sand Sulfurcrete

Reinforcement

In addition to the use of glass fibre as reinforcement, Sulfurcrete can be reinforced by conventional methods using steel reinforcing bar, mesh or prestressing strands. The bond strength to reinforcing steel appears to be at least as great as that obtained with portland cement concrete.

There has been no evidence of corrosion of steel reinforcement in Sulfurcrete products which have been exposed to the elements for a two-year period. This may be due in part to the very low moisture permeability of Sulfurcrete, e.g. prolonged soaking of 4 in. x 8 in. test cylinders results in a water absorption generally in the range of 0 to 1.0 wt%.

Durability

Much of the effort which has gone into the development of Sulfurcrete to date has been directed toward enhancing the durability of the product. The performance of Sulfurcrete has been studied under freeze-thaw cycling, thermal shock treatment (wet and dry), hot water soaking, exposure to salt water brine, sodium sulphate solution (hot and cold), saturated lime water and 50% sulphuric acid. Through the use of tests such as these, proprietary additives have been developed which provide Sulfurcrete with high degrees of durability if formulated properly.

The presence of water-expansive clay in an aggregate is detrimental to the durability of Sulfurcrete which is to be exposed to continual wetting. Sulfurcrete made with clay-free aggregate or with clay which has been kiln-fired suffers essentially no strength loss after 150 cycles of freezing in air and thawing in water. Similarly, such Sulfurcrete has stood up without visible effect to 8 months exposure to 4% salt water brine, 10% sodium sulphate and 50% sulphuric acid.

Table 3

Properties of Fiberglass Reinforced Sulphur Cement Paste and Sand Sulfurcrete

	Paste		Concrete Sand Sulfurcrete	
	Plain	2% Fiber	Plain	0.4% Fiber
Density lb/ft^3 (kg/m^3)	137.0 (2194)	128.2 (2054)	134.5 (2154)	138.7 (2222)
Compressive Strength ksi(MPa)	5.18 (35.7)	6.00 (41.4)	5.60 (38.6)	6.78 (46.7)
Splitting Tensile Strength psi (kPa)	122 (841)	---	480 (3310)	965 (6650)
Flexural Strength psi (kPa)	147 (1013)	1,320 (9100)	1,020 (7033)	1,166* (8039)
Impact Strength**	1	5	2	4

* Suspected to be lower than true value

** Impact strengths ranked on an arbitrary scale of 5, with p.c. concrete set at 3, by observation of the degree of shattering of a 4 in. x 1/2 in. disc dropped 3 ft onto a finished p.c. concrete floor

Figure 2: Introducing additives to heated transit mix truck containing Sulfurcrete mix. (Note heat-containing shroud over drum.) Loading ramp is built entirely of Sulfurcrete

Figure 3: Pouring a highway median barrier

Figure 4: Sulfurcrete being dumped from conventional asphalt batch plant mixer

Fire Resistance

One characteristic of Sulfurcrete which will limit its end-use is its relatively poor fire resistance. Sulphur cements will re-melt when raised to a temperature in excess of 113°C (235°F). This can be an advantage if one wished to recycle the product and reform it, but it is a disadvantage to its use where it might be exposed to fire.

As a result of its relatively low thermal conductivity, a Sulfurcrete object several inches thick would lose strength in a fire only slowly. Coating or cladding with fire resistant, insulating material would naturally improve its fire rating. On cooling again, Sulfurcrete will regain its original strength (although not its original form if flow has occurred).

If a Sulfurcrete surface is exposed to flame, there will be some burning of sulphur with the evolution of sulphur dioxide gas which is both noxious and toxic. With most aggregates, however, Sulfurcrete is self-extinguishing and will not propagate a flame. The flammability is greater when lightweight aggregates are used and when the sulphur content rises over 20 wt%, e.g. when no coarse aggregate is used. Additives are available which not only render Sulfurcrete non-flammable but which suppress the evolution of sulphur dioxide. Use of these additives, however, can significantly increase the cost of Sulfurcrete.

SULFURCRETE MANUFACTURE AND COSTS

The manufacture of Sulfurcrete involves simply the mixing of liquid sulphur with hot, dry aggregates, introducing proprietary additives, then pouring the molten mix into forms or molds where it cools and quickly hardens. The principal classes of equipment can be identified by the materials to be handled and the major operations as follows:

a) Sulphur - handling, storage, melting, metering.
b) Aggregates - crushing, grading, handling, storage, drying, proportioning/metering.
c) Additives - handling, storage, metering.
d) Mixing.
e) Placing - forming/molding, compacting, finishing.

Most of the necessary equipment is readily available from various suppliers with easily-made modifications required for some components (Figures 2,3 and 4). The process closely resembles that of asphaltic concrete production, substituting sulphur for asphalt, but in terms of workability, molten Sulfurcrete looks like and behaves very similarly to plastic p.c. concrete.

Forming materials may be of any construction material capable of withstanding the hot mix temperatures (120 - 150°C). Steel or aluminum provide good form/mold release unless actually imbedded in the mix. Vibration is normally used for compaction.

Due to the rapid setting properties of Sulfurcrete,.there is little time for finishing the placed material much beyond screeding and some trowelling (Figure 5). Heated screeds and trowels will extend the time available for finishing and may be necessary under certain circumstances. Slumps attainable with Sulfurcrete are continuously variable. With low-cost additives, a nearly zero slump plastic concrete of very workable consistency may be obtained. The similar handling/flow properties of plastic Sulfurcrete and plastic p.c. concrete indicate that any difficulties to be encountered in slip-forming in any direction and at any thickness would be solely associated with the high operating temperature.

The relative costs of Sulfurcrete and portland

Figure 5: The start of hand trowelling of a manhole base

cement concrete are dependent on so many factors that generalized conclusions in this regard are meaningless. Aggregate costs will usually be similar for both materials. Capital and operating costs will generally be slightly higher for Sulfurcrete. The most significant factor, however, will be the relative cost of sulphur and of portland cement delivered to the job site. Using a graded aggregate, Sulfurcrete requires about 16 wt% sulphur in the mix, or about 650 lb/yd^3 (385 kg/m^3). Where high strength is not required the quantity of portland cement can be reduced substantially below this level, but low strength Sulfurcrete cannot be achieved by a corresponding lowering of the sulphur content as liquid sulphur (not water) provides the necessary fluidity in the mix. At the present time, however, the selling price of sulphur in, for example, Edmonton is less than half that of portland cement and the price differential is steadily increasing.

For Arctic applications, many other factors will influence the cost of the finished product. Total energy requirements for producing a cubic yard (0.76 m^3) of Sulfurcrete are approximately 450 mBTU (113 cal) more than that for unheated concrete (neglecting the energy required for portland cement manufacturing). If, in the Arctic, diesel fuel at $1.00 per gal (22¢/ℓ) were used for aggregate drying and sulphur melting the additional energy cost would be approximately $2.60/yd^3 ($3.40/m^3).

No estimates are made here, however, of the savings which might result from Sulfurcrete's lack of requirement for water, lack of freezing problems after pouring, faster setting, higher strength, possible replacement of some steel by glass fibre, and better insulation. These savings will vary with different construction job requirements.

POTENTIAL APPLICATIONS AND FIELD TRIALS

As a result of the relatively poor fire resistance of Sulfurcrete, emphasis to date has been placed on demonstrating its suitability for use in applications where fire hazards would not be great and, particularly, where advantage might be taken of its unique properties. A list of some of the potential applications being considered is presented in Table 4.

Early in 1974, Sulphur Innovations Ltd. started producing precast Sulfurcrete products experimentally for field trials and general performance evaluation. These products include parking curbs (Figure 6) for use in parking lots, sidewalk slabs for residential use, highway median barriers (Figure 7), pipeline swamp weights and 2 ft (0.6 m) cubes for use in retaining walls. More than two hundred 550 lb (250 kg) swamp weights (Figure 8) were installed on natural

Table 4

Some Potential Arctic Applications for Sulfurcrete

PRECAST:
1. DOLOS, RIPRAP AND OTHER BLOCKS FOR BREAKWATERS
2. PILINGS
3. PIPELINE WEIGHTS
4. COMPRESSOR PADS
5. PIPE AND CULVERT
FIELD-POURED:
1. PAVEMENT FOR AIRSTRIPS, ROADS AND HIGHWAYS, ETC.
2. FOOTINGS AND FOUNDATIONS
3. CONSTRUCTION AND EQUIPMENT PADS
4. GROUND ANCHORS FOR TOWERS, ETC.
5. PIERS, PILINGS, BREAKWATERS
6. STORAGE TANKS
7. SLOPE STABILIZATION (SPRAY APPLICATION)

Figure 6: Sulfurcrete parking bumpers

Figure 7: Highway median barrier weighing approximately 4,000 lb (1,800 kg)

Figure 8: Swamp weights for a 6 in. (150 mm) pipeline awaiting shipment

Figure 9: Spreading a finish coat of Sulfurcrete on an existing Sulfurcrete base floor for a storage bin

gas pipelines in Northern Alberta during the winter of 1975-76 by two major gas line companies.

Since the spring of 1975, a number of field pours of Sulfurcrete have also been carried out (Figure 9). These include a 20 ft (6 m) pad at the entrance to a concrete block plant where it has successfully withstood heavy traffic for more than a year, a loading ramp and an aggregate bin floor.

CONCLUSIONS

Sulphur concrete can be considered as a material suitable for many types of Arctic construction. Its use eliminates the need for mixing water, the usual freezing problems associated with cold weather concreting, salt corrosion problems, and allows the use of lower grade aggregates. It also offers high strength, low thermal conductivity and some potential cost savings.

Sulphur concrete manufacture consumes less than half the energy required for the manufacture of the portland cement used in an equivalent amount of conventional concrete. As energy costs increase, the cost differential between Sulfurcrete and portland cement concrete is expected to increase.

Acknowledgments

Financial assistance for much of the earlier work in the development of this sulphur concrete was received from the National Research Council of Canada, the Sulphur Development Institute of Canada (SUDIC) and the Provincial Government of Alberta. The author also wishes to acknowledge the substantial contribution made by K. M. Zaun and E. D. Day to the success of this development.

REFERENCES

1. G. McKay, U.S. Pat., 643,251, 1900.
2. Pulp & Paper Mag. of Canada, 1920, vol. 17, p. 998.
3. W. H. Kobbe, Ind. Eng. Chem., 1924, vol. 16, pp 1026-28.
4. W. W. Duecker, Chem. & Met. Eng., 1934, vol. 41, pp. 583-86.
5. W. W. Duecker, Mining & Metallurgy, 1938, vol. 20, pp. 473-476.
6. J. M. Dale and A. C. Ludwig, Civil Eng., 1967, vol. 37, (12), pp. 66-68.
7. J. J. Beaudoin and P. J. Sereda, Building Res. Note No. 92, N.R.C., Ottawa, 1974.
8. B. R. Currell, A. J. Williams, A. J. Mooney and B. J. Nash, Advances in Chem. Series 140, A.C.S., Washington, D.C. 1975, pp. 1-17.
9. T. A. Sullivan, W. C. McBee and D. D. Blue, Advances in Chemistry, Series 140, A.C.S. Washington, D.C., 1975, pp. 55-74.
10. E. R. Kinkead, U. C. Pozanni, D. L. Geary and C. P. Carpentier, Toxicology and Appl. Pharmacology, 1971, vol. 20, pp. 552-561.
11. L. J. Crow and R. C. Bates, U.S. Bureau of Mines, Report 7349, 1970.
12. A. H. Vroom, "Sulphur Utilization - A Challenge and an Opportunity", N.R.C. Report No. 12241, Ottawa, 1971.
13. A. H. Vroom, Hydrocarbon Processing 1972, vol. 51, (7), pp. 79-85.
14. A. Ortega, W. Rybczynski, S. Ayad, W. Ali and A. Acheson, in "The ECOL Operation", School of Architecture, McGill University, Montreal, Canada, 1972, pp. 21-56.
15. R. E. Loov, A. H. Vroom and M. A. Ward, J. Prestress. Concrete Inst. 1974, vol. 19, pp.86-95.
16. R. M. Hardy & Associates, Calgary, Alberta, private communication.

DISCUSSION

E. P. Antoniades (Chevron Research): There is a fortunate triple coincidence that characterizes a number of sulphur-based products: 1) the need for new outlets of surplus sulphur; 2) the need for unconventional materials with processing characteristics suitable to the Arctic; 3) the proximity of the source of raw material supply (e.g. Alberta sulphur) to the potential demand.

Is there a special reason for introducing additives after the sulphur and aggregate have been mixed, rather than thoroughly dispersing the additives into the sulphur first and then introducing the aggregate?

A. H. Vroom: We prefer to introduce the additives last because they are sensitive to overheating and could be degraded by contact with particles of aggregate at over 150°C. The additive we have developed is a polymer containing sulphur so you don't get large crystals. It also seems to improve the bond between the sulphur and aggregate and reduces the moisture penetration.

E. P. Antoniades: When you make swamp weights or curbs for parking lots, do you have to vibrate the Sulfurcrete in order to get rid of voids?

A. H. Vroom: Generally speaking it is best to vibrate. You get a better surface finish, eliminate some voids, and you can use less sulphur, using a stiffer mix. We have worked very hard and succeeded in formulating a mix which gives an absolute minimum of shrinkage voids. Air-entrainment voids, however, do depend on the technique of pouring and use of vibrators. We vibrate in much the same manner as is done with ordinary concrete.

B. Hawbolt (University of British Columbia): Is there not a greater differential in the thermal expansion coefficient between sulphur and steel than with portland cement and steel? Does this limit the use of steel reinforcement where thermal cycling will occur?

A. H. Vroom: The thermal expansion coefficient of Portland cement concrete is influenced by the aggregate used and the curing conditions, but generally it is slightly lower than that of steel. The thermal expansion coefficient of Sulfurcrete is only very slightly higher than that of portland cement concrete when similar aggregates are used. From the viewpoint of thermal expansion, Sulfurcrete should be at least as compatible with steel reinforcement as portland cement concrete.

P. G. Glockner (University of Calgary): What is the problem if you do not have completely dry aggregate?

A. H. Vroom: If moist aggregate is mixed with liquid sulphur steam will be evolved until the aggregate is dry. If a Sulfurcrete mix is poured and allowed to cool while bubbles of steam are being formed within it, some of these bubbles are likely to be trapped, leaving voids in the product.

P. G. Glockner: Do you feel there is a problem with corrosion of steel reinforcing in Sulfurcrete, and if so, do you have any other reinforcing materials in mind to be used in order to enhance the tensile and flexural strength of Sulfurcrete?

A. H. Vroom: The examination of steel reinforcement in specimens of Sulfurcrete which have been exposed to the Calgary climate for 2 1/2 years has shown no evidence of corrosion. Many types of fibre may also be used for reinforcement, however, including glass, asbestos and synthetics capable of withstanding the temperature of liquid sulphur.

O. Draganiuk (Syncrude Canada): You mentioned the use of lower grade aggregates. Can lower grades of sulphur be used for Sulfurcrete?

A. H. Vroom: Lower grades of sulphur can certainly be used for Sulfurcrete and very impure sulphur has been used in much of our work with no ill effects.

O. Draganiuk: In the city of Calgary how would the cost of Sulfurcrete compare with conventional portland cement concrete?

A. H. Vroom: If manufactured on a similar scale, Sulfurcrete should be somewhat less expensive to produce than a good quality portland cement concrete in the city of Calgary.

I. Ismail (Montreal Engineering): What are the wear characteristics of Sulfurcrete?

A. H. Vroom: Wear characteristics are best related to specific end-use conditions and the tests tailored accordingly. Sidewalk slabs have shown no undue wear over a two-year period. Road tests are currently being planned to obtain information on resistance to wear by heavy traffic. A modified Los Angeles abrasion test has shown slightly greater abrasion of Sulfurcrete as compared with normal concrete but this may have been due to differences in the aggregate used.

A. Ismail: Is there a risk of explosion due to sulphur dust created by abrasion?

A. H. Vroom: It is difficult to imagine a condition which would produce sufficient sulphur dust by abrasion of Sulfurcrete to create an explosion hazard.

A. Ismail: Is there a static charge developed in this material by means of friction -- as in pure sulphur?

A. H. Vroom: We have never observed the development of a static charge on the surface of Sulfurcrete, but have not specifically attempted to produce a charge.

D. James (Indian Affairs and Northern Development): I understand that lichens are exceedingly susceptible to SO_2. Could this be a problem with the use of Sulfurcrete in the Arctic?

A. H. Vroom: Evolution of SO_2 from Sulfurcrete is likely only when it is exposed to fire.

J. Clayton (Gulf Oil Canada): Are any precautions taken against evolution of hydrogen sulphide when melting the sulphur?

A. H. Vroom: We melt in an open tank indoors and have not observed any odour of hydrogen sulphide in the atmosphere when melting at the rate of, perhaps, 200 to 300 lb (90 to 140 kg) /h. For large-scale melting, however, adequate in-plant ventilation would undoubtedly be required, although the quantity of dissolved H_2S in most solid sulphur is so low that no steps to limit atmospheric emission are anticipated.

SULPHUR FOAMS FOR PERMAFROST PROTECTION

J. W. Ankers, E. P. Antoniades
R. W. Campbell and G. L. Woo
Chevron Research Company
576 Standard Avenue
Richmond, California, 94802
USA

A test section of sulfur foam as road insulation was successfully installed in August 1974 on Dempster Highway near the Mackenzie Delta. Foam made on-site in a mobile pilot plant was applied at the rate of 100 lb/min (45 kg/min) on top of 1.5 ft (0.45 m) of granular fill. The resulting pad, 130 ft (40 m) long, 45 ft (14 m) wide, and 4.4 in (110 mm) thick, was covered with more fill to a final grade of 5 ft (1.5 m) above original ground.

The foam used had the following properties: density, 11 lb/ft^3 (180 kg/m^3); K-factor at 86°F (30°C), 0.28 Btu in./hr ft^2 deg F (0.04 W/m K); compressive strength 46 psi (320 kPa); tensile strength 9 psi (60 kPa); resilient modulus ∿16 ksi (110 MPa); closed-cell content, 5%; water vapor permeability, 10 perm-in. (without skin) 0.9 perm-in. (with skin).

Monthly temperature data showed no evidence of thermal conductivity changes and samples removed after one year contained only 0.16 vol% water. The amount of insulation used for summer installation was not enough to regenerate permafrost permanently within a year. It was calculated that the insulation would have been enough for winter installation on permafrost of higher ice content (30 to 50%).

INTRODUCTION

Seasonal freezing and thawing poses serious problems for construction and maintenance of roads, air fields, and similar structures in cold climates. Thawing, especially of water-rich soils, can cause settlement. Freezing can cause upward movements commonly called frost heave or frost boil. Results from a sulfur foam field test designed to prevent frost heave in a paved road have been reported elsewhere (1). In permafrost regions the depth of the active layer may vary from a few inches to a few feet and is very sensitive to the thermal insulation afforded by the thick carpet of vegetation in tundra or muskeg (marshlands in Northern Canada). Loss of this natural insulation increases the depth of the active layer, sometimes to the point where it collapses under its own weight.

To avoid such problems, dwellings are built on piles sunk into permafrost, leaving air spaces underneath buildings to act as insulators. Roads are commonly built on several feet of gravel piled on top of the original ground. This has the multiple effect of distributing load, providing drainage, and, more importantly, insulating the ice-laden soil below.

In recent years, synthetic cellular plastics have been considered for insulating the sub-base of roads in cold climates as a means of reducing construction time and cost. Field tests of polyurethane (2) and polystyrene (3) foams of vastly lower thermal conductivity than gravel have already been made. Interest in the performance of potentially less expensive rigid sulfur foams brought about the field test described here. Installed in August 1974, the test used sulfur foam insulation to protect permafrost under an Arctic road, and was jointly sponsored by Chevron, the Sulphur Development Institute of Canada (SUDIC), and the Department of Public Works.

SULFUR FOAMS

Foams have been developed at Chevron Research Company and are being offered by Chevron Chemical Company under the registered trademark "Chevron FURCOAT Arctic Insulation". To prepare them, chemically modified sulfur is first made in the form of a concentrate which can be diluted with elemental sulfur to make foam precursor as needed. Molten precursor is then mixed with a foaming agent to produce foam:

Foam Concentrate (17-25 Parts)	+	Local Molten Sulfur (60-70 Parts)	→	Foam Precursor (77-95 Parts)

Foam Precursor (90-95 Parts)	+	Foaming Agent (5 - 10 Parts)	→	Sulfur Foam (100 Parts)

Foam precursor can also be made ahead of time and remelted just before use. Because the system lends itself to foaming in-place, part of the present study has been aimed at exploring this capability.

Table 1

Typical Properties of Rigid Sulfur Foams

	ASTM Method	Density, lb/ft³(kg/m³) 4.5(72)	6.5(105)	10(160)	20(320)
Thermal Conductivity Btu in./ft² h °F(W/m K) at 86°F (30°C)	D2326	0.24	0.25	0.28(0.040)	0.34(0.049)
at -40°F (-40°C)		(.035)	(.036)	0.22(0.032)	
Compressive Strength[1], psi (kPa)	D1621	25(170)	40(280)	50(350)	170(1200)
Compressive Modulus, ksi (MPa)	D1621			∿2·5(17)	
Flexural Strength, psi (kPa)	D790			25(170)	60(410)
Flexural Modulus, ksi (MPa)	D790			∿5(34)	∿5(34)
Tensile Strength, psi (kPa)	D1623		1(7)	9(60)	24(165)
Resilient Modulus[2], ksi (MPa)				∿16(110)	∿36(250)
Coefficient of Linear Thermal Expansion, $°F^{-1}$ (K^{-1})	D696			19×10^{-6} (34×10^{-6})	13×10^{-6} (23×10^{-6})
Dynamic Loading[3], Cycles to failure at 15 psi (100 kPa)				$>10^6$	
Water Vapor Permeability, (perm in.)	C355				
Core		11	9	10	10
One skin intact		0.8	1.5	<1	0.5
Water Absorption, vol %	D2127	1.5		2	2
Closed Cell Content (% of Total Voids)	D1940-62T	<5	<5	<5	18

[1] Measured parallel to foam rise, as maximum stress to 10% deformation.

[2] Compressive stress/strain under repeated loading conditions (0.1 s loading at 20 applications/min).

[3] Compressions of 1.3s duration, at 26 applications/min.

Table 2

Compression Creep in Chevron Sulfur Foams

Density lb/ft³ (kg/m³)	Method	Compressive Strength psi(kPa)	Test Stress psi(kPa)	Strain, % Instant.	10^3 Hr	One Year (extrap.)
14 (220)	ASTM D674 (spring load)	91 (627)	29 (200)	0.5	0.69	0.76
			42 (290)	0.4	0.70	0.82
17 (270)	ASTM D22168	162 (1120)	42 (290)	0.3	0.51	0.54
22 (350)	ASTM D22168	141 (971)	42 (290)	0.3	0.71	1.07

Specimens: 3 x 3 in., 1.5-3 in. high (76 x 76 mm, 38-76 mm high).
Conditions: Temperature, 76°F (24°C); rel. humidity, 50%; stress perpendicular to foam rise

Table 3

Exposure of Chevron Sulfur Foam to Liquids
Encountered in Arctic Operations

Liquid in Contact with Sulfur Foam (10 lb/ft³/160 kg/m³)	Time h	Uptake vol %	Compressive Strength,[1] psi(kPa)	Approximate Solubility,[2] wt %
None (Control)	-	-	50 (340)	-
Chevron Low Lead Gasoline	96	37	34 (230)	0.8
Chevron Jet Fuel A-50	96	29	39 (270)	0.4
Chevron Diesel Fuel	96	23	37 (260)	0.3
Crude Oil (California Light Waxy)	96	28	37 (260)	0.2
Methanol (100%)	168	36	33 (230)	0.02
Aqueous Methanol (30%)	312	7	43 (300)	

[1] 95% Confidence Limit, ± 5 psi (ASTM D 1621).

[2] Measured by x-ray fluorescence as increased sulfur in solution.

Sulfur foams with a wide spectrum of properties can be prepared by the above process. Some of the more common properties are shown in Table 1. These properties can be varied by chemical modification. Compressive strength remains unaffected at least down to -60°F (-50°C). Foams can be formulated which have excellent creep properties (Table 2) for applications as load-bearing members, for example as insulation for large cryogenic storage tanks. However, creep is quite sensitive to formulation differences even for the same density. Table 3 shows the high resistance of the foam to those liquids which are likely to be encountered in Arctic operations. In these tests, 2 x 2 x 1.5 in. (51 x 51 x 38 mm) samples were submerged in 1.75 ℓ liquid under a 2 in. (51 mm) head (cf. ASTM D2127).

FIELD TEST

A field test was undertaken in order to explore the potential of on-site foaming in remote Arctic environments, and to test the endurance of the foam in a typical field situation.

The site selected was a section of Dempster Highway, a highway that is destined to connect the Mackenzie Delta with the Yukon Territory and Alaska. (See Figures 1 and 2). Located about 40 mile (64 km) south of Inuvik, Northwest Territories, the site is nearly 100 mile (160 km) north of the Arctic Circle and not far from the treeline. The terrain is transitional between that of subarctic forest and tundra proper, which is treeless. Poorly drained, it tends to be swampy (muskeg) and is covered by moss and lichens, low shrubbery, and a scattering of trees such as alder, willow, and spruce, stunted from their customary height.

The site was on the main road between the arms of a Y formed by two side roads leading to a newly-opened borrow pit near Mile 923. This permitted traffic to bypass the site and afforded freedom of movement without disrupting road building operations.

Soil Conditions

Disturbed bag samples recovered in August, 1974, from 4 in. (100 mm) diameter holes, drilled for the ground thermistors with a Nodwell 100 rig, furnished all subsoil data. Soil analysis and instrumentation of the site was done by Klohn Leonoff Consultants, Ltd., Calgary. The four strata encountered to the drilled depth of 20 ft (6 m) are as follows:

	Depth, ft(m)	Water Content, wt%
Peat	<0.5(0.15)	14-23
Silt	0-11(0-3.4)	14-23
Silt Till	11-16(3.4-4.9)	10-15
Silt Shale (Bedrock)	>15 (4.6)	7-10

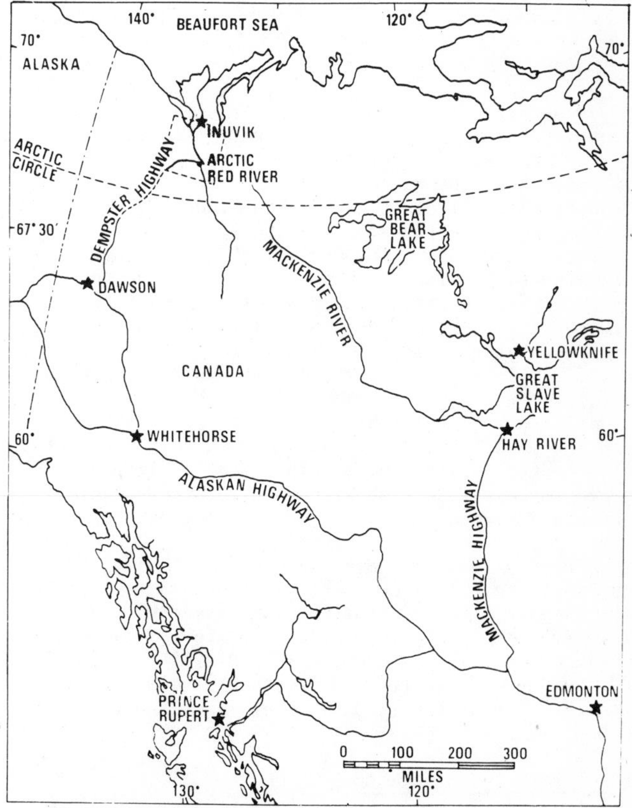

Figure 1: Northwestern Canada

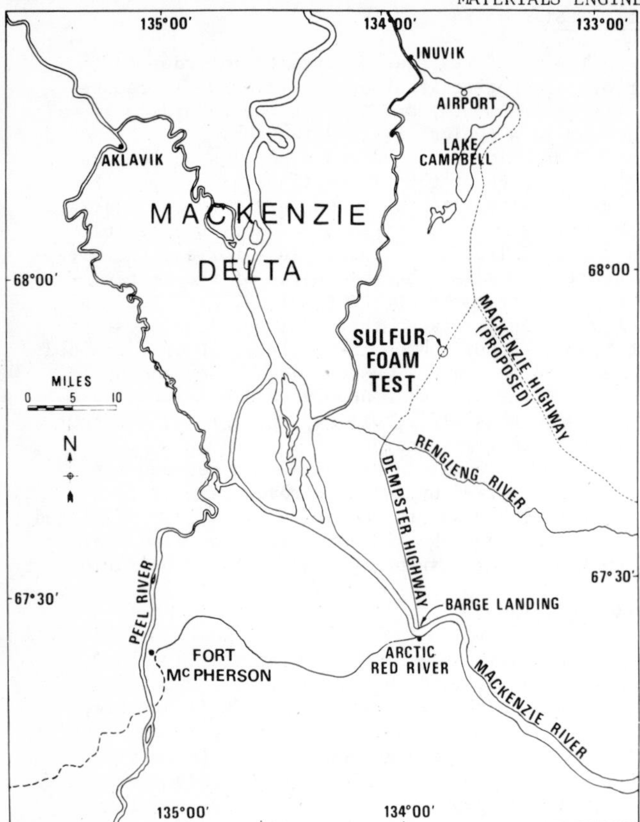

Figure 2: Location of test site near the Mackenzie Delta

Ice present was generally not visible except for sparse tiny inclusions or thin lenses. The small thickness of peat and the low water content (10-20 wt%) did not make the ground particularly susceptible to settlement.

Equipment

A melter and a foam unit were specially-designed for the test, each mounted on a truck, fitted with its own electric generator. They were barged from Hay River down the Mackenzie River to a landing opposite the village of Arctic Red River, 30 miles (48 km) away from the site (Figure 2).

The melter was a 100 USgal (380 ℓ) LPG-fired, oil-jacketed, stirred tank constructed at Chevron Research. It prepared foam precursor by melting together a mixture of sulfur and foam concentrate to make a batch of 1000 to 1300 lb (450 to 590 kg) in 5 h. This was the bottleneck of the entire operation.

Molten precursor was transferred by pressure into the reservoir of the foam unit through an electrically-heated flexible hose. In so doing, it was forced through a 30-mesh filter to remove particles that could damage the pump and flowmeter of the foam unit.

The foam unit (Figure 3) was custom-built by Fluidyne, Inc. Its power-driven mixer and XY-spreader were designed and built at Chevron Research. It produced foam at the rate of 100 lb/min (45 kg/min) by mixing molten foam precursor (220-276°F/93-129°C) and foaming agent. Foam so made would rise to the desired height a few seconds after discharge and become rigid in a few hours.

Sulfur Foam Installation

For the road in question, calculated stresses under a 50,000 lb (7 MN) tandem axle load were 5 to 6 psi (34 to 41 kPa) compressive and 2 to 3 psi (14 to 21 kPa) tensile. Thus, foam of 10 lb/ft^3 (160 kg/m^3) density, the lowest practical at the time, with a compressive strength of about 50 psi (340 kPa) was considered adequate. Its thermal conductivity was about 0.28 Btu in./hr ft^2 deg F (0.04 W/m K). The thickness used was not based on thermal analysis of the site but corresponded to what has been generally required in Arctic operations in this region (thermal resistance 15 ft^2 h deg F/Btu or 2.6 m^2 K/W).

Figure 3: Sulfur foam pilot-scale field unit

Figure 4: Movable head of power mixer discharges foam on granular fill

Foam was installed on top of the 1.5 ft (0.46 m) thick "pioneer fill", as shown in Figure 4. This is the first layer of granular overfill (in this case ripped shale), which is laid down by end-dumping on the cleared right-of-way. Equipment can thus travel back and forth on temporarily stable ground, put in culverts, and finish the road with more fill to a final lift of 5 ft (1.5 m) above ground.

The sulfur foam pad (Figure 5) was about 130 ft (40 m) long and 45 ft (14 m) wide with an average thickness of 4.4 in. (110 mm). A total of 25 batches of foam was used, each batch generally covering an area of about 260 ft^2 (24 m^2). Four consecutive 6 ft x 11 ft (1.8 m x 3.4 m) grids of the spreader were used, requiring a tankful of precursor.

Sulfur foam was also placed adjacent to the road, directly on a 10 x 10 ft (3 x 3 m) section of ground freshly stripped of its vegetation. This

Figure 5: Sulfur foam pad near completion

Figure 6: Foam being covered with 3.5 ft (1.1 m) of granular fill

foam was left uncovered and will serve for future observations of its effects on surrounding plant life.

To make the insulated section level with the rest of the finished, though unpaved, road, 3.5 ft (1.1 m) of granular fill was end-dumped on top of the foam and leveled with a bulldozer (Figure 6). The foam took this punishment remarkably well. Even when 1 to 2 ft (0.3 - 0.6 m) rocks rolled over it, they produced only minor scuff marks.

Foam Properties

Although weather varied considerably and abruptly during installation (air temperatures ranged from 28°F (-2°C) to 70°F (21°C), the objective of preparing 10 to 12 lb/ft^3 (160 to 190 kg/m^3) sulfur foam with an average compressive strength of 40 to 50 psi (280 to 345 kPa) and an average thickness of 4.5 in. (110 mm) was achieved. Density and compressive strength by batch are listed in Table 4. Cell structure was very fine and uniform, (Figure 7) characteristic of the best laboratory foams.

The surface of the foam was wavy as a result of the zigzag spreading pattern. Gusts of wind caused bumps by distorting the foam stream. Light rain or cold temperatures did not seem to affect the foam as much as water puddles on the ground. Evidently, water trapped inside the foam gave rise to voids, as was the case with foam batch No. 12 (Table 4). We were careful thereafter to fill rain puddles with dirt before foaming.

Foam batch No. 12 was remarkable in another sense. Whereas newly-poured foam generally developed stress-relief cracks every 2 to 3 ft (1 m or less) soon after cooling, this batch remained free of cracks. On the assumption that rainwater was acting as a heat release agent for this batch, two other release agents were tried in separate experiments off the main test section. Thus, when polyethylene sheet was placed between the foam and road surface, or when the road surface was first coated with heat transfer oil, again no cracks developed. This demonstrated that the foam can shrink without cracking when

Table 4

Properties of Sulfur Foam Batches for Dempster Highway Insulation Test

Batch No.	Foam Density lb/ft^3 Skin Off	Skin On[1]	Average Foam Thickness[2], in.(mm) Calculated	Found	Compressive Strength psi(kPa)	Air Temperature During Foaming, °F(°C)
1	10.7	12.2	4.3(110)	3.5(89)	47(320)	45(7)
2			6.0(150)	5.3(130)		55(13)
3	9.5	10.3	6.1(155)	4.9(125)	46(320)	50(10)
4			5.0(130)	4.4(112)		54(12)
5			5.0(130)	5.3(135)		48(9)
6			4.5(115)	4.1(104)		46(8)
7			4.5	4.5(115)		45(7)
8			4.5	4.3(110)		54(12)
9	9.9	10.3	4.5	4.3(110)	47(320)	46(8)
10	9.8	11.2	4.5	4.3(110)	56(390)	50(10)
11			4.5	4.3(110)		43(6)
12	9.1	11.1	4.5	4.7(120)	35(240)	37(3)
13			4.5	4.3(110)		28(-2)
14			4.5	4.4(112)		41(5)
15			4.5	4.3(110)		45(7)
16	9.9	10.6	4.5	4.6(117)	42(290)	41(5)
17	9.3	10.8	4.5	4.4(112)	41(280)	45(7)
18	11.3	12.1	4.5	4.1(104)	48(330)	45(7)
19	9.9	10.5	4.5	4.4(112)	38(260)	41(5)
20			4.5	4.5(114)		50(10)
21	9.5	10.6	4.5	4.3(109)	42(290)	55(13)
22	9.9	10.5	4.5	4.3(109)	45(310)	45(7)
23	11.1	12.0	4.5	4.5(115)	55(280)	68(20)
24	9.6	10.7	4.5	4.4(112)	50(340)	70(21)
25	9.5	10.1	4.5	4.4(112)	50(340)	63(17)
Avg.	9.9	10.9	4.5	4.4(112)	46(320)	

[1] Only top skin on. Bottom skin removed before measurement due to adherence of gravel and other small particles.

[2] "Calculated" values derived from foaming time, foaming rate, area covered, and foam density. "Found" values are average of several direct measurements.

Figure 7: Foam sample from Dempster Highway field test

it does not adhere strongly to the substrate.

Instrumentation

In order to assess performance of the insulation over the next few years, provisions were made for measuring ground temperatures and ground settlement. Figure 8 shows the location of instruments. For monitoring ground temperatures, thermistors were installed to a depth of 20 ft (6 m) using a string of 13 thermistors for each vertical location. Six such strings were placed in the insulated section, 5 in an adjacent (non-insulated) control section and one in undisturbed ground 50 ft (15 m) away from the road. Single thermistors were installed just above and just below the foam at 13 locations, and 5 comparable locations in the control section. Finally, a vertical string of five thermistors was placed in the granular overfill at the center of the insulated section.

Thermistors were made by Cantech Controls, Calgary. Thermistors strings were packed with vermiculite inside 1.5 in. (38 mm) PVC pipe. Multistrand cable leads entered this pipe through a flexible (pleated) conduit. The tips of single thermistors were protected with heat-shrinkable sheaths. All wiring terminated in a splitter box to which a portable meter could be attached when taking readings.

In order to measure ground settlement, ten 10 in. (250 mm) square steel plates were placed on top of the foam and in the control section. From time to time, holes will be drilled through the overfill to these feeler plates so that surveying stakes can be rested on them and sighted against benchmarks

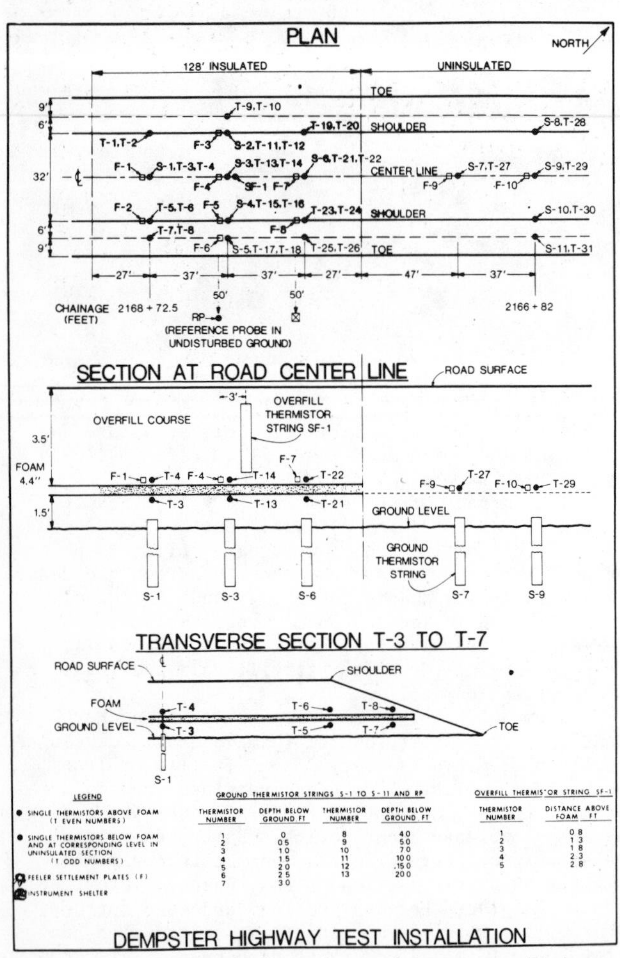

Figure 8: Plan and elevations of Demptster Highway test installation

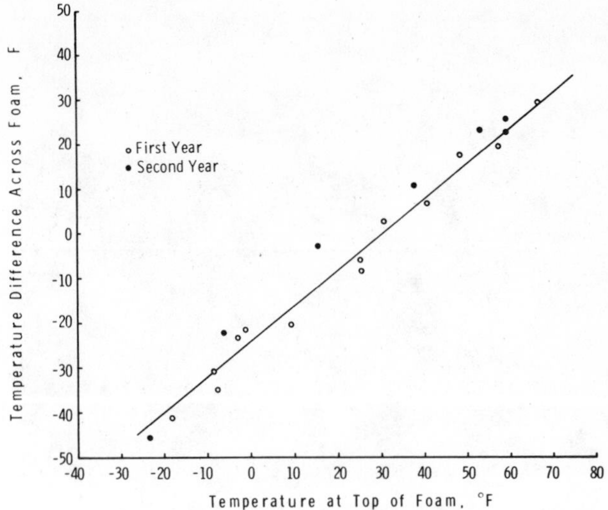

Figure 9: Plot of temperature difference across the foam against temperature at top, near center of insulated section (thermistors, T-13 and T-14). Line is fitted to first year's points.

sunk into bedrock on either side of the road. Exact location of feeler plates was marked by alignment pins driven into permafrost on either side of the roadway.

Performance

With skin removed, the present foam had an appreciable water vapor permeability in laboratory tests. This makes it possible under certain conditions for water to enter into the foam at cracks or other places where the skin was damaged. One question, therefore, this field test is expected to answer is whether, and to what extent, this takes place with time.

When the difference in temperature between top and bottom of the foam is plotted against temperature at the top of the foam, a full year's measurements dispose themselves around a straight line. Their position above or below this line depends on whether temperatures are ascending or descending. The slope of a straight line fitted through these points would be expected to decrease with increasing thermal conductivity. Measurements for two full years have not yet been completed to permit a rigorous year-by-year comparison. Nevertheless, inspection of the plots does not reveal a trend toward diminished slopes (see example in Figure 9). This is true of 11 of 12 thermistor pairs above and below the foam.

For the most part, therefore, thermal conductivity appears to have remained essentially constant, indicating that to date neither water intrusion nor mechanical collapse has occurred to any significant extent. A sample of foam under the road center line, removed one year after installation, furnished corroborative evidence. Its moisture content was only 0.16 vol%. [It takes a water content of approximately 15 vol% to increase the thermal conductivity by a factor of 2].

Ground temperature data indicate that regeneration of permafrost under the insulated section is not yet complete (Figure 10 and Table 5). However, thaw depth has been reducing with each succeeding year. This is due at least in part to slow dissipation of heat trapped during summer construction. In Figure 10, the integers above and below the curves are "thaw and freeze" indices (deg F.days) taken from mean air temperatures at Inuvik airport.

Figure 11 shows isotherms for July 4, 1976. The

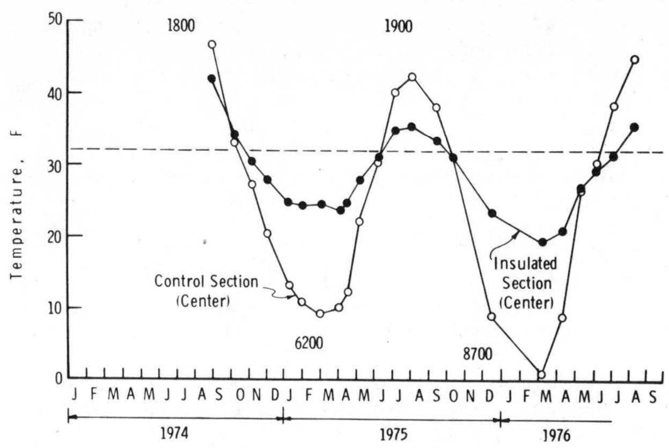

Figure 10: Temperatures below roadway at original ground level (thermistors No. 1 of strings S-3 and S-9)

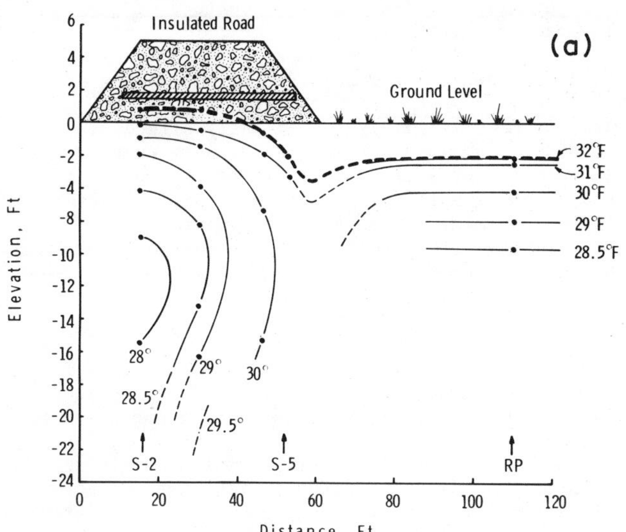

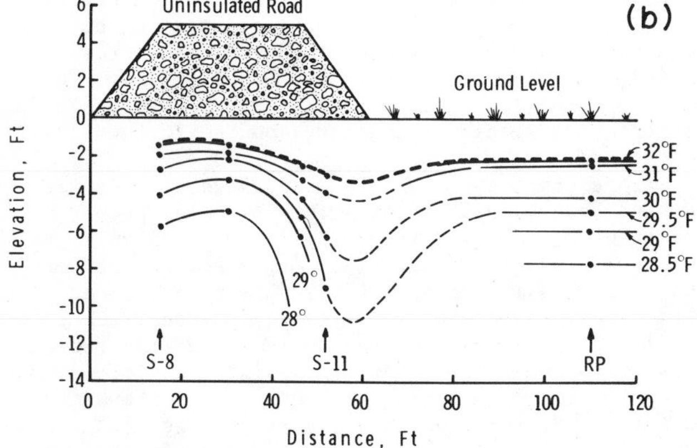

Figure 11: Isotherms for July 4, 1967, (a) under insulated road (cross-sections S-2 to S-5); (b) under noninsulated road (cross-section S-8 to S-11).

Table 5

Maximum Depth of Thaw at Dempster Highway Test Section, Feet (Metres) Below Ground Level

Year	Insulated Section	Control Section	Undisturbed Ground
1974	6.0 (1.8)	6.0 (1.8)	3.0 (0.91)
1975	2.2 (0.67)	4.0 (1.2)	3.8 (1.16)
1976 (August)	1.4 (0.43)	2.9 (0.88)	3.9 (1.19)

disturbance caused by absence of insulation at the toe of the road is seen here, and the lack of symmetry about the road center line probably arises from unsymmetrical exposure to the sun.

Thermal Analysis

One-dimensional heat conduction analysis was used to predict ground temperatures. It was based on an explicit finite difference technique and utilized ground temperatures and soil data that became available after installation. This analysis, made by a previously-published (4) method, predicts that full regeneration of permafrost would not be accomplished even after three years, with the present 4.4 in. (110 mm) of insulation (thermal resistance, 15 h ft^2 deg F/Btu or 2.6 m^2 K/W). To prevent thawing in the following summer, approximately 7 in. (180 mm) of 10 lb/ft^3 (160 kg/m^3) foam would have been needed for summer construction and 5.5 in. (140 mm) for winter construction. However, the present thickness would have been adequate for winter construction at a site of higher ice content (e.g., 30 to 50% instead of 10 to 20%).

CONCLUSIONS

In-place foaming of sulfur foam in the Arctic environment has proved feasible. The process appears adaptable for road, airfield, or building pad construction without significant changes in conventional operations.

Cracking is due to thermal stress relief and can be reduced or eliminated by lubricating the ground underneath. Although the foam has a largely open-cell structure, its performance in the first two years of installation on Dempster Highway does not indicate measurable loss of insulative properties, either through moisture intrusion or mechanical failure.

The 4.4 in. (110 mm) of insulation used was not enough to fully regenerate permafrost of 10-20% water content within a year. To accomplish this, about 20% more insulation would have been required for winter construction, or 60% more for summer construction.

Observations on the sustained use of the foam-making equipment in remote areas has led to many ideas for improvement in a commercial prototype. Development of a larger unit that will lay foam faster and more evenly is under way. The operational ability of this unit at -50°F (-46°C) ambient temperature will be tested in 1977. Lower density, acceptably strong foams and foams with high closed-cell content are at various stages of development.

Acknowledgment

The site was arranged through the Department of Indian Affairs and Northern Development and the Department of Public Works, Canada. We are particularly indebted to N. A. Huculak, Regional Highways

Engineer, Edmonton, and Carl Yurchak, Project Engineer on location, for their cooperation and for making the necessary arrangements with the contractors. We wish to thank G. H. Johnston of the National Research Council for helpful discussions, and J. T. Christison and B. P. Shields of Alberta Research Council for the heat conduction analysis.

REFERENCES

1. R. W. Campbell, G. L. Woo, E. P. Antoniades, and J. W. Ankers, unpublished paper, Proceedings, Annual Conference, 1975, Canadian Technical Asphalt Association, Toronto.
2. N. Smith, R. Bert, and L. Muller, in "Permafrost: N. American Contribution to the 2nd Int. Conference, Yakutsk, Siberia, 1973", 1973, National Acad. of Sciences, Washington, p. 736.
3. G. E. Johns, in "Symposium on Cold Regions Engineering", 1971, J. L. Brudick, ed., U. Alaska, vol. 1, p. 1701.
4. J. T. Christison and K. O. Anderson, Third International Conference on Structural Design of Asphalt Pavements, London, 1972, p. 41.

DISCUSSION

B. Ladanyi (Ecole Polytechnique): The sulphur foam used in the tests is essentially a brittle-porous material, with its compressive strength about five times its tensile strength. It is therefore probably prone to cracking under flexure when used as a mat and subject to unequal settlement. These cracks may bring about a gradual destruction of the mat. Has this effect been investigated?

E. P. Antoniades: We have not yet uncovered a large enough portion of the insulated section to count frequency of cracks. This would be definitely worth doing. No rigid insulation will survive cracking when subjected to unequal settlement. However, insulation is expected to reduce or eliminate settlement.

B. Ladanyi: If the foam has an open-cell structure it is probably subject to frost damage. How does it perform under freeze and thaw cycles?

E. P. Antoniades: Foams containing up to 10 vol% water, an amount that roughly doubles their thermal conductivity, showed no freeze-thaw cracking in air after 100 cycles (0°F to 73°C), nor loss of compressive strength.

W. M. Drope (Northern Engineering Services): What would happen to your product in the many grass and forest fires in the Arctic?

E. P. Antoniades: Exposed foams would burn in an intense forest fire. However, most of the envisioned uses are underground.

W. M. Drope: If it does burn, how do you see it being used in Arctic revegetation programs?

E. P. Antoniades: Even in this case the foam would probably be covered with soil. However, the use for revegetation is speculative and has not yet been tested. At any rate, the idea is to do this where the ground has been stripped of vegetation due to heavy construction.

L. Luyckx (Reactive Metals and Alloys): This is not my field, but it seems that any insulation system protecting permafrost under the road from decaying is welcome for the Arctic. I am impressed by the efforts of the oil industry to put its waste material to good use. Is there not a way to circumvent the sulphur foam cracking problem by applying a top and bottom plastic sealant coat which would flow somewhat to fill the cracks, a bit like our asphalt driveway sealants?

E. P. Antoniades: Yes, there are a number of approaches that are being studied. One, as you mentioned, is a sealant coating. Another would be increasing the closed-cell content.

L. Luyckx: It looks like this permafrost insulation issue is a mandatory precaution. What are the competing alternatives to your material development?

E. P. Antoniades: Urethane and polystyrene foams are among competing alternatives not entirely problem free. Urethane foams tend to pick up moisture and various coatings are used to seal them. Polystyrene foams have poor resistance to gasoline and other hydrocarbon fuels and additionally must be shipped and installed as preformed slabs.

L. Luyckx: Can you give an idea of the projected $ cost per mile, at least as a percentage of the whole roadbed cost?

E. P. Antoniades: The insulation effectiveness of sulphur foam is such that with certain types of embankment material it is economically effective to consider foam-in-place insulation when overfill coats reach about $5.50/yd^3 ($7.20/m^3). Since the crossover costs vary as a function of design, size of job, embankment character, and location it is difficult to give a precise cost/mile of road.

SESSION CHAIRMAN'S SUMMARY

E. I. Carefoot

After listening to the papers, one begins to see what modern technology is developing for northern development.

Ice is a product of environmental conditions. Its characteristics in a natural state are subject to the random variations that are usually associated with anything that depends upon the weather. The ability to control its properties and increase its shear and tensile strength could provide a whole new material product, already situated in the north in unlimited supply. The research and testing being done in the way of providing domed ice structures for temporary enclosures has been highlighted. Bond and creep behaviour are critical, but when stresses are kept to a specified maximum, good performance is attained.

Fibre composites cover a wide range of materials and have been used in natural form by polar people for centuries. Modern technology has opened up a whole new product possibility. Dr. Street encountered considerable difficulty in literature research on Arctic applications, as there is an apparent lack of written information on the subject. He invites anyone with knowledge on Arctic applications of composites to contact him. Of particular interest would be when, where and how the product reacted to cold temperature, temperature cycling effects and aging.

Sulphur foams and sulphur concretes, by-products of the petrochemical industry are shaping up with real potential in the supply of materials for Arctic construction. The structural strength and ease of handling in cold weather and durability make sulphur concrete a very desirable material. One characteristic which presently limits its versatility is its flammability.

Sulphur foams show promise as an insulation for road constructions in permafrost terrain. Mr. Antoniades dealt in some length with a field test on the Mackenzie Highway about 40 mile south of Inuvik. He concludes that in-place foaming under Arctic environment is quite feasible and appears adaptable for road, airfield and building pad construction.

Following the initial introduction to Arctic Engineering provided by the first conference Session, the papers presented herein served to bring the attention of the conference to the potential of new products. Subsequent sessions tended to investigate adaptations and properties of traditional materials.

ARCTIC CONSTRUCTION

INTRODUCTION

E. C. Hamre

From the papers of this session it is apparent that the level of quality is as important for construction in the Arctic as it is for mainline gas transmission pipe. Quality requirements for Arctic material are generally an upgrading of those normally specified for construction in more temperate climates or in less fragile environments. The most critical aspect of quality appears to be the assurance that materials possess adequate impact toughness at very low temperatures; typically -45°C. Other aspects of quality are equally demanding. For example, the frequency of inspection is increased often to 100%, weldability parameters are strictly specified and allowable flaw sizes are calculated and specified.

The particular methods used to attain the levels of quality deemed necessary for individual projects are as varied as the projects themselves. In the case of power line construction, brittle fracture is avoided by using materials which are not particularly susceptible to low temperatures. For example, even the most exotic of new materials cannot compete with wooden poles for tower structures. It is interesting, however, that while welding of steel clamping members is not permitted due to possible quality problems, the impact toughness is specified at a temperature of only -30°C.

To attain the required toughness in rolled shapes for support structures of the Trans-Alaska Pipeline it was necessary to employ controlled rolling techniques normally used only on flat plate and coil. Service life of ditcher teeth for permafrost trenching conditions was increased by specifying a more highly alloyed steel and carefully controlling the heat treatment.

The papers in this session do provide information on what is done to solve particular problems but they give little background information on the reasons for the specifications which have caused the problems. For example, information on the reasoning behind the determination of various safety factors for power line construction, or the minimum Charpy energy values required for pipeline support systems would have been interesting. In a similar context, the papers on power line construction and ditcher teeth performance both state that the economics of their particular situations dictate that failures could not be tolerated. It would have been informative had the authors given details in this regard; for example, the increased cost of building a power line to guarantee continuity of service *versus*, say, a system of backup generating stations, or the cost of ditcher teeth as proposed in the paper *versus* the cost of decreased excavating efficiency or downtime to replace failed teeth.

In any event, it is apparent that construction in the Arctic environment is a difficult challenge, but one that will be met successfully.

USING STEEL IN ARCTIC CONSTRUCTION

H. C. Cotton
British Petroleum Co., Ltd.,
London, England

and

I. M. Macaulay
BP Alaska Inc.
San Francisco, California
USA

Modular construction is favoured for Arctic construction on the grounds of cost and productivity. Steels presently available are adequate for most, if not all, Arctic applications. Examples are given of steel qualities which have been used successfully on Alaska's North Slope. The basis for choosing them is described. Improvements in the notch ductility of weld metals is thought to be worth further study.

INTRODUCTION

In the lands beyond the Arctic Circle the climate is extremely variable. On the North Slope of Alaska at Prudhoe Bay the weather is mostly very cold. There are 9 months of winter during which the temperature sometimes falls even below -57°C and for 56 days the sun never rises above the horizon. Yet, during the short summer, for a few days at least, the weather may be pleasantly warm. For 3 months the temperature is in the range 4°C to 20°C and it is then that construction activity on hard permafrost is most intense. But during this warm period the 0.5 m blanket of tundra, which insulates the underlying ice-rich permafrost from changes in the weather, begins to melt and the surface becomes wet and marshy. Transport on land comes to a standstill. Official permission to work on the sensitive tundra is only given for the period mid-November to mid-May when the ground is frozen hard. Coincident with reasonable working weather comes a total ban on movement and, for those who are unprepared, it can be a wasted summer. If, during those few summer months, transport across wet permafrost is required hard roads must be built and these must be insulated from the tundra by a 1.5 m thick pad of gravel. For example, in order to be able to develop the Prudhoe Bay area, BP found it necessary to build 80 km of wide road to link the several wellhead sites with the service centres and living quarters.

CONSTRUCTION IN THE ARCTIC

Arctic regions are mostly remote and the provision of supplies involves problems. Roads, railways and ports are usually non-existant and the sea may be frozen for much of the year. It is then that aircraft are a boon. During a space of 3 months in 1969, BP flew into the Prudhoe Bay area some 20,000 ton of supplies. But flying is costly and other methods must be devised when large construction projects are involved.

For such huge undertakings it is hardly practicable to embark upon complicated structural and mechanical engineering projects in the winter without all-embracing protection from the cold. However, earthworks and some civil engineering projects may be feasible where manual skills and precision are not so important. The low air temperatures are all right for steel but for man, subject to a chill factor of 1°C per each km/h of wind speed, the effective temperature can be below -70°C. Bulky clothing and thick gloves must be worn which inhibits manual dexterity. Frost obscures vision and loss of horizon in white-outs gives rise to disorientation. Productivity falls to very low levels.

Even in the summer the cost of production is very high. Food and accommodation costs about $100 per man day at BP's North Slope site and, in addition, for various reasons such as climate, premium payments etc., the base cost per unit of work is about 4 times that at warmer locations. It is good economics to keep Arctic construction to the minimum and, where possible, to supply to the Arctic site in modular form part-finished assemblies made in warmer and more efficient locations. Construction at the site should be limited, as far as possible, to the preparation of roads and foundations and to linking up modules in sheltered conditions. Pipelining, which cannot be tackled in this way, begins in May and ends in October. Production welding at very low temperatures exists mainly in the imagination. It is neither economic nor feasible for large projects.

MATERIAL SUPPLY

The decision to bring large modules to Prudhoe Bay was based upon the occasional availability of a sea route through the Bering Strait via Point Barrow. For a short period of about six weeks in the months of August and September the ice usually,

Figure 1: North slope modules set on pile caps

but not invariably, becomes thin enough to allow ice breakers to smash a way through and thus provide a passage for ships and barges into the Arctic Ocean and on to Prudhoe. In the month of July, a convoy of 70 or more barges, tugs, etc. leaves its rendezvous on the U.S. west coast for the Bering Strait. There the ships lie in wait for a chance to slip through the transient ice window towing their valuable loads into the open sea beyond. The convoy must not be late, for the exact date the channel will be unlocked is uncertain. Sometimes the window never fully opens and the barges with their precious cargo may be trapped in the unyielding ice for 11 whole months, waiting to be freed by the next fleeting thaw.

If the passage is safely made, time is of the essence for the barges must be speedily discharged if they are to succeed in slipping back home before the window closes. Much of the cargo consists of part-finished assemblies (modules) mounted on skids. They weigh between 400 and 1000 ton and their discharge and transport in the absence of conventional port facilities could present a problem. At the landfall, large crawlers, specially designed to fit beneath the tunnel of the skid are waiting. Their speed of 2 km/h is slow but their carrying capacity is prodigious. Hydraulic jacking facilities on the crawler allow the huge modules to be lifted from the deck of the barge and carried away by road to the site some 40 km away where a swivel arrangement allows the crawler to position its load accurately upon the pile caps already prepared to receive it (Figure 1). The modules are mostly metal sheeted and present the appearance of large houses. Inside, protected against the winter weather, man may work in reasonably congenial surroundings on unfinished tasks and the linking together of the various modules which go to make up the particular construction.

Protection from the environment is the key to successful Arctic engineering. The situation is almost exactly analagous to offshore working in the inhospitable waters of the North Sea. There, BP modules for offshore working weigh about 1800 ton, their weight being restricted by marine lifting capacity. On the North Slope the economic module size depends on several factors. Very large packs may be unduly cumbersome even if lifting and transport facilities are capable of handling heavier loads. Planning the content and linking points of the individual modules is given careful attention. Ideally the location of the connecting points between the modules should allow for very simple and convenient working and involve a minimum of exposure of individuals to the harsh climate outside.

DANGER IN WARMTH

It is common to dwell upon the effects of cold when thinking of Arctic construction and this will be the general theme of this paper, but it is worth mentioning that the effects of warmth may present equally complex problems in construction. Sunshine falling upon exposed pile surfaces may cause the permafrost substratum, upon which the integrity of the supporting foundation depends, to thaw and thus become unstable. Crude oil as warm as 80°C can, as it gushes up to the surface, heat the well casing to unacceptably high temperatures. There is grave risk of melting the 650 m deep permafrost local to the well casing, causing the supporting soil to lose its strength with consequent collapse and irreparable damage. Unbelievably in these icy regions, refrigeration is in regular use to offset the damaging effects of warmth.

STEEL SELECTION

Of the many metallic materials used in Arctic construction by far the most common is steel. Steel is strong and cheap but it is the metal most affected by the Arctic cold, both in respect of its weldability and its notch ductility. Other metals in common use are almost unaffected by changes in temperature in the range under consideration, but the behaviour of steel can seem to be unpredictable and even capricious. At the same time it must be remembered that even now thousands of tons of fabricated steel are giving satisfactory service in Arctic locations.

In choosing steel for Arctic construction two aspects are of special concern. These are weldability and low-stress fracture. So much has been written on these two subjects that it is hard to believe that there can be any dubiety as to the best course of action for a given set of circumstances. Yet this is far from the case. Perhaps the decision is more difficult now than ever because of the multiplicity of alternatives offered.

The practicing engineer, even the materials engineer with specialised skill, finds difficulty in choosing materials, welding techniques, etc. which will be at once successful and economic. Even on very large projects the staff numbers engaged upon materials selection may be miniscule. Except, perhaps, for rather special considerations of cost or risk, simplified rules must be applied to rather generalised situations in the interests of expediency.

Instant decisions are often required and that is why the 15 ft lbf (20 J) Charpy-V concept, however unsatisfactory, has stood the test of time and, because of its simplicity in use, why fracture arrest considerations are often favoured. Applying criteria relating to the initiation of unstable fracture, which for common steels is usually more economic in terms of steel quality required, is more difficult in use because design loadings and the effects of these upon strain requirements is often difficult to compute in the limited time available.

WELDING AND PREHEAT

Welding is a most potent method for damaging steel and the effects of this must be taken into account when choosing steel grades for low temperature applications. In doing so it is useful if basic

CORRELATIONS SHOWN ASSUME WELD SHAPE $\frac{W}{D} \leq 2$ ARROWS SHOW INCREASED H.A.Z. HARDNESS FOR FLATTER WELD ($\frac{W}{D} \geq 2$)

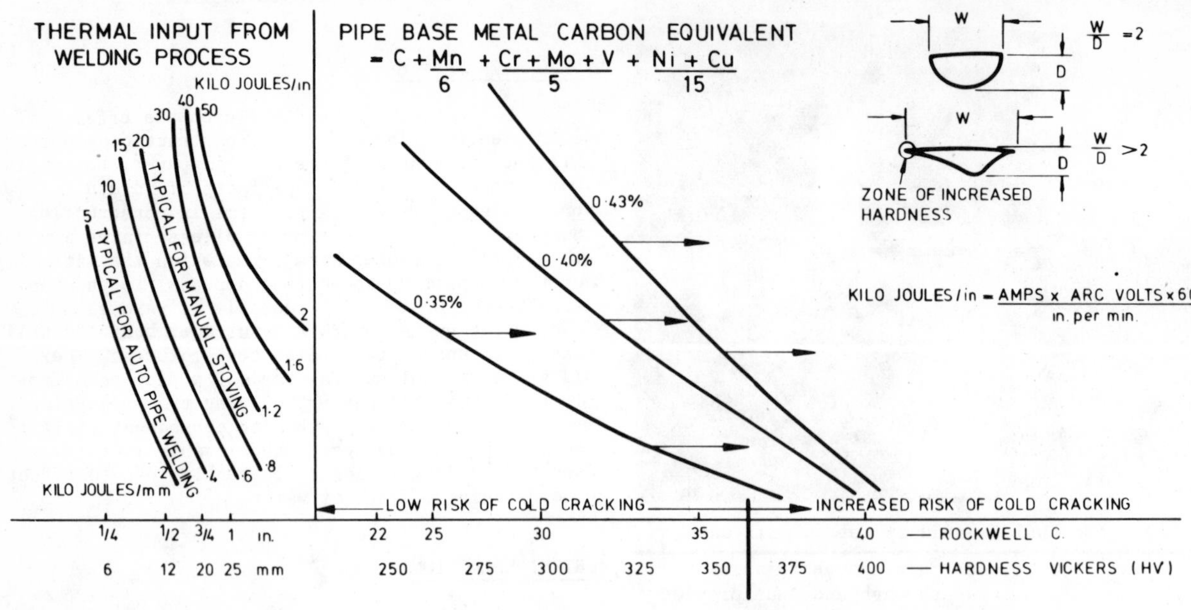

Figure 2: Relationship between weld heat input, pipe composition and weld heat affected zone hardness

and practical assumptions are made. The most important of these is the thermal input of the welding process. High heat input processes may reduce notch ductility in the heat affected zone (HAZ) enormously, mainly because of grain growth and consequent softening. Conversely, unduly low thermal input may give rise to hard HAZ's sensitive to cracking and with low resistance to unstable fracture initiation. A convenient assumption, which has been found to work in practice, is that the minimum thermal input arising out of the welding process itself when welding in any position other than vertical-down will not be less than about 40 kJ/in. (1.6 kJ/mm) for a 0.25 in. (6 mm) fillet. For downward vertical welding an input of 15 kJ/in. (0.6 kJ/mm) should be assumed as a minimum when using manual metal arc welding processes (E6010, E7010). If automatic welding processes are use for vertical-down welding of pipelines for example, lower values of thermal input may be appropriate.

On this basis, welding procedures are chosen and qualified to provide the level of thermal input assumed plus a moderate factor of safety where appropriate. The use of welding processes producing very high thermal input (electroslag, electrogas, etc.) requires special consideration because of the coarse grain size of the welded joint. Such welding techniques are generally not suitable for low temperature applications unless the weld and its HAZ are normalized. Preheating requirements are chosen for the various thicknesses involved by reference to Figure 2. The thermal input, composition and thickness must be known in order to make the necessary estimates. The accuracy of these predictions is checked in the procedure test. Allowance must be made for the effect of ambient temperature upon the preheating requirements, but this is not as great as might be imagined as can be judged from Figure 3 which was constructed from practical observations in transmission linepipe welding in cold climates. Safety factors are applied as deemed necessary, bearing in mind the importance of the construction and the reliability and reproducibility of the data used. Most of these diagrams are based upon private work done by BP, but other sources of information have been utilized (1). It is recognized that the Carbon Equivalent formulae may not be strictly accurate, especially for very-low-carbon low-alloy steels, but the use of the formula given in Figure 2 is thought to be rather pessimistic and thus provides for an additional small safety factor (2).

As far as possible steel is purchased in bulk and this is especially the case for linepipe. For all projects, wherever situated, standard steel qualities are used as far as possible. Supplementary requirements are only added where it does not reduce availability or increase cost disproportionately to do so. The aim is to minimize the necessity for especially close control during welding, either of preheat or run size. Table 1 gives some examples of typical standard steel grades which have been used successfully in Arctic locations and in low

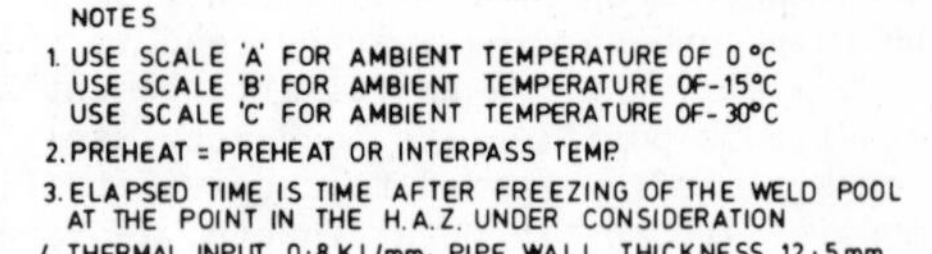

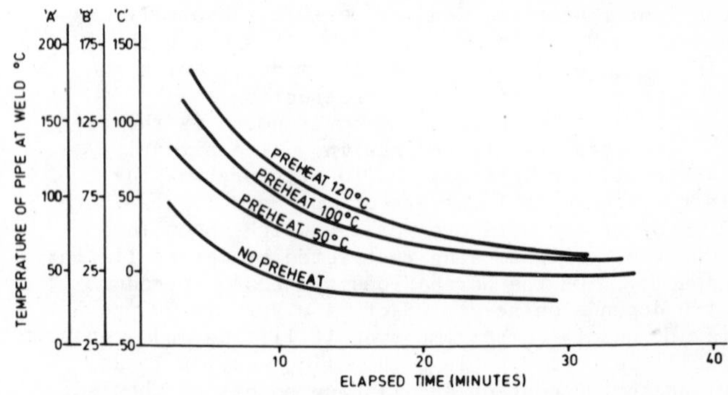

Figure 3: Effect of ambient temperature on weld interpass temperature

Table 1

Materials Used in Arctic Construction

Item	Application	Materials
Tankage	Plate	ASTM A516 Grade 70 - Normalized
	Nozzles	ASTM A333 Grade 6 Pipe
	Flanges	ASTM A350 Grade LF 1
Module Skids	Main structural members	ASTM A537 Grade A modified (Cv 47J at -45°C)
Piling	Low Temperature Sections	ASTM A537 Grade A
	(Thickness ≤ 20 mm)	ASTM A516 Grade 70 (Cv 20J at -45°C)
		ASTM A333 Grade 6
	Warm Environment Inside Modules	ASTM A283
Pipelines	Flowlines (150 to 250 mm)	API 5LX Grade X52 (Seamless Q and T) Cv 47J at -45°C)
	Transit & Flare Lines (760 to 965 mm dia.) (Maximum Thickness = 14 mm)	API 5LX Grade X52 (Longitudinal welded) (Cv 68J at -30°C)
	Piping outside modules (low temperature service)	ASTM A333 Grade 6 (seamless)
Pressure vessels and heat exchangers inside modules	Shell and Heads (Stress relieved over 30 mm)	ASTM A516 Grades 60 to 70 normalized
	Nozzles	ASTM A333 Grade 6
	Flanges	ASTM A350 LF1 or LF2
Piping (-20°F to 400°F) (-30°C to 200°C)	Pipe	ASTM A106 Grade B
		API 5L Grade B
	Flanges & Fittings	ASTM A103
		ASTM A234 Grade WPB
Piping (-50°F to 400°F) (-45°C to 200°C)	Pipe (thickness 5 mm to 13 mm)	ASTM A333 Grade 6
	Flanges & Fittings	ASTM A350 Grade LF2
Cranes		ASTM A537 Grade A (Cv 47J at -50°C)
Pile Caps		ASTM A537 Grade A (Cv 47J at -50°C)

temperature applications.

LAMELLAR TEARING

Lamellar tearing is a serious inconvenience during fabrication, wherever the location, and it is specially important when constructing modules and structures for destinations such as the North Slope because by delaying completion, it enhances the risk of missing the ice window (3). It is an absolutely unacceptable risk, if restrained-fillet welded constructions are to be fabricated in remote and inclement locations where the difficulties in normal fabrication may be almost insurmountable even without this added complication. For fabrication under these conditions, steel is supplied with enhanced ductility in the through-thickness direction. This is achieved mainly by reducing the sulphur content to low values, say an average ladle S of 0.004%, and 0.007% max., coupled with vacuum degassing to ensure cleanliness and reduce hydrogen cracking during production. Approximately 100,000 ton of such steel have now been used by BP in applications involving considerable through-thickness restraint where lamellar tearing is usually a serious problem (4). No single case of lamellar tearing has been experienced in these steels. Typical examples of composition and mechanical properties together with through-thickness reduction of area of such steels are given in Table 2.

Through-thickness tensile tests (Figure 4) are reasonably convenient for use in investigating compositional variables or as a mill production

Table 2

Chemical Composition and Mechanical Properties of Lamellar-Tearing-Resistant Steel

Material BS 4360 Grade 50D: Thickness 63.5 mm

Element %	Number of Variates	Arithmetic Mean	Standard Deviation	Smallest Variate	Largest Variate
C (x 100)	36	14.3	0.53	13	15
Si (x 100)	36	46.8	1.70	43	51
Mn (x 100)	36	146.9	2.55	140	154
P (x 1000)	36	6.2	0.76	5	7
S (x 1000)	36	2.5	0.82	1	4
Cu (x 100)	36	14.6	0.73	13	16
Nb (x 1000)	36	2.7	0.51	2	4
Al (x 1000)	36	33.8	5.96	18	47
Carbon Equivalent (x 100)	36	43.0	0.79	42	45
Mechanical Properties					
Yield Strength (MPa)	172	396	16.3	358	447
Tensile Strength (MPa)	172	545	9.4	517	571
Charpy-V Energy ft lbf	516	162.1	14.01	118	187
(long. at -20°C) J	516	220.4	19.05	160	254
Through-Thickness Properties					
Yield Strength (MPa)	1032	384	16.9	338	429
Tensile Strength (MPa)	1032	547	14.9	452	583
Reduction of Area (%)	1032	61.6	7.93	36	73
Elongation (%)	1032	29.1	4.10	19	38

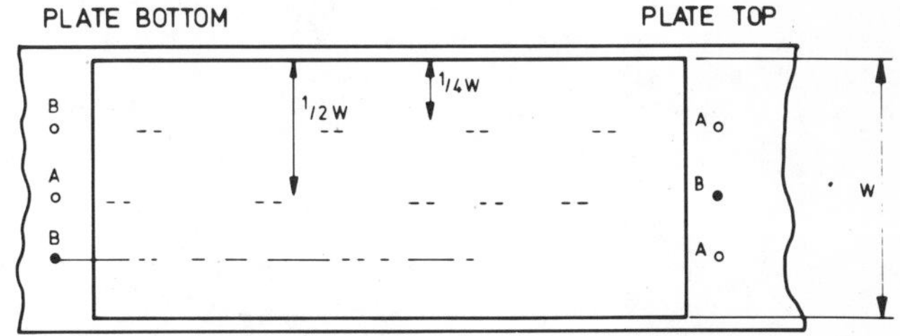

TEST PIECES 'A' SHALL BE TAKEN FROM ONE SURFACE OF THE PLATE.

TEST PIECES 'B' SHALL BE TAKEN FROM THE OPPOSITE SURFACE OF THE PLATE

LOCATION OF THROUGH THICKNESS TENSILE TEST PIECES

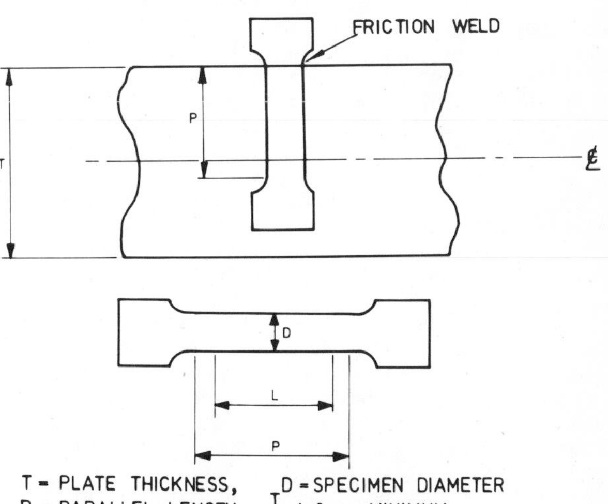

T = PLATE THICKNESS, D = SPECIMEN DIAMETER
P = PARALLEL LENGTH = $\frac{T}{2}$ + 6mm MINIMUM
L = GAUGE LENGTH = D x 3·54 = $\frac{T}{2}$

Figure 4: Position and size of test specimens

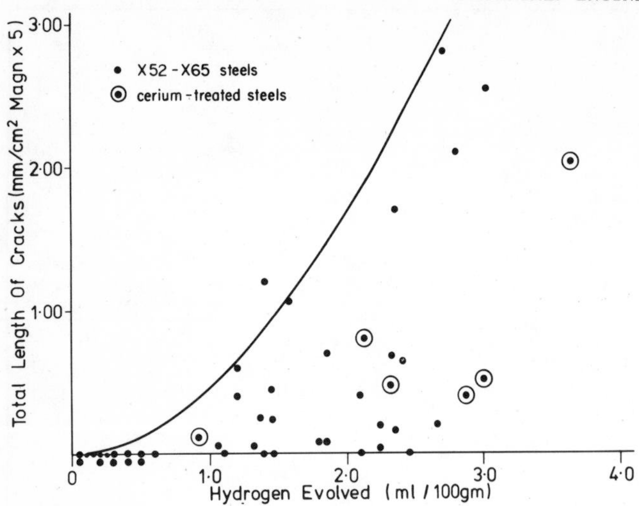

Figure 5: Cracking observed in wet hydrogen sulphide test after 96 h exposure

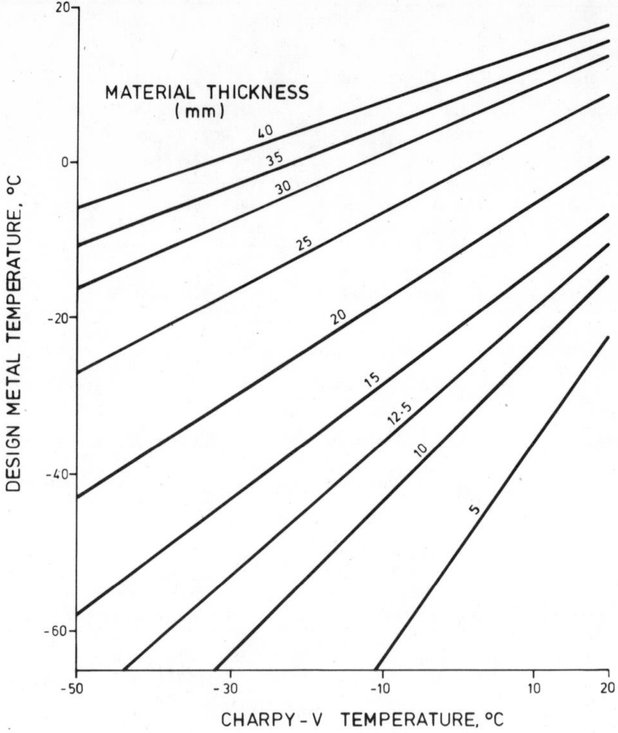

Figure 6: Thickness, metal temperature and Charpy-V test temperature relationships

test for thick plates (say, over 1 in. or 25 mm) but for thinner plates the through-thickness tension test is not so satisfactory. This is largely because of the lateral constraint offered by the welded ends and the short parallel length which interferes with the true development of reduction in area and so other methods of assessment seem to be more appropriate. Immersion in a 3% sodium chloride solution saturated with hydrogen sulphide provides a good method of assessing the risk of lamellar tearing, as well as the resistance to delamination by hydrogen absorption. This may occur as a result of corrosion effects or by overcharging when using impressed-current cathodic protection. Details of the test have been given by Moore and Warga (5), and the result of applying it to various steel qualities together with the degree of cracking observed in the test pieces as a result of this exposure is shown in Figure 5.

LOW-STRESS FRACTURE

Techniques for assessing brittle fracture risk are many and varied but Charpy-V impact testing is still most widely used as a workshop or steel mill acceptance test. Nowadays the absorbed energy value required of the Charpy test at the chosen test temperature is based increasingly upon experimental work using sophisticated tests. Drop weight and Drop Weight Tear Tests find some application in petroleum industry work where resistance to the propagation of fracture initiated by dynamic effects such as explosion or collision is required, but for most applications in that industry, Yielding Fracture Mechanics (COD) seems to be more appropriate and is gaining in popularity. Sometimes COD is supplemented by Cross Welded Wide Plate Tests where confirmation of residual stress effects or the effects of differences between the base metal and the welded joint in strength or work hardening exponent is required. COD tests show a pronounced thickness effect and this is allowed for in writing steel purchasing specifications or designing welding procedure tests either by adjusting the Charpy test temperature relative to the design temperature or by changing the absorbed energy requirement. Figure 6, which was derived from a subjective assessment of numerous COD tests, is included here as a practical guide to the general thickness effect and is regarded as a good guide to Charpy-V requirements for general purposes (6).

If applied to all parts of the joint, COD testing is very rigorous and some statistical assessment of the results is worthwhile. When assessing the significance of flaws it is worth considering the wisdom of discarding especially low values where these are evidently extremes. Figure 6 is not considered to be ultra-conservative, but it is sufficiently so for most practical applications.

STRESS RELIEF

The effect of using Figure 6 is to discriminate heavily against steels thicker than about 40 mm and for such thicknesses, unless very careful fracture analyses are made, post heat-treatment in the stress relieving range of temperature is recommended. Post heat-treatment, because of its tempering, over-ageing and stress relieving effects, is of great value in reducing the risk of low-stress (brittle) fracture and this is an important factor when choosing steel qualities based upon fracture initiation criteria.

After stress relief, 20 ft lbf (27 J) Charpy V-energy at the service temperature for base metal, HAZ and weld metal for Grades 43, and 30 ft lbf (40 J) for stronger steels seems to be adequate for all thicknesses and structural steel grades in common use.

ESTIMATING ALLOWABLE FLAW SIZE

For estimating the flaw sizes tolerable for a given value of COD and strain, Figures 7 and 8 are useful and provide a good guide when mathematical analysis is not practical (7). β is the total allowable length of a through-thickness crack.

Examples of typical COD transition curves for typical materials and welding procedures are

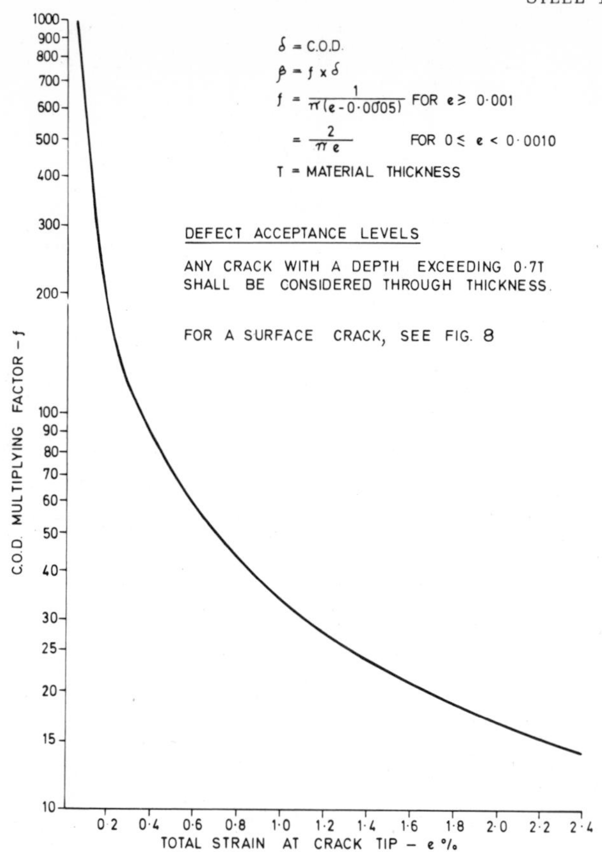

Figure 7: Relationship between COD multiplying factor and total strain at crack tip.

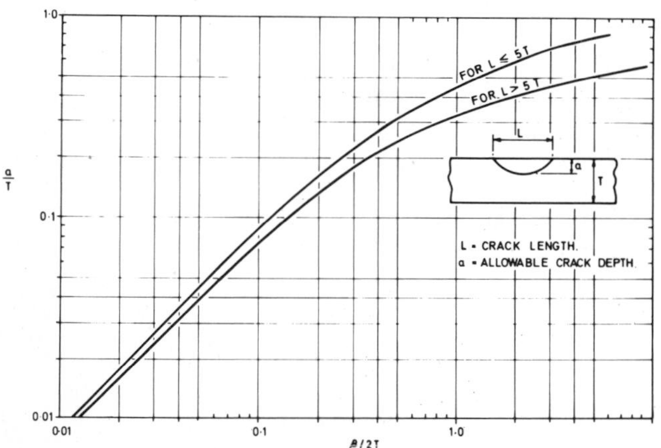

Figure 8: Relationship between surface flaw dimensions and β(= f x δ, see Figure 7)

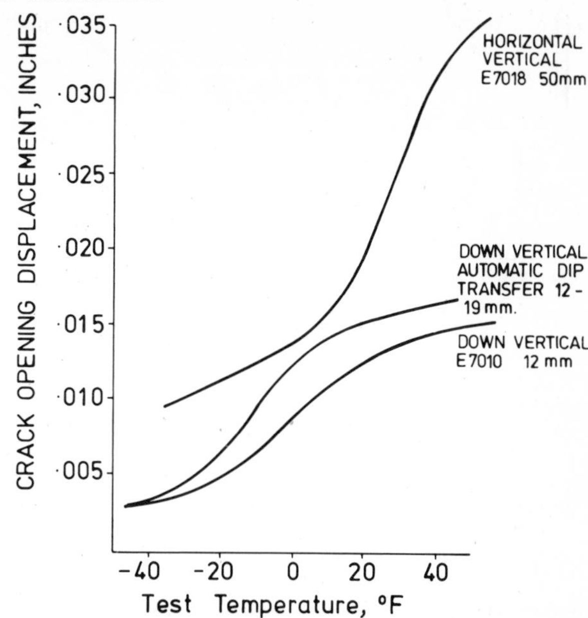

Figure 9: Typical minimum crack opening displacement for various weld metals

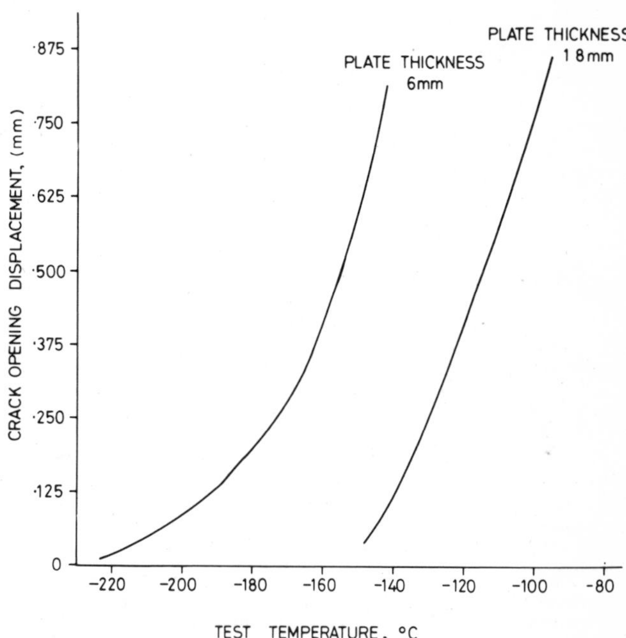

Figure 10: COD transition curves for typical materials used for Arctic construction

given in Figures 9 and 10. These have been used successfully in low temperature applications and provide a guide, in the absence of actual testing, to the critical value of COD which may be anticipated in common weld metals and steels.

Allowable sizes for weld imperfections may be estimated more accurately from calculations based upon actual COD test results. Draft BS Standard Rules for the Derivation of Acceptance Levels for Defects in Fusion Welded Joints, Document 75/77081 DC, defines an acceptable technique. British Standards has suggested methods for calculating allowable flaw sizes for safe conditions using the COD method. Diagrams of allowable flaw size which have been used as a basis for judging the safety of constructions built in the Arctic, to devise acceptance standards and to judge the adequacy of particular welding procedures are illustrated in Figure 11.

CHOOSING DESIGN TEMPERATURE

Estimating the design and service temperature is difficult but very important. It must be remembered that it is the temperature of the construction and not that of the air which should be considered. Chill factors do not apply. Where very short times at exceptionally low temperatures are involved, insulation may be less expensive than the provision of extra notch ductility. Constructions which are buried even in cold permafrost rarely reach temperatures below -20°C. Most constructions can easily be housed in simple protective buildings and such protection is often necessary in any case to permit

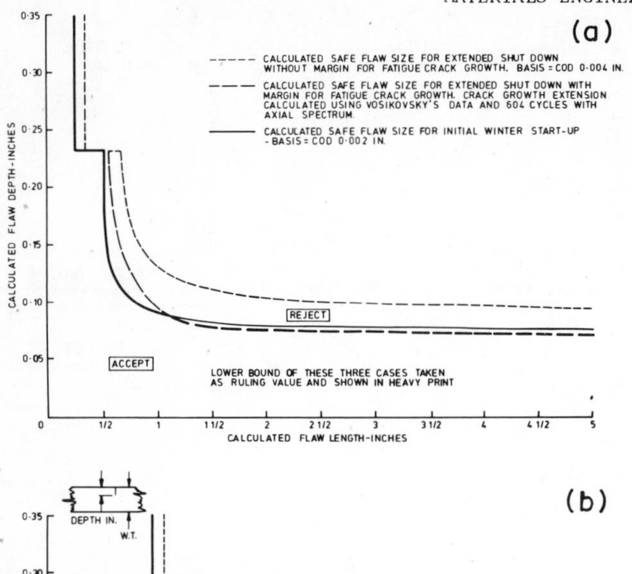

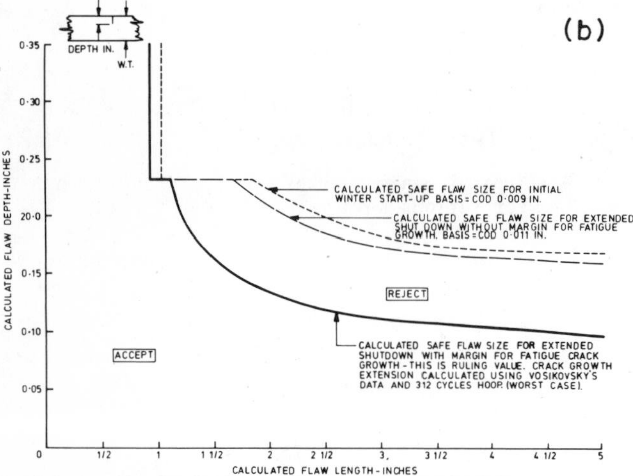

Figure 11: Calculated safe flaw sizes for (a) buried weld and HAZ imperfections; (b) outside surface imperfections on base metal -- arc burns etc.

operators to work in reasonable comfort. The temperature of pipelines is influenced greatly by the material being transported within them. Even when a pipeline is offstream it is usually many months before the pipe cools to the average outside temperature. A design temperature of -50°C is very low and rarely met in Arctic construction.

Typical carbon-manganese steels are suitable for even that low temperature, provided that the thickness of the joint in the "as-welded" condition does not exceed about 20 mm. Thinner materials in these steels are suitable for use even in the "as-welded" condition at extremely low temperatures. Figure 12 provides a useful guide to what is presently thought to be safe.

RELATED EXPERIENCE IN LOW-TEMPERATURE STORAGE

In the oil and chemical industries the necessity of storing, at low or ambient pressure, huge quantities of liquefied gases (e.g. butane, propane, ethane and methane) has provided ample experience of the effect of cold upon pressure vessel steels, piping, ship and storage tank plates and sections. On Das Island in the Persian Gulf a large LNG installation consisting of two 1 M bbls. (160,000 m^3) liquefied methane tanks, two 300,000 bbl. (48,000 m^3) propane, and two 230,000 bbl. (37,000 m^3) butane tanks has recently been completed. The design stress for the propane and butane tanks was UTS/2 + YS/1.5.

The propane and butane is stored at -50°C

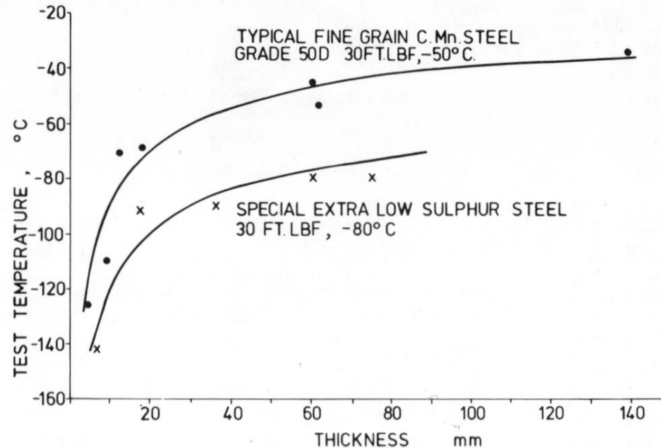

Figure 12: Transition temperature for 0.25 mm COD as a function of thickness of unwelded base metal

and 0°C respectively in huge tanks constructed from plain carbon steel, with notch ductility in accordance with Figure 6. The maximum thickness employed in the tank shells was 20 mm. Even for these very large tanks a greater thickness was not required because of the high design stresses used. The base metal COD was adequate for the temperature but at thicknesses over about 1 in. (25 mm) the welded joint was thought to be marginal at -50°C. This was not because of any deficiency in the base metal but because of the difficulty of preserving adequate COD properties in the weld and HAZ, even when using the best conventional welding techniques. It has been shown by COD and confirmed by Wide Plate testing and by service experience that plain C-Mn fine-grained steels are adequate up to thicknesses of 20 mm for temperatures down to -50°C, even in the as-welded condition. Thinner sections of C-Mn steels can be used down to even lower temperatures and this accounts for the successful use of thin plain-carbon steels at extremely low temperatures.

The thickness of the material, the strain intensity and the rate of strain are significant parameters. The recommendations of Figure 6 provide for applied strain equal to that at yielding in the as-welded condition, allowing for the HAZ degradation arising from normal welding processes, i.e. HAZ notch-ductility need not be considered. The intercepts are considered to be applicable to normal rates of strain, say 10^{-3}/s -- a typical earthquake strain rate.

It is important to realize that Charpy-V requirements for unwelded steel can be significantly less severe than for welded structures. Figure 12 indicates that a margin of about 20 deg C is thought to be necessary to cater for welding damage in the HAZ. It can be seen that for unwelded structures subject only to static strain Charpy V-notch ductility requirements need only be minimal. This accounts for the excellent service provided by simple steels not subject to notch ductility requirements in northern cities like Fairbanks and Edmonton where numerous riveted and bolted bridges, street furniture, and other constructions testify that thin unwelded structures are not in danger, even at very low temperatures, despite the uncertainty regarding the notch ductility of the materials used in their construction.

For the enormous LNG tanks on Das Island, 9% nickel steel was used for a design temperature of -162°C at a design stress of about 40 ksi (280 MPa) -- considerably higher than that permitted by ASME and API Standards. The welding consumables used were all of the high-Ni variety. For seams transverse to the principal stress the strength of the weld metal was increased by the addition of Mo

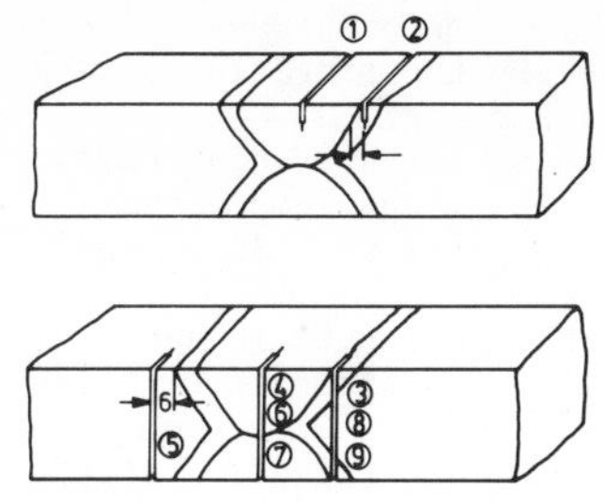

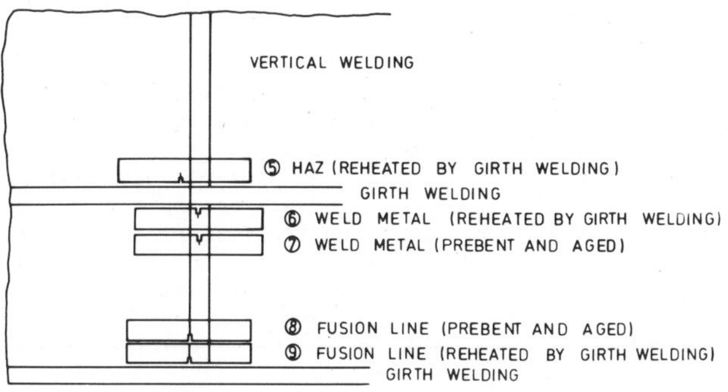

Figure 13: COD notch locations

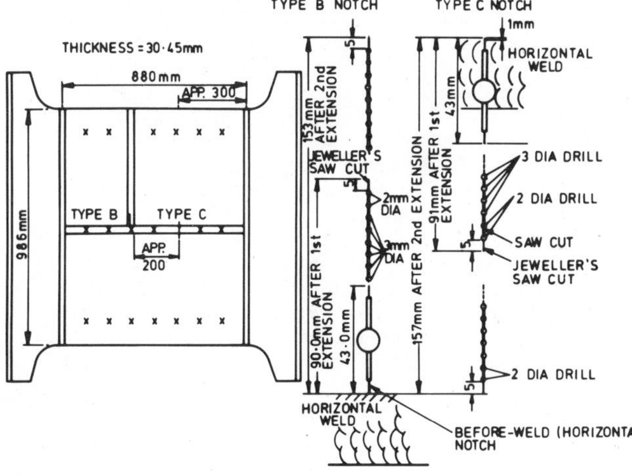

TYPE B NOTCH: HAZ OF VERTICAL WELD (1 mm FROM FUSION LINE)

TYPE C NOTCH: HAZ OF HORIZONTAL WELD

Figure 14: Specimen for welded plate notched to HAZ portion of vertical welding

and W, resulting in an all-weld-metal yield strength of over 60 ksi (410 MPa).

The adequacy of this design was checked by COD and by cross-welded wide plate tests, Figure 13 and 14. At the design metal temperature of -162°C some instability was noted in 9% Ni plates over 30 mm thick and this demonstrates that the effect of thickness is significant even in 9% Ni steel, normally regarded as quite adequate for this temperature irrespective of thickness. When 9% Ni steel is used at high design stresses for service at liquid oxygen temperatures an upper limit of thickness not exceeding 20 mm seems to be prudent. However it is worth noting that there appears to be no Arctic location requiring the use of 9% Ni steels other than for cryogenic applications of the type just mentioned.

WELD METAL

A glance at the COD transition diagrams in Figures 9 and 10 illustrates the importance of weld metal notch ductility in non-stress-relieved fabrications in the range of temperature of Arctic constructions. The choice of welding procedures, electrodes and other consumables must be made very carefully if good COD values are required at temperatures below about 0°F (-20°C) and if the thickness exceeds about 25 mm. It appears that this difficulty emanates from dynamic strain ageing effects in the weld metal near the centre of the thickness and this is especially noticeable in sections over about 30 mm. The damage is wiped out by post-heat-treating at temperatures around 600°C and this, together with the tempering of HAZ's, is perhaps the most persuasive argument for the application of post-heat-treatment to weldments thicker than 30 mm for service at low temperatures. The significance of residual stress appears to be marginal except in rather brittle structures.

PIPELINES

Pipelines seems to have become classified in a group by themselves, presumably because of the preoccupation with fracture arrest processes in gas transmission pipelines. It is evident from burst test results and from the work of Shoemaker et al (8) that even a very high Charpy-V shelf energy is not successful in arresting fast fracture in large diameter gas pipelines. This does not seem to be a problem in oil lines because of the speed of the decompression front and it is questionable if it is a real problem in gas lines. There have been few if any cases of long distance fracture propagation even in large diameter gas lines, except when the steels used have displayed very low shelf energies. The risk of such an occurrence appears therefore to be largely hypothetical now that high shelf energy steels are widely available as a result of desulphurization. Mechanical crack arrestors are used by BP when such an eventuality is thought to be credible and these are applied at arbitrary intervals.

A simple form of arrestor which is easy to apply and does not require welding is shown in Figure 15 and this design is already in use in the prevention of catastrophic buckling in undersea pipelines (9).

Figure 15: Example of non-welded crack arrestor

It is believed that it would be equally successful in arresting a propagating fast fracture. The lack of metallic continuity between the material of the pipe and the outer annulus, which serves to reduce the stress and to prevent the opening of flaps of the fractured pipe behind the crack tip, has a special advantage inasmuch as further propagation of the crack front would require the reinitiation of the crack in the outer ring. This is unlikely owing to the reduced hoop stress arising out of the diametral constraint.

Increasing the Charpy-V upper plateau energy is facilitated by using materials with high resistance to delamination and this tends to increase the transition temperature because of the increased thickness effect arising out of the absence of delamination. The competing aspects of transition temperature and plateau energy require study so that service performance versus the cost of linepipe can be maximized. Pursuit of very high levels of plateau energy now seems hardly justifiable. For the purposes of fracture initiation the weld and its HAZ appear to be the most critical and more study is required of this aspect for all forms of construction.

FUTURE REQUIREMENTS

Some subjects which require special attention if we are to improve the efficiency of our selection of steel for Arctic engineering are:

(1) - An improvement in the notch ductility of weld metal designed for down vertical welding E6010, E7010 etc., and for the various automatic welding processes for service temperatures below -30°C (especially if base metal thickness exceeds about 15 mm).

(2) - Improved notch ductility in weld metal for all-position welding for thicknesses greater than 20 mm for service below -30°C. This requires better knowledge of dynamic strain ageing effects.

(3) - The significance of rate of strain in establishing critical values of COD should be quantified and confirmed.

(4) - The effect of machine compliance upon the behaviour of the COD test specimen and the significance of this upon the behaviour of transient instabilities during testing, should be studied. Many transient effects presently recorded as critical values of COD may prove to be innocuous provided that they can be shown to arrest in a stable or rising stress field.

CONCLUSIONS

The large scale fabrication of steel constructions in the Arctic is best avoided unless artifical working conditions can be contrived. This is not so much because welding and notch ductility requirements are so severe but rather that productivity is low and the cost per ton is exhorbitant. The use of thin sections in redundant constructions is recommended.

Notch ductility requirements for steel for normal engineering and structural applications in the Arctic are not particularly severe provided that the thickness of the base metal does not exceed about 20 mm. This thickness is sufficient for most structures.

Base metal properties of common steels are adequate for very low temperatures provided they are not damaged by welding. Bolted or rivetted structures present little danger especially if the maximum thickness is controlled.

Fracture arrest is gas pipelines through the medium of notch ductility has not been shown to be feasible. Mechanical arrestors appear to be effective and make unnecessary the provision of high levels of transverse plateau energy.

Better welding consumables are required for (a) thickness greater than 20 mm and temperature below -30°C; (b) thickness greater than 30 mm and temperature below -20°C.

The significance of dynamic strain ageing damage in weld metal and the importance of brittleness in narrow HAZ's as measured by the COD test require further study. A more precise understanding of the effect of strain rate in the range 10^{-3} to 10^{-1}/s would be helpful.

Pipeline steels stronger than X70, or with greater notch ductility than is presently available, is not a general requirement. Increasing strength intensifies notch ductility and weldability problems and is not recommended for general purposes.

After spending more than 30 years on the study of fracture, practically no progress has been made in applying any of the findings to the improvement of Codes and Standards for the type of hardware commonly used in Arctic construction. Despite such inspired notions as Pellini Drop Weight Test and N.D.T., the Navy Tear Test, K_{IC} and COD, a Charpy-V energy of 15 ft lbf (20 J) at the service temperature is still the most widely applied criterion in practice. More benefit would be gained in consolidating and quantifying what we already know and introducing this into Codes and Standards than in pursuing esoteric mathematical solutions which are often beyond the comprehension of the practising engineer and find little application in engineering solutions. Practical engineering solutions exemplified by the mechanical crack arrestor typifies what is required. Perhaps accurate solutions are required to design problems in the construction of space vehicles and some aircraft where weight is of great consequence and where ultra-strong, and therefore notch-sensitive materials must be used. But for much of the engineering required for Arctic constructions present knowledge is adequate. It is time Codes and Standards were brought into line with present day knowledge and unnecessary mysteries clarified. This is especially important in Arctic locations where statutory requirements, Federal and State embodying antiquated National Codes are binding.

ACKNOWLEDGEMENT

Permission to publish this paper has been given by the British Petroleum Company Limited.

REFERENCES

1. H. Kubota et al., "Controlled Rolling of Steel Plates", Nippon Kokan Technical Report - Overseas, 1971.
2. K. Winterton, Welding J. Research Supplement, 1961, vol. 40, pp. 106s-109s.
3. J. C. M. Farrar, R. E. Dolby, R. G. Baker, ibid., 1969, vol. 48, pp. 274s-282s.
4. H. C. Cotton, Proc. Roy. Soc., 1976, vol. 2828 (A1307) pp. 53-64.
5. E. M. Moore and J. J. Warga, Unpublished paper, Corrosion/76, NACE Houston, 1976.
6. British Standard BS.4741.1971.
7. H. C. Cotton, J. B. Denham, K. R. Doble, First International Symposium, Japan Welding Society, Tokyo, November 1971.
8. A. K. Shoemaker, R. F. McCartney and K. D. Ives, This Volume, pp. 298-305.
9. U. S. Patent 3860039, J. Ells, January 1975.

DISCUSSION

P. A. Peters (Mannesmannrorhen-Werke): One of the most remarkable sentences in your paper is "Welding is a most potent method for damaging steel". Supposing you chose the right steel, what did you do under the severe environmental conditions in Alaska to prevent such damage?

H. C. Cotton: The welding procedures approved for use were examined to ensure that the damage caused by welding would be acceptable. Welding, by affecting the properties of the base metal by hardening, strain age embrittlement, grain growth etc., can be most damaging to the properties in the region of the HAZ. Welding processes outside the range 20-100 kJ/in. (0.8-3.9 kJ/mm) were not permitted. The steels selected were chosen so as to be adequate to withstand damage arising from thermal effects within the prescribed range.

P. A. Peters: You say that the arresting of a propagating fracture in the shear mode may be impossible. What is the reason for this opinion, and do you know other long-running shear fractures besides the three in 1969?

H. C. Cotton: I prefer not to pursue this as it is the subject of a later paper at this meeting. However I believe it is now generally accepted that arresting fast fracture by the sole means of high Charpy plateau energy will not succeed in large diameter high strength pipelines at the operating stresses presently in use. For this reason if it is believed that fast fracture will initiate and that other effects will not cause it to arrest, then the use of mechanical arrestors would seem to be indicated. Personally I think that the possibility of a long propagating high energy fracture in a large diameter pipeline using the notch-ductile steels presently available is unreal.

R. Culbertson (Brown and Root): What requirements do you impose on your metal suppliers for the Z-direction properties of elongation and reduction of area?

H. C. Cotton: Farrar et al (Welding J., July 1969) approached this problem and concluded, to the best of my recollection, that a through-thickness reduction in area of 15% min/20% average would be adequate. Such tests are usually made at the ends of plates as-rolled and thus give only a notion of what the properties at the plate centre might be. It is thus a matter of confidence. Table 2 of our paper shows a range of 36% to 73% with a mean of 61.6%, and these results refer to a very large tonnage. On this basis I would venture that a minimum value of 30% would seem to be achievable in practice and this would provide a high level of confidence that the properties at locations remote to the test sample would be adequate.

R. Culbertson: In Figure 6 you show a relationship of Cv temperature vs design metal temperature. What Cv energy value is applicable?

H. C. Cotton: The paper is in error in not making this clear. The values of absorbed energy required at the indicated test temperature for a given design temperature/thickness intercept are: 20 ft lbf(27 J) for grades weaker than X42, e.g. common structural grades, and 30 ft lbf (40 J) for Grades stronger than X42.

R. Culbertson: You indicate that a margin of 20 deg C is thought necessary to account for welding damage. Do you normally use this criterion for your material specifications?

H. C. Cotton: This is a rather simple generalization. The COD for 0.25 mm for an undamaged steel is shown in the upper curve of Figure 12. This is a fine grain steel with 30 ft lbf (40 J) at -50°C. The allowable minimum temperature for this steel after damage by average welding processes can be derived from Figure 6.

R. Culbertson: You indicate that code limits for allowable weld imperfections are frequently unreliable and that non-destructive test methods are often unrelated to the real significance of flaws in welds. Since it appears that we are on diverging paths with inspection requirements for flaw acceptance, is there any work or effort by BP or others planned to correlate the weld defect significance with non-destructive acceptable flaw size.

H. C. Cotton: British Standard 4515.1969 "Field welding of carbon steel pipelines" permits fracture mechanics (COD) to be used to derive safe dimensions for imperfections. These may be used in lieu of the entirely arbitrary requirements listed therein, which for all intents and purposes are a carbon copy of API 1104. Presently requirements listed in almost all, if not all, codes and standards bear no relationship to critical flaw sizes. Repairing imperfections outside these wholly arbitrary limits is costing huge sums of money and making a mockery of refined non-destructive testing.

R. J. Cooke (National Energy Board): Could you comment on the validity of present defect acceptance standards as a quality control tool designed to keep the welder honest and provide a measure of how much qualified welding procedures are being varied in practice? In effect, should a double standard be applied? One to monitor workmanship during installation, and the second to assess defect stability and fitness for purpose after installation?

H. C. Cotton: I think that perhaps there is some validity in applying defect acceptance standards based upon what seems to be reasonably achievable in practice as a means of keeping a general check that welders are reasonably competent and that procedures and consumables used are in order. It is the extension of these requirements to the repair of welds found to be unacceptable on the basis of these criteria that requires examination. Repair welding is always costly and may be harmful and better reasons than failure to meet arbitrary requirements should be advanced to justify unnecessary remedial action.

D. L. Cheever (John Deere): The authors have presented an excellent guide for designers of steel structures. The provision of sufficient data to allow estimation of critical crack sizes at specific temperatures makes this paper especially useful. After working through this data, I would appreciate the following clarifications: 1) Do points that fall on the left of the ordinate of Figure 6 indicate combinations of thickness and temperature where stress relief or higher alloying is necessary? 2) Are the COD values in Figure 8 the lower bounds for weldment values? Are these values for the weld only or the HAZ? 3) Does the data in your figures apply to all the alloy steels you found to be suitable for Arctic use? 4) You list four areas where further data is necessary to extend the use of this procedure. Is work planned or in progress to provide this needed data?

H. C. Cotton: Your questions draw attention to some deficiencies in our paper. Figure 6 is limited to C-Mn steels and the ordinate marks the limit at which it is thought not to be advisable to use steel weldments without taking some additional precautions unless applied stresses are rather low. Post heat treatment, as already mentioned can have a remarkable effect in improving the properties of HAZ's damaged by welding and its application at the margin to which you refer would allow the steels mentioned and the upper limits of thickness defined to be extended considerably. The COD values given in Figure 8 are the lower bound values for weld metal. They are thus highly conservative. The data given in the various figures relate to C, C-Mn and low alloy steels (for example, 2% Ni).

All the questions listed as worth further examination are presently being studied by BP, at Cranfield Institute of Technology and at The Welding Institute.

E. Shelton (Alberta Gas Trunk Line): The recognized value to be taken as the critical value of Crack Opening Displacement (COD), δ_c, for specimens failing on the "upper plateau" is the value of COD at the first attainment of maximum load. Fractures initiated from imperfections in such materials do so by a ductile tearing mechanism. Conditions giving rise to fracture in the ductile tearing mode in actual constructions usually, if not always, entail very high strains approaching the flow stress in the remaining nett section or perhaps very deep flaws relative to the thickness of the material containing the imperfection, which under some conditions can give rise to a "snap through" effect. For practical applications the first indication of an instability in the COD versus stress trace or, in its absence, the first achievement of maximum load is adequate and may under some conditions be highly conservative. Flaw sizes calculated as being safe for a through-thickness or for a surface crack, by reference to Figures 7 and 8, will be very large if maximum load values are used in the calculation. Figure 7(a) takes into account "snap through" as well as ductile tearing and perhaps for a more accurate method of safe flaw size calculation which will be larger than derived from Figure 7, reference should be made to the British Standard Draft Doc. 75/77081 D.C.

G. L. Archer (The Welding Institute): For those not familiar with the COD approach, it may be useful to expand a little on the subject. The testpiece usually takes the form of a full-plate thickness notched rectangular bar which is loaded in three point bending. (Other specimen geometries can be used, but this is usually the most convenient experimentally). The notch must be as sharp as possible if reliable answers are to be obtained and for this reason the last portion is usually grown under fatigue loading. British Standard DD19 (1), which is only a draft standard at the moment, suggests a standard way of doing the test. It is intended that this standard will be revised and issued in the near future. As with most other types of fracture toughness test, clip gauge instrumentation across the notch is used and thus the test method is compatible with other tests. During the test a plot of clip gauge displacement against applied load is obtained on an x-y recorder. Notch tip displacement can be calculated from the critical clip gauge displacement by means of a simple formula. The notch tip displacement is also referred to as crack opening displacement (COD) and this is the fracture-characterising parameter.

There has been criticism of the concept because the COD is not uniquely defined (2). It is now considered that the analyses on which these criticisms were based were not valid (3). Nevertheless, there is a problem of how to define precisely where the COD occurs. Most evidence (4-8) suggests that the original notch tip is the most logical place. Current methods of specifying COD will not always be in line with this. The errors involved are small compared to the errors incurred due to material inhomogeneity and in the subsequent fracture analysis. These factors are far more important than the definition of COD. There are several other elastic-plastic fracture parameters available, such as J-integral, equivalent energy, K, and it can be shown that there are certain consistent relationships between them (9). The method of application is probably more important than the parameter measured. COD is convenient practically however because it is a physical measurement, whereas some of the other parameters are not.

The test is usually done to assess the risk of fracture initiation under a slow loading rate. Typically, the test may take anything from a few seconds to a few minutes to complete (1), depending on the size of the specimen and the toughness of the material. Small variations in loading rate will not affect COD levels. In fact, as already mentioned by Mr. Cotton, an increase in loading rate of several orders of magnitude is needed to bring about a significant change. Methods are being developed for testing at high strain rates (10). In order to design against fracture initiation, it is essential to locate and assess that part of the structure with the lowest toughness. This area will invariably be some part of the welded joint and hence it is logical to concentrate on this area. When designing fracture specimens for weldment regions, it is more important to consider carefully the relationship of the chosen specimen to the actual joint design and the types of defects which will occur in practice, than to adhere rigidly to one standard piece. For this reason, several specimen geometries are allowed in BS DD19.

The design of specimens for assessing weld metals and HAZ regions are discussed in various reports (11,12). Due to microstructural variations in welded joints and the fact that most tests are done in the transition temperature range between low and high toughness, the COD-values obtained are often subject to scatter. At the moment it is usual to test a minimum of three specimens at each temperature and use the lowest result obtained. It is recognized that this is not sufficient to obtain a statistically meaningful answer, but follows past practice as in Charpy testing. Also cost is usually a factor which limits the amount of testing. The statistical side of fracture toughness testing is now receiving attention at The Welding Institute.

The analysis for calculating maximum allowable flaw size is based on empirical relationships between crack length, COD and applied strain (13, 14,15). The relationships were derived from tension tests on large flat plates with various forms of notches. Since we are dealing with a yielding situation, the analysis is expressed in terms of applied strain rather than applied stress. Simple methods for dealing with stress (or strain) concentrations and welding residual stresses have been proposed (15). The latter certainly cannot be ignored, as shown by the occasional "spontaneous" fracture which occurs under the action of residual stresses alone. It is necessary to make simplifications in order to provide a method which can be easily understood and applied by practical people in industry. As a result of the simplifications, the flaw size estimates have been found (16) to incorporate safety factors of at least 2. For this reason the flaw sizes obtained are referred to as maximum allowable, rather than critical. Despite the simplifications which are made, the method can supply flaw size information to an accuracy which is well within that required for present-day NDT techniques. Even if the answers obtained were divided by a further factor of 2 for added safety, the majority of repairs, which are both costly and time-consuming, could probably be avoided. This is because the typical construction defect is not a gross crack, but a rather harmless defect such as a slag inclusion, a pore, a small lack-of-fusion etc. which most construction codes will not permit except at minute levels. Putting these defects into true perspective worldwide would save the construction industry countless millions of dollars. As already mentioned by Cotton, some parts of industry are using the method with considerable gain. An attempt has been made to specify material defect acceptance levels in a document submitted to the British Standards Institution (17). Some of the above ideas are used in that document which, it is hoped will be published in some form in the future.

References

1. British Standard DD19: "Methods for crack opening displacement (COD) testing", 1972.
2. J. E. Srawley, J. L. Swedlow and E. Roberts, Jr., "On the sharpness of cracks compared with Well's COD", Report SM-44, Carnegie Institute of Technology, Pittsburgh.
3. A. A. Wells and F. M. Burdekin, International J. Fracture Mechanics, 1971, vol. 7, p. 233
4. J. R. Rice and M. A. Johnson in "Inelastic Behaviour of Solids", 1970, McGraw-Hill.
5. R. M. N. Pelloux, Eng. Fracture Mech., 1970, (1), p. 697.
6. B. A. Fields, J. Pressure Vessel Tech., 1976, vol. 98, p. 81.
7. J. N. Goodier and F. A. Field, "Fracture of Solids", 1963, Wiley, New York, pp. 103-118.
8. G. L. Archer, 1975, Welding Institute Report, E/63/75.
9. J. D. Harrison, 1975, Welding Institute Report E/64/75.
10. Proceedings, Conference on "Dynamic Fracture Toughness", The Welding Institute and ASM, London, 1976, to be published.
11. M. G. Dawes, Welding Institute Research Bulletin, June 1973, vol. 14, (6) p. 157
12. R. E. Dolby and G. L. Archer, Proceedings Conf. on "Practical Application of Fracture Mechanics to Pressure Vessels", 1971, I. Mech. E., London.
13. F. M. Burdekin and D. E. W. Stone, J. Strain Analysis, 1966, vol. 1, p. 145.
14. A. A. Wells, British Welding J., 1963, vol. 10, (11), p. 563.
15. F. M. Burdekin and M. G. Dawes, Proceedings, "Practical use of linear elastic and yielding fracture mechanics with particular reference to pressure vessels", 1971, Inst. Mech. E. London, p. 28.
16. M. G. Dawes, Welding J., 1974, vol. 53 (Research Suppl.), pp 369s-379s.
17. British Standards Draft Document BS 75/77081 D.C.

H. C. Cotton: Alan Wells must be credited with introducing the COD concept which he described in a very interesting paper published about 1955. The technique has gradually increased in popularity as a natural extension of the notched wide plate test, also attributable to Wells. The significance of strain rate in propagating fractures in the so-called yielding steels lead to a sharp conflict in basic philosophy between the protagonists of the arrest concept (Robertson, Pellini et al) and those favoring initiation concepts (Wells, Burdekin etc.). The notion that R-curve theory and COD are competitive and contemporary is misleading. R-curves are a natural extension of COD into the ductile tearing mode beyond general yield. R-curves seem to provide a most interesting technique for showing the basic ductility of materials beyond the maximum load value in the COD test, but it is in the region between K_{Ic} and maximum load that COD is most valuable and interesting and irreplaceable by J or R methods.

I wish to point out that many large storage tanks for liquified gases -- methane, propane and butane and oil storage tanks with a capacity exceeding 1 million bbl have been designed and constructed to higher design stresses on the basis of COD principles. The huge 50,000t North Sea Platforms for developing BP North Sea Forties Field were similarly fabricated on the basis of COD principles. The COD methods presently in use, although perhaps not exactly accurate in some theoretical aspects, have nevertheless been shown to be highly satisfactory, if somewhat conservative, in predicting the results of large wide-plate tests and full scale burst tests. These COD methods which are now in general use by the British Atomic Energy Authority, Central Electricity Generating Board, and Gas Council, to name but a few, can be used to show that present codes and standards for weld imperfections are wildly inaccurate in terms of what is really required for safety. Rate of strain is important in the context of fracture initiation in structural steels but not excessively so and the strain rate applied in COD testing appears to be sufficiently rapid for most practical purposes.

A. K. Shoemaker (United States Steel): This discussion of COD tends to be confined primarily to the local events in the vicinity of a crack. However, in any fracture control plan the entire structure and its service performance must be considered in light of toughness requirements.

Are the redundancy and compliance of a structure considered when establishing a critical COD value for a material and service application?

H. C. Cotton: I agree with the philosophy expressed in this question. However, by the very nature of things, COD tends to be applied to welded connections in locations with the least redundancy and hence where continuous and reliable performance is essential. Pressure vessel and storage tank shells exemplify the type of construction most often subject to fracture mechanics assessments and these of course show no redundancy.

FABRICATION OF ABOVEGROUND SUPPORT STRUCTURES FOR THE TRANS - ALASKA PIPELINE

H. Matsubara, T. Irie, H. Yozishawa
and Y. Nakamura
Nippon Kokan K.K.
Yokohama, Japan

Nippon Kokan K.K. fabricated the steel structures, including production of the steels themselves, to support the pipeline in the Trans-Alaska Pipeline and Road Project, and contracted to deliver the fabricated products to Alyeska Pipeline Service Company (ALPS). The steels adopted complied with the requirements of ASTM A537, A572 and A441, with special requirements for Charpy V-notch energy at -50°F (-46°C).

Controlled rolling was adopted in the manufacture of steel plates 25 mm thick or less and a normalizing process was adopted for plates thicker than 25 mm. In particular, niobium (columbium) was added to the 89 mm thick steel plates. Steel shapes were controlled-rolled from material of low carbon and high manganese content.

Gas metal-arc welding and covered arc welding were adopted to weld steel plates and shapes. Preheating was conducted in conformity to the requirements of ALPS specifications. To ensure the stiffness of welded areas, a maximum welding heat input of 4.0 kJ/mm was adopted, and welding was performed at an interpass temperature of a maximum of 200°C.

INTRODUCTION

The Alyeska Pipeline Project requires construction of 798 miles (1280 km) of pipe across Alaska to supply 9.6 million barrels of oil from Prudhoe Bay to American industry. To carry out this project, Alyeska Pipeline Service Company (ALPS), has been promoting investigation, planning, design and construction work. The project is expected to be completed by mid-1977.

As shown in Figure 1, the pipeline starts from Prudhoe Bay, passes over the 1440 m high Dietrich Pass and finally arrives at the ice-free port of Valdez. The pipeline, when completed, will be exposed to temperatures of 90°F (32°C) in summer and -80°F (-62°C) in winter. Most of the pipeline is being built on permafrost, some of it in the south being within a significant seismic zone. In order to prevent the pipeline construction from destroying the environment, local wildlife and vegetation, special features were designed, for example an overpass was built straddling a section of the pipeline so as not to partition the area where caribou live. According to the condition of permafrost and topography, some of the pipeline was buried underground and some elevated. Nippon Kokan K.K. (NKK) has supplied the 48 in. (1220 mm) main pipes, steel pipe-piles, support beams and anchor supports. This paper covers only the support beams and anchor supports. Figure 2 shows two views of the built pipeline in the vicinity of Valdez.

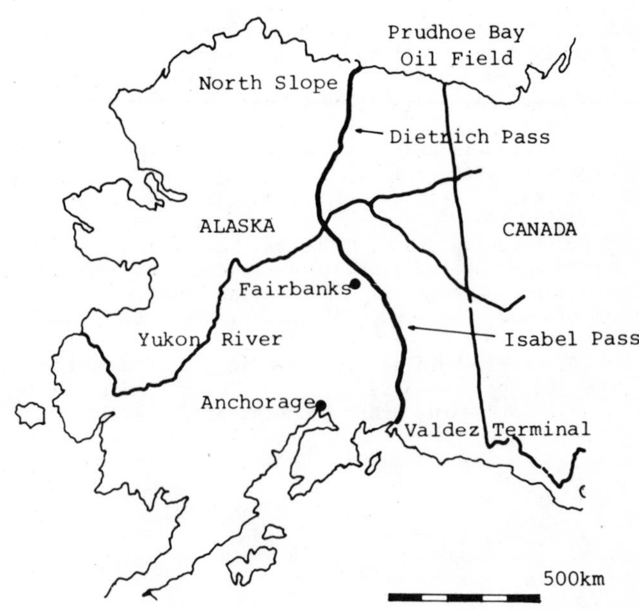

Figure 1: Trans Alaska pipeline route

Figure 2: Sections of the aboveground pipeline laid in the vicinity of Valdez

SUPPORT BEAMS

The support beam is a beam whose ends are fixed to two 14 in. (360 mm) diameter steel piles, as shown schematically in Figure 3. Mounted on the support beams is the main pipe, attached by means of a sliding shoe placed thereunder. The support beams are placed at 50 to 70 ft (16 to 21 m) intervals. The total of 23,211 support beams were fabricated by NKK, weighing 16,359 tons (14,841 metric tons).

In order to minimize the field work to be performed under the rigorous weather conditions, provision was made for the beam to be set on a pipe-bracket and jointed by means of a single bolt on each side. In this way, the loadings due to temperature change, earthquakes and the dead load of the pipe can be accommodated, and the permissible tolerances on the pipe-piles driven on site can also be readily met.

ANCHOR SUPPORTS

To accommodate temperature changes and seismic loadings, the pipeline is built to a zigzag pattern, shown in Figure 4. The pipeline is supported by anchor supports (Figure 5) which secure it at 800 to 1800 ft (240 to 550 m) intervals. The anchor support is designed so that the top of the support, in the shape of a hemisphere and fixed to the underside of the pipe, is set on a drum-shaped base placed on the anchor support. All anchor supports are of the same shape and, with this design, are unaffected by the site grade.

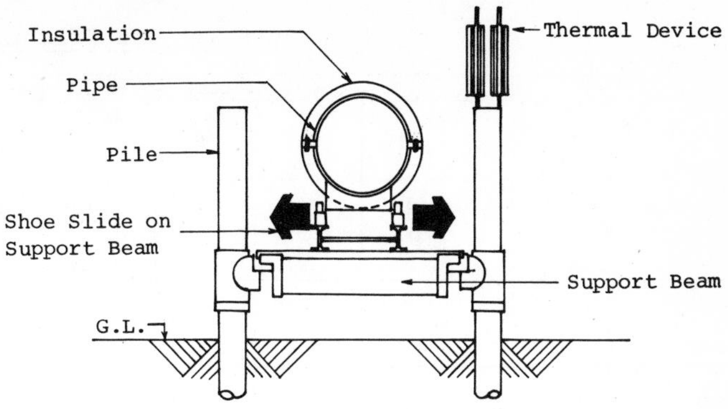

Figure 3: Support beam arrangement

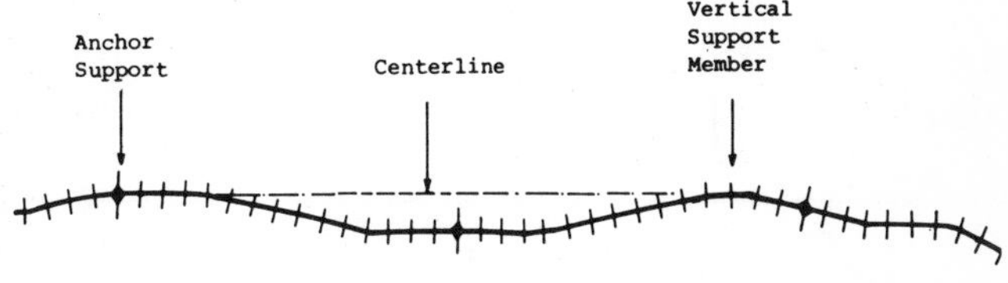

Figure 4: Typical pipeline zigzag layout

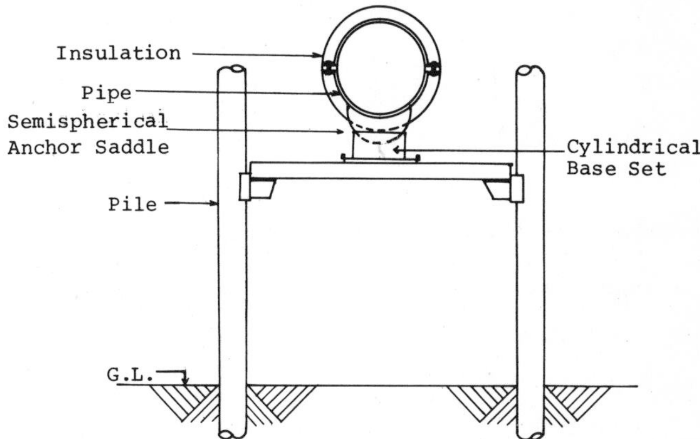

Figure 5: Anchor support design

SPECIFICATIONS

Steels

Steel plates must meet, or be equivalent to, the requirements of ASTM A537 Class 1 and satisfy the requirements for a Charpy V-notch impact test at -50°F (-45.5°C), as shown in Table 1. Steel shapes must meet, or be equivalent to, the requirements of ASTM A572, or A441 as modified or A537 Class 1 and satisfy the requirements for a Charpy V-notch impact test as shown in Table 1. Bolts, nuts and washers must meet the requirements of ASTM A320 Grade L7.

Fabrication

Dimensional tolerances of steel materials must satisfy the requirements of ASTM A6. Welding must be performed in accordance with the requirements of AWS D1.1-73. Welded metal and the heat-affected area thereof must be subjected to a Charpy V-notch impact test. The notch toughness of weld metal at -50°F (-45.5°C) must be 20 ft lbf (27 J) on average and 18 ft lbf (24 J) minimum, and that of a heat-affected area must be two-thirds of the values specified

Table 1: Specification of Steel Plates

Thickness mm	Chemical composition (ladle analysis) %										Tensile properties		
	C	Si	Mn	P	S	Cu	Ni	Cr	Mo	Nb	Yield point MPa	Tensile strength MPa	Elongation %
38.1 or less	≦0.24	0.15 - 0.50	0.70 - 1.35	≦0.035	≦0.040	≦0.35	≦0.25	≦0.25	≦0.08	-	≧345	483 - 621	≧18 in 200mm
38.1 - 63.5	"	"	1.00 - 1.60	"	"	"	"	"	"	-	"	"	≧22 in 50mm
88.9	"	"	1.00 - 1.60	"	"	"	"	"	"	≦0.04	"	"	≧22 in 50mm

Thickness mm	Bending properties		Notch toughness (longitudinal)			Heat treatment
	Bending dia.	Bending angle	Temp. (°C)	Absorbed energy (Joules) Average	Absorbed energy (Joules) Minimum	
31.8 or less	$1\frac{1}{2}t$	180°	-45.5	20	16	t ≦ 25.4mm Controlled rolling or normalizing
31.8 - 63.5	2 t	"	"	"	"	t > 25.4mm Normalizing
88.9	$2\frac{1}{2}t$	"	-28.9	47	38	Normalizing

Table 2: Steel Plates Used

Designation	Max. Plate Thickness (mm)	Applicable Standard	Tonnage
Support Beam	25.4	ASTM A 537-1	3,800
Anchor Support	88.9	ASTM A 537-1	3,000

for the parent metal in Table 1, or at least 15 ft lbf (20 J).

MATERIALS

Steel Plates

6800 metric tons of steel plate were required, as shown in Table 2. Although the ASTM specification requires normalization as a heat treatment, independent of plate thickness, ALPS's specifications permit the steel to be manufactured by controlled-rolling. Thus, we have produced steel plates of less than 1 in. (25 mm) in thickness by this process, of which the final reduction of 50% to 60% is made below 900°C. 1.25 in. (31.8 mm) and 3.5 in. (88.9 mm) thick plates were normalized, conforming to ASTM A537 Class 1. For the 3.5 in. (88.9 mm) thick plate, which exceeds the thickness specified by ASTM, niobium (columbium) was added to satisfy the yield strength requirement.

In order to obtain the required impact value at low temperature, the sulfur content of hot metal was reduced to less than 0.007% by desulfurization, by addition of nickel, copper and chromium.

Figure 6 shows the actual chemical compositions of steel plates of less than 1 in. (25 mm) thickness and Table 3 gives those for the 1.25 and 3.5 in. (32 mm and 89 mm) plates. Figure 7 shows the tensile test results of 1 in. (25 mm) or less

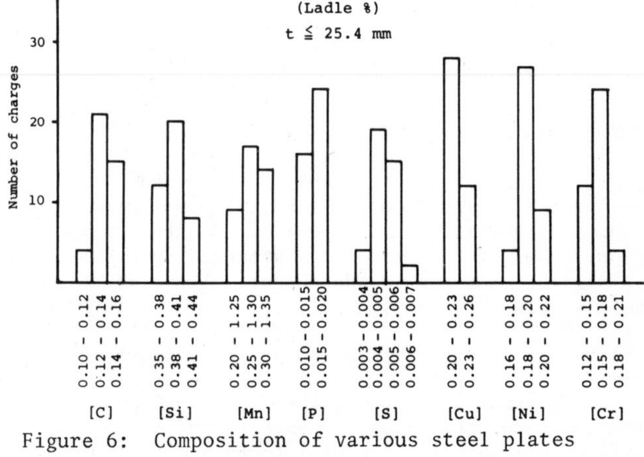

Figure 6: Composition of various steel plates

Table 3: Chemical Composition of Steel Plates

Thickness (mm)	Heat No.	Chemical analysis (Ladle %)								
		C	Si	Mn	P	S	Cu	Ni	Cr	Nb
31.8	A	0.16	0.45	1.32	0.020	0.004	0.27	0.19	0.18	-
	B	0.16	0.38	1.23	0.015	0.005	0.22	0.19	0.22	-
	C	0.17	0.39	1.32	0.018	0.004	0.24	0.18	0.22	-
	D	0.16	0.42	1.26	0.014	0.005	0.23	0.20	0.24	-
	E	0.15	0.39	1.29	0.016	0.005	0.25	0.18	0.24	-
	F	0.15	0.40	1.28	0.019	0.006	0.23	0.20	0.21	-
88.9	G	0.16	0.42	1.52	0.019	0.006	0.23	0.18	-	0.02
	H	0.15	0.40	1.48	0.018	0.004	0.24	0.19	-	0.02
	I	0.15	0.42	1.53	0.019	0.005	0.24	0.19	-	0.03
	J	0.14	0.39	1.48	0.016	0.005	0.23	0.17	-	0.02
	K	0.15	0.41	1.51	0.016	0.006	0.24	0.20	-	0.03

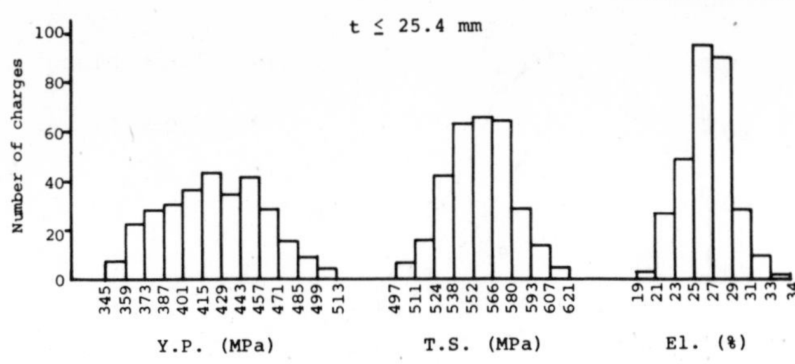

Figure 7: Tensile test results of steel plates (Transverse direction: gauge length = 200 mm)

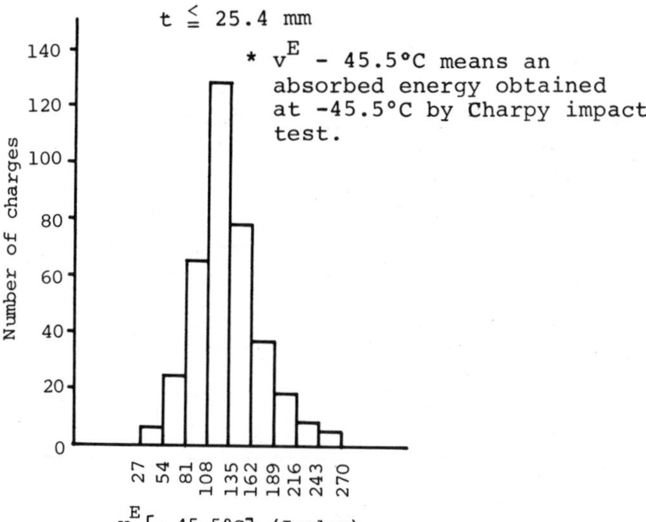

Figure 8: Impact test results of steel plates (Longitudinal direction)

Table 4: Test Results of Steel Plates

Thickness (mm)	Y.P. (MPa)	T.S. (MPa)	El. (%)	Absorbed energy (Joules)
31.8	345 - 400	511 - 566	27 - 34	108 - 189
88.9	373 - 428	511 - 587	28 - 37	149 - 243

Table 5: Required Mechanical Properties of Shapes

Tensile Test				Impact Test
Y.S. (MPa)	T.S. (MPa)	Elongation		Absorbed energy at 45.5°C (Joules)
		Thickness (mm)	(%)	
≥345	≥449	5 - 16	≥18	≥ Average 34
		≥16.1	≥22	≥ Minimum 30

Table 6: Specified Chemical Composition of Shapes

(Maximum ladle values)

(%)

C	Si	Mn	P	S	V
0.15	0.50	1.50	0.025	0.015	0.10

Note: Component bases shall be established by the manufacturer.

steel plates. Figures 8 and 9 summarize the impact test results, where "v^E[- 45.5°C]" is the Charpy-V absorbed energy at -45.5°C. Table 4 gives the tensile and impact test results for the thicker steel plates, and shows examples of impact transition curves for the four plate thicknesses.

Steel Shapes

Table 5 gives the ALPS material specifications for steel beams, channels and angles. The rigorous limits on the Charpy impact test values requires the manufacture of steels with low carbon and high manganese content (Table 6).

Conventionally, normalizing is the usual process for such low-temperature steels, but we have used them as-rolled in order to achieve as high a yield stress as possible and permit mass production. In recent years, although greatly improved rolling technology can produce rolled steel plate with excellent toughness and strength, the controlled rolling technology has not been widely used because of the complications of steel profiles. After some effort, we have succeeded in making effective use of controlled-rolling technology and this has led to the successful production of low-temperature steels.

The steelmaking employed a 250 t basic oxygen furnace. Taking into consideration the weldability and low temperature toughness, efforts were made to reduce carbon content and "carbon equivalent" values as far as possible, with manganese and vanadium added to make up strength. Phosphorus and sulfur, which are said to be injurious to ductility and toughness, were used in the minimum possible amounts. Rolling was performed from the heating temperature of 1250°C, finishing at 750°C or lower.

Tables 7 to 10 and Figures 10 and 11 illustrate the characteristics of the beams and channels made. All heats were excellent with respect to their strengths and toughnesses as well as maximum hardnesses. Figure 12 compares these results with those obtained by the conventional SM50 steel (JIS), equivalent to ASTM A441. The steels specifically developed for this project clearly have greatly improved toughness. The histograms of Figure 13 indicate the small deviations of mechanical properties of these mass-produced steels.

Bolts

1 in. (25 mm) diameter bolts of lengths 3.5 in., 4 in. and 4.5 in. (89, 102 and 114 mm) totalling about 65,000 pieces, 2 in. (51 mm) diameter x 2.5 in. (64 mm) bolts aggregating 16,000 pieces, 5,000 stud bolts, 1 in. (25.4 mm) diameter x 17 in. (430 mm), and the requisite nuts and washers were supplied to the Project.

Notwithstanding the requirements of ASTM A320-L7 for these products, none of the Japanese manufacturers had any experience in making such material. For this reason, there were many difficult problems to be solved in interpreting the ASTM requirements, the low temperature impact test and galvanizing.

The matter of greatest concern was whether an average Charpy-V impact strength of 20 ft lbf (27 J) could be obtained at -150°F (-100°C). However, with tempering temperature set at a higher level, a satisfactory result was obtained such that the hardness remains at a low level after heat treatment, e.g., tempering a 25 mm diameter bolt at between 610°C and 620°C.

With the exception of 2 in. (51 mm) bolts and nuts, ASTM A164 GS calls for electrogalvanizing other steel materials to a coating thickness of 25 μm or more. Due to this large thickness requirement,

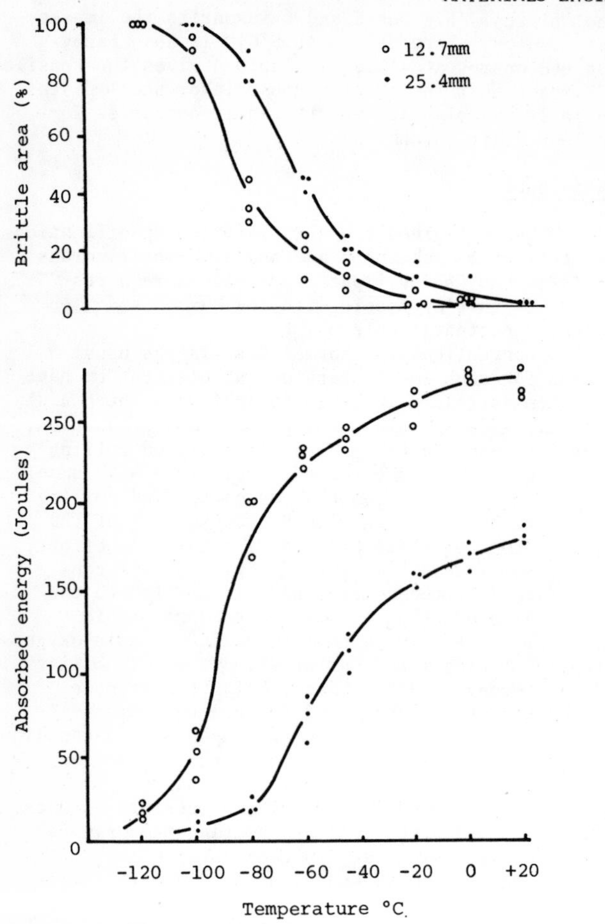

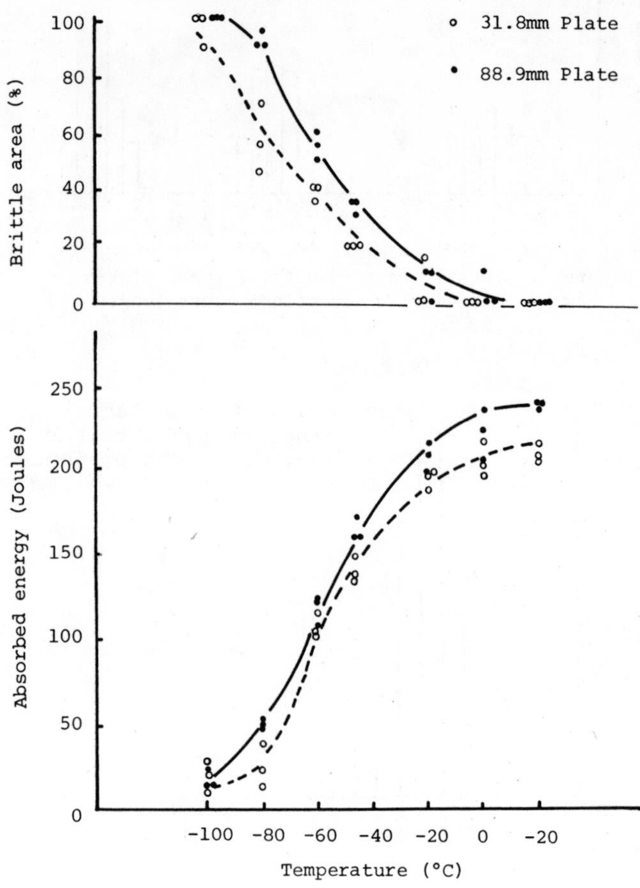

Figure 9: Impact transition curves for steel plates

Table 7: Chemical Composition (Wt %) in Test Results of Wide Frange Shape (H - 606 × 201 × 12 × 20)

	C	Si	Mn	P	S	V
Ladle	0.12	0.42	1.42	0.018	0.006	0.043
Check	0.13	0.40	1.40	0.017	0.005	0.040

Table 8: Mechanical Property and Impact Test Results of Wide Flange Shape (H - 606 × 201 × 12 × 20)

Y.S. (MPa)	T.S. (MPa)	El. %	Absorbed energy at 45.5°C (Joules)
419	538	29	162

Table 9: Chemical Composition in Test Results of Channel [380 × 100 × 13 × 20

(%)

	C	Si	Mn	P	S	V
Ladle	0.12	0.41	1.37	0.015	0.006	0.041
Check	0.12	0.38	1.36	0.017	0.005	0.039

Table 10: Mechanical Property and Impact Test Results of Channel [380 × 100 × 13 × 20

Y.S. (MPa)	(MPa)	El. (%)	Absorbed energy at -45.5°C (Joules)
440	560	23.7	223

efforts were made to effect a uniform coating by hanging bare bolts from a rack.

WELDING

Table 11 shows the ALPS welding requirements and the principal results of the NKK study of them, which obtained the subsequent approval of ALPS.

Considerations of Welding Conditions

Generally speaking, the impact characteristics of a weld metal and the associated HAZ deteriorate as the welding heat input is increased. Therefore, research was conducted into various welding methods, centering on submerged-arc welding, in conjunction with welding heat and impact characteristics, to determine the upper limit of weld heat input. The heat input limit for submerged-arc welding was set at 102 kJ/in. (4.0 kJ/mm).

An increase in interpass temperature also adversely affects the impact characteristics of a weld, as shown in Figure 14. Based on these results, the interpass temperature was set at 200°C.

In order to satisfy the requirements of AWS given in the ALPS specifications, careful consideration was given to use of adequate jigs, satisfactory welding practice, weld materials and welding efficiency to effect a fillet weld of satisfactory profile. Figure 15 and Table 12 summarize the major welding conditions which were adopted.

Welding Performance Test

Table 13 gives, as a representative example, the results of a joint performance test using each

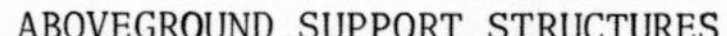

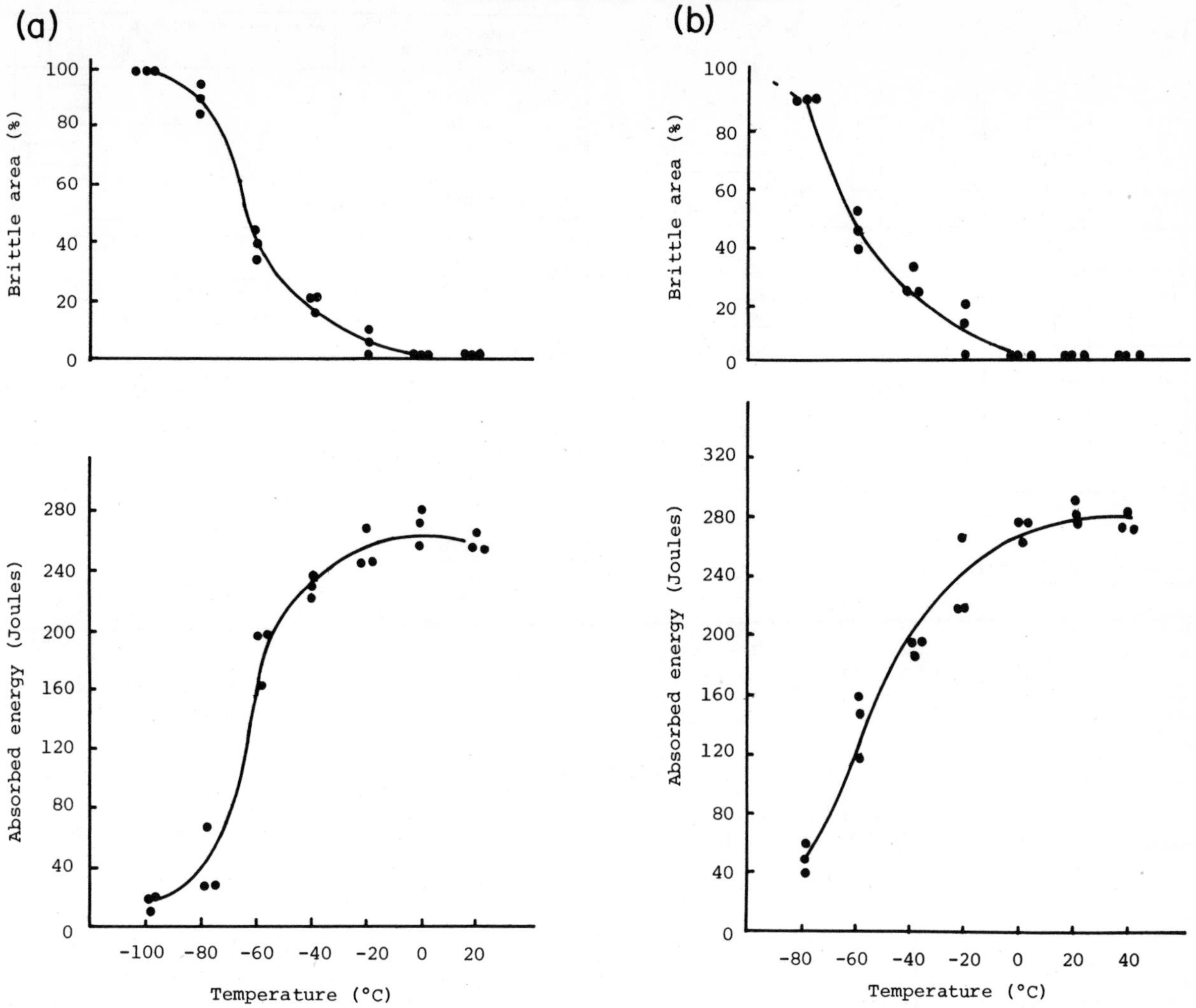

Figure 10: Transition curves of (a) wide flange shapes (H - 606 x 201 x 12 x 20) and (b) ([- 380 x 100 x 13 x 20)

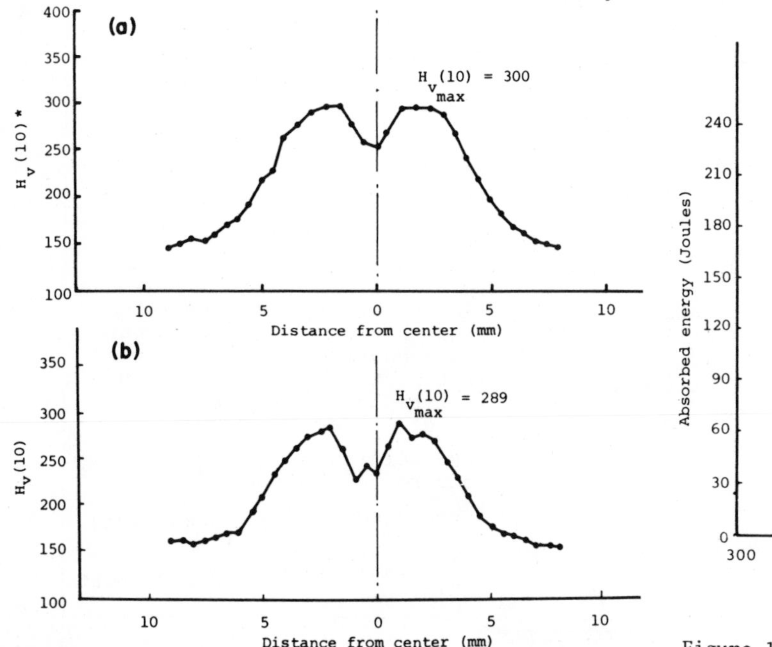

Figure 11: Hardness of welded area of (a) wide flange shapes, and (b) channel ([- 380 x 100 x 13 x 20)

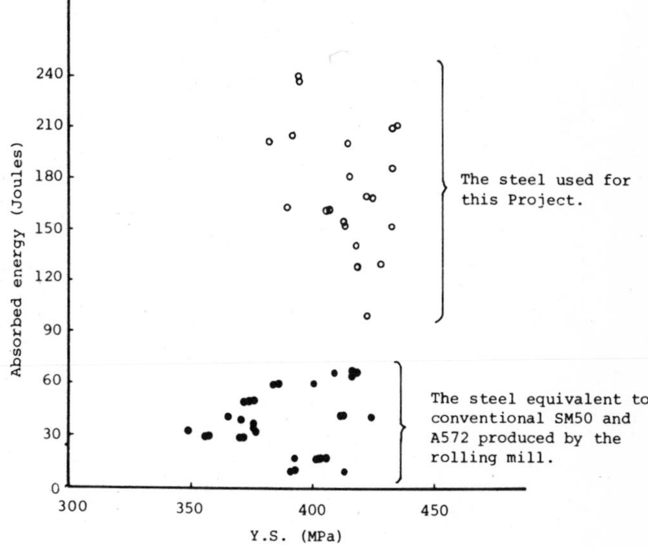

Figure 12: Comparison of mechanical properties of the steel specifically used for this Project and conventional steels

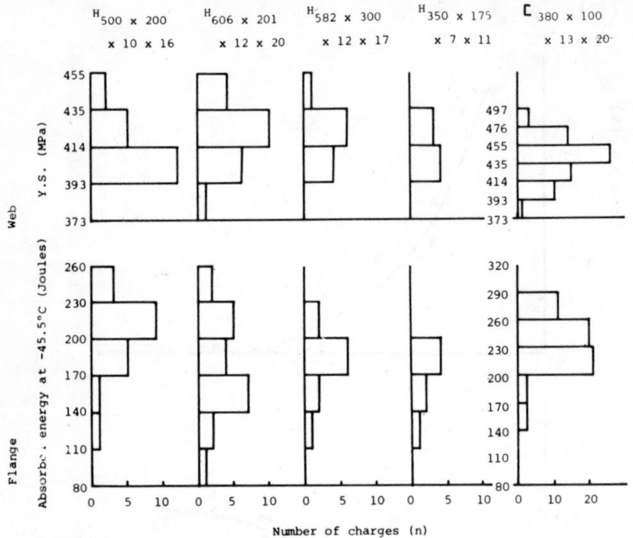

Figure 13: Test results of steel shapes

Interpass temperature	Absorbed energy at -45.5°C (Joules) 10 20 30 40 50 60 70
100°C	
200°C	
Nearly continuously welded	
Continuously welded	

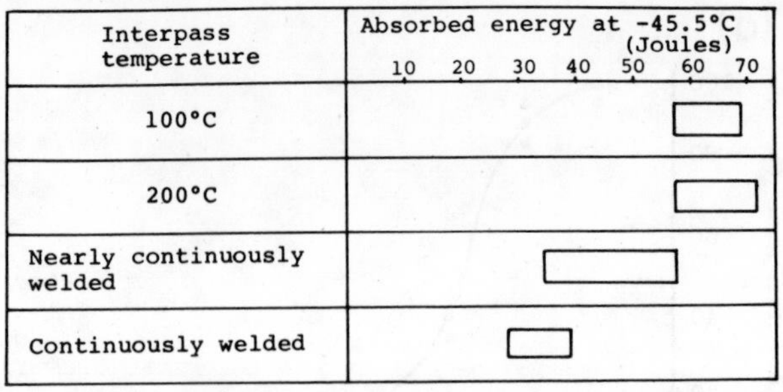

CO_2 welding, MG60 1.6mmϕ, welding heat = 1.18 - 2.36 kJ/mm

Figure 14: Effect of interpass temperature on CO_2 gas arc weld metal impact properties

welding method. Both the weld metal and heat-affected zone met the impact specifications. Welding performance conditions were thus deemed to be adequate and the strength, ductility and fillet weld appearance of the joints satisfactory.

Other Welding Problems

In addition to the considerations noted above, various new jigs were designed, sufficient training was carried out to provide skilled welders, ample consideration was given to drying and controlling all welding materials, and to tacking so as to prevent occurrence of welding defects, achieve higher efficiency and prevent deformation.

QUALITY CONTROL

All materials, components and finished products were voluntarily inspected by NKK and rigorously inspected by ALPS, in accordance with the particular specifications. Quality control consisted not only of making rigorous inspections at each manufacturing stage, but also in assuring the quality of products from raw material through fabrication.

With the adoption of this quality control system, the chemical compositions, heat treatment and mechanical properties of the raw materials for major components could be followed up in respect

Table 11: Major Welding Requirements

Items	Requirements Originally Proposed by ALPS	Requirements Revised by Mutual Discussion
° General rule of welding	Comply with AWS D1.1-73.	
° Approval of welding procedures and welders	Comply with AWS D1.1-73.	
° Impact value of welded zone	Weld metal Av. value 27 Joules Max. value 24 Joules } at -45.5°C Heat-affected zone More than 2/3 of required value of base metal, or more than 20 Joules. Refer to table 2.	
° Welding Materials	Arc welding with covered electrode: AWS A5.1, AWS A5.5 E70XX Submerged arc welding: AWS A5.17, F7X-EXXX Gas metal arc welding: AWS A5.18 E70S-X or E70U-1	Subject to mutual discussion and that test be made on certain characteristics of weld metal, the use of following materials (Kobe Seiko K.K. make) was approved: ARc welding with covered electrode: LB-52N Submerged arc welding: US49 + MF38 Gas metal arc welding: MGS50, HG60
° Preheating, and Interpass Temperature	Plate Thickness (mm) / Temperature (°C): ≦ 38.1 / ≧ 21 38.1 < ≦ 63.5 / ≧ 65 63.5 < / ≧107	

Table 12: Welding Conditions for Major Welded Zones

(a) Support Beam

Mark	Fabricated Steel	Welding Method	Welding Material	Preheating, and Interpass Temperature °C	Welding Heat kJ/mm	Edge, Layer	Remarks
W1	A537 x A537	CO_2 Semi-automatic welding	MG60 1.6 mmφ CO_2 22 - 31 ℓ/m	21 - 200	1.7-3.5	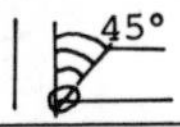 45°	Rotating jig be used.
W2	A572 x A572	CO_2 Full-automatic welding	"	"	1.4-2.6	Leg length 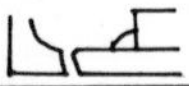 9mm	Locking jig be used.
W3	A572 x A537	Manual welding	LB-52N 4.0, 5.0 mmφ	"	1.3-2.7	Leg length 6mm - 12mm 1 - 3 passes	

(b) Anchor Support

Mark	Fabricated Steel	Welding Method	Welding Material	Preheating, and Interpass Temperature °C	Welding Heat kJ/mm	Edge, Layer	Remarks
W4	A537 x A537	Manual welding	LB-52N 6 mmφ	21 - 150	2.6	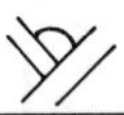 Leg length 16mm	Inverse deformation required. Locking jig be used.
W5	"	Submerged arc welding	US49.4 mmφ x MF38	"	3.1	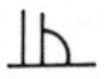 Leg length 16mm	
W6	"	"	"	"	2.4-3.6	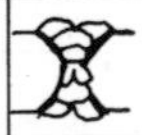	
W7	A572 x A572	Manual welding	LB-52N 6 mmφ	"	2.7-3.5	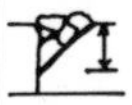 6mm - 12mm	
W8	A537 x A537	Gas metal arc welding	MGS50, 1.6 mmφ Ar 20 ℓ/m, CO_2 5ℓ/m	107 - 150	1.5-2.4	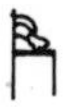 Leg length 10mm - 12mm	Inverse deformation required.
W9	"	Submerged arc welding	US49.4 mmφ x MF38	"	2.2-3.6	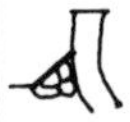 Bevel angle 55°	

Table 13: Typical Examples of Welding Performance Tests

Welding Method	Steel	Welding Material	Edge and Position	Preheating and Interpass Temperature °C	Welding Heat kJ/mm	Layer	Mechanical Properties of Welded Joint: Tensile Strength (MPa)	Bending Test Result	Absorbed Energy at -45.5°C (Joules): Weld Metal	Absorbed Energy at -45.5°C (Joules): Heat-affected Zone
Manual welding	A537 Cl.1 + A537 Cl.1	LB-52N 3.2 mmφ 5.0 mmφ	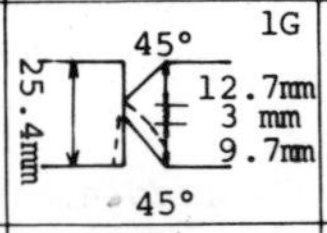45° 1G 25.4mm 12.7mm 3 mm 9.7mm 45°	21 - 150	1.7-3.4	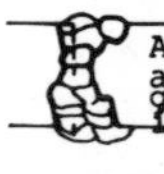 Arc air gouging	587 585	Satis-factory	151 128.9 81.0 Av. 120.1	195.3 217.8 85.9 Av. 166.1
Gas metal arc welding	"	MSG50 1.6 mmφ Ar 20 ℓ/m CO_2 5 ℓ/m	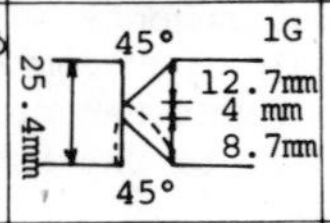45° 1G 25.4mm 12.7mm 4 mm 8.7mm 45°	"	1.5-2.4	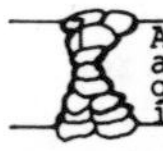 Arc air gouging	580 581	Satis-factory	64.4 61.6 51.7 Av. 59.5	83.0 173.7 75.2 Av. 110.3
	"	MG60 1.6 mmφ CO_2 25ℓ/m	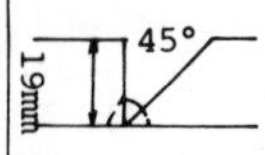45° 19mm	21 - 198	1.6-2.0	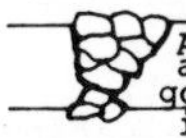 Arc air gouging	573 559	Satis-factory	55.0 58.1 51.8 Av. 55.0	74.7 98.6 314.8 Av. 162.6
Submerged arc welding	"	US49.4 mmφ MF38	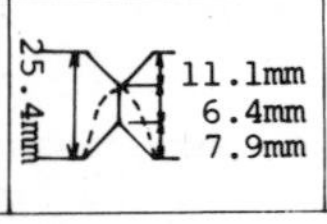25.4mm 11.1mm 6.4mm 7.9mm	21 - 150	2.4-3.9	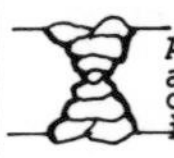 Arc air gouging	575 585	Satis-factory	56.7 51.7 53.7 Av. 53.7	25.4 24.4 39.0 Av. 30.2

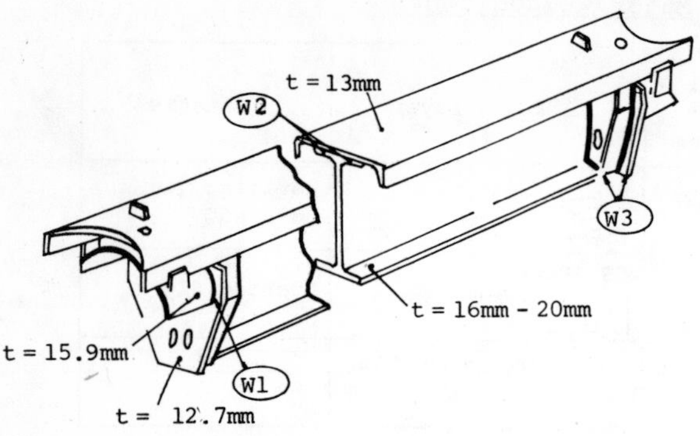

(a) Support beam

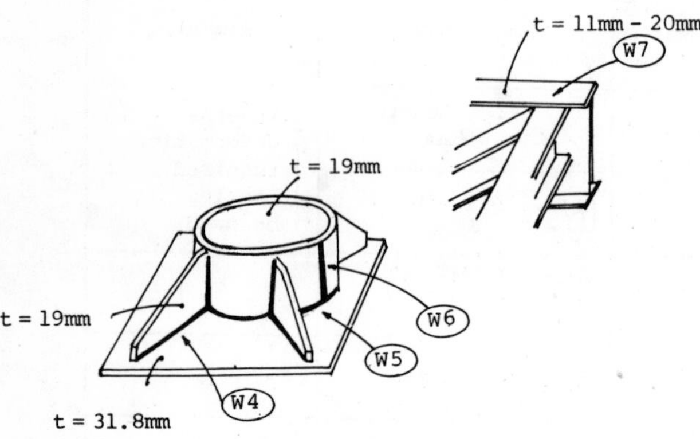

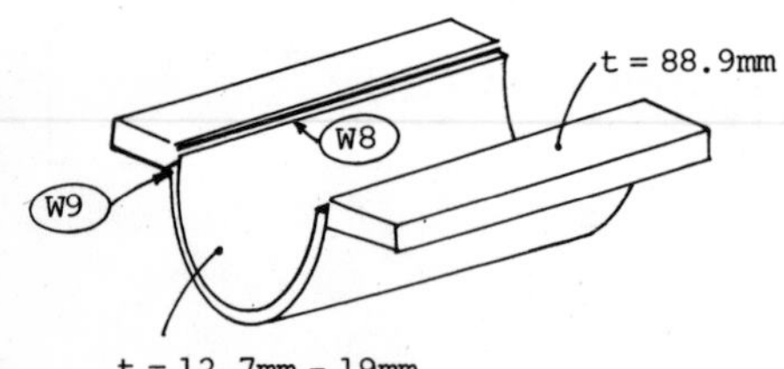

(b) Anchor support

Figure 15: Designs for major welded areas

of many thousands of product pieces, including the welding conditions and the names of welders relating to important welded areas. In the event of an accident occurring on the site, use of this quality control system made it possible to follow up the cause from various angles and to cope adequately with subsequent actions.

Another important point in quality control was that all fabricating orders, conditions and the methods of inspection were thoroughly standardized. For this purpose, the greatest efforts were made to effect as much automated work and uniform pattern of work as possible by means of jigs. We could pinpoint any anomaly in material quality well in advance at each stage by means of a check sheet, and could thereby maintain accuracy while fabricating materials and before passing them over to the next process line. Dimensional accuracy, coated surface and coating film thickness of each product were recorded.

Given the importance of these structures and the adverse effects which might result from their failure, we succeeded, with the co-operation and guidance of Bechtel Incoporated and Exxon Research Engineering Liaison, in completing the NKK portion of this Project.

CONCLUSION

It was for the rigorous conditions of -45°C ambient temperature that the aboveground support structures were designed and fabricated. In order not to lose toughness in the Alaska climate, consideration was given to the use of appropriate materials and the best methods of welding.

The controlled-rolling process was employed for steel plates of 25 mm or less thickness, and the normalizing process was employed for steel plates exceeding 25 mm thickness, especially for 88.9 mm thick plate with addition of niobium (columbium).

Steel shapes were made of low carbon/high manganese steel and were processes by controlled-rolling to assure the required strengths and toughnesses.

Before adopting the specified welding preheat treatment, thorough checks were conducted to see that the required strengths and low temperature toughness of steels could be safely assured to resist welding cracks. Since welding heat could have a significant effect on the toughness of welded areas, various tests were made to ensure a welding heat input limit of 4.0 kJ/mm for submerged arc welding. Also a ceiling temperature of 200°C was set as the interpass temperature.

Acknowledgments

The authors are most grateful to Dr. J. Maple of the Alyeska Pipeline Service Co. for his valuable suggestions. The cooperation of Bechtel Inc., Mitsubishi Corp. and Kokan-sakurada Corp. is also acknowledged.

DISCUSSION

J. E. Hood (Steel Company of Canada): This paper is particularly interesting because it illustrates a trend to the application of quite sophisticated processing techniques, such as strict sulphur control and controlled rolling, to what would normally be considered very conventional steels. Would the authors please comment on the procedural changes required to control-roll shapes, and indicate any methods used to control sulphide shape as well as volume.

Y. Nakamura: The soaking temperature of the continuous reheating furnaces is controlled at the temperature suitable for continuous controlled rolling, without any cooling interval between each stand, and at least 30% reduction is given at temperatures under 900°C, and the finishing temperature is controlled above 700°C. Also, some procedures for shape control during the finishing rolling are added based on the experimental rolling. Sulphide shape control was not applied for these steels.

J. E. Hood: While recognizing that the specification of toughness requirements was not the responsibility of the authors, could they comment on the logic behind them. Also, what was the orientation of the toughness tests with respect to the rolling direction?

Y. Nakamura: We understand that the Alyeska specifications were based upon the authorized specifications such as API, ASME, ASTM, etc. and their own studies. Steels having low sulphur contents tend to have no orientation for toughness with respect to the rolling direction.

W. G. Wilson (Molycorp): You show that the sulphur content of the plates made for this project range from 0.001 to 0.007%. Do the Charpy V-notch ductility curves shown for these plates represent the 0.001% S steel or the 0.007% S steel or the complete spectrum of sulphur contents?

Y. Nakamura: The examples given are for the 0.005% S steel.

M. L. LaFrance (Usinor): You use controlled rolling for thicknesses up to 25 mm and a normalizing process for thicker plates. What is the reason for this thickness limitation? Is it an economical or a technical problem?

Y. Nakamura: The customer's specification shown in Table 1 specified the normalizing practice for over 1 in. (25 mm) thickness, and this is a reasonable limitation for the rolling practice.

M. L. LaFrance: Do you have the same limitations for shapes and do you use normalizing in this case?

Y. Nakamura: All shapes were rolled by the controlled rolling method.

C. Parrini (Italsider): What transverse impact energies did you have on the plates produced by control rolling?

Y. Nakamura: In this case, we made no transverse impact test. But I am sure the transverse value is 2/3 of the longitudinal.

C. Parrini: Did you use any continuous casting for the control-rolling plates?

Y. Nakamura: No, we did not.

C. Parrini: Comparing the 25 mm thick plate formed by controlled rolling and the normalized 31 mm thick plate, a much better transition temperature is given by the controlled rolled one. Is this a general experience in your case?

Y. Nakamura: Yes, because the normalized plates were also controlled-rolled before normalizing.

P. A. Peters (Mannesmannrohren-Werke): What is the reason for the small differences in transition temperature for the 31 and 88 mm normalized plate? Under standard normalizing conditions a much greater difference would be expected. Were there differences in rolling or cooling conditions or in the chemical composition?

Y. Nakamura: The chemical composition of 88 mm thickness is different from 31 mm (see Table 3) and also the rolling practice is different.

G. D. Uttrachi (Union Carbide, Linde Division): The allowable maximum weld heat input of 4 kJ/mm is quite high. What was the criteria for selecting this value and what was the reduction in CVN value in the HAZ with this heat input level?

Y. Nakamura: Meeting the required impact values in the HAZ was the criterion used for setting the maximum heat input. The HAZ impact values at the 4 kJ/mm heat input level were about 2/3 those of the parent material. The lowest values were in the coarse-grained area adjacent to the fusion line.

J. N. Cordea (Armco Steel): The controlled rolling of steel shapes is a very interesting development. Does the procedure involve low finishing temperatures or heavier deformation at lower temperature? If it is the latter, how do you control the extent of deformation in the various sections of the shapes (i.e. web vs. flange)?

Y. Nakamura: The shape is rolled with at least 30% reduction in the rolling temperature range of from 900°C to 700°C. For size control, we have the same procedures based on our experience.

MATERIAL SELECTION AND DESIGN PRACTICES FOR ELECTRIC POWER SYSTEMS IN THE ARCTIC

Vernon F. Crowley
The Shawinigan Engineering Company Ltd.
620 Dorchester Blvd. W.
Montreal, H3B 3L7 Canada

Extremes of temperature and the harsh environment in much of Canada are notoriously onerous for electric power systems. In the Arctic these conditions are even more extreme and the difficulties of design, construction and operation are compounded by the presence of continuous permafrost and the inability to use heavy construction equipment on the sensitive tundra except during the main winter months.

This paper covers design principles and details and in particular those aspects of material selection and application for transmission lines and low-voltage distribution systems constructed under Arctic and sub-Arctic conditions in North America. Due to the necessity of providing power lines with a high degree of reliability many fail-safe design concepts are required, together with special installation methods designed to minimize both the amount of work and construction costs.

INTRODUCTION

The prime requisite for the settlement of the Arctic areas of North America is energy. The most efficient and adaptable form is electricity. In the past, most of the generation has been by means of small local fossil fuel plants, but the ever-increasing demand for larger bulk supply dictates larger fossil fuel plants or hydro-electric generation plants. In the case of the former, power must be transmitted from a central generating station to remote locations. In the hydro-generation case, generation is usually remote from the load centers, and also creates a need for electric power transmission lines.

Future high voltage transmission lines may transmit power from hydro sites south of the Arctic, or laterally across the Arctic, and will, for many years to come, be single radial lines requiring a high degree of reliability. Continuity of service means not only living comfort and industrial efficiency, but often actual survival. Thus the selection of materials and application of construction practices is of prime importance.

The basic parameters and details of design and construction must be such that operation and maintenance problems will not occur or must be kept to an acceptable minimum. Transmission line troubles are more likely to occur during the periods of worst weather conditions and in the Arctic these can be such that it is impossible to get to the trouble area for days or weeks. Long power lines are often difficult to access, even in the summer.

While a number of small systems of overhead distribution lines have been constructed, it is only in very recent years that high voltage transmission lines have been constructed north of the Arctic Circle in North America. The 69 KV 80-mile (130 km) line from Inuvik to Tuktoyaktuk in the North West Territories was constructed in 1972 and a 69 KV transmission line system on the North Slope, Alaska erected from 1973 to 1976. Low voltage distribution lines have been in service in the Point Barrow area for a number of years and some 13.8 KV lines are presently being installed on the North Slope.

The general principles of design and construction of overhead transmission lines in the Arctic are similar to lines constructed in temperate climates. However, to cope with the protracted periods of sub-zero temperatures, combined with extremely high winds, inaccessible terrain and the necessity for continuity of service, requires special materials, designs and techniques.

Certainly, the capital cost of such a line is considerably more than an equivalent line built in lower latitudes, but undoubtedly this higher cost is more than justified. The costs involved in the loss of a line for even a short period will far outweigh the interest charges on the extra initial capital cost required to install a trouble-free line. The loss of revenue, especially for an oil field, together with the cost of keeping trained personnel on site in the event of trouble, the cost of making repairs under the hostile winter conditions or attempting the work on the sensitive tundra in the summer, could be many times more expensive than additional safety features in the design and construction.

For many years, Arctic weather charts and data have been accumulating and general maximum weather conditions may be predicted within a reasonable degree. Thus, by using suitable design and construction techniques and adequate safety factors, a transmission line may be constructed with a predictable service reliability factor. However, the main source of line failure comes from man. Any line is vulnerable to an improperly controlled ground or air vehicle. Certain precautions may be taken to minimize such occurrences but complete protection is not possible.

The design and construction techniques that have been used to date for Arctic transmission lines have been established from distribution and communication lines constructed in the Arctic, power lines in sub-Arctic areas, as well as from field and laboratory experiments.

A characteristic of overhead transmission lines is that the design involves many engineering disciplines - civil, mechanical, electrical, meteorology, geology, metallurgy and environmental engineering. A change in any one factor may result in a change or changes in the other line design and construction factors. The construction specification of a transmission line should be prepared concurrently with the detailed design. This is especially true for lines installed in the Arctic.

ROUTE SELECTION, SURVEY AND SOILS

While the terminals of a transmission line are usually fixed, some flexibility is available in selecting the best route. The main criteria are soil conditions and accessibility. Ponds, lakes and extensive muskeg areas should be avoided. Although most of such areas are relatively shallow, the extra cost of installing foundations in such locations is generally greater than the cost of detouring onto more suitable foundation conditions.

The exact location of streams, rivers, ponds, lakes and muskeg may be more accurately determined in the summer than in the winter and it is possible to take advantage of the longer daylight hours. It is also less costly, especially when it is necessary to use helicopters to transport survey crews. Conversely, during the winter months, the setting up of survey instruments is more time-consuming, visibility is reduced by blowing snow and there are fewer daylight hours. Aerial photographic profiling may be extremely useful where access is difficult and under summer conditions in unwooded areas, may be done with acceptable accuracy.

From terrain mosaics, obtained from aerial photographs, locations for field tests may be made to determine more accurately the types of soil and depths. These are usually classified for transmission foundation design purposes as:

1. Clay and/or silt-sediments deposited in quiet waters or marine, lacustrine or floodplain origin.
2. Gravel and/or graded sands -- mainly sands in outwash plains and valley trains.
3. Shallow moraine -- mostly coarse sandy or gravelly and bouldery basal (lodgement) till over bedrock; shallow residual soils included in this unit.
4. Deep moraine -- mostly coarse sandy to gravelly and bouldery ablation till containing appreciably stratified drift (sand, gravel).
5. Shallow peat -- organic, decayed vegetation on gentle slopes mainly string (ribbed) peatland with shallow stagnant pools.
6. Deep peat.
7. Rock
8. Sand -- includes marine, estuarine, lacustrine, floodplain and ablation deposits.
9. Talus -- boulders
10. Other types of soil may be encountered such as eskers and raised beaches, and all types may be found in combinations or complexes.

Test drilling and sampling of soils should

be carried out along selected routes as well as standard penetration tests (ASTM-D-1586) taken at regular intervals to provide guidance on the relative depth of the mineral and organic soil deposits.

To identify and classify soils beyond the level which is possible from a visual examination and to assist in the assessment of frost susceptibility of the soils, laboratory tests should be carried out to determine grain size characteristics, natural water content, and specific gravity. Considerable research on Arctic foundation materials, especially muskeg and tundra, has been completed and reported (1).

DESIGN LOADING PARAMETERS

To provide a transmission line with the required high degree of reliability, a careful study of all available meteorological data must be made. While there is a wide variation in temperature over a 12-month period in the Arctic, and winds from zero to 100 and 120 mile/h (160 to 190 km/h) may be expected, it may be predicted that they will occur on a regular basis. The basic loading parameters of transmission lines are formed on assumptions, i.e., it is presumed that the line will be subjected to certain temperatures, certain wind forces, and possibly, ice loading.

As the temperature decreases the conductors and overhead ground wires contract, thus increasing the tension in the cables and decreasing the sag between supports. An accretion of ice on the cables would increase the tension in the cables, as would wind blowing on them. In order to assure that the maximum tensile strength of the cables is not exceeded, certain loading parameters must be determined, based on known or assumed climatic conditions. Also the maximum conductor temperature must be known, since the conductor will expand, increasing the sag between structures and reducing the clearance to the earth's surface.

On recent transmission lines in Alaska the following parameters were applied:

A minimum temperature of line conductors and grounding wires at -70°F (-60°C), with no ice and with no wind.

A maximum temperature of line conductors at 150°F (70°C) with no wind.

A maximum temperature of grounding wires at 70°F (20°C), no ice and no wind.

As an alternative loading, the wind was taken at 100 mph (160 km/h) at 0°F (-20°C), equivalent to 26 lbf/ft^2 (1.2 kPa) on the whole projected area of line conductor and grounding wires, with no ice.

After installation, stranded cables, especially those made with aluminum wires, will creep over a period of time and/or when mechanically loaded at abnormally low temperatures by ice or wind. From extensive tests by the cable-producing companies, a close approximation of the amount of creep is known and the conductor and overhead ground wire sags can be calculated. The line is therefore designed by applying both the initial and final tensions and sags.

In order to provide for contingency conditions, an overload factor is assumed for an initial unloaded tension in the cables not exceeding 0.25 x UTS at -30°F (-35°C). The final unloaded tension is not to exceed 0.20 x UTS at a normal ambient temperature of 10°F (-12°C).

The minimum installed factor of safety for the conductors and grounding wires on maximum loading conditions at -70°F (-55°C) was 2.75 x UTS. The installed factor of safety on the insulators was 5.0, on the wood poles 4.0, and 2.5 on the guy wires and anchors.

STRUCTURES

Due to the permafrost over most of the Arctic, the most practical material for transmission structures is wood in the form of poles. With a thermal conductivity much less than that of steel or concrete, the summer heat penetration down and around a wooden pole is considerably less than steel towers with steel grillage foundations or concrete piles or piers.

The fabrication of concrete piles or piers in the Arctic, summer or winter, is extremely costly. Obtaining suitable sand, aggregate and water is difficult and the problems of heating, mixing and protecting the concrete until set, especially when spread out over long distances, is prohibitively expensive.

A disadvantage of steel structures is that on the tundra all construction work must be carried out in winter and the assembly of bolted connections is an extremely time-consuming process under low-temperature conditions. Whereas a wood pole structure has not only fewer bolts, but may be pre-assembled and transported to the erection site.

Some of the finest wood poles for transmission line construction are available in North America and in lengths up to 120 ft (37 m) in heavy duty sizes. The preferred species is Western Red Cedar, as it is durable, straight and strong. Under Arctic conditions, without a preservative treatment it would have a life span of 20 to 25 years and if impregnated with a chemical preservative, such as pentachlorolphenol, would have a life of 55 to 60 years. Western or Douglas fir is also a suitable species but has two disadvantages over the Western Red Cedar. It is a heavier -- and thus more expensive to transport and erect -- and harder wood, so that it is more difficult to climb using spurs, especially in the extreme cold.

North American poles used for transmission, distribution and communication purposes are produced to rigid government specifications and standards of quality and dimensions. The treating materials and procedures are also covered by government standards. Poles are supplied in five-foot increments of length from 20 to 125 ft (6 to 38 m). A class 1 pole has a minimum top diameter of 27 in. (710 mm) with butt dimensions depending on the natural taper of the species. Class 2, 3, etc. poles have smaller top diameters, decreasing in two-inch increments. For piling and where extra strength in a structure is required, a heavy duty classification is available. Average fibre strengths for the various species of wood are also listed in the standards to assist in calculating structure strengths. References to government specifications are included in the Appendix.

STRUCTURE LOADINGS

In order to provide against abnormal loads and to compensate for any material deterioration, structures should be designed not to exceed 25% of their ultimate fibre stress when subjected to a wind pressure of 25 lbf/ft^2 (1200 Pa) on the projected area of each member, together with the maximum conductor loads.

The structure should also withstand the following stresses: a) stresses produced by conductor tension at dead-ends; b) compression stresses due to guy tensions; c) transverse stresses due to angles in the line; d) vertical stresses due to the weight of conductors; e) stresses imposed by wind and ice; f) seismic loadings -if deemed necessary.

FOUNDATIONS AND ANCHORS

Techniques have been developed for the efficient installation of wood poles and anchors for guy wires in permafrost (2-4). Using the proper equipment, holes can readily be augered through most permafrost types of soil. The depth of hole is dependent on the pole length, the type of soil and, in permafrost, the depth of the active layer.

The following table shows the depth of pole setting (normal) where good gravel, or equivalent soil, exists from below the bottom of the pole to the surface.

Pole Length ft (m)	Setting Depth ft (m)
55 (17)	7.5 (2.3)
60 (18)	8 (2.4)
70 (21)	9 (2.7)
80 (24)	10 (3.0)
90 (27)	11 (3.4)
100 (30)	12 (3.7)

Where permafrost exists to depths of 20 ft (6 m) or more and the active layer consists of muskeg, tundra or soft silty soils an allowance must be made for this condition. The augered pole setting is then equal to the maximum depth of the active layer plus twice the depth of the active layer into the permafrost, with a minimum depth in the permafrost equal to the normal setting depth. In this way, the pole will not be "jacked" out of the ground by frost action of the active layer during the freezing cycle and it will have adequate resistance to overturning during the thaw cycle.

With the pole or assembled structure erected by a mobile crane, it is plumbed and held while placing the backfill. As the excavated material generally has an unacceptable amount of ice, stones and boulders too large or too difficult to fit between the pole and the side of the augered hole, it is better to replace the excavated material by backfilling with a slurry of sand and water. The sand is mixed with clean water (i.e. without visible organic material in suspension) at 70 to 90°F (20 to 30°C) in a heated cement mixer to a consistency similar to concrete. As the slurry is poured into the hole it is vibrated to bring the excess water to the surface. When the hole is completely backfilled some of the excavated material is used to crown up (surfill) around the hole to provide insulation over the backfill.

The type and size of anchor will depend upon the nature of the soil and the load to be restrained. Where permafrost occurs near the surface it is necessary to ensure that the anchor is placed well into the permafrost. Where the active layer is 8 to 10 ft (2.5 to 3 m) in depth, different types and methods of installation may be used.

As augering is the simplest method of excavating in permafrost a plate-type anchor is the most practical. Screw-type and expanding-plate type patented anchors are almost impossible to install in permafrost. For high-strength anchors a curved steel plate set in a vertically augered hole provides adequate holding strength and is relatively economical. It must however be set completely below the active layer so that it will not be subject to "ad-freeze" forces. When soil impregnated with moisture freezes it binds or adheres to foundation material. The force of adhesion will depend on the type of soil, the amount of moisture and the type and surface of the foundation. The upward "ad-freeze" force may damage or lift the anchor.

Any type of standard quality steel is quite suitable and, being installed in permafrost, does not require galvanizing. A high strength steel anchor rod is set in line with the guy wires from the pole through a small-diameter diagonally (at the angle of the guy wire) augered hole to meet a connection point in the center of the anchor plate. The material of the anchor rod must be ductile in a Charpy-V impact test to -20°F (-30°C) and be of sufficient tensile strength to resist the guy load plus a safety factor. Where the rod passes through the active layer it must be galvanized against corrosion.

A recent innovation in backfilling is the use of rigid polyurethane foam. Although the material and techniques were first perfected and commercially used during World War II, its advantages as a pole backfill material, over native soil or even crushed rock, have only been recognized during the past four to five years. It has excellent environmental resistance and a very low water-absorption factor. The compound used for this purpose is a cellular plastic and is formed by the reaction of two liquids, a special blended polyisocyanate and a blend of polyolols in the presence of a gas-producing blowing agent (usually fluorocarbon). When these two components are mixed, a chemical reaction occurs, releasing the blowing agent and the material expands 15 times in volume. A standard 4 lb/ft^3 (64 kg/m^3) formulation has a compressive strength of over 100 psi (700 kPa), shear strength of 76 psi (520 kPa) and a tensile strength of 90 psi (620 kPa). Although costs may vary considerably, depending on the amount required per pole, etc., it may save in labour costs and, from a design point of view, the foam backfill has a predetermined strength from butt to groundline and eliminates much of the problems and costs in the heating of water and sand required for the slurry method of backfilling.

In the past few years installations using this material have been placed in northern areas subject to deep, annual soil freezing, and their performance to date has been quite satisfactory. There is no available accurate data on the behaviour of this material under Arctic conditions and, especially, in permafrost. However, this material and method of backfilling would appear to offer significant cost savings.

STRUCTURE DESIGN

While single-pole structures may be used for communication circuits and low-voltage distribution circuits (up to 50 kV) two-pole structures are recommended for high voltage lines when a high degree of reliability is required.

In order to keep costs to a minimum the wood cross-arms and cross-braces should be to the same standards and specifications as the poles. In order to make full use of the strength in the poles and cross-arms they should be connected by means of steel clamping devices. Holes drilled in the poles and cross-arms will reduce the strength of the member. In addition, on-site assembly costs are reduced, as field drilling and matching of the holes to pass long bolts through two or more poles is expensive and difficult under Arctic winter conditions. A certain amount of pre-drilling at the pole yard may be done, especially for multiple sets of cross-bracing.

While the timber members are supplied to close standard and reasonable tolerances there is always several inches between limits. Thus the clamping hardware and bolt lengths must be designed to readily accommodate these variations. Poles and other wood members should be measured in the depot and matched as closely as possible, and will materially assist in determining the quantities of the various bolt lengths required. The conventional grid gain (a flat or curved plate with small teeth on each side and a central hole for the bolt) may be used in wood connections to increase the holding power of the connection. Under extreme cold it may be difficult to force the metal teeth of the grid gain into the wood and thus the bolts should be strong enough to take the torque necessary to seat the teeth.

All steel used in clamping connections and bolts should be specified to a Charpy-V energy of 15 ft.lbf (20 J) at -20°F (-30°C). Steel produced to ASTM Specification A-325 has been found to have characteristics commensurate with the climatic conditions and service requirements.

Welding of clamping members is not recommended, due to the high degree of damaging vibration possible in lines exposed to the constant winds of the Arctic. It has been found that for transmission line applications the cost of obtaining suitable welds, with quality assurance by ultrasonic or X-ray testing, is not normally justified.

CONDUCTORS

The basic types of stranded conductor for power lines are: 1) all aluminum; 2) aluminum alloy; 3) galvanized steel core, aluminum-stranded; 4) copper; 5) aluminum or copper-clad steel.

Copper as a fully-tensioned line conductor is subject to brittleness by continuous, extreme low temperatures and today is extremely expensive.

Steel-core aluminum conductor has the disadvantage of being made up of two dissimilar metals which have different coefficients of expansion and, under protracted extremely low temperatures, may result in strands being displaced (birdcaging).

As aluminum alloy conductors do not exhibit these symptoms, they are generally considered to be more advantageous. Aluminum alloy conductors are, however, lighter per specific length than equivalent steel-cored conductors and somewhat larger in diameter. Thus, they may be more susceptible to conductor galloping. This phenomenon can be more prevalent in the Arctic than many other areas, especially where the open flat terrain exposes the conductors to high winds.

Overhead conductors of transmission lines are subject to two different types of vibration: aeolian and galloping, both produced by wind. Aeolian vibration is a high frequency, low amplitude oscillation created by a regular formation of air vortices behind the conductor. The frequency is generally between 5 and 100 Hz for wind speeds up to 15 mph (24 km/h). Galloping is a low frequency and high amplitude oscillation. The frequency is approximately 0.25 to 1.25 Hz and is generally caused by wind velocities between 10 and 45 mph (16 and 72 km/h). Both types may cause severe damage by failure of line conductors and materials. The solution to the problem is complex and depends on many factors. The installation of patented damping devices may often control the vibrations within acceptable limits.

In erecting and sagging the conductors and the protecting overhead ground cables, a very careful study must be made of the loading parameters. It may frequently be found that the longitudinal tension in the conductors under extremely low temperatures could be the governing factor in maintaining adequate safety factors in the conductors, hardware and structures. Thus, the conductor tension must not be too high, to keep aeolian vibration to a minimum but not too low, to prevent excessive galloping. The actual percentage of ultimate strength used in the sagging of the conductors and grounding cables depends upon the type of conductor, its size and the desired safety factor.

HARDWARE

Where steel is used for clamping structure members together, it is imperative that the material be suitable for this purpose and for Arctic conditions. As there have been a significant number of failures of steel, as used in transmission lines, considerable investigation has been carried out on this subject. The most specific and practical study was prepared by the Canadian Electrical Association (5). The most important phenomenon to consider is brittle fracture and the factors which contribute to it, such as material toughness, presence of flaws, state of stress, rate of loading and material thickness.

Although the short summer season reduces the hazard of corrosion to steel members, the proximity of the Arctic Ocean provides a fairly strong salt-laden atmosphere. Zinc galvanizing is recommended and steel galvanized to ASTM standard 123 or A-153 should provide adequate protection for 40 to 50 years.

To prevent over-tightening and consequently excessive stress under sub-zero temperatures, all ferrous bolts and nuts, including U-bolts and those in cable suspension clamps, should be tightened to specified torque values. For example, 0.5 in. diameter bolts at 0°F (-20°C) should be torqued to a minimum of 400 lbf in. (45 N m) and a maximum of 600 lbf in. (67 N m).

For clamping and supporting conductors to the insulator strings, aluminum alloy clamps are recommended as more compatible with the aluminum alloy conductor than malleable iron or steel. Under certain conditions of contamination an electrolytic action between the ferrous material and aluminum is set-up with consequent damage to the connection. In addition an electrostatic field is generated by a ferrous material clamp and in the case of heavy current and long lines will create an electrical power loss.

The aluminum conductor suspension clamps are fabricated from Aluminum Association Inc. casting grade material 356.2 or Alcan 135. The aluminum compression conductor terminals are fabricated from Aluminum Association Inc. extrusion material grade 1050 with a clamping pad of 6061 material.

INSULATION

Although most of the area north of the Arctic Circle in North America is relatively pollution free, the dry conditions during summer cause dusting of gravel beds and sand dunes. Most of the alluvial deposits include silicate silt materials which, under unfavourable weather conditions, may be picked up by the winds and deposited on surfaces, including insulators. The contamination on insulators, when dampened by fog, may cause electrical tracking to occur. Also, along the Arctic Ocean, further insulation contamination may be experienced, from salt-laden air masses when the temperature is above freezing and by frost crystals in sub-freezing temperatures. The problem can be aggravated by the lack of sufficient summer rainfall to clean the insulators.

In order to reduce the possibility of arcing caused by contamination several preventative measures may be taken. One innovation is a bell-shaped insulator with a semi-conducting glaze (RC type, resistance graded). The performance of this insulator depends on whether the insulators were energized before contamination. If the units are energized before contamination, the leakage current increases the insulator temperature and this significantly improves its performance. If a line outage occurs and the units are contaminated, when the line is re-energized the insulator performance in this cold condition is poor.

Some manufacturers have recently developed self-cleaning insulators which perform much better under contaminating conditions. The self-cleaning insulators are usually formed of smooth, aerodynamic-shaped discs.

While considerable experimental work has been carried out, actual field experience over a long period and especially under Arctic conditions is lacking. Recent pollution tests on various types of insulator indicate that a slightly better operating performance might be expected from glass insulators than from the standard glazed porcelain type. The insulator manufacturing companies are continuously carrying out tests on new types and materials for insulators. In addition, considerable testing for pollution effects on insulators is being done by most of the government testing laboratories. Some very interesting studies have recently been made on insulator pollution effects on lines for northern Canada by the Hydro-Quebec Institute of Research. An investigation on an actual pollution case over an 18-month period showed (6) that pollution may be present in the Arctic in type and quantities sufficient to cause insulator flash-over. Furthermore, while pollution may not necessarily be washed free during the summer months, careful choice of insulator material can assist in preventing flash-overs.

Permafrost areas have a very high resistance and hence faults to ground on a high voltage system may not produce sufficient ground current for reliable operation of protective relays and may cause dangerously high step-and touch-potentials. Built-up gravel pads for generating and transformer stations also have a high resistivity. The possibility of a fallen conductor failing to penetrate hard-packed snow and make direct physical contact with the ground also presents a high grounding resistivity.

From extensive field tests, it has been determined that a satisfactory station ground system consisting of a grid of conductors buried in the active layer could be designed and installed (7,8). It is thus possible to obtain a ground resistance low enough to keep the ground, step- and touch-potentials within safe limits.

As the isoceronic level (annual thunderstorm days) in the Arctic is one or less, it is not considered necessary to add overhead grounding wires to protect line conductors from lightning.

As it is generally impractical to install adequate grounding at each structure where very high resistance may be encountered, other methods must be employed. To ensure that a sufficient ground current will be transmitted to operate the protective relays in the event of a conductor falling to ground, an effective but relatively expensive precaution is the installation of overhead ground wires, running from structure to structure and connected directly to the station grounding system at each end. These wires, identical to the conductors in type and size, should be located on the poles some distance below the conductor cross-arms and connected to a metal frame installed on each structure. Any broken conductor would then contact the frame. These frames should be connected to grounding wires coiled under the bottom of the poles, to obtain whatever grounding capacity is available.

SUMMARY

Suitable materials and special design techniques have been developed to cope with the extremely low temperatures, high winds, permafrost and the environmental problems of the Arctic to provide electric transmission lines with a high degree of reliability. Service experience and continuing research and study are required to provide further reliability and economy of capital cost and maintenance.

Acknowledgment

Mr. A. Banks, The Shawinigan Engineering Company Limited, is gratefully acknowledged for his research assistance.

REFERENCES

1. Proceedings, 13th Muskeg Research Conference, Technical Memo No. 99, NRC, Ottawa, 1970.
2. R.K. Rowley, G.H. Watson and B. Ladanyi, Proc., Permafrost International Conf., National Academy of Sciences, Washington, 1973, p. 712.
3. G. H. Johnson and B. Ladanyi, Canadian Geotech. J. 1972, vol. 9, (2), pp. 176 - 194.
4. B. Ladanyi and G. H. Johnson, Canadian Geotech. J. 1974, vol. 11, (4), pp. 531 - 553.
5. "Brittle Fracture", Can. Electrical Assoc., Montreal, 1974.
6. B. Richards, Shawinigan Engineering Co. Report No. 5268-26-2-75, Montreal, 1975.
7. R. Breton, The Canadian Consulting Engineer, August, 1973.
8. H. A. Erith, The Canadian Consulting Engineer, August 1974.

APPENDIX

Wood Pole and Preservative Treatment Specifications and Standards

ANSI 05.1-1972	American National Standard Specifications and Dimensions for Wood Poles
AWPA* C1-73	All Timber Products. Preservative Treatment by Pressure Process
AWPA C8-73	Western Red Cedar and Alaska Yellow Cedar. Preservative Treatment by the Full Length Thermal Process
EEI** TD-100	Full Length Thermal Process, Preservative Treatment of Western Red Cedar Poles
AWPA C4-73	Poles -- Preservative Treatment by Pressure Process
CSA*** Standard 015.2-1969	The Physical Properties of Western Red Cedar Poles and Reinforcing Stubs
CSA Standard 015.3-1960	Specification for the Physical Properties of Jack Pine, Lodge Pole and Red Pine (3rd. Editn.)

* American Wood Preservers Association
** Edison Electric Institute
*** Canadian Standards Association

DISCUSSION

B. Ladanyi (Ecole Polytechnique): How do you use the standard penetration test if the soil is frozen?

V. F. Crowley: Standard penetration equipment, such as is specified in ASTM D-1586/74 and D-1587/74, the A. B.

Chance Test Probe (a calibrated hand-torqued rod), or the French Penevane impact soil tester (which determines soil bearing by dynamic penètration) cannot effectively be used in frozen soil. The usual method is to auger a small diameter hole, taking samples at regular intervals. The classification of soils from such test pits is generally based on the Modified Unified Classification System.

B. Ladanyi: Do you have any experience with grouted rod anchors? According to reference 3, plate-type screw anchors need much more displacement for the same load than rod anchors embedded in frozen soil.

V. F. Crowley: We have had considerable experience with grouted rod anchors. The direct-current 450 kV transmission line from the Nelson River to Winnipeg in Manitoba employed the deep-drilled, over-burden grouted anchor rods. These were installed in all types of soil, including permafrost, both continuous and discontinuous. The Churchill Falls 735 kV transmission lines in Labrador also employed the same type of anchor. Each of these anchors were tested to 200,000 lbf uplift without failure.

Screw-type anchors are difficult to install even in un-frozen soil, as they generally require such powerful equipment as to be uneconomical, and they disturb the soil to a degree that adequate holding power is not worth the cost, compared with other types of anchor. The statement in reference 3 is correct.

B. Ladanyi: What design criteria have been used for grounding?

V. F. Crowley: Measured resistance of permafrost and frozen soils may be 4000 ohm or more. To apply directional ground relays with a transfer trip requires a high source impedance. We use a figure of Z_0 equal to 300 ohm or grounding equal to 100 ohm, restricting the fault current to a maximum of about 400 A. Stability is not a consideration, but we do have to avoid evolving faults and consequent effects on switchgear. On this basis the grounding system should not exceed 100 V for building, structure or pipeline to ground.

B. Ladanyi: Do you have any information on insulator pollution in the Arctic? Is it possible to study this problem under laboratory conditions? How can field conditions be simulated in that case?

V. F. Crowley: Yes. Pollution in the form of dust particles and salt from sea fog has been found on insulators. Rather than simulate field conditions in the laboratory, polluted insulators were removed from the line and carefully transported to the laboratory to determine the type of pollution, the quantity and adherence factor. During the short summer period, the precipitation is generally light, thus washing off of pollutants may be minimal, leading to critical build-up. At present, the data are not sufficient to determine if this is a problem, but it is being monitored for future reference.

E. C. Hamre (Interprovincial Steel and Pipe): Why was a Charpy impact test specified at only -30°C (-20°F)?

V. F. Crowley: At one time we had specified a Charpy impact test of 15 ft lbf (20 J) foot pounds at -50°F (-46°C). However, to guarantee this figure the manufacturer insisted on normalizing the material at a considerable increase in cost. Testing showed that this material would withstand a Charpy Impact of 15 ft lbf (20 J) at -50°F without normalizing. Subsequent investigation showed that a specified figure of -20°F would provide material which would perform adequately to -50°F (-46°C).

E. C. Hamre: What is the reasoning behind the selection of the various safety factors?

V. F. Crowley: Fundamentally, to assure fail-safe operation. The criteria used to evaluate the safety or overload factors are (a) years of service, (b) allowances for quality of material, fabrication and assembly deficiencies, (c) climatic conditions beyond known or envisaged limits and, (d) relative importance of required continuity of service.

E. C. Hamre: What would be the cost of building a powerline to guarantee continuity of service versus a system of back-up generating stations?

V. F. Crowley: The extra cost in building a powerline of standard construction versus a line to guarantee continuity of service in the Arctic is about 15% on material and 5% on labour depending on the line capacity, type and location. Against this is the cost of stand-by generating units and equipment, maintenance, continuous on-duty operators (salaries and living costs) and the transportation of the fuel. On this basis the extra cost of constructing a fail-safe line is usually justified.

ABRASION RESISTANT ALLOYS FOR EXCAVATION EQUIPMENT

C. P. Hoogensen, P. C. Lichtenberger
R. M. Hardy and Associates

and

J. E. Rymes
J. E. Rymes Engineering Ltd.
Calgary, Alberta
Canada

This paper deals with improvements in low alloy steels used for high-stress abrasion applications in Arctic environments. Standard earth-working tools, such as ditching teeth, have been shown to be totally inadequate when used in most permafrost conditions.

Improvements in physical properties, such as impact resistance and strength were obtained by reduction of the level of impurities, reducing the grain size and modifying the chemical composition to offset the loss of ductility which tends to accompany the increase in hardness.

Crack opening displacement results seem to indicate that cast steels could perform equally as well as forged steels for these types of high-stress abrasion applications.

INTRODUCTION

Improvements have been made in low-alloy steels for combined high stress abrasion and high impact applications. In order to appreciate the requirements of excavating in the Arctic, a brief overview of Arctic terrain systems is necessary.

The terrain system north of the 60th parallel falls in the broad classification of permafrost. To excavate the permafrost terrain systems, it was initially important to define the types of permafrost terrains in terms of an excavation classification, rather than a standard geotechnical classification.- The soil classifications for excavation by means of a wheel ditcher have been divided into seven preliminary classifications with the soil code No. I being the most difficult and the soil code No. VII being the least difficult. These soil excavation classifications are listed in Table 1.

The resistance to excavation or resistance to penetration is essentially dependent on three fundamental factors of the terrain system: viz. type and composition; temperature; and moisture content.

Near the Yukon/Alaska border and in the major portion of Alaska close to the Beaufort Sea, the soil composition is silty and ice wedges are quite prevalent (Figure 1). In contrast, some areas south of Fort Good Hope have similar types of silty sands with higher abrasion characteristics and in addition, boulders are often prevalent. Figure 2 depicts this type of terrain system.

Typical terrain systems near Parsons Lake in the Northwest Territories, are characterized by Figure 3 which shows an ice-lens inclusion, and Figure 4 which shows a deposit of gravel some 4 to 5 ft (1 to 2 m) below the surface.

Figures 5 and 6 were also taken in the same general area, but show a gravel terrain; Figure 5 shows the effect of ripping with a D9 Caterpillar in the undrained gravel area and Figure 6 shows a close-up of the gravel and of the sand matrix which holds the gravel together.

Figure 7 depicts a test ditch excavated in the general Sans Sault region of the Northwest Territories some 70 miles (110 km) north of Norman Wells. This permafrost terrain system was composed primarily of silty clays and sands with some horizontal ice lenses. The ditcher was produced by Banister Pipelines and was the initial attempt at upgrading mach-

Figure 1: Silty terrain with ice wedges -- Yukon-Alaska Border ["a" - ice wedge]

Table 1 PRELIMINARY SOIL CLASSIFICATION FOR WHEEL DITCHERS

Soil Code	Soil Definitions* Silt & Clay (%)	Sand (%)	Gravel (%)	Average Predicted Penetration Pressures (psi) @ 24% Moisture Content and Minimum Temperatures. (-24 deg. C)	*Remarks
I	26	50	24	9,000 - 14,000	Cobbles and Boulders encountered.
II	34	51	15	8,000 - 10,500	Cobbles and Boulders encountered.
III	44.5	54.5	1	5,800 - 7,800	Miscellaneous Cobbles.
IV	Fines, some sand, little medium to fine gravel			5,000 - 6,000	Some Cobbles.
V	95	5	-	3,500 - 4,500 5,000 - 5,900	Virtually no cobbles.
VI	86	13½	½	2,500 - 3,250	Virtually no cobbles.
VII	Fines, some sand, little fine gravel			2,000 - 2,500	Cobbles and Boulder pavement encountered at bottom of active layer.

NOTE: Pressures shown are under maximum critical condition - variations in % moisture content and ground temperatures will have a reducing effect.

Figure 2: Silty sands with high boulder content -- south of Fort Good Hope

inery for Arctic ditching operations.

Test ditches have also been excavated near Churchill, Manitoba, where the type and composition of the permafrost terrain system was similar in most respects to that of extremely strong concrete. This terrain corresponds to soil Type I. Figure 8 shows one of the test ditches and a close-up of the actual wall of the ditch, to indicate that ditcher teeth must not only cut the matrix of the permafrost terrain system, but also the rock and boulders contained therein. This particular ditch was excavated with a wheel ditcher which was considerably larger than the one used at Sans Sault. Figure 9 shows one of the ditchers at the Churchill site.

EVALUATION OF TEETH USED IN EARLY FIELD TESTS

From ditcher tests that were conducted in the permafrost regions described above, representative samples of ditcher teeth were sent to the metallurgical laboratory. After receiving about 85 teeth samples, compilation of historical data (with regard to physical and chemical properties) of the excavation teeth was started. Documentation of all submitted teeth was carried out according to the following format:

1. Each tooth was photographed in its as-received condition.
2. Chemical analysis of each tooth was undertaken using standard wet chemical techniques. Specific analytical procedures for individual elements were:
   for C, S - induction furnace ignition
   for Mn, P, Cr, Ni - volumetric techniques;
   for Si, Mo - photometric techniques;
   for V, Cu, Al, B, Cb, Ti, W, Co - Semi-quantitative spectrographic analysis.
3. Each tooth was sectioned and examined metallographically. Rockwell C (Rc) hardness measurements were also conducted on sectioned pieces.
4. Charpy V-notch impact specimens were prepared from the teeth specimens.

Figure 10 shows some of the teeth in the as-received state. Figure 11(a) shows a typical example of a fractured tooth. Sometimes the fracture surface was not disturbed by abrasion forces because it occurred so close to the shank and did not contact

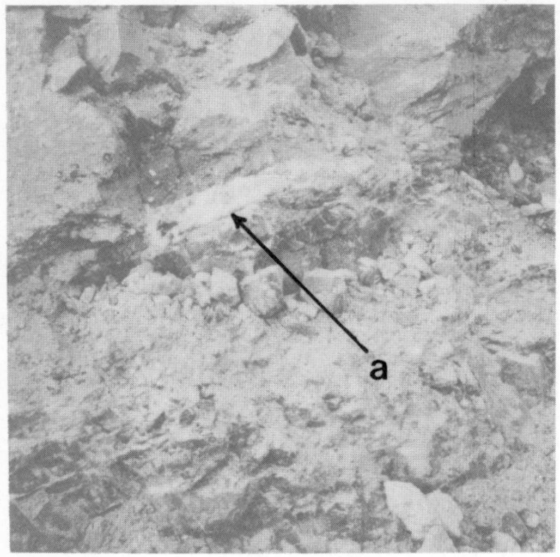

Figure 3: Ice lens in silty till -- near Parsons Lake, NWT, Canada ["a" - ice lens]

Figure 4: Gravel deposit under silty till -- near Parsons Lake, NWT, Canada ["a" - gravel deposit]

Figure 5: Undrained gravel from 10 in. (250 mm) deep D9 ripper -- near Parsons Lake, NWT, Canada

Figure 6: Close-up of undrained gravel showing sand matrix --near Parsons Lake, NWT, Canada

Figure 7: Ditch excavated in silty clays and sands -- near Sans Sault, NWT, Canada

the soil. From studying such fracture surfaces the origin could be determined. It was found that fractures occurred when the teeth started digging (i.e. at the lowest point in the ditch). Fractures also occurred when the teeth were at a higher position in the ditch due to the force of the ditcher which pushed the teeth in the opposite direction away from the ditch face, (Figure 12).

To illustrate the harshness of ditching conditions, Figure 11(b) shows the failure of two teeth which had carbide insert tips. As can be seen, the longer of the two bent, whereas the shorter one fractured. It is obvious that the forces acting upon the teeth were so large that the cemented carbides did not have a chance to break-up the frozen soil. Instead they tore the base metal in which they were inserted and fell out, or they fractured because of the large tensile stresses acting.

Table 2 gives the chemical analysis, hardness and grain size of some of the tested teeth. It appeared that the alloys were mostly proprietary grades, and for general classification purposes, corresponded approximately to A.I.S.I. series such as 4000 and 8600. Cast teeth such as #76 and #77 have too high a silicon content to fit the A.I.S.I. 4000 specification. The higher silicon content facilitates the casting practice. It appears that the chemistry of the steel was not closely controlled. For example,

Figure 8: (a) Ditch excavated in hard sand and silt with boulders -- near Churchill, Manitoba; (b) close-up of Churchill ditch showing rocks fractured by ditcher teeth

Figure 9: A large ditcher used for excavations at Churchill, Manitoba, Canada

Figure 10: As-received teeth after first ditching trial

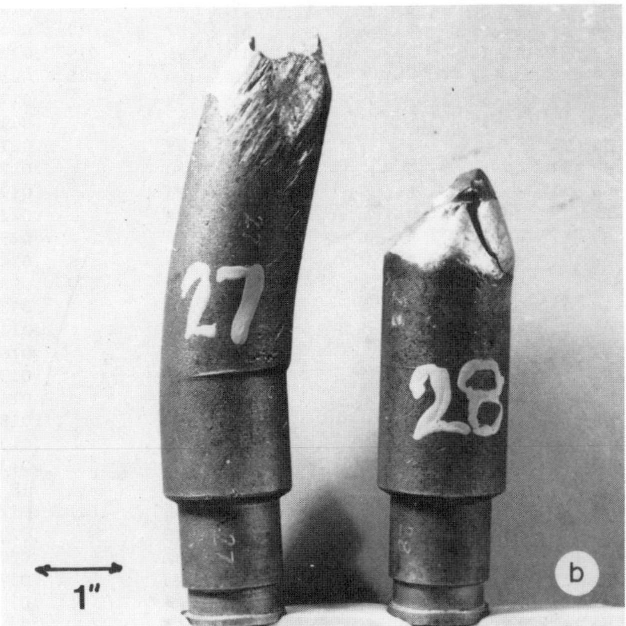

Figure 11: (a) Fractured tooth tip -- Churchill tests; (b) Bent and fractured carbide insert teeth from Churchill tests

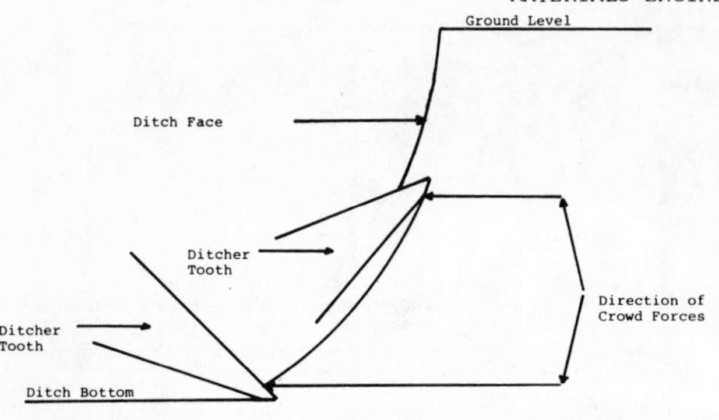

Figure 12: Crowd forces imposed on teeth at two-tooth positions on ditcher wheel

samples 64 to 67, which are from one manufacturer, were apparently ordered as an AISI 4340 alloy. It can also be seen in Table 2 that the carbon content varies between 0.26 and 0.37 which is an indication of the product variation. It should be emphasized here, however, that these teeth materials had previously been used in the prairies and usually during the summer. Winter ditching was very seldom carried out. The main purpose had been to produce teeth as economically as possible.

Since the alloys for teeth were subjected to shock loading, it was felt that the Charpy V-Notch (CVN) Impact test would give some insight into the teeth fractures. Some results of impact tests on standard 10 mm x 10 mm specimens are shown in Figure 13. The results are interesting in that they show the large variations which occurred. The impact resistance of all teeth, except #80, was quite low.

Despite the better impact properties of tooth #80 material, it did not fare much better, as judged from the samples received. Unfortunately the fracture surface had been severely damaged and could not be evaluated. One tooth of this material had not been subjected to a field test, but in a three-point bend test in the laboratory it failed at a low value because of a quench crack present in the tooth. This may have been coincidental, but it is possible that a number of failures were initiated in the field due to similar material flaws.

To improve tooth wear resistance, weld-on hard facings have often been used. When a hard-faced tooth starts digging at the bottom of the ditch, the force acting on the tooth tends to bend it. The hard facing is therefore subjected to a tensile stress often resulting in tip deflection which may cause it to crack and then spall off the tooth surface. Such cracks may also act as crack initiators similar to the artificially induced cracks used in conventional drop weight tests. The majority of the hard-faced teeth which were examined had broken. The location of fractures varied from tip to shank.

When the ditching wheel rotates so that the teeth move towards the top or rim of the ditch, the forward movement of the ditcher will produce a force on the tooth which tends to bend the tooth away from the ditch face. Figure 14(a) shows a hard-faced tooth which was bent such that the hard facing could

Table 2

Chemical Composition, Hardness and Grain Size of Some of the Teeth From First Ditcher Trails

Sample No.	Base Macro-Hardness (RC)	Austenitic Grain Size (ferric chloride etch)	C	Mn	P	S	Si	Cr	Ni	Mo	V*	Cu*	Al*	B*	Cb*
4	50	8	.44	.78	.014	.022	.22	.85	1.78	.20			.01		.02
18	51	8	.41	.78	.010	.023	.21	.87	1.61	.21			.01		.02
20	45	8	.37	.77	.011	.018	.21	.87	1.78	.21	.044	.07	.005	.0006	.02
26 (a)	44-45	7½	.51	.87	.012	.024	.19	.57	.51	.20			.05		.02
28 (b)	35-36	8	.41	.95	.019	.029	.31	.90	.12	.16	.003	.15	.033	.0005	.02
29 (b)	30-32	8½	.40	.88	.015	.023	.32	1.01	.12	.19	.002	.16	.034	.0006	.02
45 (a)	47-50	9	.45	1.04		.027	.27	1.11	< .05	.15			.03		.03
48	35-36	8	.58	.96		.029	.26	.46	.50	.14			.02		.03
52 (b)	28	8½	.41	.95		.027	.28	.87	.14	.11			.02		.02
64 (a)	45	7	.35	.80		.017	.25	.78	1.87	.20			.03		.02
65 (a)	49-51	8	.36	.84		.019	.25	.78	1.72	.20			.03		.02
66	48	7½	.37	.84		.022	.24	.78	1.72	.20			.03		.02
67	46	7½	.26	.72		.025	.24	.75	1.75	.16			.02		.01
68	43	7	.45	.79		.026	.16	1.11	.18	.14			.04		.03
69	52	1½	.41	.86	.007	.025	.25	.85	.18	.14	.002	.15	.033	.0007	.03
70 (a)	32	6½	.58	.86		.033	.28	.49	.40	.14			.04		.03
71	49	3½	.29	.84		.014	1.42	1.98	.10	.31			.04		.03
72	49	2	.28	.74		.016	1.42	1.93	.09	.31			.04		.03
73	49	2	.27	.91		.013	1.44	2.05	.09	.32			.04		.03
74 (a)	46	5½	.26	.71		.016	1.48	1.91	.11	.56			.01		.01
75 (a)	47	3½	.23	.71		.018	1.52	1.91	.10	.56			.02		.01
76 (a)	47	4½	.23	.67		.018	1.56	1.91	.10	.56			.02		.01
77	48	6	.29	.84	.026	.013	1.46	1.93	.08	.21		.12	.041		.03
78	49	6	.28	.80		.15	1.44	1.86	.09	.26			.03		.03
79	49	2	.29	.99	.028	.012	1.46	1.88	.09	.22		.13	.044	.0012	.03
80	41	8	.30	.75		.020	.27	.77	1.72	.16			.01		.01
81 (a)	48	8½	.38	.86		.020	.24	.78	1.71	.20			.01		.01
82 (a)	48	9	.35	.80		.017	.24	.77	1.72	.20			.01		.01
83 (a)	46	8½	.35	.84		.015	.24	.77	1.76	.18			.01		.01
84	44	7½	.37	.64	.023	.035	.26	1.33	1.31	.06	.014	.16	.009	.0009	.02

(a) Hard Faced
(b) Carbide Tipped

The microstructure of all specimens was a tempered martensite

*Semi Quantitative Spectrographic Analysis

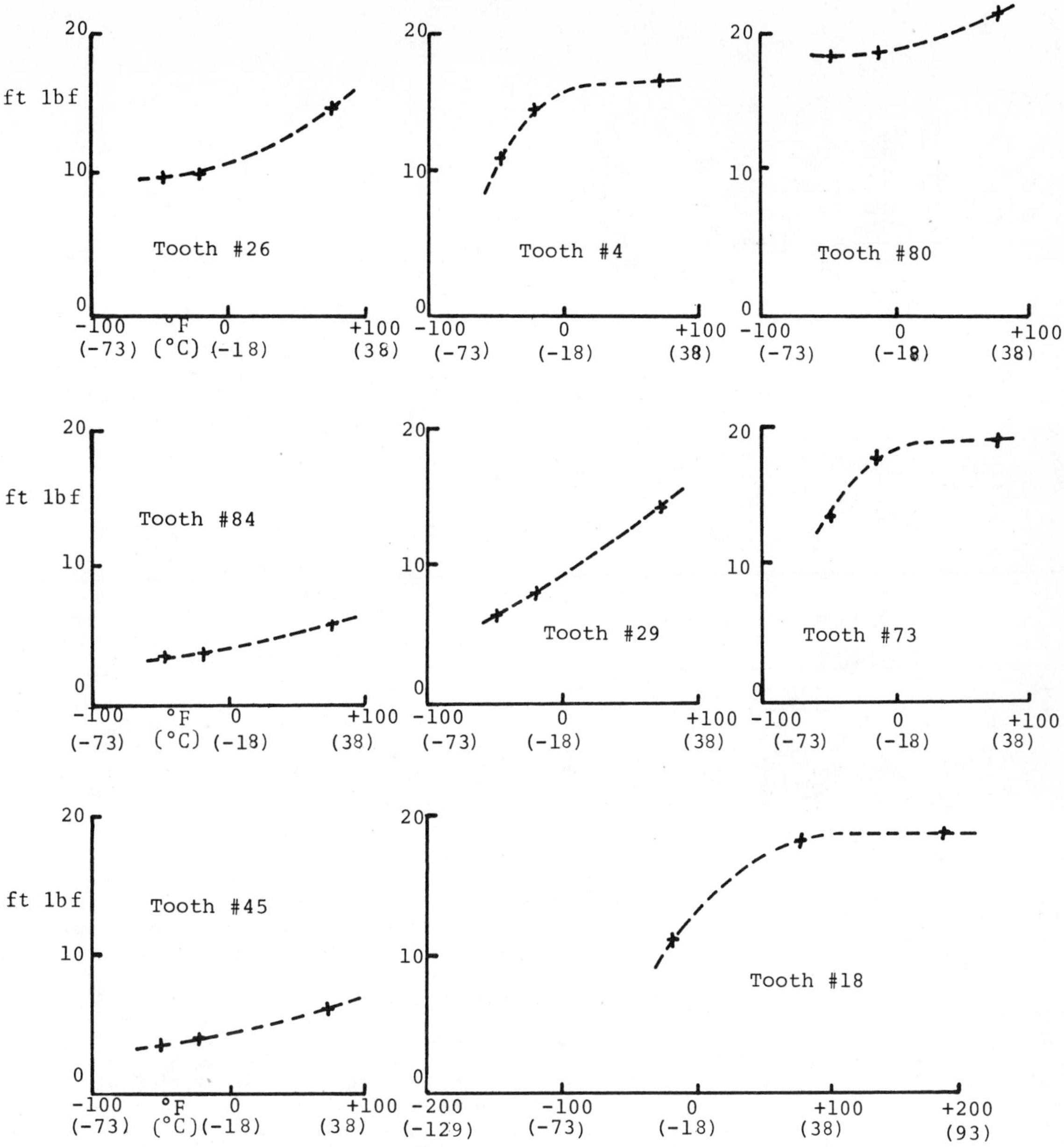

Figure 13: Charpy-V energy as a function of temperature (ASTM E23 Type A, 10 mm x 10 mm)

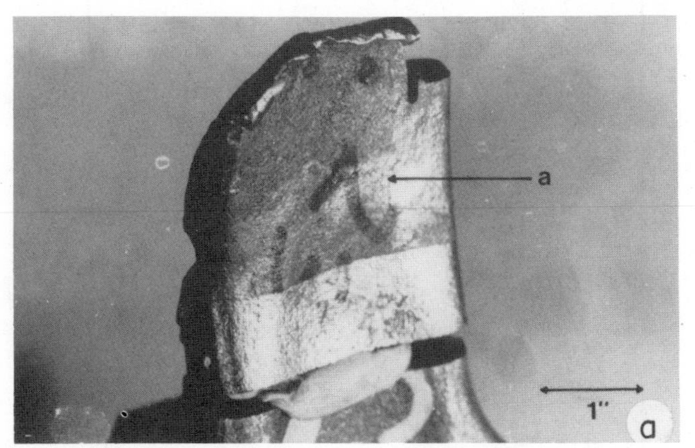

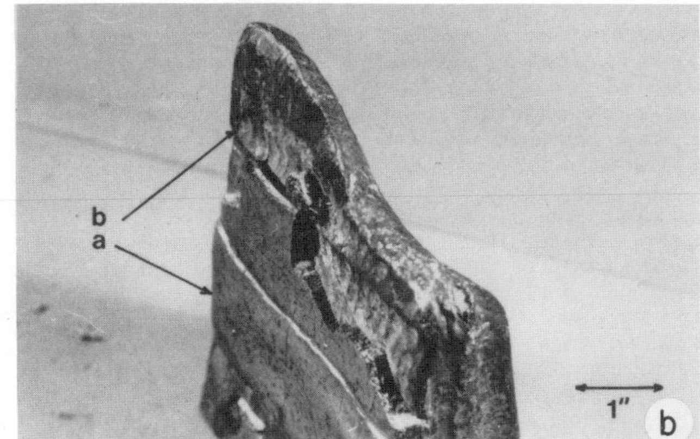

Figure 14: (a) Bent hard-faced tooth, (b) Spalling of hard facing ["a" - hard facing, "b" - base metal]

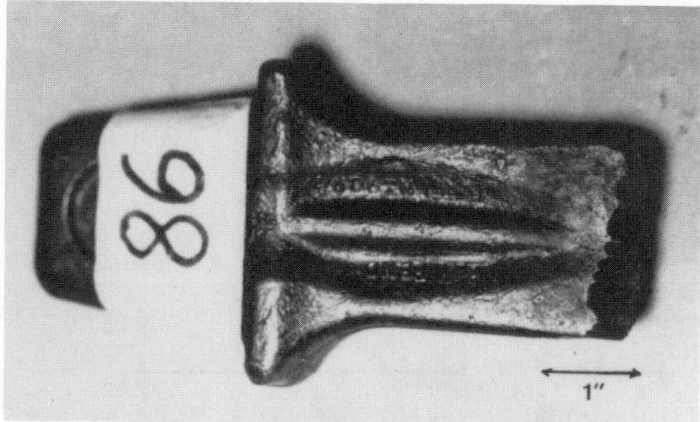

Figure 15: Hard-faced tooth tested at Sans Sault

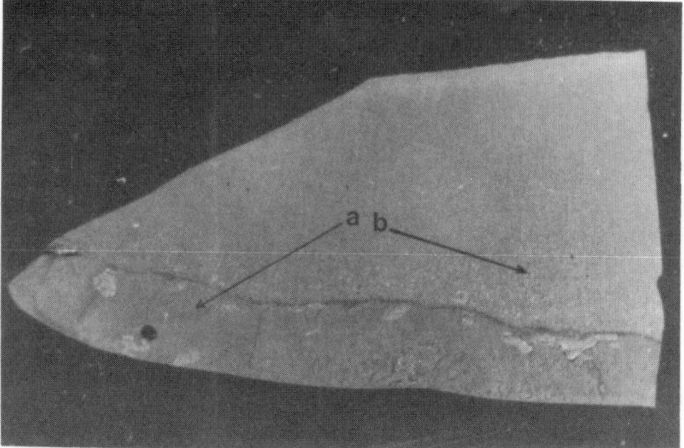

Figure 16: Cross-section of tooth tip of Figure 15

not act as a wear surface.

Figure 14(b) shows a hard-faced tooth with a thick hard-facing layer. The hard-facing has spalled away from the tooth material. The spalling could be caused by tensile stresses resulting in small tip deflections, or it could be caused by compressive stresses on this very brittle material. Three-point bend tests were made with the facing in both compression and tension and it was found that the modes of failure were, in each case, brittle.

Another problem with weld-on hard facing is that their application softens the base material. This increases abrasion of base metal and was evident in all hard-faced teeth. It invariably resulted in a thin, unsupported layer of hard facing at the tooth tip which fractured.

Rapid wear due to low hardness was also found on carbide-tipped teeth. Softening occurred due to the brazing of the carbide onto the base metal. Hardnesses as low as 30 Rc were measured. Such teeth failed in a short time, not because the carbide insert failed, but because the metal around the carbide tip abraded away and the carbide fell out. These teeth also failed in overload due to the unsupported extension of the carbide tip.

There was a single application where hard facing appeared to be successful. A sample tooth is shown in Figure 15. This tooth was tested at the Sans Sault site and performed better than similar non hard-faced teeth tested at the same time at Sans Sault.

Figure 16 shows a cross-section of this tooth. Its wear characteristics are entirely different from those shown in Figure 14 for teeth tested at other sites. The tooth tip, as shown in Figure 16, has been subjected to abrasion. It is clear from the numerous cracks in the facing that it would spall off when subjected to impact loading. The hard facing acted as a means by which a sharp edge could be maintained. For low stress applications hard facing therefore can be very successful.

Conventional (tungsten carbide and chromium carbide) hard facings typically have good abrasion resistance. It was, however, apparent from the collected field data that their impact resistance was low and they could tolerate little tip deflection without fracture.

Perhaps the most striking correlation between conventional ditcher teeth and their suitability to Arctic ditching was observed in relation to high stress abrasion. The majority of teeth examined showed severe abrasion wear after just a few minutes of ditching time which was so severe that ditching was terminated. This combination of a short ditching time and numerous fractures made it impossible to gather statistically meaningful data on wear lifetimes. The effective tooth lifetime was a few minutes and a qualitative feeling of lifetime on the basis only of wear could only be guessed.

EVALUATION OF TEETH USED IN RECENT FIELD TESTS

It had been found that under carefully controlled laboratory heat treat conditions the impact properties of teeth could be improved considerably. Furthermore, lowering the sulfur content and decreasing the grain size of the steel would result in a steel of high hardness while maintaining good ductility. The main difficulty was to estimate from the field tests what would be the most important requirement. Because of the many fractures, combined with the low impact resistance, the emphasis was placed on an increase of the impact resistance as determined by the Charpy "V" Notch. The temperature at which the earlier field test had been carried out was reportedly of the order of -40°C. From the data obtained, it was evident that a material with a Charpy-V energy of 12 ft lbf (16 J) at that temperature was insufficient to prevent premature failure.

For the high stress abrasion and impact conditions encountered in the Arctic, it was attempted to produce a tooth which had a hardness of 50 Rc minimum, and a Charpy-V energy of 20 ft lbf (27 J) at -40°C. The alloy composition of a forged tooth found to meet these requirements is shown in Table 3. The teeth submitted for testing had an ASTM Grain Size 9, as determined by a ferric chloride etch.

Two test sites were used for evaluating the teeth, the Seebe and McPherson locations.

The Seebe test site is situated within the

Table 3

Chemistry of Forged Tooth Materials used in most recent Field Trials

Element		Content
Carbon	-	.33 - 0.35
Manganese	-	.35 - 0.70
Phosphorus	-	.015 max.
Sulfur	-	.005 max.
Silicon	-	.30 - 0.35
Chromium	-	1.25 - 1.50
Nickel	-	2.50 - 4.00
Molybdenum	-	.40 - 0.60
*Vanadium	- <	.03
*Tungsten	- <	.03
*Cobalt	- <	.02
*Titanium	- <	.04

* Semi-Quantitative Spectrographic Analysis

valley of the Bow River in Alberta and comprises grey silty mud stone and silt stone. This soil type does not fit the classifications presented in Table 1. It was intended to represent a qualifying test site for ditcher teeth before they were accepted for testing in the Arctic. During the test at Seebe, it was revealed that this type of rock was considerably harder in the frozen state than had been anticipated. Because the quarry is subjected to an upward seepage flow of water, ice was formed within the discontinuities, providing a cementing agent. As a result there was a considerable increase in the resistance to excavation and under these conditions the silt stone had characteristics similar to concrete. This test site was abandoned because the machine conditions were such that sufficient penetration could not be achieved.

The McPherson gravel pit (located close to Calgary, Alberta) was composed of clay silt, glacial till with a predominance of gravel ranging from 0.5 in. (13 mm) pebbles to small boulders 15 in. (380 mm) in diameter. The McPherson gravel pit cannot be classified according to the soil types presented in Table 1. It would come closest to Type III, with roughly 5% silt and clay, 40% sand and 55% gravel. The depth of the seasonal frost averaged 7 ft (2 m). A detailed geotechnical analysis has been carried out on both test sites in order to ensure that future tests can be compared.

To illustrate the difference in ditcher conditions, Figure 17 shows the frontal view of the ditch at Seebe and Figure 18 the frontal view of the ditch at the McPherson test site. Figure 19 shows some sheared boulders at the McPherson site, indicating that the teeth were subjected to large impact forces.

For the tests at Seebe and McPherson, six types of test teeth were available:

Forged Steel: 50 Rc, non hard-faced
50 Rc hard-faced
40 Rc hard-faced

Cast Steel: 40 Rc hard-faced (a)
40 Rc, plus butter layer & hard facing (b)
40 Rc, plus butter layer & hard facing (c)

The forged material had a chemistry corresponding to that in Table 3. The manufacturer of the cast teeth could not, at the time of testing, provide a material with a similarly low S and P content. The chemistry of these teeth is presented in Table 4. In order to meet the impact requirement, the

Table 4

Chemistry of Cast Tooth Material† Used in most recent Field Trials

Carbon	0.15
Manganese	0.82
Phosphorus	0.012
Sulfur	0.020
Silicon	0.59
Chromium	1.04
Nickel	2.89
Molybdenum	0.25
*Vanadium	< 0.03
*Tungsten	< 0.03
*Cobalt	< 0.02
*Titanium	< 0.04

* Semi-Quantitative Spectrographic Analysis

† Grain Size ASTM 7

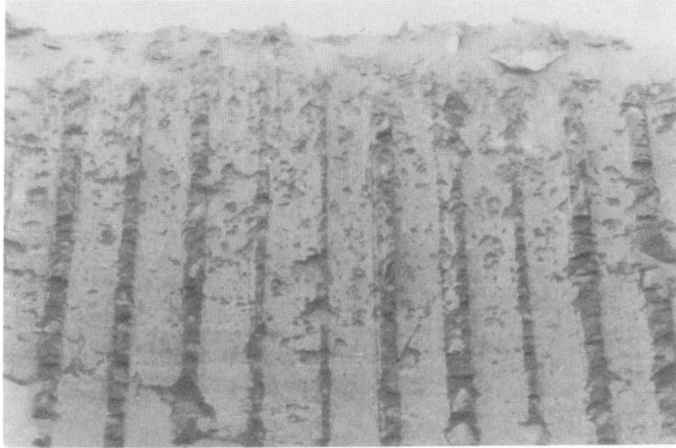

Figure 17: Seebe ditch no. 1, frontal face

Figure 18: McPherson ditch no. 1, frontal face

Figure 19: McPherson ditch no. 1, typical gravel gradation (frozen to ditch bottom)

Figure 20: Bottom face of cast tooth after testing at Seebe and McPherson test site

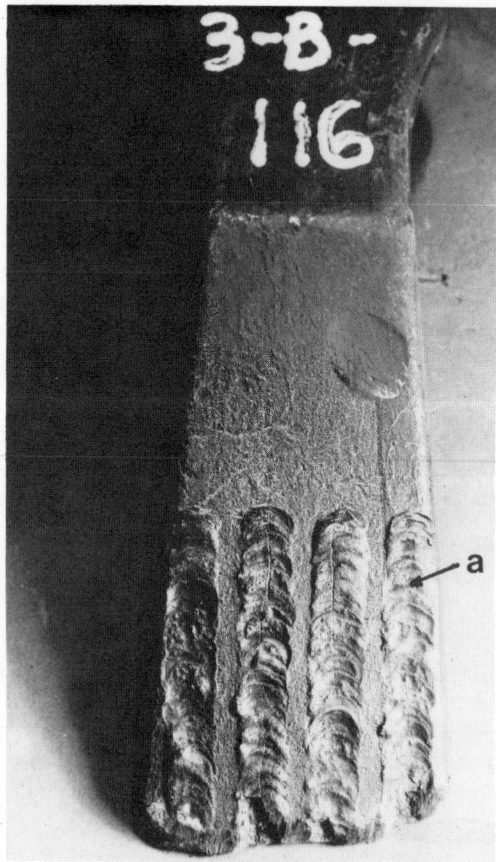

Figure 21: Bottom face of forged tooth after testing at Seebe and McPherson test sites ["a" - hard-facing inlays]

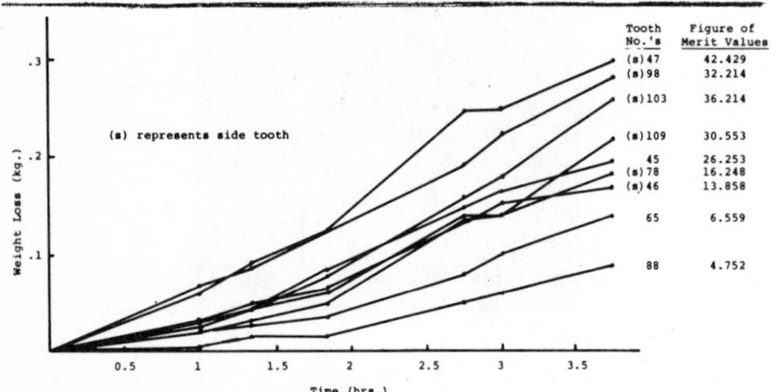

Figure 22: Weight loss data for forged teeth tested at Seebe and McPherson

carbon content was lowered to 0.15%.

All test teeth had a Charpy-V energy of greater than 20 ft lbf (27 J) at -40°C.

The hard facing of the forged teeth was a proprietary grade consisting of tungsten carbide in an iron matrix.

The hard facings that were applied to the cast teeth were: a) Tungsten carbide in an iron matrix welded directly onto the base metal; b) tungsten carbide in an iron matrix welded over a butter layer of 310 stainless steel; c) tungsten carbide in a nickel matrix welded onto a butter layer of nickel. Butter layers were applied to prevent cracks originating in the hard facing from propagating into the base material.

Approximately 360 teeth were tested. After the tests were completed, all teeth were visually examined. No forged tooth was found which had fractured. This would imply that a Charpy-V energy of 20 ft lbf (27 J) is adequate for this type of ditching. It should be emphasized, however, that these tests were carried out in soil of seasonal frost. In permafrost, locations are expected where the soil is more dense with large boulders.

In order to evaluate the performance of the teeth, the ditching wheel was stopped at intervals and a group of control teeth were removed and weighed. Figures 20 and 21 show a cast and a forged tooth after completion of the test. After a total ditching time of approximately two hours, all teeth were photographed. A detailed visual description of all 195 control teeth was carried out to determine their relative performances. To obtain a quantitative measure of this description, a parameter describing wear characteristics was formulated. This parameter, called a "figure of merit", quantifies such wear characteristics as burring, chipping, gouging, spalling and cracking of hard facing and the wear pattern on the teeth as gauged by length measurements taken on both the front and back surfaces.

Figure 22 shows weight loss as a function of time, combined with figures of merit, for the 50 Rc non hard-faced teeth. In order to evaluate the performance of each individual tooth location, the teeth were numbered and placed in given positions on the ditching wheel. Those marked S were located at the side of the wheel and these side teeth wore considerably faster than the front teeth.

Weight loss averages were computed for front teeth, as well as side teeth. The data was then fitted by a least squares analysis to a polynominal function of order 2, as shown in Figure 23. The lifetime, or service time, of a ditching tooth on a wheel is determined by the amount of weight a tooth can lose. Termination of ditching occurs when the tooth becomes either too short or the surface in contact with the soil becomes too large. If the contact area of the tooth and the soil becomes too large, the power required to turn the ditching wheel and/or the crowding of the ditcher is insufficient.

In order to compare teeth performance, an arbitrary 1000 g weight loss was chosen, as indicated in Figure 23. Based on this criterion, a non hard--faced 50 Rc tooth could ditch 600 min, while a 50 Rc tooth with hard facing would require 360 min before losing 1000 g. It appears that the non hard-faced 50 Rc teeth are far superior to any other type tested.

Figure 23 also shows that it was the base metal which determined the performance and the hard facing tested here shortened, rather than extended, the tooth life.

In spite of the fact that the performance of hard-faced teeth in the early field test was not promising, hard faced teeth were again tried on the most recent trials. The reason for this was two-fold. First, at the time of the trials it was very difficult

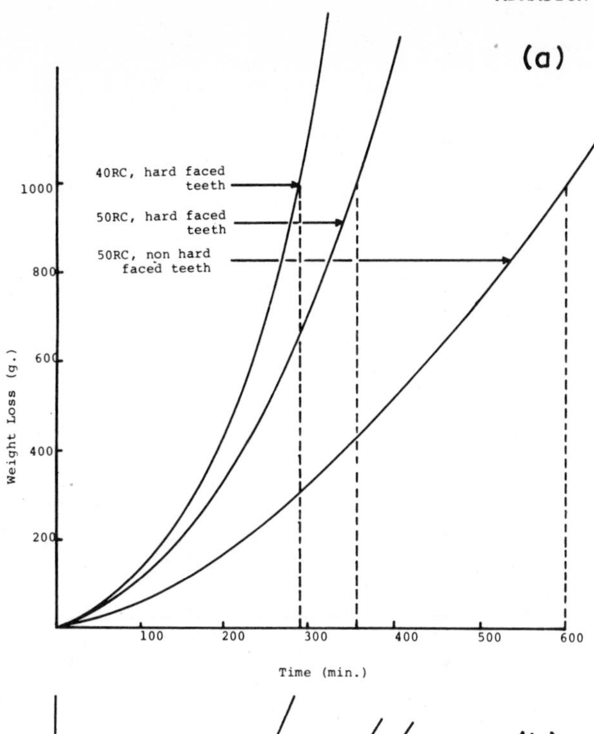

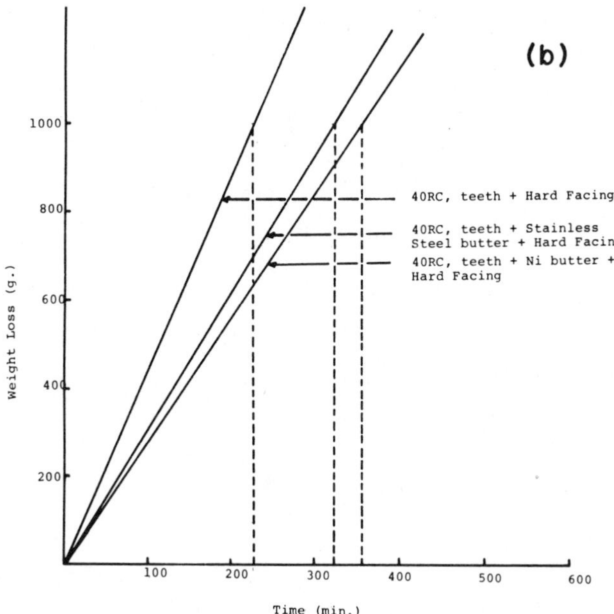

Figure 23: (a) Weight loss predictions for forged teeth tested at Seebe and McPherson; (b) Weight loss predictions for cast teeth tested at Seebe and McPherson

to obtain a low alloy steel with the required properties. Secondly, utilization of hard facings was attractive because of the high hardness and hence high abrasion resistance that is possible. The advantage of hard facing is that it can be applied to a tooth wear surface in locations where it can be most effective. Therefore, different hard facing approaches were tried.

One approach was to apply a butter layer as shown in Figure 24. Another approach was to utilize the hard facing as an inlay (Figure 25). The hard facing was expected to provide wear resistance, while any impact could be absorbed by the base metal.

It is believed that the brittle failure of conventional hard facings is inherent for this particular application. This can be illustrated by studying the microstructure. Both the matrix and the carbide particles are found to be considerably cracked, as shown in Figure 26. Such is not the case for carbide particles found in cemented carbides (Figure 27). The carbide particles embedded in cobalt as a cemented carbide insert are very small. If cracks were present in such carbide particles, the soft cobalt would arrest propagation. However, the weld-on tungsten carbide hard-facings dissolve and the result is a particle which is not pure tungsten carbide, but a complex carbide. The matrix surrounding these particles is quite brittle due to diffusion of carbon and tungsten from the carbide particles. The analysis of powder X-ray diffraction data indicated that the carbide in hard facings was complex, whereas that of pure tungsten mono-carbide, as found in cemented carbides, was a far simpler structure (1). The implication of the above is that the hard facings so far tested are incapable of absorbing impact and fracture.

A very small number of tooth tip fractures in cast teeth was observed during these recent field tests, in contrast to the predominance of tip breakages in the earlier trials. The reasons for this are two-fold. First, a considerable improvement in low temperature impact strength has been achieved. A minimum of 20 ft lbf (27 J) of Charpy-V absorbed energy at -40°C was accepted. This represented an average of 3 to 5 times increase over the impact strength of previously tested proprietary grades of teeth. Secondly, the section size of ditcher teeth was increased to resist tip beaming. The design criterion for section size determination was calculated from consideration of machine horsepower, wheel weight, rake angles and some penetration data for

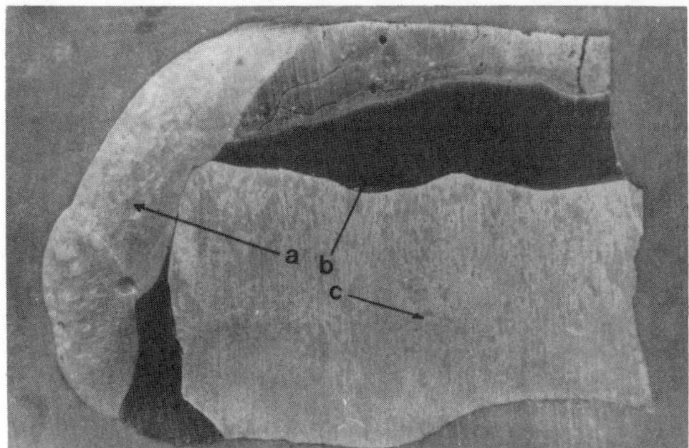

Figure 24: Hardfaced tooth with butter pass ["a" - hard-facing; "b" - butter layer; "c" - base metal]

Figure 25: Hard-face inlays ["a" - inlays; "b" - base metal]

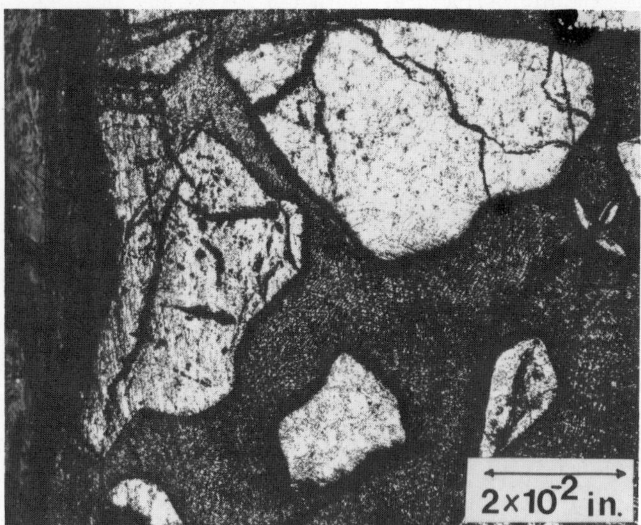

Figure 26: Cracking in hard-facing carbides

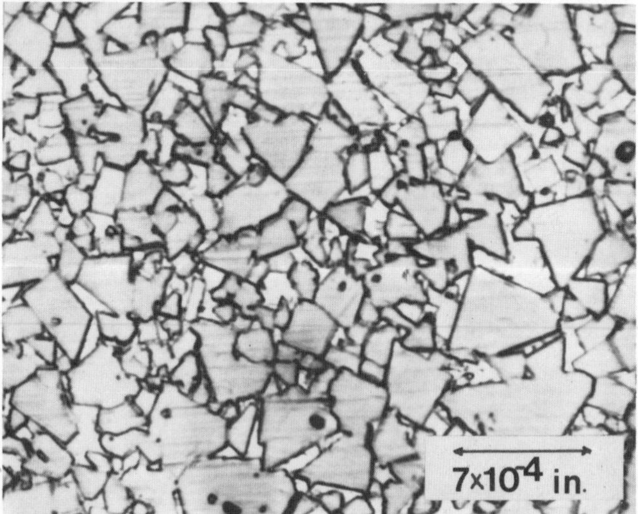

Figure 27: Tungsten mono-carbide sintered with cobalt

Arctic terrains.

The second notable improvement in material properties for Arctic ditcher teeth has been due to the excellent correlation between tooth hardness and lifetime. Figure 23 demonstrates this relationship. Because of the predominance of tip fractures, this correlation could not be definitively established in the earlier tests. Figures 23 clearly show the appreciable extension of tooth lifetime for teeth of 50 Rc hardness, compared with teeth of 40 Rc hardness.

Finally, in the recent tests, in every case of tip failure, crack initiation could not be identified as a gross material flaw such as was found in previous tests. In this regard, the quality of material was improved.

Figure 28 shows the improvement which has been achieved in the impact properties of a forged tooth material by lowering the sulphur and phosphorus residuals and by vacuum arc remelting. Both materials are from the same manufacturer. Data labelled "present submission" has the chemistry given in Table 3, a hardness of 50 Rc, a grain size of ASTM 9 and a tempered martensitic microstructure. Data labelled "initial submission" has the chemistry given as tooth #4, Table 1. It also had a tempered martensitic microstructure.

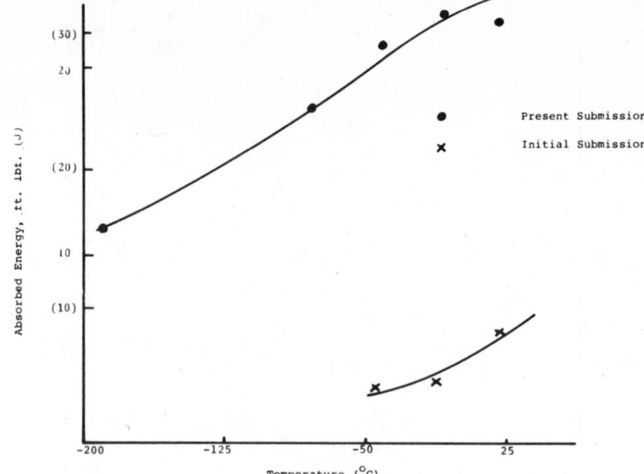

Figure 28: Improvement in Charpy Impact results for forged material

Summing up the results of recent field test trials, it is found that:

1) A Charpy-V impact energy of 20 ft lbf (28 J) at -40°C appears to be sufficient, from the very few fractures (16 out of 360 teeth) which occurred.
2) A minimum hardness of 50 Rc appears to be effective for ditching the frozen soil tested.
3) The few fractures which occurred on the test teeth indicate that quality contributes as much to tooth performance as does impact strength.
4) Tungsten carbide hard facings again proved inadequate in increasing the teeth life.
5) Ditcher teeth lifetime has been extended to several hours, a tremendous improvement from the lifetimes of a few minutes in previous tests.

Further improvements in material properties have now been made which promise to provide even better results than those obtained in the southern test site. Table 5 presents the physical and chemi-

Table 5

Physical and Chemical Properties of Newest Generation of Arctic Ditcher Teeth

	Cast Material	Forged Material	Differentially Hardened Forged Material
A) Chemistry			
Carbon	0.28	0.33	0.49
Manganese	0.77	0.44	0.37
Phosphorus	0.015	0.006	0.015
Sulfur	0.004	0.007	0.010
Silicon	1.48	0.23	0.95
Chromium	3.07	1.25	1.35
Nickel	0.23	3.76	0.21
Molybdenum	0.41	0.21	0.27
*Vanadium	<0.1	<0.1	<0.05
*Tungsten	<0.3	<0.3	<2.4
*Cobalt	<0.2	<0.2	<0.2
*Titanium	<0.04	<0.04	<0.04
B) Rockwell C Hardness	50	52	57
C) Austenitic Grain Size (ASTM)	7	9	9
D) Charpy "V" Notch Absorbed Energy, ft lbf (J) at -40°C	20(47)	26(35)	5(7) at tip 15(20) in shank
E) Heat Treatment	Quenched and Tempered	Quenched and Tempered	Quenched and Tempered

* semi-quantitative spectrographic analysis

cal properties of three improved varieties of ditcher tooth material. The Charpy V-notch impact test values are averages of 3 individual measurements. In the quenched and tempered specimens the total spread in individual values was always less than 4 ft lbf (5 J).

The improvements in both the cast and forged material are due mainly to a reduction in phosphorus and sulphur residuals. Although the differentially-hardened tooth is of low toughness at the tip, it should be recognized that the 5 ft lbf (7 J) energy is measured close to the tip where low values of outside fibre stress are expected. The increased hardness to 57 Rc is interesting and gives an excellent indication of hardness required for efficient ditching in the Arctic.

FRACTURE MECHANICS

The early development of material selection criteria for Arctic ditcher tooth material relied heavily upon toughness criteria as established by the Charpy V-notch impact test. The minimum impact energy was established by field experience. The usefulness of this test lies in the fact that it reproduces the ductile-brittle transformation of steel in about the same temperature range as is actually observed in engineering structures. But the test, or energy values extracted from it, says little about fracture properties or initiation under given loading conditions.

In the large-scale production of Arctic ditcher teeth the inclusion of small defects, both surface and sub-surface, is inherent. Although we expect from past experience that 20 ft lbf (27 J) in a Charpy test is an acceptable guide, manufacturing defects could lead to premature failure. Applying a safety margin (e.g. an absorbed energy of 30 ft lbf (41 J) at -40°C) by sacrificing hardness is not acceptable because of the exceptional demands for high-stress abrasion wear. There is, therefore, a need for a failure criterion which will accurately predict, for dynamic tooth loadings, a relationship between stress and the fracture toughness of the tooth material.

During the past few years a powerful new engineering tool -- fracture mechanics -- has evolved, and such tests have been performed in our laboratories.

Linear elastic fracture mechanics K_{1c} values were estimated in accordance with ASTM E399, even though the specimens failed to conform to the constraint equation. Crack opening displacement (COD) values were determined in accordance with proposed specification BSI DD19 (2). A K_{1c} value was also computed from the relationship between COD and linear elastic fracture mechanics, viz.

$$COD = K^2/E(YS)$$

where E is the elastic modulus. J-integral calculations giving K_{1c} predictions were performed along the lines of ASTM STP 560, following Rice, Paris and Merkle (3). All results were compared for internal consistency. Figure 29 presents a summary of the relative differences in fracture toughness properties (COD test) as a function of temperature. A lack of sufficient material prevented the presentation of a complete curve of COD versus temperature for each material. The curves drawn through the data are eyeball fits designed to separate the groups of data, and no attempt was made to deduce a functional relationship.

Using estimated K_{1c} values, a relationship between applied stress and critical flaw size for the tested materials was attempted. Two surface defects were considered, a semi-circular and semi-

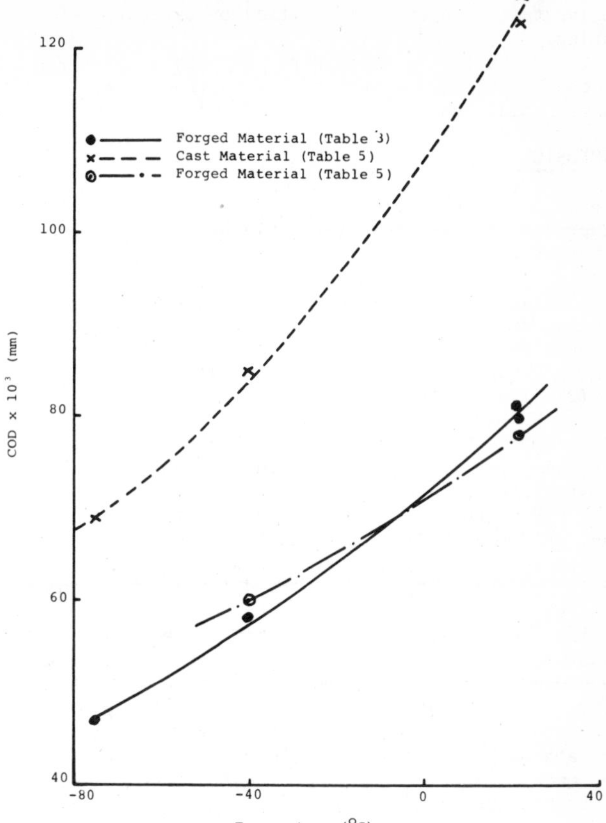

Figure 29: COD values

elliptical crack, in a bar loaded in cantilever fashion, using the stress-flaw size relationship given by Irwin and Paris (4). The static nominal bending stress versus crack surface depth, a, for the lowest predicted value of K_{1c} for each material at -40°C was plotted. Figure 30 illustrates a typical stress flaw-size relationship for the materials investigated. The results shown in Figure 30, which is typical of the other materials, suggests that in this material of hardness 52 Rc and 200 ksi (1380 MPa) yield strength, semi-elliptical surface cracks less than 2 mm in depth and less than 20 mm in length should not lead to fracture at static stresses below the yield stress. This assumes a high degree of confidence in the value of K_{1c}. Testing is now underway with properly-sized specimens to improve

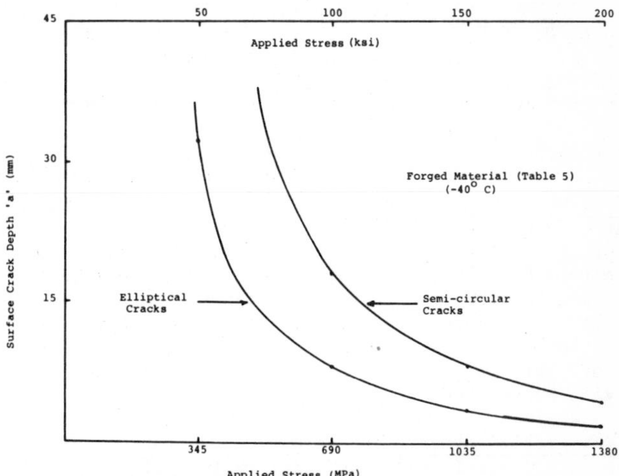

Figure 30: Stress/flaw-size relationship for forged material (Table 5)

the reliability of K_{1c}. The validity of these and similar tests can only be verified by extensive field testing.

The data presented here provides a base-line for continuing development of COD testing under dynamic conditions.

CONCLUSION

It has been demonstrated that the physical properties of low-alloy steels can be improved such that they may be successfully used for high stress abrasion combined with high impact applications. By reducing the sulfur and phosphorus levels, and by using vacuum arc remelted low-alloy steels, high hardness levels (>50 Rc) can be achieved, while maintaining Charpy-V energy absorption values of 20 ft lbf (27 J) at -40°C.

New techniques of evaluating steel, such as the COD test and J-integral methods will, it is felt, aid significantly in the further development of materials for uses such as ditching teeth.

From the full scale ditcher tests described here, and which have been conducted within the last two years, there is no question that most of the Arctic permafrost terrain can be ditched. This point is stressed because doubts have been expressed concerning the feasibility of combining such antagonistic properties as hardness and impact toughness to meet the unusual demands required for ditching in the Arctic. These properties have not, until now, been developed simply because there has never been a need. The data presented here show the progress that has been made in Arctic ditcher teeth and further improvements are anticipated.

Acknowledgment

This work has been made possible through the support of Northern Engineering Services Company Limited, engineers for Canadian Arctic Gas Study Limited. In this regard, we especially thank Mr. Murray Drope for his co-ordinating efforts.

REFERENCES

1. W. Hume-Rothery and G. V. Raynor, "The Structure of Metals and Alloys", 1962, Institute of Metals London, pp. 279-282.
2. B.S.I. Proposed Specification DD19, "Methods for Crack Opening Displacement (COD) Testing", 1972.
3. J. R. Rice, P. C. Paris and J. G. Merkle, 1973, STP 536, ASTM, Philadelphia.
4. G. R. Irwin and P. C. Paris, "Fracture", Vol. III, 1968, ed. H. Liebowitz, Academic Press, London and New York, p. 9.

DISCUSSION

D. L. Cheever (John Deere): The authors illustrate the effort that must first go into characterizing a problem before solutions can be proposed and tested. The forged alloy appeared to have adequate toughness but was limited by abrasion resistance. Have the authors considered mechanically pinning an abrasion-resistant sheath over a shank made of this forged alloy? This is currently used on conventional earth-moving bucket teeth.

P. C. Lichtenberger: The abrasion resistance of the forged steels was found satisfactory if accompanied by a minimum hardness of 50 Rc although there is certainly room for further improvement.

D. L. Cheever: What subsequent work is planned? Will COD measurements be used to screen materials for toughness instead of the Charpy level that was selected intuitively?

P. C. Lichtenberger: The subsequent work will depend on the outcome of field tests to be conducted in January 1977 in the Arctic. Laboratory tests will continue to be used as a guide for this further development. Teeth of different designs and teeth containing tungsten carbide inserts will also be tested. As indicated in the paper, carbide insert teeth previously tested were not successful but new concepts of the supporting base material will hopefully improve their performance.

We also hope to establish better criteria for material selection by performing both static and dynamic COD tests, as well as instrumented Charpy tests and dynamic tear tests.

D. L. Cheever: Tip fracture of 16 cast teeth compared to no fracture of the forged teeth appears highly significant. Does this not contradict the COD results and suggest the Charpy criteria were not adequate?

P. C. Lichtenberger: The higher incidence of fractures in cast teeth does not indicate that the Charpy results were inadeqaute. First of all the COD data for cast teeth reported in Figure 29 was determined for improved cast teeth and not those field tested in which the fractures were observed. We do not have values of COD for the field tested cast teeth because they were hard-faced and hence samples of sufficient size could not be prepared. The presence of cracks in the hard facing of the field tested cast teeth containing no butter layer as well as a lower hardness (40 Rc) and hence lower bending strength all combined to cause fractures of these particular cast teeth.

D. L. Cheever: Was the weight loss observed for hardfaced teeth concentrated in the hard-facing, the heat affected zone, or the base metal?

P. C. Lichtenberger: The weight loss was not concentrated in the hard facing although the spalling contributed to the general weight loss. No indications were found which suggested that the heat affected zone abraded faster than the base metal.

D. L. Cheever: Did the hard facing cover the entire working surface of the teeth?

P. C. Lichtenberger: Only the top part of the cast teeth has a hard face cover. The forged teeth had the hard face inlays evenly distributed on top and bottom.

D. L. Cheever: What was the hardness of the hard facing?

P. C. Lichtenberger: The hardness of the carbides measured with a "Dunimet" 100g loading using a "Knoop" diamond was of the order of 2200 HV. The base material hardness measured under the same conditions varies from 800 to 1100 HV.

D. L. Cheever: Did your field test data correlate with any laboratory wear tests?

P. C. Lichtenberger: It is extremely difficult to arrive at a laboratory wear test which simulates conditions of both high impact and high stress gouging abrasion.

B. Hawbolt (University of British Columbia): Your

data indicates some success with the Charpy approach -- a dynamic test procedure. You suggest that future fracture toughness tests will include COD and other low strain rate tests. For this particular impact loading application I would suggest that a more sophisticated dynamic test, such as instrumented Charpy, would better duplicate your application conditions -- in particular an assessment of the energy to nucleate a flaw or running crack.

P. C. Lichtenberger: Yes, the instrumented Charpy test may be quite suitable for the evaluation of fracture toughness of ditcher tooth material. However it is often found that the application of any test technique to a new problem requires not only careful consideration but also experimental verification. We plan to evaluate both COD and Charpy tests in the near future.

The COD test is currently being evaluated in order to assess the crack arresting properties of ditcher tooth material, under static conditions as might arise when the tooth contacts frozen soil and fractures without too much impact exerted on the tooth. The next stage of COD evaluations will be to attempt such tests in a dynamic mode.

O. Draganiuk (Syncrude Canada): Was the stainless steel buttering layer prior to hard facing successful in preventing propagation of inherent cracks from the laid down layers into the parent metal?

P. C. Lichtenberger: A stainless steel or nickel butter layer was quite successful in arresting cracks and therefore prevented such cracks from extending into the base metal. The hard facing failed by spalling off the butter layer. The approach of utilizing a butter layer between hard facing and base metal is considered very viable, however more development is required to obtain compatability of butter with hard facing. In the case of ditcher teeth for Arctic excavation, the first and foremost difficulty is to improve the performance of the hard facing itself.

J. M. Wallbridge (Foothills Pipe Lines): You stated that in your laboratory tests of teeth from previous ditching tests only one tooth had adequate properties. Do you have any further details on what this tooth was and how it related to your more recent teeth?

P. C. Lichtenberger: During the evaluation of teeth of the early field test, a used tooth was received from the Sans Sault site. The tooth was hard-faced and reportedly lasted longer than other teeth tested at the same site. The tooth is shown in Figure 15. For reasons unknown there was only one tooth left from this particular group tested. Hence the results of our findings for this group are based on this tooth only. As stated, this tooth would have failed in a manner similar to the other hard-faced teeth when subjected to impact loading.

V. G. Behal (Dominion Foundries and Steel): Is your statement that forged teeth were found to be superior to cast teeth based upon comparison of similar materials, suggesting that the casting manufacturing process as such is not suitable, or was the superiority of the forged product simply due to the poor quality of the specific castings under investigation, rather than to metallurgical considerations?

P. C. Lichtenberger: Our findings in no way suggest that the casting manufacturing process is not suitable for ditching teeth. Our test results from the Seebe and McPherson test locations did however show that the particular group of cast teeth tested there did not perform as well as the particular group of forged teeth tested. However, there is no problem finding forged teeth which are inferior to a given set of cast teeth. As it turned out, the forged teeth tested had better impact properties and higher hardness than the chosen group of cast teeth and hence the forgings performed somewhat better than the castings under this circumstance. It is however expected that cast teeth which will be tested during January and February 1977 will perform as well as the forged teeth to be tested at that time.

Our conclusions generally indicate that forgings and castings (when both are of high quality) can be used interchangeably in ditcher applications in the Arctic.

B. Ladanyi (Ecole Polytechnique): From the materials science point of view, frozen sand is essentially a particulate composite. That is why it is so tough and abrasive. It would seem to me that it would be logical to beat one composite material with another one. Have you considered the use of some composite material for the teeth of your ditching equipment?

P. C. Lichtenberger: Composite materials are being considered and will hopefully be tested in the future. Ditching frozen sand does not pose a serious problem. However, ditching permafrost with large boulders dispersed throughout it poses a significant problem. The latter has a close similarity with strong concrete and when such terrain areas are encountered teeth have a very short lifetime. It is possible that particular composite materials will provide increased tooth lifetimes.

F. S. Jeglic (CANMET): Have you noticed any microstructural damage at the tips of the abraded teeth?

P. C. Lichtenberger: Yes, we did find microstructural changes at the very tips of the teeth. The outside fibres of the tooth surface may be heated above the critical temperature. The mass of the tooth forms an excellent heat sink and may result in the formation of untempered martensite. The thickness of such layers was of the order of 3-5 mil (76-127 μm) and very localized. The entire wear surface did not show a complete layer of untempered martensite but rather only isolated surface areas of about 50 mm^2.

Machine operation will strongly influence microstructural changes at the tip of the abrading teeth.

F. S. Jeglic: What is the effect of temperature on the abrasion resistance of the tooth material?

P. C. Lichtenberger: It is not expected that the temperature range at which the teeth are being used will seriously influence their abrasion resistance.

T. Kunitake (Sumitomo Metal Industries): In laboratory abrasion tests which were done some time ago we found the addition of 0.5 to 1.0% Ti and/or more than 2 to 3% Cr is effective in reducing the abrasion loss. Have you ever investigated the effect of Ti and/or Cr in your field tests?

P. C. Lichtenberger: We have not field-tested alloys with additions of Ti. Low alloy steels with Ti additions were evaluated in the lab. However, the impact properties were too low to consider these materials for field testing.

T. Kunitake: Is your newly-developed martensitic steel superior to austenitic high Mn steel for service in the Arctic environment, both in terms of toughness and abrasion resistance?

P. C. Lichtenberger: Modified Mn steels will be evaluated in the near future. The problem with conventional Mn steel is that the strength is relatively low and would require a much larger section size than martensitic steel.

P. R. Slimmon (Bethlehem Steel): Does your work indicate that although 20 ft lbf (27 J) at -40°C is adequate for tooth design, what is really needed is greater hardness at this toughness level? For instance, is Rc 60 material obviously going to be better if toughness is maintained at 20 ft lbf (27 J) at -40°C?

P. C. Lichtenberger: The increase of hardness is very beneficial. It is conceivable however, that the incremental increase in abrasion resistance decreases with increased hardness beyond, say, 55 Rc. Free carbides are expected to further improve the abrasion resistance. The problem here however is to maintain a high enough impact resistance to resist fracture.

D. Fleckenstein (Union Carbide): Since different types of stresses are involved in ripping vs excavation, does your 50 Rc martensitic forged material work equally in both applications?

P. C. Lichtenberger: The example of a D9 caterpillar ripping the permafrost was shown as another example of soil to be ditched in the Arctic. The tooth used was not related to our ditcher program.

MATERIAL SELECTION CONSIDERATIONS IN THE MINING AND EXTRACTION OF TARSANDS

O. B. Draganiuk
Syncrude Canada Limited
Edmonton, Alberta
Canada

The Syncrude Canada Project for the extraction of oil from tarsands consists of three distinct but closely related and integrated operations, namely: mining, extraction and upgrading.

Mining in the extremely cold temperature plus the abrasive condition of the tarsands make it expensive, risky and complex. Materials must withstand the varying static and dynamic loads, while being wear-resistant, yet easily weldable. Extraction and tailings disposal requires the handling of different sand-water, sand-oil slurries through a variety of equipment while separating the oil from the sand and the water. In upgrading, coke and sulfur are removed from the bitumen to produce a synthetic crude. The consequences of failure require extra considerations in the selection of materials.

Failure to comply with specifications can lead to brittle failure under severe winter temperatures. Equipment installed according to specifications can still experience problems due to certain fabrication and process variables, leading to severe corrosion. Examples of fabrication problems are presented.

INTRODUCTION

Syncrude Canada Limited is currently approximately halfway to completion of a $2 billion mining, extraction and an upgrading project in the Athabasca Tarsands of Northeastern Alberta. The plant site is 23 mile (37 km) north of the community of Fort McMurray and about 260 mile(416 km) north of Edmonton. When the facilities achieve their ultimate design capacity, the plant will produce 125,000 barrels (20,000 m^3) per day of synthetic crude oil.

The mixture of sand, clay and heavy oil known as "tarsand" occurs in three major deposits throughout northeastern Alberta. Two of these occur in the vicinity of Cold Lake and Peace River but are at such a depth that recovery can only be contemplated by in-situ techniques. Collectively, these three deposits have the long term potential for producing 300 billion barrels of oil. Moreover, the mineable deposits could, with existing methods, recover approximately 26 billion barrels of oil -- sufficient to supply Canada for 50 years.

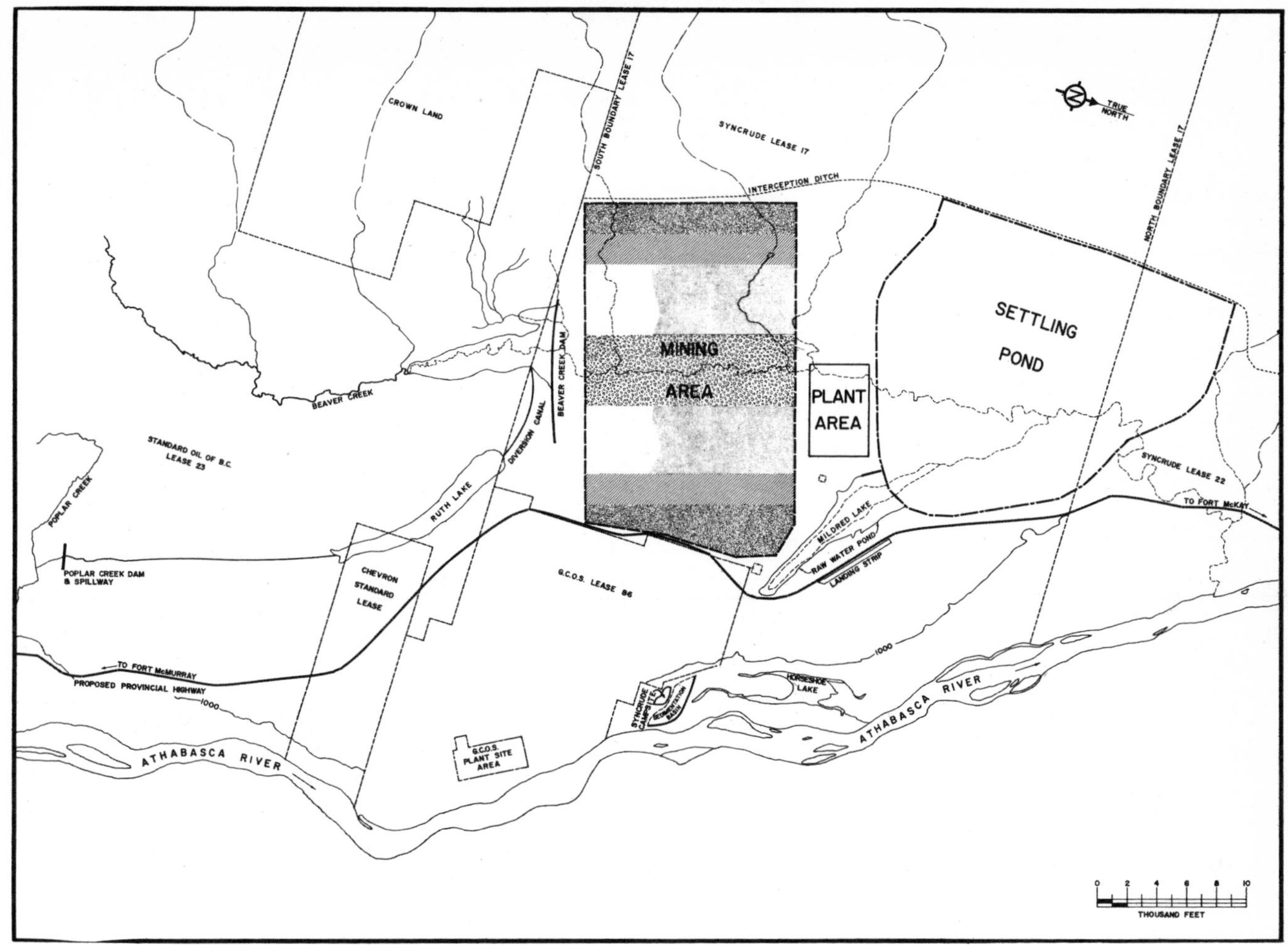

Figure 1: General site plan

THE ATHABASCA TARSAND

The Athabasca deposit covers an area of approximately 12,000 mile^2 (31,000 km^2). Figure 1 is a general Site Plan of Syncrude's "Lease 17" mining area which is 14,000 ft (4,300 m) by 23,000 ft (7,000 m) and contains sufficient tarsand to feed the plant for the 25 year period of the project permit. It is covered by overburden varying in depth from 7 ft (2 m) to 111 ft (33.3 m). About 40% of the mining area is overlain with muskeg to a depth of a few inches to 16 ft (5 m).

The oil is accumulated in the McMurray Formation of the Cretaceous Age. From outcrops along the Athabasca River, where saturation thicknesses range up to 150 ft (46 m) the beds slope to the southwest, eventually becoming overlain by the sand and shale deposits to over 2,000 ft (600 m). Eighty per cent of the oil reserves are located in the 40% total volume of the oil-bearing sediments. Under such varying conditions, some areas are appropriate for oil production, while others are beyond the practical limits of recoverability.

Tarsand varies widely in quality and is intermixed with a variety of other materials, most of which are barren sands and clay. Sand grains are water wet, averaging 4.5% water content. This allows separation by water washing. The raw oil is a black, naphthenic-base hydrocarbon which has a specific gravity of about 1.01 and a viscosity which ranges from 3000 to several hundred thousand poise at 60°F (15°C). The sulfur content of the oil is high for most areas and ranges from 4% to 6%. In addition, the oil has a relatively high nickel-vanadium porphyrin content.

Tarsand oil saturation is usually expressed as a weight percentage, with actual measurements varying from 18-20 wt% down to zero. Those sands containing 10% or more oil have a definite recoverable potential. Where overburden thickness does not exceed 350 ft (110 m) and where saturated beds are usually between 100 and 200 ft (30 and 60 m) thick, recovery by tested mining techniques is possible, but is limited to areas containing 6% or more of oil. The tarsand fed to the Syncrude plant will average about 11% oil. Current economics, however, limit the practical overburden-to-ore ratio to a maximum of 1:1.

DESIGN CONSIDERATIONS

All Syncrude steel structures (i.e. draglines, reclaimers, conveyors, steel-framed buildings, supports and supporting structures, storage tanks, pressure vessels and piping) exist under ambient temperature conditions, which vary between -59°F and 96°F. Table 1 shows the winter climatic conditions at Fort McMurray, compared with the major Canadian cities. For approximately 10 days of the year the temperature is -39°F (-39°C). The general philosophy considered during the design and engineering stages was that the Syncrude complex must be safe for operation at low ambient temperatures of -59°F and must be safe for cold start ups at from -50°F (-46°C) to 60°F (15°C), depending on service conditions, design factors, stress factors and the feasibility of utilizing startup warming procedures.

Table 1

Winter Climatic Conditions

Location	Elevation ft(m)	Lowest Temperature on Record °F(°C)	Average Annual Minimum °F(°C)	Winter Design Temperature* °F(°C)	Average Wind Velocity mph(km/h)
Montreal	187(57)	-29(-34)	-16(-27)	- 9(-23)	12(19)
Toronto	379(116)	-22(-30)	- 7(-22)	0(-18)	14(23)
Vancouver	22(7)	0(-18)	13(-11)	11(-12)	8(12)
Winnipeg	786(240)	-44(-42)	-35(-37)	-29(-34)	12(19)
Ottawa	339(103)	-38(-39)	-26(-32)	-15(-26)	11(18)
Quebec	296(90)	-32(-36)	-19(-28)	-12(-24)	12(20)
Edmonton	2219(677)	-55(-48)	-39(-39)	-33(-36)	8(12)
Calgary	3540(1080)	-46(-43)	-31(-35)	-29(-34)	11(17)
Syncrude Plant Site Ft. McMurray (approx.)	1000(305)	-59(-51)	-50(-46)	-39(-39)	8(13)

* Temperature at or below this value experienced for 2.5% of the January hourly records.

For example, mining equipment, (e.g. draglines and bucketwheel reclaimers) were designed for -50°F (-46°C), while unheated equipment such as storage tanks, pressure vessels and piping were designed for -39°F (-39°C). Code requirements were recognized only as minimum standards. Considerable effort was expended to choose materials compatible with end use, including atmosphere, product, contaminants, expected corrosion conditions, maintenance, etc. We believe that the standard 15 ft lbf (20 J) Charpy-V criterion is a very poor index of the usefulness of a material.

Tensile strength and yield stress increase markedly as temperature is lowered, though there does not appear to be any marked consistency between the different steels and there is considerable difference between a steel in different metallurgical conditions. However, the undesirable feature of the low temperature mechanical properties of steels is the loss of ductility. Loss of ductility is important since the stresses encountered are not likely to be static or constant. These may vary smoothly with time as in heating or cooling a boiler, but they may also occur instantaneously as when the dragline bucket encounters sandstone seams, boulders, or frozen lenses, while the dragline boom is momentarily but simultaneously subjected to an enormous additional bending moment by a gust of wind. The effect of impact loading must therefore be considered.

For the Syncrude complex, the design required that ferrous alloys for use at low temperatures should possess an impact transition temperature below the lowest service temperature contemplated. Therefore, consideration had been given to the most significant practical effect of low temperature on the mechanical properties of ferrous alloys. Diminished ductility is also sensitive to a great variety of metallurgical and environmental features and is the least consistent of all mechanical properties. The Charpy V-notch requirements shown in Table 2 were used as a general guideline. It can be seen that the requirements for absorbed energy increase as the material strength and thickness increase.

DESCRIPTION OF THE PROJECT

The main steps of the processing operation are illustrated schematically in Figure 2, and the layout of the plant shown in Figure 3.

The tarsand deposit averages 120 ft (36 m) in thickness with lenses increasing to 180 ft (45 m). It is covered by overburden which varies in depth from 7 to 111 feet (2 to 33.3 m). The complex will obtain its raw material from an open pit mine. Mining will begin in the centre on the mine site, with a cut the full length of the pit. First it is necessary to strip the muskeg from the mining area. This will be stockpiled for later use in revegatation, since reclaimation will commence once the mined-out area has been filled back to final grade with the sand tailings. After this final cut has been made, two mining faces will be developed, one on the east and one on the west wide. Each will be the full length of the mine and will reach a depth of 200 ft (60 m). Two draglines will operate on each face, removing overburden, and mining the abrasive tar sand, which they will pile in windrows behind them. The ability to freecast the overburden is a major advantage enjoyed by the dragline mining scheme.

Table 2

Impact Requirements for Syncrude Project Steels

Specified Minimum Yield Strength ksi(MPa)	Specified Minimum Tensile Strength ksi(MPa)	Thickness in.(mm)	Charpy V-Notch at Design Temp. ft lbf (J)
	Rimmed and Semi-killed Steels		
35(240)	65(450)	≤2(51)	10/8(14/11)
		>2(51)	25/20(34/27)
45(310)	80(550)	≤0.5(13)	10/8(14/11)
		0.5-2(13-51)	15/12(20/16)
		>2(51)	35/28(47/38)
	Fully-killed Medium Strength Carbon & Low Alloy Steels		
35(240)	75(520)	≤0.63(16)	13/10(18/14)
		0.63-2(16-51)	15/12(20/16)
		>2(51)	35/28(47/38)
55(380)	90(620)	≤0.5(13)	20/16(27/22)
		0.5-2(13-51)	25/20(34/27)
		>2(51)	40/32(54/44)
65(450)	100(690)	≤0.5(13)	25/20(34/27)
		0.5-1(13-25)	30/25(41/34)
		1-2(25-51)	35/28(47/38)
		>2(51)	45/36(61/49)

Draglines

Each dragline has a bucket capacity of 80 yd^3 (61 m^3). The booms are 360 ft (108 m) long. With a boom angle of 30°, they are designed to operate at a radius of 340 ft (102 m) and a suspended load of 435,000 lb (20,000 kg). It is planned that these machines operate continuously, with time out for scheduled maintenance. A design temperature of -50°F (-46°C) was considered mandatory. Particular attention to notch toughness criterion at service temperature was focused on the following areas of the machines: buckets, bucket teeth, booms, masts, backlegs, tristructures, fairlead girders, cam girders, bottom plates, and walking shoes.

Syncrude materials specifications require that all materials designed for "cold weather service" exhibit notch toughness as demonstrated by Charpy "V" notch impact tests, an average value from 3 specimens of 20 ft lbf (27 J) at -50°F (-46°C), with no single specimen lower than 16 ft lbf (21 J). Orders for the machines were placed with two separate manufacturers. Each had distinctly different design concepts which are manifest in the outward appearance of the respective machines. As an example, one

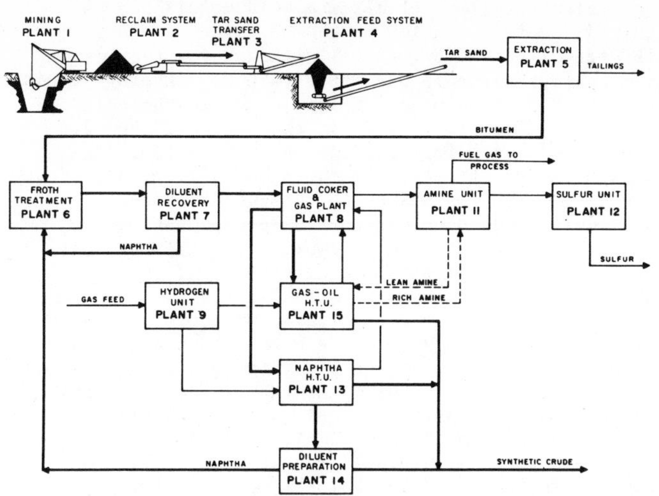

Figure 2: Tarsand processing sequence

manufacturer utilizes a tubular structure for the boom members, the cords and diagonal bracing, whilst the other uses conventional wide flange beam members with tubular diagonal bracing.

Low temperature steels were supplied in accordance with ASTM A572 Grades 42 and 50 with additional supplementary provisions for notch toughness at -50°F (-46°C). These grades are intended for riveted, bolted or welded construction of bridges, buildings, and other structures. Materials for shafting and gearing are AISI 4140, 4150, 4340. The tubular boom cord material was supplied in accordance with ASTM A618 Grade 2, 16 in. (410 mm) diameter, and 0.75 in. (19 mm) wall thickness. Its corrosion resistance is enhanced by the presence of small amounts of copper. The conventional wide flange beam boom material is ASTM A441.

In the tub, most of the cold-weather steels are in the tub circular base and top plates, and the walking shoes. The 80 ft (24 m) diameter tubs have 2 in. (51 mm) thick bottom plates, 0.75 in. (19 mm) top plates in cold-weather steel from one manufacturer, whilst the other utilized 2 in. (51 mm) bottom plates conforming to the supplementary specification requirements of ASTM A572, and 1.25 in. (31.7 mm) ASTM A36 material for the top plates. All tubs are of welded box construction.

Welding procedures used were qualified with impact test requirements. Extensive use of submerged arc welding (SAW) was made for shop fabrication supplemented by flux cored arc welding (FCAW) and shielded metal arc welding (SMAW). For field welding, we adopted electroslag welding (ESW) for vertical bulkhead welds in one tub structure. FCAW was used predominantly with E90 T and E80 T wire for cold weather steels and E70 T for all other ferrous materials. CO_2 gas shielding was mandatory for all classes of steels. SMAW using E8018 C1 electrodes was used on cold weather steels where FCAW was not considered suitable. Other steels were welded with E7018 electrodes.

The walking shoes, also of welded-box construction, are approximately 70 ft (21 m) long and 15 ft (4.5 m) wide. All bottom plates are cold-

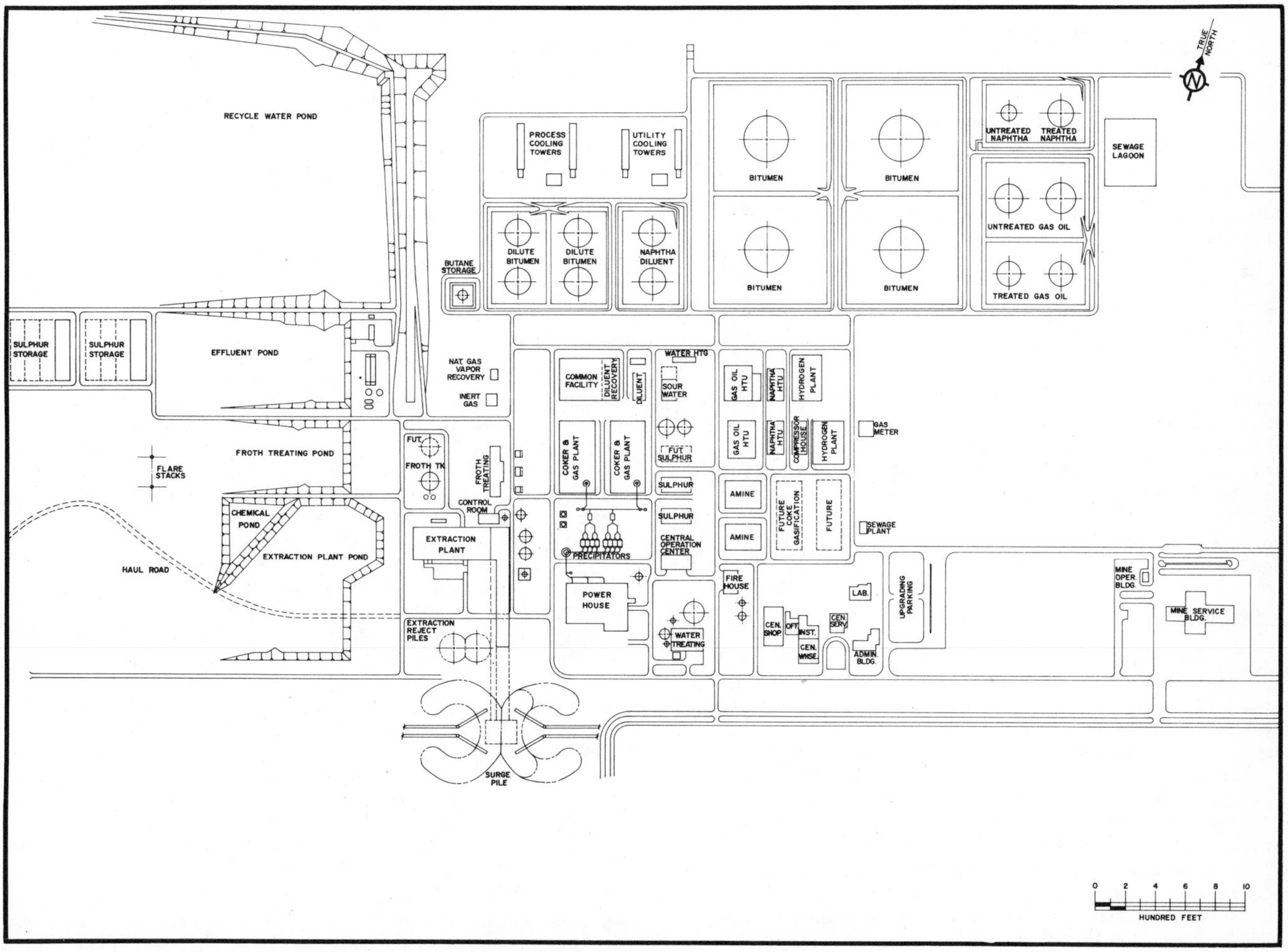

Figure 3: Plant site layout

weather steel ranging from 1.75 in. (44 mm) to 2.5 in. (64 mm) thick. Top plates vary from 0.75 in. (19 mm) to 1.7 in. (44 mm), although only one manufacturer incorporated cold-weather steel.

Extensive field welding is involved in the erection of the machines. Because many of the components, and in particular the boom, mast and backlegs, are subjected to dynamic loading during operation, close surveillance of all welding operations is maintained. Because of the material thicknesses and joint geometries, ultrasonic testing is used for quality control. This is supplemented by magnetic particle testing, during and on completion of the joint welding. Some of these will be subjected to dynamic stress tests. Both impact strength and fatigue were considered in the design and welding of the boom butt joints and the lacing connections. For the welding of the wide flange members, joints were designed to avoid lamellar tearing.

Dragline Buckets

There are eight dragline buckets, four of which are standby units. All are 80 yd^3 (61 m^3) capacity and supplied by 3 separate manufacturers. Resistance to extreme forces of tension, shear, fatigue, abrasion and impact are primary prerequisites in material selection. Material selection is as follows:

STRUCTURALS:	Astralloy, Con-Pac, RQC-80, LT-75HS. USS 50-N
TRUNNIONS:	ASTM A514: ASTM A148: Modified Ni-Cr-Mo
SHROUDS:	AISI 4330, modified Q & T, castings
ARCH:	USS 50-N, Con-Pac, and RQC-80
LIPS:	ASTM A148 modified; ASTM A543
TEETH:	AISI 4330, ASTM A148
JAW PLATES:	ASTM A514, Astralloy
CHAINS:	AISI 4330, AISI 8630

The above materials were selected by the bucket manufacturers as having suitable resistance to the abrasive tarsand and in addition, exhibiting the required fracture toughness properties at -50°F (-46°C). The buckets are shipped in four sections for field erection and welding using FCAW and SMAW. E80 T, E90 T and E110 T cored wire is used for FCAW and E8018 C1, E9018 and E12018 electrodes for SMAW. Preheating and interpass temperatures are maintained in the range 200°F to 250°F (93°C to 120°C). Strict compliance with detailed weld metal deposition sequences is necessary to obviate the deleterious influence of shrinkage stresses that promote solidification cracking. Moreover, to enhance the attainment of fine grain structures when using FCAW, supplemental CO_2 shielding is mandatory.

Bucketwheel Reclaimers

To properly utilize the draglines, a rehandling step for the tarsand in the windrows is necessary. This will be accomplished by bucketwheel reclaimers which will load tarsand onto conveyor belts for transport to the extraction plant. These comprise a crawler-mounted bucketwheel excavator with connected crawler-mounted discharge bridge conveyor. A series of toothed buckets on a revolving drum will dig the tarsand from the windrows.

The reclaimer superstructure, turntable, undercarriage, boom crawlers and discharge bridge are the main components and all are fabricated from cold-weather steel conforming to CSA G40.21-50T, normalised. Many structural parts were also made in Germany using DIN TT Ste 36 material, which is equivalent. All materials and weld metals are required to exhibit notch toughness values of 20 ft lbf (27 J) at -50°F (-46°C), although in practice the test temperature was -58°F (-50°C). Average impact values (Charpy-V) of 46 ft lbf (62 J) in the weld metal and 38 ft lbf (51 J) in the HAZ were typical from tests taken from production test plates. The design of the structural members was also greatly concerned with resistance to fatigue stresses. Considerable development work on procedures was necessary to obtain the optimum weld metal physical properties conducive to the attainment of these qualities.

Forgings for mechanical components are supplied primarily in accordance with DIN standard 24 CrMo 4. Other forgings comply with such DIN standards as 20 Mn 5; 34 CrNiMo 6; 33 NiCrMo 145; and 24 CrNiMo 554. Comparable ASTM standards would be A 237-67 classes D through G. SAW, GMAW, FCAW, and SMAW processes were used in weld fabrication, with preheating in the range 100°F (38°C) to 250°F (120°C). All full-strength, full-penetration welds are subjected to 100% ultrasonic examination supplemented by radiography and magnetic particle testing where deemed appropriate.

Yield strengths of these forgings range from 70 ksi (480 MPa) to 115 ksi (790 MPa). All are normalized, quenched, and tempered. Notch toughness (longitudinal values) at -50°F (-46°C) are 20 ft lbf (27 J) for the lower yield strengths, and up to 35 ft lbf (48 J) for the higher yield strength grades. High-strength steel castings conform to DIN GS-CK-16V, GS-CK 24V, GS-26 CrMo 4V, GS-30 CrMo V 64 V. (ASTM A148 grades 80-40 to 105-85). Here also, the notch toughness provisions specified for forgings are applied, i.e., 20 ft lbf (27 J) for 40 ksi (275 MPa) yield strength, and 35 ft lbf (48 J) for 85 ksi (586 MPa) yield strength.

The reclaimer bucketwheels were made in Germany. TT STe 36 material (G40.2 21-50T) was used in construction. Buckets were made from AISI 4340, HY80 and T1 steels. The abrasion on these machines is not expected to be as severe as that on the dragline buckets because the tarsand material has been loosened.

Conveyors and Extraction Feed System

The Syncrude conveyor system, utilizing a belt moving at high speed, transports the tarsand through radial stackers to a surge pile and on to the extraction building. The system includes a 16 in. (400 mm) vibrating grizzly screen lump separator and a 6 ft (1.8 m) wide belt. Total length of the conveyor system is 36,000 ft (10,000 m). While no particular requirements for components with cold weather properties were specified some were supplied.

Severe wear is expected on the grizzly bars, the conveyor support rollers, return idlers and bearings or bushings. Four radial stackers distribute the tarsand onto two semicircular surge piles. Recovery from the surge piles is via 16 mass flow bins controlled by apron feeders. Feed is discharged onto gathering conveyors which in turn discharge to the extraction feed conveyors. As the stackers operate in the open, special consideration was given to low temperature properties of the steel used in their construction. Parts of the stackers made in Canada utilized steel conforming to CSA G40.21-50T; those from Germany complied with DIN TT STe 36.

The feed bins, which are 27.6 ft (8.3 m) high and located below ground, do not have special low temperature requirements, although consideration had to be given to the severe abrasive characteristics of the tarsand. Therefore, wear resistant materials are incorporated in their construction. Structural steel to CSA G40.21 -44W was used for the most part and in thicknesses of 1 in. (25 mm). Since most of the wear is expected at the bottom of these bins, wear resistant plate was used there, grading to plain carbon steels in the upper portions.

Extraction Equipment

The tarsand consists primarily of a water-wetted, semi-consolidated sandstone, the interstices of which are filled with tar, or bitumen as it is generally called. The extraction process utilizes hot water to effect disintegration of the tarsand and liberation of the oil flecks from the grains of sand. The extraction is achieved in the largest shippable diameter, horizontal, rotating, tumblers approximately 100 ft (30 m) long, with shell thicknesses varying from 0.75 in. (19 mm) to 2.25 in. (56 mm). From here, the aerated bitumen in the form of a slurry is discharged into large primary separation vessels, enabling the bitumen which floats on the surface as a froth to become separated from the bulk of the mineral matter. Primary froth is collected in launders, and subsequently deaerated.

As the equipment associated with extraction operates in an enclosed structure and in association with high temperatures, no impact strength requirements are necessary for the materials of its construction. Steels conforming to ASTM A283 Grade C; A 515 Grade 70 and A 516 Grade 70 were used. Wear and abrasion are the main areas of concern here. They are expected at the inlet chute end, at the rock movers, in the water and steam pipe ports, at the sand lifters, and at the outlet end. The design philosophy incoporated the use of plain carbon steel, plus air-hardening, work-hardening, weldable, wear-resistant, sand retaining strips to enhance movement of sand layers, as Figure 4.

The extraction process produces a bituminous froth consisting of about 65 wt% bitumen, 25% water and 10% mineral matter. It is necessary to remove most of the physical contaminants before the bitumen can be upgraded to synthetic crude. This involves dilution with naphtha to reduce the viscosity followed by a two-stage system of centrifuges to remove the fine abrasives and the water.

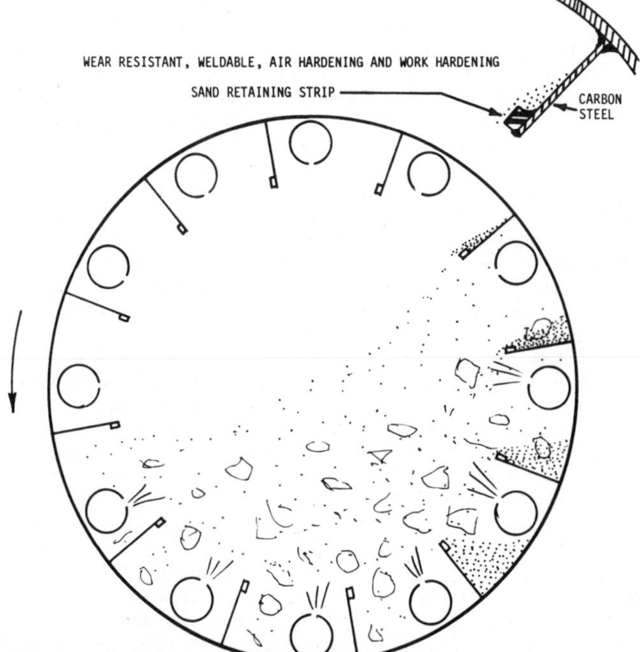

Figure 4: Schematic drawing of tumbler cross-section

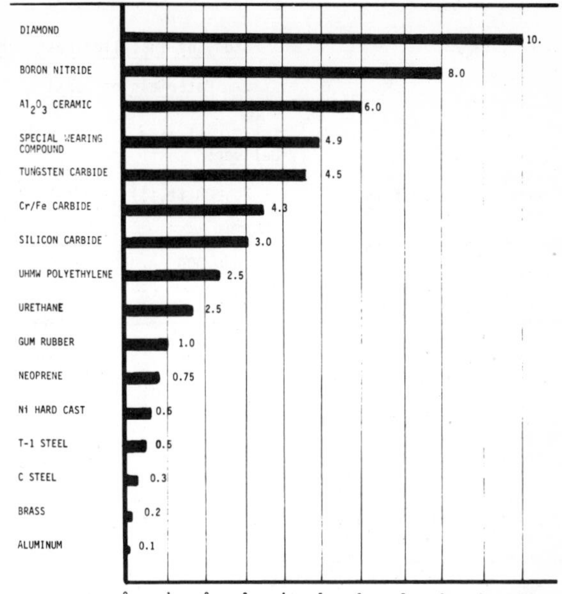

Figure 5: Relative wear resistance scale for sliding fine grain abrasion at 70°F (21°C)

A variety of materials were used to minimize wear, abrasion and corrosion. These range from carbon steel, to rubber- and polymer-lined equipment and pipe, to abrasion-resistant wear plate, to ceramics and special stainless alloys. Many other alternatives were considered, evaluated and may yet be tried after the complex commences operation.

Tailings Disposal

One of the most comprehensive materials studies carried out for Syncrude Project was that of wear resistant materials for the tailings disposal lines. The system will consist of five 24 in. (610 mm) diameter pipelines, each approximately 4000 ft (1200 m) long, designed to hydraulically transport the tailings, at 46% to 50% concentration of solids by weight, to the tailings disposal pond.

Alternative materials systems receiving consideration are shown in Table 3. Costs were based on 1974 quotations for the alternatives listed plus an estimated installation cost. The estimated pipeline life was based on actual 0.5 in. (13 mm) thick carbon steel samples in slurry experience which were rotated 120° every 3000 to 4000 h, and on the sliding fine grain abrasion index shown in Figure 5.

While the carbon steel system has the lowest capital cost, Table 3 indicates that a concrete lined pipe is the most economical based on the cost/life ratio. However, it was judged undesirable because of mechanical damage to the concrete linings during rotating, relocating, and/or unplugging operations after sanding out, and the resultant turbulent, highly-erosive conditions. Lining with hard-facing was not accepted because of the extremely high initial cost. Polymer-lined systems present some excellent cost/life ratios but do present difficulties with in-service monitoring of wear rates on the lining itself. Similar problems as noted for concrete linings would result after wear. It must be realized that while the actual costs today are meaningless, the comparative cost data are useful and are favourable with other current cost/life ratios. Inflation to date has increased the purchase price of the carbon

Table 3

Study of Installed Costs and Replacement Costs of Alternative Materials of Construction for Tailings Disposal Lines

Alternative Systems	Total Estimated Delivered Cost Including Freight* for 20,000 ft ($)	Installed $/ft($/m)	Installed Cost Factor	Est. Approx. Life,(a)	Cost/ Life	Average Annual Replacement Cost $/ft($/m)	Average Annual Replacement Cost,$	25 Year Material Cost Delivered $
0.5 in.(13mm) thick steel 40 ft(12 m) lengths	630,000	32(103)	1.0	1	1	32(103)	630,000	15,750,000
0.5 in.(13mm) thick steel 20 ft(6 m) lengths with 0.38(9.5 mm) concrete	697,400	34(113)	1.1	3.3	.34	10(34)	208,300	5,696,700
0.25 in.(13 mm) thick steel 20 ft (6 m) lengths with 0.25 in. (6 mm) neoprene	1,388,400	69(228)	2.2	2.5	.88	28(91)	555,400	14,711,700
0.25 in.(6 mm) thick steel 20 ft (6 m) lengths lined with 0.25 in. (6 mm) CPE	1,531,200	76(248)	2.4	3.3	.75	24(77)	471,100	12,838,500
0.25 in. (6 mm) thick steel 20 ft (6 m) lengths lined with 0.25 in. (6 mm) urethane	2,267,600	113(372)	3.6	8	.45	14(46)	283,500	9,070,400
3/8" thick steel 40 ft (12 m) lengths lined with 0.19 in. (5 mm) hardfacing	4,471,000	224(733)	7.1	10	.71	22(73)	447,100	15,201,400

* Does not include duty and/or sales tax

steel alone by a factor of three.

Material replacement cost studies of the six different alternatives over a 25 year period are shown to the right side of Table 3. These have confirmed that concrete-lined systems are most economical, while polymer alternates are intermediate and carbon steel is the most expensive.

Fluid Coking

Syncrude will upgrade the bitumen by converting it to naphtha and gas-oil in two parallel fluid coking units. The total capacity of these two units is greater than the combined capacity of the other ten fluid coking units currently in existence in the world. Their size alone and the supporting structural steel, which towers approximately 210 ft (64 m), dictated special designs, material specifications and non-destructive examination. While the cokers operate at elevated temperatures they are refractory lined and internally insulated to varying degrees. This, therefore, exposed the steels of pressured units to varying atmospheric conditions and dictated impact-tested steel for the cold-wall designed pressure vessels. Up to 2 in. (52 mm) thick ASTM A 516-70 impact tested plate at -30°F (-34°C) was used for parts of these vessels. Even the bolting studs used in the cold-wall designed flanges were subject to impact requirements.

Structural steel in the support structure received special consideration. Bridge design and fabrication practices for northern Canada and Alaska were reviewed and it was decided that there was a good possibility that certain primary beams in the coker structure and/or the gusset-type connections to the columns may be subjected to higher strain rates than normally occur in bridges. Certain maintenance activities, if required during the extreme low ambients and cold weather start-ups or emergency procedures, could cause strain rates which more nearly approach laboratory impact conditions. CSA-G40.8 Grade B material, with required longitudinal Charpy V-notch impact of 12 ft lbf (16 J) at -40°F (-40°C) were specified.

Approximately 180 t of steel used in bracing members, their connection plates, and the connection plates for the plate girders was stressed in tension below a project-set minimum guideline and was not Charpy-tested. Also, 284 t of structural shapes were rolled for these structures. It is difficult to obtain high energy impact values in structural sections because of inherent problems with grain size control and inability to cross-roll. The results of impact testing on six heats of wide flange members indicated high values of Charpy impact energy, but with a wide spread in these values. Weld procedures were qualified with impact testing requirements. At -40°F (-40°C) weld metal impacts were 38 to 28 ft lbf (51 to 38 J) and HAZ impacts were 45 to 19 ft lbf (61 to 26 J).

The load-carrying members supporting the fluid coker vessels are fireproofed by magnesium oxychloride which will in the future preclude any obvious examination of the members and/or weldments for fatigue cracking. Since the fatigue strength of a metal or alloy is a function of its ultimate strength, and since the latter increases with decreasing temperature, it follows that fatigue strength also increases. True brittle fracture arising from a stress concentration in a material at a low temperature is not necessarily associated with fatigue failure. It appears that under conditions of low-frequency, high amplitude stresses, the notch sensitivity is not seriously increased. As a result, the Syncrude design did not consider fatigue, but where fatigue was expected, members and joints were designed to permit the expected stress. Weldments in these instances were checked for penetrations, completeness and presence of defects.

Sulphur Removal

The Syncrude complex will include facilities for removal of sulphur by hydrotreating the gas-oil stream and the naphtha stream produced in the fluid cokers. Associated with this requirement there are parallel hydrogen plants for desulphurization, hydrotreaters, amine plants for scrubbing the hydrogen-sulphide-rich hydrocarbon streams, and sulphur plants. For two fired heaters, cold weather steel was not readily available for certain key and exposed members judged to be critical. Since a delay of 8 to 12 months could not have been tolerated, redesign to lower levels was undertaken. Other design requirements included impact testing of column anchor bolts, but the allowable stresses for support skirts were lowered.

Pressure vessels here vary from 2 to over 50 ft (0.5 to 15 m) in diameter, from 3 to 175 ft (1 to 53 m) in height and from 0.19 to 6.25 in. (5 to 150 mm) in thickness. Materials of construction vary from carbon steel, through 1.25Cr-0.5Mo, 2.5Cr-1Mo, 5Cr-0.5Mo, 11 to 13Cr-0.5Ni, 17Cr-13Ni-2.5Mo. Special considerations were required for the low-alloy steels with the higher transition temperatures. Some equipment and structures will be cold even when operating, and sufficiently tough steels will be required where brittle fracture could be catastrophic.

Storage tanks also vary in size and service. The largest tanks are 288 ft (88 m) in diameter and will store hot bitumen. These tanks were designed in accordance with a minimum Charpy V-notch energy of 30 ft lbf (40 J) longitudinal and 20 ft lbf (27 J) transverse at the lower design temperature.

FABRICATION PROBLEMS

While the foregoing dealt with considerations to minimize the chance of service failures, there have been a number of fabrication failures relating to steel fracture. They are worthy of mention here because they were the result of "people errors".

One rapid failure occurred in 1.94 in. (49 mm) thick ASTM A 387-Grade 11, Class 2 (1.25Cr-0.5Mo) plate when a 15 ft (4.5 m) diameter cylindrical section was being rerolled after longitudinal seam welding. The fracture surface exhibited a cleavage type structure, typical of brittle fracture. Chevrons indicated that fracture initiated at a tackweld made to hold the guide rail for the semi-automatic welding head. It is believed that no preheat was used in making the tackweld, and rerolling was well below the 75°F (24°C) temperature considered to be good practice. The fractured edges overlapped each other by some 3 to 4 ft (0.9 to 1.2 m).

Another failure occurred in a 2.75 in. (30 mm) thick ASTM A 387 Grade 22 (2.25 Cr-1Mo) torch-cut petal section that was being hot pressed into shape for a hemispherical head. The torch-cut edge had not been ground prior to forming. The crack initiated at a notch in the rough edge resulting from the torch cutting. The crack was 18 in. (460 m) long, without branches, and without necking. The fracture surface was brittle in nature. It did not penetrate the full plate thickness. The depth ranged from 2 in. (51 mm) at the edge to about 1 in. (25 mm) at the point of arrest. Although the material toughness probably influenced the crack arrest, it is believed that the primary reason it stopped was stress decay. Chevron patterns pointed directly to the "notch" or rough edge. Both mechanical and metallurgical notches were the cause of this failure.

One stainless steel-clad vessel failed by cracking along a longitudinal weld seam during a hydrostatic shop test. While a number of factors may have contributed to the failure, the failed weld and some other back-cladding welds were found to be magnetic. Brinnell hardness readings were high, (300-327 BHN). The balance of the welds were non-magnetic and hardness was in the expected range of 180 to 200 BHN. Improper welding procedures had been used.

Molten copper embrittlement of austenitic stainless steel heat exchanger tubes was one of the most interesting fabrication failures encountered on this project to date. Embrittlement occurred during a 1900°F (1050°C) resistance annealing cycle of the cold-bent/cold-worked 304 & 321 stainless steel tubing. One inch (25 mm) by 12-gauge tubes were rapidly cracked by this treatment. Molten copper had penetrated into the parent metal. Cracks were associated with small copper deposits on the surface of the tubes and/or with tiny arc burns. In one tube sample examined, no cracking or copper penetration was visible when a cross-section was examined at low magnification. Observation at 500X magnification revealed copper deposition between the grain boundaries to approximately a 6 mil (150 μm) depth.

A number of fabricators have experienced cracking of plate edges during or after rolling carbon and low-alloy steel. There seems to be some difficulty in emphasizing to shop personnel that during the cutting of any steel, the metal facing the cut expands. The physical restraint of the adjoining cold metal causes the metal to upset. After cooling, the contraction of the upset metal produces severe local stresses. This results in checking and cracking, which tends to increase with increase in carbon content. It is difficult to persuade shops to preheat prior to torch cutting.

Two fabricators experienced cracking in hardenable steel along weldments made with 8018-C2 and 12018 electrodes. Investigation revealed lack of baking and heating ovens and improper control of low-hydrogen welding electrodes. While other factors, such as restrained weldments, etc. may have contributed to the cracking, hydrogen cracking is believed to have been the main cause.

Fabrication failures are the result of "people errors" arising from lack of knowledge of failure prevention. This lack covers design, material selection, fabrication and weld procedures, heat treatment, handling, inspection and so on. Service failures are also the result of people errors stemming from the same lack of knowledge. People errors can be avoided only by education and conferences such as this.

Acknowledgements

This paper is presented by kind permission of the management of Syncrude Canada Limited, to which sincere thanks are extended. The author also expresses his appreciation to colleagues in the Engineering Department for their kind assistance in its preparation and review.

DISCUSSION

J. R. Broderick (Imperial Oil): For many years, design engineers have used operating temperatures as design parameters in Alberta. We have many processing facilities utilising materials good for only -20°F, yet ambient temperatures in Alberta drop to lows of -59°F during the winter period.

In view of the project cost and appreciating the Alberta experience with -20°F steels, how does Syncrude justify a specification philosophy in applying the -39°F figure for all pressure vessels, tankage and structural steels?

O. Draganiuk: I am sorry if I gave the impression that all pressure vessels, tankage and structural steel was designed for -39°F. -39°F was a design quote, not a standard. Only those vessels that will operate below -20°F were designed for -39°F. Those that operate hot, or could be easily warmed up before pressurization were not designed for -39°F. The paper lists temperatures like -20°F, 32°F, and 60°F. Only those structural components that are critical were designed for the specified temperatures below -20°F, e.g. fluid coker structures, draglines, reclaimers. Pipe-support structures and conveyor supports were not impact tested.

Items were reviewed with the consequences of failure in mind. First, safety was considered. Would a brittle failure be hazardous? How hazardous? Would personnel be involved? Would other equipment be involved and how many? Secondly, would the required repair/replacement/ redesign be urgent? What would be the time delay? Thirdly, would growth potential, profit picture, earnings possibility, rate of return be affected? How seriously? After all factors were considered and weighted, we believe a safe operating complex was designed.

J. R. Broderick: Due to procurement difficulties and/or the vendor being unable to meet Charpy impact requirements, I understand that Syncrude, in relaxing structural steel specifications, adopted a minimized stress intensity criteria in purchasing the structural steel members. What stress level guidlines did Syncrude use and why?

O. Draganiuk: As in my first reply, each item was evaluated and when impact-tested steels could not be supplied within our time frame, redesign to lower allowable stress levels was undertaken, with safety, urgency of repair and growth potential in mind. These then varied between 8 and 12 ksi (55 and 83 MPa), depending on component member and location.

J. L. Gerlitz (Shell Canada): In order to meet weld impact requirements for plain carbon or low-alloy steels what type (class) of electrodes were used? Did they contain nickel additions?

O. Draganiuk: Yes, the electrodes used in the draglines and the bucket wheel reclaimers did contain nickel, where required for impact tests. Electrode classification 8018 C2 contains about 2.25% nickel.

L. Malik (Dominion Bridge): You mention in the paper that for the welding of the wide flange members of the boom of one of the draglines, "joints were designed to avoid lamellar tearing". Would you please expand on the statement and explain if lamellar tearing was avoided by: (a) modifying groove shapes and/or relocation of joints or (b) establishing a steel quality criterion, such as minimum reduction in area in the ST direction. If so, what did the specification ask for?

O. Draganiuk: In the design of dragline booms there are many cross members and bracing supports. Prevention of lamellar tearing in the booms with wide flange members meant relocation of joints to avoid the concentration of many large welds with resultant high stresses. In most cases it was possible to weld to members which were free to deform. For the tubular booms, relocation of joints and welds was not possible and avoidance of lamellar tearing was based on material selection, e.g. cleanliness of steel, with a through-thickness ductility of at least 20%.

G. L. Archer (The Welding Institute): Could you please enlarge on the use of electroslag welding in fabricating your structures. In particular could you tell us what thicknesses were electroslag-welded, what parts of the structures were they used in and what were the stress levels, and were the welds given any heat treatment?

O. Draganiuk: Electroslag welding was used by only one manufacturer in the tub on the vertical bulk-head. All section were T-sections with a 1 in. (25 mm) gap. Most plate thicknesses were 1.5 to 2 in. No preheat and no post-heat was applied. I do not know the stress levels. Charpy V-notch impact testing was not a requirement for these members or welds. During the development work, impact energies of the HAZ at 25°F (-4°C) were 15 ft lbf (20 J).

F. S. Jeglic (CANMET): With the improved qualities of concrete (for example "Sulfurcrete") a special shape of pipe could be used for the transport of two-phase materials having a very thick wall thickness at the bottom, the philosophy being that the solid phase travels on the bottom surface of the pipe.

O. Draganiuk: Pipe with either wear-resistant alloys or concrete, with a special shape (such as greater thickness in the lower half where most of the wear occurs) is indeed of interest if it were readily available. It would need to be more economic than the system in use at the time. I think the suggestion is a good one.

C. A. Parrini (Italsider): I would like to understand why, after your detailed economic analysis, you have chosen C-Mn steel.

O. Draganiuk: Carbon-manganese steels were chosen because they are suitable for the service required, and are conventional materials with which most fabricators are familiar. Complexes such as Syncrude's are built on compliance with the ASME pressure vessel values and the ANSI pressure piping codes. Also, designers and engineers are more familiar with Charpy V-notch testing than with fracture mechanics methodology. Thirdly, costs cannot be forgotten. While it is important to design and fabricate a safe complex, nuclear-type quality cannot be justified.

A. K. Shoemaker (U. S. Steel): I am interested in knowing what background and what type of fracture toughness criteria were used to develop your Charpy V-notch toughness requirements for different yield strengths and plate thicknesses. I would like to call your attention to the fact that there now is a fracture-mechanics-based methodology in combination with a Charpy toughness and fracture mechanics toughness correlation which can be used to develop such toughness requirements (See J. M. Barsom, Engin. Fracture Mech., 1975, vol. 7, pp. 605-618).

O. Draganiuk: Charpy V-notch energy levels were chosen to prevent crack propagation. As I said before, Charpy V-notch testing was the method chosen as the one that is more easily understood and applied in the field. Our requirements were established in 1972-73 and most of the pressure vessels were built in 1974 and 1975, prior to the methodology published in 1975.

K. N. Street (R. M. Hardy and Associates): Why was a design temperature of -39°F selected when the recorded minimum temperature at the site was reported to be -59°F? Does this infer that a finite probability of brittle failure is allowed for in the design and materials selection?

O. Draganiuk: -39°F was set as a project guideline, in that we believe there is approximately a 30 deg F safety factor below the impact test temperature. Many vessels in Alberta operate near these low ambient temperatures without having their materials of construction impact tested at any temperature without any brittle failure. Many of these vessels were not built utilizing fine grain steels as are vessels in present-day construction. ASME code does not require impact testing for vessels whose temperature occasionally drops below -20°F due to ambient temperature. Our design was more conservative than that of the ASME code. Where shock loading is known to occur at -50°F, those items were indeed designed for that operating temperature. Where brittle failure would be of little consequence, e.g. in tailings disposal lines, a risk of brittle failure was accepted, although the possiblity is small because of the high erosion allowance and the low resultant stress. We do not believe we have knowingly taken undue risks in the design.

K. N. Street: You mentioned the rejection of a concrete-lined pipe. Would fiber reinforced concrete have provided you with the necessary enhanced damage resistance in this particular application?

O. Draganiuk: We would have to consider the properties of fiber reinforced concrete before we could reply in the affirmative. Carbon steel was chosen as the first material of construction. There will be many chances and pressures to try the other alternatives or any other designs and materials in the future. The study had supplied some initial data. Other laboratory data plus field data is now required to improve on the system.

SESSION SUMMARY

J. D. Makarchuk

A review of this Session, and particularly the discussion, leads to the conclusion that the necessary changes in specifications pertaining to construction materials must be introduced by promulgation. The authors have pointed out, however, that extensive development programs have been underway to influence current design and material selection concepts, and that some specification changes have taken place as a result of these programs. The industry has, however, not progressed far enough. Acceptance levels related to specific material defects have failed to gain universal acknowledgment, resulting in highly inflated construction costs.

Cotton and Macaulay have provided a prolific "good news - bad news" picture. Within a temperature range of -50°C to 20°C, an excellent material selection guide based on COD tests has been developed, along with a correlation which allows the design engineer a simplistic selectivity approach based on the more economical Charpy-V criterion. But while considerable information has been provided on base material properties, the authors have pointedly identified the need to study the welding and HAZ properties for the purposes of fracture initiation. Germane to this topic is the fact that codes and standards requirements bear little or no relationship to critical flaw size. Discussion brought out the question of crack arrest through high Charpy shelf energy. Mr. Cotton clearly favoured mechanical arrestors and on Friday morning we were shown, via a dramatic film, (Shoemaker et al.) that the high energy approach may be the wrong one. The pipe owners seem not to have achieved unanimity on this question, identifying the need for further study.

Meeting the Aleyeska Pipeline Service Company's support structure specifications has been a readily approachable task by Nippon Kokan. Controlled-rolling techniques, coupled with phosphorus and sulphur suppression, achieve a 24 J minimum energy requirement at -45°C. In thicknesses exceeding 25 mm, controlled rolling is to a major degree replaced by alloying additions. Welding heat imputs have been limited to 4 kJ/mm with a maximum degradation of the Charpy-V energy in the coarse HAZ region of 33%. Nippon Kokan has shown that the technology exists to upgrade the heretofore common steels, and to apply this technology to the processing of difficult steel shapes.

A good degree of experience has provided a basis upon which power transmission lines are constructed. The problems imposed by climatic conditions, service continuity, fabrication and assembly deficiences have been studied in situ and have been reasonably well overcome. The prime construction material being wood, decreases the scope of material selection. It is interesting to note the author's estimation of incremental increase in cost to provide guaranteed continuity of service. One wonders if this same premium would be applicable in other Arctic construction areas.

The investigative program undertaken to develop ditcher teeth capable of performing in permafrost conditions is an excellent example of a scientific approach supplemented by necessary field testing. The correlation between practical success and dynamic or static test methods will undoubtedly provide the materials engineer with a much-needed short-cut for selection optimization. It is encouraging to see the utilization of identical matrix materials in both forged and cast form. Certainly the authors are optimistic that a solution to our future excavation problems is just around the corner.

The Syncrude paper makes it clear that a number of compromises are made when the materials/design engineer has an opportunity to weigh all of the variables influencing selection. Factors such as: personnel safety, production stoppage, re-design necessity, profit and earnings picture, replacement frequency, initial cost, long-term cost, and fabrication familiarity are all considered in conjunction with the basic design criteria question, and the choice made for a "safe" operating mining and extraction complex. An interesting sequel would be the verification of the "best-fit" choice by comparing the fracture mechanics methodology existing today, with the fracture toughness criteria used at the time of the tarsands complex design. Indeed, technology is advancing so rapidly that it would be interesting to use this same comparison for almost any aspect of an Arctic construction project, and analyse the over-or-under safety factor that the materials engineer has "best-guessed".

MATERIALS IN ARCTIC TRANSPORTATION

INTRODUCTION

F. E. King

This session features four speakers who are well qualified to speak on the problems of selection of materials for Arctic transportation. Mr. Maughan, by virtue of his participation in a study entitled "Arctic Oil and Gas by Rail", is qualified to speak on some aspects of material selection discussed by other authors. As keynote speaker, he has deliberately avoided doing so, in order to avoid repetition and to present some other considerations on operating a transportation system in the Arctic. Mr. Maughan describes the climatic conditions and how these affect ground transportation systems. Although the provision of materials having adequate fracture toughness and fatigue properties is important, Mr. Maughan points out that the secondary effects of the Arctic climate such as permafrost, ice in the ground, in the river and in the open sea, the requirements of minimum outdoor maintenance in winter, etc., must be given adequate consideration.

Mr. Deeks discusses the design of railway tank cars for use in Arctic service. He draws on his experience as car designer to assess the possibilities of brittle failure and fatigue failure in cars and in the components under Arctic service conditions. Since railway cars with good fatigue resistance have in the past evolved by cut-and-try rather than by scientific methods, there is a scarcity of good design data available. The field of fracture mechanics appears to have great possibilities for car design, but its application to railway car design problems has been extremely limited. However, since the early 1970's, a tremendous cooperative research effort has been mounted in North America, involving the Association of American Railroads, the equipment manufacturers and carbuilders, the governments of the United States and Canada, and the individual railroads. The information arising out of this joint effort has already been used to improve railway operations and will have considerable impact in the future. Mr. Deeks discusses two reports on fracture mechanics arising out of this joint effort and suggests a procedure involving performance specifications, structural analysis, testing and manufacturing standards which could be used to insure car designs which are both adequate and economical.

Roney and Deno describe how system reliability requirements influence the selection of materials. These reliability requirements are obviously much more demanding for a high traffic density railway. The authors discuss the suitability of materials presently being used for assisting vehicles for the Arctic environment. They show how the application of innovations in equipment design and expanded maintenance programs offer alternatives to expensive materials upgrading.

Tenge and Solli outline their experience with the application of fracture mechanics for the design and construction of liquid natural gas tanks and ships. The subject is covered in considerable detail and is an important contribution to the design and construction of tanks for carrying liquid natural gas; not only in ships, but also in the railroad. The governing principle for an L.N.G. ship is that it should be of fail-safe construction. The structure should leak before failure, and a system for detection and protection against small leaks should be installed in the ships. The authors show how fracture mechanics, when combined with accurate detailed stress analysis, can be used to meet these requirements.

With the exception of the last paper, the papers in this session are oriented toward the railway transportation mode. But what will be the role of aircraft and highway vehicles in the Arctic? In all probability, the role of aircraft and highway vehicles will be a supporting one, although this is by no means a foregone conclusion. In fact, proposals for using giant tanker-type aircraft to move oil and liquid natural gas have been advanced. Certainly aircraft and highway vehicles will play an important role in the transportation of the resources in the Arctic regardless of the mode of transportation selected. Since aircraft operate for most of their flying time in a sub-zero environment, it is unlikely that any important design or material changes will be required. Specialized motor vehicles have also been operative for years in the Arctic and the designers and builders of these vehicles can probably extrapolate their present experience to meet possible future requirements. In view of the above considerations, it is hoped that the absence of papers dealing with the special requirements of these two modes of transportation has not been a serious omission.

MATERIALS SELECTION AND PERFORMANCE IN ARCTIC TRANSPORTATION SYSTEMS

R. G. Maughan
Montreal, Quebec
Canada

If the large quantities of energy, minerals and other riches contained in the Arctic are to be extracted, an effective transportation system will be a fundamental requirement.

The principal characteristics of the unusual Arctic environment are reviewed, including temperature (extremes, means, duration and wind-chill), precipitation, ice and icing, permafrost and the ecology. Their influence on material selection and performance and effectiveness of the transportation system is discussed.

It is apparent that the Arctic entails a total service environment for transportation systems that has a profound effect on materials selection and performance, and on system effectiveness.

INTRODUCTION

Only to a limited extent throughout the world have the resources of the Arctic territories been effectively tapped. In Canada particularly, the large quantities of energy, minerals, and other riches contained within these vast areas remain virtually undeveloped.

As more accessible world supplies are depleted, it can be expected that the demand will grow for extraction of these resources. Effective transportation will be a fundamental requirement for that process, and for the continuing development of the Arctic.

Obviously, no single transportation mode or routing will forever meet all needs. Additions will ultimately become necessary regardless of the initial choice, but these will be constrained by extremely high Arctic construction costs. Careful planning will therefore be necessary to ensure that the maximum possible combination of development needs are met by the mode and routing selected. The utmost care must be taken to ensure that its construction does not unnecessarily prejudice the practicability or economics of the additions which may ultimately be required to meet future demands for a more comprehensive transportation network.

In the meantime, realistic scenarios must be developed for each of the modal candidates. That process must be directed towards maximizing system performance and minimizing cost. Achievement of that goal will demand the optimum in material selection and performance and it is to these matters that this section of the Conference is addressed.

What is it about the Arctic which demands that special care be taken in selection of material design criteria? The answer seems apparent -- the cold.

Such an answer, while correct, is incomplete. To the materials scientist, climate represents a whole spectrum of design considerations. Extremes of temperature are important, but it is the frequency and duration of low temperature thresholds that defines the risk of brittle fracture. Wind loads, wind-chill, rainfall and snowfall are further climatological parameters which profoundly influence transportation system design and performance. The Arctic environment is unique in its secondary climate effects -- permafrost, ice and icing and blowing snow. Each of these phenomena also influences the total service environment in which a material must perform.

Much of the background material for this paper was derived during the Federal Government sponsored study of the feasibility and cost of a railway to move crude oil and natural gas from the Arctic (1).

CLIMATE

It is perhaps not generally appreciated that within the area we generally think of as the Arctic, there are in fact two distinct climatic zones -- Arctic and Northern (Figure 1). The chief distinction between these two climatic zones is not in the winter, which is characteristically long and cold in both, but in the summer, which is cooler in the case of the Arctic zone.

The Arctic climate zone lies north of a line extending inland from the Alaskan North Slope, across the mouth of the Mackenzie River to Churchill, Manitoba, roughly delineating the northern limit of the tree line. In this zone, the summers are colder than those in the Northern zone as a result of the unfavourable influence of the adjacent Arctic seas.

Transportation systems, or elements of them, already exist in both of these climatic zones, but their scale and diversity can be expected to grow. Within the Arctic zone, the Alaskan North Slope

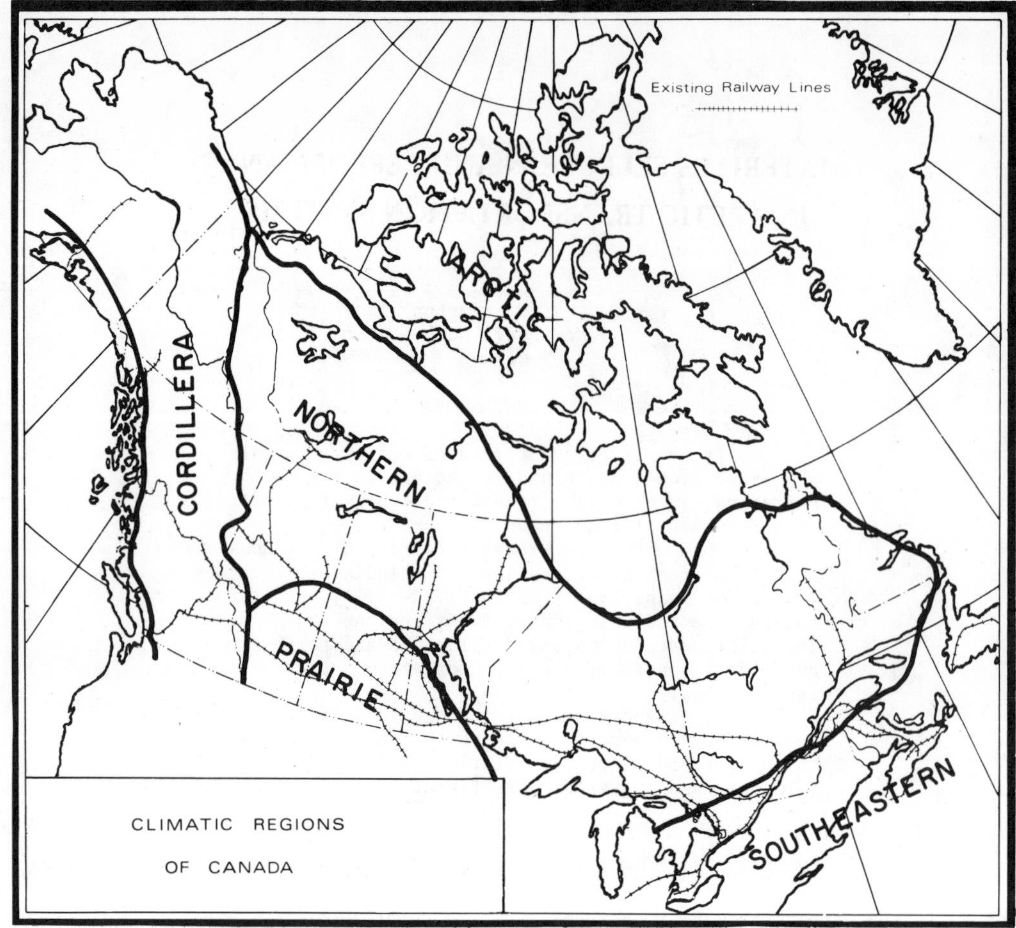

Figure 1: Climatic Regions of Canada (after ref 2)

has already received attention as the possible location for both a pipeline and a railway. Further east in that zone, a pipeline to carry petroleum products from the Arctic Islands area has been examined. There already exists considerable shipping activity within the zone and the possiblity of a much heavier concentration is very real.

Within the Northern zone, the most likely location for transportation systems is the Mackenzie Valley. Highway and marine (barge) transportation modes already exist there, and it has been selected by both the pipeline and railway planners as the location for their respective systems if and when such are built.

Although as already noted there is some difference in the summer temperatures between the two zones, winter temperature conditions within the two are very similar. It is interesting to note (Figure 2) that minimum recorded temperatures in the two zones are not significantly lower than those in other areas of Canada, such as north of Lake Superior where effective road and rail transportation systems have been in operation for many years. As may be seen from Figure 3, however, the mean January minimum temperature for the two zones is somewhat lower than is found in those areas.

Of greater significance than extreme or mean temperatures is the frequency and duration of temperatures below a certain threshold. Figure 4 shows that the area of Canada we are talking about is subject to an appreciably greater number of daily minimum temperatures below -30°F (-34°C) than are most other parts of Canada. The significance of this will be discussed later.

Annual snowfall is not heavy in those parts of either the Arctic or Northern climatic zones in which transportation systems currently exist or might be expected to ultimately exist. On the North Slope, snowfall averages less than 30 in. (760 mm) per year with a normal maximum ground accummulation of 20 in. (510 mm). However, the treeless, open country is exposed to the full force of the prevailing winds from the north, causing the dry, granular, northern snow to blow about, frequently lifting it high enough to create severe visibility problems. The same winds compound the already low temperature problems, producing wind-chill levels much in excess of those normally encountered in populated regions.

In the Mackenzie Valley, the mean annual snowfall is approximately 50 in. (1300 mm) with ground accummulations seldom exceeding 40 in. (1000 mm). There, local topography and the dense forest cover combine to appreciably reduce winter mean wind velocities. The result of this is that the mean January wind chill level in much of the Valley is no worse than in the city of Winnipeg.

DESIGN IMPLICATIONS OF THE ARCTIC CLIMATE

From the designer's standpoint, the first and most obvious factor to consider is the cold. However, highways and railways already operate in areas of Canada where temperatures fall to -50°F (-45°C) and the minimum temperature likely to be encountered by an Arctic transportation system is -70°F (-57°C). Although this is not a great difference in degrees, Figure 5 shows almost 20% of winter days in the areas with which we are concerned have minimums at or below -30°F (-34°C) as compared

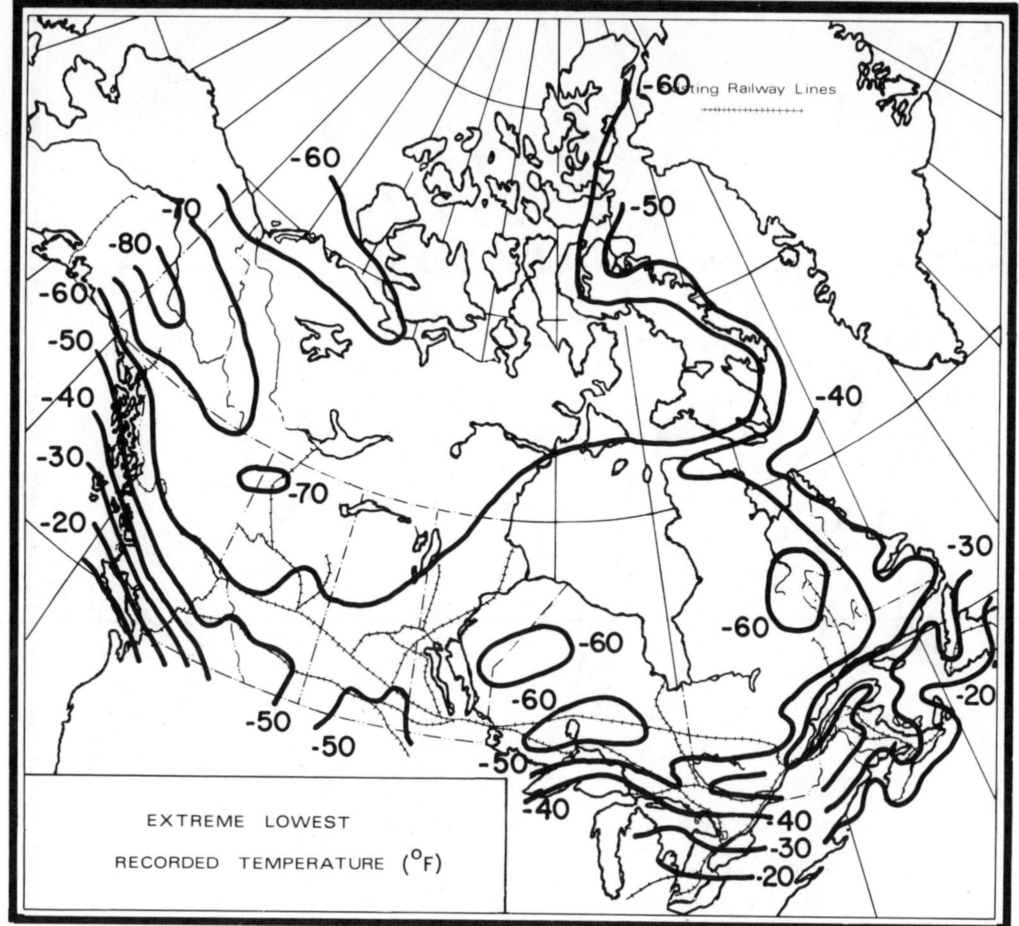

Figure 2: Extreme Lowest Recorded Temperature (after refs. 3.4)

with parts of Northern Ontario, for example, where daily minimums below this temperature occur on only about 3% of the days.

For the materials scientist, this is translated as a higher risk of brittle failures, particularly for materials operating close to the Nil Ductility Temperature, whether they be found in the hulls of tankers or in the shells of tank cars. Particular attention must be given to weldments and the minimization of stress concentrations. The development of improved fracture toughness tests, specifically tailored to materials for Arctic service, may be required.

Transportation equipment is particularly sensitive, as critical components must be protected from high frequencies of brittle failures. Contraction of machine parts and sluggishness of lubricants at low temperatures is a further problem, producing a high frictional drag in equipment. Any air that is allowed to cool, as in the cylinders of idle equipment, is likely to condense moisture. Nonmetallic materials, such as rubber, plastics, glass and leather, in air hoses, tires, windshields and drive belts may become sufficiently brittle to break when flexed or struck.

The requirement for careful materials selection is made more critical by the system reliability demanded because of the time required to obtain replacements parts can be mitigated to some **extent** by careful inventory control but little can be done to ease the hostile outside working conditions.

So-called "comfort classes" for outside working conditions have been developed as follows, and are illustrated in Figure 5.

I Comfortable with normal precaution

II Work and travel become uncomfortable unless properly clothed

III Work and travel become more hazardous unless properly clothed. Heavy outer clothing necessary

IV Unprotected skin will freeze with direct exposure over prolonged period. Heavy outer clothing becomes mandatory

V Unprotected skin can freeze in one minute with direct exposure. Multiple layers of clothing mandatory. Adequate face protection becomes important. Work and travel alone not advisable

VI Adequate face protection becomes mandatory. Work and travel alone prohibited. Supervisors must control exposure times by careful work scheduling

VII Personnel become easily fatigued. Buddy system & observation mandatory

Table 1 represents the percentage frequency of occurrence of the comfort classes at Norman Wells (roughly midway down the Mackenzie Valley) and Inuvik (adjacent to the Mackenzie Delta). These statistics enable estimates to be made of the feasibility and scheduling of outdoor maintenance activities. For example, it can be expected that during January, the coldest month, wind-chills necessitating controlled exposure times and work scheduling will occur 13% of the time at Norman Wells and 5% of the time time at Inuvik. All but emergency operations will likely cease for 1% of the time at Norman Wells, as conditions requiring mandatory observation of

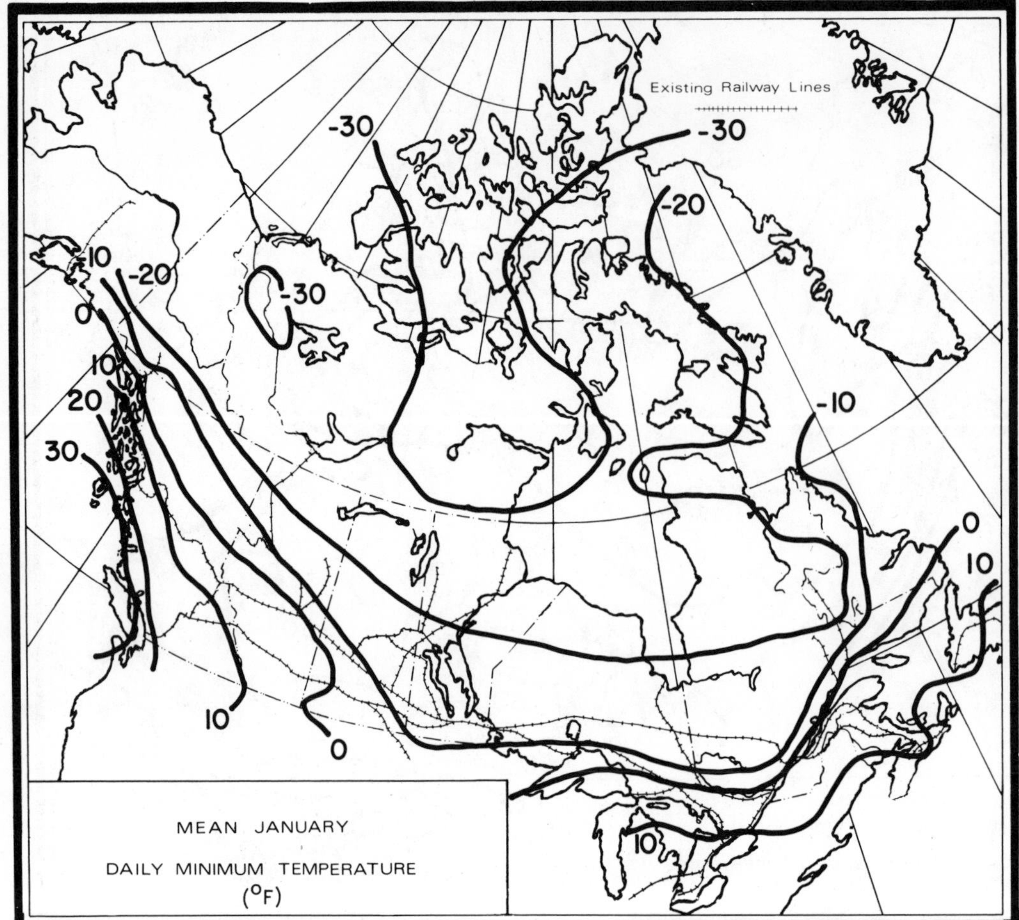

Figure 3: Mean January Daily Minimum Temperature (after refs. 3,4)

personnel will prevail.

Stated somewhat less scientifically, it has been estimated that the general efficiency of outdoor labour at -20°F (-29°C) is reduced to about 25% of that at 70°F (21°C) dependent upon the extent of manual dexterity involved in the maintenance operation. Safety considerations dictate that outside activities come to a halt as -40°F (-40°C) is reached. It is therefore apparent that the transportation system must be designed so that it will operate during the winter months with a minimum of outside maintenance work. For the materials scientist, this probably implies a certain amount of "over-designing" by standards applying in a more temperate environment. Consideration of temperature must pervade all aspects of design, from lubricants through insulation, with the emphasis placed on high system reliability.

SECONDARY EFFECTS OF THE ARCTIC CLIMATE ON DESIGN

Not only is the North currently cold, but it has been cold for thousands of years, and over this time the frost has penetrated into the ground so that large areas of subsoil or rock are now permanently frozen to depths of several hundred feet. The permanently frozen ground is overlain at the surface by an active organic layer, varying in thickness from a few inches to several feet, which thaws annually in summer. This condition, termed "permafrost", varies from isolated zones with a thickness of a few feet, to a continuous layer 1,000 to 1,500 ft (300 to 450 m) thick along the Arctic coast.

In all permafrost zones, careless construction

TABLE 1

PERCENTAGE FREQUENCY OF OCCURRENCE OF COMFORT CLASSES DUE TO A COMBINATION OF ALL HOURLY WIND SPEEDS AND TEMPERATURE

STATION: Norman Wells Airport (1957-1966)

	COMFORT CLASS						
Month	I	II	III	IV	V	VI	VII
Jan	1	20	19	20	26	13	1
Feb	1	25	22	22	24	6	*
Mar	5	31	22	18	14	2	*
Apr	22	44	13	7	3	*	
May	22	27	2	*			
June	22	26					
July	7	8					
Aug	17	20					
Sept	55	19	*				
Oct	29	47	10	3	*	*	
Nov	5	38	28	19	9	1	*
Dec	1	26	26	20	20	7	*

STATION: Inuvik Airport (1961-1970)

	COMFORT CLASS						
Month	I	II	III	IV	V	VI	VII
Jan	1	27	25	22	20	5	*
Feb	3	28	25	19	21	4	*
Mar	5	31	26	17	17	2	*
Apr	12	43	20	10	7	1	
May	41	45	5	1	*		
June	34	11	*				
July	25	4					
Aug	32	8	*				
Sept	25	28	*	*			
Oct	26	8	52	2	*	*	
Nov	7	58	24	15	7	*	
Dec	2	32	27	19	18	2	*

* Indicates less than 0.5%

Source: B.M. Burns, Climate of the Mackenzie Valley-Beaufort Sea - Vol. 1

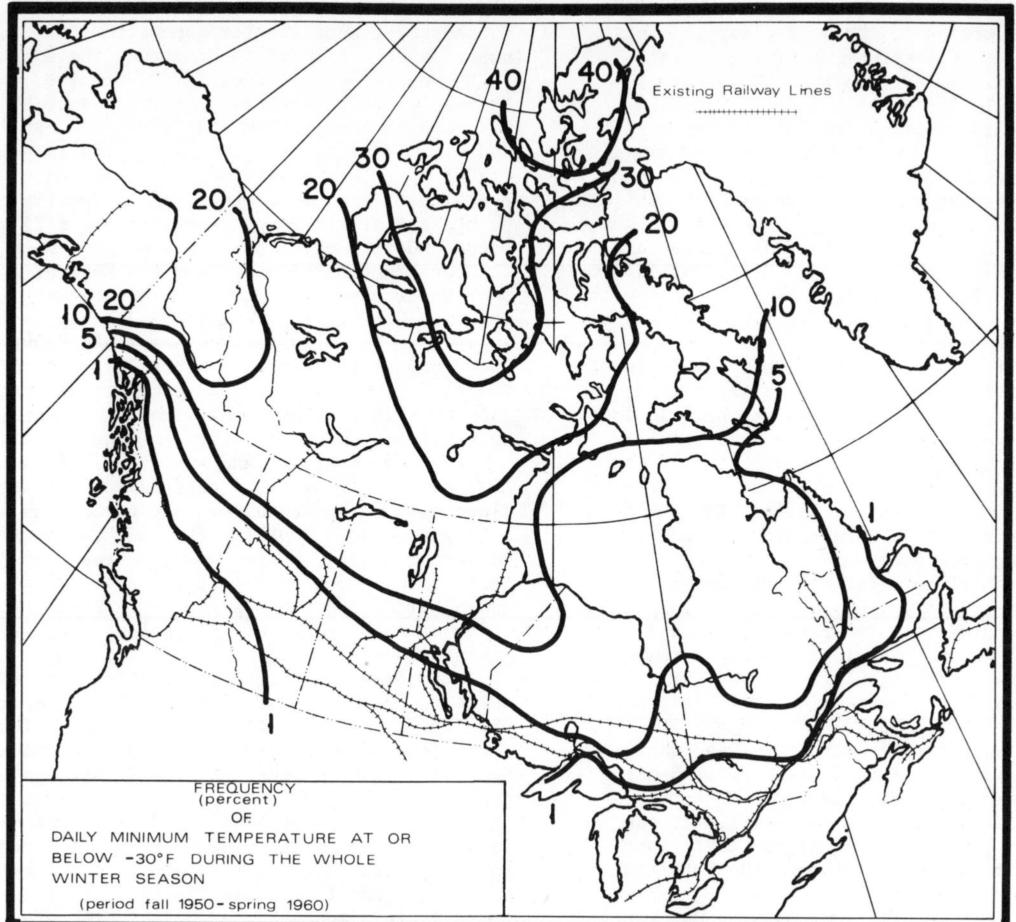

Figure 4: Frequency (per cent) of Daily Minimum Temperature at or below -30°F during the whole winter season (after refs. 3,4)

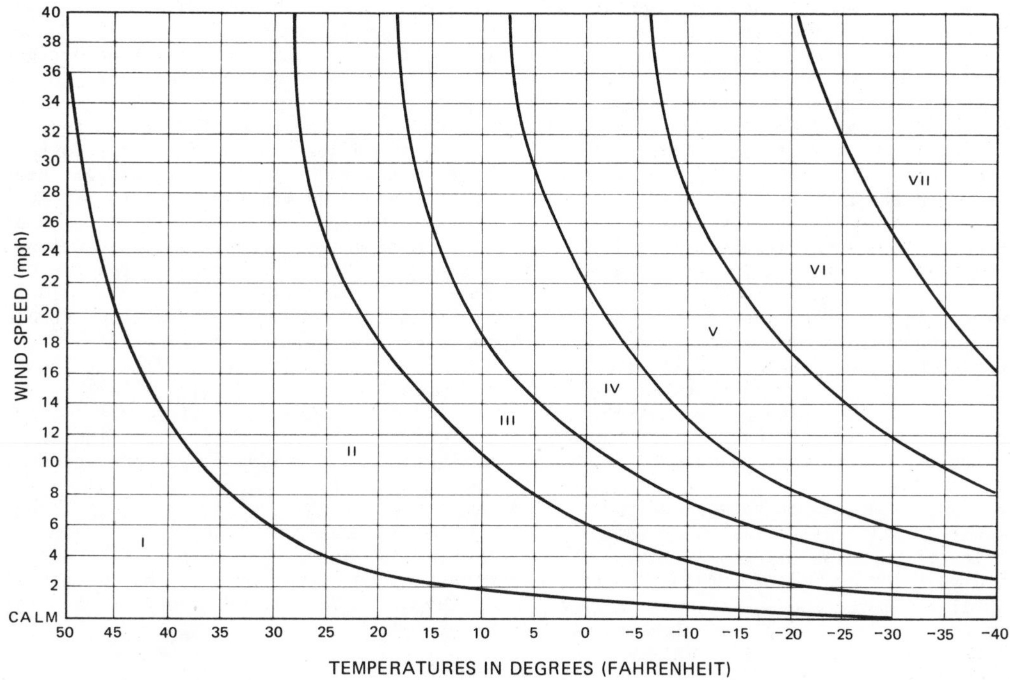

Figure 5: Temperature/Wind Chill Index (after ref. 5)

procedures can drastically alter the thickness and geotechnical properties of the active layer. This occurs as a result of compression of the organic ground cover by fills, or even by vehicles, thus reducing its insulating value and permitting the top layers of frozen material to melt during the summer. This melting is accompanied by settlement of the ground surface due to draining and thaw consolidation of subgrade soils. Clearing of brush and trees will have the same adverse effect on the temperature balance, and for that reason fires are especially serious in these areas. Differential settlement obviously has important implications with respect to structural integrity and hence for materials selection.

In this regard, precipitation is an indirect factor. The interruption of natural surface and subsurface drainage by a rightofway may have serious consequences if adequate alternative drainage is not provided. Ponding of water on one side of the rightofway causes increased absorption of solar radiation, creating a warmer subsurface temperature regime which can result in accelerated degradation of the underlying permafrost.

Precipitation through infiltration results in the formation of ice lenses in some soils under severe winter conditions. The resultant annual "frost heaving" is well known to residents of even temperate, continental climates, particularly in the form of latewinter heaves in highway surfaces. This type of frost heave is attributable to the migration of soil moisture toward the "freeze front" as frost penetrates subsurface soil or fills. Frost heaving is usually nonuniform because of local differences in soil and its moisture characteristics. It can be expected that artificially changed temperature gradients would materially influence the rate and extent of differential heaving.

Due to their capacity for drawing up water from below the frost line, ice layers can contain far more water than the volume originally available in the soil. This is the case with ice layers in permafrost ground. Such layers may in some cases comprise most of the volume of the soil mass near the ground surface. As a result, when soil containing ice layers is thawed, a great deal of excess water can be squeezed out by the weight of overburden, causing settlement of the ground surface. If the ground ice in permafrost is present in the form of vertical ice wedges, several feet thick at the top but thin at the bottom, as commonly occurs, surface thawing of the ground will result in considerable loss of volume in the form of sinkholes.

In the absence of specific provision for thermal protection, it seems inevitable that the infrastructure for any type of ground transportation system in the Arctic will be subjected to significant differential heaving in the winter and cumulative subsidence in the summer. The proper design of thermal protection, whether by granular fills or manufactured materials, involves sophisticated engineering techniques. Provision of adequate protection involes a substantial increase in construction costs as compared with corresponding work in nonpermafrost areas.

A basic requirement common to many of the fixed installations of all transportation systems is large quantities of granular materials - sand and gravel or crushed rock for concrete, for subgrades of highways, pipeline service roads, railways and airport runways, for wearing surfaces of highways and pipeline installations. The quality and availability of these materials can profoundly influence the performance and cost of all transportation modes.

Prosaic though this matter may appear, it has a particular importance in Arctic territories because of the general scarcity of these materials. Furthermore, much greater quantities than usual are needed there in order to construct the supporting fills, up to several feet thick, required to provide thermal protection where permafrost must be preserved. To compound the problem even more, the usual "cut and fill" construction techniques are largely precluded by the necessity to avoid thawing of the permafrost, and consequently an abnormally high percentage of the large quantities of fill material needed must be obtained from sources remote from the construction site. Along the Mackenzie Valley, sources of hard rock for crushing are very limited. The only potential material of adequate quality appears to be dolomite rock available from some locations in the Franklin Mountains some miles to the east of the Valley. On the Alaskan North Slope, good rock is available only from the mountains five to ten miles south of the coast line.

Good quality sand and gravel are not abundant. Limited sources of these materials are scattered along the Mackenzie Valley as far north as approximately Fort Good Hope (at the Southern apex of the Mackenzie Delta), but are very scarce throughout the remaining 300 mile (480 km) distance to the Mackenzie Delta. On the Alaskan North Slope they are somewhat more abundant, in inactive river flood plains.

Compounding the difficulties created by the scarcity of these basic construction materials in the Arctic is the absence of roads or railways over which to transport them to the work location. The Mackenzie Highway, when completed, will be an exception to this, but its presence will not preclude the need for large expenditures for service roads to gain access to material sources. The necessity to comply with rigid environmental regulations will add significantly to that financial burden.

River and sea ice in the North present very significant design problems for transportation systems. Because the Mackenzie River flows south to north, the first melting occurs at the headwaters in the south, and until the river mouth in the north is free of ice --several weeks later -- massive ice jams can result. Normal water levels can rise by 45 to 50 ft (14 to 15 m). The effect on bridge and dock structures that have not been designed to accommodate this annual rampage needs no elaboration. Buried pipeline crossings require particular attention due to the distinct possibility of ice scouring.

Consideration of ice conditions likely to be encountered will of course affect the material selection and design for ships to be employed in Arctic service. Their hulls must be capable of withstanding the enormous forces developed as the vessel makes its way through sheet ice or pressure ridges. Equally important, they should be able to withstand the pressures encountered should the vessel be beset and forced to remain that way for some time. The crushing strength of Arctic ice has been recorded at up to 900 psi (6.2 MPa).

The Siamese twin of permafrost is the delicate ecological balance of the area. The same climate that produces permafrost produces an ecology that must continually fight for survival. Imprudent action can bring devastating results to the land surface and to the transportation system occupying that land. Service failures, for example, take on particular significance if they entail the operation of repair equipment or vehicles over unprotected terrain.

SUMMARY

It is apparent that the Arctic entails a total service environment that has much more of an effect on materials selection for transportation systems than simply the provision of adequate fracture toughness and low temperature fatigue properties. The designer must be prepared to consider how the secondary effects of the Arctic climate the permafrost phenomenon, and the formation of ice in the ground, in rivers, and in the open sea affects his selection of materials. He must also keep in mind the necessity of creating a highly reliable system that will function with the minimum of outdoor maintenance in winter. Finally, the materials engineer must have an understanding of how to tailor his design to jointly complement the delicate Arctic environment and protect the integrity of the transportation system.

These objectives are all compatible with careful and conservative materials selection. With these considerations in mind, the following papers discuss some specific solutions to materials problems posed by the peculiar environment of the Arctic.

REFERENCES

1. R. G. Maughan, J. S. Smith and R. W. Lake: "Arctic Oil and Gas by Rail", Transport Canada, 1974, vol. 1-6.
2. "The Climate of Canada", Meteorological Branch, Department of Transport, 1960.
3. M. K. Thomas, Climatological Atlas of Canada, 1953.
4. M. G. Hagglund and H. A. Thompson: "A Study of Sub-Zero Canadian Temperatures", Meteorological Branch, Department of Transport, 1964.
5. B. M. Burns: "The Climate of the Mackenzie Valley-Beaufort Sea", vol. 1, Environment Canada, 1973.

DISCUSSION

L. Luyckx (Reactive Metals): When a railroad is being built on permafrost, is there any Canadian Government regulation which specifies maximum heat transfer through the bedding or roadbed to limit the damage to the permafrost?

R. G. Maughan To the best of my knowledge, no. The major considerations are economic, to reduce maintenance costs.

A. Glover (Canadian Welding Development Institute): In a railway system for the Arctic, is it envisaged that continuous welded rail will be used? How do you propose to overcome the difference in summer expansion and winter contraction?

R. G. Maughan: Yes, the problem of differential temperatures (summer vs winter) would be less severe in the Arctic, with winter minimum say of -70°F and summer maximum of 60°F; a difference of 130 deg F. In Manitoba, the difference can be 150 to 160 deg F and adequate rail anchorage takes care of that differential.

W. M. Drope (Northern Engineering Services): Where did you get your information that there was no gravel in the Arctic?

R. G. Maughan: I did not say that there was no gravel in the Arctic. I said that good quality sand and gravel are not abundant. Limited sources exist along the Mackenzie Valley as far north as approximately Fort Good Hope but are very scarce throughout the remaining distance to the Mackenzie Delta. On the Alaskan north slope they are somewhat more abundant, in inactive river flood plains. To some extent, availability is limited by restrictive environmental regulations which can preclude use of river gravels.

D. James (Indian Affairs and Northern Development: Does the 25% efficiency figure apply only to totally exposed manual labour?

R. G. Maughan: Essentially, yes. It would not apply, for example, to work being done by a machine operator in a heated cab - except to the extent that the machine itself was affected by low temperatures.

D. James: Would you please elaborate on the -40°F safety cut-off. Does it too apply just to total exposure?

R. G. Maughan: Again, essentially yes, although also dependent upon whether or not the man is working alone.

J. E. Rymes (J. E. Rymes Engineering): To state that work must stop for safety reasons at -40°F is just not true. A review of northern and high Arctic operations (e.g. drilling) will reveal the mis-statement.

MATERIAL SELECTION FOR KEY COMPONENTS OF RAILROAD CARS DESTINED TO SERVE IN THE ARCTIC

R. G. Deeks
Procor Ltd.
Oakville, Ontario
Canada

Materials presently specified for key components of tank cars are reviewed. Arctic service conditions are compared with those normally experienced in southern Canada. Material selection is seen to be improved by the application of fracture mechanics concepts. Test methods, inspection and any factors affecting service safety are indicated, with a proposal for the methodology of future designs.

INTRODUCTION

The Canadian Institute of Guided Ground Transport, The Canadian National Railway and Canadian Pacific Railway have all considered the concept of a railway to move oil and gas from the Arctic to more southerly points of Canada. The reports issued vary in depth but in general conclude that the project is technically feasible and recommend that further study be carried out. While this paper is oriented to the selection of materials for Arctic service, it is also necessary to discuss the design aspects of railway vehicles which must operate under the conditions of the proposed Arctic railway.

TANK CAR CLASSIFICATION

Broadly speaking, tank cars may be classified as either pressure or non-pressure types. The products which are carried in these cars are again broadly divided into two categories, regulated and unregulated. The regulated commodities are those which necessitate caution in handling due to their fire risk, toxicity, corrosion characteristics or vapour pressure. Some regulated commodities like propane combine both fire risk and have a relatively high vapour pressure at normal ambient temperature. Such commodities are classed as flammable compressed gases.

Products like gasoline and solvents primarily present a fire risk. A product such as anhydrous ammonia presents both a toxic and vapour pressure risk. A typical example of an unregulated commodity is residual fuel oil ("bunker oil"). The bodies which decide whether a product is to be regulated or unregulated are the Canadian Transport Commission in Canada and the Department of Transport in the USA. The same bodies lay down the specification to which a railway car must be designed and manufactured if they are to carry a regulated commodity. The American Association of Railroads (A.A.R.) issues specifications governing cars for unregulated commodities as well as all the other railway equipment involved such as running gear, draft gear, and brake equipment. An Arctic railway would provide a means of transportation for regulated and unregulated commodities in both non-pressure and pressure tank cars.

OPERATING CONDITIONS

In the studies referred to above it was assumed that the minimum temperature which will occur is -70°F (-57°C) and that the annual distance travelled will be as high as 200,000 mile (320,000 km). A mileage accumulation of this magnitude virtually demands the use of unit train movement in order to achieve maximum equipment utilisation. This mileage is about ten times the annual mileage of cars in interchange service and twice as much as those presently used in unit train service. Cars which are in interchange service are subject to impacting in hump yards but are not generally subjected to the train loads that apply in the case of cars in unit train service.

This is because a mixed train consist is not comprised of cars which are all loaded to their maximum capacity as is the case with unit trains. Unit trains of 10,000 ton total capacity are quite common and some are even as high as 15,000 ton capacity. With the utilisation envisaged, the necessity of thorough fatigue analysis requires consideration of the dynamic forces from train action which produces loading due to run in, run out and rock and roll. However, the topography of the route travelled has a large bearing on these considerations, but in this respect the Arctic conditions are relatively mild when compared, for example, with unit trains crossing the Rocky Mountains.

BRITTLE FAILURE

The severity of loading together with the very low temperature naturally gives rise to the risk of brittle failure. It has been the author's experience that while a number of catastrophic brittle failures have occurred with static storage tanks, very few incidents have occurred with railway vehicles. The author has seen only two catastrophic brittle failures in tank cars, one of these was in an old forge-welded chlorine car and the other in a ferritic stainless nitric acid car. Catastrophic brittle failures which have occured as a result of high speed impacts during the course of a derailment can be discounted since the strain rates involved are so great that ductile failure is unlikely. Even for the latter conditions there have not been very many catastrophic brittle failures. However, cracks are quite common in railway car sills and these generally vary in length from about 3 in. (76 mm) to 9 in. (230 mm) which upon metallurgical examination have proven to be brittle failures. There have also been a number of cases of fatigue initiation and brittle propagation resulting in cracks of several feet in length. The steels used in all of these cases have shown transition temperatures in the region of 50°F (10°C) to 65°F (18°C) and failures occurred under winter ambient temperatures. When the propagation velocity of a brittle crack is considered, it is also evident that this type of crack must be of low energy and is apparently quite easily stopped by whatever crack-arresting mechanism happens to be present -- most frequently, a transverse weld. For brittle failure to occur, a tensile stress of sufficient magnitude, a stress raiser and brittle material at the specific ambient temperature must all be present simultaneously, and perhaps it is this that has kept the incidence very low. In the case of flammable compressed gases, the hoop stress increases with increasing temperature but so also does the notch toughness of the steel. Therefore the maximum hoop stress can never occur together with a brittle condition of the shell material. However, the train loads always exist whether the car is loaded or not, and no matter what the ambient temperature happens to be.

FATIGUE CONSIDERATIONS

At present, there is insufficient data to enable thorough fatigue analysis to be carried out. It is necessary to know the magnitude and sense of all the loading that can occur and the frequency with which any part of the load spectrum is applied. However, the U.S. Department of Transport and the A.A.R. are both presently involved in track train dynamic studies which, it is hoped, will provide the necessary information. In the author's experience, the most frequently encountered initiation of a brittle crack has been due to fatigue. Workmanship factors such as arc strikes, weld undercut and burning notches have not generally been responsible for crack initiation. Railway cars have been developed with good fatigue resistance but by "cut and try", rather than scientific methods. It is unfortunate that what appears from experience to be the most likely cause of crack initiation is lacking in necessary design data, but perhaps this will be satisfied by work presently in progress.

EXPERIENCE WITH EXISTING STEEL SPECIFICATIONS

Most non-pressure general purpose cars are fabricated from ASTM A285C, A515 Grade 70 or A516 Grade 70 steels. The first two of these steels would definitely not be used in the Arctic since their normal transition temperature is too high. A516 Grade 70 however, may, in the normalized condition, be very satisfactory. This would be certainly the case for a car carrying a hot material such as residual fuel oil. A516 Grade 70 has given excellent service with no known failures for pressure cars in such ladings as liquid carbon dioxide and anhydrous hydrogen chloride. For these latter products, the material is ordered in the normalized condition and is impact tested at -50°F (-46°C) using full-size Charpy specimens with an average of 15 ft lbf (20 J) obtained from three specimens, and a minimum of 10 ft lbf (14 J) from any one specimen.

Pressure cars are also fabricated from TC128B material, which is a steel specification contained in the tank car specifications of A.A.R. This steel is somewhat similar to A516 Grade 70 but with a low alloy addition giving higher yield and ultimate strength. This material has also been used in the normalized condition and impact tested for cold service similar to A516 Grade 70. Cryogenic cars usually have a carbon steel exterior tank fabricated from one of the previously mentioned steels and the inner tank is invariably an austenitic stainless steel, most frequently Type 304.

The standard materials specified for the car sills are ASTM A572 or A441. Neither of these materials is suitable for Arctic service, since both exhibit relatively high transition temperatures in the as-rolled condition.

Couplers, yokes and knuckles are available in an AAR specification M211 Grade E and this is probably suitable for Arctic service. Draft gears are usually of the friction or elastomeric type and some low temperature testing will probably need to be done to determine the suitability of these components. Trucks may be satisfactory in carbon steel if normalized, but may need to be cast in 2 to 3% nickel steel. Low temperature testing will be advisable with these components. Wheels are made from a steel specification which is not particularly desirable for low temperatures and further research will be needed. Axles are probably satisfactory to the present specifications. Truck springs are another component that will probably need testing. It will be necessary to carry out a thorough test programme in view of the extremely large number of cars anticipated (from 10,000 to 20,000 has been suggested). The objective should be to establish railway cars which have integrity for the operating conditions and which can be produced as economically as possible.

FRACTURE MECHANICS

In recent years, developments in the field of fracture mechanics promise the design engineer information of much greater value than has existed in the past. In particular, two reports (1,2) deal with current and formerly-used steels for tank cars and with both brittle failure analysis and problems resulting from geometric instability as a result of derailment damage. The reports also deal with the cars being involved in a fire environment as a result of damage caused by derailment.

In one study (1) four specific toughness tests were carried out. These were Charpy V-notch (CV) Drop weight test (NDT), Drop weight tear test (DWTT), and Dynamic tear test (DT). Table 1 shows the averaged results of the four tests for TC-128B and ASTM 515-70 in various metallurgical conditions.

The dynamic tear 50% shear area transition temperature and the drop weight tear test 80% shear area transition temperature can be seen to be reasonably close. There is an average temperature of 75°F (24°C) for the dynamic tear 50% shear area transition temperature and an average temperature of 84°F (29°C) for the Drop weight tear test 80% shear area transition temperature. This suggests that the Dynamic Tear 50% shear area transition temperature provides an indication of the full scale ductile to brittle transition temperature provided that the test specimen thickness is close to the tank thickness.

Table 1

Average Fracture Toughness Properties of Shell and Head Plate Alloys†

	Charpy V-Notch Impact Test					Drop Weight Test	Dynamic Tear Test			
	15 ft lbf (20 J) temp.	50% shear temp.	15-mil lateral expansion	Shelf Energy ft lbf(J) trans.	long.	80% shear transition	Plateau Energy ft lbf (J) trans.	long.	50% shear transition	50% max energy transition
AAR TC128 Grade B										
Shell Plate (rolled and normalised and stress relief)	2°F(-17°C)	57°F(14°C)	4°F(-16°C)	41(56)	72(98)	84°F(29°C)	331(445)	554(750)	92°F(33°C)	75°F(24°C)
(rolled and normalise and stress relief)	-72°F(-58°C)	-32°F(-36°C)	-50°F(-46°C)	58(79)	99(134)		400(542)	810(1098)	35°F(2°C)	25°F(-4°C)
Head Plate (various treatment)	-16°F(-27°C)	3°F(-16°C)	-9°F(-23°C)	46(62)	61(83)	83°F(28°C)	363(492)	502(680)	51°F(11°C)	46°F(8°C)
ASTM A515 Grade 70 Shell Plate (rolled and stress relief)	3°F(-16°C)	49°F(9°C)	8°F(-13°C)	40(54)	78(106)		281(380)	505(684)	76°F(24°C)	77°F(25°C)
Head Plate	20°F(-7°C)	55°F(13°C)	10°F(12°C)	47(64)	72(98)		325(440)	473(641)	94°F(34°C)	87°F(30°C)
ASTM A516 Grade 70 (rolled and normalise and stress relief)*	-20°F(-29°C)	5°F(-15°C)	-40°F(-40°C)	40(54)	89(121)	85°F(29°C)	340(461)	640(868)	55°F(13°C)	33°F(1°C)

* one sample only; † (after ref. 1)

Individual measurements of the Dynamic Tear transition temperature were 50 deg F (28 deg C) to 125 deg F (69 deg C) above the Charpy V-notch 15 ft lbf (20 J) or 10 mil lateral expansion values. This is partly due to the different specimen thicknesses. However, the dynamic tear test provides true transition temperatures significantly higher than the arbitrary 15 ft lbf (20 J) Charpy V-notch temperature.

The dynamic tear test appears to be the most useful tool to the design engineer in assessing the risk of brittle failure in relationship to stress level and operation temperature.

Figure 1 illustrates the salient features of dynamic tear (DT) transition curves (2). It can be seen that the fracture mode changes from flat to brittle to gross yielding. The force-time plots (inset) show the initial load for break on first contact and the load required to continue the fracture. It is of interest to note the relatively high loads required to initiate the crack and the sudden load drop required to propagate the crack at the NDT point, compared with the much more gradual force decay at the gross yielding point. The yield criterion is shown as the point YC, which is the point at which yield level stresses are required for continuation of a through-thickness crack.

Figure 2 shows a summary of test results (2) demonstrating a clear separation of the transition bands of the as-rolled and stress-relieved specimens from the normalized and stress-relieved specimens. Figure 3 shows the fracture properties superimposed on the fracture bands of Figure 2. The three types of behaviour represent brittle or plain strain frac-

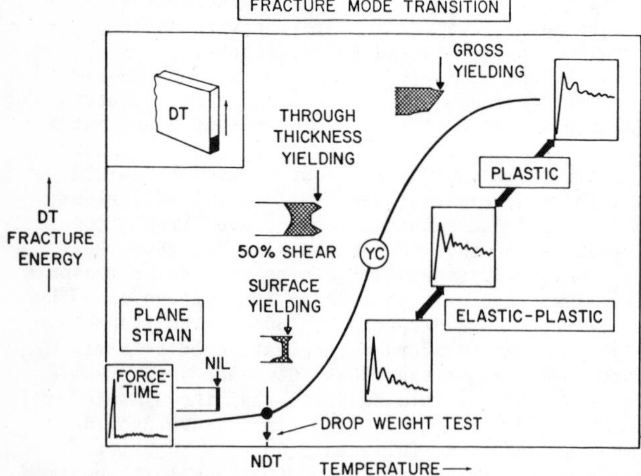

Figure 1: Features of Dynamic Tear Transition Curves (after ref. 2)

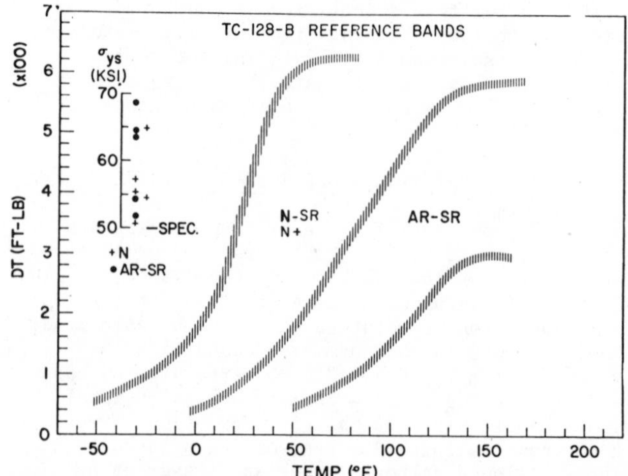

Figure 2: Summary of Alloy TC128B Reference Bands (after ref. 2)

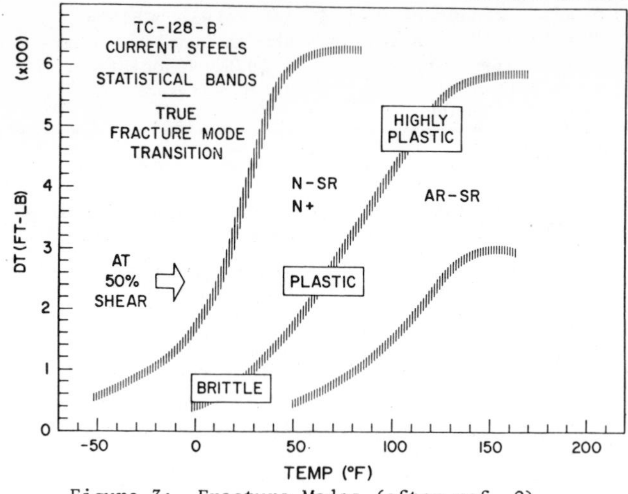

Figure 3: Fracture Modes (after ref. 2)

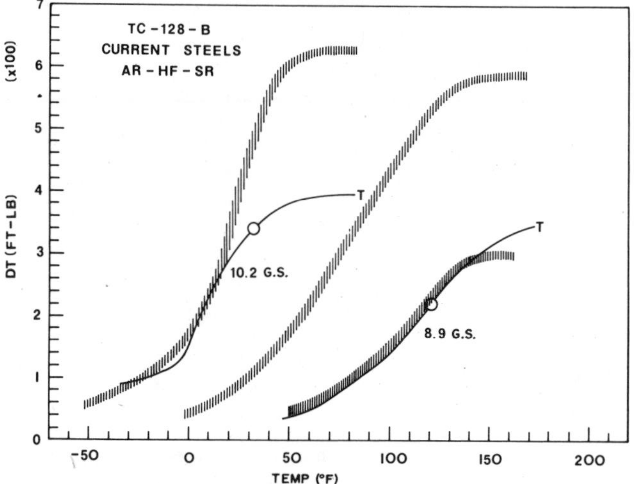

Figure 4: Dynamic Tear Curves Superimposed on Reference Bands (after ref. 2)

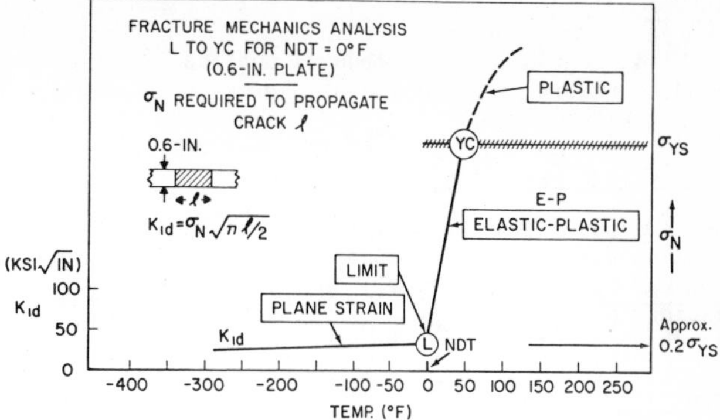

Figure 5: Fracture Mechanics Interpretation of Transition Curves (after ref. 2)

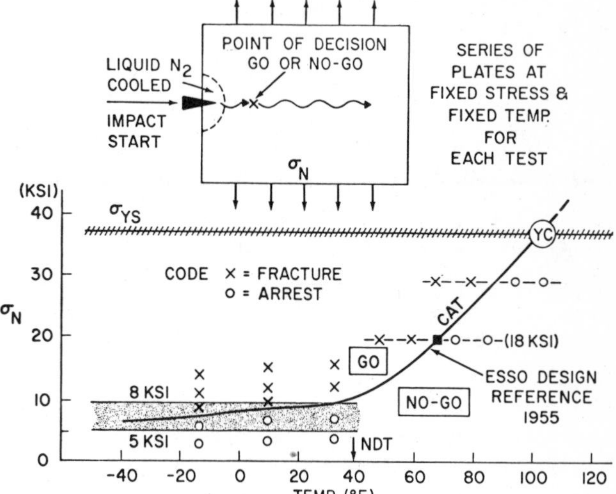

Figure 6: Typical Robertson Crack Arrest Curve (after ref. 2)

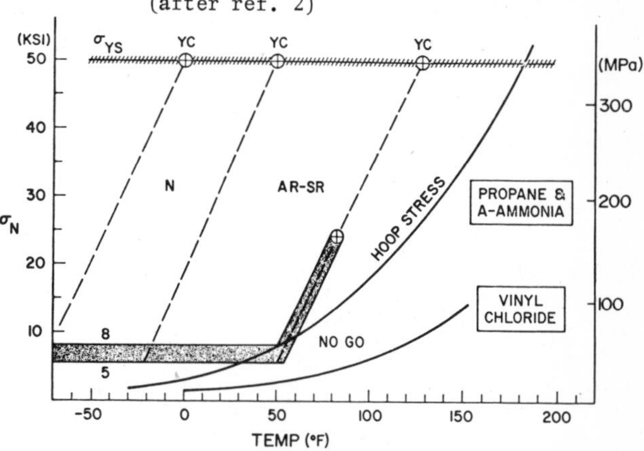

Figure 7: Actual Hoop Stress -- Temperature Relationship compared with Stress to Propagate Fractures in Tank Cars (after ref. 2)

ture, the YC level or plastic properties, and highly plastic properties.

Figure 4 shows the tested properties of two samples M17 and M19 (YS 46 ksi, 386 MPa), superimposed on the fracture bands (2). Both samples were from hot-formed steel. M17 had an ASTM grain size 10.2, but M19 had a grain size of 8.9, which explains why it falls into the as-rolled-and-stress-relieved band. It appears that M19 had been exposed to excessively high temperature, resulting in large pearlite colonies. There was such good agreement between grain size and the locations in the as-rolled or normalized bands in these tests, that micrographic examination could be used in lieu of physical tests to place the steel in a particular fracture band.

Figure 5 shows the fracture mechanics interpretation of the transition curves. The most interesting feature is that stress level, shown on the right ordinate, can be related to the temperature and the fracture behaviour. This information is extremely valuable to the design engineer.

Figure 6 is a crack arrest curve, showing the stress-temperature relationship for the "GO" fracture condition above the curve and the "NO GO" fracture condition below the curve. When the relationship between hoop stress and fracture characteristics with temperature is superimposed on the crack arrest curve (Figure 7) it can be seen that the hoop stress is on the "NO GO" side of the required stress to propagate fracture.

The fracture mechanics approach therefore permits the metallurgist to provide information which can be directly adopted for stress analysis and materials selection. The particular results referred to above are significant enough to suggest a new design approach to the problem of railway cars in Arctic service. It is clear that the materials presently used for tank car construction are unsatisfactory for Arctic service, with the possible exception of hot-product service. It will probably be necessary to look to one of the nickel steels for satisfactory low temperature characteristics.

CONCLUSION

In conclusion a procedural outline is suggested to ensure car designs which provide integrity together with economy.

Specification Committee

A specification committee should be established to agree on a performance type specification which can be used for the car and its components. Existing specifications may be used as a guide but considerable changes will be necessary.

Structural Analysis

The original analysis should be made making use of the most modern techniques. Finite element analysis is an example of this approach but at this time insufficient elements have been developed to make a precise determination.

Static Test

An indoor test facility with a squeeze capability of 1,000,000 lbf (4,500,000 N) and computerised strain gauge readout should be established. Initially a brittle lacquer test should be conducted to determine strain gauge locations. This should be a very thorough test to establish stress patterns and compare with finite element analysis. It would also be desirable to review the analysis in the light of test results.

Running Test

A running test should be conducted in which the magnitude and frequency of stress levels for all components can be established. The test should preferably be conducted over similar terrain, and the car used with a similar unit train movement, to that expected in service.

Fatigue Testing

It will be desirable to fatigue test all components in the light of the running test results.

Manufacturing Standards

It is most important to set up quality control standards to which the cars will be inspected. Particular care will be necessary to avoid weld undercut, burning, notches, etc. Non-destructive testing methods must be established.

Metallurgical Testing

Dynamic tear tests should be carried out on those materials which metallurgists consider to have the greatest possibility of satisfying the operating conditions. The results should be provided to the design engineers in a form similar to that reported above.

The prospect of an Arctic railway is a very exciting one to the engineer, since the northland could be opened up as a result of such a railway in a manner similar to that provided to the more southerly parts of Canada by the east-west transcontinental railway.

REFERENCES

1. "Material study on steels used in current and former tank car construction and from cars involved in accidents", 1975 Association of American Railroads, Report RA-03-5-33(AAR R-193), Chicago
2. "Fracture Properties of Tank Car Steels -- Characterization and Analysis", 1975, Association of American Railroads, Report RA-03-4-32 (AAR R-192), Chicago.

DISCUSSION

C. Parrini (Italsider): How do you think it would be possible to utilize the experience in developing steels for pipes to the applications you have discussed, for example, controlled rolling, low carbon steels?

R. G. Deeks: I think the work that has been done in the development of pipeline steels is extremely useful. However, one difference with our materials is that they are subjected to dynamic loading. I think we could start by selecting materials based on their properties for pipelines but we must in addition test them for their dynamic properties due to the nature of the loading experienced by railroad cars.

A. Glover (Canadian Welding Development Institute): I would just like to say as a metallurgist that you are going to have to design your tank cars either on initiation or propagation, depending on what you are going to carry in them. You will not be able to use a unified approach for everything you want to carry, for example, oil products, LNG products and gas.

R. G. Deeks: It is true that the same considerations as for pipelines could apply to the pressure vessel of a tank car. However, as I indicated in the paper, we are not only concerned with hoop stresses and longitudinal stresses in the pressure vessel. In my experience the more significant stresses are those that are related to the load input as a consequence of the train action. We consider extremely high stresses on railroad cars. For example, the AAR standard test is a one million pound static squeeze held for 60 s, or 1.25 x 10^6 lbf impact as measured on a dynamometer coupler. The stress levels in cars are controlled more by these factors than by the product contained in the car. The nature of the product relates primarily to the degree of hazard that any tank car failure might produce.

L. Luyckx (Reactive Metals and Alloys): You mentioned steels in various conditions, such as semi-killed, full-killed and normalized, etc. and effective grain size. I would like to suggest that when considering various steelmaking practices, more consideration be given to inclusion control, which you have not mentioned. Inclusion control can assist in lowering the transition temperature improving the transverse impact and weldability, laminar tearing resistance, for example.

R. G. Deeks: Sometimes I feel that too many of our steel specifications are oriented to mill practices on the assumption that if they miss one specification they will hit another. For example, I had a case of a 285 C plate with stringer inclusions in it and when we welded it under 100% X-ray quality we kept opening up cracks and yet the mill insisted that it met the specification, which it did -- except you could not weld it without cracks opening up. I agree that the control of inclusions is very important.

L. Luyckx: Very often one is willing to spend $50 a ton for normalization but one is not willing to spend the $12 a ton required for inclusion control.

R. G. Deeks: I agree.

G. L. Archer (The Welding Institute): Is it your experience that the fractures you have seen in welded cars have started in welded areas and if this is so, are you going to give these some attention in evaluating the fracture toughness of the weld metal and heat affected zone?

R. G. Deeks: We have done a large amount of testing on weld metals and I wish the steels we use would have as good properties as the weld metals. The heat affected zone, however, is a different matter. Most of the fatigue initiations that we see are adjacent to fillet welds securing either the reinforcing plate to which the sill is attached or the head shoe which takes the vertical force. I don't think it is so much a problem of the weld as of the stress concentrations in those critical areas of the cars. Certainly, there is a need for some redesign of cars to avoid these regions, but also we are going to need steels with better fatigue properties and brittle fracture characteristics. More research is definitely necessary and we are proposing to build a simulator in which we will get dynamic and stress level input from ride trials and feed them into a computer to determine optimum design against fatigue. I don't think that fillet welding will be a problem in that regard once we know what the stress pattern is.

T. Kunitake (Sumitomo Metal Industries): For components used in a cold climate, the fracture toughness should be one of the most important properties, therefore, I agree with Mr. Deeks' opinion that the material selection is seen to be improved by the application of fracture mechanics concepts. We have evaluated the fracture toughness of solid railroad wheel for service in cold climates and I would like to present some of our test results.

Our investigation was conducted to improve the fracture toughness of railroad wheel used in winter in the northern part of Japan, where the lowest temperature encountered is around -10°C. Since on-tread type braking is being used in this case and the material is a high carbon (0.70%) steel, the accumulated thermal residual stress plus thermal cracks initiated on the tread might cause failure of the wheels.

Figure 1 shows the fracture toughness of a carbon steel as a function of carbon content.

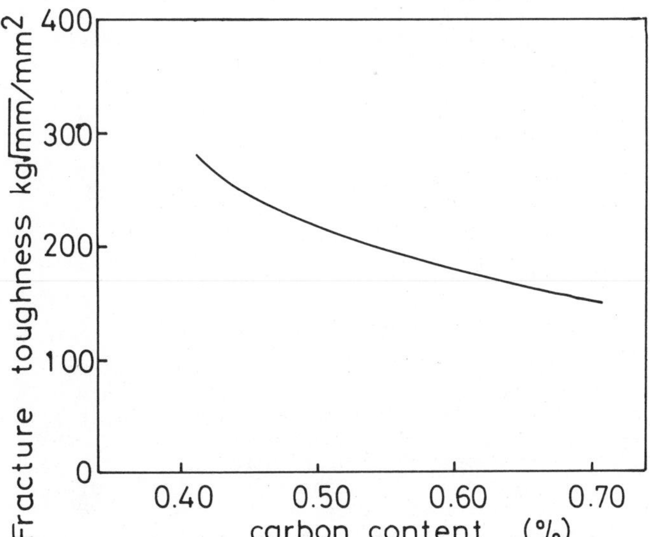

Figure 1: The effect of carbon content on fracture toughness

Table 1

Ferrite Network Size and the Corresponding Fracture Toughness of Vanadium Steels Studied

V	Normalized K_{Ic}	Normalized d	Quenched & Tempered K_{Ic}	Quenched & Tempered d
(%)	($kgf/mm^{3/2}$)	(μm)	($kgf/mm^{3/2}$)	(μm)
0	145	28.9	224	-
0.03	200	19	276	13
0.055	185	19	336	12
0.10	274	12	314	13
0.15	262	15	330	12
0.21	255	15.5	315	10

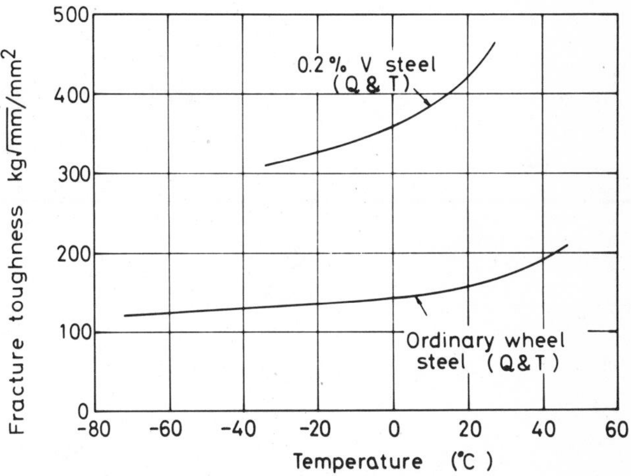

Figure 2: The effect of temperature on fracture toughness for traditional and new wheel steels (ASTM WOL Test)

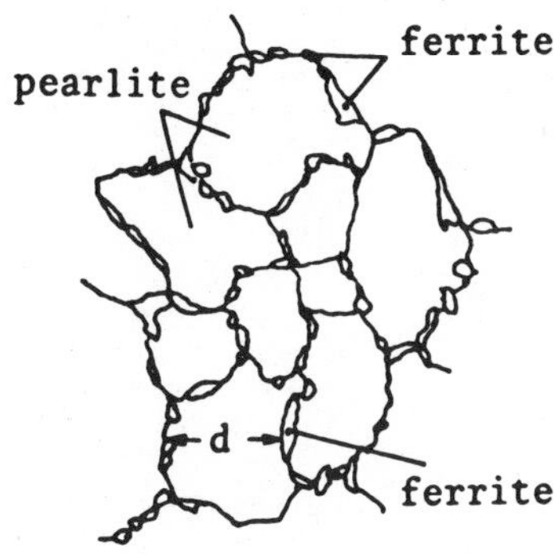

Figure 3: Schematic of ferrite network

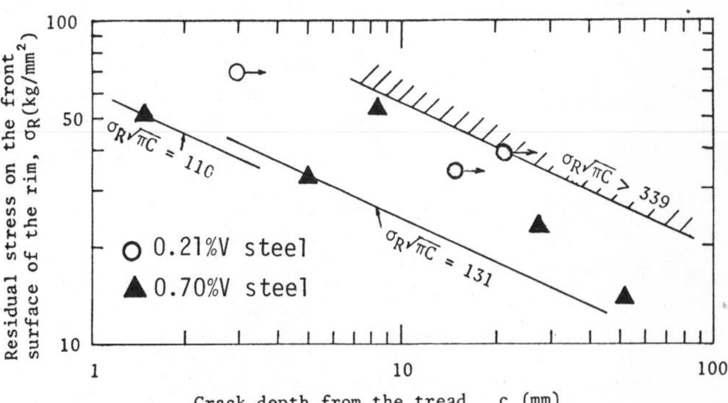

Figure 4: Relationship between circumferential residual stress in wheel rim and the crack depth at fracture

Fracture toughness was measured by the ASTM WOL test. Lowering of carbon content of a steel increases the fracture toughness.

The effect of various alloying additions on the fracture toughness of a steel was investigated and the addition of 0.2% vanadium was found to be particularly effective for the improvement of the fracture toughness, as shown in Figure 2. The improvement is due to the refinement of microstructure as shown in Table 1, where ferrite network size, d, was measured as defined in Figure 3. With the vanadium addition, microstructural unit size, measured by the ferrite network, became smaller.

The chemical composition of the test wheel steel which was produced as a result of the fundamental research was 0.57C, 0.29Si, 0.86Mn, 0.008P, 0.011S, 0.06Cu, 0.12Cr and 0.21V. The tread was heat-treated by quenching after 5 h at 850°C, tempered at 560°C for 6 h, followed by air cooling.

The fracture toughness of this new steel was evaluated on the bench test. By the repeated application of braking on the tread, residual stresses and thermal cracks were introduced until fracture occurred in the wheel. It was shown that the new steel possesses a much higher resistance to brittle fracture, as shown in Figure 4, thus assuring enhanced safety for service in cold climates.

RELIABILITY CONSIDERATIONS FOR UNIT TRAIN SERVICE UNDER ARCTIC CONDITIONS

M. D. Roney
Canadian Institute of Guided Ground Transport
Queen's University, Kingston, Ontario

and

M. C. Deno
CP Rail, Montreal, Quebec
CANADA

The operation of a low density, resource grade railway in the far North would not entail significant upgrading of the materials used in existing operations. These systems have performed adequately in periods of extreme low temperature in the past. Faced with increased frequencies of brittle failures, the most likely approach would be to accept the reliability penalty incurred with the use of conventional railway materials.

As traffic levels and reliability requirements increase, such an approach is no longer feasible. A number of components would require materials upgrading to improve both fatigue and low temperature properties. Fracture toughness tests tailored to railway applications and tighter material specifications would undoubtedly yield dividends in system reliability.

As the ultimate objective is to maintain high system reliability at the lowest cost, innovative equipment designs and expanded preventative maintenance programs offer alternatives to extensive materials upgrading. Among these, improvements to locomotive air filtration, air compressors and cooling systems, on-board data acquisition, and the cab control car concept are particularly attractive for high density unit train service under Arctic conditions.

INTRODUCTION

Although the resource scenario remains uncertain, there is little doubt that we can expect a burgeoning demand for transportation services in the North. Given the most recent estimates of mineralization in the western Arctic, one of the likely components of an expanded northern transportation network will be a railway.

For a railway, the Arctic does not represent a venture into the unknown; the technology is well proven in northern latitudes. Permafrost construction is expensive, but presents no technical difficulties. The Hudson Bay Line, for example, has been operated over discontinuous permafrost and 140 miles of continuous permafrost for close to half a century.

The greatest concern that will face the builders of future Arctic railways will be the effects of increased frequencies and durations of very low temperatures on system reliability. For example, although the Quebec North Shore and Labrador Railway has successfully operated 225-car unit trains at temperatures below -40°C, and presently moves large volumes of iron ore reliably through very adverse climatic conditions, it does not do so with the same facility as an equivalent system in the south.

Four possibilities are open for future projects in the Arctic:

1) The reliability penalty attending the introduction of conventional materials and equipment into an Arctic environment can be accepted.
2) Reliability can be maintained at an acceptable level with materials improvements.
3) Expanded preventative maintenance programs can be implemented.
4) The service demands made on equipment and materials can be mitigated by design alterations.

The optimal strategy is obviously the combination of the above options which yields the greatest cost effectiveness, within the constraints imposed by acceptable limits of reliability and safety. As the achieved level of reliability is dependent upon the performance of a wide range of components in a diversity of service environments and is profoundly influenced by utilization, the economics are extremely difficult to compute. Both achieved and specified levels of reliability tend to be very much a function of the system envisaged.

For example, high quality metallurgy could do little for the Hudson Bay Line, as system reliability is dominated by the existing rail section, which consists in some sections of 1896-1920 vintage "80 lb" (39 kg/m) relay* rail, salvaged 50 years ago from main line track. In this case, the impact of rail renewal with "132 lb" (65 kg/m) relay rail (or even with "100 lb" (49 kg/m) rail removed from other lines) would completely overshadow any other materials improvements. On the other hand, where a uniform standard of component quality is adhered to, a multitude of materials improvements could yield substantial payoffs. It is apparent from these considerations that it is difficult to make generalizations concerning materials selection for an Arctic railway service. The overriding concern is the maintenance of an acceptable level of reliability at minimum cost. Clearly, reductions in the frequency of brittle failures through materials improvements is only one method of meeting this objective and cannot be dealt with in isolation from alternative strategies.

However, as an Arctic railway is hypothetical at this time, we must consider these strategies without the benefit of specific failure analyses. Although it is not possible to present more than a tentative assessment of materials selection considerations, it is appropriate in this conference to examine some of the weak links in the railway armour. Since the proposed solutions are to a very large extent system-specific, reliability will be discussed within the context of both a low density, resource-grade railway and a high density bulk-haul system.

MATERIALS SELECTION FOR A RESOURCE-GRADE ARCTIC RAILWAY

In a report identifying likely generators of demand for transportation services, Lake et al (1) developed expected rail tonnages for mineral products over a Mackenzie Valley railway, arriving at a figure of 6.4 Mt (6.5 Gg) annually by the year 2000. In a similar study of the mineral endowment adjacent to the Mackenzie Valley, Freyman (2) postulated the annual rail traffic for the period from 1991 to 2000 as

a 10% probability of 1 to 5 million tons
a 10% probability of 5.1 to 10 million tons
a 40% probability of 10.1 to 20 million tons
a 40% probability of 20.1 to 30 million tons

This would yield an expected traffic of 17 Mt (17 Gg). Since the 432 mile (695 km) Great Slave Lake Line was constructed (at a cost of $75 million) with an immediate traffic expectation of less than a million tons annually, the projected levels of mineral traffic should be sufficient to merit construction of such a single track resource-grade railway. The demand for the transport of lumber, petroleum and mineral exploration supplies, fuel, building supplies and consumer goods would constitute additional tonnage.

Such a railway would encounter minimum temperatures that would not differ significantly from those presently encountered along CN and CP main lines north of Lake Superior. Although these occasional encounters with extreme temperatures would tend to "weed out weak sisters", they have not posed serious problems for the conventional grades of metals used. They have, however, resulted in slight increases in the frequencies of brittle failures of certain railway components. This effect can be expected to be amplified as longer duration of very low temperatures are encountered with greater frequency as, for example, in the Mackenzie Valley.

Car Castings

Predictably, the most vulnerable components have traditionally been castings, such as yokes, couplers, knuckles, truck side frames, and truck bolsters. The element of risk of brittle fracture is attributable to three-dimensional continuity in combination with a thick cross-section and dynamic transients that can impose a rapidly changing rate of stress. The brittle fracture problem in these components is aggravated by fatigue, since cracks initiated by fatigue can develop into brittle fractures. Thus, the selection of suitable materials must be based on both fatigue and low temperature properties. Results of Dynamic Tear and Pre-Cracked Charpy tests on the Association of American Railroads (AAR) specification M-211/Grade C steel most commonly used in railway castings are shown in Figure 1 (3). They indicate a Nil Ductility Temperature (NDT) of -20°C. It is likely that the reliability benefits accrued with the use of AAR specification M-211/ Grade E steel, a quenched and tempered steel with a NDT of -75°C in these same tests, will out-weigh the additional costs, even for a low density railway.

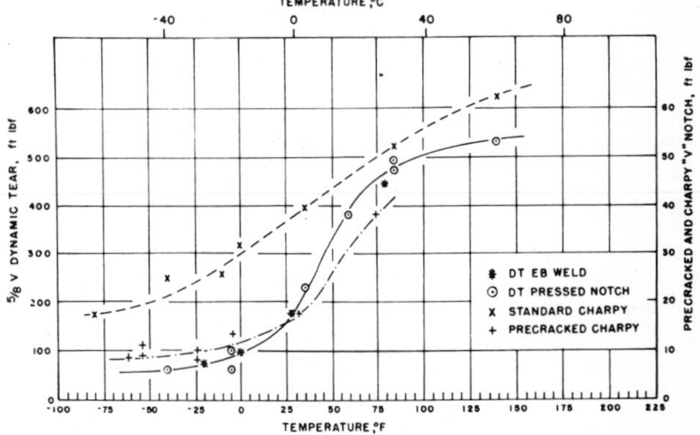

Figure 1: Brittle-ductile transition of Grade C Castings as Determined by Dynamic Tear, Precracked Charpy, and Charpy V-Notch Tests (3).

* Rail which has reached condemning limits of wear as far as main line track is concerned, but with further economic life under less demanding branch line service conditions

Air Brake System

A second perennial problem area experienced in existing operations relates to the performance of braking systems in cold weather. Commencing at about -10°C, leakages in the air brake system are intensified by the contraction of metal fittings and the stiffening of the reinforced rubber air hose (hose bag) connecting the brake pipes of adjacent cars*. The pressure loss in the line also allows more moist air to be pumped into the system, which, upon cooling, condenses at critical points in the brake system, restricting air flow. To put the problem into perspective, an inspection conducted by the AAR in 1966 (4) in temperatures ranging from -20°C to -30°C uncovered an average of 1.4 leaks per car in a sample of 292 freight cars. A solution which has proven to be quite effective on the Quebec North Shore and Labrador Railway is the use of one-piece hose bags with screw-type fittings and all-welded brake pipes.

A further braking problem relates to the performance of organic friction materials used in composition brake shoes. It has often been observed that it is difficult to brake a train equipped with composition brake shoes at low temperatures (5). Although not a major problem, this phenomenon is an aggravation for any scale of railway system, and is a likely candidate for future materials research.

Wheels and Rails

Although both rails and wheels are presently constructed of steels which are shown in Charpy V-notch tests to be brittle over all normal operating temperatures, existing failure rates during periods of minimum temperatures have been considered satisfactory. This is probably a result of the particular care taken in manufacture to eliminate cracks, notches and inclusions. Both CP Rail and Canadian National do, however, report an increase in rail failures during the winter months, when the cold reduces the dynamic fracture toughness, causing the rail to be more susceptible to breaks caused by impacts. Closer attention to the elimination of surface irregularities in the riding surfaces of both wheels and rails is probably a more practical solution than higher quality rail metallurgy.

Rail surface irregularities occur in the form of corrugations, rail head damage, mill defects, high joint welds or rail end mismatch, which contribute to unfavourable dynamic load increments. If caught in time, all of these conditions can be eliminated or reduced by periodic passes of a rail grinding train. The most critical impacts result from defects or flat spots on loaded cars and locomotive wheels. The risk of brittle fracture arising from wheel defects can be controlled, to a certain extent, by the specification of a condemnable size of wheel flat. The present specification allows 2.5 in. (6.35 cm) which would likely prove to be suboptimal under Arctic conditions.

A particular concern with rails is in the joint area, where rails often develop fatigue cracks at the bolt holes, which can propagate in a brittle manner. Fortunately, these cracks can be detected ultrasonically before they reach critical dimensions. However, the added risk of brittle fracture should be estimated and matched by a corresponding increase in the frequency of rail inspections. As this problem is alleviated by the substitution of welded for jointed track construction, it is suggested that the minimum traffic criterion for continuous welded rail, currently set somewhat arbitrarily at about 10 Mt/a (gross), be reduced with the northward expansion of the railway network.

Generally speaking, the AAR Class C heat treated wheel used in existing heavy tonnage service shows no evidence of unsatisfactory performance under low temperature conditions. At any rate, a reduction in the carbon content (currently at 0.67 to 0.77% for a dynamic fracture toughness K_{Id} of 27 ksi$\sqrt{\text{in.}}$ (30 MPa$\sqrt{\text{m}}$)) to obtain increased toughness would sacrifice wearability. Even on railways with very severe operating conditions, such as the Quebec North Shore and Labrador Railway, wheel wear continues to account for some 94% of wheel turnings(6). Unless it is matched by increases in rail hardness, any wholesale improvement in wheel surface hardness is likely to result in excessive rail wear.

Reliability Requirements

It is apparent from the preceding discussion that the requirements for improved materials for a low density, resource grade operation are light. Existing sub-Arctic railways have performed adequately in climatic extremes not unlike those to be encountered further north. With the exception of failures in welded bodies of derailed tank cars, most current railway materials problems relate more to fatigue than to brittle fractures, although brittle fractures occasionally propagate from fatigue cracks. Present experience in extreme low temperatures suggests that the severity of the situation would not be expected to change substantially with the superimposition of conventional railway materials into an Arctic environment. Given the equipment utilization and reliability requirements characteristic of a resource grade system, increased failure rates could, if necessary, be absorbed.

Consequently, the materials improvement decision is likely to hinge upon the ability of the railways' existing rolling stock fleet to meet the transportation requirements of a new Arctic branch line. If freight cars are presently available to handle the additional tonnage, then it is likely that they will be pressed into Arctic service without modification. If, on the other hand, it is necessary to purchase new equipment, then it would be advantageous to tighten materials specifications and to specify Grade E steel for castings, with air brake assemblies incorporating one-piece hose bags with screw-type fittings and all-welded brake pipes. In either event, the emphasis on preventative maintenance should be expanded to give more frequent attention to the minimization of unfavourable dynamic conditions. Similarly, flaw detection cycles should reflect the higher risk of brittle fracture imposed by an Arctic environment.

INNOVATIONS FOR A HIGH DENSITY BULK HAUL SYSTEM

The materials problem takes on a significantly different complexion as rail traffic projections reach very high levels. If, for example, it were decided to follow the Soviet example (7) and move hydrocarbons as well as mineral resources by rail, component utilization and reliability specifications would place a premium on the performance of materials. The authors have had an opportunity to study such a railway through their recent association with a study group formed to investigate the feasibility of a railway in lieu of pipelines for the transport of Arctic oil and gas (8). A study railway was designed for operation between the Mackenzie Delta petroleum region and/or Prudhoe Bay, Alaska and a

* The hose bag is a reinforced rubber or chloroprene tube, attached to a nipple that screws into the angle cock at the end of the brake pipe of each car or locomotive. The brake pipe is that section of the air brake piping of a car or locomotive which acts as a supply pipe for the reservoirs.

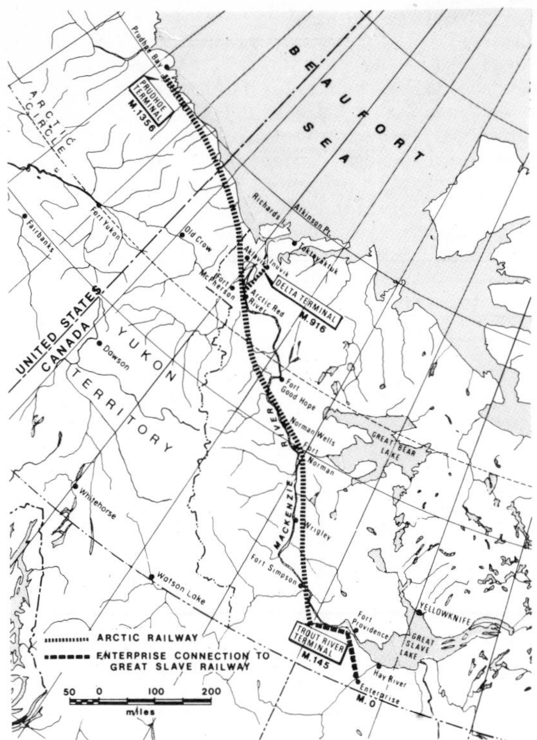

Figure 2: Routing of Study Railway

hypothetical southern terminus below the limit of significant permafrost (Figure 2). A variety of oil and gas production options were costed. As an indication of the traffic levels under consideration, the detailed study case entailed an average of 21- to 27-unit trains per day in each direction to handle a daily traffic volume of 2 million barrels of oil and 3 billion ft^3 (85 Mm^3) of gas. The oil train would be comprised of 225 cars in summer and 150 cars in winter, powered by both head-end and remote controlled mid-train locomotive units (liquefied natural gas was assumed to be moved in 110-car trains).

At these traffic levels, rolling stock and track would undergo a high level of utilization, and line blockages due to component failures would seriously disrupt system throughput. Frequent and/or severe disruptions translate as heavy requirements for storage facilities and makeup capacity. As tight delivery requirements are characteristic of this type of traffic, the provision of a high quality of components is paramount.

The materials improvements discussed with reference to the low density, resource grade railway would be highly desirable for a heavy tonnage operation in the Arctic. Metallic components used in high density, bulk haul service would require careful evaluation for both low temperature and fatigue properties. The preferred method of ensuring that metals have the necessary properties is through placing more stringent limits on present material specifications and making more careful inspection.

Fracture Toughness Testing

At present, materials selection and quality control is seriously hampered by the inadequacy of existing fracture toughness testing techniques for railway applications. In general, fracture toughness testing techniques have not been used in the railway industry except for the limited use of Charpy V-notch tests to control the quality of the material. By presently accepted tests, rail and wheel steels would be considered brittle at all operating temperatures (eg. NDT for conventional rail steel = 200°C), yet existing performance in cold weather has been considered satisfactory. A high density system in the Arctic would require the development of inexpensive and reproducible tests that do not employ notches or cracks to evaluate the toughness of the material. The objective is to identify the temperature range over which the steel becomes brittle, and correlate these results with service experience (9).

The economic advantage of new fracture toughness tests specifically developed for railway materials in an Arctic environment could be substantial where a large scale operation is envisaged. These tests would have several important applications. For example, they would enable an evaluation to be made of the risk of brittle fracture for each material, ranking prospective replacement materials according to incremental costs and benefits. In the past, the railways have had little control on the quality of materials purchased from suppliers. With the added risk of brittle fracture imposed by an Arctic environment, fracture toughness testing will be required to ensure the continuing reliability of the product.

Rail

As traffic forecasts approach very high levels, there may be economic advantages to an improved rail steel. As a result of a need to have high wear resistance, rail steels are customarily brittle, room temperature Charpy V-notch impact energies of 2 ft lbf (3J) being common (10). The brittle/ductile transition that occurs over a temperature range in rail steels is shown in Figure 3. Note also the importance of the mode of testing on the toughness determination. High strain rates, simulated by dynamic fracture toughness tests, are characteristic of the state of loading of most railway materials.

Although conventional rail steels have performed adequately in existing service, the brittle fracture initiation in the head of the rail that has been responsible for increases in rail failures during winter months may require particular attention under frequent passages of heavy axle loads at very low temperatures. Overall, a decrease in rail yield strength to reduce brittleness is not a practical solution as this will increase the tendency for the rail head to flow plastically. As head flow is presently an acute problem under heavy axle loads,

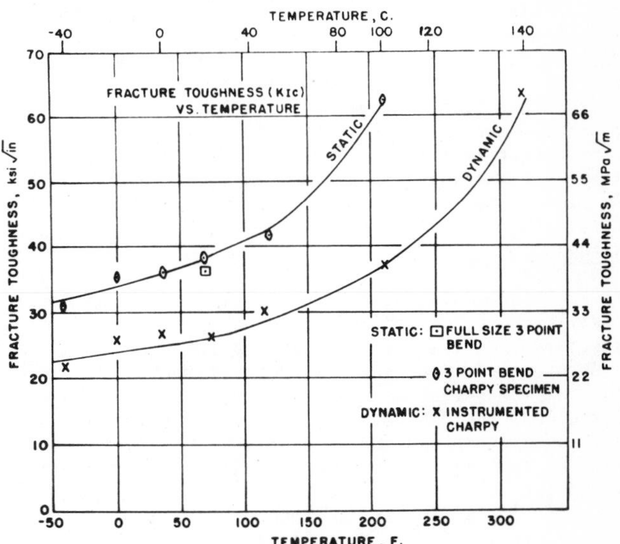

Figure 3: The Effect of Temperature on the Static and Dynamic Fracture Toughness of Rail Steel (3)

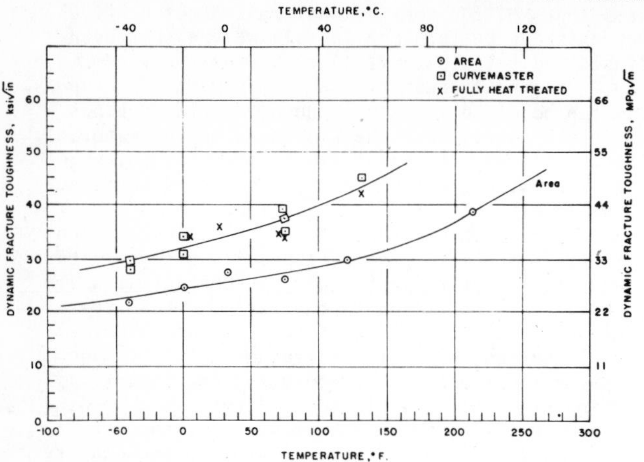

Figure 4: Effect of Temperature on Fracture Toughness of Standard and Heat Treated Rail Steels (3)

an increase in the fracture toughness of the rail steel is a more expedient solution. According to fracture mechanics analysis, a doubling of the plane strain fracture toughness of the rail steel would enable a fourfold increase in the size of crack to cause brittle fracture initiation in the head of the rail. In the web of the rail, the effect is similar, however, as plane strain conditions do not prevail, the material toughness is increased above the plane strain value (11).

Grain refinement of steels offers a simultaneous increase in strength, wearability and toughness. The toughness improvement achievable with heat-treated in place of standard (AREA) rail is illustrated in Figure 4 (3). At a cost premium of some 30%, heat-treated rail would offer a means with which to counteract the high wear and plastic flow to be expected under heavy traffic levels, in addition to reducing the probability of brittle fracture. A similar effect is obtainable with certain alloying elements (e.g. silicon, manganese, vanadium). These could also provide compatibility with surface-hardened wheels if these were found to be economically justified.

Truck Castings

As service failures in truck castings have potentially catastrophic results, an immediate priority should be the minimization of surface defects through more stringent manufacturing specifications and inspections, and design reviews to decrease the risk of brittle fractures by eliminating such causal factors as abrupt changes in cross section. Although these measures will undoubtedly exert a positive improvement in truck failures, the 40 to 50% cost premium attending the use of 2 to 3% nickel steel in side frames and bolsters is likely to be justified.

Bridges

Bridges will also be subjected to high fatigue under temperature conditions amenable to brittle fractures. Consequently, conservative design criteria are suggested. In view of the large number of minimum-maximum stress cycles attending a high density operation, in combination with working temperatures as low as -60°C, an increase of 40% over current railway loading has been suggested (8). Particular attention must be directed at welds, to minimize their potential for stress concentration and fracture propagation. The CSA G.40.21 Type 50A steel should perform adequately in the Arctic environment. This high strength, (YS = 50 ksi, 340 MPa) low-alloy steel, offers improved low temperature properties over conventional structural steel.

The cost of further materials improvements can be expected to be substantial. As an alternative to widespread improvements to maintain a high-reliability heavy-tonnage system, a higher benefit/cost ratio may be attained through the implementation of innovative equipment design concepts and expanded preventative maintenance programs. This alternative approach was explored in some detail by the study group (8), and has yielded several innovations for high density service under Arctic conditions.

Locomotive Innovations

As the conventional diesel locomotive has been designed primarily for the average American operating environment, locomotives subjected to more severe environmental conditions, as during the Canadian winter, exhibit increased failure rates of certain components*. It appears that design deficiencies are at least partially responsible.

Locomotives on the study railway (8) would be subjected to a high level of utilization while operating from 800-1200 miles (1300-1900 km) without the benefit of running repair depots, access by highway, or standby units. Any failure of a unit or units would have an immediate adverse reaction on the speed of following trains and might upset the overall traffic pattern. Under these operating conditions, the conventional diesel locomotive would be the weakest link in the reliability chain, outweighing reliability benefits attributable to materials improvements.

New forms of motive power show good promise for Arctic service -- in particular the gas turbine locomotive†. Such a locomotive was designed by the study group but not included in the economic analysis. In accordance with the terms of reference of the study, which specified the adherence to proven technology for cost estimation purposes, the basic 3000 hp (2.2 MW), six-axle diesel locomotive design was accepted "off-the-shelf" as representing the latest in technological development.

Nevertheless, it was decided to look at ways in which the most sensitive components could be eliminated. Failing this, attempts were made to create less demanding service environments. As a result of this review, it was recommended that the locomotive cooling system be separated into primary and secondary sections to obviate the need for radiator shutters and their pneumatic control magnet valves, operating

* A 1973 survey found that during the months of January, February and December, the number of diesel unit miles run per defect ranged from 20,000 to 40,000, while the range for the remainder of the year was from 45,000 to 70,000 unit miles per defect (11).

† The gas turbine electric locomotives do not require the elaborate diesel engine radiator cooling systems with their fans and shutters, and onboard fuel heating and pumping equipment is eliminated. The fuel system and spray nozzles are also simplified. The result is more reliable cold weather operation and an estimated 50% reduction in engine maintenance. The inherent fuel consumption efficiency characteristic of gas turbines operating under nearly continuous high load factors is accentuated by low ambient temperatures. With the aim of evaluating the economics of gas turbine motive power for operation over the Baikal-Amur railway in eastern Siberia, scheduled for completion in 1982, the Soviet Railways have recently announced plans to build an 8000 hp (6.0 MW) gas turbine prototype. The use of two 12,000 hp (9.0 MW) gas turbine locomotives to power each train is ultimately envisaged (12).

rods and linkages -- all potential candidates for failure. This measure would also materially decrease the amount of anti-freeze required and reduce by approximately one-half the amount of chromate-treated cooling water which might have to be drained and stored in an emergency due to freezing temperatures.

A further weak area was the current arrangement of locomotive air compressors and drives which has each engine drive an air compressor which runs continually at the engine speed. The compressor cylinders load and unload in response to the train braking air demands. A trainline and electrical load control arrangement unloads all the compressors in the locomotive consist when the first compressor control switch in any unit reaches its "stop pumping" pressure setting. This arrangement results in a great deal of non-essential high-speed rotation of compressors in the unloaded condition and an unequal division of work between the compressors. This superfluous operation carries a penalty of increased maintenance and shorter service life of air compressors. Consequently, it was recommended that the entire air compressor and its drives, flexible couplings, intercooler, lubricating and cooling systems be replaced with one or more of the main engine cylinders as the source of air supply.

Elimination of the air compressor and drive as separate components would reduce the maintenance and spare parts requirements as well as releasing space that could be used to improve air brake line moisture removal equipment essential to the prevention of ice formation in the air line. Icing is also a potential concern for the system used to filter air for combustion and cooling. This possibility has precipitated a proposal for rotation of the inertial filter plus the addition of heat, and a change in configuration.

Data Acquisition System

Perhaps the most attractive means of achieving an improvement in system reliability is the utilization of preventative maintenance procedures to the greatest extent possible. Although most North American railroads follow some program of preventative maintenance on diesel electric locomotives, their effectiveness in preventing costly equipment damage and resultant excessive out-of-service time is limited. This is largely a result of the relative accessibility of certain parts for visual inspection and measurement and the influence of short term reductions in maintenance allotments. While the level of preventative maintenance on North American railroads has increased in recent years through the development of various "measuring devices", no system of on-board monitoring of total locomotive performance with a view to identifying potential failures has proven successful. Recent advances in technology in this area have spurred renewed interest in developing a workable on-board data acquisition system, culminating with the design of software for such a system in conjunction with the Arctic Railway study. The proposed data acquisition system would provide continuous monitoring of locomotive component performance and would permit headquarters maintenance staff to alert the crews concerned and advise corrective action before component failure occurs.

In contrast to existing railroad preventative maintenance programs which characteristically include the calibration of certain parts at regular intervals followed by their renewal if necessary, or the replacement of certain parts at regular statistically established intervals, a system such as is planned would provide continuous monitoring of critical parts, including those not readily accessible for visual inspection or measurement. The end result would be the prevention of a high percentage of costly equipment damage and the consequent out-of-service time.

The data acquisition system is presently undergoing further development and testing by CP Rail. The system under development will detect thermal, vibration, and pressure levels on the diesel engine and associated auxiliary systems. In a like manner, departures of electrical control and propulsion system parameters from acceptable standards will be sensed. A partial list of locomotive parameters to be monitored follows:

Key Locomotive Parameters Monitored on-Line

DIESEL ENGINE
- Timing
- Cylinder Pressures
- Temperature
- Coolant Flow
- Fuel Consumption vs Power Output vs Electrical Load

TURBOCHARGER
- Bearing Temperatures
- Speed

TRACTION MOTOR
- Suspension Bearing Temperature

WHEELS
- Flat Spot Detection

ELECTRIC CONTROL SYSTEMS

In the event that the predetermined limits of any parameter are exceeded, immediate remedial action will be initiated in one of three forms, viz: unit shut-down, unit isolation, or partial reduction of output. Data pertaining to safe train operation, such as skidded wheels on any of the locomotive units in a train consist, will be displayed immediately on the console in the controlling cab and a brake application will be initiated automatically.

Only significant information from any locomotive unit in a train consist will be gathered and transmitted by a control car; this information will be suitably coded and relayed through the railway communication system to a central control depot.

Using on-board data acquisition, defective units arriving at the maintenance shop would not require the present time-consuming diagnostic examination to locate and identify the malfunction; this information would have been formulated prior to unit arrival. The resultant effect would be a decrease in technical staff and increased unit availability.

Information received at central control can be separated out and stored by diesel unit number, thus providing an historical background for each unit. This can be scrutinized periodically by the computer, permitting a forecast of component behaviour patterns, and all information would be processed as to priority for sequential maintenance planning. The data acquisition would also serve to reduce the probability of brittle fracture in wheel and rail by detecting excessive vehicle vibrations, often associated with high impact loads (eg: flat spots on wheels), further alleviating the necessity for extensive materials upgrading to achieve a high system reliability.

The Cab Control Car

The data acquisition equipment would be housed

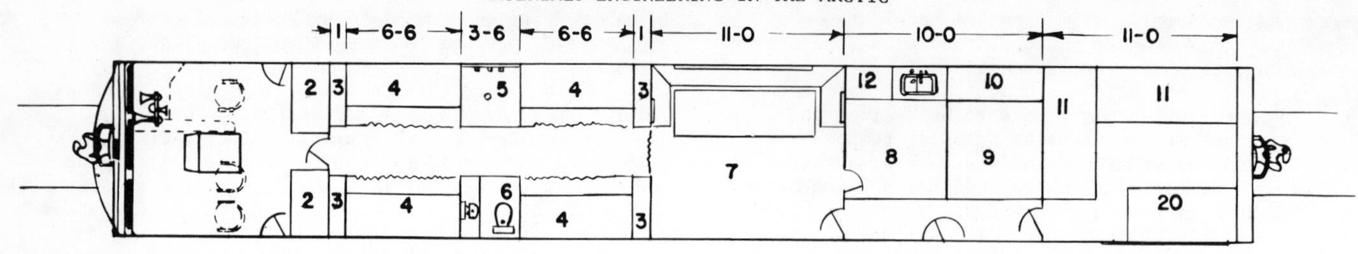

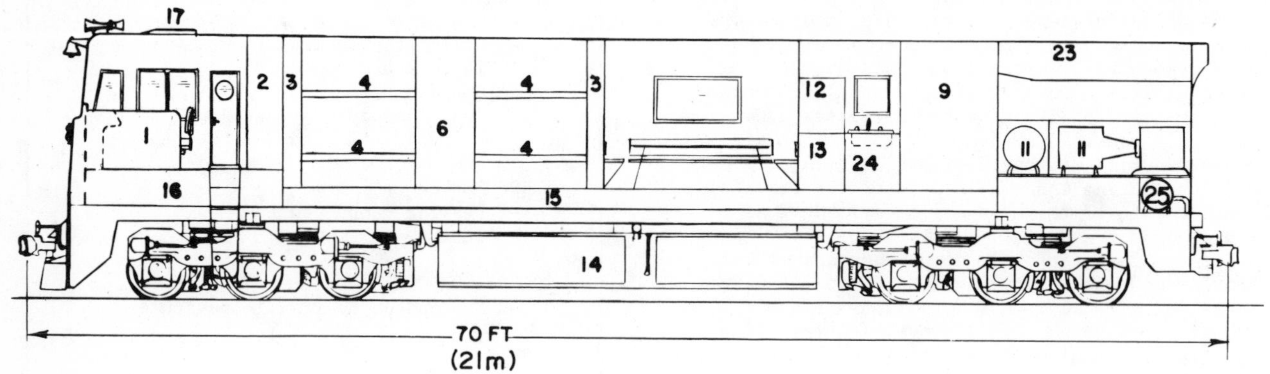

1 - LOCO. CONTROL
2 - LOCOTROL EQUIP
3 - LOCKERS
4 - BUNKS
5 - SHOWER
6 - TOILET & SINK
7 - DINING & REC. ROOM
8 - KITCHEN
9 - FOOD FREEZER
10 - REFUSE COMPRESSOR
11 - TURBINE
12 - MICRO OVEN
13 - DISH LOCKER
14 - BELLY FUEL TANK
15 - FRAME & FLOOR FUEL TANK
16 - AIR BRAKE EQUIP
17 - ESCAPE HATCH
20 - SNOW CAT
23 - WATER TANK
24 - KITCHEN SINK
25 - FUEL TRANSFER PUMP

Figure 5: Cab Control Car Layout

in an innovative vehicle for unit train service termed the "cab control car". The cab control car would be the lead vehicle of the head-end locomotive consist but would not have tractive power. All of the necessary equipment for the control of the leading locomotives, remote locomotives and communications links with the dispatcher and shops would be located in the cab control car, shown in Figure 5. Within the central car body, sufficient space would be available to accommodate a crew of four plus one steward and three other personnel. These facilities would enable the implementation of a "ship-at-sea" approach to train crewing whereby train crew members would embark from the southern terminal and accompany the train for the round trip to the loading terminal, working alternate shifts. The availability of extra crew members during an emergency is expected to represent an attractive supplementary feature for improving reliability.

A further reliability benefit of the cab control car results from the replacement of locomotive starting batteries with the control car as the starting power source. At the present time, any locomotive unit that has failed in service must be drained within one hour of shutdown to prevent possible freezing of the electrolyte and cracking of the battery. The elimination of the starting battery would allow the train to continue under reduced power to the load/unload terminal.

CONCLUSION

The requirements for improved materials for a railway operating in the Arctic environment are a function of the scale of the system envisaged. A resource-grade railway can be expected to operate with a minimum of modification, as the basic equipment used in more southerly applications has a record of proven reliability under a wide range of operating conditions. A high-density bulk-haul system, on the other hand, although feasible from a metallurgical point of view will require particular attention to the reliability penalty resulting from increased frequencies of brittle fracture.

The cost effectiveness of improvements in low temperature and fatigue properties of railway materials must ultimately be considered in light of alternative strategies for maintaining an acceptable level of rail system reliability, such as improved locomotive performance and expanded preventative maintenance practices. With a combined approach including materials upgrading, improved manufacturing quality control, new fracture toughness tests, expanded maintenance practices, and innovations in rolling stock, the rail mode can operate with a high level of reliability under extreme climatic conditions.

REFERENCES

1. R. W. Lake, J. A. Macdonald, C. Schwier, et al, "Forecast of Demand for Transportation Services in a Mackenzie Valley Corridor", prepared for the Canadian Arctic Resources Committee, Kingston, 1975.
2. A. J. Freyman, "The Potential Impact of a Mackenzie Valley Railway on Mineral Development in North", Appendix III of "Arctic Oil and Gas by Rail", vol. 3, 1974, Montreal.
3. A. S. Tetelman and D. H. Stone, "An Introduction to the Fracture Mechanics of Railroad Materials", Association of American Railroads Research and Test Department, AAR Report R-157, Chicago 1974.
4. Association of American Railroads, Operations and Maintenance Department, "Report of Committee on Brakes and Brake Equipment", Circular No. D.V. -1629, Chicago, 1966.
5. J. T. Wilson, "Braking Systems Research Needs", prepared for The Railroad Research Study, Transportation Research Board, Woods Hole, Massachusetts, 1975, Canadian National Railways, Montreal.
6. H. A. Tyler, "Wheel Mileage Performance on Ore Cars Operating Over the Quebec North Shore and Labrador Railway", American Society of Mechanical Engineers Railroad Division, Paper 64-WA/RR-6, New York, 1964.
7. Oil and Gas Journal, April 8 1974, vol. 72 (14) p. 56.
8. R. G. Maughan, J. S. Smith and R. W. Lake, et al, "Arctic Oil and Gas by Rail; Vol. 3, part 4, and vol. 5, part 2, " Montreal 1974.
9. P. R. V. Evans, N. B. Owen and B. E. Hopkins, J. Iron Steel Inst., 1970, vol. 208, pp. 560-567.
10. R. I. Mair, "Material Aspects of Rail Design", Melbourne Research Laboratories, 1972.
11. D. H. Easun, T. D. Ganton, D. H. Page, and M. Salidas, "Diesel Electric Locomotive Performance During Winter Operations", prepared for the RAC/TDA Railway Advisory Committee, Canadian Institute of Guided Ground Transportation, Kingston, 1974.
12. Railway Gazette International, 1974, vol. 130, p. 406.

DISCUSSION

R. G. Deeks (Procor): I cannot agree that it is appropriate to make no equipment modifications for a low-density Arctic railway. The Quebec North Shore Railway does not use standard materials and equipment. They have made many changes to obtain greater reliability, both in materials and operating conditions.

M. D. Roney: The Quebec North Shore has also increased the car payloads, requiring upgrading of equipment. I would also like to distinguish between what should be done, and what would be done. If cars were readily available from other lines, there would be very little done to produce more reliable equipment -- that is what would happen in fact.

J. Clayton (Gulf Oil Canada): Is high silicon rail a beneficial factor in Arctic operation? What about concomitant wheel wear?

M. D. Roney: High silicon rail offers increased resistance to both contact fatigue and brittle failure at a cost premium that would likely be justified for a high density bulk haul Arctic service. Its projected cost effectiveness must, of course, be compared to benefits offered by other alloys and by heat treatment. In this context, it is interesting that fully heat treated rail has been adopted as standard for the extensive Soviet Railways System, which carries an extremely high average annual traffic density of 56 million gross tons per mile, and which will shortly have two trans-Siberian lines in operation. After extensive test programs aimed at combatting rapid defect formation, a fully heat treated rail was chosen over alloy rails using various combinations of manganese, chromium, silicon and nickel.

It is, of course, important that wheel hardness be in balance with rail hardness. The AAR Class C wheel used in existing heavy tonnage service is surface hardened. However, multiple-wear 38 in. (965 mm) diameter wheels would likely be required to maintain acceptable service lives for wheels operating over fully heat treated rail. With very high utilization levels, it may be economical to go to special alloy steels. A prime candidate would be a steel with a low carbon content in combination with additions of manganese and chromium, which would offer increased resistance to both wear and surface fatigue.

J. Clayton: Are high density polyethylene tie plates useful in Arctic Rail? They do tend to minimize sink in wooden ties and absorb vibration. They have virtually no impact resistance at 32°F (0°C) but have been in use in Alaska and Alberta for 18 months without reported failures.

M. D. Roney: It is difficult to make an assessment at this stage, as mainline service tests of polyethylene tie plates have been of limited duration and are for the most part, ongoing. Although laboratory tests have been very promising, it is difficult to extrapolate these results to long term performance in the field. Laboratory tests have, however, shown the brittle point of these tie plates to be below -100°F (-73°C) so that brittle failure in Arctic service should not be a major concern.

By the manufacturer's own admission, the field tests have indicated that the polyethylene tie plate should not be used in track carrying over 40 million gross tons annually or on curves with extreme elevation. I do not believe that the existing data are sufficient to set specific limits on their use, however, they do indicate that polyethylene tie plates are not suitable for severe operating conditions. The present thrust of marketing efforts has been towards their employment in industrial spurs and sidings, particularly where chemicals play havoc with steel plates. In addition, it is important to note that they must be recessed in dapped crossties in track carrying traffic exceeding roughly 10 million gross tons annually at over 20 mph (32 km/h) or on curves in excess of 5°. This reduces their relative cost advantage over steel tie plates.

Nevertheless, their lightweight feature makes them particularly attractive for northern locations where transportation costs become a particularly significant component of materials costs. I believe that the accumulation of further service experience and future steel price movements will dictate whether or not the high density polyethylene tie plates will become commonplace in branch line trackage. If these tieplates come to be accepted by the railway industry then it is quite possible that we will see them in light service applications in the North.

J. Clayton: I do not feel that on-board vibration analysis to diagnose wheel or rail incipient failure would be viable -- it would be constantly giving false indications.

M. D. Roney: Not having had any personal experience with vibration analysis, I have some difficulty in commenting on your statement. My co-author, Mr. Deno of CP Rail, who has been involved personally with the development of the on-board monitoring system, does report success with the detection of incipient crankshaft failure through vibration analysis on test locomotives in the West. Although the system is admittedly in the early stages of development, CP Rail is optimistic about its extension to a wider range of operating parameters.

L. Luyckx (Reactive Metals): Taking exception with your statement that more emphasis is now put on rail abrasion resistance than on fracture toughness, I would like to point out that many premature rail failures occur by spalling on major inclusions a fraction of an inch below the top bearing surface.

In addition to the excellent trend towards higher strength rail with Cr-V or Cr-Mo to improve wear life, I suggest that inclusion control would minimize these spalling effects at much lower cost than Cr-V or Cr-Mo alloying and should be considered at least concomitantly with these alloying steps. Continuous casting of rail steel should be of considerable help in improving inclusion control of rail steel.

M. D. Roney: My comments referred to the situation in Canada where the heaviest unit train movements are concentrated in the Rockies, where curvature and gradient interact to cause high relative sliding of wheel/rail contacts. Consequently abrasion of the high curve rail, which is the prime location for spalling, occurs at a rate which is too rapid to permit the development of surface fatigue. Rails in curves exceeding 4° characteristically have a service life in these locations of some 1.5 to 3 years. This is not to say that spalling is not a problem, and in fact excessive plastic flow and surface fatigue have been occurring with increasing frequency. Where freight volume is high, very little rail is now replaced because of excessive vertical wear.

It is my understanding however that improved fracture toughness will serve to delay crack initiation by increasing the critical crack length to produce unstable fracture. This also allows a greater opportunity for detection prior to final fracture. In the higher cycle fatigue failures, initiation usually occupies a very significant proportion of the rail life, so that this would be a significant factor.

Spalling and shelling, however, are due to a low cycle fatigue, propagating from cracks initiated very rapidly by gross plastic deformation. In this case, the crack propagation stage occupies the greater proportion of the rail life. Consequently, although increased fracture toughness would aid in delaying high cycle fatigue (e.g. bolt hole breaks), and reducing the frequencies of brittle fracture, the critical surface fatigue problem would not be substantially affected. On the other hand, any increase in ultimate tensile strength, which would accompany improved rail steels would exert a distinctly positive effect.

You mention inclusion control, and I must agree with you that it deserves close scrutiny. The surface fatigue mechanism is not well understood, and it is very likely that cracks initiate from inclusions in many instances.

A. Sage (Highveld Steel and Vanadium): With reference to the toughness of rails -- is the author aware of the rails of increased toughness containing vanadium developed by British Steel Corporation and British Rail? These steels were not adopted because conditions in the U.K. did not justify the slightly higher cost, but they could be justified in Arctic conditions. This development was published in the Rail Conference sponsored by the Iron and Steel Institute, 1971. We are at present developing a vanadium rail steel for improved wear resistance which is more weldable than chromium rail steels. It is being tested in six practical locations.

M. D. Roney: In the paper, I have made reference to the attractiveness of a higher toughness, higher strength steel for high density Arctic service. There are several candidates for higher quality steels, including those employing vanadium. What is presently lacking to my knowledge is consistent results from long term service tests on these steels.

J. L. Mihelich (Climax Molybdenum): What is the fracture toughness criterion to be applied to rails? [This target would be useful to designers of new steels for this application. Work on alloy rails, e.g. Cr-Mo type, indicates alloy approval is similar in performance to fully heat treated grades]. What about fracture toughness requirement in the weld zones?

M. D. Roney: At the present time, there is no fracture testing criterion for rails. As I have mentioned, traditional toughness tests employing notches are of little use as rail steel is a characteristically brittle steel, Charpy V-notch energies of 2 ft lbf (3 J) at room temperature being common. It appears that a Charpy test which does not employ a notched specimen would be useful. However no correlation of this kind of test is presently available. Present specifications dwell on hardness and strength capabilities. Brittle failures are at present relatively infrequent, particularly under today's heavier wheel loads, which cause plastic flow and abrasion to predominate. Obviously a fracture toughness specification would be particularly valuable in high-density Arctic service.

M. R. Krishnadev (Laval University): Your paper tends to suggest that we have already sufficient technology to build an economically viable railway system in the Arctic because of our experience with the Quebec, Labrador and other railway systems. This is not entirely true. There is considerable scope for developing improved materials, even for conventional railway systems. Much more so when one considers the hostile environment and remoteness of the Arctic.

M. D. Roney: I do believe that a railway system incorporating our present knowlege of materials would be economically viable. The entire basis for the evaluation of technical and economic feasibility made by the Arctic Railway Study Group was the reliance on existing technology. It is true that considerable materials optimization should be done, but this would merely enhance the economics.

APPLICATION OF FRACTURE MECHANICS FOR DESIGN AND CONSTRUCTION OF LIQUID NATURAL GAS TANKS IN SHIPS

P. Tenge and O. Solli
Det norske Veritas
Veritasveien 1, 1322 Høvik,
Oslo, Norway

Five years' experience in fracture mechanics testing and analysis applied to liquid natural gas (LNG) ship tanks of 9% nickel steel and aluminum alloy 5083-0 is reviewed. Many of the principles are also relevant to LNG storage tanks. The main design criteria, with emphasis on "leak-before-failure", and the derived material requirements with respect to mechanical properties, fatigue strength, and fracture toughness are treated.

Fatigue crack propagation parameters at -162°C are given and used in a computation procedure developed for analysis of crack propagation rate and crack geometries of surface cracks in various types of stress fields. Fracture toughness properties at -162°C and -196°C using small scale tests and wide plate tests are reported. Also the fracture toughness of plates and welded joints of 9% nickel steel in running production is presented.

The significance of defects is analysed, and the requirements for non-destructive inspection and acceptance criteria are discussed, along with experience in the application of the requirements to the inspection of LNG-tanks during construction.

INTRODUCTION

Natural gas has become an energy source of prime importance, and in the years ahead there will be a considerable increase in its use. Some natural gas is handled as liquid, which for the last twenty years has been stored and transported with excellent safety and performance records. Experience gained in the design and production of LNG tanks is to a large extent incorporated in present standards and rules, and there is every reason to believe that present-day practice will ensure safe construction in the future. However, developments are rapidly moving towards higher allowable stresses, larger tank sizes, new types of tank design, and new materials and consumables, which must be managed carefully to prevent failures.

In 1970 the interest in LNG-ships with large cargo capacities was growing, and several designs were developed. One of these designs was the Moss-Rosenberg ship type having large spherical tanks with a system of protection against small leaks. The first ships were planned with cargo capacities of 29,000 m^3 and 87,600 m^3 and are today being built with a capacity of 125,000 m^3. A picture of a 87,600 m^3 LNG carrier is shown in Figure 1, and a tank shell section with the characteristic load carrying ring is shown in Figure 2. In 1969, only the main design principles had been approved. The procedures of stress and buckling stability analysis and evaluation of material properties had to be established. Part of the necessary extensive stress analysis and materials testing and evaluation was performed by the research branch of Det norske Veritas. In particular, the material compliance and design requirements imposed by the "leak-before-failure" criterion had to be demonstrated. In this respect, fracture mechanics was a proper tool to be used in defining the resistance against unstable fracture, the rate of propagation and geometry of fatigue cracks, and in establishing rational acceptance criteria for material defects and non-destructive testing (NDT) requirements.

This paper reviews experiences in the application of these different aspects of fracture mechanics testing and analysis to LNG-ship tanks of 9% Ni steel and aluminium alloy 5083-0. Many of the results are also applicable to other types of LNG ship tanks. The discussions regarding the fracture toughness properties are likewise relevant to land-based storage tanks and floating terminals for LNG.

Figure 1: 87,600 m^3 LNG carrier with 9% Ni steel tanks under construction

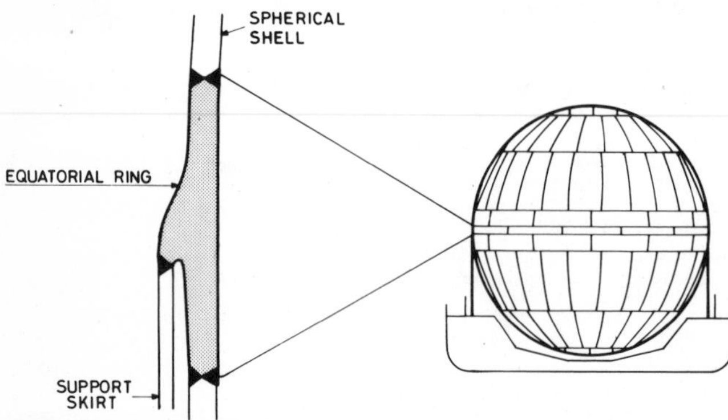

Figure 2: Section of spherical LNG tank and equatorial load-carrying ring in Al 5083-0

DESIGN CRITIERIA AND DERIVED MATERIAL REQUIREMENTS

The rules for ship construction are primarily set by the various ship classification societies. These rules are naturally much influenced by national and international standards. Also national authorities, such as the U.S. Coast Guard, may influence the requirements directly through the establishment of national codes. Spherical tanks protected against small leaks are today classed as "independent tanks, Type B" in the Rules of Det norske Veritas (1).

The overall governing principle for an LNG ship is that it should be a "fail safe" construction. A supplementary and ultimate safeguard is the requirement to "leak before failure" and that there be a small leak detection system. The cracks to be considered are fatigue cracks propagated by dynamic loads imposed by wave-induced forces. To satisfy the "leak-before-failure" criterion the following requirements must be fulfilled: a) Fatigue cracks shall not reach a critical size before penetrating the tank wall; b) critical crack size for through-wall cracks shall, with ample margin, be large enough to allow safe sailing from the time of leak detection until discharge and repair is possible.

The implications of these requirements are:

- the tank must be subjected to accurate stress analysis in all regions and details, and the stresses must be acceptably low;
- the size and geometry of fatigue cracks in critical regions and details at penetration must be determined;
- the fatigue crack propagation rate in the actual material (parent material, heat affect zone (HAZ), and weld deposit) must be established for the allowable dynamic stresses, in order to determine the extension of the crack after penetration;
- it has to be demonstrated that the critical crack size for static and dynamic loading is safely above the size of the total crack length after the worst 15-day period;
- the tank is to be provided with a small leak protection system which is able to detect and deal with a gas leak of a size corresponding at least to the maximum leak rate occurring during the worst 15-day period;
- during production, the absence of welding defects above the specified tolerable sizes is to be ensured by NDT.

To meet these requirements it is necessary to use fracture mechanics and accurate detailed stress

NOMENCLATURE

a	depth of surface crack, mm
a_o	initial depth of surface crack, mm
c	one half of total crack length, mm
c_o	one half of initial crack length, mm
d	tensile specimen diameter
E	modulus of elasticity, kgf/mm^2
K_c	stress intensity factor based on fracture load in wide-plate tests, $kgf/mm^{3/2}$
K_{max}	stress intensity factor based on maximum load in the load-deformation curve
K_{pop-in}	stress intensity factor based on first pop-in load in the load-deformation diagram
K_{Ic}	critical stress intensity factor for plane strain
ΔK	variation in stress intensity factor per cycle of loading
ΔK_{th}	threshold ΔK value for non-propagation
N	number of cycles
da/dN	crack growth rate, mm/cycle
R	stress ratio, $\sigma_{min}/\sigma_{max}$
rT	ambient temperature
t	plate thickness
δ_c	critical crack opening displacement, mm
δ_{pop-in}	critical crack opening displacement, based on first opo-in load, mm
δ_{max}	critical crack opening displacement, based on maximum load, mm
δ_5	elongation at fracture over 5d gage length
σ	stress, kgf/mm^2
σ_a	axial stress; σ_b bending stress
σ_{max}	maximum stress; σ_{min} minimum stress
σ_{mean}	mean stress; $\Delta\sigma$ stress variation

Table 1a

Materials for LNG tanks - Chemical Composition (wt %)

Designation	C	Si	Mn	P	S	Ni
Steels:						
ASTM A353/553	0.13[1]	0.13-0.32	0.90	0.035	0.040	8.5-9.5
NV-20-2[2]	0.08	0.15-0.35	0.40-0.70	0.025	0.020	

	Cu	Fe	Si	Mn	Mg	Zn	Cr	Ti
Aluminum alloys:								
ASTM B 209 5083-0	0.10	0.40	0.40	0.3-1.0	4.0-4.9	0.25	0.05-0.25	0.10
NV-AlMg4,5Mn[2]	0.10	0.50	0.5	0.3-1.0	4.0-4.9	0.30	0.05-0.25	0.10

[1] Single values are maximum values; [2] According to the Rules of Det norske Veritas (see ref. 1)

Table 1b

Material for LNG tanks - Mechanical Properties

Designation	Tensile Strength kgf/mm² (MPa)	Yield Stress $\sigma_{0.2}$ kgf/mm² (MPa)	Elongation $\delta_{2''}$ % min	Charpy-V impact (long transverse) Test temp. °C	Impact energy kgf m (J)
ASTM-A353	70-84 (690-820)	52.5 (515)	20	-195	3.5 (34)
ASTM-553	70-84 (690-820)	59.5 (584)	20	-195	3.5 (34)
NV 20-2	70 (690)[1]	52.5 (515)	20[2]	-196	3.5 (34)
	25 mm < t < 38 mm				
5083-0	28.1-35.9 (275-352)	12.7-20.4 (125-200)	16		
NV AlMg4.5Mn	28.1 (275)	12.7 (125)	16[2]		
	38 mm < t < 76 mm				
5083-0	27.4-35.1 (265-344)	12.0-20.4 (118-200)	16		
NV AlMg4.5Mn	27.4 (265)	12.0 (118)	16[2]		
	76 mm < t < 102 mm				
5083-0	26.7 (262)	11.3 (111)	16		
NV AlMg4.5Mn	27.4 (265)	11.2 (110)	12[2]		

[1] Single values are minimum values; [2] Elongation δ_5

analysis. In fact, designing and constructing to "leak before failure" is a situation where the full potential of fracture mechanics can be realised.

The tank system has, of course, to satisfy other design critieria specifying yield and ultimate stress safety levels and instability by buckling. Treatment of these criteria is, however, outside the scope of this paper. Various aspects of design safety of LNG carriers have been treated by Hansen (2).

MATERIALS AND TENSILE PROPERTIES

The principal materials used in LNG tank structures are 9% Ni steel [ASTM Specification for Pressure Vessel Plates, Alloy Steel, 9% Nickel, Double-Normalized and Tempered (A 353-74) and ASTM Specification for Pressure Vessel Plates, Alloy Steel, Quenched and Tempered 8% and 9% nickel (A 553-72)], aluminum alloy 5083-0 [ASTM Specification for Aluminum-Alloy Sheet and Plate (B 209-73)], austenitic stainless steels and a 36% Ni-Fe alloy (Invar). New 5% to 6% Ni steels have also been developed for LNG application, but have not yet been used for this purpose. Test results indicate that these materials may find application in the future.

9% Ni steel in ship tanks seems to be welded almost exclusively with high Ni consumables, whereas Al 5083-0 is generally welded using 5183 and 5356 Al wires. Only the properties of 9% Ni steel, Al 5083-0, and their weldments are considered in this paper.

An extract of the tensile property requirements and chemical composition for the two materials is given in Table 1. Normally, the specifications refer to the longitudinal tensile properties of plates and extrusions. The shell plates for spherical LNG-tanks were also tested in the long transverse direction to find the weakest direction. For Al-5083-0 the strength in the two directions was very similar and well above the requirements, and it was accepted that the specimens could be taken in any of the two directions.

The equatorial ring of the spherical tanks built of 9% Ni steel is produced from forged sections. The ring for the 29,000 m³ cargo capacity ships is produced from extrusions and for the 125,000 m³ ships from heavy plate approximately 200 mm thick, both of Al 5083-0. The equatorial ring is partially stressed in the short transverse direction, and the tensile properties in this direction were investigated. For the forged section in 9% Ni steel and the extruded section in Al 5083-0, the requirements for yield and ultimate tensile strength are the same in all three directions. For the 200 mm heavy plate, however, the requirements are lower in the short transverse direction. Initially, the short transverse properties were investigated for various parts of the plate. It is now required that each material producer carry out initial tensile testing with the specimen positions shown in Figure 3. For the heavy plates the elongation requirement (δ_5) is 10% in the short transverse direction. If this requirement is not fulfilled, a fracture mechanics investigation of the short transverse properties is required.

FRACTURE TOUGHNESS

Small scale fracture mechanics tests, as well as wide plate tests, employing linear elastic and crack opening displacement (COD) principles (3), have been used.

9 Ni Steel

As part of the initial feasibility study, 33 mm plates for the tank shell and 60 mm thick sections intended for the equatorial profile were tested (4). The ASTM procedure (E 399-72) was used, employing three-point bend specimens. The maximum, or pop-in, loads were taken as critical loads. Using K_{max} means generally an extrapolation of the linear elastic fracture mechanics. However, this procedure has given quite satisfactory calculated values for critical crack sizes determined experimentally in wide plate tests. It was judged that the K_{max} values could be applied for engineering purposes, provided the steel is tested in the thicknesses to be used in the construction. A summary

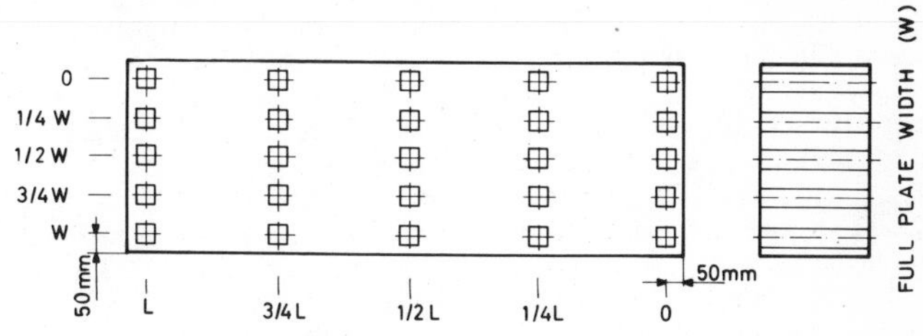

Figure 3: Position of tensile specimens for qualification testing of 200 mm heavy plate in Al 5083-0

Table 2

Fracture Toughness of 9% Ni Steel

	Test Temp. °C	Fracture toughness, K_{max} kgf/mm$^{3/2}$(MN/m$^{3/2}$) mean	min.	δ_c [1] (mm) mean
PLATE (35 mm)				
Parent Material	-162	567(176)	546(169)	0.26
	-175		594(184)	0.25
	-191	440(136)	434(135)	0.19
HAZ	-162	472(147)	405(126)	0.64
	-175		432(134)	0.36
	-185		340(104)[2]	> 0.21
Weld Metal	-162	483(150)	460(142)[3]	> 0.87
(Inconel 82)	-187	493(153)	463(143)[3]	> 0.84
EQUATORIAL SECTION (65 x 110 mm)				
Parent Material	-162	708(219)	705(218)	> 1.05
	-187		690(214)	0.44
HAZ	-162	676(210)	656(204)	> 0.86
	-189		367(114)[2]	0.15
Weld Metal	-162	609(188)	580(180)	0.47
(Inconel 112)	-188		561(174)	0.32

[1] δ_c at max load. For calculation of δ_c the 0.5 ligament depth has been used as center of rotation; [2] Valid or approximately valid K_{Ic}; [3] Failed by slow tearing

of the test results is given in Table 2. The material for the equatorial ring was electroslag remelted and the values given are for the transverse direction.

The production of the first LNG-carrier with 9% Ni steel tanks of 87,000 m^3 cargo capacity was followed by investigation of a large number of steel plates (5). The material was delivered with two different heat treatments:

23.5 mm plate: 900°C/12 min(air) + 790°C/25 min (forced air cooling) + 570°C/2.5 h (air)

30.5 mm plate: 900°C/15 min(air) + 790°C/30 min (water quenching) + 570°C/2.5 h (air)

Figure 4 shows the distribution of K_{max} values at -196°C from static tests. The higher toughness values obtained for the thicker plates are explained by the quenching treatment given to this material. The crack lengths were corrected for plastic zone size. Without corrections, the K_{max}-values are on an average 58 kgf mm$^{-3/2}$ lower for the 23.5 mm plate and 165 kgf mm$^{-3/2}$ lower for the 30.5 mm plate.

The dynamic fracture toughness of the same steels were investigated in the same study (5) using three point bend specimens with similar rectangular section, W = 2B. The specimens were impact loaded in an instrumented drop weight test machine using a damped blow. The specimens were tested at strain rates of the order of magnitude which may occur due to slamming and sloshing. It was clearly demonstrated that the fracture toughness of 9% Ni steel was not impaired by high strain rates. Figure 5 shows the comparison between the static and dynamic K_{max}-values. The correlation diagram for Charpy-V energy versus K_{max} is shown in Figure 6. Here, the results from the earlier investigation (4) are included, and they have here been corrected for plastic zone size.

During building of the first 87,600 m^3 ship, workmanship test weldments produced for each 50 m of production weld were also subject to fracture toughness testing (6). Three point bend specimens of square section were tested with the fatigue crack tip located in the HAZ 1 to 3 mm from the fusion

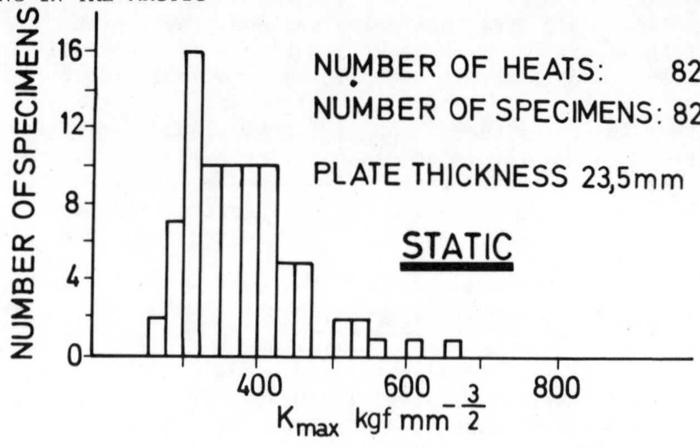

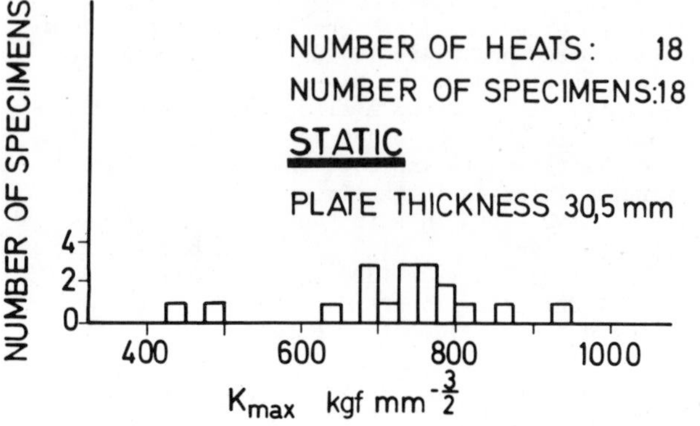

Figure 4: Static K_{max} values of 9% Ni steel plate

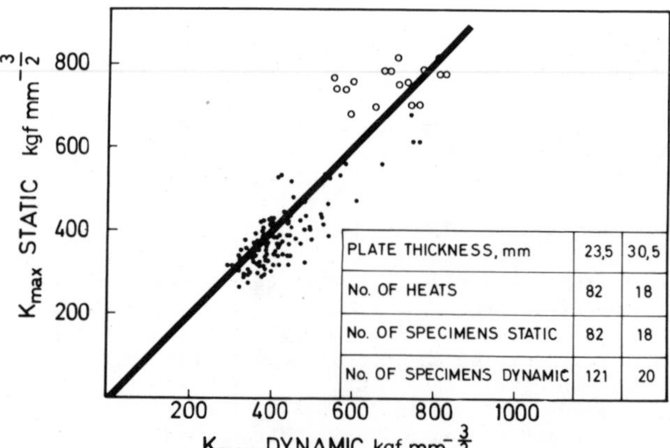

Figure 5: K_{max} static versus K_{max} dynamic for 9% Ni steel plate

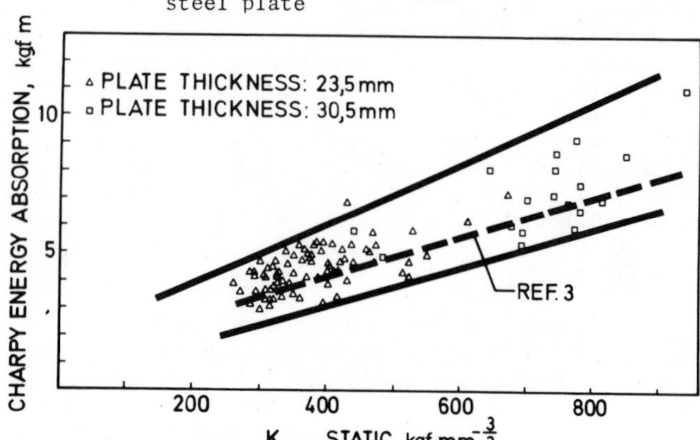

Figure 6: Static K_{max} values versus Charpy-V impact energy at -196°C for 9% Ni steel plate

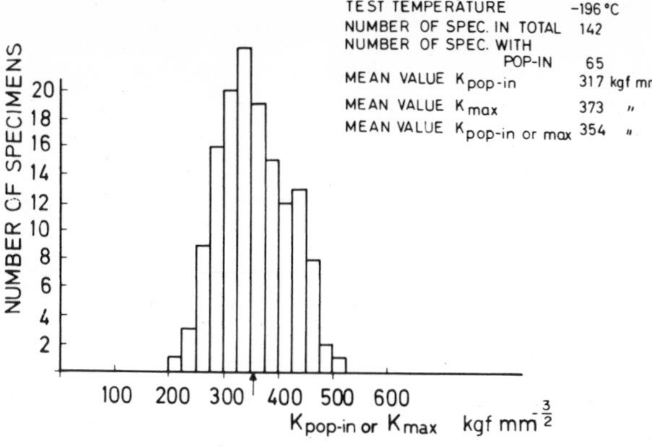

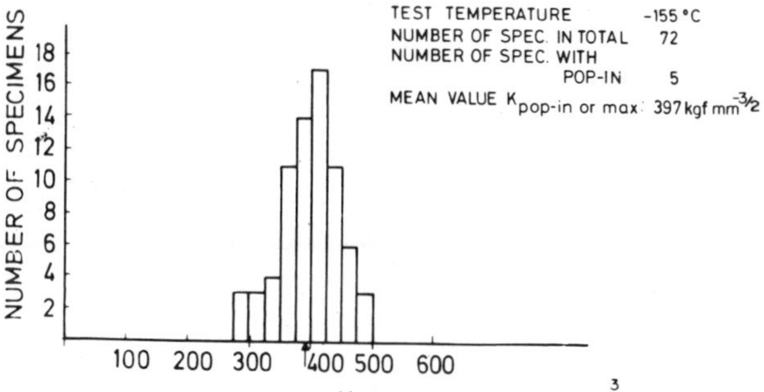

Figure 7: Static K_{max} or K_{pop-in} values in HAZ of 23.5 mm 9% Ni steel

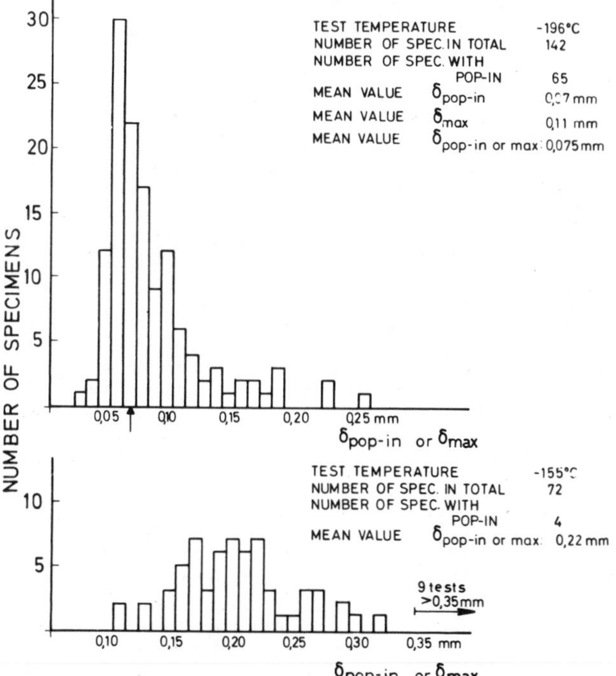

Figure 8: Static δ_{max} or pop-in values in HAZ of 23.5 mm 9% Ni steel

line. The notches were perpendicular to the plate surface. Figure 7 shows the distribution of the K_{max} values at -196°C and at -155°C in 23.5 mm plate. The distribution of the COD values is given in Figure 8. The K_{max} values are not corrected for plastic zone size. The mean K_{max} value at -155°C is 397 kgf $mm^{-3/2}$. This value is somewhat lower than that measured on the parent plate. However, K_{max} values as determined for specimens with different size and shape do not lend themselves to an exact comparison

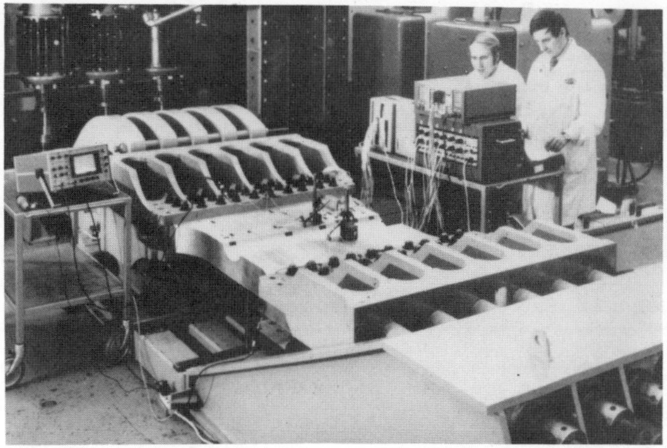

Figure 9: Wide plate testing of Al 5083-0 in a test machine of 800 t static and 320 t dynamic load capacity

of toughness. The mean COD value at -155°C is 0.22 mm, which is also somewhat lower than found earlier for the plate material and the HAZ.

Wide plate testing has been performed in a testing machine (Figure 9) of 800 t static and 320 t dynamic capacity with facilities for testing at all temperatures down to -196°C. Welded plates and plates containing a transverse surface groove, for simulation of the combined axial and bending stress in the equatorial ring, were used. When statically loaded to final fracture, the fatigue crack lengths ranged from 196 to 304 mm. An extract of the results is given in Table 3. The calculated K_c values for the grooved specimens were all high. The reason is clearly that the material permits local yielding around the crack tips in the surface region, and thus is able to sustain high surface stresses before final fracture. The K_c data obtained in wide plate testing for representative degrees of production tolerance deviations (misalignment, angular distortion) have given a lowest value of 401 kgf $mm^{-3/2}$ at -162°C for through-cracks extending from the weld toe in welded joints to 20 to 30 mm thickness. This is in good agreement with small tests. This fracture toughness level demonstrates the ability of 9% Ni steel weldments to sustain through-thickness cracks of at least 80 mm length in the weld HAZ of large plate sections (at least 80 mm) in LNG-tanks at the yield stress level of the weld metal. For the design stresses used today, the critical through-crack sizes in the same region of the weld will be at least 300 mm, the normally accepted tolerance deviations being considered. Extensive wide plate testing in Japan (7) has produced still higher toughness values. A comprehensive literature survey of the low temperature properties of nickel steels has recently been presented by Pense and Stout (8).

Al 5083-0

When first considering Al 5083-0 for use in the spherical LNG-tanks, it was well documented and supported by experience, that this material, including welds, has considerable ability to deform plastically even in the presence of sharp notches. However, the material was not tested in the large thicknesses to be used in the tanks. Therefore, small scale fracture mechanics tests and wide plate tests were performed.

The small scale three-point bend testing covered thicknesses of 20, 40, 100 and 200 mm of parent material, HAZ, and weld metal. The load displacement curves were characterized by ductile tearing, and the toughness improved from room temp-

Table 3

Wide plate fracture tests of 9% Ni Steel

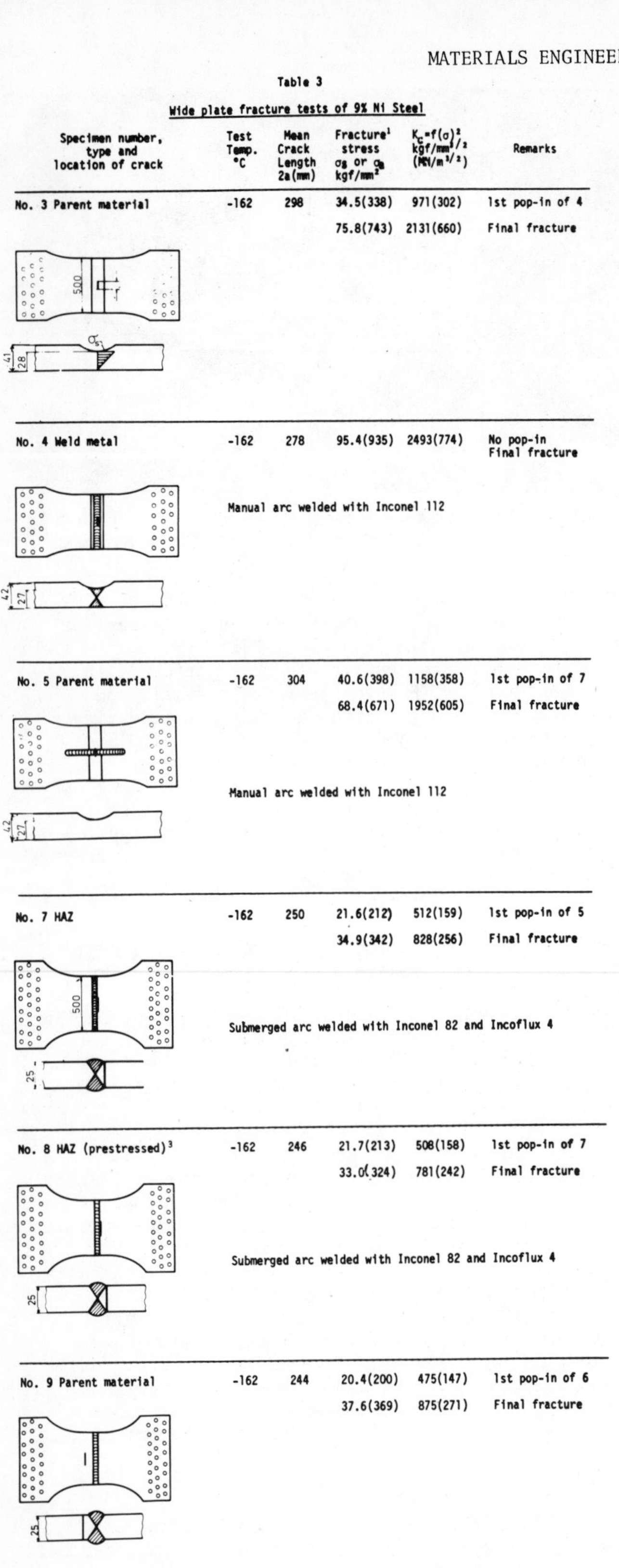

Specimen number, type and location of crack	Test Temp. °C	Mean Crack Length 2a(mm)	Fracture[1] stress σ_s or σ_a kgf/mm²	$K_c=f(\sigma)$[2] kgf/mm$^{3/2}$ (MN/m$^{3/2}$)	Remarks
No. 3 Parent material	-162	298	34.5(338)	971(302)	1st pop-in of 4
			75.8(743)	2131(660)	Final fracture
No. 4 Weld metal	-162	278	95.4(935)	2493(774)	No pop-in Final fracture
Manual arc welded with Inconel 112					
No. 5 Parent material	-162	304	40.6(398)	1158(358)	1st pop-in of 7
			68.4(671)	1952(605)	Final fracture
Manual arc welded with Inconel 112					
No. 7 HAZ	-162	250	21.6(212)	512(159)	1st pop-in of 5
			34.9(342)	828(256)	Final fracture
Submerged arc welded with Inconel 82 and Incoflux 4					
No. 8 HAZ (prestressed)[3]	-162	246	21.7(213)	508(158)	1st pop-in of 7
			33.0(324)	781(242)	Final fracture
Submerged arc welded with Inconel 82 and Incoflux 4					
No. 9 Parent material	-162	244	20.4(200)	475(147)	1st pop-in of 6
			37.6(369)	875(271)	Final fracture
No. 10 HAZ	-193	244	17.5(172)	407(126)	1st pop-in of 15
			30.7(301)	715(222)	Final fracture
Submerged arc welded with Cromete 6 and Incoflux 6					
No. 12 Parent material	-162	299	14.3(140)	401(124)	1st pop-in of 4
			33.3(327)	935(290)	Final fracture
No. 13 Weld metal	-194	199	20.6(202)	407(126)	1st pop-in
			46.5(456)	920(286)	Final fracture
Manual arc welded with Nyloid 2					
No. 16 Weld metal	-196	196	38.5(378)	753(234)	Final fracture
Manual arc welded with Nyloid 2					

[1] For grooved specimens, fracture stress means the max. surface stress (σ_s) in the bottom of the groove, based on gross area. For the plane specimens the fracture stress equals the gross axial stress (σ_a).
[2] $K_c = \sigma\sqrt{\pi a}[1-0.1(2a/W) + (2a/W)^2]$; $\sigma = \sigma_s$ or σ_a
[3] Prestressed prior to introduction of crack to a stress level of 25 kgf/mm² corresponding to water pressure testing of the tank

erature down to LNG-temperature. Neither the linear elastic nor the COD fracture mechanics methods has been applicable to thicknesses up to 200 mm.

Table 4 shows the results from a number of wide plate tests with through-plate fatigue cracks (9,10). All specimens fractured by large initial slow crack growth and ductile tearing. Therefore valid assessment of the fracture toughness was not possible. The net section fracture stress/yield stress ratios are in all cases greater than unity. The ductile failure mode and above-yield stress fracture do not permit exact evaluation of the critical crack sizes in the spherical tanks. The wide plate testing has demonstrated that the tank shell and the equatorial region will be able to sustain at least 500 mm through-cracks at the yield stress level. This indicates that the critical crack lengths at the design stress are considerably larger.

FATIGUE PROPERTIES

Fatigue Strength

The dynamic stresses due to the wave-induced loads are generally described by a long term distribution curve, such as shown in Figure 10. The number of load cycles during the lifetime of a ship (20 years) is 10^8. The damaging effect of all load cycles in the tank lifetime has to be considered, covering both initiation and propagation of fatigue cracks. Further, LNG tanks are subjected to low cycle thermal fatigue during cooling and heating of the tanks.

The weldments in fatigue testing should be produced under workshop conditions in full plate thickness and should have a quality which meet the specification for the tanks in question. The testing conditions, such as mean stress or stress ratio, should be close to that in the tanks. The fatigue strength of butt welds in 9% Ni steel and the aluminum alloy 5083-0 is presented in Figures 11 and 12. An example of the long-term distribution of the

Table 4

Wide plate fracture tests of Al 5083-0

Specimen number, type and location of crack	Test temp. °C	Mean Crack Length 2a(mm)	$\sigma_{0.2}$[1] kgf/mm² (MPa)	NSFS[2] kgf/mm² (MPa)	NSFS/$\sigma_{0.2}$
No. 1 Parent material	- 70	532	13.8(135)	17.0(167)	1.2
No. 2 Parent material	- 70	521	13.8(135)	18.2(178)	1.3
No. 3 HAZ	-162	290	14.3(140)	20.3(199)	1.4
No. 4 Parent material	RT	397	15.6(153)	24.4(239)	1.6
No. 5 Parent material	RT	383	15.6(153)	21.4(210)	1.4
No. 6 Parent material	-162°	354	16.9(166)	17.9(176)	1.1

[1] Longitudinal direction; [2] NSFS = Net section fracture stress = fracture load/Net section area

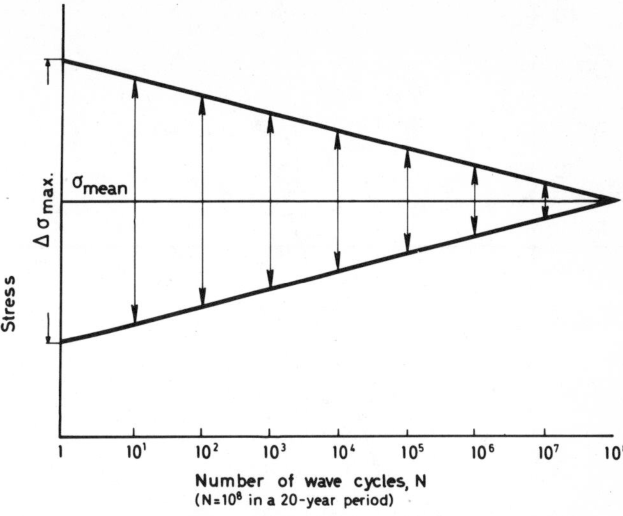

Figure 10: Long term distribution of dynamic (wave-induced) stresses in a 20-year ship operation period

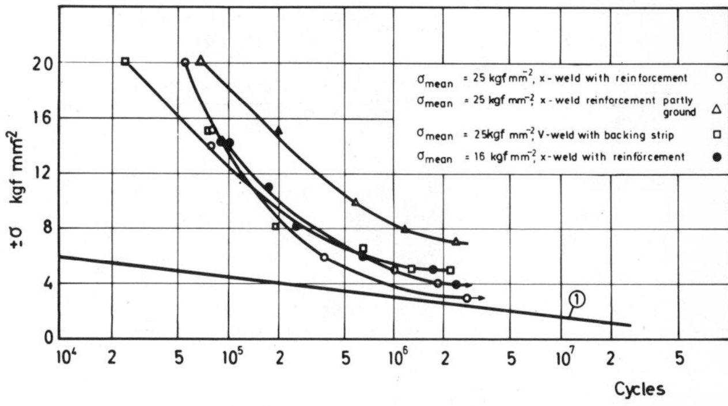

Figure 11: Fatigue strength of welded joints in 9% Ni steel. ["1" denotes example of 20-year distribution curve of wave induced stresses]

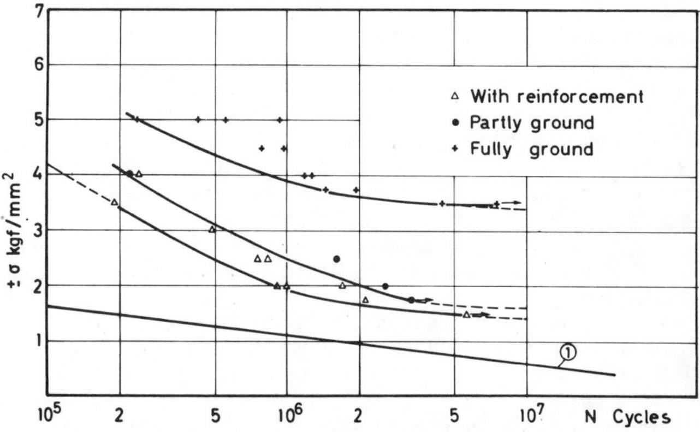

Figure 12: Fatigue strength of welded joints in Al 5083-0. ["1" denotes example of 20-year distribution curve of wave induced stresses]

wave-induced stresses in the lower part of the shell is also given. The Miner-Palmgren criterion (11) is normally used for evaluation of the cumulative fatigue damage. The basis for this criterion is:

$$\sum n_i/N_i = n_1/N_1 + n_2/N_2 \; .... \; n_i/N_i$$

n_1, n_2 .... n_i is the actual number of stress cycles on each stress level during the total lifetime of the ship, and N_1, N_2 .... N_i is the number of cycles to fracture for the respective stress levels according to the relevant endurance curve. According to the Rules of Det norske Veritas (1) the $\sum n_i/N_i$ should be less than 0.5 including the low cycle thermal fatigue. In the spherical LNG tanks approved by Det norske Veritas this sum value has always been less than 0.2 .

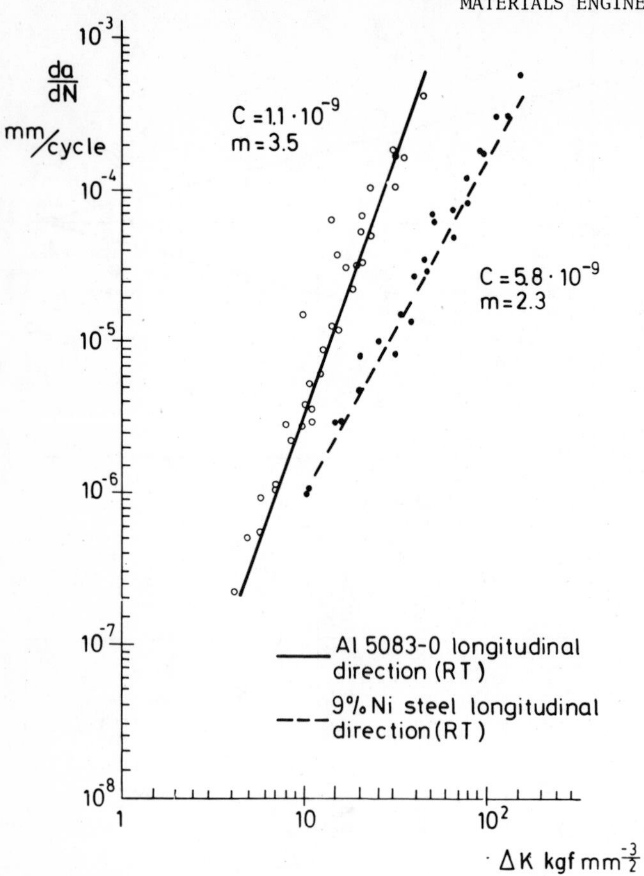

Figure 13: Fatigue crack propagation diagrams

Fatigue Crack Propagation

The propagation rate of fatigue cracks has been investigated applying the equation:

$$da/dN = C(\Delta K)^m \qquad (1)$$

The constants C and m were determined using center-slotted specimens by testing over a wide range of ΔK-values for different mean stresses. A linear relationship between log (da/dN) and log ΔK in the double logarithmic diagram was established, and the material constants were calculated by linear regression analysis. Typical relationships are shown in Figure 13 and the results are summarized in Table 5. It is demonstrated that the effect of mean stress is minor and that the propagation rate decreases with decreasing temperature.

The overall stress state in LNG tanks in ships is characterized by a constant mean stress with superimposed dynamic stresses. Therefore, the C and m values used have been established for certain representative mean stress levels. In the majority of laboratory tests performed elsewhere, the propagation parameters are determined for certain stress ratios, R. To illustrate the difference in propagation rate curves, three typical curves obtained for R = 0.33 and 0.40 (12,13) are included in Figure 14. The higher propagation rate in the low ΔK range for the constant σ_{mean} curves, due to higher σ_{max} when testing in this range, is significant. This difference should be borne in mind and corrected when applying propagation rate parameters obtained by testing at constant R-ratio structures subjected to a certain mean stress.

The largest number of load cycles in the long term distribution of dynamic stress (Figure 10) will, in general, give stress variations associ-

Table 5

Fatigue crack propagation parameters for Al 5083-0 and 9 Ni-steel

Material			Test No.	Test Temp. °C	σ_{mean} kgf/mm²	ΔK-range kgf/mm$^{3/2}$	Propagation rate parameters (metric units) C	m
	Plate	L	1	rT	7	3.4 - 42.2	1.1×10^{-9}	3.5
	Plate	L	2	-162	7	7.8 - 41.2	2.0×10^{-10}	3.7
	Plate	LT	3	rT	5	4.3 - 30.6	8.9×10^{-10}	3.6
Al 5083-0	Plate	LT	4	rT	7	5.2 - 70.9	3.1×10^{-9}	3.2
						4.3 - 5.2	1.1×10^{-17}	14.7
	Plate	LT	5	rT	9	5.0 - 40.5	7.5×10^{-10}	3.6
						4.5 - 5.0	3.2×10^{-15}	11.7
	Extruded section	LT	6	rT	7	5.1 - 41.8	6.2×10^{-9}	2.9
	Weld metal (Al 5183)		7	rT	7	6.0 - 63.2	6.0×10^{-9}	2.9
						4.5 - 6.0	2.3×10^{-13}	8.3
	Plate	L	8	rT	16	10.3 - 152.8	5.8×10^{-9}	2.3
	Plate	L	9	-162	16	15.3 - 152	5.6×10^{-10}	2.7
9% Ni	Plate	LT	10	rT	16	5.9 - 179	1.5×10^{-9}	2.6
	Plate	LT	11	rT	25	7.4 - 62.5	5.9×10^{-10}	2.9
	Weld metal (Inconel 82)		12	rT	16	10.2 - 152	2.3×10^{-10}	3.0
	HAZ		13	rT	16	9.9 - 173.5	5.4×10^{-11}	3.4

Specimen axis oriented in longitudinal direction (L) or specimen axis oriented in long transverse direction (LT)

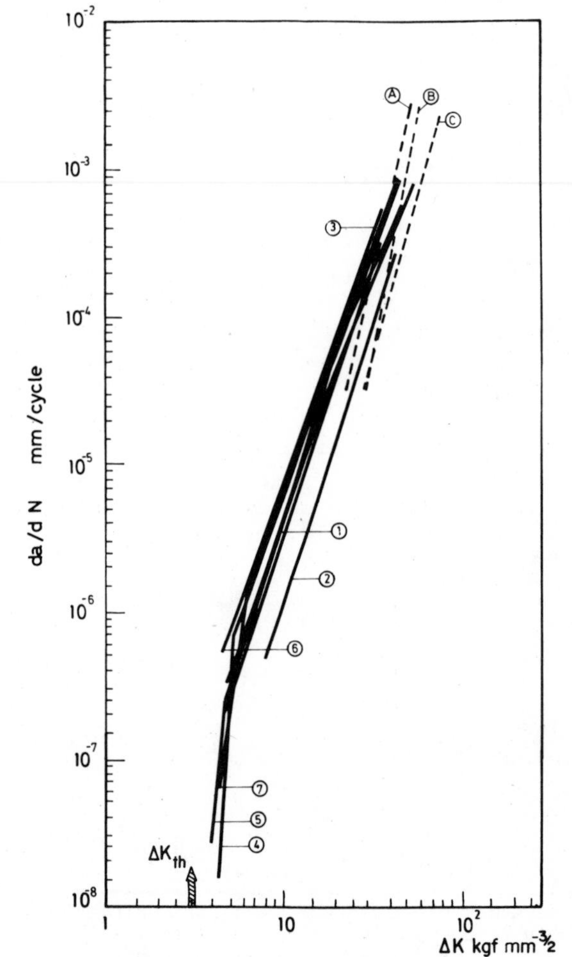

Figure 14: Fatigue crack propagation in Al 5083-0 (Numbers refer to test, see Table 5, constant σ_{mean}; (A) ref. 13, R = 0.4; (B) ref. 12, R = 0.33; (C) ref. 13, R = 0.4)

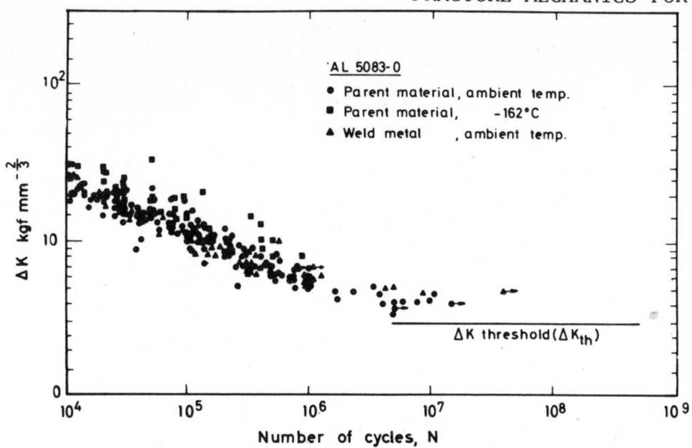

Figure 15: Dependence of ΔK on number of cycles in fatigue crack propagation testing

ated with low ΔK-values in the crack propagation diagram. By using propagation parameters based on constant R values in crack propagation calculations for ship tanks, the crack growth rate may therefore be under-estimated. Furthermore, published data are often limited to a narrow ΔK range and rather high ΔK values, also illustrated in Figure 14, ignoring the range of interest when dynamic stresses are low and cracks are small.

It has been shown that the threshold ΔK-value for nonpropagation for a number of materials can be rationalized in a general form through the ratio $\Delta K/E < 5.10^{-4}$ $mm^{0.5}$ (14). The fatigue crack propagation test data obtained in earlier investigations (9) have been used in an evaluation of the threshold ΔK values (ΔK_{th}) for both the 9% Ni steel and 5083-0 alloy. Tests were performed up to a maximum of 5 x 10^7 load cycles. The results are presented in Figure 15 for Al 5083-0. Each point represents a crack extension of approximately 0.5 mm. Points with arrows represent nonvisible crack growth. The ΔK_{th} value for Al 5083-0 is estimated to be 3 kgf $mm^{-3/2}$ at a mean stress of 7 kgf mm^{-2} and for 10^8 load cycles, representing 20 years of ship operation. The corresponding ΔK_{th} value for 9% Ni steel is 5 kgf $mm^{-3/2}$ at a mean stress of 16 kgf mm^{-2}. The test data indicate that the nonpropagation limits at low temperatures will be somewhat higher. It is considered that the values chosen in the later calculations are, on the whole, representative of the propagation properties of the materials investigated. The weld metal propagation properties have been found to be very similar to the properties of the parent plate.

Wide Plate Testing

A number of wide plates with synthetic surface defects have been tested under fatigue loading. The testing covered plate thicknesses from 25 to 85 mm. Some specimens contained a surface groove designed by a finite element method to give a stress distribution through the plate equalling the stress distribution in the equatorial ring.

The synthetic defects were produced by spark erosion to a depth of 3 mm and a width of 0.2 mm. From these defects a fatigue crack was initiated, after which fatigue crack propagation testing was performed. The stress amplitudes were changed in steps, and in part of the testing the stress distribution in 15 day and 6-month periods were simulated. The crack growth rate and the geometry of the propagating cracks have been compared with fracture mechanics calculations. The calculations have been performed using a specially developed computer procedure (15). Mathematical expressions for the stress intensity factors as a function of crack size, plate thickness, and varying stress distributions were established. Stress intensity factors for semi-elliptical surface cracks obtained by Rice and Levy (16) and Aamodt (17) were applied. Equations of the form of equation (1) for fatigue crack propagation in length and depth are integrated numerically, employing the propagation parameters, C and m, obtained for constant mean stress. One pair of C and m values are applied without taking account of the shift in propagation rate at low ΔK values. The program applies to all combinations of axial and bending stresses and plate thicknesses. The program can also take account of the long time distribution of dynamic stresses in a ship at sea (Figure 10). A constant threshold value of ΔK for nonpropagation, ΔK_{th}, is also applied in the program. Some results are shown in Table 6.

The agreement between calculated and experimentally measured crack dimensions after the various load steps is very satisfactory. This is also the case for crack geometry, as shown in Figure 16 where crack depth/crack length (a/2c) is plotted as a function of crack depth.

Calculations for other wide plate tests and also separate studies by Aamodt (17,18,19) have given similar results. All these results give confidence to apply this procedure to other stress conditions, crack sizes, and materials. The same procedure has been used to analyse the geometry of cracks at penetration in connection with evaluation of the "leak before failure" criterion. In Figure 17 the crack length at penetration for various ratios of axial and bending stresses is presented for a typical plate thickness and initial crack size.

To investigate the significance of real defects, a number of welded wide plates with internal lack-of-fusion defects have been tested. The testing covered both Al alloy 5083 and 9% Ni steel. One of the lack-of-fusion defects is seen in the fracture surface in Figure 18. The length is 103 mm and its depth varies from 6 to 9 mm. The plate containing this defect was fatigue loaded in a number of steps with varying stress amplitudes, as summarized in Table 7. The testing was performed until the fatigue crack had penetrated the plate and reached a length of approximately 270 mm on both sides. It was difficult to determine the crack extension by ultrasonics during fatigure testing. Fatigue crack front lines associated with the load steps given in Table 7 are indicated in Figure 18. A fatigue crack propagation

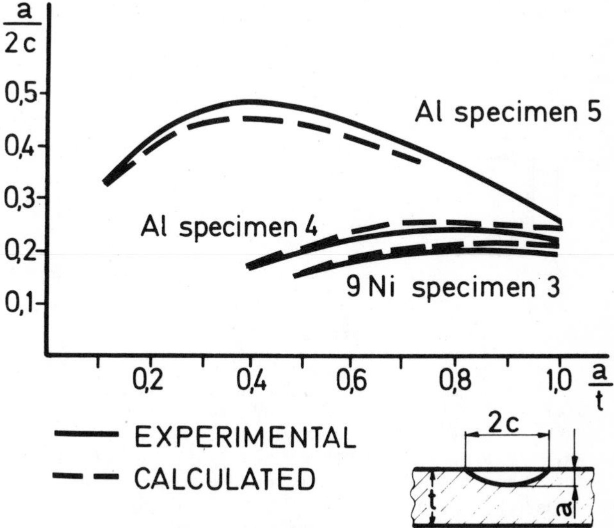

Figure 16: Geometry of propagating surface fatigue cracks. (Specimen Nos. refer to Table 6)

Table 6a

Fatigue crack propagation rates of surface cracks in 9% Ni steel wide-plate

Test Conditions	$\Delta\sigma_s$ kgf/mm² (MPa)	Number of Cycles per Load level N_i	Experimental a (mm)	Experimental 2c (mm)	Calculated a (mm)	Calculated 2c (mm)	Calculated[1] ref. (17) a (mm)	Calculated[1] ref. (17) 2c (mm)
Specimen No. 3								
			13.1	90.8	13.1	90.9	13.1	90.8
	22.0(216)	50000	19.8	105.2	22.2	107.4	17.3	96.7
	22.0(216)	20000	22.1	113.0	25.3	118.4	18.8	99.6
	22.0(216)	30000	24.8	128.7	29.7[2]	146.6[2]	21.07	104.4
	22.0(216)	20000	27.0	141.4	32.8[2]	173.8[2]	22.47	108.1

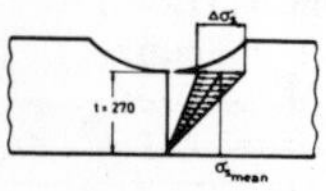

$\sigma_{s\ mean}$ = 16 kgf/mm²

Test temp. = -162°C

m = 2.7

C = 5.6 x 10^{-10}

[1] Reference (17) used m = 2.67; C = 2.4 x 10^{-10} (preliminary data); [2] Computer extrapolation

Table 6b

Fatigue crack propagation rates of surface cracks in Al 5083-0 wide-plate

Test Conditions	$\Delta\sigma_s$ kgf/mm² (MPa)	Number of Cycles per Load level N_i	Experimental a (mm)	Experimental 2c (mm)	Calculated a (mm)	Calculated 2c (mm)	Calculated[1] ref (17) a (mm)	Calculated[1] ref (17) 2c (mm)
Specimen No. 4								
			13.7	83.9	13.7	83.9	14.0	87.3
	2.20(22)	225000	15.2	85.7	15.1	85.4	15.3	89.2
	3.30(32)	22500	16.0	87.0	15.7	86.0	15.8	90.0
	4.50(44)	2300	16.2	87.0	15.9	86.2	16.0	90.4
	1.16(11)	2225000	18.6	90.3	17.4	88.0	17.4	92.6
	5.60(55)	225			17.4	88.1	17.5	93.0
	6.80(67)	50			17.4	88.1	17.5	93.0
	5.60(55)	225	19.3	90.8	17.5	88.2	17.5	93.2
	4.50(44)	2300	20.0	91.2	17.6	88.4	17.7	93.5
$\sigma_{s\ mean}$ = 7 kgf/mm²	3.30(32)	22500	21.0	92.9	18.2	89.2	18.2	94.7
Test temp. = ambient	2.20(22)	225000	21.6	94.5	19.6	91.2	19.6	97.7
m = 3.5	6.80(67)	17900	23.2	103.1	24.8	101.6		
C = 1.1 x 10^{-9}	5.60(55)	12000	23.4	108.8	26.4	106.0		
	4.50(44)	120000	34.2	159.2	33.3	145.6		

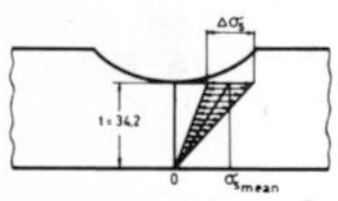

[1] Reference (17) used m = 3.5; C = 1.4 x 10^{-9} (preliminary data)

Table 6c

Fatigue crack propagation rate of a through-crack in Al 5083-0 wide plate

Test Conditions	$\Delta\sigma_a$ kgf/mm² (MPa)	Number of Cycles per Load level N_i	Experimental 2a (mm)	Calculated 2a (mm)
Specimen No. 6			186.8	186.8
	0.85(8.3)	5000	186.8	187.0
	1.67(16.4)	22000	195.2	197.1
	1.64(16.1)	22000	207.4	208.0
	1.62(15.9)	24000	222.6	221.3
	2.49(24.4)	2800	223.3	229.5

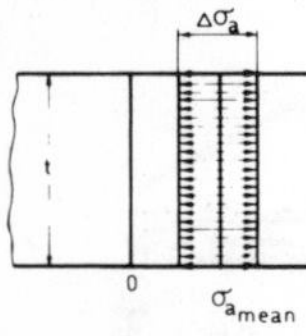

$\sigma_{s\ mean}$ = 7 kgf/mm²; spec. width = 500 mm/ Test temp. = ambient; m = 3.5; C = 1.06 x 10^{-9}

calculation has been performed by treating the defect as a semi-elliptic surface crack of length, 2c = 103 mm, equal to the length of the interior defect. Further, the depth, a = 20 mm, has been chosen as the distance from the bottom front of the defect to the plate surface. This calculation showed that the crack will penetrate the plate during step 11 (Table 7) in the testing program, while the experiments showed that penetration occurred during step 38. Similar calculated early penetration has also been obtained for a second 70 mm welded plate with a lack-of-fusion defect.

Table 6d

Fatigue crack propagation rate of surface cracks in wide plate of Al 5083-0

Test Conditions	$\Delta\sigma_s$ kgf/mm² (MPa)	Number of Cycles Per Load Level N_i	Experimental a (mm)	Experimental 2c (mm)	Calculated a (mm)	Calculated 2c (mm)
Spec. No. 1			3.0	50.0		
	6.00(59)	186000		53.5		
	5.10(50)	62000		61.0		
	5.10(50)	18000		63.9		
	0.56(5.5)	2220000	22.1	63.9	22.10	63.90
	1.70(16)	220000	22.6	65.0	22.59	64.58
	2.84(28)	22000		65.3	22.86	65.02
	3.96(39)	2000		65.8	22.97	65.14
	5.10(50)	220		65.8	23.00	65.18
	6.24(61)	22		65.8	23.00	65.18
	5.10(50)	26000	24.6	70.5	25.95	69.08
	5.10	20000	26.2	74.6	28.12	73.74
	5.10	22000	28.7	79.8	30.55	78.48
	3.96(39)	40000	31.7	85.4	32.42	82.38
	3.96	32000	33.2	90.6	33.94	85.70
	3.96	28000	35.2	96.0	35.29	88.74
	5.10(50)	16000		100.5	37.19	93.18
	5.10	20000	37.7	106.8	39.61	99.06
	5.10	21000	40.7	113.0	42.21	104.66
	5.10	20000	43.7	119.5	44.72	112.28
	5.10	20000	46.6	127.5	47.27	119.24
	3.96(39)	19000		132.3	48.28	122.04
	3.96	30000	48.3	139.6	59.87	126.56
	3.96	18000		146.2	50.83	129.32
$\sigma_{s\ mean}$ = 7.5 kgf/mm²	3.96	20000	49.8	152.4	51.30	132.44
Test temp. = ambient	3.96	21000		162.1	53.03	135.74
m = 3.5	5.10(50)	21000	51.3	171.7	55.76	143.92
C = 1.1 x 10^{-9}	5.10	12000		177.2	57.32	148.70
ΔK_0 = 3.0 kgf mm$^{-3/2}$	5.10	21000	52.8	186.4	60.03	156.20
	5.10	9000	55.8	192.3	61.19	160.88
	5.10	21000	60.8	202.6	63.87	169.72
	5.10	8000	63.3	207.6	64.88	173.28
	5.10	31000	69.3	225.6	68.63	189.72
	5.10	21000	71.8	238.0	71.61	204.32
	5.10	19000	73.0	248.8	74.28	221.38
	5.10	29000	76.5	267.9	78.97	260.06

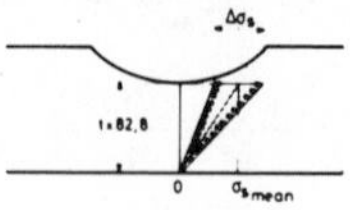

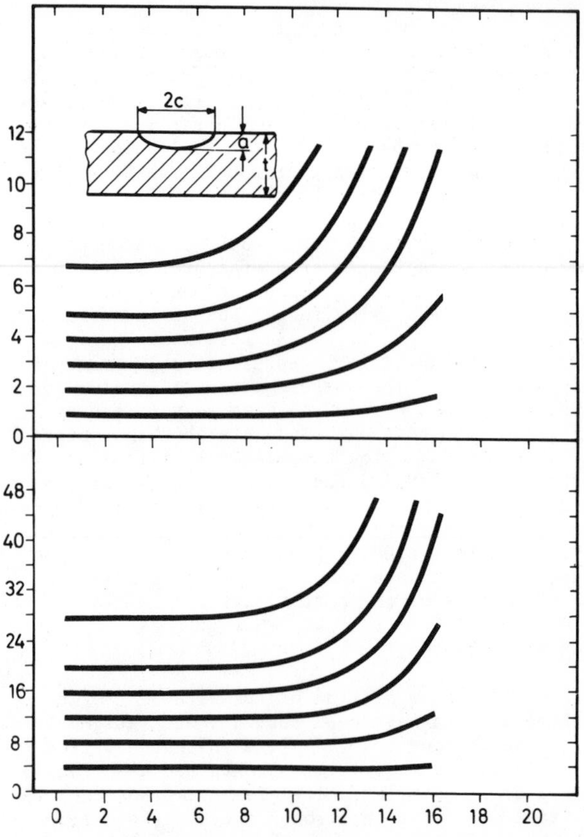

Max. stress variation in a 20 year ship operation period. $\Delta\sigma_{max}$, kgf mm^{-2}

Figure 17 Crack length at penetration for combined axial and bending stresses calculated for Al 5083-0 [C = 1.1 x 10^{-9}; m = 3.5 (metric units); ΔK_{th} = 3 kgf/mm$^{3/2}$; $\Delta\sigma = \Delta\sigma_a + \Delta\sigma_b$, $\Delta\sigma_a = \Delta\sigma_b$; $a_o/2c_o$ = 0.25; t = 71 mm]

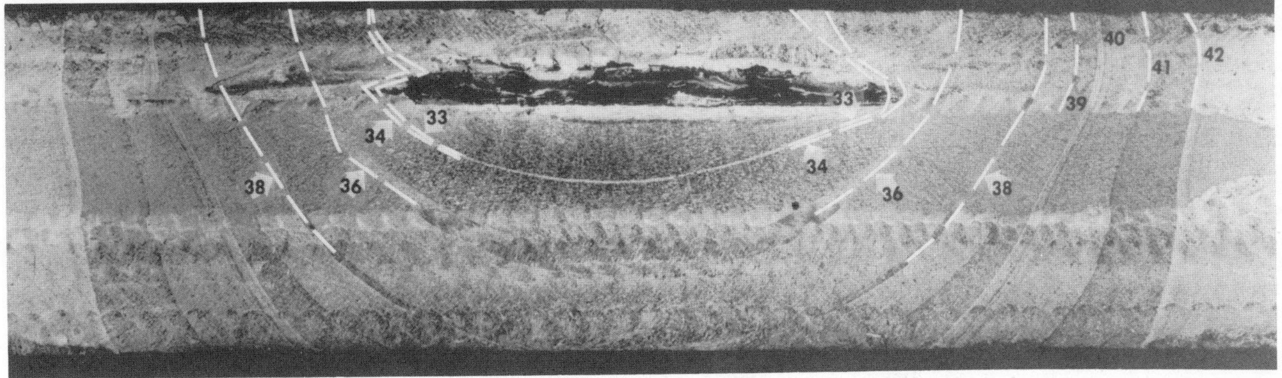

Figure 18: Fracture surface of welded Al 5083-0 wide-plate specimen with a lack-of-fusion defect. [Numbers refer to test steps indicated in Table 7]

This simplified model for treating interior defects has clearly given conservative results. It is believed that this procedure will also give conservative evaluations when analyzing the significance of other types of interior defects.

SIGNIFICANCE OF DEFECTS

Defects in 9% Ni Steel Welds

The welding methods mostly used in welding 9% Ni steel are automatic and semi-automatic gas metal arc (MIG), submerged arc and manual shielded arc welding. Only high Ni consumables are used for ship tanks today. Incomplete fusion is a frequent defect in MIG-welding due to the sensitivity to variations in welding conditions, including groove preparation. Both lack of side wall fusion and lack of interrun fusion may occur. Regarding solidification cracks, the fully austenitic type of microstructure in high-Ni steel deposits may, under certain circumstances, be hot-crack sensitive. Occurrence of incomplete root penetration and slag inclusions seem to be normally distributed. Porosity is seldom encountered.

Hydrogen cracks do not seem to have been found in 9% Ni steel weldments. This observation is ascribed to the high hydrogen solubility in the weld deposit, and also to the low carbon content. The presence of finely dispersed austenite may also contribute.

Among the type of defects observed, lack of fusion along the side wall is considered the most severe. This defect is planar, is found in planes oriented nearly perpendicular to the main acting stress direction and is located in a region of the joint which can have reduced fracture toughness. Besides (and this is relevant for other welding defects) such defects are located in a region where residual welding stresses and local stress concentrations will invariably occur. Solidification cracks and lack of interrun fusion are equally severe from the point of view of sharpness.

Table 7

Dynamic Loading of Al 5083-0 Plate with a lack-of-fusion defect

Test step	$\pm\sigma$ kgf/mm²	Test cycles (x 10^5)	Test step	$\pm\sigma$ kgf/mm²	Test cycles (x 10^5)
1	1.5	0.15	23	2.0	0.4
2	1.0	0.3	24	2.0	1.4
3	2.0	0.5	25	2.0	1.5
4	1.0	0.5	26	2.0	1.6
5	2.0	0.15	27	2.0	1.5
6	1.0	0.25	28	2.0	1.5
7	2.0	1.0	29	2.0	0.2
8	1.0	0.5	30	3.0	0.86
9	2.0	0.35	31	2.0	1.0
10	1.0	0.25	32	3.0	0.35
11	2.0	0.5	33	2.0	0.35
12	2.0	0.5	34	1.0	0.65
13	1.0	0.25	35	2.0	0.35
14	2.0	1.0	36	1.0	0.81
15	2.0	1.0	37	2.0	0.2
16	2.0	0.37	38	1.0	0.1
17	2.0	0.63	39	2.0	0.05
18	2.0	0.80	40	1.0	0.2
19	2.0	1.0	41	2.0	0.05
20	2.0	1.0	42	1.0	0.25
21	2.0	0.3	43	2.0	0.03
22	2.0	1.0			

Defects in Al 5083 Welds

In the welding of large LNG-tanks in aluminum alloy, only automatic, semi-automatic and manual MIG-methods are in use today. Lack of fusion will readily occur with deviation from the tightly specified welding parameters and the comprehensive requirements of joint preparation. Hot cracking is observed from time to time and porosity is frequently encountered. Lack of fusion and hot cracks are considered to be the defects of the greatest severity.

Unstable Fracture Initiated at Weld Defects

Initiation of unstable fracture directly from defects in plate butt welds at -162°C seems in practice to be virtually impossible for both 9% Ni steel and Al 5083-0. The high toughness values imply correspondingly large critical crack sizes even at the yield stress. Only grave errors in the treatment of the material or in welding can lead to weld defects corresponding to critical cracks. This situation will, however, be critical only if such a defect is missed during NDT, which would also have been an extremely grave error. In general, these remarks will probably also cover most welded connections in LNG tanks, although the material dimensions, local stress conditions, and possible NDT difficulties can reduce the large margins of safety.

Propagation of Fatigue Cracks from Weld Defects

The significance of welding defects in LNG tanks in ships is primarily that they may act as initiators for possible fatigue cracks. A fracture mechanics calculation procedure to determine fatigue propagation of surface cracks in tank butt welds subjected to a long-term spectrum of wave-induced forces has already been presented (15,20). Correspondence between calculations and large plate fatigue tests has been good and thus has given confidence in the application of the method.

Some examples of propagation of surface cracks in typical butt welds of 9% Ni steel are presented in Figure 19 for various sizes of starting defect of semi-elliptical shape with aspect ratio of $a_o/2c_o = 0.25$. The height and length after twenty years of ship operation is given as a function of the stress. The stress refers to the maximum stress variation, $\Delta\sigma_{max}$, occurring in the long-term distribution diagram of dynamic stresses. The example in Figure 19 refers to a linear through-thickness stress distribution consisting of equal tensile and bending components. This stress distribution is assumed to be normal and is caused by stress concentrations representative of the usual workmanship and workshop practice. A plate thickness, t, of 25 mm has been chosen and fatigue crack propagation assumed at -162°C.

Figure 20 gives examples of crack propagation diagrams for Al 5083-0. The conditions are similar to those applied in Figure 19, except that a plate thickness of 45 mm has been chosen.

When defects occur because of lack of fusion, they may naturally be very long. Practical experience tells us that these defects will appear from time to time. It is therefore realistic to assume infinitely long defects ($a_o/2c_o = 0$) as the worst case in a fracture mechanics analysis. Figure 21 gives the height extension of long surface cracks of various initial height in Al 5083-0, where a pure tensile stress has been assumed.

Diagrams of the type presented can be used as a basis for the determination of acceptance criteria for sharp defects. Estimates can also be made with respect to interior cracks, the stress intensity factor being approximately the same for a semi-elliptical surface crack and for a buried elliptical crack with the same axis. This procedure applies to cracks of much smaller height and length than the plate thickness and to shallow, long defects

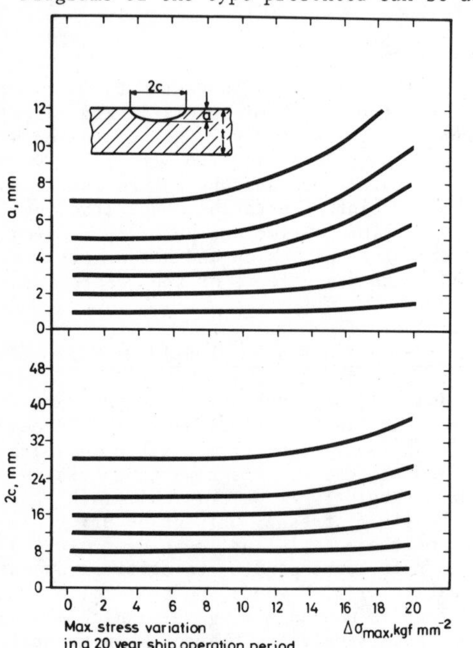

Figure 19: Fatigue propagation of semi-elliptical surface cracks in 9% Ni steel at -162°C. [$C = 5.6 \times 10^{-10}$, m = 2.7 (metric units); $\Delta K_{th} = 5$ kgf/mm$^{3/2}$, $\Delta\sigma = \Delta\sigma_a + \Delta\sigma_b$, $\Delta\sigma_a = \Delta\sigma_b$, $a_o/2c_o = 0.25$, t = 25 mm]

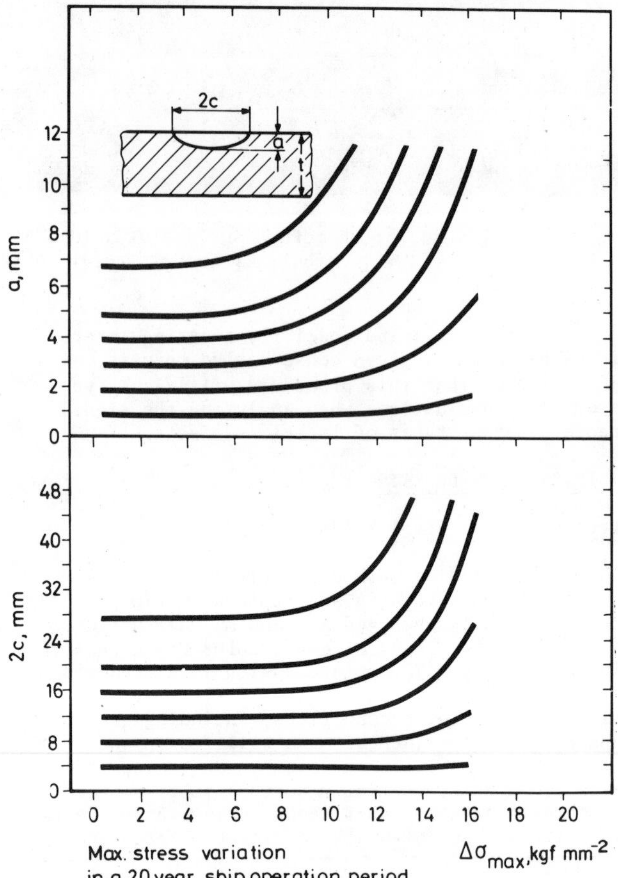

Figure 20: Fatigue propagation of semi-elliptical surface cracks in Al 5083-0 at -162°C. [$C = 2.0 \times 10^{-10}$; m = 3.7 (metric units); $\Delta K_{th} = 3$ kgf/mm$^{3/2}$; $\Delta\sigma = \Delta\sigma_a + \Delta\sigma_b$, $\Delta\sigma_a = \Delta\sigma_b$; $a_o/2c_o = 0.25$; t = 45 mm]

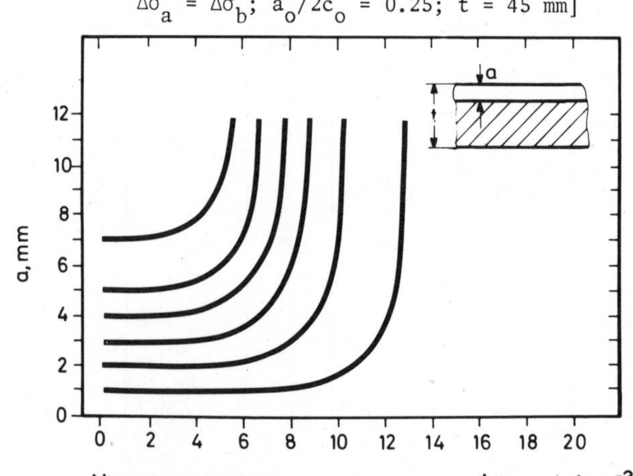

Figure 21: Fatigue propagation of long surface cracks in Al 5083-0 at -162°C. [$C = 2.0 \times 10^{-10}$; m = 3.7 (metric units); $\Delta K_{th} = 3$ kgf/mm$^{3/2}$; $\Delta\sigma = \Delta\sigma_a$; $a_o/2c_o = 0$; t = 45 mm]

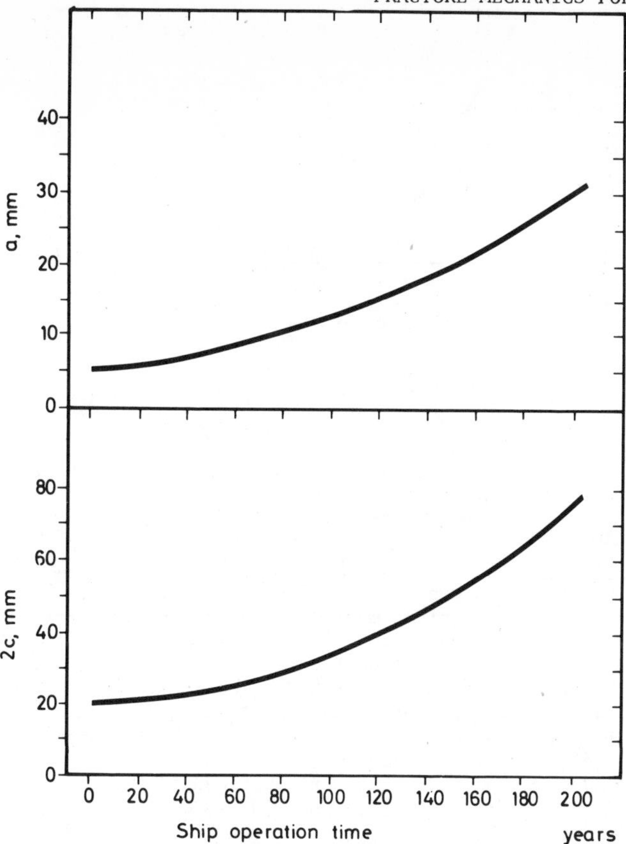

Figure 22: Crack length and depth in Al 5083-0 versus ship operation time. [$C = 2.0 \times 10^{-10}$; $m = 3.7$ (metric units); $\Delta K_o = 3$ kgf/mm$^{3/2}$; $\Delta\sigma = \Delta\sigma_a + \Delta\sigma_b$; $\Delta\sigma_a = \Delta\sigma_b \cong 4.5$ kgf/mm^2 $a_o/2c_o = 0.25$; $t = 45$ mm]

away from the surface. However, a more precise evaluation for interior cracks situated at different depths for combined tensile and bending stress distributions is more complex. The assessment of crack extension of interior defects using approximations from the propagation of surface defects have proved to be on the conservative side for reasons discussed elsewhere (20). This is supported by the fact that fatigue tests of welded wide plates with real defects gave less crack extension of the lack-of-fusion type than calculated.

For evaluation of safety margins for fatigue crack growth, it may be appropriate to perform calculations for periods exceeding the lifetime of the ship. This is exemplified in Figure 22.

The significance of hot cracks in the surface region has been investigated in one special, practical case. Small cracks, 0.5 to 2 mm high and 1 to 6 mm long, appeared in production and were detected by dye penetrant inspection. The hot cracks were formed in regions of the weld having a feathery microstructure (21) and strong microsegregation of magnesium. The fatigue properties were investigated and compared with a fracture mechanics analysis. The conclusion was that the behaviour of the cracks could be predicted well by the analysis, and that crack propagation in the micro-structure surrounding the hot cracks was similar to that in the weld metal. In principle, this was also a confirmation of the validity of the curves of the type shown in Figures 19 to 21.

NON-DESTRUCTIVE TESTING

Current Practice

Radiography is at present the NDT method most generally relied upon for testing welded joints in cryogenic tanks. The most widely used standard for LNG storage tanks, (API 620, 1973) as well as the newest standard, the British Standard "Draft for public comment" (73/37611 DC), specify radiography as the only NDT method. A condensed survey of acceptance criteria for different weld defects, as well as NDT methods and extent of testing required, has been given by Wintermark et al. (22).

Possibilities and Limitations of Defect Evaluation

The limited ability of radiography to find and size planar defects must be realized. For instance, if only radiographic testing is applied to inspect welds in 9% Ni steel and Al 5083-0, most lack-of-fusion defects will not be detected, but hot cracks perpendicular to the plate surface, lack of penetration, porosity, and slag inclusion will normally be detected. However, only the length can be determined.

The inspection of welded joints in 9% Ni steel and Al 5083-0 for sharp surface defects is best done with dye penetrants. However, the depth extension of the defects has to be determined by other methods.

Ultrasonic testing is at present the only practical and satisfactory method for detecting and sizing embedded planar defects. Detection and evaluation of side-wall and interrun lack-of-fusion, incomplete penetration, longitudinal cracks, and inclusions is at present best done using conventional angle-beam pulse-echo testing. The determination of size is then done by a combination of amplitude and edge location techniques, as the allowable height is usually smaller than the sound beam diameter and the allowable length usually greater. The absolute errors in size determination using ultrasound under field conditions are not at all negligible (23,24). The amplitude technique is especially burdened with uncertainties, as the ultrasound echo amplitude varies with defect orientation, defect surface geometry, and the ability of the defect to reflect and transmit ultrasound. Lack of fusion in aluminum with the surfaces of the defect in contact will transmit the greater part of the sound (25). Residual stresses may be able to close such a planar defect to a higher degree than in steel because of the greater contraction of aluminum. Edge location errors are associated with errors in positioning and angulation of the probe and the definition of the sound beam diameter. Furthermore, in making allowance for the total errors in the determination of size by ultrasonic testing, the mapping procedure and human errors also must be considered. Defects near the surface of an unmachined weld are difficult to detect because of the reflections from the uneven surface. In 9% Ni steel welds with high Ni deposits, sound transmission and therefore ultrasonic testing, is inhibited by large attentuation. The detection and evaluation of sidewall lack of fusion is, however, possible.

Choice of Testing Methods

The choice of testing method must be based on its ability to detect and evaluate the defects encountered in the actual construction. Evaluation against real defects using destruction tests (bend tests, metallographic sections) is therefore of importance. In the specifications of Det norske Veritas for independent spherical LNG tanks with a small leak protection system, ultrasonic testing is required as the principal method for the detection of internal planar defects. To detect surface defects, the use of dye penetrants is required.

Investigation of Real Defects

To evaluate the ultrasonic method and to establish its acceptance level, the ultrasonic response from real defects in butt welds has been investigated (26). Separate investigations have also been carried out to establish test procedures for special structural details.

Investigation of 9% Ni steel welds did not reveal special problems connected with the detection of cracks and lack of fusion in the weld sidewall. These defects gave echoes well above those from the transition weld/parent metal, which have amplitudes of 6% to 8% compared with those from a 3.2 mm diameter reference hole. Evaluation of defects in high-nickel weld metals by ultrasound is, however, as stated earlier, impossible.

A metallographic and ultrasonic investigation of planar, long, internal defects in butt welds in Al 5083-0 produced under workshop conditions in 40 to 50 mm thick plate is described in the following. The investigation involved X-welds with 60° grooves similar to the production welds. The main part of the investigation was done on six different weldments. These defective weldments were chosen after ultrasonic testing in an initial classification of a larger number of test welds. In addition, twelve defects cut from different production welds were included in the investigation.

The ultrasonic investigation was performed using Krautkramer MWB series miniature narrow band angle beam probes of nominal frequencies of 2 and 4 MHz and nominal angles of 41°, 56°, 65° and 43°, 54°, 66° for the two probes respectively. The procedure was similar to the ASME method (27) except that a 1 mm diameter drilled hole was used as reference. The plates were examined from both sides. Approximately forty defects were detected, excluding the twelve from different production welds. When investigated from both sides of the plate each defect usually gave the same echo heights. The defect lengths were determined using the 6 dB drop method and were generally longer than 15 mm.

All plates examined ultrasonically were investigated metallographically. Metallographic sections approximately 10 mm apart were microscopically mapped with registration of defect positions, type, size, orientation, and opening. Some defects were opened by careful cutting and bending and subjected to a more thorough investigation using an electron scanning microscope and analysed with respect to Mg and other elements.

The majority of the defects encountered were of the lack-of-fusion type, most containing oxides. However, bright metallic surfaces were also observed when opening the defects, and it seems reasonable to believe that partial metallic contact between the opposite surfaces also existed. The defects were situated mainly along the weld sidewall and in the root region. The positions and sizes of all the defects are plotted in a compiled form in Figure 23. The sidewall defects were oriented more or less parallel to the sidewall. The defect sizes ranged from 0.3 to 8 mm in height, and the openings were sometimes almost 0.3 mm. The metallographic investigations confirmed the length measurements obtained from ultrasonic testing.

Figure 24 shows the correlation between echo amplitude and the defect main parameter, height, for the 4 MHz probe at 60°. The defect height is the largest extension of a defect measured in the metallographical sections. The projection of the defect in a plane perpendicular to the plate surface is usually considered as the effective crack height

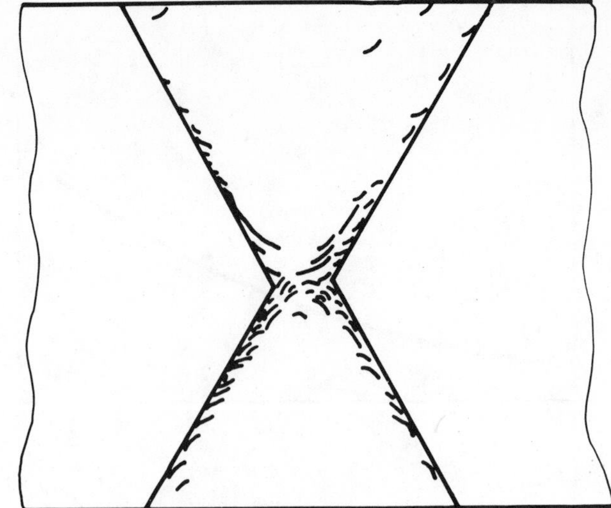

Figure 23: Compilation of studied defects in 45 mm plate of Al 5083-0

in the fracture mechanics analysis. Therefore the indicated defect sizes may be considered somewhat conservative from a fracture mechanics point of view.

When two different echo heights were obtained from the same defect, the smallest only is plotted in Figure 24. All the indicated defects are long with lengths of approximately one sound beam diameter or more. The twenty-eight defects not revealed by the ultrasonic examination are included in the figure. The lines corresponding to the 100% reference level (RL, 1 mm diameter hole), 20% RL, ASME 20% RL (3.2 mm diameter reference hole), and the noise level represented by response from the weld deposit (up to 8% RL) are also drawn. Echo heights, including scatter-bands, for 1 and 2 mm flat machined reflectors oriented normal to the ultrasonic beam are also given.

The most obvious result of this investigation is the scatter in recorded echo heights and the low level of most echoes. The orientation of the defects and their surface geometry is favourable for the ultrasonic probe used. The scatter and low echo levels are to a great extent probably a result of the varying ability of the lack-of-fusion defects to transmit and reflect the ultrasound. A lower boundary curve is indicated in Figure 24. This curve must, however, be regarded as somewhat uncertain owing to the limited number of measurements. When

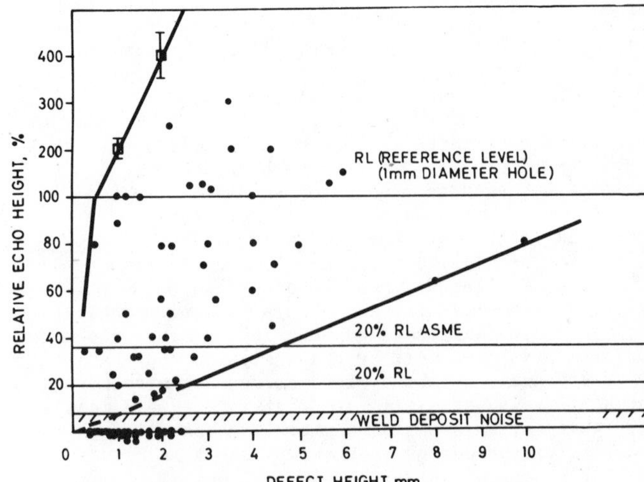

Figure 24: Ultrasonic response versus height of long planar defects in Al 5083-0 butt welds for 4 MHz, 60° angle probe. (● - real defects; ⊕ - artificial flat reflectors.)

using this lower boundary, and assuming twice the weld deposit echo height as a practical noise level, it should be possible to detect all defects greater than 2 mm in height. When using 20% RL as acceptance level, all defects 2.5 mm or more in height will be detected, whereas 20% RL ASME corresponds to detection of all defects above 4.5 mm in height.

Acceptance criteria and NDT Procedures

The consequences of a failure will be the overall governing factor in establishing acceptance requirements for weld quality and control procedures. In LNG ships a complete break-down of the tank system following production errors cannot be tolerated. In a refined assessment of the significance of defects the tank type in question should be considered. In principle, the requirements should be more rigorous going from secondary barrier systems to small leak protection systems and even more to primary tanks without any protection system.

As an example, the acceptance criteria applied to butt welds in LNG ships with spherical tanks in Al 5083-0 of Moss-Rosenberg design are discussed. Even if these tanks are designed to the leak-before-failure concept, defects which would probably lead to a leak cannot be tolerated. No repairs, or only a minimum, during service is naturally a production goal. The highest dynamic stresses in butt welds are found in the region of the tank bottom, where a typical nominal $\Delta\sigma_{max}$ value of 39 MPa may occur.

Considering fracture mechanics fatigue crack propagation analyses, a safety factor on the calculated nominal stresses, and also test results from large-scale experiments with welds containing real defects, it has been judged safe to accept long internal defects up to approximately 2 mm. It is, nevertheless, not realistic to specify that such defects are generally acceptable since their presence indicates something wrong with respect to materials or welding procedures.

The ultrasonic reference criteria should be correlated to the height of real defects, and detectability down to approximately 2 mm is obviously required. To detect defects of 2 mm the ultrasonic acceptance criteria have been chosen in accordance with correlation diagrams such as Figure 24. The general requirements with respect to the acceptance criteria for ultrasonic testing butt welds are presented in Table 8.

One implication of the 20% RL requirement is that many long defects even shallower than 2 mm may be repaired, but occasionally long defects 2 mm high may pass. When a planar defect is shorter in length than one third of the plate thickness, it is allowable if the echo is below 100% RL. This

Table 8

Acceptance requirements for ultrasonic testing of butt welds in Al 5083-0

	Ultrasonic acceptance requirements (l = length of defect, t = plate thickness, RL = reference level, 1 mm hole)
Embedded, planar defects	Echo < 20% RL, allowable 20% RL ≤ echo < 100%, allowable if l < t/3. Echo ≥ 100% RL, not allowed

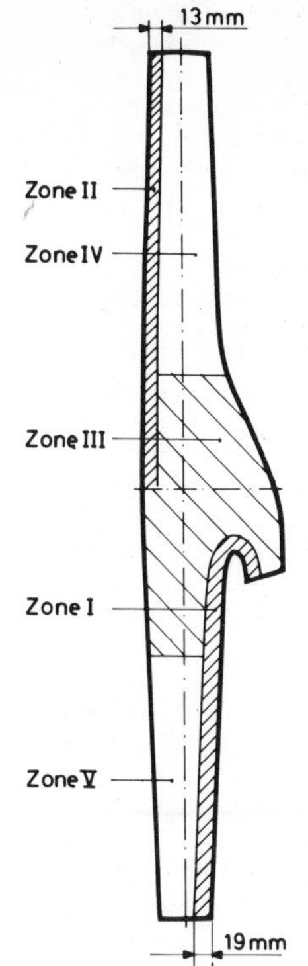

Zone	Largest acceptable dimension of internal discon-tinuities	Minimum acceptable distance, A, between two discon-tinuities		
	d(mm)	Size d(mm) from	to	Amm
I and II	6,4	4,0	6,4	4d
III	9,5	6,4	9,5	4d
IV and V	12,7	9,5	12,7	4d

Figure 25: Acceptance levels for an equatorial profile in Al 5083-0

means that, according to Figure 24, a defect 15 mm long and 10 to 12 mm high in a 45 mm plate may be acceptable.

The margins between tolerable defect sizes and the sizes that would cause unacceptable fatigue crack growth are quite large and are primarily a safeguard against possible uncertainties in NDT. The acceptance requirement for dye penetrant and visual inspection is that planar surface defects are not allowed. In radiographic testing butt welds for internal non-planar defects, such as slag inclusions and porosity, the requirements of the ASME Boiler and Pressure Vessel Code, (Sec. VIII, Div. 2, AI 531) are applied. The extent of testing butt welds in LNG spheres is in principle 100% ultrasonic, and in the initial production 100% radiographic testing has also been applied. Limited dye penetrant testing is required. However, depending on factors such as weld location in the tank, welding position, and the general workmanship quality, the extent of testing may be increased or decreased.

The requirements in ultrasonic testing 9% Ni steel are in principle similar to those applied for Al 5083-0, except that less rigorous ultrasonic acceptance criteria are used. Radiography, is, to a larger extent than for Al, required to test the weld deposit itself.

A special structural detail where fracture mechanics has been used to define acceptance levels for materials defects is the equatorial load-carrying ring. The acceptance defects for specific tank sizes are specified in Figure 25.

Experience Gained from Non-Destructive Inspection

The ultrasonic test procedures for aluminum tanks have until now been applied to two LNG ships of 29,000 m^3 cargo capacity and two of 125,000 m^3 capacity. Several other ships of 125,000 m^3 cargo capacity are under construction, and the same requirements are applied. Present experience is that the requirements are well met by proper workmanship and welding procedures. Investigations of defects removed for repair also indicate satisfactory correspondence with requirements. Inspection has to date been carried out manually, but automated and mechanised procedures may be introduced in the future. Nowadays, the yards' inspection and control systems, as well as the qualification of their inspectors, must be approved by the classification body. Furthermore, the NDT is supervised by a surveyor from the classification society, qualified and specially trained in ultrasonic testing. Reports from individual inspectors are kept for approval and records.

Concerning radiographic testing, there is ample confirmation that planar defects detected by ultrasonics are rarely found on the films.

Dye penetrant inspection is extensively used in production to detect possible lack of penetration or surface cracks between layers. A final inspection for surface defects is made to reveal possible hot cracks. Dye penetrant testing has proven to be a necessary complement to ultrasonic testing.

As a general rule, the specifications also have room for separate approval of defects extending outside the specified requirements, judgment being based on whether or not a repair will improve the overall situation. Experience shows that in several instances special evaluation by fracture mechanics and special NDT has saved repairs.

Acknowledgments

The authors wish to thank the many co-workers who have been engaged in the different investigations, S. Fredheim, O. Førli, A. Karlsen, Th. Kristoffersen, E. Onsvaag, P. Solberg and H. Ulle. In addition the authors are specially grateful to P. Solberg for assistance in the preparation of the paper.

REFERENCES

1. Det norske Veritas Rules for the Construction and Classification of Steel Ships. 1976 edition, 773 pages. Det norske Veritas, Veritasvein 1, 1322 Høvik, Norway.
2. H. R. Hansen, "Some aspects concerning the design of LNG-carriers". Det norske Veritas, Information No. 10, 1972.
3. British Standard DD19:72, "Methods for Crack Opening Displacement (COD) Testing". British Standards Institution.
4. P. Tenge, O. Solli, European Shipbuilding, 1972 (1) p. 9
5. P. Tenge, A. Karlsen, B. Mauritzon, Norwegian Maritime Research 1975, (1), p. 11.
6. "Fracture toughness of production welds in 9 Ni steel". Det norske Veritas Report, to be published.
7. "Studies on 9 Per cent Nickel Steel for Moss-type Liquified Natural Gas Carriers", Nippon Steel Corp., Japan, 1973.
8. A. W. Pense and R. D. Stout, "Fracture Toughness and Related Characteristics of the Cryogenic Nickel Steels". WRC Bulletin 205/May 1975.
9. P. Tenge and O. Solli, Norwegian Maritime Res. 1973, vol. 1, (2), p. 1
10. R. A. Kelsey, R. H. Wygonik and P. Tenge, "Crack Growth and Fracture of Thick 5083-0 Plate under Liquified Natural Gas Ship Spectrum Loading", ASTM STP 579, 1975, p. 44.
11. M. A. Miner, J. Appl. Mechanics, 1945, vol. 12, pp. 159-164.
12. J. G. Kaufman and R. A. Kelsey, "Fracture Toughness and Fatigue Properties of 5083-0 Plate and 5183 welds for Liquified Natural Gas Application", ASTM STP 579, p. 138, 1975.
13. G. Argy, P. C. Paris and F. Shaw, 1975, ASTM STP 579, p.96.
14. J. D. Harrison, Metal Construction and British Welding J.,1970, vol. 2, pp. 93-98.
15. O. Førli, Det norske Veritas, 1973, Report 84 5064.
16. J. R. Rice and N. Levy, J. Appl. Mech., 1972, vol. 39, pp. 185-194.
17. B. Aamodt, P. G. Bergan, and H. S. Klem, Proc., 2nd. Intl. Conf. Press. Vessel Tech., San Antonio, Texas, 1973, pp.911-921.
18. B. Aamodt, Dissertation, Div. Struct. Mech., Univ. Trondheim, Norway, 1974.
19. B. Aamodt, Proceedings, World Congress, Finite Element Methods in Structural Mechanics, Bournemouth, England, 1975. (Reprinted in Det norske Veritas Pub. No. 92, 1976)
20. P. Tenge, O. Solli and O. Førli, 1975, ASTM STP 579, p. 10.
21. H.Nakagawa, M. Katoh, F. Matsuda and T. Senda, Welding Research Abroad, Jan. 1974, p.45.
22. H. Wintermark, P. Tenge, O. Solli, "Acceptance Criteria and Inspection of LNG-tanks," IIW meeting, Public Session, Budapest, 1974.
23. "NDT aspects of the significance of weld defects", Proc. SANDT Special Seminar NDT 17, Weling.Inst. 1972.
24. V. N. Whittaker, Non-destructive Testing, 1972, vol. 5 (2), pp.92-100.
25. B. G. Martin and C. J. Adams, Materials Research and Standards, 1966, vol. 6 (9), pp. 440-442.
26. P. Tenge, O. Solli and O. Førli, Acceptance criteria for weld defects and non-destructive inspection procedures for LNG tanks in Ships", Proc., Quality Control and Non-destructive Testing in Welding, The Welding Institute,Institute of Quality Assurance,Non-Dstructive Testing Society of Great Britain, London, Nov. 1974.
27. Boiler and Pressure Vessel Code, Section VIII, Rules for Construction of Pressure Vessels. (Div. 2, Alternative Rules, 1974) ASME.

EDITORIAL NOTE: P. Tenge was not able to present this paper in person at the conference, but the background philosophy to the paper was reviewed by D. J. Burns (University of Waterloo). The short discussion which ensued was consequently not directly related to the content of the paper and has not been included in this Volume.

CONCLUDING REMARKS

J. F. Clayton (Gulf Oil Canada): I would like to make a couple of comments on aircraft in the Arctic in contention with the introductory remarks of the Session Chairman.

Aircraft can be a problem in the Arctic. The maximum stresses in an aircraft occur on landing and at other times landing gear is usually at ambient temperature. As failures do occur, and high strength Cr-plated steels are used, this matter deserves special attention in the Arctic.

Landing strips in the Arctic are often on or near the sea and float planes land in the sea. Thus salt can be picked up. In jet turbines, where the blades have a high Ni content, hot corrosion is a problem. Sodium chloride accelerates this. Another engine problem in the Arctic stems from engine manufacturers' allowance of up to 25 h running on any available fuel. If this fuel is an aviation gasoline it contains lead, which has a disastrous effect on turbine life.

F. E. King (CN Rail Research): My introductory observation that it is unlikely that any important design or material changes will be required for aircraft operating in Arctic service was based on the fact that aircraft have operated safely and successfully for years in this environment. Also, it was assumed that the aircraft would be used in a supportive role. If, however, the role of the aircraft increased appreciably in the future, then specially designed aircraft would be justified to cater to problems such as those mentioned by Mr. Clayton.

SESSION CHAIRMAN'S SUMMARY

F. E. King

The session on "Materials in Arctic Transportation" was mainly concerned with rail transportation considerations. Three of the four papers, and one prepared discussion, were directed towards materials selection for this mode. There are two reasons for this. Railways have, for many years, operated in rather harsh winter environments in North America where minimum temperatures were not much higher than those expected in the Arctic. Consequently, there is a large body of knowledge regarding the problems of maintaining a service under conditions of blowing snow and very low temperatures. The other reason is that studies on the feasibility of rail transportation in the Arctic, funded by the Government of Canada, have provided a comprehensive survey and evaluation of this body of knowledge, prior to this conference. Since many of the people attending the conference were metallurgists, or engineers familiar with the problems associated with low temperature metallurgy, there was some surprise at the rather limited use of special alloys, or heat treatment, to overcome low temperature problems. The speakers also pointed out the limited applicability of the experience of development of specifications for pipe line steel to railroad operations.

In summary, it appears that the position of the speakers is tenable and an Arctic railway based on existing technology could be built and operated successfully. There is obviously room for considerable materials optimization to enhance both the safety and the economic position of such a railway and this would no doubt occur if an Arctic railway becomes a reality.

Unfortunately, Mr. Tenge was not able to make an oral presentation of his paper dealing with the application of fracture mechanics to the design and construction of liquid natural gas tanks in ships and, therefore, no discussion on the contents of his paper was possible. In addition to this, no paper was offered on the construction of ships with ice-breaking capability for use in transportation in the Arctic. There is no doubt that ships have a role in the transportation of Arctic resources and it is hoped that future conferences on materials selection will be able to deal more fully with this subject.

PIPELINES

INTRODUCTION

A. B. Rothwell and J. D. Embury

In the preparation of a preamble to the papers on pipelines, it is perhaps fitting to have a joint statement from an author interested in the development and sales of alloy steels and an academic. A glance at the papers in these sessions indicates very clearly the emergence of a new relationship between basic research and engineering utilization in this area.

A decade ago, the properties demanded of structural steels were relatively unsophisticated and easily within the bounds of existing technology. The stringent demands for engineering performance in the Arctic, however, have resulted in a real crisis in the ability to spell out the materials requirements: One of the writers, who a little while ago was directly involved in the development of materials for these applications, vividly recalls the bewildering uncertainty at that time as regards ultimate specification requirements. This did not, and does not, arise because of ignorance or lethargy on the part of regulatory bodies, but because the known requirements really refer to systems rather than materials. The need to specify the safe loading and operating conditions for a pipeline demands consideration of strength, fracture toughness, performance of welds in large-scale tests, freedom from environmental effects and the ability to specify crack arrest characteristics. The real metallurgical understanding of the control of these parameters in terms of steelmaking practice and fabrication techniques is minimal, at least for steels which lie at the limit of what can currently be considered tonnage steels. In essence, the structure of the material is by-passed as a metallurgical control; the parameters of the fabrication method (e.g. controlled-rolling practice) are being used to establish correlations with the results of a system test (e.g. crack arrest in a pressurized vessel). The structure of the material is now too complex to provide a simple vehicle for quality control. The papers which deal with the importance of yielding behaviour clearly indicate this. The yield characteristics are altered by the presence of non-ferritic constituents too complex to be unambiguously identified even in the electron microscope, and by the pattern of residual stresses associated with these constituents. Ten years ago, the relationship between yield stress, however defined, and structure in anything which could be considered a tonnage steel was well defined. Today, we find ourselves bound to admit that we no longer understand in a quantitative fashion the form of the initial stress-strain curve in the tensile test, and thus cannot predict, on the basis of structure, the most basic design parameter of the system. Hence, the vital need to direct research toward the meaningful specification of properties and the importance of imbuing young metallurgical engineers not only with a basic understanding of microstructure, but also of the elements of plastic design and stress analysis.

Similarly, it is of value to consider the function of both alloy development and process optimization. The work from France, Japan and Canada all clearly indicates not only the need to understand the basic science behind the use of desulphurization, controlled rolling, and microalloying additions, but also the need for a systematic economic analysis of their value. It is worthwhile to ask not only whether we can produce an 80 or 90 ksi (550 or 620 MPa) yield strength structural steel, but also whether it is really economical in the long term. To what extent should we use alloy additions, not to provide strength per se, but for the reliable attainment of properties, in lieu of the ability to control the fabrication process to a sufficient degree? A paper on the comparative economics of the approaches taken in the structural steel area would have been of real value in these sessions.

The papers on materials selection and property specification clearly indicate the difficulty in designating the salient mechanical properties of the materials in question. It is useful to take stock of the situation; the properties demanded are on the fringe of currently available technology, which raises the question of product reliability for a product of which more than 5 Mt are likely to be produced in the next few years.

It would be inappropriate, however, to end on this note. The challenge of the Arctic has stimulated the most rapid and widespread development in the quality of tonnage steels which has ever been known. Some ten years ago, one of the writers was involved in the production of some 30,000 t of API 5LX60 skelp to a guaranteed transverse impact energy -- the first time, it is believed, that such a criterion was ever applied in this field. The major pipe mills of the world have truly revolutionized their approach in the intervening years, and specifications which would have been considered outrageous ten years ago are now met as a matter of course. Nor are the major companies standing still; we hear in these sessions of new process developments, many of which are directly stimulated by the needs of the Arctic. It must be acknowledged, then, that much has been, and is being done. It is hoped that this conference will help not only to stimulate this effort still further, but also to orientate it in productive directions.

Finally, it remains to say that the topic reveals to all of us that the challenge of engineering in the Arctic is in part economic, in part technological or ecological, but above all educational. It is to put ourselves simultaneously at the frontiers of technology and science and to realize that the problems which will be encountered can only be dealt with if we are able to broaden our scope and integrate the materials requirements into the overall systems approach.

PROPERTY REQUIREMENTS FOR PIPELINES

F. S. Somerville
Canadian Arctic Gas Study Ltd.
550 Sixth Ave. S.W.,
Calgary, Alberta T2P OS2
Canada

and

T. C. Slimmon
Northern Engineering Services Co., Ltd.
635 Sixth Avenue S.W.
Calgary, Alberta T2P OT5
Canada

At present there is no significant demand for line pipe having strength levels in excess of Grade 70 (480 MPa yield strength), but rather for larger diameter pipes of thicker wall having low temperature notch toughness. Full scale fracture initiation tests on 48 in. (1220 mm) pipe at temperatures down to -57°C have shown that the critical crack size, 2c, can be predicted by the relationship,

$$K_c^2\pi/8c\sigma_F^2 = \ell n[\sec(\pi M\sigma_H/2\sigma_F)]$$

For fracture control of gas pipelines, Charpy energy levels suggested by various investigators may be employed for moderate designs. For extreme design conditions either further testing is necessary or crack arrestors may be utilized. Consideration must also be given to girth welding, including the weldability of the parent material, the properties required in the girth weldment, and the properties and characteristics which can be achieved by various welding procedures. Further development work is necessary to increase the number of available processes for welding Arctic pipelines, although present day technology does provide acceptable solutions.

PROPERTY REQUIREMENTS

Strength

"Super projects", such as the Alyeska oil pipeline presently under construction and other oil and gas pipeline projects which are under study to move Arctic resources, involve high pressure transmission systems using large diameter pipe. In order to optimize pipeline economics, pipe of the highest commercially available grade is specified. It appears that for as-rolled materials, a practical limit to yield strength may be in the 70 to 80 ksi range (480 to 550 MPa). At present, the highest grade which has been offered by most manufacturers has a yield strength of 70 ksi (480 MPa), although higher strength levels are certainly possible. For the time being, the users appear to be content with strength levels up to and including 70 ksi (480 MPa).

Increasing requirements for large diameter pipe having moderate and heavy wall thicknesses for the "super projects" challenge the technology to produce the required notch toughness properties for low temperature Arctic applications and maintain the strength and weldability desired.

The use of quenched and tempered materials may offer a metallurgical solution to the attainment of high strength levels in heavy wall thickness materials of lean chemical composition while maintaining suitable notch toughness properties down to low temperatures. The use of quenched and tempered plate for pipe manufacturing, or the quenching and tempering of formed pipe, are alternatives which will see continued use.

Perhaps the only restriction on strength (manufacturing problems excluded) is the increasing tendency towards environmental cracking in higher strength materials. Figure 1 shows the increasing susceptibility to stress corrosion cracking of X70 steels as compared with X52 steels, reported by Fessler (1).

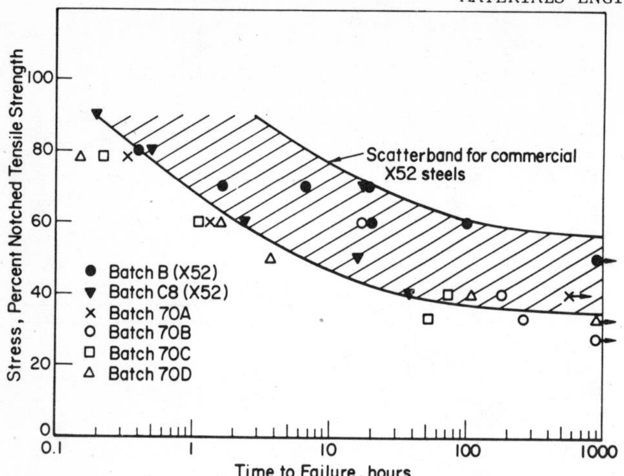

Figure 1: Comparison of Stress-Corrosion-Cracking Susceptibilities of X52 and X70 Steels in a Boiling 20% Ammonium Nitrate Solution at -170 mV versus Cu-CuSO$_4$.

Additional work needs to be done on the relevance of microstructure or strain history, since the higher strength materials may be processed in a variety of ways.

In addition to strength level, the effect of temperature on stress corrosion cracking is an important consideration (2,3). Since it is desirable even under Arctic conditions to maintain high fluid temperatures in an oil pipeline to promote flow, the use of significantly higher strength pipeline materials may be limited to gas transmission service. In particular, higher yield strength materials may find utility in Arctic pipelines where it is necessary to lower the temperature of the gas below the thawing temperature of the soil in order to prevent degradation of the ground and subsequent instability of the pipeline.

Since stress corrosion cracking is not likely to occur without a liquid phase present, operating pipelines below 0°C may allow the use of significantly higher strength materials up to the threshold at which hydrogen stress cracking becomes a consideration (3).

Fracture Initiation

It is necessary to guard against fracture initiation in line pipe and, in the particular case of a gas pipeline, to prevent extensive fracture propagation. In order to design against fracture initiation, one must consider the material's resistance to fracture initiation, (i.e. its notch toughness) and the expected defect size. Fortunately, quality control tests suitable to prevent crack initiation in line pipe have been defined.

Hahn et al (4) have suggested that for very tough ductile materials, failure of flaws is controlled by large scale yielding, such that

$$\sigma_H M = \sigma_F \qquad (1)$$

where σ_H is the hoop stress at failure (ksi), M is the Folias correction, σ_F is the flow stress (YS + 10 ksi).

Materials which can be characterized by this equation are said to be flow-stress dependent, i.e. the failure stress is dependent only upon crack length, yield strength and pipe geometry. The behaviour of pipe materials which are toughness-dependent have been characterized by Maxey(5) through the following relationship

$$K_c^2\pi/8c\sigma_F^2 = \ell n[\sec(\pi M\sigma_H/2\sigma_F)] \qquad (2)$$

where K_c^2 is a parameter related to the material's resistance to fracture, and 2c is the length of the throughwall flaw. It is suggested by Maxey that K_c^2 may be calculated from

$$12C_V/A_c = K_c^2/E \qquad (3)$$

where C_V is Charpy V-Notch shelf energy (ft lbf), A_c is the area of the fracture surface in a Charpy specimen (in^2) and E is Young's modulus.

Figure 2 shows the relationship between Charpy energy and critical crack length of a 48 in. (1220 mm) x 0.720 in. (18.3 mm) Grade 70 pipe operating at 80% of its yield strength. The critical crack length for flow stress dependent behaviour is also shown. It is seen that for this particular pipe size and stress level, a Charpy energy of 50 J provides for a critical crack length approximately 85% of the theoretical maximum.

Although the validity of Equation (2) has been repeatedly verified (6), additional tests have recently been conducted on high strength pipe having improved low temperature properties. West Jefferson Tests (7) were conducted on 48 in. (1220 mm) x 0.720 in. (18.3 mm) nominal wall thickness Grade 70 pipe manufactured by both the UOE and spiral weld processes. Test temperatures down to -57°C were used. The results of these tests are summarized in Table 1. It is seen that for a range of material properties, the failure pressure can be predicted with considerable accuracy. For the tests shown, failure pressures were predicted with an average error of 3%.

Approaches such as that of Figure 2 are suggested for the determination of notch ductility values to prevent fracture initiation in line pipe. It is worthwhile noting that extensive full scale testing has shown that the familiar Charpy test provides sufficient control over the material properties to assure resistance against fracture initiation.

Fracture Propagation

In the design of a pipeline, consideration must also be given to arresting a fracture in the event that one is initiated.

If a rupture were to occur in an oil pipeline, the decompression would be so rapid that there would be insufficient pressure to drive the fracture and it would stop within a relatively short distance of the point of initiation. This quick arrest would occur even if the temperature were below the fracture propagation transition temperature, i.e. even if the fracture propagated in a brittle mode.

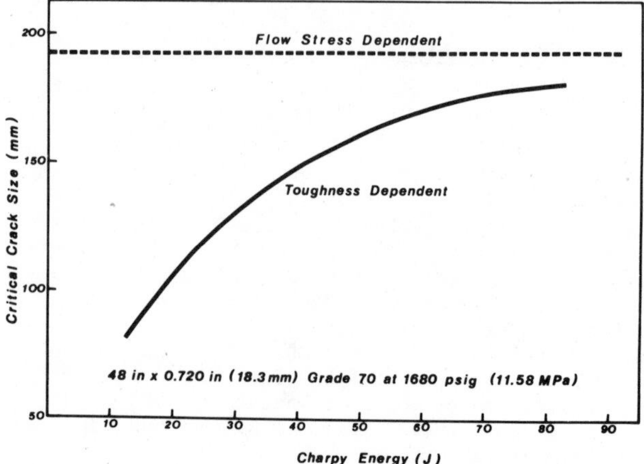

Figure 2: Critical Crack Sizes for Through-Wall Defects in 48 in. x 0.720 in. Grade 70 Line Pipe

Table 1

Summary of West Jefferson Tests on 48-Inch Grade 70 Pipe

Actual Yield Strength		Actual Thickness		Charpy Plateau Energy		Crack Size		Calculated Failure Pressure		Actual Failure Pressure		Test Temperature
ksi	MPa	in	mm	ft lbf	J	in	mm	psig	MPa	psig	MPa	°C
74.2	512	0.756	19.2	145	197	8.9	226	1720	11.86	1610	11.10	-26
86.5	596	0.720	18.3	140	190	6.9	175	2115	14.58	2190	15.10	-19
86.5	596	0.720	18.3	140	190	11.0	279	1585	10.93	1580	10.89	-19
71.9	496	0.748	19.0	43	58	6.35	161	1830	12.62	1845	12.72	-46
72.6	501	0.752	19.1	29	39	6.35	161	1705	11.76	1775	12.24	-57

In the case of a gas pipeline, the design must prevent long failures from occurring. A fracture propagating in a brittle mode can be very long and serious. (The longest brittle fracture reported to date was approximately 13 km) Brittle fractures travel at speeds up to 900 m/s. The acoustic velocity, and hence the initial decompression, of natural gas is approximately 400 m/s. Therefore, brittle fractures travel faster than the gas can decompress and the pressure level at and ahead of the crack tip maintains a high driving force on the crack tip. To avoid brittle fracture, it is necessary to specify a high percentage of shear area on a full thickness test such as the Drop Weight Tear Test (8). Notwithstanding the above, the possibility of brittle fracture arrest at lower stress levels has been documented (5,9).

Until relatively recently, it was felt that one only had to avoid brittle fracture to avoid a long failure in a gas pipeline. Approximately eight years ago, a fully ductile fracture occurred in a natural gas pipeline and ran for over 250 m. Since that time, at least eight shear fractures of 100 m or more have occurred in the United States and Canada. Thus a gas pipeline should be designed to prevent long shear fractures as well as to prevent brittle fractures.

Considerable research has been done on how to avoid long shear fracture (5,9,10,11). Initial indications were that these fractures could be arrested in relatively short distances if the Charpy toughness values were sufficiently high. The exact values to specify and even the best method that should be used are subjects of intense current study.

The most commonly used parameter for specifying a material's resistance to propagating ductile failure is the Charpy V-Notch absorbed energy. In general, higher absorbed energies are required for higher operating stress levels, larger diameter pipe, higher strength pipes, and heavier wall thickness pipes. Maxey (5) has suggested that for certain pipe geometries, yield strengths and stress levels, the Charpy energy required to provide fracture arrest, C_V(ft lbf) is given by:

$$C_V = 0.0873\ \sigma_H^{2}(Rt)^{0.33}A_c$$

where σ_H is the operating stress level (ksi), R is the pipe radius (in.) and t is the pipe thickness (in.).

The required Charpy V-Notch energy to provide fracture arrest has also been suggested by other investigators, and Figure 3 compares the values calculated from Maxey's formula with values of Mercer (12), Dick et al (10) and the AISI (11). It is seen that the suggested values are not significantly different.

For larger diameter, high strength and heavy wall thickness material, property requirements to provide fracture arrest are not always clear. The particular fracture appearance ("separations") which characterizes these materials (13), as well as the decompression phenomena which may occur (14) is important in characterizing the fracture propagation and arrest behaviour. Until relationships are developed for these materials, full scale burst tests under the particular operating parameters selected for the pipeline will be required to demonstrate fracture control.

Under certain conditions it may not be possible to ensure fracture arrest using pipe of extremely high toughness, and the use of mechanical crack arrestors may be necessary to provide fracture control. Mechanical crack arrestors have been successfully tested by Battelle, the American Iron and Steel Institute, and Italsider. The exact mechanism by which crack arrestors stop a crack is not clearly understood, but full scale tests under simulated pipeline operating conditions have shown their usefulness (14,15).

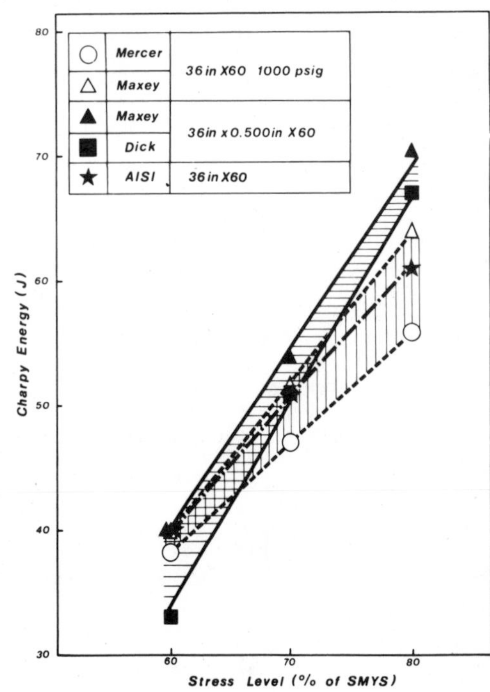

Figure 3: Charpy V-Notch Energy Required to Produce Fracture Arrest, as Suggested by Various Investigators

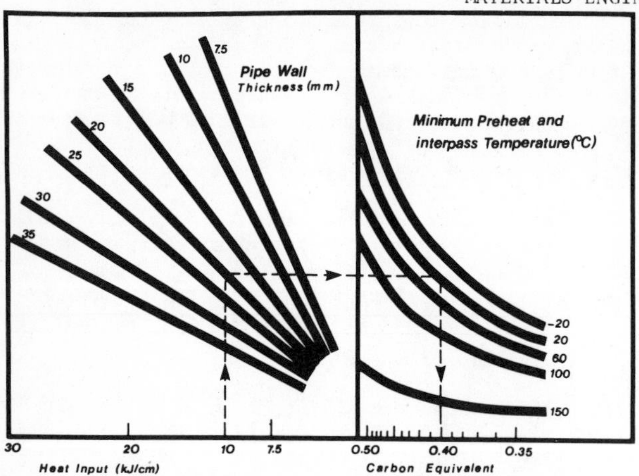

Figure 4: Nomogram for the determination of allowable Maximum Carbon Equivalent for Butt Welds in Line Pipe using Cellulosic (EXX10) Electrodes

Chemical Composition and Weldability

Suitable controls are necessary to ensure that the composition selected for pipe production is weldable. Figure 4, adapted from the work of Cotton and Thomas (16), is a nomogram for deducing the carbon equivalent limit when the welding procedure and wall thickness are known. This figure, based upon field experience and laboratory data, is designed to prevent Vickers hardness in excess of 365, which is considered a critical threshold for underbead cracking when using cellulosic electrodes. (For low hydrogen processes, 0.05% may be added to the allowable maximum carbon equivalent).

The use of carbon equivalents is only justified if prior experience with materials in the composition range expected has shown this approach to be valuable. Rapid development of high-strength low-alloy steels has produced multiple chemical compositions which do not conform to previously established guidelines but are eminently suitable for pipeline application. In particular, materials having low carbon content (less than 0.10%) may have better weldability than this carbon equivalent calculation would suggest.

Notch Ductility Requirements for Welds

Only recently have pipeline companies given specific consideration to notch ductility requirements for welds. Welds using conventional electrodes and procedures produce adequate ductility for low strength pipes in moderate service, but the increasing interest in the use of higher strength materials in low temperature environments has prompted investigation and specification of notch toughness properties for welds.

A survey of companies requiring notch toughness values indicates that a Charpy V-notch energy in the range 25 to 40 J is most often specified at or below the design temperature, although there is increasing interest in the use of "crack-opening-displacement" (COD) testing for investigation of weldment properties since it provides a more realistic simulation of service conditions.

Welding Processes

Historically, the shielded metal arc process using cellulosic coated electrodes has been employed for pipeline construction. The increasing use of high strength materials, together with a need for low temperature weldment properties for Arctic environments, requires a re-examination of these practices.

Figure 5 shows Charpy impact test results obtained by various investigators on pipe welds made using a pipeline electrode of AWS classification E8010G. It is suggested that the impact properties may not be suitable for the lowest temperatures which may be specified for Arctic construction.

Tensile tests on this representative electrode indicate satisfactory weld strength for use with Grade 65 pipe, but borderline properties for Grade 70 material. Present efforts by the electrode manufacturers are directed towards providing cellulosic electrodes having ample strength for Grade 70 pipe, together with enhanced low temperature notch toughness.

Other solutions for the particularly difficult welding requirements of high strength Arctic pipelines are the use of gas metal arc welding, automatic gas metal arc welding, or the use of low hydrogen electrodes for downhill welding.

The gas metal arc welding process has been used for pipeline welding, both semi-automatically and automatically. With suitable filler metal selection, high strength weldments with low temperature notch toughness are readily produced. The major drawbacks are the limited availability of pipeline welders familiar with the semi-automatic technique, the prevalence of lack-of-fusion defects in multi-pass welds, and the concern over productivity using automatic equipment.

An interesting approach to the problem of welding high-strength Arctic pipelines is the development of a low hydrogen electrode for downhill pipeline welding. While tests on welds made using experimental electrodes have indicated good physical properties, the operational characteristics of these electrodes require additional development.

SUMMARY

While this paper has focused on the property requirements for pipelines, it is perhaps useful in summary to note that the required materials are currently available for the construction of Arctic pipelines. High-strength low-alloy steels which have recently been developed can be produced with suitable notch ductility at expected Arctic operating conditions. Further work is necessary to increase the number of available processes for welding these materials, particularly for the higher strength alloys, although present day technology already provides acceptable techniques.

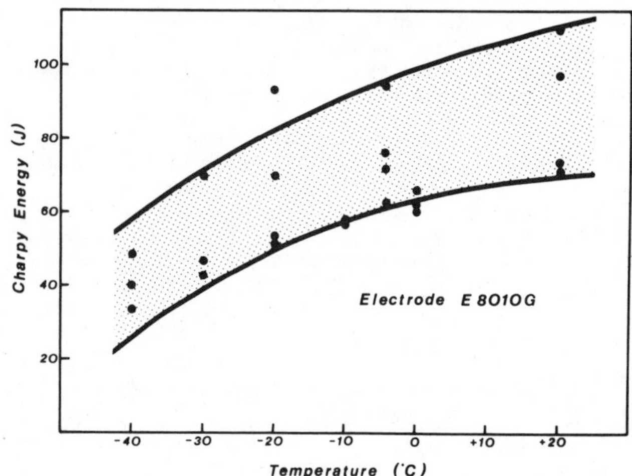

Figure 5: Charpy V-Notch Energy as a Function of Temperature for a Typical E8010G Electrode

REFERENCES

1. R. R. Fessler, 5th Symposium on Line Pipe Research, 1974 American Gas Association, Arlington, p. w-8.
2. W. E. Berry, ibid. pp. V-11 to V-20.
3. R. R. Fessler, T. P. Groeneveld and A. R. Elsea, "Stress-Corrosion and Hydrogen-Stress Cracking in Buried Pipelines", Conference on Stress-Corrosion Cracking and Hydrogen Embrittlement of Iron-Base Alloys, Firminy, France, June 1973.
4. G. T. Hahn, M. Sarrate and A. R. Rosenfield, Fracture Mechanics, 1969, vol. 6, pp. 187-210.
5. W. A. Maxey, "Fracture Initiation, Propagation and Arrest", 5th Symposium on Line Pipe Research, 1974. American Gas Association, Arlington, pp. J-3 to J-30.
6. J. F. Kiefner, W. A. Maxey, R. J. Eiber and A. R. Duffy, in "Progress in Flaw Growth and Fracture Toughness Testing", 1973, ASTM, Philadelphia, pp. 462-468.
7. A. R. Duffy, Symposium on Line Research, 1965, American Gas Association, New York, pp. 43-47.
8. R. J. Eiber, ibid. pp. 83-118.
9. G. D. Fearnehough, J. Pressure Vessels and Piping, 1974, vol. 2, pp. 261-279.0
10. J. A. Dick, P. McK. Jamieson and E. F. Walker, in "Crack Propagation in Pipelines", 1974, The British Gas Corporation, Newcastle-Upon-Tyne.
11. AISI Committee of Large Diameter Line Pipe Producers, "Running Shear Fractures in Line Pipe", 1974, AISI, New York.
12. W. L. Mercer, Developments in Gas Pipeline Technology, 1973, AWRA, Sydney, p. 9.
13. E. Miyoshi, M. Fukuda, H. Iwanaga and T. Oazawa, in "Crack Propagation in Pipelines", 1974, The British Gas Corporation, Newcastle-Upon-Tyne.
14. W. A. Maxey, F. A. Syler and R. J. Eiber, "Fracture Propagation Experiments on 48-in. x 0.720 in. X70 Line Pipe", 1976 Battelle Columbus Laboratories, Columbus, Ohio.
15. R. J. Eiber and W. A. Maxey, "CAGSL Crack Arrest Experiments 1 and 2", 1975 Battelle Columbus Laboratories, Columbus, Ohio.
16. H. C. Cotton and D. B. J. Thomas, "Tube and Pipe Production", 1970 The Iron and Steel Institute, London, p. 41.

DISCUSSION

R. J. Cooke (National Energy Board): I was interested to note that you attributed the Grade 70 limitation on strength to a fear of regulatory reaction. This reaction appears to be associated with a distrust of new technology. Could you develop this thinking, particularly if you assume that properly engineered and supported materials technology should be favoured by regulatory authories.

F. S. Somerville: The present user interest in pipes not higher in strength than Grade 70 stems only in part from potential regulatory reaction. We should strike a balance between concerns over new technology in an Arctic environment, and the economics of the new technology. I believe the Canadian Arctic Gas Pipeline does this. However, within the time period of construction for even this one project, it should be possible to introduce properly researched technology.

R. J. Cooke: It would seem unlikely that a critical longitudinal crack-like defect would escape detection during pipe manufacture or field testing. The only possible mechanism available to form such a defect in service would be environmental cracking or fatigue, both of which are unlikely in a chilled gas pipeline. However, such a pipeline may be subject to large and perhaps unpredictable bending stresses due to such things as frost heave or differential settlement. This suggests that a more probable fracture initiation site may be related to plastic instability in the pipe causing such things as buckles. Could you discuss the relevance of your proposed fracture initiation design criteria which is based on an idealized crack-like defect and the hoop stress alone, to the more complex and perhaps more realistic case of fracture initiation at an area of buckling or plastic instability in the pipe wall?

F. S. Somerville: I do not believe there is any rigorous analysis which speaks to the question of fracture initiation at buckles. Since the buckling due to frost heave or differential settlement occurs over a number of years, it is possible to monitor a pipeline through the use of "pigging" devices which would indicate slope changes prior to buckling. The designer should also be aware that prior to the incidence of buckling, substantial longitudinal tensile stresses will exist and consideration should be given to this in weldment design.

C. A. Parrini (Italsider): Why are you using the mechanical crack arrestor approach instead of Charpy-V criteria?

F. S. Somerville: Mechanical crack arrestors have been selected as a result of extensive full scale burst testing and economic analysis. The burst tests have shown us that pipe having notch toughness greater than has been commercially offered would not arrest a running crack under the proposed operating conditions of the Arctic Gas pipeline. Economic studies suggested that crack arrestors provided the best solution.

C. A. Parrini: How far apart will you put the crack arrestors?

F. S. Somerville: Crack arrestor spacing of approximately 100 m has been suggested by our early studies.

C. A. Parrini: Did you consider the possiblity of using thicker pipe rings of, for example, 15 ft (5 m) lengths, as crack arrestors?

F. S. Somerville: Crack arrestors manufactured of heavy wall pipe were found to have an economic penalty, mainly due to extra material costs.

W. G. Wilson (Molycorp): If you are going to arrest cracks with crack stoppers can %-shear requirements be relaxed or removed?

F. S. Somerville: For the crack stopper itself, the most common proposal is to arrest a ductile crack, although brittle crack arrest with a crack stopper system is also possible. For the pipeline between crack stoppers, from the theoretical standpoint it would be possible to reduce or remove shear area requirements.

M. R. Krishnadev (Laval University): I am not yet fully convinced of the wisdom of using conventional Charpy energy level alone as the criterion for toughness of pipeline steels. I think there is a need to develop a more meaningful and convenient type of quality control test

F. S. Somerville: In view of our tests (Table 1) as well as the work of the original researchers (reference 6), I do not see any need for a more meaningful test. The Charpy test is, to my way of thinking, a convenient quality control test.

M. R. Krishnadev: Did you consider the effect of microstructural cleanliness on fracture characteristics? Apart from any Charpy energy criterion, microstructural cleanliness of the steel is a very important parameter, particularly for Arctic application, but this is often ignored.

F. S. Somerville: Microstructural cleanliness is reflected in the absorbed energy values observed on such tests as the Charpy and is therefore more important to producers than users. I cannot imagine a dirty steel which would meet our impact energy requirements.

E. C. Hamre (Interprovincial Steel and Pipe): You indicated that you would be willing to consider pipe stronger than Grade 70. Given current restrictions on composition and carbon equivalent, does this mean you are considering heat treated plate or pipe? Conversely, if you are considering relaxing the carbon equivalent restriction in order to obtain higher strength steel, then would you also consider a similar relaxation for Grade 70?

F. S. Somerville: For higher strength pipe, heat treatments would be considered. The present Canadian Arctic Gas limitations on carbon equivalent are based upon welding 0.72 in. (18 mm) medium carbon (0.15% max.) pipe using cellulosic electrodes and minimum preheat. Higher strength materials for the same pressure would be of lighter wall thickness, probably very low carbon and would most likely be welded with a low hydrogen process. Accordingly, an increase in carbon equivalent may be appropriate. For the present design, no increase is being considered, except an allowance is made for low-carbon materials, in accordance with the specification.

B. Fruck (Imperial Oil): In an experience I read about recently, a small diameter gas pipeline exploded killing 3 people about 6 months ago. The reported cause was selective corrosion of the longitudinal seam. What possibility was given to such a situation starting a propagating fracture in large diameter pipelines in the Arctic? Was this a factor in selecting spiral-welded pipe?

F. S. Somerville: I am somewhat at a loss to comment on a field failure with which I am not familiar, although I am aware of a failure in ERW pipe carrying corrosive fluids. For the design of the Arctic Gas pipeline, all small diameter pipe in high pressure service will be seamless. For large diameter pipes, control of weldment properties as well as fluid composition provides freedom from weld cracking.

CRITERIA FOR MATERIALS SELECTION FOR THE FOOTHILLS PIPELINE PROJECT

J. M. E. Wallbridge
Foothills Pipe Lines Ltd.
205 Fifth Ave. S.W.
Calgary, Alberta T2P 2W4
Canada

Studies have demonstrated that criteria can be established for a Mackenzie Valley gas pipeline which will ensure a safe, reliable system. Steels are available for the Foothills Project which meet these criteria. For line pipe and high strength fittings it will be necessary to use steels approaching the present technological limit. For other components conventional standard steels will be adequate.

INTRODUCTION

The Maple Leaf Project is a proposal to transport Canadian gas by pipeline from the Mackenzie Delta to consumers in the Mackenzie Valley and southern Canada from British Columbia to Quebec. Foothills Pipe Lines Ltd. would be responsible for that section of the Project in the Northwest Territories. This comprises the mainline system shown on Figure 1, roughly parallel to the Mackenzie River. The mainline is a buried 42 in. (1070 mm) diameter by 0.540 in. (13.7 mm) wall, Grade 70 system with seventeen compressor stations. There are also approximately 500 miles (800 km) of small diameter laterals feeding gas to the main pipeline and providing gas service to northern communities.

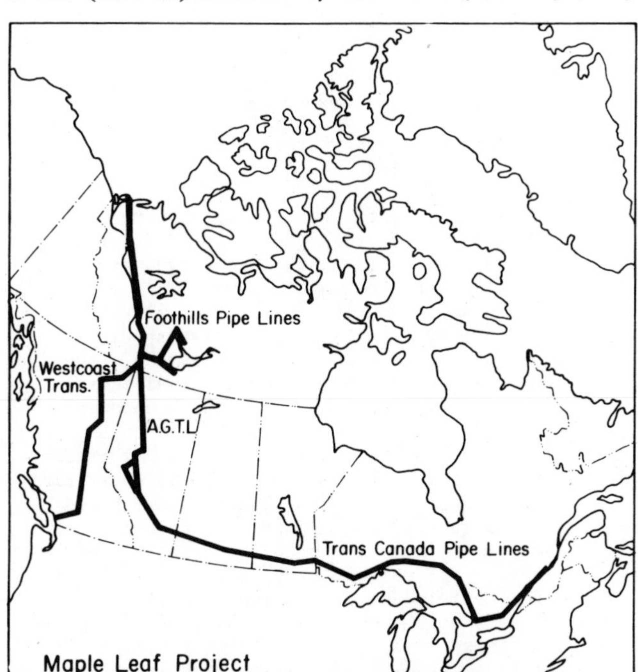

Figure 1: Map of the pipelines comprising the Maple Leaf Project

The majority of the route falls in either the continuous or the discontinuous permafrost regions and therefore it is considered necessary in these regions to operate the pipeline in what is known as the chilled mode. For the chilled mode the gas temperature in the pipeline is maintained below the freezing point of the ground at all times. This is accomplished by installing refrigeration units at each of the compressor stations within permafrost regions. These refrigeration units cool the gas coming out of the gas compressors down to approximately 25°F (4°C).

This portion of the country is subject to long periods of extremely low ambient temperatures during the winter. Temperatures below-50°F (-46°C) are relatively common and they have fallen as low as -69°F (-55°C). These temperatures drastically limit suitable materials for use in exposed service.

The majority of the Foothills system would have to be installed in the winter so as not to damage the permafrost, imposing further severe restraints on materials.

MATERIALS SELECTION CRITERIA AND THEIR APPLICATION TO SYSTEM DESIGN

Three primary criteria were established to aid in the materials selection.

1. Materials should be conventional and readily available;
2. Materials should be readily assembled in the field into a high integrity system;
3. Materials should be such that they provide a long, safe working life.

These three primary criteria were then developed into specific selection criteria, discussed separately below.

Strength

The design pressure of pipelines is based on the specified minimum yield strength of the mainline pipe. The mainline pipe comprises the vast majority of the steel used in the system and is a major cost item for any pipeline system. Pipeline codes base the maximum level of pressure in the system on the specified minimum yield strength of the pipe. Since pipeline economics are a very strong function of pressure, the selection of the pipe diameter, wall thickness and grades are of extreme importance. Within the range of common pipeline materials, minimum cost for a given pressure is obtained with the highest strength pipe available. For this reason Foothills elected to use Grade 70 pipe, (i.e. a 70 ksi (483 MPa) minimum yield strength pipe) for their system. Pipe for gas transmission service in North America has not generally exceeded 42 in. (1070 mm) x 0.5 in. (13 mm) wall so this has been accepted as a guide to the maximum size. Forty-two in. (1070 mm) Grade 70 pipe has been used in the Alberta Gas Trunk System over the last 5 years. It would be desirable from the cost point of view to go to even higher strengths and perhaps heavier wall thicknesses, but it was considered that these had not been proven and therefore did not meet the first criterion.

The pipe should exhibit uniform properties and therefore a maximum yield strength of 85 ksi (590 MPa) was also specified. This was to prevent a situation where one weak pipe in a string of strong pipes would be required to take all the deformation in the event of overloads. It was also considered important that there be a reserve of strength in the system in the event of overloads, and for this reason a high tensile strength and a very high ductility have been specified.

The measured strength of the pipe should in fact be the strength of all of the pipe not just that at the test specimen location. For this reason samples have been taken to measure the variation of properties along the length of the pipe.

Weldability

All materials used in the system should be readily weldable in the field using conventional welding practice. For the welding of mainline pipe the Foothills design is based on manual downhill welding. It is possible that fully automatic welding will be used in the field, but this would involve less constraint in terms of weldability than manual welding.

For the welding of compressor station components, it is likely that an uphill low-hydrogen technique will be used. This imposes less restraint on the materials as regards weldability, but it is still necessary to ensure that they are weldable using this technique.

Dimensional Tolerances

The ease of assembly of components in the field is very strongly dependent on the dimensional tolerances of the components. As an example, tolerances at the pipe bevels (e.g. inside diameter, land width, out of roundness and squareness) all contribute to the ease of fitup and the ability of internal line-up clamps to bring the two pipes into perfect alignment, thereby reduce the likelihood of cracking. We have therefore specified the tightest tolerances which the manufacturers can meet.

Bendability

Pipelines must be bent in the field in order to match the contour of the ground. Bending is done using a hydraulic bending machine with an internal mandrel to prevent buckling of the pipe. It is important that the pipe so bent does not have significantly inferior properties to that of mainline pipe. Due to the strains introduced during this bending, the yield strength of the pipe rises on one side where the loading was tensile and may fall on the other where the loading was compressive. If the pipe material has a low work hardening exponent, yield strength will not be significantly affected. It is also important that this strain not adversely affect the toughness properties of the pipe.

Fracture Considerations

Brittle fracture is an unacceptable failure mode for pipelines. Experience has indicated that brittle fractures can propagate for long distances with arrest being a chance event occurring eventually, usually as a result of change in thickness (e.g. at a valve). Tests reported by Maxey (1) have indicated that full scale behaviour will be ductile if the Drop Weight Tear Test exhibits 85% or more shear area when tested at the minimum operating temperature. We have adopted this criterion with a 0°F (-18°C) minimum design temperature to prevent brittle fracture of the pipe.

Ductile fractures, when initiated in pipelines, have generally arrested after a very short propagation. The very few that have propagated any significant distance have, according to our information, all been in pipe exhibiting low fracture toughness. We have therefore placed primary emphasis on prevention of initiation.

Initiation

Various correlations exist between toughness as measured on test specimens and full scale behaviour. These correlations enable us to calculate the maximum size defect which can exist in a structure without initiation occurring. They do, however, provide only a gross approximation of the real case because of the following factors:

(a) CRACK SHAPE -- Correlations are only available for a limited number of crack shapes. Most real defects do not fit one of these ideal cracks. A conservative assumption regarding crack shape must therefore be made.

(b) STRESS FIELD -- Correlations are based on simple stress fields, generally uniaxial tension, while the stress state surrounding a pipeline defect is generally triaxial and only approximately known due to geometrical and secondary loading factors. This can result in a nonconservative estimate of initiation.

(c) PROPERTY VARIATIONS -- Test specimen results apply to one location in the structure, while in fact properties vary significantly in each direction throughout the component. Test specimen location is selected to be representative of the component and therefore there is no bias, only a degree of uncertainty.

(d) DEFECT SIZE -- Correlations are based on the general assumption that defect sizes are small in relation to the size of the component. If this is true, the stress across the crack is not a function of crack size. Because of the desire for maximum safety high toughness is specified, which yields a large critical crack size. This crack is no longer small compared with the component size, which leads to a nonconservative estimate of the critical crack particularly at lower stresses. This is not, in practice, a major problem.

(e) DEFECT TYPE -- Correlations are all based on sharp cracks. Real cracks may be initially sharp but hydrotesting at high stress levels blunts the ends of the defects; therefore, in service the calculated critical crack size is conservative.

The overall effects of all these factors result in calculated critical crack sizes which are a conservative estimate of the real behaviour.

For the Foothills Project we have used two primary correlations for critical crack size calculation. The most important, developed by Battelle (1), applies to cracks oriented in the longitudinal direction. Because the pipe is round, pressure can cause extensive bulging in the area of a longitudinal defect. This bulging increases the stress across the crack and therefore results in a smaller critical crack than for plate. Combining and simplifying the following two equations from the Battelle work for a sharp through-thickness crack,

$$K_c^2\pi / 8c\sigma_F^2 = \ln(\sec \pi M_T\sigma_p / 2\sigma_F) \quad (1)$$

$$12\, C_V / A_c = K^2_c / E \quad (2)$$

we obtain

$$3C_V E\pi / 2A_c c\sigma_F^2 = \ln(\sec \pi M_T\sigma_p / 2\sigma_F) \quad (3)$$

The same equation can be used for partial thickness cracks if M_p is substituted for M_T, where

$$M_p = (1-d/M_T t) / (1-d/t) \quad (4)$$

C_V = Charpy V-notch energy (ft lb)
A_c = Area of Charpy specimen (in^2)
$2c$ = length of the through wall flaw (in.)
σ_F = Flow stress (yield strength + 10 ksi)
E = Young's modulus
M_T = $(1 + 1.255c^2/Rt - 0.0135c^4/R^2t^2)^{1/2}$, the Folias correction
R = pipe radius (in.)
t = pipe thickness (in.)
σ_p = hoop stress at failure (psi)
d = flaw depth (in.)

Figures 2, 3, and 4 are plots of the results of calculations using this equation for the Foothills pipe. This calculation assumes a through-wall sharp crack. All other defects would result in a longer critical crack size.

The second correlation we have used is based on standard linear elastic fracture mechanics concepts and was used to check critical crack size for circumferential defects. For pipelines this yields a very conservative estimate of critical crack size but demonstrates that the longitudinal defect with bulging is more critical. These calculations only predict what will happen if a certain size defect develops, they give no indication of the probability of development of certain defect sizes. In general, no method exists for predicting initiation probability other than past performance.

Calculations of critical flaw lengths for various crack sizes, shapes, directions and stress levels combined with the expected variation of toughness as a function of orientation within a pipe led to the following minimum toughness requirements regarding initiation. (These values apply to all parts of the components, including welds, except that for pipe and fittings a lower value is permitted for directions other than the longitudinal because defects in other directions are less serious as the lower stress and reduced bulging lowers the toughness requirements for the same critical crack size.)

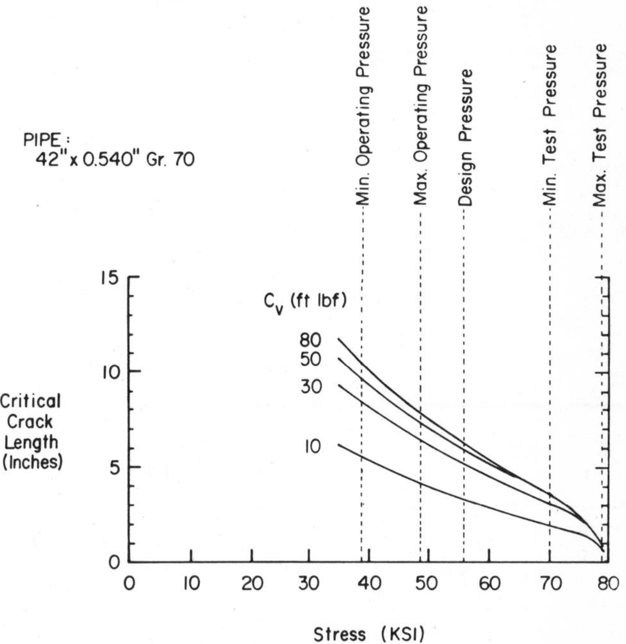

Figure 2: Critical crack size for a sharp through-wall longitudinal defect as a function of stress level and pipe toughness for 42 in. (1070 mm) x 0.540 in. (13.7 mm) wall Grade 70 pipe (Foothills mainline pipe with a design factor of 0.80)

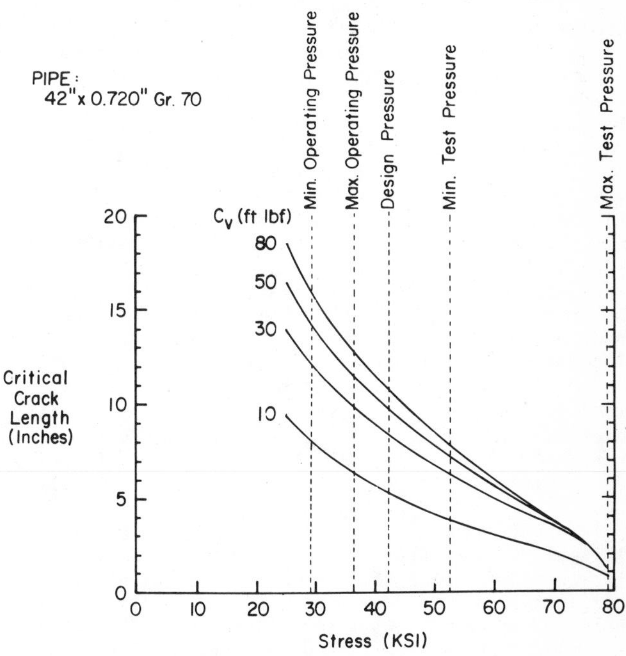

Figure 3: Critical crack size for a sharp through-wall longitudinal defect as a function of stress level and pipe toughness for 42 in. (1070 mm) x 0.720 in. (18.3 mm) wall Grade 70 pipe (Foothills heavy wall mainline pipe with a design factor of 0.60)

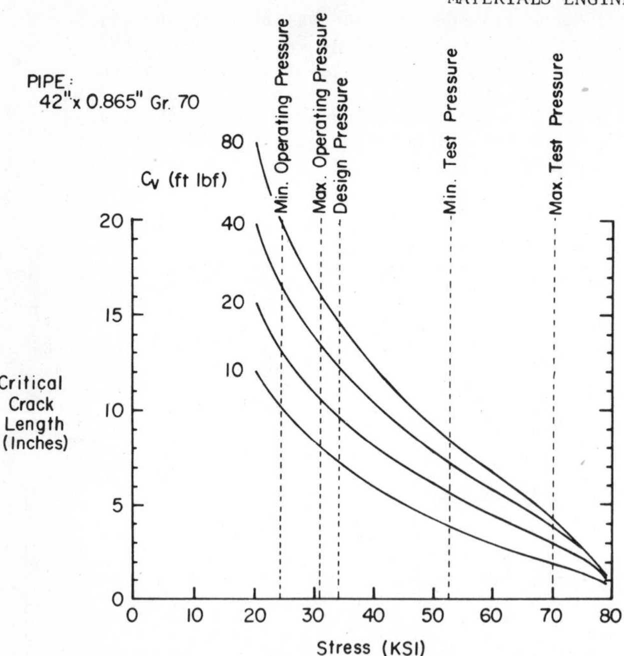

Figure 4: Critical crack size for a sharp through-wall longitudinal defect as a function of stress level and pipe toughness for 42 in. (1070 mm) x 0.865 in. (22.0 mm) wall Grade 70 pipe (Foothills compressor station pipe with a design factor of 0.50)

mainline pipe	50 ft lb (68 J)
station pipe	40 ft lb (54 J)
high strength fittings	40 ft lb (54 J)
flanges	20 to 30 ft lb (27 to 40 J) (dependent on strength)
other components	20 ft lb (27 J)

The risk of initiation will be minimized by inspection of all components prior to and during installation. Inspection techniques are designed to detect all defects larger than a certain size which is very much smaller than that of the critical crack. All large defects and many smaller ones are removed. Hydrotesting provides a subsequent check for defects.

Critical crack size at a given toughness level is a strong function of stress level (Figure 2) and therefore any existing defect larger than about half the critical crack shows up as a leak during hydrotesting, and can be removed. The large critical crack size ensures that the defect will penetrate the pipe wall prior to initiation and therefore can be detected as a leak. On-line internal inspection also can detect defects prior to initiation; in fact, for the Foothills pipeline it is intended to detect defects long before they even leak. The only defects which should initiate are those very large defects that are formed too fast to allow shutdown of the system prior to initiation. These could conceivably occur by third party damage or major sudden earth movements (landslides, earthquakes, etc.). One additional possible source of initiation would be extreme overstressing, which would reduce the critical size drastically. If a large enough load is applied to the pipe, it is not possible to prevent its failure. This source of failure is minimized by consideration of applied stresses in the pipeline design.

Propagation

Although initiation of a fracture is a very remote possibility, propagation considerations have been included in the Foothills design for mainline pipe because of the extreme consequence of any long failure, the relative inexperience with pipelines in permafrost and the emphasis which others have placed on propagation. Recent information (2) gives a rupture frequency of .000189 ruptures per year per mile (1970-72) in the USA for 18 in. (460 mm) and larger pipe. Alberta Gas Trunk Line experience between 1952 and 1974 with the same size pipe is .000207 ruptures per year per mile. Although both these frequencies are very small we expect the Foothills frequency to be an order of magnitude lower because of the lack of other activity adjacent to the right-of-way, the frozen annulus around the pipe which provides protection from mechanical damage, the negligible corrosion rate expected at below-freezing temperatures, and the high quality level and rigid inspection planned during manufacturing and construction. A long fracture would be especially unacceptable for a northern pipeline project because of the remote location, the environmental sensitivity and the difficulty of repair in certain seasons of the year. Propagation does not have to be considered for stations because of the short length of runs, the lower stress level and the presence of flanges, valves, etc. which would probably arrest any fracture.

Once a ductile fracture is initiated it will propagate for some distance as a result of the rupturing process. The length of propagation depends on factors which include the pipe size and wall thickness, stress level, impact properties of the pipe and gas composition. Fractures can, under some circumstances, be arrested after a short propagating length. If the speed of fracture propagation can be reduced significantly, the gas in the pipeline can escape, thereby reducing the stress at the tip of the fracture. This lower pressure eventually results in the stress on the crack falling below that necessary to extend the fracture. This arrest stress level is a function of initial stress level, toughness, crack geometry etc. but is in the order of 30% of the specified minimum yield strength. The method and theory for predicting the toughness necessary to result in arrest have been developed as a result of three different research programs, conducted by Battelle (1), American Iron and Steel Institute (AISI) (3), and the British Gas Corporation (4). Battelle's work under AGA sponsorship has been the most extensive in terms of both the different field conditions simulated and the range of pipe sizes studied. They have also done the only low temperature tests. Based on this work, Battelle has developed a hypothesis which can be used to predict pipe properties necessary for arrest, failure lengths, etc. AISI's work has been primarily on large diameter pipe. This has only reached the stage of predicting the toughness necessary to arrest the fracture in a reasonable length. Much of the AISI work has been devoted to developing a better way of measuring the properties of the steel that result in an arrest, as opposed to Battelle's use of the Charpy V-Notch test as a predictor of performance. The British Gas Corporation work has been primarily on smaller diameter pipe. It is understood that they have recently tested very large diameter pipe, but this has not, to our knowledge, been published yet.

The three predictions are in general agreement although the agreement is much poorer when any one of the hypotheses is applied outside the range in which it has been tested. The three correlations also, in general, agree on the effect of changing the variables although they predict different rates of change. Increased diameter and/or wall thickness increases the difficulties of arrest. Increased stress greatly increases the difficulty of arrest. Battelle's work indicates that gas composition can have a large

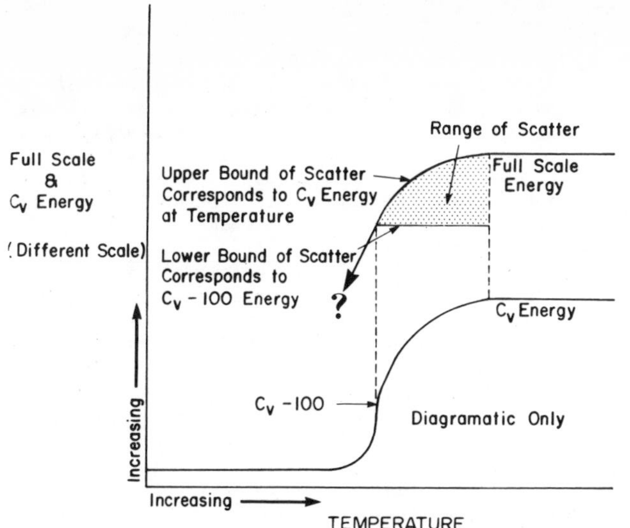

Figure 5: Relationship between full scale pipe toughness for a propagating fracture and toughness measured on a Charpy "V" notch specimen

effect if two-phase behaviour is encountered. The effect of temperature has not been thoroughly studied as it was thought initially to have no effect as long as the test temperature was above the transition temperature of the pipe. Recent burst tests demonstrated that there is a major effect, at least for separated materials, of a change in temperature above the transition temperature.

Recent burst tests have also indicated that problems exist in predicting the behaviour of pipe which undergoes splitting during fracture. These splits (or separations) are not in the pipe prior to fracture, but they develop during the fracture process. They have been ascribed to a high transition temperature in the through-thickness direction. Under particular combinations of stress, strain rate, and temperature, the material fails in a brittle manner in the through-thickness plane in front of the crack tip. There are differences in the severity of separations and the temperature range where separations occur between full scale behavour, drop weight tear tests, and the Charpy tests.

Full scale burst tests which have exhibited separations have not in general agreed with the original fracture propagation hypothesis. If an energy between that at the minimum 100% shear temperature on a Charpy specimen and the Charpy energy at temperature is used in the Battelle equation, agreement with full scale behaviour can be obtained. Unfortunately, the energy correlation in this range is not consistent from one test to another (see Figure 5). We have consequently selected the lowest estimate of toughness, i.e. the energy at the minimum 100% shear temperature, which is termed the "CV-100" energy. This energy will not yield an accurate prediction of fracture velocity when inserted in the equations below, but it will establish a "worst case" estimate of fracture velocity. We have continued to use this approach even though pipe purchased to our specification from both Canadian pipe producers has not exhibited separations for the majority of heats.

All the existing hypotheses regarding fracture propagation are based on single-phase gas decompression in the region of interest. Because of our low temperatures, high pressures and richer gas, two-phase behaviour (i.e. gas and liquid phases) occurs prior to fracture arrest. This increases the severity of the fracture propagation problem.

Battelle's hypothesis (1) states that arrests will occur if a plot of gas pressure versus the propagation velocity of that gas pressure level is tangent to or below a plot of gas pressure versus pipe fracture velocity. The fracture problem can therefore be resolved into two parts: (1) prediction of gas decompression, and (2) prediction of fracture velocity versus pressure. We have used a computer program developed using test data and theoretical thermodynamic predictions to construct gas decompression diagrams. These diagrams are a complex function of gas composition and there is no simple model applicable to our system. The curves relating fracture velocity and pressure were calculated from the relations:

$$V_f = c\sigma_F(P_d/P_a - 1)^{1/6} \,/\, (C_v/12A_c)^{0.5} \qquad (5)$$

$$C_vE \,/\, A_c\sigma^2{}_f(Rt)^{0.5} = (2/\pi)\ell n \sec(3.33\pi\sigma_a/2\sigma_f) \qquad (6)$$

where V_f = fracture velocity at pressure P_d
P_d = decompressed pressure level
P_a = arrest pressure
σ_a = arrest stress
c = constant (0.470 for buried pipe, 0.648 for above-ground pipe)

and the remainder of the symbols were defined previously.

From such plots, using 0.470 as the constant, we have determined that for our system, operating at 1250 psi (8630 kPa) and 10°F (-12°C), an 80 ft lb (110 J) CV-100 energy would result in arrest. This condition is shown in Figure 6. This is our worst case condition of temperature and pressure. The 50 ft lb fracture velocity curve indicates that less than 50 ft lb (68 J) would be necessary for arrest at our worst case station section conditions. A statistical study has indicated that if half of the pipe joints have this energy there is a very high probability that the fracture will stop in a very short distance. We have therefore specified for our line pipe that 50% of the heats must have a CV-100 energy greater than 80 ft lb (110 J) in addition to the requirements for initiation control.

In summary, rupture in pipelines is expected to be a very infrequent occurrence. This is a result of specifying high toughness for components, comprehensive inspection procedures, high pressure hydrostatic

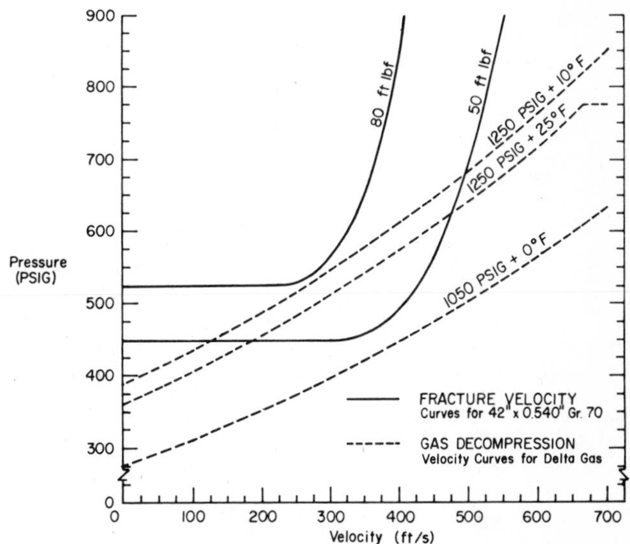

Figure 6: Illustration of method of determining pipe toughness necessary to arrest a propagating ductile fracture in Foothills mainline pipe

testing, and careful consideration of design parameters. However, if rupture did occur there is a chance it may propagate for a relatively long distance and therefore, the system has been designed to minimize the risk of a long fracture in the environmentally sensitive and remote areas in which the Foothills pipeline will operate.

Long Term Stability

It is necessary to ensure that all materials will not be subjected to adverse longterm effects, or, if these effects are significant, that they are allowed for in the design. For pipelines there are three particular long-term effects that are important: strain ageing, fatigue, and creep.

For all components which may be subject to being strained after testing the materials must be checked for strain ageing. The most common place where this straining occurs is at the field bends. It is therefore important to include artificial ageing to simulate the long term field use. Test programs have demonstrated that bending, including artificial ageing, does not adversely affect the properties of some pipe materials. We have such a program presently underway for our proposed mainline pipe.

In most pipeline systems fatigue is not an important consideration. We will be utilizing centrifugal compressors. Therefore, even in this area fluctuating stresses will be low. Sophisticated design practices, nevertheless, will be used for the pipe supports and the compressor foundations to minimize fluctuating stresses. We also plan to stress-relieve welds in critical areas. Piping flexibility analysis will be used to ensure that piping is not subject to high thermal fatigue stresses during operation. We have participated in studies to assess stresses present in pipe being shipped by rail to ensure that mean stress and fluctuating stress during this rail shipment will be kept well below the fatigue limit.

Creep will only be of importance in the internal components of the gas turbines and the associated equipment. The creep strength of these materials will be assessed to ensure that either they have infinite life or, if not, they have more than adequate life to cover the time span between major overhauls, at which time they would be replaced.

APPLICATION OF SELECTION CRITERIA TO CANDIDATE MATERIALS

Mainline Pipe

We have assessed three pipe materials supplied by three Canadian steel companies. Stelco and IPSCO have proposed similar low carbon, high manganese, molybdenum, columbium steels to be produced on their spiral pipe mills. Alberta Gas Trunk Line Limited has ordered from each of these five miles of pipe made to the Foothills specification. The Stelco pipe was produced in 1975 and installed in winter, 1975-76. The IPSCO pipe was produced in spring 1976 and installed in summer, 1976. Both these orders in general met our specification and proved suitable for field construction. Algoma Steel has proposed a low-carbon, medium manganese, columbium, vanadium steel for use on longitudinal seam pipe mills. Algoma Steel does not own a pipe mill for producing line pipe, therefore, this plate would be made into pipe on either the IPSCO or Stelco longitudinal seam pipe mills. Algoma has produced a trial run of this material, but the results are not yet available.

In summary, at least two, and probably three, steel makers can provide steel that will result in pipe meeting all our criteria.

Station Piping and Fittings

A large number of steels have been proposed for station piping and fittings. If the heavy wall pipe is manufactured on a pipe mill, it would probably use a similar, though somewhat richer chemistry, to that used in the mainline pipe. Stelco's new "Stelform" mill is the most likely choice in this area and therefore the heavy wall pipe would then be a low carbon, high manganese, molybdenum, columbium grade. If the heavy wall pipe were to be made on a rolled-and-welded type mill, materials similar to those used for fittings are most appropriate because of the need for heat treatment after forming. Some of the materials suggested by fitting manufacturers are : IN-787; a richer-chemistry version of the carbon, manganese, molybdenum, columbium grade used for line pipe; modified Hy80; some of the vanadium nitrogen grades; a number of proprietory grades; and some special plain carbon manganese steels. All these grades appear potentially able to meet our selection criteria. The manufacturers have not yet made a choice because of the possible manufacturing problems of some grades such as high costs, the greater care required to weld the higher alloy grades, and the need for a quenching and tempering operation with some grades. It appears likely that lean compositions will be used for most fittings, with the higher chemistry compositions being reserved for the thicker, heavier components where greater hardenability is required. All compositions can be welded in the field using current techniques. The sophistication of the techniques decreases as the composition becomes leaner. Therefore, we too would prefer the leaner, lower cost compositions. We are encouraging manufacturers to work toward the leanest composition which can meet our requirements.

Valves, Heat Exchangers, Pressure Vessels and Aerial Coolers

These components will in general use normal low-strength materials. Where minimum design temperatures are above -20°F (-30°C), materials such as A516 Grade 70, A350 LF 2, A216 WCB, A352 LCB, and A333 Grade 6 are adequate. They more than meet the 20 ft lb (27 J) requirement, included in our specifications, are readily weldable and have adequate mechanical properties.

Where these components are exposed to the low minimum ambient temperatures we again expect to use conventional materials, such as A537, A350 LF3, A333 Grade 3 or 9, A352 Grade 2, 2-1 or 3, or A203. These materials require more sophisticated welding procedures but reduced weldability must be accepted in order to obtain the low temperature fracture toughness properties required.

SUMMARY

Materials selection for the Foothills Project is based on a philosophy of soliciting candidate materials from various manufacturers and then assessing these by means of a number of criteria based on the known operating conditions of the system. Using this method we have determined that we can obtain the necessary products as conventional materials from a number of manufacturers. In a few cases these materials will be processed or otherwise treated to yield improved fracture toughness properties over that conventionally expected.

REFERENCES

1. W. A. Maxey, "Fifth Symposium on Line Pipe Research",

American Gas Association, Pub. L. 30174, 1974, p. J1.

2. Battelle Columbus Laboratories, "An Analysis of Reportable Incidents for Natural Gas Transmission and Gathering Lines, 1970 Through 1972", Report to American Gas Association, 1973.
3. K. D. Ives, A. K. Shoemaker and R. F. McCartney, J. Engineering Materials and Technology, Series H, 1974, vol. 96, P. 309.
4. W. A. Poynton, R. W. E. Shannon and G. D. Fearnehough, ibid.

DISCUSSION

B. A. Graville (Dominion Bridge): As you say your material selection is based on the philosophy of soliciting candidate materials then evaluating them on the basis of criteria determined by the known operating conditions, I was disappointed that your paper touches on weldability so lightly when this is one of the central considerations. How do you evaluate weldability? What aspects do you include? Do you ask the steel supplier to "prove" the weldability? Do you use tests, or do you use formulae and are they reliable for your application?

J. M. Wallbridge: Our approach to weldability is to ask the manufacturers to provide a weldable composition within a maximum carbon equivalent limitation. Using pipe from substantial-sized trial orders we then conduct laboratory tests to determine cracking tendency, hardnesses, etc. and to establish a welding procedure. We then conduct the real test of weldability; that is, we take the pipe to the field and have it welded under field conditions using a contractor's crew. We have done this with pipe from our two approved pipe suppliers, IPSCO and Stelco.

T. C. Slimmon (Northern Engineering): Canadian Arctic Gas has recently conducted some cold temperature full-scale burst tests at Battelle using a rich gas. In over half the pipe joints which fractured (not counting the origin lengths) the measured fracture speed was higher than predicted by the CV-100 toughness of the pipe. These test results contradict the statement in your paper that the CV-100 will establish a "worst case" estimate of fracture velocity. Battelle has developed 2 correlations, one for backfilled pipe and one for non-backfilled pipe. If the non-backfilled correlation is used, the CV-100 toughness comes much closer to predicting the maximum fracture speed. However, the non-backfilled correlation would require a much higher toughness to arrest a fracture than the 80 ft lbf (109 J) level you specify. It seems to me that more research is necessary before one can specify required toughnesses for arrest under Arctic pipeline conditions. I would consider "Arctic pipeline conditions" to include rich gas, frozen backfill and steels that exhibit separations. Do you have any comments?

J. M. Wallbridge: We believe that in many of these joints the CV-100 toughness was overestimated because of insufficient data. Fracture speeds have also historically had a wide scatter on burst tests. The pipe used for these tests also exhibited very heavy separation. These tests were conducted outside the range previously tested with regard to wall thickness and pressure and therefore may indicate that continued extrapolation from previous tests to systems with greater amounts of contained energy may not be valid.

Our calculations indicate that less than 80 ft lbf (109 J) is required for arrest under back filled conditions and about 85 ft lbf (115 J) under non-backfilled conditions. Statistical calculations have indicated that fracture lengths, even under the worst case non-backfilled condition, would not be unrealistically long even ignoring the probability that the pipe will have greater than the specified minimum toughness.

We do not agree that more research is necessary before one can specify adequate toughness for Arctic service, but would agree that it is desirable to reduce the cost involved in all the conservative assumptions we have made.

I do not see how Arctic pipeline conditions can be considered to include rich gas or separations on the fracture surface although I would agree that Arctic pipelines may have to consider one or both of these situations.

W. G. Wilson (Molycorp): Is four miles of pipe an acceptable sample size, based on statistically-based quality control procedures?

J. M. Wallbridge: We believe that the approximately 400 field welds included in the installation of the four miles of pipe gave an accurate and valid sample. With regard to the five miles of pipe obtained from each of the two pipe mills, this has given us enough experience to demonstrate their ability to make the pipe on a day-after-day basis. Five miles of pipe represents a substantial number of heats of steel or joints of pipe, which are the two important considerations.

C. A. Parrini (Italsider): Considering the Canadian Arctic Gas approach of using mechanical crack arrestors, why are you using the approach of conservative Charpy toughness to arrest any ductile fracture in the line?

J. M. Wallbridge: We consider that the possibility of fracture propagation is very remote (we know of only two fully documented cases of long ductile cracks when there was no unusual contributing factors) and therefore that it is poor judgment to install fracture arrestors, with their own expected problems, to deal with it. The problems with crack arrestors are a function of design but include increased initiation probability due to stress concentration, restriction on critical curvature of the pipe, logistic and installation problems, corrosion under the crack arrestor and stress corrosion of the arrestor. We have also not seen sufficient evidence to demonstrate this long term reliability. In one test, reinitiation on the opposite side of the crack arrestor occurred and we feel that under field conditions with lower toughness pipe this might be a real concern.

J. N. Cordea (Armco Steel): From the material-producer standpoint I am concerned with the very high impact energy requirements (i.e. 50 ft lbf (68 J) at low temperature) especially when it is shown that a different impact energy (30 ft lbf or 41 J) does not make a significant difference in critical crack size for brittle fracture initiation. In addition, the high energies necessary for crack arrest (50/80 ft lbf) may be attained, at some expense, in plate but not in the HAZ and in some cases the weld metal. In light of these factors, how do you rationalize your material toughness criterion?

J. M. Wallbridge: We are considering ductile rather than brittle fracture initiation, as our DWTT requirement will insure that the initiation transition temperature will be well below our operating temperature. We feel that, for example, the difference between 7.2 and 8.2 in. (180 and 210 mm) for a 42 in. x 0.600 in. grade X65 at 1250 psig, which is the result of a change from 30 to 50 ft lbf (41 to 68

J), is significant. Also, the same change in toughness under the same conditions results in a 25% greater critical crack size for a partial through-wall crack (d = 0.3t to 0.5t).

We are unaware of any propagating ductile fractures which have propagated down either the weld metal or the heat affected zone and therefore do not feel that propagation considerations apply.

Also we feel this is even less important in our case, as most of our pipe will be spiral weld and we cannot conceive of a fracture accurately propagating in such a narrow zone around and around the pipe without arrest occurring.

F. S. Somerville (Canadian Arctic Gas): As is shown in Figure 2 of our (previous) contribution, at 37 ft lbf (50 J) the critical crack size at the operating conditions of the Arctic Gas Pipeline is 85% of the maximum. We have specified this as the pipe toughness, since we intend to use crack arrestors, and we are not prepared to pay for the extra toughness.

P. E. Bedford-Jones (Steel Company of Canada): The emphasis shown on fracture initiation and critical flaw size seems to represent a return to industrial research programs that were underway prior to the crash programmes which were carried out due to the occurrence of propagating shear failures caused by the presence of very large external damage defects. The need for more control of the steel properties related to fracture initiation suggests that an improved toughness test method for routine quality control testing needs to be developed. A closer similarity between the field and mill welding processes may be important in achieving a better understanding and control of the weldability factors of the pipe. I would ask Mr. Wallbridge to comment on the welding practices envisaged for the Foothills project.

J. M. Wallbridge: We would agree thit it would be desirable to have an improved toughness test. We have a program that is just getting underway that includes this as one of its aims.

I would disagree that a close similarity between field and mill welding is desirable or practical. The primary difference between them is in heat input and hydrogen content. A low hydrogen process for field welding would be desirable but I do not believe the high heat processes such as submerged-arc can be developed in the near future for field welding (excluding double jointing).

Foothills present planning is based on conventional downhill welding, but we are continuing to assess the fully automatic processes.

G. L. Archer (The Welding Institute): Mr. Bedford-Jones raised the question of an improved toughness test for quality control in place of the Charpy test. We have in fact proposed a simplified COD test for this purpose in the U.K. A rough machined full thickness specimen with a simple, narrow, machined notch is sufficient. Instrumentation could be simplified. The resulting test would probably still be more expensive than the Charpy, but correlation with the normal fracture mechanics type of test would be more direct, more valid and more dependable.

F. S. Somerville: I cannot agree that improved toughness testing is necessary for linepipe. The results of West Jefferson Tests show the Charpy energy to predict critical size with good accuracy. The COD test is also suggested to investigate initiation, particularly for welds and heat affected zones or for prediction of fracture initiation transition temperature.

E. C. Hamre (Interprovincial Steel and Pipe): You stated that the Foothills specification requires at least 50% of the pipes to have a minimum of 80 ft lbf (109 J) to prevent fracture propagation. How far apart do you propose placing these pipes, or how long a fracture are you prepared to accept? Assuming this distance to be quite small, will not this present a very significant materials handling problem?

J. M. Wallbridge: We do not intend to install these high energy pipes at any particular location but rather to allow their semi-random distribution along the line. We have not established a maximum allowable fracture length. Our analysis is based on a statistical distribution of fracture lengths. This study which includes the distributions of Charpy energy of the pipe, the C_v required for arrest as a function of location and arrest length, various degrees of non-random distribution of pipe and the effect of various lengths of joints of pipe, has indicated that the present design has a probable distribution of fracture length as follows: 50% of fractures less than 150 ft (46 m), and 99% of fractures less than 600 ft (180 m).

K. N. Street (R. M. Hardy and Associates): We have listened with interest to the technical pros and cons of the two pipeline proposals being discussed here this morning. Would you care to give us your views on the non-technical pros and cons of the two proposals, as seen by the people of Canada, including the native peoples of the Arctic? This would appear to be well within the aims of this conference.

J. M. Wallbridge: In making this response I have assumed that a basic understanding exists as to nature of the various projects currently being proposed to transport northern gas to the market areas of both Canada and the United States.

In addition to the benefits common to all of the proposed northern pipelines there are, in our opinion, many benefits which our projects (the Maple Leaf and Alcan) will offer over that of the competitive project, Canadian Arctic Gas:

The fact that the Maple Leaf and Alcan projects are manageable in size and design, and they also make use of most of the existing pipeline and operating facilities in Canada and the expertise available within the projects' two Canadian-sponsored companies.

The fact that the financial requirements of our projects are within the financial capacity of Canada. In Canada the cost of putting the Alcan Project into service is $2.5 billion. The Maple Leaf Project which will come into service two years later will require $2.9 billion by the first year of operation. By comparison, the cost of putting the Canadian Arctic Gas Project into service is about $7.5 billion.

The fact that all sections of the Maple Leaf and Alcan Pipelines which are contained within Canadian territory will be 100% Canadian-owned. The competitive project, Arctic Gas, will not.

The fact that nearly all the requirements of the Maple Leaf Project and Canadian portion of the Alcan Project can be supplied by Canadians. Most of the pipes, valves, fittings and other equipment can be made by Canadian manufacturers. Because of the diameter and pressure rating of the Arctic Gas components, a number of Canadian companies will be ruled out as suppliers for their requirements, but would be able to make the Foothills components. Being conventionally sized, the pipeline can be built by Canadian pipeline contractors and will, therefore, make maximum use of Canadian labour and construction capability.

The fact that the Alcan and Maple Leaf projects will be constructed sequentially will result in a number of years of pipeline activity. This should greatly assist the creation and expansion of the Canadian economy in both the industrial and service sector, especially in the field of engineering, environment and project management, where expertise gained will be marketable abroad.

The fact that the Arctic Gas project will traverse a large part of the extremely harsh yet environmentally sensitive North Slope and the Mackenzie Delta. The Maple Leaf and Alcan Projects will not.

The fact that Foothills Pipe Lines Ltd. has as one of its prime objectives the maximization of northern participation in both of its projects.

The fact that Foothills in both its proposed Maple Leaf Project and Alcan Pipeline Project has included the supply of natural gas to some 45% of the population of the Northwest Territories and the Yukon. The competitive project, Arctic Gas, has not.

The fact that Foothills Pipe Lines intends to give residents of the NWT and the Yukon the opportunity to purchase equity-ownership in our pipeline projects on attractive terms and thus northerners will have a say in how the projects should be operated.

Add to these the fact that the Alcan Pipeline Project provides the United States the quickest means of obtaining the Alaskan gas which they urgently require. With governmental approvals by late 1977, gas deliveries can commence on January 1, 1981. The competitive project, Arctic Gas, can only commence deliveries of Alaskan gas in late 1983.

And finally, the fact that the immediate urgency for new gas supply is in the United States, not Canada. The Alcan Project, if approved, removes this urgency. It thus provides Canada reasonable time to settle the matter of Northwest Territories native land claims in a rational manner and also provides reasonable time to decide how the Mackenzie Valley pipeline should be constructed in order to provide the most benefit to Canada. This is not to say that Canada will not need to connect new sources of gas supply. In the early 1980's, Canada's established gas supply areas will not be able to satisfy its demand for natural gas and new supply areas will have to be connected.

When authorization is given to build the Mackenzie Valley Pipeline, the Maple Leaf project can be built as soon as, if not sooner, than the competitive project since ours is a smaller project requiring much less capital outlay and resources to complete.

Faced with these facts, in our opinion, a northern pipeline system can and will be a benefit and a necessity to the people of Canada.

ARCTIC PIPE PRODUCTION AND DEVELOPMENT

J. E. Hood
The Steel Company of Canada, Limited
Hamilton, Ontario L8N 3T1
Canada

This paper describes aspects of Arctic pipe production from acicular ferrite steel. The acicular ferrite provides sufficient work hardening to compensate for Bauschinger effect strength losses during spiral pipe forming and meets the fracture toughness requirements for Arctic pipe.

Acicular ferrite can be readily welded during pipemaking to meet submerged-arc weld toughness requirements and, in addition, has a field weldability comparable with conventional ferrite-pearlite steels.

Full-scale tests on 48 in. (1220 mm) diameter by 0.72 in. (18 mm) wall X-70 pipe have demonstrated the integrity of the acicular ferrite product.

INTRODUCTION

Pipe for planned Arctic pipelines has special requirements. These stem from the low ambient temperatures of the Arctic, from the high operating pressures, and from the large diameters necessary for economic gas transport over the vast distances between the northern gas sources and the southern consumers. The Canadian Arctic Gas Study, Limited, for example, has translated these needs into the following design parameters:

Outside Diameter:	48 in. (1220 mm)
Thickness:	0.72 in. (18 mm)
Grade:	X-70
Operating Pressure:	1680 psi (11.6 MPa)

Moreover, for gas pipelines the environment has imposed a minimum design temperature of -13°F (-25°C), thereby increasing the difficulty of achieving satisfactory pipe fracture behaviour. Although there are different fracture design philosophies for different pipelines, the general requirements are for high ductile toughness and low fracture mode transition temperatures.

Also, the low temperatures of the Arctic make weldability a particularly important property of pipe steel, especially when coupled with the thick pipe walls and high yield strength. A large technical effort was required to achieve these desired characteristics in a single pipe: higher strength, thicker walls, improved toughness, larger diameter, and adequate weldability. Added to this, Stelco has the additional consideration of making this pipe by the "Stelform" process.

HIGH-STRENGTH SPIRAL WELDED PIPE

Stelco will make much of its pipe for Arctic applications at its new Stelform spiral weld pipe mill (1) located in Welland, Ontario. There are two major differences between spiral weld pipe and the more common UOE or longitudinal seam pipe: i) the skelp rolling direction is at an angle to the pipe axis, and ii) spiral pipe is not cold expanded.

The Stelform Mill utilizes plate rather than the coiled strip skelp normally used for spiral pipe-making. Another feature of this process is the replacement of submerged-arc welding at the forming station by a continuous, high-speed MIG tack welder. The spiral seam submerged-arc welding is done "off line" at a number of welding stations. The sequence of operations at this mill is illustrated schematically in Figure 1.

In both longitudinal seam and spiral seam pipe-making, the skelp is bent so that the inner portion of the pipe experiences compressive plastic strain and the outer fibers experience tensile strain. In spiral pipe-making, the levels of strain at the two surfaces are approximately equal while in longitudinal seam pipe-making, the compressive strain at the inside surface is greater than the tensile strain at the outer surface because of the compression applied during the "O"-ing operation.

The pipe yield strength after forming by either process tends to be less than the original skelp yield strength. This is a manifestation of the Bauschinger effect arising from the strain reversal (compression in forming, then tension in testing) experienced by the inner half of the pipe wall. Figure 2 shows the drop in yield strength suffered by conventional ferrite-pearlite skelp (polygonal microstructure) formed into spiral pipe. The yield strength loss in the compression side of the pipe wall generally is not fully compensated by the strain hardening developed in the tension side, resulting in a net loss of yield strength. The effect of forming on the through-wall yield strength distribution in a spirally formed ferrite-pearlite skelp is shown in Figure 3, where the individual yield strength values were determined

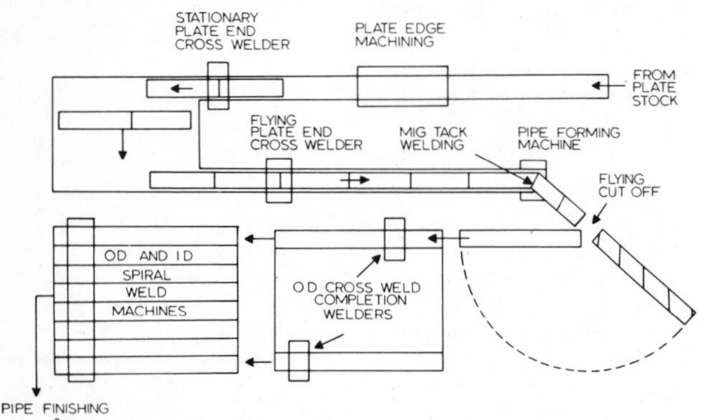

Figure 1: Stelform Mill - Sequence of Welding Operations

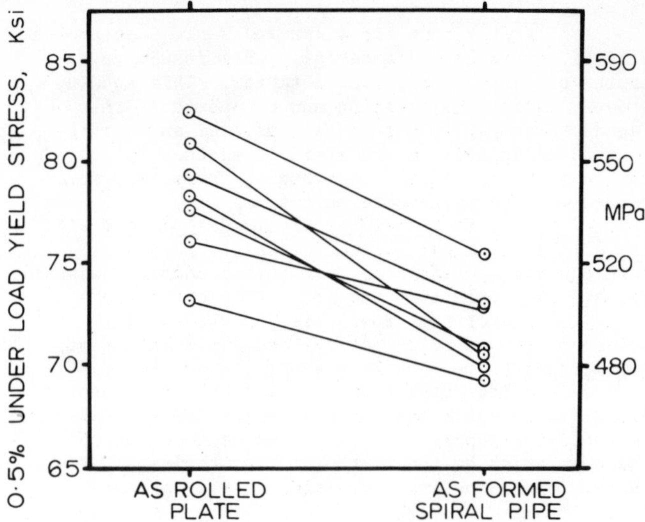

Figure 2: Yield Stress Change During Forming Ferrite-Pearlite Spiral Pipe

from 0.125 in. (3.2 mm) diameter transverse-to-the-pipe-axis tensile specimens machined from the pipe wall.

The influence of the Bauschinger effect is reduced in longitudinal seam pipe by cold expanding the formed pipe by 1% to 1.75% hoop strain. The Bauschinger effect yield loss can also be counteracted by using a steel with a high rate of strain hardening. A steel containing a high proportion of acicular ferrite has a sufficiently high strain hardening rate during pipe forming that it can provide a net increase in yield strength and so dispense with the need for a separate expansion cycle. The change in through-wall yield strength distribution from forming an acicular ferrite skelp is shown in Figure 4, while the different strain hardening rates of acicular ferrite and a conventional ferrite-pearlite skelp are illustrated in Figure 5.

A suitable steel analysis was developed from a series of full-scale trials (2). The development of an optimum analysis was complicated by the interrelation between rolling practice (prior austenite grain size), chemical analysis and transformation temperature. For the particular rolling practice used, a relationship was developed between yield strength, structure and total alloy content, as

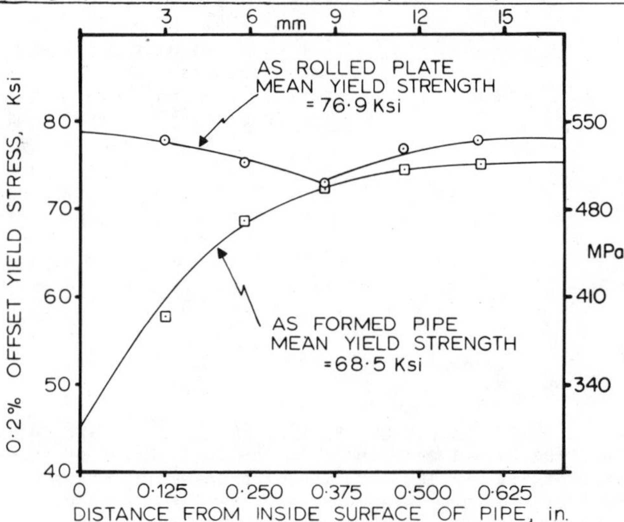

Figure 3: Through-Wall Transverse to Pipe Axis Yield Strength Distribution Before and After Forming Ferrite-Pearlite Spiral Pipe

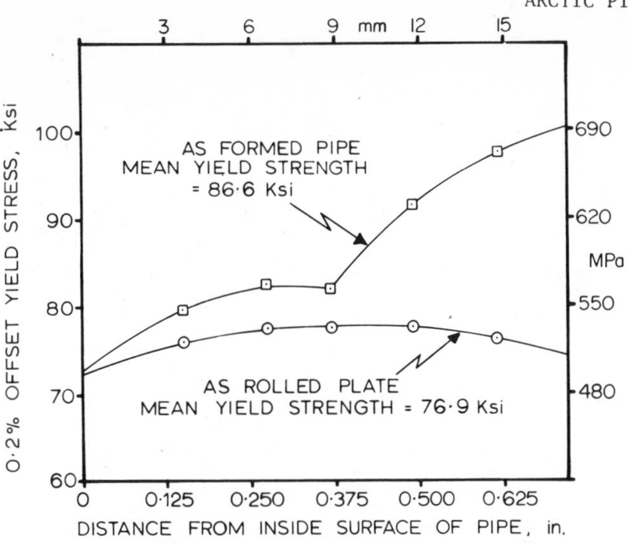

Figure 4: Through-Wall Transverse to Pipe Axis Yield Strength Distribution Before and After Forming Acicular Ferrite Spiral Pipe

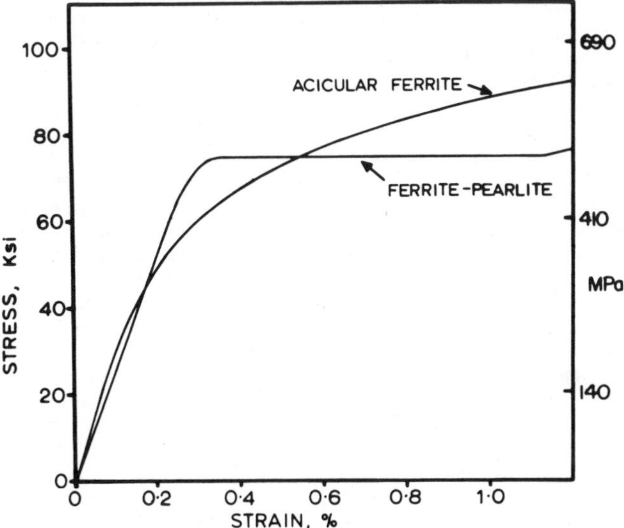

Figure 5: Yielding and Strain Hardening Characteristics of Ferrite-Pearlite and Acicular Ferrite Plate

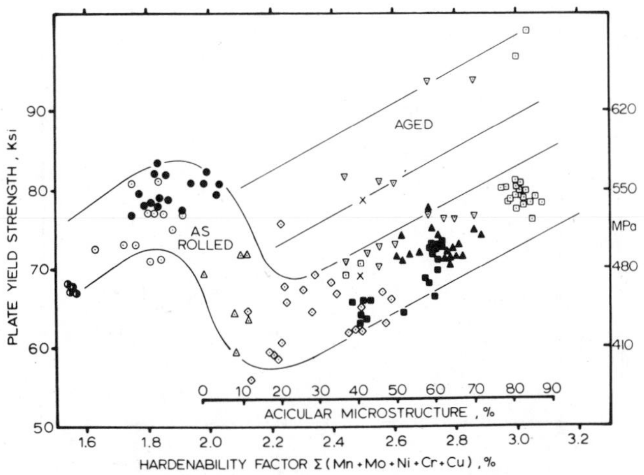

Figure 6: Relationship Between Alloy Content, Structure and Yield Strength for Controlled Rolled Plate

Table 1

Typical Analysis of High Acicularity Steel

C%	Mn%	P%	S%	Si%	Ni%	Mo%	Cb%	Al%
0.05	2.00	0.01	0.007	0.25	0.25	0.55	0.06	0.03

illustrated in Figure 6. The different symbols in Figure 6 relate to different alloy groups. An alloy level of approximately 2.8% to 3.0%, giving more than 70% acicularity, provides sufficient skelp yield strength and strain hardening rate to meet the requirements for an X-70 grade in 48 in. (1220 mm) diameter by 0.72 in. (18 mm) wall pipe. A typical analysis of such a skelp is given in Table 1. The Cb does not play a significant strengthening role in these low transformation temperature steels except through grain refinement.

PIPE BODY TOUGHNESS

The toughness of the pipe body can be separated into two parts: i) the transition temperature, and ii) the ductile toughness or level of toughness above the transition temperature.

Methods of achieving both a low transition temperature and a high ductile toughness in plate rolling are well documented (3-6) and for this reason they will be discussed only briefly here. In general, the fine prior austenite grain size needed to achieve a fine transformed grain size, and hence low transition temperature, can be achieved by controlling austenite grain growth during slab reheating and applying large plate reductions at low finishing rolling temperatures. It is also advantageous to achieve complete recrystallization of the austenite at high rolling temperatures to provide the finest grain size at the start of the lower temperature rolling sequence. The large reductions needed to achieve this recrystallization are, however, frequently unattainable on lower powered plate mills. High ductile toughness is achieved by minimizing the inclusion content in general and the sulfur content in particular. Controlled rare earth additions improve ductile toughness by making the sulfides less plastic during hot rolling and thereby shortening the average inclusion length. Ductile toughness is also improved by reducing the carbon content. These techniques for developing high toughness ferrite-pearlite pipe are equally applicable to acicular ferrite pipe for Arctic applications.

PIPE WELD TOUGHNESS

Methods of achieving high toughness in the submerged-arc pipe welds are less well documented. Minimum values of weld toughness were set only recently with the development of specifications for Arctic pipe and are typically in the region of 40 ft lbf (54 J) at 0°F (-18°C). Heavy wall Arctic pipe creates special problems because the high weld heat inputs decrease the toughness of the weld metal and HAZ. Figure 7 shows the effect of heat input on weld metal toughness. One way of reducing heat input and yet achieving the same weld penetration is by "edge gapping" -- welding with a fixed gap between the lands of the edge preparation. Although not yet applied in production, significant increases in penetration for a given heat input can be achieved in the laboratory. This is shown in Figure 8. While further improvements to weld toughness through process improvement can be expected, the main thrust has been through metallurgical improvement of the weld metal by decreasing the inclusion content and

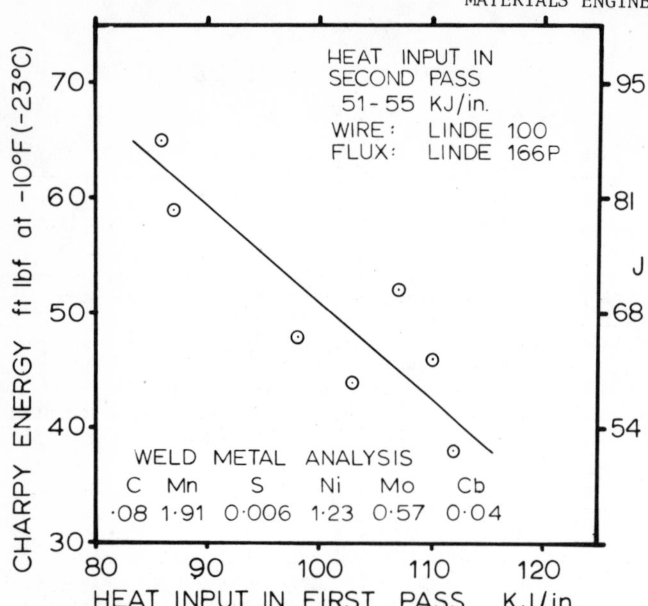

Figure 7: Effect of Heat Input on Weld Metal Toughness of Two-Pass Submerged-Arc Weld.

refining the structure.

The two most important components of the weld metal inclusion content are sulfur and oxygen. Sulfur is introduced into the weldment through the welding wire and the parent metal, and within the usual sulfur range, exerts a strong effect on toughness. Some reduction in weld metal sulfur can be achieved by using very low sulfur welding wire, although with the 65 per cent dilution of the weld by the parent metal that is typical of pipe welding this is only a partial solution. The oxygen content of the weld varies, depending mainly on the welding flux. Basic fluxes tend to provide a lower oxygen level in the weld compared to neutral fluxes and so give higher weld toughness. The currently available basic fluxes are, however, more difficult to use and have an increased tendency to cause undercutting and poor bead appearance. The influence of oxygen on weld toughness is illustrated in Figure 9.

A clear picture of how alloying elements influence the weld metal structure and how the structure, in turn, relates to the toughness has not yet been developed. Some general agreement does seem to be emerging, however, and it appears that a uniform, fine acicular structure is the most desirable. Most authorities agree that the presence of coarse proeutectoid ferrite, generally surrounding the columnar regions, causes a reduction of toughness (7,8). This microstructural constituent can be eliminated by lowering the transformation temperature of the weld.

The most frequently used alloy additions are Mn and Mo. These promote the formation of acicular ferrite. There is an optimum alloy level beyond which further reductions in transformation temperature are accompanied by a reduction in toughness. This loss of toughness due to increasing alloy content is shown in Figure 10. Insufficient data were available to show the reduction of toughness at lower alloy levels but this is well known to occur with increasing amounts of proeutectoid ferrite. As the alloy level rises, the yield strength of the weld metal increases and the loss of toughness appears to be associated with a coarsening of the microstructure and the appearance of larger regions of "upper bainite". Figure 11 illustrates typical microstructure of underalloyed (proeutectoid ferrite surrounding columnar zones), correctly alloyed (no pro-eutectoid ferrite, fine acicular structure) and overalloyed

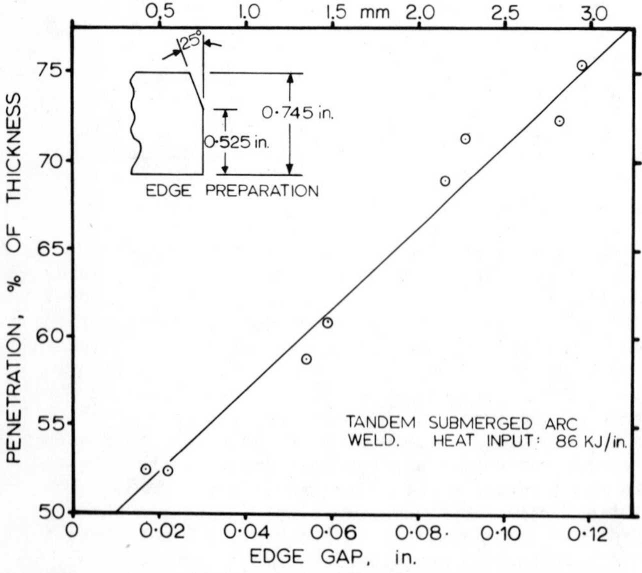

Figure 8: Effect of Edge Gap on Penetration

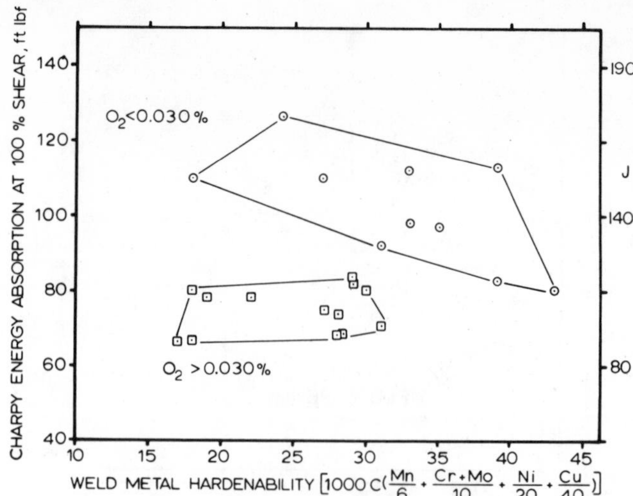

Figure 9: Influence of Weld Metal Oxygen Content on Charpy Shelf Energy

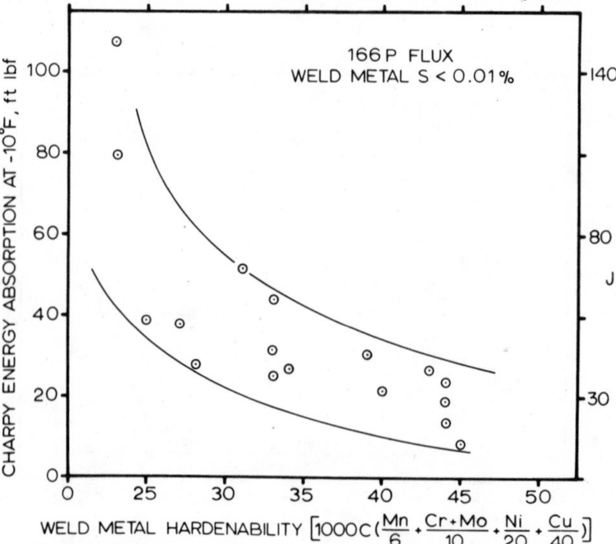

Figure 10: Reduction of Weld Metal Toughness with Increasing Hardenability

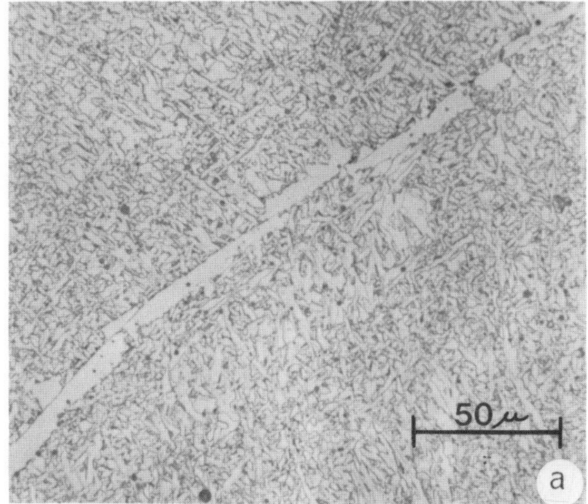

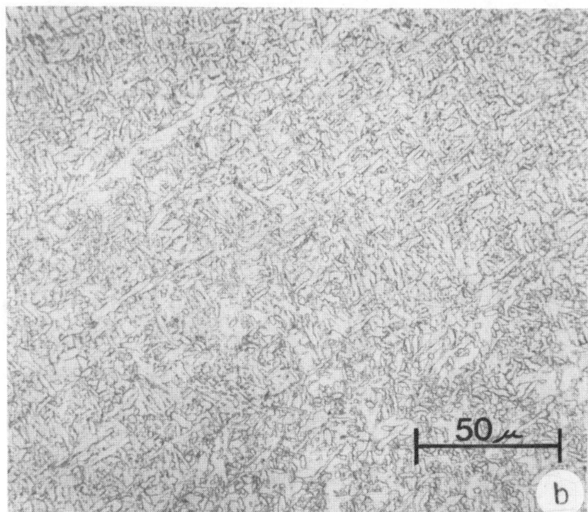

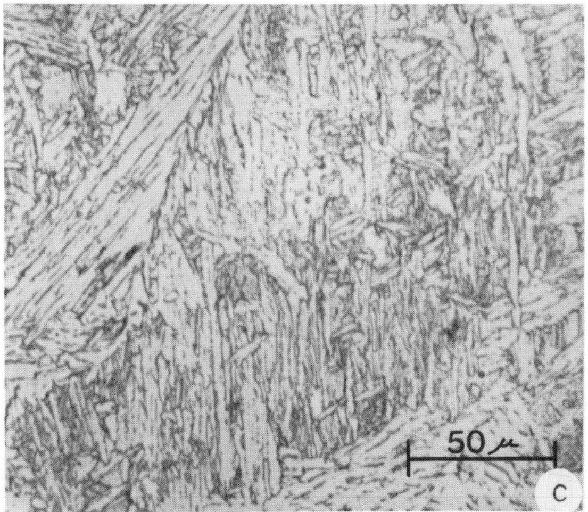

Figure 11: Weld Metal Microstructures of (a) "Underalloyed", (b) "Correctly Alloyed" and (c) "Overalloyed" Welds

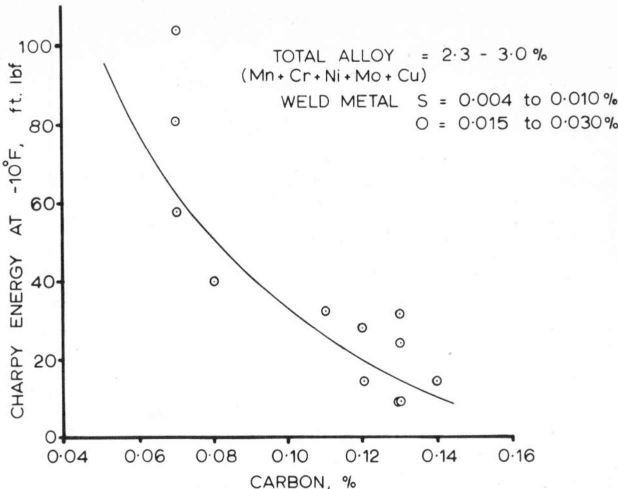

Figure 12: Influence of Carbon Content on Weld Metal Toughness

(coarse acicular structure; martensitic regions) weld metals.

The alloy level used in Figure 10 was calculated simply as a "carbon equivalent" of alloying elements multiplied by the carbon content. This rather arbitrary indicator of hardenability has been used by Stout (9) as an indication of carbon equivalence in weldability work and is used here because it seems to provide a reasonable means of predicting toughness. The influence of carbon can be accounted for adequately only when it is used as a multiplier.

Because of the powerful effect of carbon on toughness, it is essential to maintain the level of carbon in the weld metal at a low level. Until recently, most commercially available welding wires contained over 0.10% C. Reductions of welding wire carbon level down to around 0.06% C would be both feasible and desirable. The effect of carbon content on weld metal toughness is illustrated in Figure 12 although, as carbon has a complex influence through both hardenability and second phase effects, this figure only indicates a trend.

Nickel is frequently added to welding wires to improve weld toughness. It is often found in levels up to 2.5 per cent, although there may be more economic methods of achieving the same level of toughness. Nickel provides an effective method of providing hardenability without loss of toughness.

The chemical analysis of the parent metal plays an important role in fixing the weld toughness level by diluting the welding wire. Between 60 and 70 per cent of the weld nugget comes from the parent material in pipe mill welding. As it is the final analysis of the weld metal that determines the weld toughness, the relative contribution of both the welding wire and the parent metal must be estimated. This can be done quite readily for most elements through the type of correlation made in Figure 13. The level of some elements in the weld metal, such as Si, strongly depend on the flux type.

While it is not present in welding wires, Cb is an element that is commonly a key component of pipe steels and so finds its way into the weld metal. Its effect on weld metal toughness is not well characterized , although it is known to influence the metallographic structure and generally increase the Charpy transition temperature (10). Increasing additions of Cb reduce the amount of proeutectoid ferrite through the effect on hardenability but seem to coarsen the acicular component of the microstructure. In addition, Cb precipitation strengthening occurs in the reheated region of a two-pass weld causing marked local changes in strength and toughness. The effect of Cb on the strength and toughness of a two-pass submerged-arc weld is illustrated in Figure 14. While Cb seemed to increase the transition temperature, no effect on energy absorbed at -10°F (-23°C) was noted. These effects of Cb should be taken only as typical of this particular weld metal analysis.

Some recently developed welding wires contain Ti, which is thought to have a beneficial effect on toughness through refining the structure and,

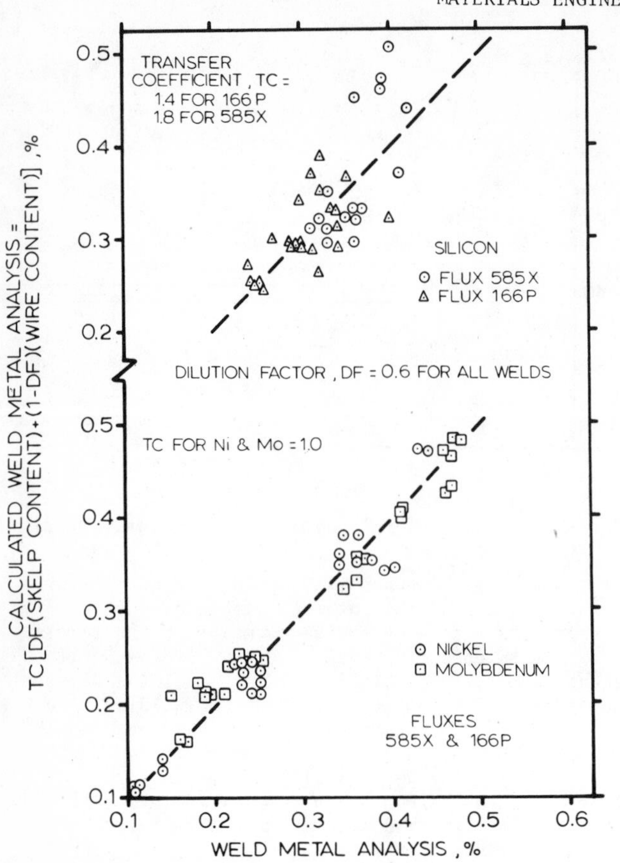

Figure 13: Prediction of Weld Metal Analysis

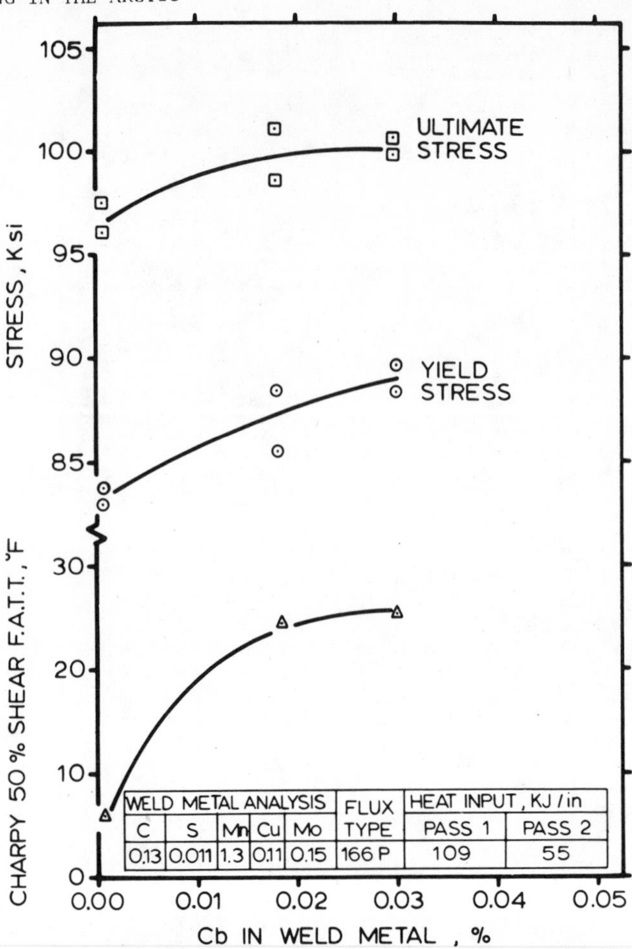

Figure 14: Effect of Cb on the Strength and Toughness of Weld Metal

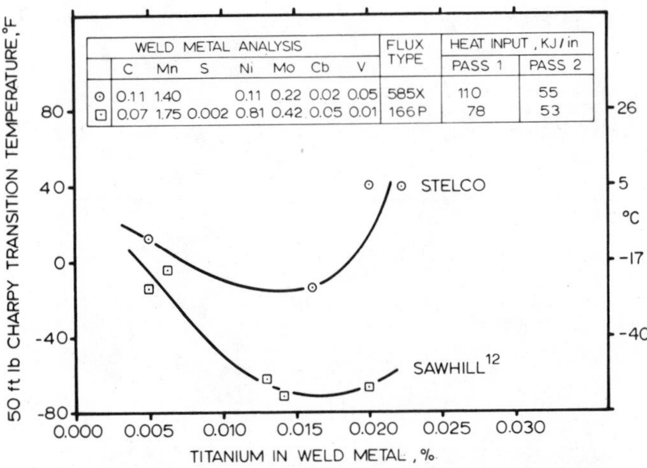

Figure 15: Influence of Titanium on Weld Metal Transition Temperature

perhaps, tying up nitrogen (11). When present at a level of about 0.015 per cent, Ti causes a significant reduction in transition temperature. The effect of Ti, the magnitude of which is not entirely predictable, is shown in Figure 15.

The higher alloy chemistry of the acicular ferrite contributes to the weld metal analysis so that lower alloy welding wires can be used to achieve the same strength and toughness level. In addition, the low carbon content of the acicular ferrite makes it easier to achieve a low carbon content in the weld metal and so improve toughness.

The weld metal toughness levels required for Arctic pipelines can be met by applying the technology discussed above. There remains, however, a good deal of research required to optimize the welding procedures and consumables so that these requirements can be met at a minimum cost.

HEAT-AFFECTED ZONE (HAZ) TOUGHNESS

Some proposed specifications for Arctic pipe contain weld heat affected zone (HAZ) toughness requirements. Toughness is measured by the Charpy test in these specifications, and there is a good deal of uncertainty about whether HAZ toughness measured in this way really relates to full-scale behaviour. It was shown (12) that the 50-50 notch location (i.e. the Charpy notch is located 50 per cent within the HAZ and 50 per cent within the weld metal) provides the measure of lowest toughness. Many investigators have used the COD (13,14) test to investigate HAZ toughness, and while it provides a more definitive measure of local HAZ toughness, its high cost and difficulties in relating results to full-scale fracture behaviour have precluded its use as a specification test, except in isolated cases.

The HAZ toughness of a submerged-arc weld is primarily controlled by the composition and structure of the parent material and the heat input of the welding process.

The heat input of the welding process is more or less fixed by pipe thickness for most pipe mills. As a result, the higher heat input required for heavier wall pipe tends to create a wider coarse-grained HAZ, thereby increasing the width of the lowest toughness zone of the weldment.

The structure and composition of the parent material has a complex relationship to the properties

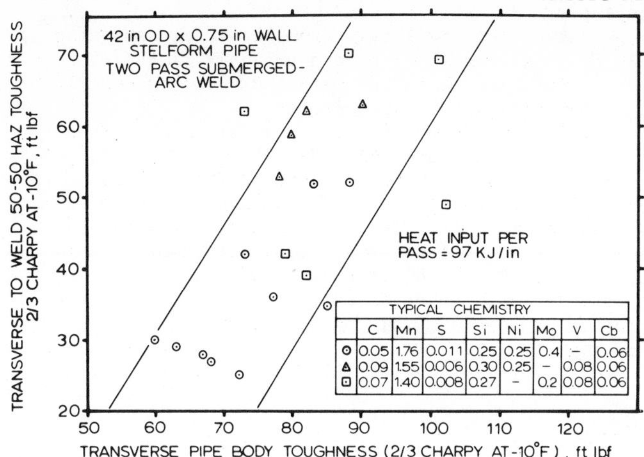

Figure 16: Relationship Between Pipe Body and HAZ Toughness

of the coarse-grained HAZ. In general, for a particular type of steel chemistry, the toughness of the coarse-grained HAZ increases with increasing skelp toughness. Elements such as Cb and V can have deleterious effects by precipitation hardening areas of reheated HAZ in two-pass welds. On the other hand, it is thought that small additions of Ti can improve toughness by inhibiting grain growth.

The HAZ toughness properties of acicular ferrite pipe steels are not significantly different from the more conventional ferrite-pearlite pipe steels. Figure 16 shows how the HAZ toughness of three different high strength pipe steels varies predominantly with the pipe body toughness. The correlation is quite strong considering the degree of scatter common to HAZ toughness testing.

FIELD WELDABILITY

Any line pipe to be used in the Arctic must have adequate field weldability. Weldability is a difficult property to define, not referring to any specific characteristic of the steel being welded and being intimately related to the procedures and competence of the pipeline construction crew. It is most commonly understood to mean the resistance to hydrogen-induced HAZ cracking in the context of girth welding of pipe in the field.

The most common parameter for predicting the sensitivity of the steel to this mode of failure is the carbon equivalent. This is a rough measure of hardenability and therefore of the tendency of the steel to form an HAZ microstructure sensitive to hydrogen. Many equations are available for predicting hydrogen cracking susceptibility in this way, two examples (15) being as follows:

$$CE = C + Mn/6 + (Cr+Mo+V)/5 + (Ni+Cu)/15 \quad (1)$$

$$CE = C + Si/30 + Mn/20 + Cu/20 + Ni/60 + Cr/20 + Mo/15 + V/10 + V/10 + 5B + (\text{thickness, mm})/600 + (\text{diffusible H, m}\ell/100\text{g})/60 \quad (2)$$

where elements are quoted in wt %. The greatest drawback of these equations is that they are applicable only within restricted analysis ranges and most of them overestimate the susceptibility to hydrogen cracking of very low carbon steels. In an attempt to bring these low carbon steels in line with more conventional analyses, Stout (9) introduced the following carbon equivalent equation with carbon as a multiplier.

$$CE = 1000C[Mn/6 + (Cr+Mo)/10 + Ni/20 + Cu/40] \quad (3)$$

The HAZ hardness developed under a weld laid with a similar heat input (and therefore same cooling rate) to a field weld, is considered to be a useful measure of susceptibility because hydrogen cracking susceptibility correlates quite closely with strength level. Table 2 shows typical peak HAZ hardness levels for three skelp steels as a function of carbon equivalence. This table emphasizes the danger of indiscriminate use of carbon-equivalent equations.

There are a large number of tests for measuring hydrogen cracking susceptibility, none of which will predict the field welding performance of the pipe with precision. One of the most sophisticated and quantitative is the implant cracking test (16). In this test, the pipe material is subjected to the welding process and heat input of interest so that a notched section of test specimen is situated in the HAZ of a real weld, as shown in Figure 17. The test specimen is loaded and the time to failure recorded. The critical stress below which failure does not occur establishes a level of susceptibility to hydrogen cracking for the material. Data for various pipe materials are presented in Figure 18, where it can be seen that acicular ferrite again shows up in a favorable light relative to its carbon equivalent. These data demonstrate that low-carbon fully acicular steels have a weldability comparable to the best low-carbon-equivalent ferrite-pearlite steels. Note that the individual data points may not be compared directly with the data of Civallero (17) because of possible differences in testing procedure.

Table 2

Peak HAZ Hardness Levels for Different Steels welded at -40°F(-40°C) with heat input, 15 kJ/in(590 J/mm)

Plate Analysis wt %	CE eq.(1)	Maximum Underbead Hardness HV (500g)
0.16 C, 1.59 Mn, 0.32 Si 0.07 V, 0.06 Cb, 0.023 Al	0.45	386, 396
0.05 C, 2.07 Mn, 0.30 Si 0.46 Mo, 0.07 Cb, 0.039 Al	0.51	330, 343
0.05 C, 1.98 Mn, 0.30 Si, 0.55 Mo, 0.06 Cb, 0.22 Ni, 0.040 Al	0.52	356, 356

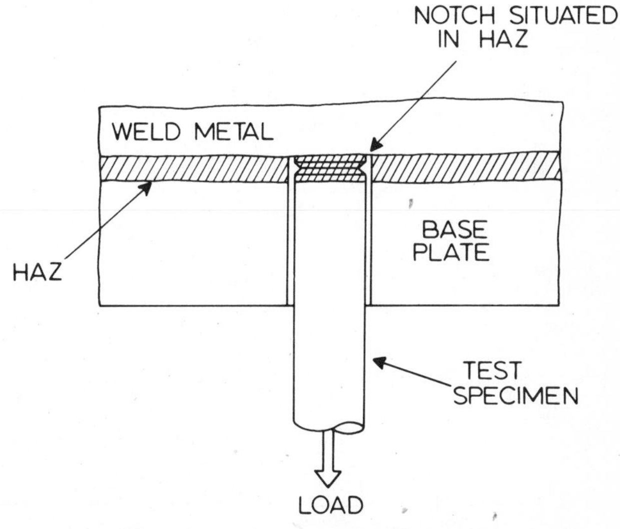

Figure 17: Implant Cracking Test

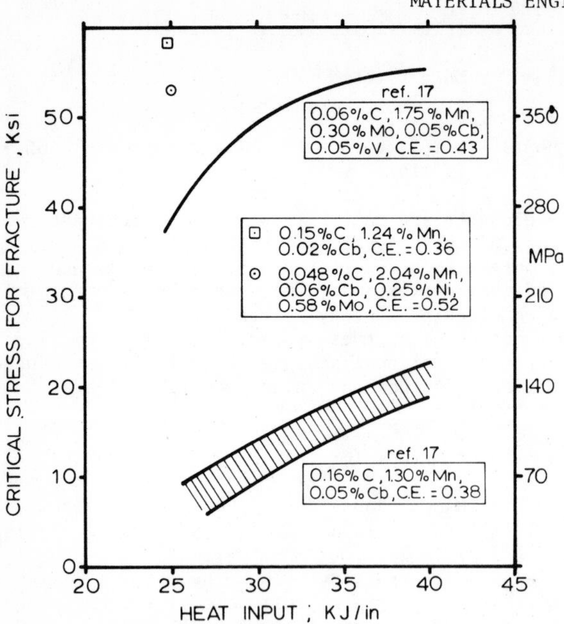

Figure 18: Implant Cracking Test Data for Various Pipe Steels

FULL-SCALE TEST BEHAVIOUR

A continuing full-scale test program is being carried out on acicular ferrite pipe made by the Stelform process.

The purpose of the tests is to confirm that the strength and ductility of the pipes are as predicted from the laboratory testing.

To date, six tests on 48 in. (1220 mm) diameter by 0.72 in. (18 mm) wall X-70 pipe have been completed.

The test involves hydraulically pressurizing a 30 ft (9 m) length of pipe previously fitted with end closures and measuring both the yielding behaviour and final failure characteristics.

In two of the tests, pipes were monotonically pressurized to failure while in the remaining four tests the pipes were pressure-cycled above yield before loading to failure. The purpose of the pressure-cycling was to intensify the effect of any defects.

The results of these tests are summarized in Table 3. They indicate that, in general, the laboratory tests underestimated full-scale performance and that low-cycle straining had no significant effect.

SUMMARY

A number of processing routes are being examined in the attempt to meet the stringent requirements for heavy wall Arctic pipe.

Acicular ferrite can provide the strength-toughness combination in spiral pipe required for Arctic service and is compatible with the recent developments in welding technology aimed at meeting weldment toughness requirements.

Weldability of low carbon acicular ferrite is comparable with the lower carbon equivalent ferrite-pearlite steels as measured by HAZ hardness and implant cracking tests.

Full-scale testing of production pipe confirmed their integrity and showed that they were at least as strong as predicted from laboratory tests.

Acknowledgement

The author thanks Mr. D. E. Osborne for his

Table 3

Full Scale Test Data

Test No.	Flattened Strap Properties: 0.5% Strain Under Load Yield Stress (MPa)	Flattened Strap Properties: Ultimate Stress ksi (MPa)	Flattened Strap Properties: Elongation on 2 in. (%)	No. Cycles	Full Scale Test Properties: 0.5% Strain Under Load Yield Stress** ksi (MPa)	Full Scale Test Properties: Maximum Cycle Stress ksi (MPa)	Full Scale Test Properties: Mean Hoop Strain (%)	Full Scale Test Properties: Thickness Reduction (%)
1	84.7(584)	115.3 (795)	36	1	83.6(576)	122.4(844)	3.83	45
2	83.8(578)	113.8 (785)	32	1	84.8(585)	123.2(849)	-	-
3	82.4(568)	113.9 (785)	36	1	84.8(585)	116.1(800)	1.39	-
				2		119.8(826)	3.76	41
4	87.3(602)	114.9 (792)	36	1		107.6(742)	0.57	-
				2	85.1(587)	109.0(751)	0.60	-
				3		120.1(828)	3.17	45
5	89.6(618)	117.0 (807)	37	1		112.1(773)	-	-
				2	81.0(558)	120.1(828)	0.98	-
				3		115.5(796)	0.98	-
				4		122.0(841)	2.92	48
6	89.8(619)	114.6 (790)	36	1		105.4(727)	0.35	-
				2	85.6(590)	112.7(777)	1.34	-
				3		119.0(820	-	-
				4		121.6(838)	-	-
				5		122.5(845)	3.78	49

* Effect of biaxial stress on yield taken into account.

assistance in assembling this paper.

REFERENCES

1. P. E. Bedford-Jones et al: AIME, Mechanical Working and Steel Processing XIV, 1976, pp. 33-51.
2. D. B. McCutcheon et al: "Controlled Rolling of Acicular Ferrite Plate", Journée Internationale de Sidérurgie, Paris, France, 1974.
3. F. B. Pickering: Microalloying '75, 1976, Union Carbide Corp., New York, p. 9.
4. T. Gladman, D. Dulieu, I. D. McIvor, ibid., p. 32.
5. T. Tanaka, N. Tabata, T. Hatomura, C. Shiga, ibid., p. 107.
6. I. Kosazu, C. Ouchi, T. Sampei, T. Okita, ibid., p. 120.
7. J. G. Garland and P. R. Kirkwood: Metal Construction, 1975, vol. 7 (5) pp. 275-283.
8. G. Bernard: Microalloying '75, 1976, Union Carbide Corp., New York, p. 552.
9. R. D. Stout: Progress Report - "Weldability Tests for 5LX Pipeline Steels" -- To API-Division of Production, 1975.
10. J. M. Sawhill: "The Effects of Cb in Low Alloy Steel Weld Metal", Climax Molybdenum Report L-176-115, 1973.
11. S. Nakano et al: "Optimizing the Titanium Effect on Weld Metal Toughness", IIW Document XII-B-182-75.
12. J. M. Sawhill and T. Wada: "Properties of Welds in Low-Carbon Mn-Mo-Cb Line pipe Steels", Climax Molybdenum Report L-176-136, 1974.
13. E. Myoshi et al: "Fracture Initiation Characteristics of Heat Affected Zones Assessed by COD Test", IIW-LX 878-74, 1974.
14. G. G. Saunders, in "Heat-Treatment Aspects of Metal Joining Processes", 1972, Iron and Steel Institute, pp. 18-28.
15. Y. Ito and L. Bessyo: Sumitomo Bulletin No. 0280, 1972.
16. P. Hart and F. Watkinson: Welding J. Res. Supp. 1972, vol. 51, pp. 349s-357s.
17. M. Civallero et al: "Experience in the Development and Welding of Large-Diameter Pipes", WRC Bulletin 201, 1974.

DISCUSSION

C. Sargent (University of Saskatchewan): High rates of work hardening and large Bauschinger effects are exhibited by plastically inhomogeneous materials. You have described a material with increased work hardening rate and lowered Bauschinger effect. What microstructural features are responsible for these effects?

J. E. Hood: The change in the magnitude of the Bauschinger effect as one goes from a polygonal to an acicular ferrite steel is not well understood. The volume fraction of carbides is much reduced in acicular steels. However, the relatively hard martensite-austenite phase is introduced. It is not known whether this phase has an effect equivalent to carbide on Bauschinger yield losses.

H. C. Cotton (British Petroleum): Are the inadequacies of the flattened strap tensile test arising, *inter alia*, out of the Bauschinger effect sufficient justifications for the efforts you describe to get around them? To put it another way, does it not seem strange that the chosen steelmaking process and composition should be so constrained by the necessity of passing a test which is so irrelevant to the real properties of the finished pipe? In my experience, X-65 pipes presently supplied are in fact stronger when measured by the flattened strap tensile test than X-70 when measured by the ring expander. This seems to be a waste of resources. I normally take the Bauschinger effect into account when evaluating safety factors in my designs. I assume your X-65 pipe is really X-70 and I do other things with that strength.

J. E. Hood: It is true that the real yield strength of the pipe is underestimated by the flattened strap test. However, there is a significant Bauschinger effect yield loss arising simply from the pipe forming operation which is independent of the pipe testing method and it was this loss of strength that prompted the development of a steel with a higher rate of strain hardening. I should note that the loss of strength from pipe forming is common to both the UOE and spiral pipe making processes and is largely recovered by a cold expansion operation.

I should also note that all pipe-makers would agree with you about the inaccuracy of the flattened strap tensile test, but they are forced to use it by pipe users who have found that it gives them a certain amount of "free" yield strength.

J. T. McGrath (Canadian Welding Development Institute): It was mentioned that proeutectoid ferrite was detrimental to weld metal toughness. Could you please expand on the reasons for this detrimental effect.

J. E. Hood: The detrimental effect of proeutectoid ferrite is thought to be due entirely to its large effective grain size, promoting the formation of cleavage cracks.

J. L. Mihelich (Climax Molybdenum): To make best use of the work hardening potential of acicular ferrite or continuous yielding pearlite-reduced steels, a pipe-expansion step, as practiced in UOE pipemaking, would be very desirable. What are the prospects of developing this type of procedure for spiral-welded pipe?

J. E. Hood: We think that the mechanical expansion of Stelform spiral pipe is quite feasible and in fact Stelco has made the decision to follow this route. We expect that expansion will allow us to reduce the alloy level of the steel and so reduce material costs.

K. N. Street (R. M. Hardy and Associates): During your full scale burst tests, did you attempt to monitor the pipes utilizing acoustic emission techniques? I am asking because other people have found very little noise from pipes tested in the same fashion. The potential of the technique however would appear to warrant its inclusion in the burst experiments.

J. E. Hood: We have not used acoustic emission to monitor our full scale burst tests, primarily because we felt that while the technique might be able to give some warning of failure, it would not give us information on pipe quality, which was the purpose of the tests. One of our tests was monitored by Dr. Hay of Ecole Polytechnique using acoustic emission. His measurements indicated that it may be practical to predict failure location.

G. L. Archer (The Welding Institute): John Hood gives the impression that it is so difficult to assess HAZ toughness that it is not even worth trying. I would agree that it is a difficult problem, but meaningful assessments can be made. First of all, one must use a realistic specimen which is of full-plate thickness and notched in a way which simulates the orientation of likely defects, e.g. hydrogen cracks. This implies that some sort of fracture mechanics approach is required and it is my opinion that Charpy tests on HAZ are a complete waste of time. For pipe materials, which are thin and usually ductile, the COD test is the most useful, small-scale test currently available for assessing fracture initiation. The essence of HAZ testing is careful notch location and careful metallurgical examination of the broken specimen after testing. This will enable spurious results to be detected and hence rejected. The most likely reasons for rejection will be a) the notch tip being in the wrong region, e.g. weld metal; b) spurious short crack or pop-in indications initiating at defects, such as inclusions or separations in the pipe material, which cannot be regarded as significant events. Sizeable short-cracks initiating at the notch tip must be regarded as significant however, unless it can be proven otherwise by energy and crack arrest considerations. Critical flaw sizes can be obtained in the usual way, but again, thought must be given to the assessment of these. Unduly small estimates often arise from one of the following mistakes: a) failure to refer back to the geometry of the weld, i.e. is it physically possible for the estimated flaw size to exist in such a small region as a weld HAZ? b) over-estimation of local strains -- it is often forgotten that the stress concentration at a weld toe diminishes very quickly as one gets into the plate thickness; c) over-estimation of residual stresses -- most HAZ flaws are parallel to the weld direction and hence the relevant residual stress component is the transverse one which is not likely even to exceed half yield, not full yield level as is often assumed. Reliable HAZ assessments are made at the Welding Institute, using the above methods.

Future work on HAZ assessment will move into the area of what happens immediately after fracture initiation when the crack moves into parent plate or weld metal. This will involve careful considerations of the compliance of the test set-up and the structure and crack arrest properties of the materials.

Finally, I would like to say that after being involved in many fracture tests on pipe weldments from a variety of sources, it is my experience that achieving adequate weld metal toughness, particularly in deposits made by cellulosic electrodes, is usually the biggest problem. The HAZ of the current generation of high quality pipe steels usually has more than adequate toughness.

J. E. Hood: I agree with the majority of Mr. Archer's statements but remain sceptical about the ability of the COD test to provide really useful information that can be used to improve the integrity of linepipe. There just are not enough data.

G. L. Archer: On the question of weldability, we have found correlations between the implant test and full scale field weldability trials to be very variable. For this reason we have developed a laboratory test which reproduces actual conditions more closely than does the implant test. This test is referred to as the "restrained butt-weld cracking test", and was described in a paper presented at the 1976 AWS meeting, shortly to be published. Using this test, better correlation with full scale trials is obtained.

PIPES TO BE USED AT LOW SERVICE TEMPERATURE

C. Parrini, M. de Lisi and P. Cibecchini
Italsider, Taranto
ITALY

Materials for use at low temperatures (below -10°C) need to be designed by steel producers taking into account the optimum balance between strength, toughness, weldability, etc., all as a function of temperature. Traditional tests need to be complemented by some more sophisticated material testing like the Charpy transition curve and BDWTT Energy curve by instrumented pendulum, COD evaluation, implant weldability tests at different temperatures, full-scale pipe burst test.

All these results are discussed and comparison is made between various processes capable of producing the high quality pipes required. Referring to controlled-rolling, there is a comparison between classical ferrite-pearlite and new structural ferrite (MOLYTAR) steels. Results from both laboratory and on-order production of more than 500,000 t of X70-grade for very low service temperature will be presented, and further developments, indicated.

INTRODUCTION

Projects involving significant quantities of large diameter Arctic gas pipelines are primarily in Canada and the Soviet Union. In Canada, a total of 18,000 km of large diameter pipe of "Arctic" quality is represented by the various projects expected to be completed by 1981. In the Soviet Union, a total length of 15,000 km Arctic pipeline is expected to be completed. The specific projects for these pipelines are noted in Table 1. The Canadian pipelines are being designed for diameters up to 48 in. (1220 mm) and those in the Soviet Union for up to 56 in. (1420 mm) diameter.

The first U.S.-Canadian project designed to exploit the Prudhoe Bay and Mackenzie Delta gas reserves was proposed in 1970-71 and involved the introduction of radically new pipeline design with consequent severe restrictions on pipe manufacturing specifications. Since the early seventies there has been a continuous increase in the various design and technical specifications resulting in significant world-wide competition among the large pipe manufacturers. To date, data on large pipelines for Arctic application have been scarce, primarily because the Arctic pipelines are few and most of them lie in the Soviet Union.

However, the correct application of these new design criteria requires cooperation between pipe producers and users with equal responsibility. It is clear that producers are forced by the pressure of a highly competitive market to produce high quality pipe even at an economic penalty. Producers cannot afford even the smallest quality error without running the risk of disqualification from the marketplace. In such a situation, the economic penalties are far greater than the advantages resulting from a production "bluff" or an intentionally inferior quality level.

Therefore, rather than placing limitations on steel chemistry and particular production practices, attention must be focussed on the attainment of the appropriate material properties required by the design and not on the process chosen by the producer to obtain them. Examples of linepipe material specifications for typical Canadian and Soviet Union projects are listed in Table 2.

PIPE SIZE

Simple economic considerations dictate a maximum diameter for gas-line capacity which is limited by compressor station capability, transportation, installation and operation costs of the line. Table 3 provides examples of the operating conditions for some typical gas pipelines. In Canada, there is a tendency to limit the pipe diameter to 48 in. (1220 mm) and increase capacity by increasing operating pressure or by adopting smaller safety factors. In the Soviet Union, pipelines have currently a maximum diameter of 56 in. (1420 mm) and a lower operating pressure and safety factor. Future pipelines in the Soviet Union will operate at a gas pressure of up to 1 kgf/mm^2 (9 MPa). To provide even greater capacity, it would be possible to enlarge the pipe diameter above 56 in. (1420 mm). For example, a 64 in. (1630 mm) diameter pipeline would, under the same operating conditions, provide an increased capacity of 40% over a 56 in. (1420 mm) line. At the same time, there would be: 1) an increase in steel cost due to the greater difficulty in obtaining strength and toughness properties at the greater wall thickness required; 2) a weight increase and commensurate general cost increases of more than 30%; and 3) increases in transportation, installation, and operating and maintenance costs of the line.

TABLE 1

Reported Length and Distribution of Arctic-type on-shore Gas-line Projects to be realized by 1981

CANADA		
Polar	3,200 km	36 in. (910 mm) to 48 in. (1220 mm)
North West	2,700 km	42 in. (1070 mm)
Gas Arctic	4,100 km	36 in. (910 mm) to 48 in. (1220 mm)
East Coast	1,600 km	36 in. (910 mm)
Foothills	1,200 km	42 in. (1070 mm)
SOVIET UNION		
Orenburg	2,700 km	40 in. (1020 mm) to 56 in. (1420 mm)
Urengoiskoje	2,900 km	48 in. (1220 mm) to 56 in. (1420 mm)
Yakutskya	2,700 km	56 in. (1420 mm)
Tyumen Fields	6,500 km	48 in. (1220 mm) to 56 in. (1420 mm)
TOTAL LENGTH	27,600 km	

A similar increase in capacity could be obtained by increasing the operating pressure and pipe thickness using the same safety factors. It is conceivable that spiral-welded pipe up to 100 in. (2540 mm) diameter could be used in Arctic gas line application.

PIPE TENSILE PROPERTIES

The measurement of tensile properties depends critically on the test method and conditions of the samples employed. Different results can be obtained from each of a cold-flattened API 2 in. (51 mm) tensile specimen, a specimen with gauge length of different proportions to the cross section, a micro-specimen, a ring expansion test method, or a small cylindrical specimen obtained from the pipe wall. Clearly, the more the specimen simulates the final condition of the pipe, the more realistic will be the information provided on tensile properties. We believe it would be more realistic for the user if the pipe elastic limit were determined by hydraulic tests in the mill at 100% specified minimum yield stress (SMYS) for the actual pipe thickness.

The X70 Grade mainly used in Arctic gas lines for thicknesses between 16 mm and 25 mm poses no particular metallurgical problem relating to restrictions on carbon equivalent values imposed by field welding conditions. The "Super X70" requested by the Soviet Union does place more critical restrictions. This steel has a minimum tensile strength of 86 ksi (590 MPa) and a carbon equivalent less than 0.40. A conventional process, such as quench and temper, could provide the required balance between steel grade and carbon equivalent but it is too expensive a process for active consideration at this time. However, by controlled-rolling (CR) it is possible to obtain grade X70 and Super X70 by two different methods: a) Further exploiting the precipitation hardening mechanisms already developed for X60 steels by increasing the alloying elements columbium, vanadium, titanium and nitrogen but still retaining a ferrite/pearlite microstructure, or, b) promoting structural changes by lowering the carbon content and introducing manganese, molybdenum, nickel, chromium, etc. to produce the "acicular ferrite" structure or the new structural ferritic MOLYTAR steels.

Since 1971, Italsider has been producing MOLYTAR steel, which permits significant improvements

TABLE 2

Specifications for Some Arctic Gas Pipelines

	CANADA		SOVIET UNION	
PROJECT	Gas Arctic	North West	Sub-Arctic	Siberia
GRADE	X70	X65	Super X70	Super X70
SIZE	0.72 in.-0.80 in.x48 in. (18 mm-20 mmx1220 mm) 0.63 in.x42 in. (16 mmx1070 mm)	0.60 in.x42 in. (15 mmx1070 mm)	0.66 in.-0.78 in.x56 in. (17 mm-20 mmx1420 mm)	0.66 in.-0.78 in.-1.00 in.x56 in. (17 mm-20 mm-25 mmx1420 mm)
OPERATING STRESS (% SMYS)	80	80	70	70
MAX C(wt %)	0.14	No Limit	0.12	0.10
MAX C_{eq} (%)	0.43[1]	0.45[1,2] - 0.43[1,3]	0.40[4]	0.40[4] for 0.66 in. 0.43[4] for 1.00 in.
MIN. CHARPY-V (J)	40	69 on 50% Pipes 110 on 50% Pipes	48 on 50% Pipes 64 on 50% Pipes	64
BDWTT (Min. Shear %)	60	60	80	80
TEST TEMP	-5°C and - 25°C	CV 100 or - 20°C	0°C	0°C and -20°C
OTHERS		CV 100	Mesnager 48J at -40°C	Mesnager 40J at -60°C
MAX. PIPE BODY DEFECT	3000 mm^2	100 mm	90 mm	90 mm
PRODUCTION CAPABILITY	Possible	Possible	>500,000 t made in 1975-76	will produce >500,000 t in 1977

[1]C_{eq} = (C+Mn)/6 + (Cr+Mo+V)/5 + (Ni+Cu)/15; [2]for acicular ferrite steels; [3]for ferrite/pearlite steels; [4]C_{eq} = (C+Mn)/6.

in steel quality, the use of continuous casting, a smaller Bauschinger effect and a considerable improvement in field weldability and weld joint toughness.

It is possible to define a condition for the production of the MOLYTAR acicular steel in terms of the alloy composition (elements expressed in wt%) and cooling rate, V_r(deg C/s) as follows:

$$3.3[10Mo + 3Mn + 3Cr + Ni] + 2000B + 50[Nb + Ti - V] + 4Si + X > 25 - 4(V_r - 1)$$

where X is a function of the rolling condition and can be taken as zero for large rolling reductions.

Figure 1 indicates the effect of manganese on the tensile properties of continuously-cast and ingot MOLYTAR steels of 17 to 20 mm thickness. The effect of plate thickness on the properties of continuously-cast MOLYTAR steel is shown in Figure 2 for steels containing 0.07%C, 0 35%Si, 0.05%Nb(Cb), 0.3 to 0.4%Mo for two manganese levels (the effects of the other major alloy elements are similar).

Figure 3 shows the relationship between the plate yield stress and ultimate tensile strength and the increase in these parameters during the transformation from plate to expanded pipe, involving a 1.1% to 1.3% expansion.

An indication of the reduced Bauschinger effect exhibited by MOLYTAR steels is demonstrated in Figure 4, showing comparison with a ferrite-pearlite steel. Figure 5 summarizes the mechanical property distribution of plate and expanded pipe obtained during production in 1976 of more than 200,000 t of Super X70 pipe.

The effects of low temperature heat treatments on the UTS, yield stress, transition temperature

TABLE 3

Pipeline Capacity for Various Operating Conditions and Sizes

Diameter in. (mm)	Thickness Nominal mm	Thickness Minimum mm	Grade	UTS ksi (MPa)	Utilization Index % YS	Utilization Index % UTS	Operating Pressure kg/mm^2(MPa)	Capacity* X1000N m^3/h
42 (1070)	15.6	14.6	X65	78 (540)	80	66	1.0 (9.8)	1330
48 (1220)	18.3	17.3	X70	82 (570)	80	68	1.1 (10.8)	1950
56 (1420)	16.5	15.5	Super X70	86 (590)	70	56	0.75 (7.4)	2770
56 (1420)	19.0	18.2	Super X70	86 (590)	80	56	1.0 (9.8)	3760
64 (1625)	18.8	17.8	X70	82 (570)	70	68	0.75 (7.4)	3930
64 (1625)	21.7	20.7	X70	82 (570)	80	68	1.0 (9.8)	5340

*Assuming 5 compressor stations on 1000 km pipeline.

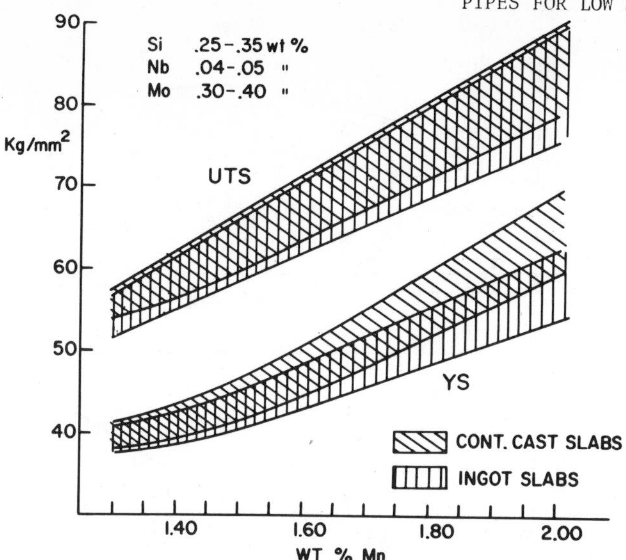

Figure 1: The effect of manganese content on the yield stress and tensile strength of MOLYTAR steel plates produced from continuously-cast slabs and from ingots

difference between Charpy-V and BDWTT, and Charpy shelf energy are summarized in Figure 6. using the Holloman and Jaffe parameter, Hp = $Tx10^{-3}(20 - \log t)$, where T = temperature (K), and t = time(h). Heating MOLYTAR steels at temperatures in excess of 250°C for more than 10 min tends to increase the yield strength and the impact toughness and slightly reduce the impact transition temperature.

PIPE TOUGHNESS AT SERVICE TEMPERATURE

The significant parameter which distinguishes an Arctic gas pipeline from a tropical one is the pipeline service temperature. Most of the other parameters are common to both conditions and are justified by economic and safety considerations. In order to optimize the toughness at the lowest service temperature with sufficient safety allowance, the material must have a predominantly shear-type fracture at that temperature. The transition temperature is best determined by the Battelle Drop Weight Tear Test (BDWTT) employing a fracture speed of approximately 100 m/s (the Charpy test involves fracture speeds of approximately 5 m/s). Even 100 m/s is less than that which might be expected during

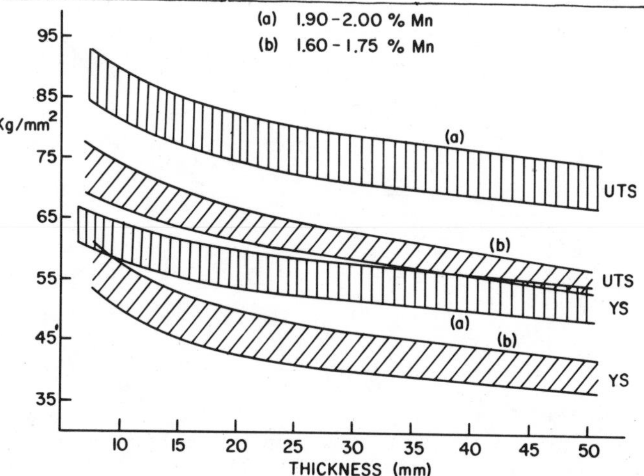

Figure 2: The effect of plate thickness on mechanical properties of continuously-cast MOLYTAR steel

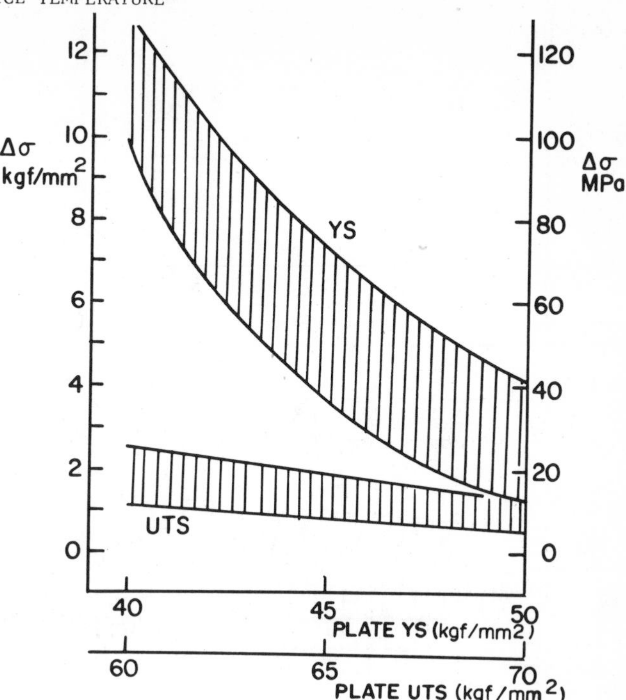

Figure 3: The change in yield strength and ultimate tensile strength of X70 MOLYTAR steel when processed from plate to pipe

shear fracture propagation in pipelines which could reach 300 m/s.

The trend to increasing pipe thicknesses to over 20 mm will introduce a problem of testing methodology, since the BDWTT is only valid for thicknesses up to 19.5 mm. Furthermore, up to this thickness the transition temperature measured by the BDWTT correlates well with that obtained from the Charpy-V test as indicated in Figure 7. It is clear that significant deviations between these two test methods occur at greater thickness.

The full-scale burst test carried out at Battelle (1) has permitted correlations between fracture propagation and arrest for pipe up to 48 in. (1220 mm) and pipe dimensions, internal pressure and steel grade. To test the validity of the various proposed correlations, we have carried out to date two full scale burst tests on 56 in. (1420 mm) pipe made of MOLYTAR Super X70 steels. Figure 8 indicates the impact properties of the steels used in these tests related to the theoretical fracture-safe design curves and the pressures employed in the test. Tests were carried out at equivalent methane pressures of 0.84 kgf/mm² (8.3 MPa) and 0.94 kgf/mm² (9.1 MPa). Each test employed four test sections of pipe of various impact properties. These sections are shown schematically in Figure 9. In the first test, a mechanical crack arrestor of wire rope was used and in the second, two wire rope crack arrestors were employed, as indicated in the figure. Measurements of fracture speeds are also summarized in Figure 9 for the two tests. The points marked "x" and "y" indicate the arrival of the crack at the shorter and longer crack arrestors, respectively. The results of the tests indicate that the Battelle relationship for fracture arrest conditions is confirmed for these pipe lengths, and that the pipe tends to ovalize approximately one to two diameters ahead of the crack tip, as reported by Shoemaker (2). These tests suggest that it is more convenient to use mechanical crack arrestors in order to obtain rapid and safe arrest than to rely on the impact energy of the pipe material. They also suggest that the

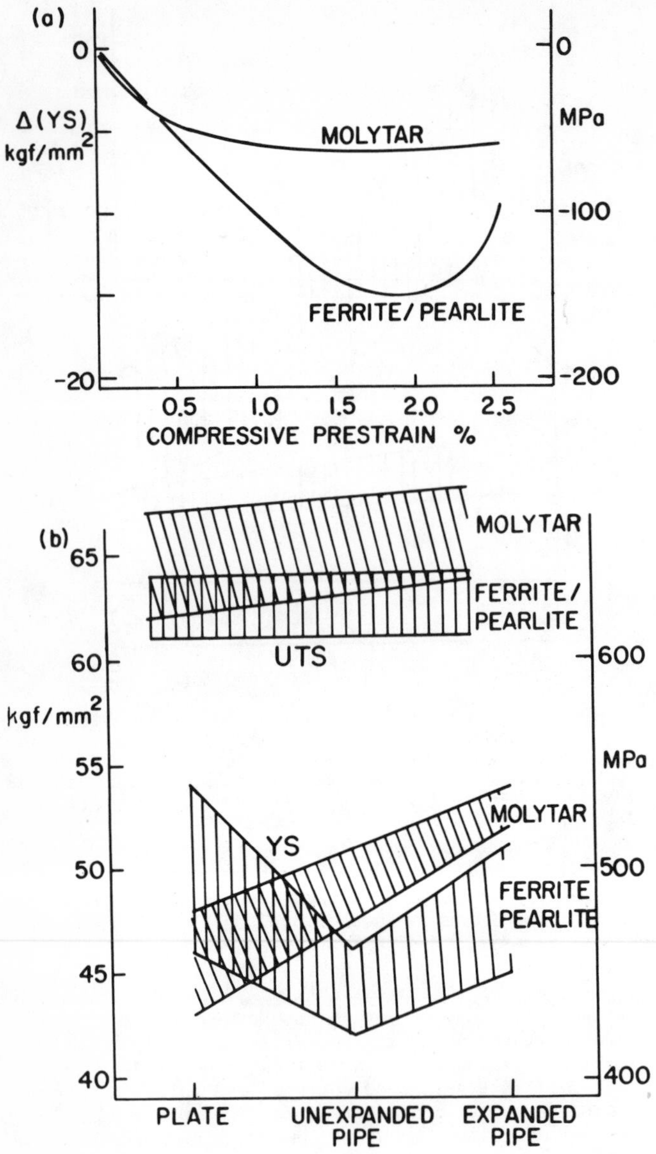

(a)
Δ(YS) kgf/mm²
MPa
MOLYTAR
FERRITE/ PEARLITE
0, -20; 0, -100, -200
0.5 1.0 1.5 2.0 2.5
COMPRESSIVE PRESTRAIN %

(b)
MOLYTAR
FERRITE/ PEARLITE
UTS
YS
MOLYTAR
FERRITE PEARLITE
kgf/mm²
MPa
65, 60, 55, 50, 45, 40; 600, 500, 400
PLATE UNEXPANDED PIPE EXPANDED PIPE

Figure 4: Bauschinger effect in MOLYTAR and ferrite-pearlite steels, (a) laboratory measurement; (b) industrial production

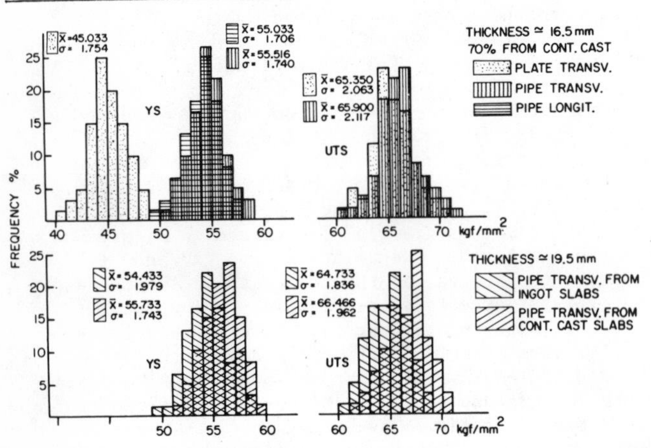

Figure 5: Mechanical property statistics for MOLYTAR plates and pipes

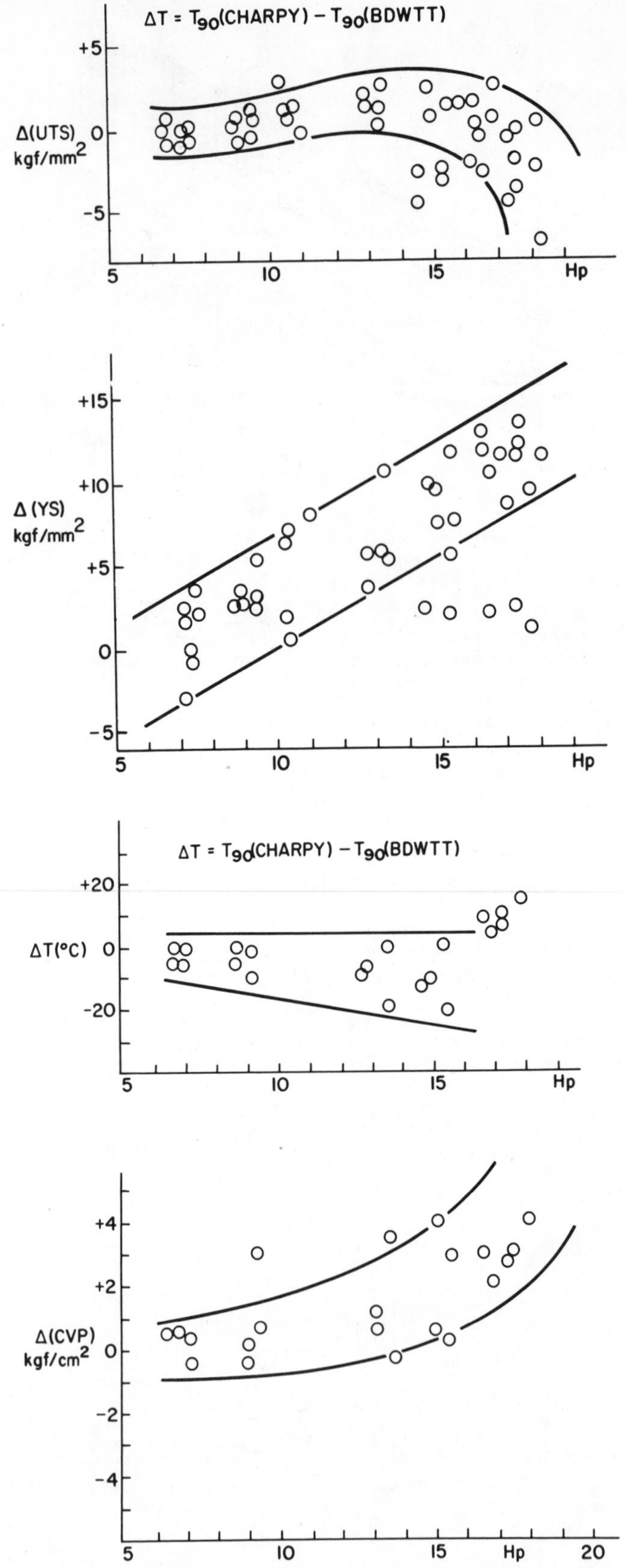

ΔT = T90(CHARPY) − T90(BDWTT)
Δ(UTS) kgf/mm²
5 10 15 Hp

Δ(YS) kgf/mm²
5 10 15 Hp

ΔT = T90(CHARPY) − T90(BDWTT)
ΔT(°C)
5 10 15 Hp

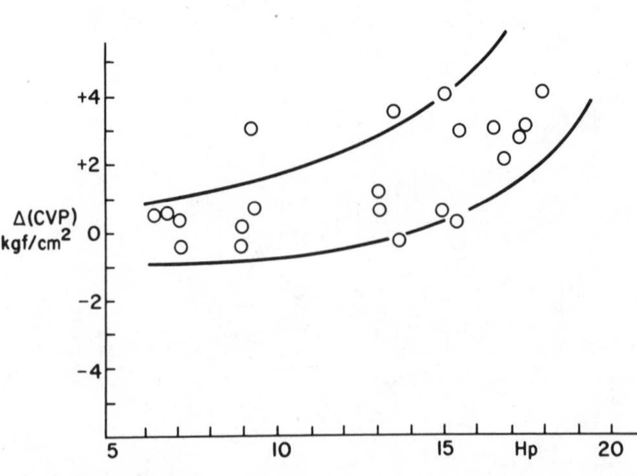

Figure 6: The effect of low temperature heat treatment (defined by the Holloman parameter, Hp) on the mechanical properties of MOLYTAR steel
$H_p = T \times 10^{-3}\ (20 - \log t) \quad [T(K), t(h)]$

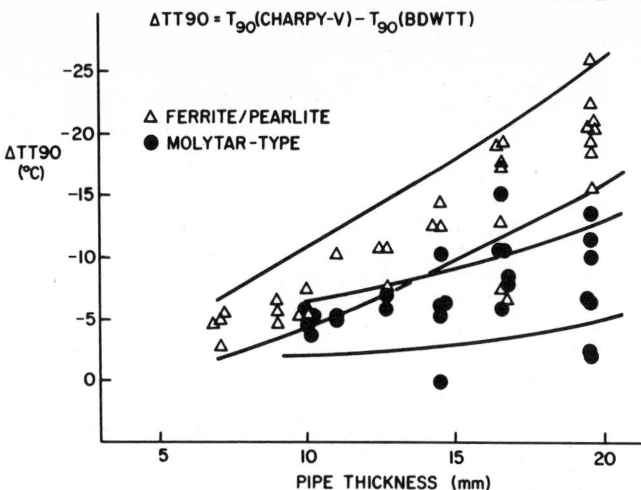

Figure 7: Comparison of transition temperature measured by Charpy-V and BDWTT, as a function of pipe thickness

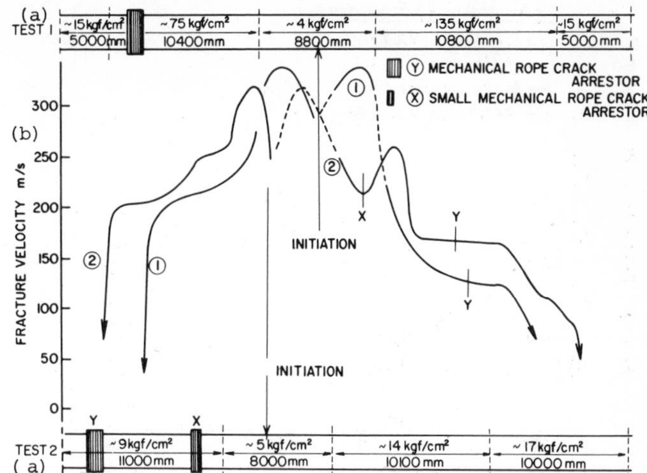

Figure 9: Full-scale burst tests on MOLYTAR Super X-70 pipes: (a) schematic arrangement of tested pipe lengths; (b) velocity profiles for propagating cracks in the two tests

speed of crack propagation, while proportional to the burst pressure, appears to be higher than that predicted by the Battelle theory (1).

Future full-scale testing is planned to determine the effect of pipe dimensions on the propagation speed and to improve the methodology of crack arrestors. It is also hoped to clarify the effects of metallurgical structure on the conditions for crack propagation and arrest.

However, from the economic point of view, it is not realistic to build a pipe in which each section has an impact energy higher than the Charpy energy required for crack arrest. Even if this were possible, it is still likely that an accidental burst would not arrest before 2 or 3 pipe lengths. Statistical analysis suggests that it is only necessary to have at least one pipe with impact energy greater than the critical Charpy-V energy within the maximum allowed fracture length. A mechanical crack arrestor could act in the same way with greater safety. Table 4 provides some results from a statistical approach to fracture arrest and compares a "crack arrestor system" with a "toughness system" required for pipes with Charpy-V values greater or less than the "required value", as a function of the number of pipe lengths through which the fracture can be expected to pass. It is clear from Table 2 that the two Canadian pipeline systems have based their projects on different design approaches. The Gas Arctic pipeline is based on a mechanical crack arrestor concept and the Northwest project

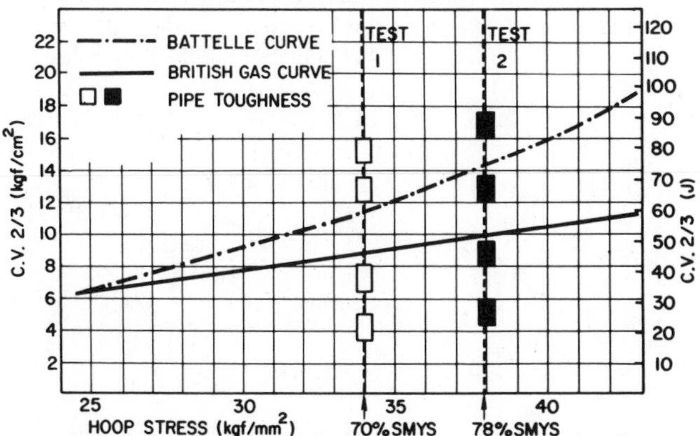

Figure 8: Impact properties of MOLYTAR Super-X70 pipes used in full-scale burst tests related to the fracture hypotheses

is based on impact energy requirements. This latter appears, from our experience, to be too conservative.

To the analysis developed to this point should also be added the positive effects of pipe laying, trench size, backfill, plinth anchorage, variations of pipe direction, pipe thickness variation, girth weld and actual average operating pressures. All these parameters make up that empirical coefficient of experience which should be given sufficient emphasis when establishing impact toughness requirements for safe pipeline operation.

When considering the impact toughness as a function of gas pressure, field testing should never be carried out with gas at 100% SMYS instead of the conventional pipe hydraulic test. The required impact values to provide safe field testing with gas could be 50 to 100% higher than the impact values for normal operating conditions (ie. 60 to 80% SMYS).

FIELD WELDABILITY

The weldability of MOLYTAR steels obtained from implant testing both with basic and cellulosic electrodes has been shown to be considerably better than conventional ferrite-pearlite steels. The improvement, mostly due to the effect of carbon, is officially acknowledged only in the Northwest project specifications that set different Ceq limits for ferrite/pearlite and acicular-ferrite steels. Figure 10 summarizes implant testing at +20°C and -20°C for the two kinds of steel. The relative effects of welding temperature and steel type on the critical stress are clearly seen for two levels of hydrogen (cellulosic and basic electrodes).

TABLE 4

Fracture-Arrest Statistics

Maximum Fracture Length (no. of pipes)	Crack-Arrestor System: Minimum % Pipes With Crack Arrestors	Crack-Arrestor System: Max % Pipes With CV < CVA	Toughness System: Minimum % Pipes With CV ≥ CVA	Toughness System: Max % Pipes With CV < CVA
3	25	75	80	20
10	9	91	60	40
20	5	95	20	80
30	3	97	15	85

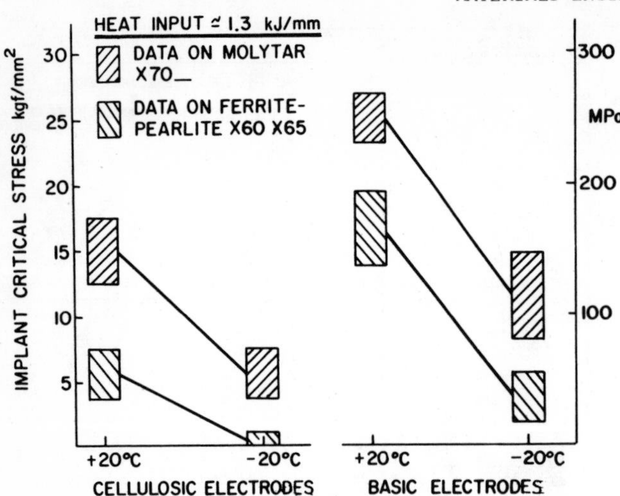

Figure 10: Implant tests results on MOLYTAR X70 and ferrite-pearlite X60 and X65 steels

PERMISSIBLE INTERNAL DEFECTS

In all pipeline specifications, internal defect areas up to a maximum individual area of 5000 mm^2 are generally allowed in the pipe body. However, when hydraulic burst tests were carried out on pipe which had been rejected as a result of ultrasonic detection of defects of densities 10 times the permissible, neither the yielding pressure nor the burst pressure appeared to be dependent upon the defect concentration, as shown in Table 5. Acoustic emission analysis during these tests also indicated that the defects were not active in the elastic range -- emission activity being restricted to the period when plastic deformation was occurring.

The sequence of non-destructive testing control currently used at the Taranto works is depicted in Figure 11. This scheme permits the detection of defects to limits lower than the specifications noted in Table 2. Furthermore, we expect soon to install automatic ultrasonic testing equipment able to survey 33% or 66% of the plate surface, instead of the present 18%.

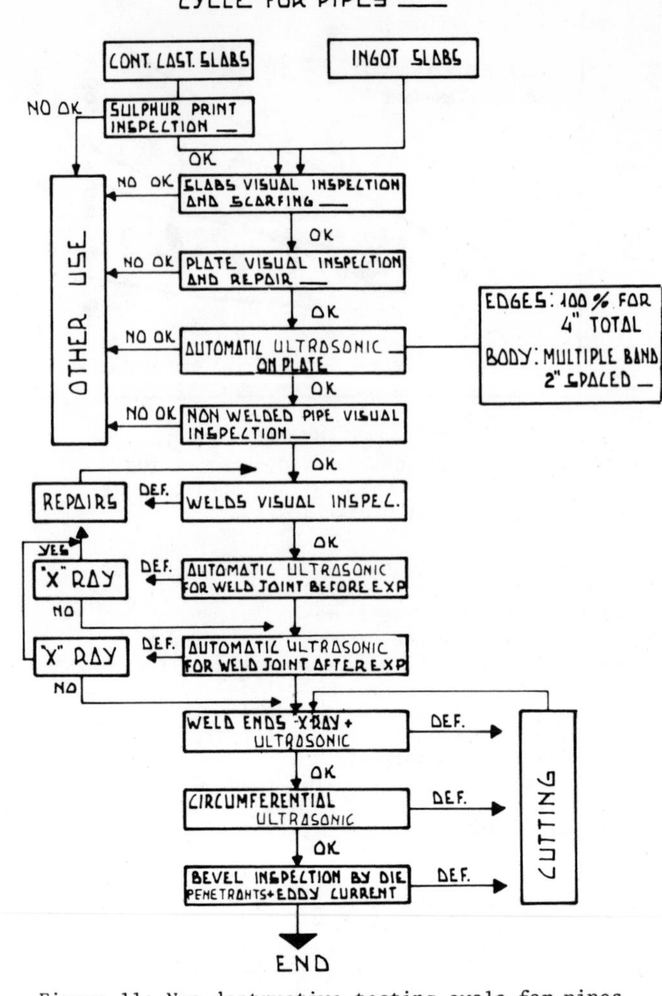

Figure 11: Non-destructive testing cycle for pipes at Taranto Works

TABLE 5

Results of Hydraulic Burst Tests of Grade-X60 Pipes Rejected by Ultrasonic Testing

Pipe	YS* (kg/mm^2)	UTS (kg/mm^2)	Pressure For 0.2% Yield (kg/mm^2) Theory	Measured	Maximum Pressure (kg/mm^2) Theory	Measured	Defects	Total Defect Area
0.50 in.x34 in.	45.0	57.0	1.36	1.43	1.72	1.66	inclusions and segregations	> 10^6 mm^2
0.66 in.x56 in.	44.3	62.8	1.00	1.07	1.42	1.45	as above	>1.5×10^6 mm^2
0.66 in.x56 in.	45.0	62.0	1.05	1.03	1.40	1.38	as above, plus laminations	>1.5×10^6 mm^2
0.78 in.x56 in.	45.7	64.1	1.27	1.31	1.76	1.75	inclusions and segregations	~7×10^5 mm^2
0.66 in.x56 in.	45.1	61.3	1.06	1.11	1.42	1.40	none	0

*measured on flattened transverse specimens.

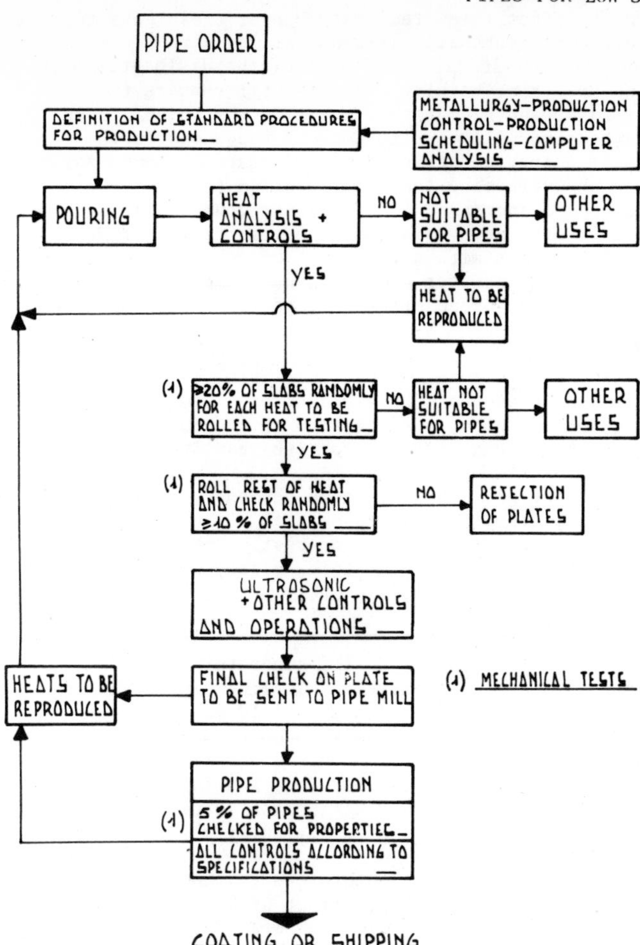

Figure 12: Production and mechanical testing cycle for pipes at Taranto Works

QUALITY CONTROL

In general, it is not difficult to obtain good quality steel in production, but to maintain quality in a reproducible manner requires a well-defined quality control operation. The solution of metallurgical problems provided by customer specifications must be readily applied to the industrial production process. At Taranto, we employ L-D type converters with which it is possible to produce 10.5 Mt steel per year. There are also three continuous casting lines, 2 slabbing mills, 2 hot strip mills, 2 plate mills, 4 pipe mills and 1 cold strip mill. Once the production practice appropriate to a certain product has been determined, an appropriate cycle of mechanical and non-destructive testing must be arranged. In Figure 12, the sequence of testing controls for pipe production is outlined. In addition to the non-destructive testing control already mentioned, mechanical testing is carried out on plate and pipe for more than 30% of the production.

CONCLUSIONS

Closer cooperation is necessary among pipeline designers, pipe users and producers, especially for projects which have special property requirements or for new steels.

In terms of future developments, we foresee a significant increase of pipe thicknesses up to 25 or 30 mm, even for the main gas line. Consequently, an alternative to the Battelle Drop Weight Tear test must be developed in order to determine the appropriate impact transition temperature of the pipe material in the service condition. If the use of mechanical crack arrestors spreads significantly, the impact toughness values demanded by pipeline designers can be expected to stabilize at approximately 6 to 9 kgf m/cm^2 (50 to 70 J, Charpy-V).

The weldability criteria should be developed considering both the effects of low and very low carbon content and proposals to modify field welding processes.

The techniques of automatic and remote control of pipeline service parameters must be developed in order to avoid the transformation of leaks into fractures.

Future pipeline developments can be expected to include the planning of a X42/X60 grade pipeline for liquid gas transport at service temperatures down to -120°C. For this latter application we are currently producing some 24 in. (610 mm) diameter pipes.

The considerations given here are also applicable to submarine gas pipelines which operate at lower pressures and have a higher thickness to diameter ratio. In this application the problems of crack arrest and crack propagation are clearly reduced, but corrosion phenomena now become significant.

The greatest impact will be provided by the development of new production processes for high-quality steel at lower prices. We will try to reduce or eliminate the need for expensive ferro-alloys such as molybdenum, nickel and cerium by developing suitable heat treatments and/or rolling processes and by the increased utilization of other economic processes, such as continuous casting.

REFERENCES

1. W. A. Maxey, 5th. Symposium on Line Pipe Research, American Gas Association, Catalog No. L30174, 1974, pp. J1-J30.
2. A. K. Shoemaker, R. F. McCartney and K. D. Ives, This Volume, pp. 298-305.

DISCUSSION

J. M. Wallbridge (Foothills Pipe Lines): With regard to the burst tests you conducted: 1) What was the gas composition? 2) What was the test temperature? 3) What measure of toughness was used (CV_{100}, CV_T, CV_{shelf} ?) and did the pipe exhibit separations?

C. A. Parrini: 1) Air. 2) Ambient temperature, with approximately 20°C outside and 10°C in the trench and in the pipe. 3) We measured the whole Charpy transition curve on transverse testpieces and we are trying to correlate results with shelf energy. We did not observe any separations in the high toughness pipe. We had some openings in the initiation pipe length because, needing a very low impact value, we had to considerably reduce the rolling temperature to reduce the shelf energy.

A. K. Shoemaker (United States Steel): I would like to point out that there is a wide range of flow stress behaviour, rather than a single behaviour as indicated in the paper, for ferrite-pearlite types of steels. The significant property which determines loss in plate to pipe yield strength is the amount of straining (for the plate stress-strain curve) prior to strain hardening. Other high carbon (ferrite-pearlite) steels demonstrate as much as 4% straining prior to work hardening whereas the new low carbon steels (not acicular ferrite microstructure) show much less, approximately 0.5% straining prior to strain hardening.

C. A. Parrini: I agree with you, but we have to consider the strain involved in the plate-to-pipe transformation. In this case, the MOLYTAR steels behave better than low carbon non-acicular steels. The effect is not only due to the reduced Bauschinger effect, which also exists for MOLYTAR steels, but we have to consider also the large work hardening coefficient of these steels, which in my experience, plays a very important role in the final results.

M. R. Krishnadev (Laval University): Did you investigate the effect of pipe forming (i.e. cold work) on the toughness of your steels?

C. A. Parrini: Yes, and we found an increase in transition temperature of 10 deg C from as-rolled to 2% strain, that remains constant up to about 5%. For shelf energy, we lost about 10 to 15% up to 2% strain and another ∿5% from 2 to 5% strain.

M. R. Krishnadev: Do you think that microstructural cleanliness should be included in the specification for Arctic pipelines?

C. A. Parrini: No, we already have too many improper limits in existing specifications. If they ask for high toughness, we will do it and we will cooperate in the best way, but we do not want to have any limits placed on the metallurgical opportunity to obtain the required properties.

A. Glover (Canadian Welding Development Institute): In the larger diameter (> 56 in. or 1420 mm) pipelines and at possibly the same or higher operating pressures, can only mechanical crack arrestors be used rather than a toughness criterion?

C. A. Parrini: There is a limit to the Charpy-V transverse toughness that is possible by controlled rolling. The limit, in my experience, is 118 J. In the Battelle analysis this will correspond to an X70, 56 in. (1420 mm) pipe with hoop stress, 80% SMYS. Adopting the particular statistical approach considered in the paper it is possible that this toughness will correspond to a 56 in. diameter by X75/X80 at 70 to 80% SMYS. Increasing above these limits will be possible only with mechanical crack arrestors. I believe also within those limits that, except in a few cases, mechanical crack arrestors will be widely utilized.

J. L. Mihelich (Climax Molybdenum): When do you plan to commercialize lean alloy heat treated direct quenched pipe grades?

C. A. Parrini: In my opinion, this could happen by 1980.

J. L. Mihelich: Low temperature ageing seems to increase YS and improve toughness. What do you believe is the cause for this behaviour?

C. A. Parrini: In the as-rolled condition we have generally low yield strength (YS/UTS ∿ 0.65). This condition can be regarded as anomalous and is due to the material structure made by pile-ups of dislocations at small islands of martensite, surrounded by low-dislocation density polygonal ferrite grains. The dislocations in the pile-ups can be considered as a spring. Under these conditions a relatively small stress will spread those dislocations into the ferrite matrix on several slip planes. Perhaps this explains the reduced Bauschinger effect. Low temperature heat treatments tend to temper martensite islands, giving carbon the possibility of "pinning" most of the dislocations in the "pool" of bainite and this will restore the yield strength. At the same time the tempering of martensite will tend to improve toughness (both shelf energy and transition temperature) compensating for or overcoming the deterioration tendency due to the YS increase. UTS will not change. We did not observe any variation of precipitation of NbC (> 20Å), even with a treatment of up to 600°C for 1 h. It is however possible that some very small precipitates of coherent NbC are formed around dislocations.

P. Boussel (Climax Molybdenum): Did you note a better increase of the yield stress from ingot casting to continuous casting with the acicular ferrite type steel than with the ferrite-pearlite steel?

C. A. Parrini: There is some tendency, for ferrite-pearlite steels, to increase both YS and UTS, when comparing CONCAST with ingot-cast. Other conditions being the same for 16 mm thick plate, we have an average of +1 kgf/mm^2 (10 MPa), both for YS and UTS.

L. Lucykx (Remacor): Carlo, congratulations on your outstanding achievement in line pipe technology and its proven success on the world market. As you may expect my questions concern rare earth metal (REM) treatment.

What are your current data and information on the mechanism of REM action for extra low temperature service? Is it strictly sulfide shape control?

C. A. Parrini: For fracture energy, however measured, there is a very positive effect of REM. For the ductile/brittle transition temperature, REM has a negligible effect in our control-rolling conditions. Actually, we are producing one pipe order, 24 in. (610 mm) x 8 mm, for LPG with a service temperature of -50°C, and we are using a fully REM-treated steel.

L. Luyckx: Has Italsider been able to demonstrate REM-nitrogen precipitation, as you have suggested earlier?

C. A. Parrini: Yes, we can confirm the data obtained about two years ago.

L. Luyckx: Is there any recorded REM-hydrogen interaction?

C. A. Parrini: As far as hydrogen is concerned, no relation exists in our experience. There is a very positive effect of hydrogen induced from outside, like "H_2S induced cracking". In this respect, we patented a steel, up to X70 for "sour gas" pipe lines which is REM-treated with a special chemical composition.

L. Luyckx: I took note of your HSNA intentions for the future (high strength NO alloy steels) because of the cost of all these alloying additives. What would you do to eliminate or replace mischmetal additions? Just adopt 0.003% max sulfur?

C. A. Parrini: We plan to avoid, if possible, REM and work for a X70 plain C, Mn steel with 100 ft lbf (136 J) at -20°C with 0.008% maximum S. It seems that in the QT structure the effect of MnS inclusions on transverse Charpy energy is much less detrimental than in other cases.

L. Luyckx: Does your current information warrant

replacement of REM by calcium or magnesium compound injection in the steel ladle, in order to meet the tough specification of the new 500,000 t, X70 very low service temperature steel pipe order?

C. A. Parrini: We will use such as approach for CONCAST material if no other solution will be available. We feel confident that working with low S and controlled amounts of REM we can obtain very high CV-transverse energies by the CONCAST process There will be no problem.using REM-treatment on ingot steels.

MOLYBDENUM-COLUMBIUM STEELS FOR ARCTIC PIPING

John L. Mihelich
Climax Molybdenum Company of Michigan
P. O. Box 1568
Ann Arbor, MI 48106
USA

Arctic pipelines place severe demands on the materials of their construction. High toughness in combination with good weldability at subzero temperatures is prerequisite for pipeline steels which will be applied in mainline pipe and specialized components such as elbow and tee fittings and heavy wall pumping station piping.

Performance of molybdenum-columbium steels, which have been developed to meet the challenge of the Arctic environment, in mainline pipe and fitting applications, is described. Strength, toughness and weldability of as-rolled and heat treated grades are emphasized. Aspects of sulfide stress cracking resistance and other important questions are discussed.

INTRODUCTION

The last 10 years has seen a flurry of alloy design and development activity by manufacturers of large diameter line pipe. This effort was brought about, primarily, by the discovery of large deposits of crude oil and natural gas in the Arctic regions of North America and the Soviet Union. Discovery of the North Slope field in Alaska in the late sixties added 26×10^{12} ft (74×10^{10} m^3) to North America's proven natural gas reserves. Gas fields estimated at more than 50×10^{12} ft^3 (140×10^{10} m^3) have also been located in the Canadian Arctic islands and in the Arctic regions of Siberia. Mainline piping and pumping station components for application in these remote areas, where temperatures as low as -80°F (-62°C) are common, must meet stringent property requirements in order to guarantee performance of the line and to protect the environment.

In the early sixties, pipe manufacturers commonly offered large diameter line pipe up to API 5LX52 grade with 52 ksi (360 MPa) specified minimum yield strength (SMYS). Wall thicknesses were usually limited to 0.50 in. (12.5 mm). The recent trend in the industry is, however, to heavy wall thickness, higher strength pipe. Large pipe, ranging in size to 48 in.. (1220 mm) diameter and, in the Soviet Union to 56 in.. (1420 mm) diameter, is being utilized. High operating pressures, up to 1680 psig (11,600 kPa) in Arctic pipelines emphasize the need for heavier wall thickness product. Pipe with wall thicknesses to 0.750 in. (19 mm) is already being used and 1.50 in. (38 mm) thick pipe will be needed for future projects.

While pipe with yield strength of 65 ksi (450 MPa) is now in common use, higher strength pipe with a minimum yield strength of 70 ksi (480 MPa) has also been placed into service in North America and in the Soviet Union. Several major projects planned for construction in the near future, including the Canadian Arctic Gas Pipeline and Polar Gas Project in North America and the Orenburg, North Star and Tyumen Projects in the USSR, are likely to use this higher strength grade for technical and economic reasons.

Installation and operation of oil or gas pipelines in cold, remote regions have led to an increase in toughness requirements by the pipeline designer. Battelle Drop Weight Tear Test (BDWTT) criteria are used as a measure to ensure that the steel will behave in a ductile manner(1). The operating temperature of the pipeline must be above the ductile-brittle Fracture Appearance Transition Temperature (FATT) of the steel. Extensive testing is carried out to insure that the pipeline operates above the BDWTT-FATT of the steel.

To guard against fast-running ductile fracture, Charpy V-notch requirements established by corelation with full-scale burst tests which simulate actual pipeline operating conditions are often specified. Recently, (2) the following empirical equation was established for the minimum, full size Charpy energy (ft lbf) that will produce fracture arrest:

$$C_V = 0.0108(\sigma_H)^2(Rt)^{0.33} \qquad (1)$$

where σ_H is the operating stress in ksi, R the pipe

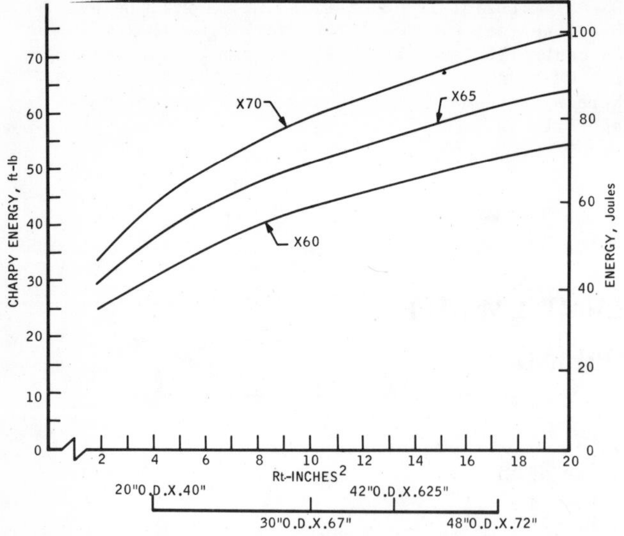

Figure 1: Charpy Impact Energy Needed for Fracture Arrest is Dependent Upon both Pipe Geometry and Operating Conditions, (after ref. 2)

radius and t the pipe wall thickness expressed in inches. SMYS of the pipe multiplied by a suitable "design factor" is equal to the operating stress σ_H.

Equation 1, using a "design factor" of 0.72 which applies to natural gas transmission pipelines located in remote areas in the United States is shown graphically in Figure 1. 30 in. (760 mm) x 0.67 in. (17 mm) wall X60 pipe (Rt = 10) operating at 72% of SMYS or 1925 psig (13,300 kPa) requires approximately 45 ft lbf (60 J) of Charpy energy to arrest ductile fracture. Under the same operating conditions, 30 in. (760 mm) x 0.57 in. (14.5 mm) wall X70 (483 MPa) pipe (Rt = 8.6) may also be used, although it is apparent that a higher Charpy energy, 55 ft lbf (75 J) will be needed. However, a significant weight-saving of 15% is obtained with the X70 grade. The higher Charpy energy requirements, in combination with low operating temperatures to -10°F (-23°C), are rapidly becoming pipeline design criteria.

Field weldability, especially in cold climates, is of prime importance. Resistance to cold or hydrogen cracking is often estimated from empirically derived Carbon Equivalent (CE) formulas which are, in general, a function of the composition of the steel. Several Carbon Equivalent formulas(3) are in use today including the following expressions:

$$C + Mn/6 + (Cr+Mo+V)/5 + (Ni+Cu)/15 \qquad (2)$$

$$C + Si/30 + Mn/20 + Cu/20 + Ni/60 + Cr/20 + Mo/15 + V/10 + 5B \qquad (3)$$

where the quantities of alloying elements in the steel are expressed in weight per cent. Since carbon is the most damaging element (it raises the hardness of the welded region, which adversely affects cold cracking susceptibility) low carbon steels, typically 0.12% or less, are clearly favored for pipeline applications. Recent information developed by Sawhill and Wada(4) and others(5) indicated that field weldability or hydrogen cracking resistance of these low carbon steels is not accurately predicted by expression. 2 because carbon is weighted too low in relation to the alloying elements. Expression 3 may offer a better correlation with hydrogen cracking sensitivity of the low carbon steels(4).

Designers of offshore and Arctic pipelines are asking pipe manufacturers for higher strength, tougher, more weldable steels. Metallurgically, a balance between composition, with special emphasis on low carbon contents, and controlled processing is needed to arrive at the desired end-product.

METALLURGICAL BACKGROUND

While carbon is an effective strengthening agent, it has undesirable effects both on weldability and toughness in controlled rolled and in heat treated steels. The adverse effect of carbon on toughness in as-rolled steels is related to the formation of pearlite and/or upper bainitic carbides. Lowering of the carbon content provides substantial improvement in Charpy impact properties with a similar beneficial effect on weldability(4). For that reason, carbon content of the new generation of Arctic quality pipe steels is usually restricted to 0.12% maximum.

As-rolled pearlite-reduced (PRS) (typically 0.10% carbon) and the pearlite-free/acicular-ferrite (AF) steels (typically 0.06% carbon) rely upon alloying elements to obtain the required strength level. This is partially achieved in AF steels by increasing manganese content to 1.60% and higher. Especially important are columbium, vanadium and molybdenum, while nickel, chromium and copper may also be employed to develop superior properties. Collectively these alloy additions in controlled rolled steels contribute to austenite grain size control, precipitation strengthening and control of the austenite to ferrite transformation. In quenched and tempered low carbon steels, these same alloying additions are employed to achieve the desired fine-grained, acicular ferritic microstructure(6). In this instance, transformation strengthening appears to be a more important contributor to strength than precipitation hardening. In steels for Arctic application, grain refinement is critical since it toughens the steel while strength is also increased.

EFFECT OF ALLOYING ADDITIONS

Columbium and vanadium are carbide and/or nitride formers which can inhibit, either directly or indirectly, grain growth and/or recrystallization of the austenite during hot deformation. Molybdenum may also act in a similar manner impeding austenite recrystallization. The steelmaker uses alloying, in combination with controlled hot-mill processing, to produce a fine-grain austenite which subsequently transforms to an ultrafine (ASTM grain size 12 to 14) grain ferrite. This controlled hot mill processing is the so-called "controlled rolling" technique.

Following transformation to the desired fine-grain ferrite, precipitation of Cb and/or V carbonitrides further strengthens the structure. Indirect evidence suggest that molybdenum increases the solubility of columbium in the austenite, which enhances Cb carbonitride precipitation in the ferrite(7).

Molybdenum, chromium, nickel and copper play an important role in heavy thickness plate steels where cooling after rolling is slow (8). Similarly, these same elements are important in heat-treated steels for special pipeline components. Together with manganese, these elements act to depress the austenite to ferrite transformation temperature (A_{r3}) which refines the ferrite. Molybdenum is particularly effective here as would be anticipated from its well known effect on hardenability.

SULFIDE INCLUSIONS

Transverse ductility or Charpy shelf energy is very much dependent on the sulfide inclusion morphology in both as-rolled and heat-treated steels.

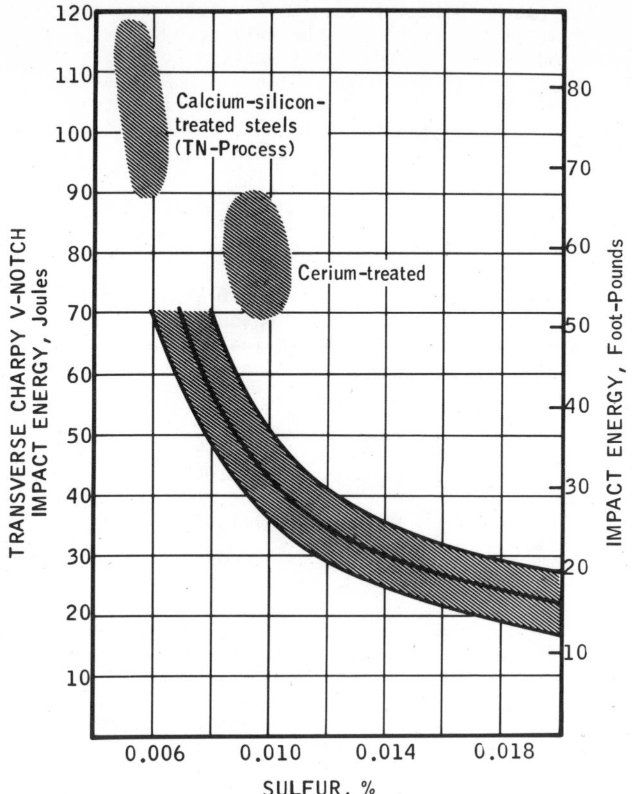

Figure 2: Low Sulfur Content With or Without Inclusion Shape Control Promotes Improvement in Transverse Toughness in X65 and X70 Pipe, (after ref. 9)

Elongated MnS inclusions, which are most pronounced in straight-away rolled steels, are detrimental to transverse toughness. However, their shape can be changed to a less damaging globular form by alloying with various elements. Alternatively, the sulfur content can be limited to 0.010% which substantially improves transverse ductility properties. Figure 2 illustrates the effects of inclusion shape control by calcium or rare earth metals (cerium) and sulfur level on Charpy energy(9).

THE INFLUENCE OF PROCESSING

Controlled Hot Rolling - The classical hot rolling of steel is designed to transform ingot or slab into plate using the least number of passes and finishing at the highest possible temperature. However, this practice produces a coarse austenite which transforms to coarse-grained polygonal ferrite with poor notch toughness. Modern hot-rolling techniques for controlled rolling of plate consist of slab reheat temperature control, control of the roughing sequence to condition the austenite and finish rolling to maximize the amount of grain refinement of the austenite (10). Usually the finishing temperature is kept low but still maintained above the A_{r3} temperature which for low carbon pipe steel is approximately 1400°F (760°C). While certain practices may call for finishing below the A_{r3} temperature, (e.g. rolling in the two-phase austenite-plus-ferrite region) care should be exercised with this practice since it tends to degrade ductility and toughness in the through-thickness direction.

A reduced slab reheat temperature of 2100°F (1150°C) is commonly used on line pipe steels requiring high toughness. The lower slab temperature insures that the austenite of a columbium-bearing steel is fine grained prior to the start of hot rolling. During the initial or rough hot rolling stage, i.e., in the temperature range 2100°F (1150°C) to 1800°F (980°C), the steel is heavily deformed and the austenite recrystallizes from the deformed structure. As hot rolling continues and temperature is reduced, the recrystallized austenite is further refined. Below approximately 1800°F (980°C), which is in the "finish" hot rolling stage, recrystallization of the austenite ceases in columbium-bearing steels. The austenite grains thereafter are elongated, offering more grain boundary surface for subsequent nucleation of fine ferrite below the critical temperature. In general, as deformation is increased and finishing temperature is decreased ferrite grain size will be refined, improving both strength and toughness properties.

Pipe Making Operation Control of the line pipe manufacturing operation is critical to the quality of the finished product(8,11). This is the second important processing step which has major influence on final properties.

Plate steels used in a UOE (longitudinal-welded) pipe making operation are susceptible to the Bauschinger Effect. The Bauschinger Effect is responsible for the loss in yield strength between the plate and the finished pipe when tested using a standard flattened tensile specimen as designated by the API specifications. This strength loss can be as high as 15% of the plate yield strength for conventional PRS steels. The discontinuous yielding stress-strain curve of conventional PRS steels is shown in Figure 3a. This loss in strength, σ_{ap}-σ_p, is not restricted to pipe formed by the UOE process, but is also observed in spiral-welded pipe fabricated from flat plate or coiled skelp(12).

Acicular ferrite and pearlite-reduced steels which contain a significant amount (20 to 30 per cent) of acicular ferrite can exhibit, in the as-hot-rolled condition, the continuous yield stress-strain behavior pictured in Figure 3b. The rapid work hardening during initial yielding which characterizes molybdenum bearing/acicular ferrite steels, serves to more than offset any loss in yield strength due to the Bauschinger Effect. The result is that the pipe yield strength, as determined by a flattened tensile specimen, is much greater than the yield strength of plate skelp. This is illustrated in Figure 4a. The strength properties of acicular ferrite-molybdenum-columbium steels, as affected by the UOE process, are detailed

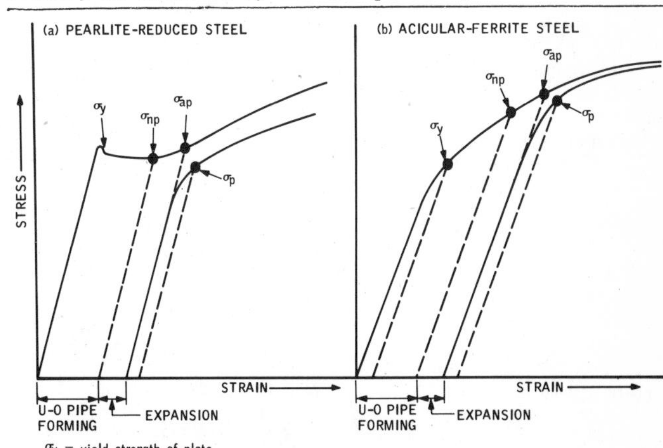

Figure 3: Schematic Representation of How the Yielding Behaviour of Pearlite-Reduced (PRS) and Acicular Ferrite (AF) Steels Affects the Yield Strength of Pipe. The Advantage of a Rounded Stress-Strain Curve (AF Steel) is Higher Finished Pipe Yield Strength.

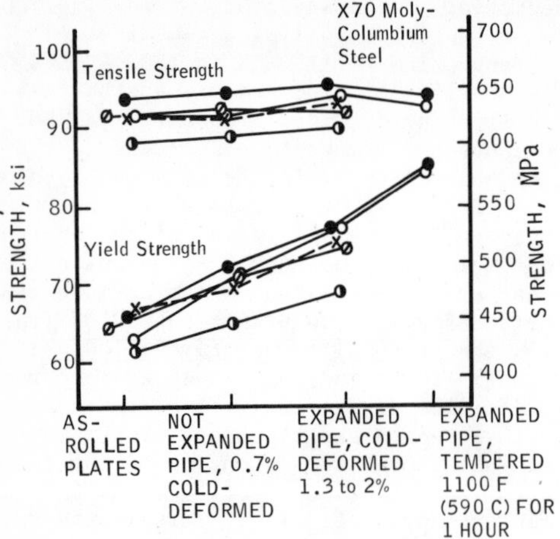

(a) AF X70 MOLY-COLUMBIUM STEELS

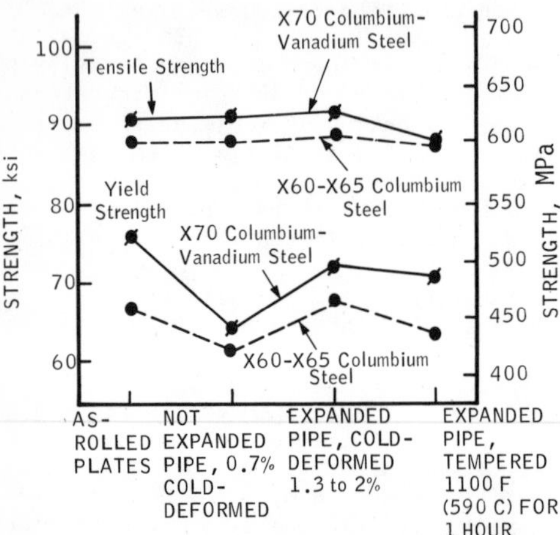

(b) PRS X60 TO X70 Cb AND Cb-V STEELS

Figure 4: Acicular-Ferrite Mo-Cb Steels Gain Strength as Compared to Cb and Cb-V Steels During U-O-E Pipe Fabrication, (after ref. 11).

in this figure. The important result is that the yield strength of the acicular ferrite steel increases continuously throughout the fabrication process. In contrast, yield strength of steels which exhibit discontinuous yield behaviour falls off on forming

Table 1

Statistical Analysis of Data on 32 in. (810 mm) Diameter x 0.78 in. (19.8 mm) Wall Thickness API 5LX-65 Pipe Made from a Mo-Cb Steel

Property	Mean Value	Standard Deviation
Yield Strength	74.3 ksi (512MPa)	2.4 (16.5)
Tensile Strength	90.3 ksi (622MPa)	2.6 (18)
YS/TS Ratio	0.82	0.03
Charpy Energy (+14 F/-10°C) (Full Size-Transverse)	62 ft-lb (84 J)	9 (12.2)
Charpy (+14 F/-10°C) (Full Size-Transverse) Shear Area	100%	0
Battelle DWTT (+14 F/-10°C) Shear Area	100%	0

as illustrated in Figure 4b. In the tempered condition (1 hour at 1100°F (490°C)), the molybdenum-columbium steel pipe showed an additional increase of yield strength to 85 ksi (580 MPa) while the Nb-V steel showed a further drop. The acicular ferrite steel, therefore, offers an effective and economical means to achieve higher strength levels to X70 grade and above.

PRODUCTION EXPERIENCE WITH LINE PIPE

Since early 1971, more than 0.5 million tons of acicular ferrite and PRS molybdenum-columbium steel pipe have been made in North America and in Western Europe. By country, the production is distributed as follows:

	Tonnage
Canada	220,000
USA	30,000
France	140,000
Italy	150,000
	540,000 ton

With the added production of several hundred thousand ton of large diameter pipe by the Japanese pipe makers for the Soviet Union, using a molybdenum-columbium-vanadium grade, and the continued activity in North America and in Europe, total production in 1976 is expected to double the past 5-year period.

Ipsco(13), Stelco(12), U.S. Steel(14), Italsider(15) and Usinor(8) have all demonstrated the "Arctic grade" capability of the family of molybdenum-columbium steels as X60, X65 and X70 line pipe. Recent results from USINOR on more than 100,000 tons of 32 in. (810 mm) x 0.78 in. (19.8 mm) wall thickness X65 pipe for a North Sea gas transmission pipeline are summarized in Table 1. The high toughness of this PRS molybdenum-columbium steel, 62 ft lbf (84 J) and 100% shear in Battelle DWTT specimens at +14°F (-10°C), demonstrates the high performance level which has been achieved.

The USINOR results were obtained from basic oxygen furnace (BOF) production of 480 heats of steel. Composition ("mean" values by statistical analysis) is 0.093C, 1.45Mn, 0.007S, 0.048Cb, 0.20Mo, 0.045Al and 0.024Ce. The cerium addition globularizes the sulfide inclusions resulting in an increase in Charpy energy in the direction transverse to the pipe axis. Carbon Equivalent, applying expression 2 to this production run, was 0.383. This C.E. is indicative of good field weldability, particularly in view of the fact that low carbon Mo-Cb steels generally exhibit better weldability than indicated by expression 2.

Submerged Arc Seam Welds - Supplementing earlier studies(4,5) on submerged arc consumables for seam welding of Arctic quality UOE and spiral pipe, additional results on several Mo-Cb base metal compositions were recently developed(16). Welds were made with a tandem electrode, Scott- connected alternating current unit. Wire diameter was 5/32 in. (4 mm) and Lincolnweld 790 flux was employed in all cases. Joint configurations are illustrated in Figure 5.

Results obtained at the centerline of the weld of a X65 PRS Mo-Cb-V grade are presented in Table 2. An average of 59 ft lbf (80 J) Charpy energy was observed on testing at -20°F (-29°C). Excellent toughness values, in excess of 40 ft lbf (55 J) at -50°F (-46°C) were also obtained on welds made in 0.75 in. (19 mm) and 0.790 in. (20 mm) thick acicular-ferrite (AF) X70 plate as shown in Tables 3 and 4. Similarly, the 1.24 in. (31.5 mm) thick Mo-Cb steel, welded in three passes, also possessed good weld-deposit notch toughness. This weld exhibited 45 ft

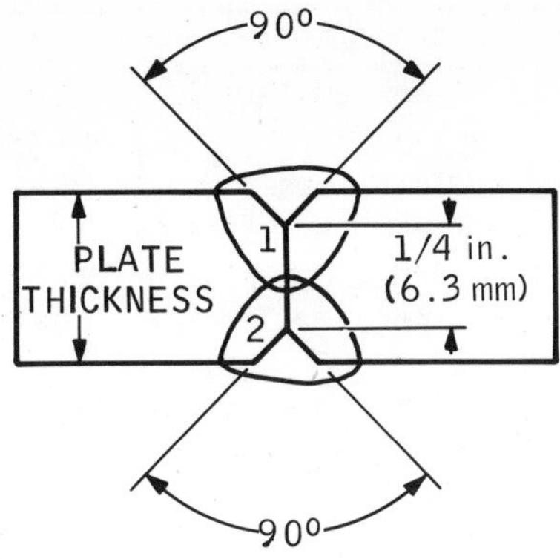

(a) Two Pass Weld

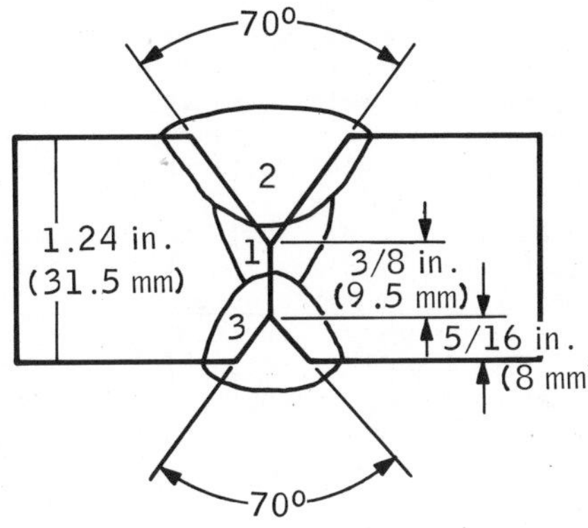

(b) Three Pass Weld

Figure 5: Joint Configuration Used in Submerged Arc Seam Welds Made in Molybdenum-Columbium Steels

lbf (61.3 J) at -40°F(-40°C) as illustrated in Table 5. Through careful selection of welding wire and flux, seam welds of high quality, suitable for low temperature Arctic applications, can be achieved in X65 and X70 grades of line pipe.

Shielded Metal Arc Girth Welds - Girth welds have been made in 42 in. (1070 mm) x 0.468 in. (12 mm) wall thick X70 pipe using Lincoln's Shieldarc-X70 (SA-X70) electrode and Westfalische Union's Phoenix Cel 90-electrode(19). In addition to meeting the

Table 2

Two Pass Submerged Arc Weld in 0.689 Inch (17.5 mm) X65 Moly-Columbium-Vanadium Steel(16)

Weld Configuration: See Figure 5a

Heat Input Pass #1: 63.4 kJ/in. (25 kJ/cm)

Pass #2: 70.4 kJ/in. (27.6 kJ/cm)

Chemistry	C	Mn	P	S	Si	V	Cb	Mo	Al
Wire (L70)	0.08/0.14	0.7/1.0	---	---	0.05 max	---	----	----	----
Mo-Cb-V Steel	0.102	1.38	0.009	0.013	0.31	0.05	0.026	0.27	0.03
Deposit	0.083	1.61	0.012	0.009	0.36	0.04	0.015	0.35	----

Hardness (HV 30):	Weld	Fusion Line	HAZ
	256 max	239 max	231 max
	230 min	226 min	203 min

Weld Metal Properties at Centerline:

Long Tensile:	Charpy Toughness:
88.1 ksi (608 MPa) Y.S.	59 ft-lb (80 J) at -20°F (-29°C)
102.2 ksi (705 MPa) T.S.	15 ft-lb (20.4 J) at -50°F (-46°C)
24% Elong.	

Table 3

Two Pass Submerged Arc Weld in 0.750 Inch (19 mm) Thick X70 Mo-Cb Steel (16)

Weld Configuration: See Figure 5a

Heat Input Pass #1: 70.4 kJ/in. (27.5 j/cm)

Pass #2 79.2 kJ/in. (31.2 J/cm)

Chemistry	C	Mn	P	S	Si	Ni	Cb	Mo	Al
Wire (L61)*	0.07/0.15	0.85/1.25	-----	-----	0.15/0.35	--	--	--	--
Mo-Cb Steel	0.05	2.15	0.009	0.005	0.28	0.23	0.053	0.51	0.06
Deposit	0.075	1.98	0.012	0.012	0.39	0.12	0.036	0.31	--

* AWS EM12K

Hardness (DPH 30 kg):	Weld	Fusion Line	HAZ
	264 max	258 max	277 max
	248 min	250 min	258 min

Weld Metal Properties at Centerline:

Long Tensile	Charpy Toughness:
83.0 ksi (572 MPa) Y.S.	48.7 ft-lb (66.3 J) at -20°F (-29°C)
105.7 ksi (730 MPa) T.S.	41.0 ft-lb (55.8 J) at -50°F (-46°C)
22% Elong.	28.0 ft-lb (38 J) at -80°F (-62°C)

Table 4

Two Pass Submerged Arc Weld in 0.790 Inch (20 mm) Thick X70 Mo-Cb Steel (16)

Weld Configuration: See Figure 5a

Heat Input Pass #1: 73.7 kJ/in. (29 kJ/cm)

Pass #2: 85.6 kJ/in. (34 kJ/cm)

Chemistry	C	Mn	P	S	Si	Cb	Mo	Al
Wire (L70)	0.08/0.14	0.70/1.0	---	---	0.5 max	----	---	---
Mo-Cb Steel	0.048	1.59	0.015	0.009	0.29	0.039	0.33	---
Deposit	0.072	1.43	0.015	0.014	0.26	0.019	0.41	---

Weld Metal Properties at Centerline:

Long Tensile:	Charpy Toughness:
87.7 ksi (605 MPa) Y.S.	79.8 ft-lb (108 J) at +25°F (-4°C)
100.2 ksi (690 MPa) T.S.	65.8 ft-lb (89.5 J) at -10°F (-23°C)
21% elong.	54.4 ft-lb (74 J) at -40°F (-40°C)

standard API 1104 requirements, the welds were subjected to detailed evaluation of microhardness and Charpy toughness. Figures 6 and 7 show the Vickers (1.0 kg) hardness traverses taken at the 3 o'clock weld position in the SA-X70 and Cel 90 welds. Full-size Charpy tests were taken, also at the 3 o'clock position, along the centre-line of the weld to establish the toughness of this zone.

In both welds the base metal, due to its low carbon content of 0.06%, exhibited heat-affected-zone (HAZ) hardness less than 250 HV. The Cel 90 deposit showed a maximum hardness value of less than 220

Table 5

Three Pass Submerged Arc Seam Weld in 1.24 Inch (31.5 mm) Thick X70 Mo-Cb Steel (16)

Joint Configuration: See Figure 5b

Heat Input Pass #1-3: 99.0 kJ/in. (39 kJ/cm)

Chemistry	C	Mn	P	S	Si	Cb	Mo	Al
Wire (L70)	0.08/0.14	0.70/1.0	---	---	0.05 max	---	---	---
Mo-Cb Steel	0.077	1.68	0.015	0.005	0.26	0.055	0.31	---
Deposit	0.09	1.60	0.015	0.012	0.30	0.024	0.40	---

Weld Metal Properties at Centerline:

Long. Tensile:	Charpy Toughness:
90.3 ksi (622 MPa) Y.S.	77.8 ft-lb (106 J) at -25°F (-4°C)
102.2 ksi (705 MPa) T.S.	65.3 ft-lb (90 J) at -10°F (-23°C)
21% Elong.	45.0 ft-lb (61.3 J) at -40°F (-40°C)

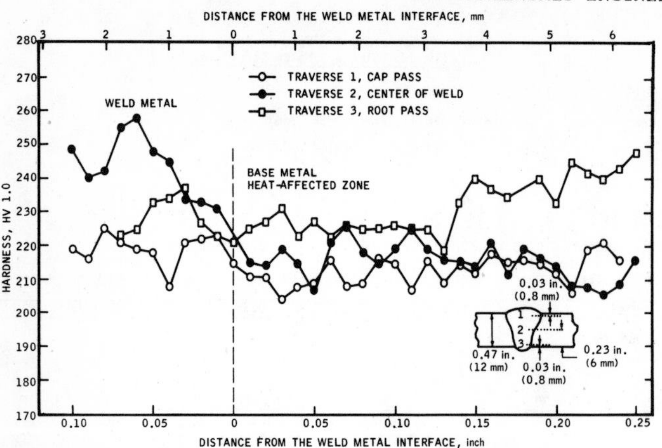

Figure 6: Vickers Hardness Traverses Across a SA-X70 Girth Weld in X70 Pipe (after ref. 17).

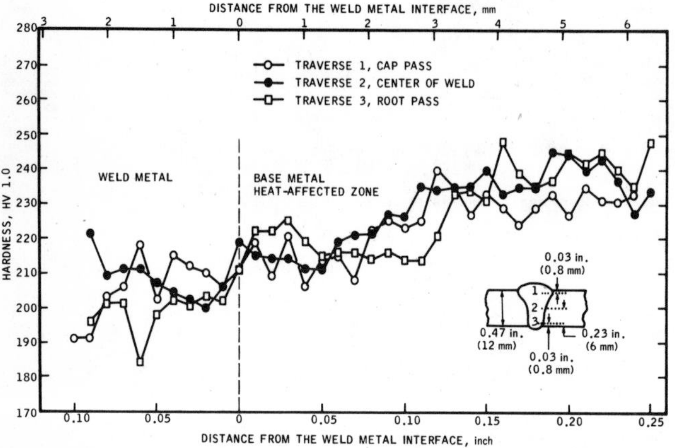

Figure 7: Vickers Hardness Traverses Across a Cel-90 Girth Weld in X70 Pipe, (after ref. 17).

HV. The SA-X70 electrode can be used for joining higher strength line pipe than the Cel 90 electrode.

The Cel 90 deposit exhibited 20 ft lbf (27 J) minimum down to a temperature of -40°F (-40°C). The SA-X70 deposit retained a 20 ft lbf (27 J) level to -20°F (-29°C). While the SA-X70 electrode may have a strength advantage, the Cel 90 deposit offers somewhat better toughness.

HEAT-TREATED WELDED FITTINGS

Molybdenum-columbium steels in the quenched and tempered (Q&T) condition offer a desirable combination of strength and toughness(6,18). Base metal properties readily meet severe Arctic pipeline requirements down to design temperatures of -80°F (-62°C).

Tensile properties of 1.38 in. (35 mm) thick Q&T Mo-Cb plates are summarized in Table 6(19). This commercially-produced plate, which was subjected to simulated plant treatments, meets X65 requirements. Excellent toughness, well above 100 ft lbf (136 J) at -80°F (-62°C) was achieved. It should be noted that the pretreatment anneal at 1700-1750°F (930-950°C) plus air cooling (AC) simulates hot-forming conditions experienced during the manufacture of elbow and tee fittings.

The 1.38 in. (35 mm) thick Mo-Cb plates were bevelled using a double-vee (65°) with a 0.25 in. (6 mm) land centered at mid-thickness. The vees were 0.56 in. (14 mm) in depth. Ten submerged-arc passes with a heat input of 46 kJ/in. (1.8 kJ/mm) were employed to fill the joint. A neutral, basic flux (Linde 166P) was used for all submerged arc welds. The

Table 6

Properties of quenched and Tempered Mo-Cb* Plates (19)

Heat Treat Schedule ***	Yield Strength** ksi (MPa)	Tensile Strength ksi (MPa)	% Elong.	% R.A.	HV 30	Avg. Charpy Values at -80°F (-62°C) ft lbf (J) Shear
24A	67.0 (450)	82.1 (566)	31.5	76.5	186	143 (194) 70%
24B	66.7 (467)	83.9 (578)	28.5	75.5	188	117 (159) 67%
27B	72.2 (497)	83.1 (574)	29.5	79.0	189	123 (167) 63%

*	C	Mn	P	S	Si	Mo	Cb	Al	Ce
	0.05	1.98	0.005	0.005	0.10	0.32	0.08	0.07	Added

** Longitudinal 0.5% Extension

*** 24A 1700 F - 2 hr - AC/1700 F - 2 hr - WQ/1250 F - 4 hr - AC
24B 1700 F - 2 hr - AC/1700 F - 2 hr - WQ/1250 F - 4 hr - AC/1125 F - 1.5 hr -
27A 1750 F - 2 hr - AC/1650 F - 2 hr - WQ/1250 F - 2 hr - AC/1125 F - 1.5 hr -

weldments were heat treated (see footnote to Table 6) and subjected to extensive testing. The results obtained on the weld deposit and the Heat-Affected-Zone (HAZ) are presented in Table 7. Across-the-weld tensile tests demonstrated essentially 100% joint efficiency. Weld metal and HAZ toughness levels in excess of 40 ft lbf (55 J) at -80°F (-62°C) were obtained, in a quenched and single tempered weld (Heat treatment 24A). Application of a second tempering treatment, followed by a water quench (24B), raised Charpy energy absorption to 66 ft lbf (89 J) at -80°F (-62°C). Double tempering followed by a water quench appears to provide for the best possible toughness in the weld region of heat treated pipeline fittings.

SULFIDE STRESS CRACKING RESISTANCE

Low carbon Mo-Cb steels in the as-rolled-plus-tempered or stress-relieved condition (1 hr at 1100°F (590°C)) and in the quenched and tempered condition (1850°F (1010°C) WQ + 1 hr at 1150°F (620°C) or 1250°F (680°C) WQ) have been subjected to the NACE T-1F-9 Sulfide Stress Cracking (SSC) test. Smooth specimens were tested under constant uniaxial load in an aqueous environment saturated with H_2S gas and containing 5% NaCl and 0.5% acetic acid. Standard tensile properties and the SSC threshold stress, defined as the highest stress which the specimen can sustain for 30 days without failure, for each condition are presented in Table 8. Results on AISI 4130 are also included for purposes of comparison (20).

Despite a high yield strength level of approximately 90 ksi (620 MPa), the molybdenum-columbium steel is quite resistant to SSC. This result is not completely unexpected as favorable low-heat-input welding experience with this family of low carbon

Table 7

Properties of Welded Zone in Quenched and Tempered Mo-Cb Plates (19)

Heat Treat Schedules	Weld Wire*	Tensile Strength Across Weld ksi (MPa)	Weld Metal HV 30	Location	Avg. Charpy Values at -80°F (-62°CO ft lbf (J) Shear
24A	L-100	82.5 (570)	219	Weld Metal	43 (58) 43%
				HAZ	91 (123) 63%
24B	L-100	84.8 (585)	219	Weld Metal	66 (89) 60%
				HAZ	83 (113) 62%
27B	W-19	83.3 (575)	194	Weld Metal	94 (127) 63%
				HAZ	118 (159) 68%

Weld Wire*	C	Mn	P	S	Si	Cr	Ni	Mo
Line - 100	0.15	2.05	0.006	0.010	0.09	0.30	2.65	0.56
Armco - W-19	0.11	0.78	0.012	0.003	0.13	0.08	3.44	0.02

Table 8

Sulfide Stress Cracking Resistance of Mo-Cb Steels*

Condition	Yield Strength(YS) ksi (MPa)	Tensile Strength ksi (MPa)	Hardness RB	Threshold Stress(THS) ksi (MPa)	THS/YS
As Rolled + 1 hr at 1100 F WQ	91.2 (629)	101.2 (699)	95	82.1 (566)	0.90
1850 F - 1 hr WQ 1150 F - 1 hr WQ	93.1 (642)	103.8 (715)	95	91.2 (628)	0.98
1850 F - 1 hr WQ 1250 F - 1 hr WQ	87.0 (600)	97.7 (673)	94	85.3 (587)	0.98
4130 (NACE) (20)	92.5 (637)	109.7 (755)	--	82.0 (565)	0.89

*	C	Mn	Si	Mo	Cb	Al	Ce
	0.046	2.1	0.07	0.29	0.07	0.07	Added

steels has demonstrated their excellent resistance to cold or hydrogen cracking(4,5). The Threshold Stress to Yield Strength (THS/YS) ratio values of 0.90 to 0.98 for the molybdenum-columbium steels compare quite favorably with the results (0.89) obtained on AISI 4130 steel(20) which is commonly used in components for oil/gas production.

CONCLUSIONS

Acicular-ferrite and pearlite reduced molybdenum-columbium steels have been developed to meet the Arctic challenge. High toughness at low temperatures has been demonstrated in X60, X65 and X70 quality pipe for mainline applications.

Additional laboratory-scale studies have been conducted on the plate and field weldability of molybdenum-columbium steels. Submerged arc welds in 0.75 in. (19 mm) thick acicular ferrite X70 plate exhibited notch toughness of more than 40 ft lbf (54.4 J) at -50°F (-46°C). Girth welds made using cellulose-coated pipe welding electrodes, Cel 90 and SA-X70 which have been designed for welding higher strength line pipe, possessed 20 ft lbf (27 J) Charpy energy down to -40°F (-40°C) and -20°F (-29°C), respectively. Overall performance of welded molybdenum-columbium steel line pipe appears to be satisfactory for Arctic applications.

Quenched and tempered molybdenum-columbium steel exhibits high strength (X65) and good toughness [over 100 ft lbf (136 J) at -80°F (-62°C]. Laboratory heat treated multipass submerged arc welds in this steel also exhibited a high degree of notch toughness; 66 ft lbf (89 J) was obtained at -80°F (62°C) using a quench+double temper followed by a water quench treatment. This grade, suitably heat treated, offers a combination of strength, toughness and weldability which is desirable for low temperature fittings and pumping station components.

Low carbon molybdenum-columbium steel in the stress relieved and in the quenched and tempered condition was shown to be resistant to sulfide stress cracking (SSC). This observation is consistent with the favorable low heat input welding behavior of these steels which has also demonstrated their high resistance to cold or hydrogen cracking.

REFERENCES

1. R. J. Eiber: Proceedings, 4th Symposium on Line Pipe Research, AGA, 1969, p. I-1.
2. W. A. Maxey: Proceedings, 5th Symposium on Linepipe Research, AGA, 1974, p. J-1.
3. Y. Ito and K. Bessyo: IIW Doc. IX 576-68, 1968.
4. J. M. Sawhill, Jr. and T. Wada: Welding J. 1975, vol 54, p. 1s.
5. M. Civallero, C. Parrini and G. Salmoni: WRC Bulletin 201, 1974.
6. G. Tither and J. W. Morrow: Met. Engr. Quar. 1975, vol 15, (3), p. 42.
7. H. Watanabe: "Precipitation Kinetics of Nb(C,N) in Austenite of HSLA Steels", Ph.D. Thesis - Univ. of Michigan, Ann Arbor, MI, 1975.
8. M. L. LaFrance, F. A. Caron, G. R. Lamant and J. LeClerc: Proceedings, Microalloying '75, 1976, Union Carbide Corp., New York, p. 367.
9. K. D. Taeffner, G. Gorges, M. A. Haneke and W. Th. Rechnagel: ibid. p. 425.
10. P. E. Repas: ibid. p. 387.
11. M. A. Civallero, C. Parrini and N. Pizzimenti: ibid. p. 451.
12. D. B. McCutcheon, T. W. Trumper and J. D. Embury: 13th Annual Conference of Metallurgists, Toronto, Canada, 1974.
13. E. C. Hamre and A. M. Gilroy-Scott: Proceedings Microalloying '75, 1976, Union Carbide Corp., New York, p. 375.
14. A. W. Hutnik and J. B. Hemphill: National Open Hearth and Basic Oxygen Steel Conference of AIME, April, 1974.
15. M. Civallero and A. C. Parrini: Proceedings, 16th Mechanical Working and Steel Processing Conference, A.I.M.E. 1974, p. 413.
16. ------ Report S245.1, The Lincoln Electric Company Cleveland, OH, Jan., 1976.
17. J. M. Sawhill, Jr.: Climax Molybdenum Company, Report ISJ936, June 20, 1975.
18. R. J. Jesseman and R. C. Smith: ASME Publication 74-Pet-9, 1974.
19. T. Wada: Climax Molybdenum Company, Report L-198-07 Nov. 25, 1975.
20. J. B. Greer, Corrosion/75, paper No. 97, NACE Toronto, Canada, 1975.

DISCUSSION

J. H. Smith (Interprovincial Steel and Pipe): What is the maximum columbium (niobium) content allowable before you have an adverse effect on field weldability? What tests have you done to evaluate the field weldability in this regard? Is martensite present in acicular ferrite microstructures?

J. L. Mihelich: With regard to columbium content, Climax usually recommends holding to a 0.07% maximum. This limit, however, is based on the adverse effect of columbium on seam weld toughness rather than on the girth weld performance. Since low heat input welding encountered in field welding does not dissolve much of the base metal, very little columbium enters into the weld deposit. We have made simulated field weld tests on Mo-Cb steel containing up to 0.10% Cb and the toughness of the weld deposit was quite good.

To evaluate field weld toughness we have made laboratory tests and also examined girth welds made in Mo-Cb steel pipes. While laboratory tests on simulated field welds may give an indication of field performance, the best method is to test the actual field welds. Columbium levels of 0.07% maximum in the base plate are consistent with good notch toughness in the girth weld deposit.

We find that martensite-austenite islands are usually present, typically 3% of the structure or less, in the Mo-Cb steels. This is true in the pearlite-reduced grades as well as in the acicular ferrite steels. It is my opinion that the martensite-austenite islands contribute, at least partly, to the rounded stress-strain behaviour of both steels. We have seen no adverse effect of these martensite islands on hydrogen-induced cold cracking during welding. Climax' Ann Arbor laboratory has also looked at the question of Hydrogen Induced Cracking (HIC) associated with hydrogen pick-up from H_2S-saturated sea water. Coldren and Tither, (J. Metals, 1976, vol. 28 (5), pp. 5-10) have indicated that the martensite-austenite islands do not have a significant influence on cracking of this type. Sulfide inclusions and their morphology seem to be important.

B. A. Graville (Dominion Bridge): One of the things people like to keep up their sleeves in case of repairs, etc., is thermal stress relief. In view of the dilution of columbium from the base material and the use of molybdenum in the weld metal, do you think you would still get good weld metal toughness after thermal stress relief?

J. L. Mihelich: Stress relieving of microalloyed weld deposits usually produces a deterioration in notch toughness. Work carried out by Jesseman (Microalloying '75, 1976, Union Carbide Corp., New York, p. 578) documents this effect in Cb-treated steels. He concludes that this loss in toughness due to a 1100°F (593°C) post-weld heat treatment is caused by the precipitation of fine columbium-carbonitride particles.

To insure good toughness after stress relieving microalloyed steels, it is important to alloy the weld properly to ensure optimum toughness in the as-deposited weld. In higher strength steels, it is essential to develop a fine grain, uniform acicular ferrite structure. Hardenability agents such as molybdenum, and also titanium (by a different mechanism), promote this desirable structure. The loss in toughness due to stress relief can be more than compensated if the as-welded deposit is tough.

C. A. Parrini: Considering the H_2S induced cracks (B.P. Test) did you make any test and what do you think is the effect of the small martensite islands in these structures?

J. L. Mihelich: Climax has examined hydrogen (H_2S) induced cracking (HIC) in steels which contain martensite-austenite islands. Since the islands are widely scattered, usually representing less than 3% of the structure, these regions do not act as nuclei for HIC. On the other hand, sulfide inclusions appear to be the preferred sites for cracking of this type. It would appear that a low-sulfur steel processed to minimize banding and containing a sulfide shape modifier would be most resistant to HIC.

We are also exploring the addition of 0.2% minimum copper, which reportedly cuts down on hydrogen absorption. Our preliminary findings indicate that copper does not always offer protection against hydrogen damage. We are currently working on several commercial steels to take a closer look at HIC.

M. R. Krishnadev (Laval University) : What is the highest yield strength that you have achieved with the "acicular ferrite" approach? At Laval University, by addition of copper to the basic Cb-Mo steel we have realized strength levels of over 100 ksi (690 MPa) with transition temperatures of -70°C and good toughness in 0.5 in. (13 mm) thick plates.

J. L. Mihelich: The results you quote are quite interesting. A 100 ksi (690 MPa) yield strength as-rolled steel with good weldability typical of these low carbon grades would be of special interest in the construction area. Excellent low temperature toughness below -70°C could make this alloy useful for structural applications in the Arctic.

With as-rolled and aged Mo-Cb steels, Climax has been able to achieve yield strength levels above 90 ksi (610 MPa) in plate products. Coiled material, due to self aging, can achieve the 90 ksi (610 MPa) yield strength level in the as-rolled condition. I would agree that an addition of copper which you have used, or vanadium, titanium and columbium, in large quantities, can be used to raise the strength of these steels. Climax, however, has not conducted any major studies in this area.

MULTIPHI - A PROCESS FOR THE PRODUCTION BY CONTROLLED ROLLING OF PLATES FOR X65 - X70 LINE PIPE

J. Leclerc, J. Bouvard and M. Lafrance
USINOR, France

and

M. Dolle, M. Grumbach and A. LeBon
IRSID, France

A new rolling process developed for a big order of API X 65 North Sea off-shore natural gas line pipe (32 in./810 mm diameter x 0.75 in./19 mm wall thickness) imparts high-strength properties to low-carbon steels through a high-temperature thermo-mechanical treatment.

The "Multiphi" process involves laboratory-simulated research, followed by industrial application in the mill, the whole rolling scheme being calculated on a computer from metallurgical data and a mathematical model by taking into account the physics and technology of rolling on the mill in question. The 3-phase rolling involves long holding times, thus impairing the productivity of the plate mill. Judiciously scheduling the different phases of rolling the slabs as they come from the reheating furnace notably improves productivity. For easier survey of the rolling results, the time-parameter is made the primary control variable. The results gained so far have permitted an extrapolation of the method to API X70 steels.

INTRODUCTION

The MULTIPHI process is used to determine the appropriate conditions for the hot-rolling of a steel to meet the precise specifications of a customer. It consists of: 1) Off-line computation of an a priori rolling schedule; 2) laboratory verification of the properties obtained by hot-torsion simulation of rolling; 3) secondary adjustment of schedules followed by another verification of properties (hot torsion); 4) adjustment on the plate mill.

By extension, the MULTIPHI process can be used to determine manufacturing processes of neighboring grades, or to define the characteristics of a new plate mill.

PRODUCTION OF PLATE FOR NORTH SEA PIPELINE

In 1974 and 1975, USINOR delivered 167,000 metric ton of plates to the VALLOUREC Company, for the manufacture of 370 km of X65 line pipe (813 mm diameter, 19.7 mm thickness), for two submarine lines connecting the North Sea FRIGG field to the Scottish Coast.

The plate steel was produced by the LD process, with silicon and aluminium ladle deoxidation. The steel was cerium-treated in the mold. The chemical analysis is given in Table 1, indicating that it is a low-carbon Nb(Cb)-Mo steel. The plates were hot rolled in the USINOR plate mills at Dunkirk and Longwy, using 3-phase controlled-rolling schedules.

The pipe was made by the U-O process in the pipe plant of VALLOUREC in Dunkirk. The mechanical properties of the pipes, given in Table 2, showed no significant differences between the plates from the two mills. They emphasize the beneficial effect

Table 1
CHEMICAL ANALYSES (wt %)

Elements	Plant analysis order	Heat analysis min	Heat analysis max	Heat analysis mean	Product analysis min	Product analysis max	Product analysis mean
C	0.08-0.11	0.072	0.130	0.094	0.073	0.135	0.099
Mn	1.35-1.55	1.285	1.550	1.446	1.255	1.585	1.433
P	≤ 0.025	0.011	0.033	0.020	0.010	0.037	0.022
S	≤ 0.010	0.003	0.013	0.007	0.003	0.016	0.006
Si	0.20-0.30	0.195	0.365	0.280	0.190	0.380	0.297
Al	0.020-0.050						
Nb	0.040-0.060	0.029	0.069	0.047	0.033	0.068	0.046
Mo	0.175-0.225	0.135	0.245	0.202	0.140	0.250	0.202
Ce	< 0.020						
C_{eq}	< 0.43				0.340	0.430	0.378

Table 2

MECHANICAL PROPERTIES

Properties	Plate			Pipe		
	mean	min	max	mean	min	max
Y.S. kgf/mm^2 (MPa)	47.5(466)	40.2(394)	61.0(598)	50.4(494)	45.7(448)	56.9(558)
U.T.S. kgf/mm^2 (MPa)	61.3(601)	52.1(511)	72.0(706)	62.3(611)	56.3(552)	72.2(708)
Y.S./U.T.S.	0.775	0.67	0.90	0.81	0.65	0.90
Elongation in 2 in., %	35	20	50	36.4	24	44
Toughness, Charpy-V (-10°), ft lbf (J)	65.9(89)	36(49)	118(160)	63.6(86)	45(61)	110(149)
Charpy-V (-10°C) / Charpy-V (+45°C)	0.903	0.57				
Charpy-V (weld axis, -10°C) ft lbf (J)				53.8(73)	35(47)	108(146)
Charpy-V (transition zone at -10°C) ft lbf (J)				58.6(80)	36(49)	138(187)

of molybdenum which provides a higher yield strength for the pipes than for the plates after forming and expansion. The nett gain is 3 kgf/mm^2 (30 MPa) on the mean value.

USINOR PLATE MILL FACILITIES

The Dunkirk plate mill began service in 1963. It has a 4300 mm x 1800 mm x 1000 mm four-high mill which can sustain a maximum separating force of 4500 tf (44 MN). In 1975, it was equipped with a slab lifter which makes it possible to interchange two half-finished plates during rolling. In the near future, a second 4500 mm x 2200 mm x 1000 mm four-high mill, which will sustain a maximum separating force of 9000 tf (88 MN), will be installed. The Dunkirk mill delivered 68,000 ton for the FRIGG contract.

The Longwy plate mill started production in April 1955. It is equipped with a roughing two-high mill (4000 mm stand) and with a finishing 4100 mm x 1500 mm x 1000 mm four-high mill, which can sustain a maximum separating force of 3500 tf (34 MN). It is fully automated with a process computer. This plate mill produced 99,000 metric ton of plates for the FRIGG contract.

CALCULATION OF ROLLING SCHEDULES

A set of models has been developed which describe the rolling of plates on reversing mills. These models, based on a physical knowledge of rolling, include the following:

- plastic deformation of the product, (variation of metal flow stress with strain, strain rate and temperature, also allowing for the influence of recrystallization retardation)
- determination of rolling load and torque;
- evolution of thermal map during rolling;
- elastic deformation of the roll-stand, including any device for roll-bending equipment (vertical deflection, camber), if available;
- threshold of flatness defect appearance of unsatisfactory flatness (centre, edges).

These models are incorporated into a system called P.L.A.T.E. (Procédé de Laminage Automatique des Toles Epaisses) which determines the optimal schedule both from the metallurgical standpoint and as regards product shape, productivity and safety of the mill (loads, torques, powers). This computation system is used both for the determination of controlled rolling schedules and for the automation or the set-up of new facilities. It requires the knowledge of the following characteristics:

a) Rolling stand characteristics
- dimension and nature of work and back-up rolls (diameters, camber, width, roll neck)
- characteristics of balancing and roll-bending systems
- maximum load, torque and power permitted
- input voltage
- reversal time of the drive motors
- speed range
- deflection of the roll stand outside the rolls (column, screws, etc.)
- roll stand separation and speed of run-out table rollers.

b) Starting product characteristics
- slab size
- type of steel (chemical analyses for estimating flow stresses)
- exit temperature of the slab, after reheating

c) Product properties required
- plate size
- controlled-rolling parameters, (i.e., number of phases; amount of deformation, and finish rolling temperature at the end of each phase).

d) Results

The computation system determines an optimum rolling schedule best suited to satisfy the above requirements. It provides a break-down of the schedule in a sequence of waiting periods and passes, each of them characterized by:
- total time (time = 0 at furnace exit)
- time per pass in the gap
- roll speed needed
- roll gap needed
- roll bending forces; if applicable
- product dimension
- plate crown
- rolling load predicted
- torque and intensity predicted
- motor overheating characteristics
- thermal map of the product after each pass
- waiting period after each pass

Figure 1: Hot torsion testing machine with on-line computer

These settings can either be fully automatic or manual (using a stop-watch)

ROLLING SCHEDULE SIMULATIONS

Being able to compute rolling schedules for a given mill does not imply automatic metallurgical optimization. It is therefore necessary to take into account metallurgical factors. This can be done by referring to the common rolling practice and setting the finish-rolling temperatures. However, limitations of load and total time of rolling restrict this approach.

The laboratory simulation of the schedule through hot torsion testing makes it possible to vary the parameters in almost unlimited ways. This is possible with the IRSID torsion testing machine equipped with a programming unit. In its latest version, seen in Figure 1, this machine reproduces exactly the deformation equivalent to each pass, the time between passes, and the thermal cycle of the plate provided by a computer model.

The observation of the microstructure of the torsion sample and the known relations between microstructure and the mechanical properties enable the prediction of the plate properties. When the structure is constituted of ferrite/ pearlite, the yield strength is simply related to the ferritic grain size, d (Hall-Petch law). The same holds for the transition temperature for a given set of steels (Cottrell-Petch law). These two laws are represented in Figure 2, for the C-Mn steels, both Nb(Cb) free and Nb(Cb)-bearing families, the latter in the as-rolled state. These graphs facilitate the determination of the yield strength and the transition temperature once the ferrite grain size is known. These diagrams cannot be directly applied to steels with partially acicular structures, in particular, certain Mo-Nb(Cb) steels. However, the heavy controlled rolling schedules used to attain the specifications required in this application (particularly, for three phase rolling) promote a ferritic structure, and this diagram (Figure 2) can be used whenever the tensile curve exhibits a short yield plateau.

The plateau length is very important for the pipe yield strength. Work hardening during pipe expansion is only significant if the plateau amounts to less than 3%, but the Mo-free steels with high yield strength (over 500 MPa) and fine ferritic grains may have plateau of more than 4%. The choice of a fine grain Mo-Nb(Cb) grade is therefore justified by the excellent mechanical properties obtained on the plate, particularly the transition temperature, and by a short plateau. It was found by simulation that breaking-down the rolling schedule into three phases allowed fine and homogeneous recrystallization of austenite grains during the second phase of rolling. As a consequence, the reduction during the third phase can be kept within mill limits.

By increasing from two to three rolling phases, one obtains a net gain of at least 25 MPa on the yield strength and of 15 deg C on the impact transition temperature.

PROPERTY VERIFICATION AND SCHEDULE ADJUSTMENT

The required properties conditioned the choice of steel composition as well as that of the type of rolling. Setting up the schedule is more difficult for an entirely new product (size, grade) than for a product resembling an established alloy. In this latter case, it is fairly easy to determine the finish rolling temperatures of each phase and the corresponding amount of deformation possible with the mill considered. Moreover, it is necessary to estimate the flow stress variation with the temperature of the steel considered, the deformation and previous passes (influence of recrystallization retardation). A good knowledge of this latter parameter is essential since it controls the precision of the *a priori* calculation of the rolling forces and torques, and so permits large reductions by working as closely as possible to the technological limits of the mill (force, power). This variation of the flow stress is obtained from numerous experiments already performed with the IRSID torsion testing machine. In the case of a new product, it is sometimes necessary to modify the metallurgical procedure. This is done by computing several schedules corresponding to different temperatures and thicknesses at the end of each phase. The results are then compared after simulation.

The schedules computed using the P.L.A.T.E. model are then simulated with samples of the steel grade tested on the IRSID torsion machine. This is done by respecting the same conditions (reheating, pass time, deformation temperature and amount, waiting period, cooling rate after deformation) and by recording the torque measurements. Two types of information are then available: 1) The mean ferritic grain size of the tension sample, the outer layer of which

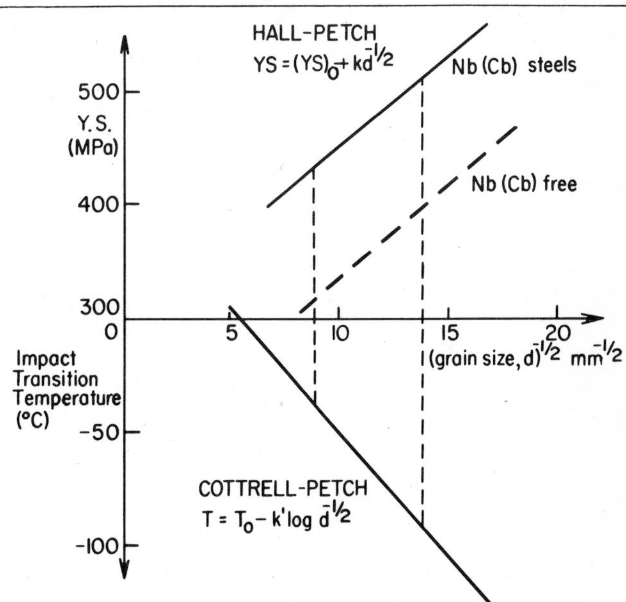

Figure 2: Yield stress and Impact Transition Temperature as a function of ferrite grain size

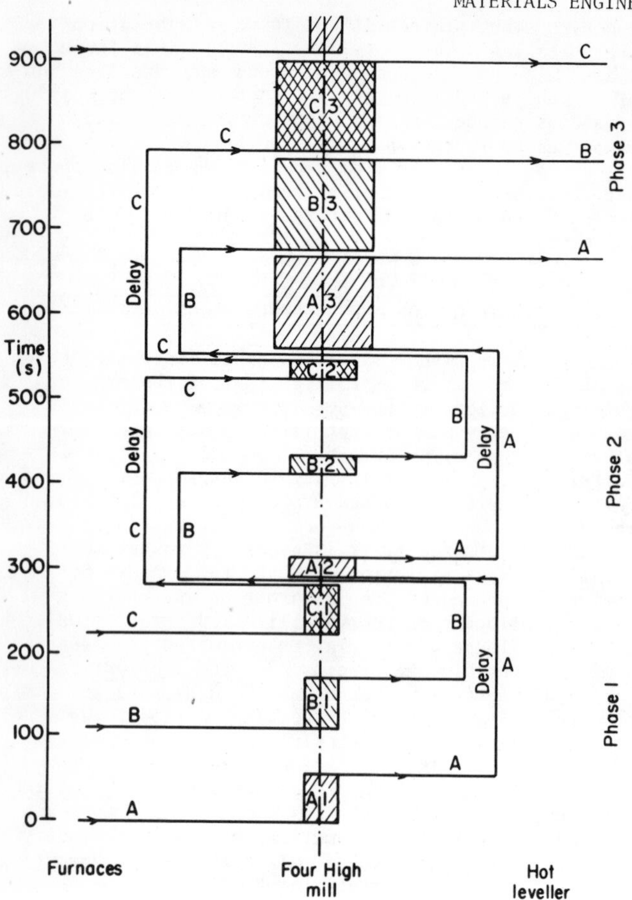

Figure 3: MULTIPHI for single-stand mill

has been submitted to a treatment wholly equivalent to that of a plate during rolling. The curves of Figure 2 make it possible to obtain the yield strength and the impact transition temperature. 2) A series of torsion torques which, through the torsion-rolling simulation equations, permits the determination of the actual flow stress of the metal in precise deformation conditions.

When the predicted and measured mechanical properties and flow stresses agree, the rolling schedule is considered as satisfactory and is put into production application on the mill. In case of substantial differences between flow stresses, the model used for that steel is modified from the measurements and a new simulation cycle, including a schedule calculation and a programmed torsion test, is performed. In general, good agreement is reached at the end of the second iteration. This method yields rolling forces and torques within 5%.

If it is needed to improve the mechanical properties, a new cycle "schedule-computation/torsion" is then started. The temperature and thicknesses at the end of each phase are then modified until the desired values are obtained.

APPLICATION TO PLATE PRODUCTION

The MULTIPHI rolling process involves long waiting periods between passes, which may seriously hamper mill productivity. For the FRIGG contract, the actual rolling procedure was a follows:

- 1st phase: passes to width and rolling of the slab down to 100 mm (5 times the final thickness, t) in 60 s.
- 230 s waiting period for cooling.
- 2nd phase: rolling down from 5t to 3t in 26 s.
- 245 s waiting period, for cooling
- 3rd phase: rolling down from 3t to **t** in 114 s.

Total controlled-rolling time	: 200 s
Waiting periods	: 475 s
Total time in mill	: 675 s (11 min, 15 s)

This prompted the devising of a sequence of schedules for the simultaneous rolling of several plates, which would minimize unproductive periods. The waiting periods needed for the slab to cool to temperature are used to perform certain phases of the rolling of other slabs.

For the case of a single-stand mill, the schedule summarized in Figure 3 was adopted. The progress of three slabs, A, B, C are depicted on a vertical time axis. However, the productivity here is still poor because of long waiting periods.

A single-stand plate mill equipped with a slab lifter (present Dunkirk configuration) makes it possible to lift a slab above the rollers, permitting another slab to pass below. This achieves slab exchange with respect to the rolling- stand. A MULTIPHI schedule for such a mill is shown in Figure 4. This system provides a substantial productivity increase through a decrease of idle periods. It also results in a more regular exit rate from the reheating furnace. Furthermore, the mill operator controls the three successive phases repeatedly. There are always three slabs or blanks in the transformation stage.

The schedule for a two-stand mill (two-high roughing mill and four-high finishing mill, as at the Longwy mill) is summarized in Figure 5. The first stand is used for the first rolling phase, the second stand for the second and third phases. The roughing stand yield is poor, but the idle periods of the finishing stand are minimized. The exit rate of the reheating furnace is regular, which contributes to product quality. There are always four slabs or blanks in the transformation stage.

Finally, Figure 6 shows the schedule for a

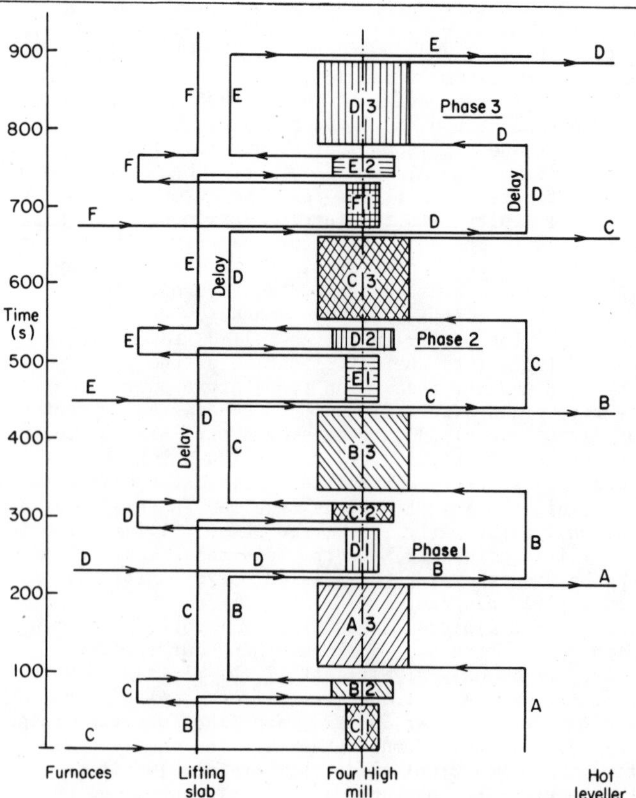

Figure 4: MULTIPHI for single-stand mill with slab lifter

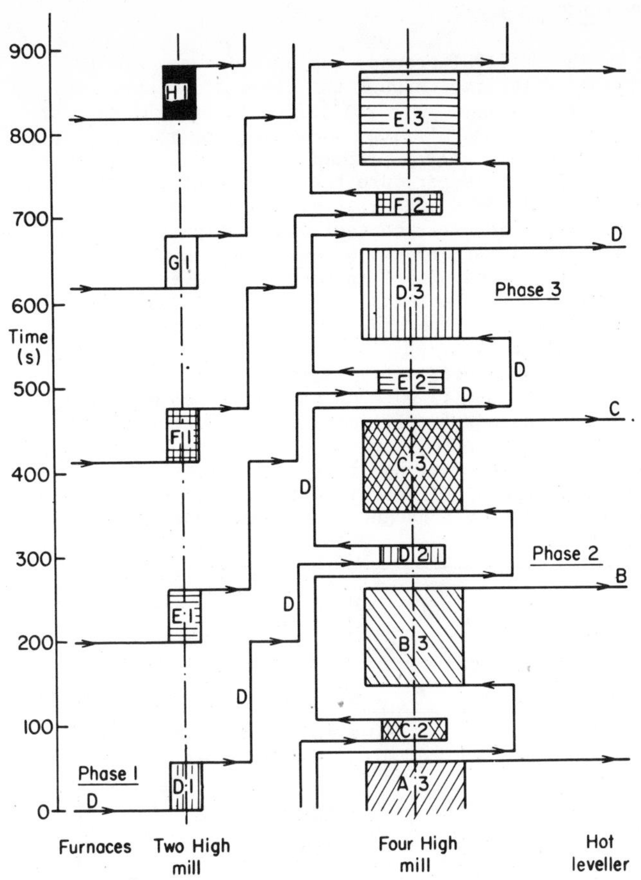

Figure 5: MULTIPHI for two-stand mill

two-stand mill (a four-high roughing mill followed by a four-high finishing mill, with a slab lifter -- the Dunkirk mill after the second stand installment). The first stand is used for the first and second phases, the second stand is used for the third phase. The two slab lifters are placed ahead of the first stand (the same configuration applies in the case of a single lifter, but it makes operations more cumbersome. It must then be large enough for two slabs).

A portion of the schedule may be described as follows (see Figure 6):

- Slab F, which has just been pushed out, passes under slabs D and E (after 1st phase) and reaches the first stand while slabs B and C (after 2nd phase) remain on the intermediate table between the stands and the finishing mill starts the third phase on slab A.
- Slab F is brought back behind the lifters while slab D is put down for its second phase.
- Slab F is placed on lifter no. 1 while slab G is pushed out of the furnace.
- Slab D (after 2nd phase) catches up with C and B on the intermediate table.
- etc. etc.

There are always six to seven slabs or blanks in the transformation stage. This schedule yields the optimum productivity of the rolling mill since the finishing stand is saturated; the idle periods of the roughing stand are kept to a low level and permit the slab handling necessary to maintain the exit rate. The rolling schedules actually established for the two mills are summarized in Table 3.

CANADIAN ARCTIC TRIALS

For the CANADIAN ARCTIC trial, the requirements to meet are even more stringent than for the FRIGG order. The pipes are to be made of X 70 steel (48 in. (1220 mm) diameter and 18.3 mm thickness), meeting the following specifications:

YS = 49.2 to 56.2 kgf/mm^2 (480 to 550 MPa)
UTS $\geqslant$ 57.6 kgf/mm^2 (570 MPa)
YS/UTS $\leqslant$ 0.87
elongation in 2 in. > 27%
Toughness (Charpy-V impact energy at -25°C) > 6.2 kgf m/cm^2 (50 J)
100% ductile (average of 3 samples).
BDWTT at -25°C < 40% crystallinity

Compared to the FRIGG order, the higher yield strength and the toughness requirements at a lower temperature have drawn us, after detailed study of the best mechanical properties previously obtained, to a steel analysis lower in carbon, with higher manganese, niobium and molybdenum content and lower sulphur. Trial heats were melted at the Dunkirk plant, aiming at the following analysis (wt% x 1000):

C	Mn	P	S	Si	Al	Nb(Cb)	Mo	Ce
80	1550	<20	<8	250	35	70	250	>20

The plate rolling was performed half at the Dunkirk plate mill and half at the Dilling plate mill. The plates were formed into pipes in the pipe plant of VALLOUREC in Dunkirk. This cross experiment enabled us to single out the main factor for the achievement of grade X 70, i.e. the finish-rolling temperature (Figure 7). All the other requirements are met; in particular, tensile strength is higher than 615 MPa (62.7 kgf/mm^2) and Charpy V-notch energy higher than 50 J (6.2 kgf m/cm^2) at -25°C.

Heavy 3-phase controlled rolling (1150°C/5t -900°C/ 3t-730°C) enables X 70 to be guaranteed in 48 in. (1220 mm) diameter and 18.3 mm thickness.

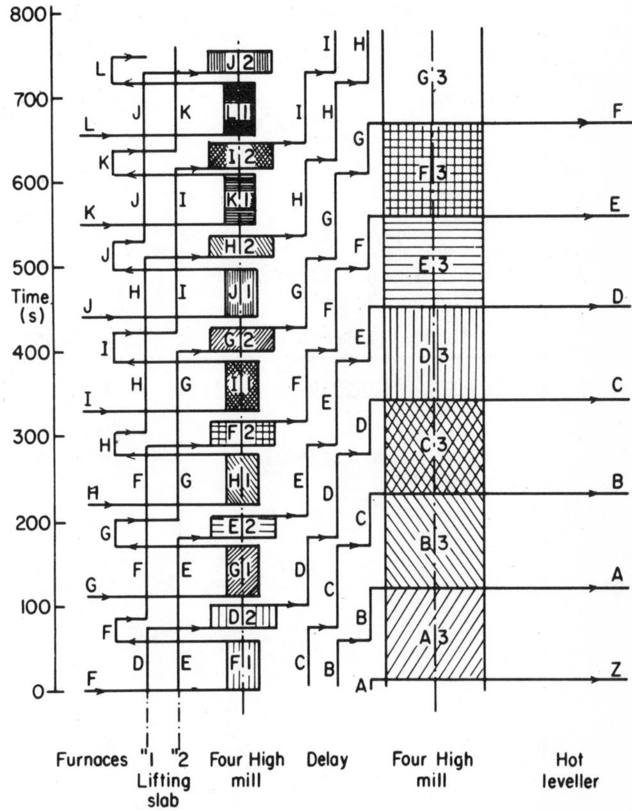

Figure 6: MULTIPHI for two-stand mill with slab lifter

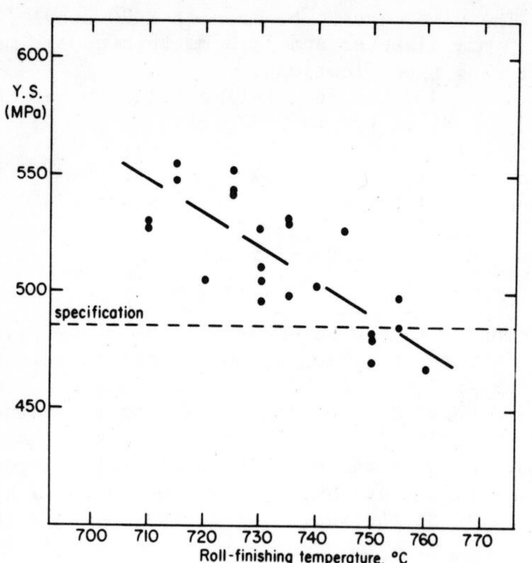

Figure 7: Influence of finishing temperature on pipe yield strength (3-phase rolling)

CONCLUSION

The MULTIPHI process has opened a new era in controlled rolling through the close association of the plant engineer, his rolling mill, and the laboratory metallurgist. Besides providing for the thickness reduction of the steel products, controlled rolling applies a high temperature thermo-mechanical treatment to the steel which endows it with higher mechanical properties than after conventional two-phase rolling. Through the joint efforts of our research, by both metallurgical and plant engineers, we have been able to move back the technical limits of an industrial facility and have therefore been in a position to meet specifications which, only a few years ago, would have been considered unrealistic.

We continue to work on new processes which will be adapted to new facilities and specifications of the type now proposed for the Arctic. We are also exploring a promising new route, viz. accelerated cooling of plates after rolling. In this context we are developing a quenching machine capable of keeping up with the mill output (cooling rate from

TABLE 3

Actual Rolling Schedules

	Dunkirk			Longwy		
Slab sizes	155 x 1640 x 2910 mm			210 x 1640 x 2150 mm		
Furnace setting						
-- heating zone	1180/1240°C			1235/1240°C		
-- equalizing zone	1150°C			1190°C		
1st rolling phase	passes to width : 30 s			passes to width : 70 s		
-- waiting period between 1st and 2nd phases	220 s			230 s		
-- initial temperature	890°C (on surface)			930°C (on surface)		
2nd rolling phase	3 passes in 30 s			3 passes in 26 s		
Schedule:	Thicknesses (mm)	Forces (tf)	T°C	Thicknesses (mm)	Forces (tf)	T°C
	80.0	2900	890	76.8	2500	930
	69.0	3000	-	65.5	2950	955
	59.0	3100	880	58.1	2600	950
-- waiting period between 2nd and 3rd phases	225 s			245 s		
-- initial temperature	790°C (on surface)			820°C (on surface)		
3rd rolling phase	8 passes in 60 s			10 passes in 117 s		
Schedule:	Thicknesses (mm)	Forces (tf)	T°C	Thicknesses (mm)	Forces (tf)	T°C
	51.5	3200		49.0	3200	
	45.6	3400	800	43.5	3300	810
	39.6	3500		38.6	3400	
	33.9	3700	780	34.3	3350	805
	29.1	3800		30.4	3500	
	25.2	3900	775	27.1	3450	795
	22.1	3800		24.3	3350	
	19.7	3500	760	22.1	3350	790
				20.7	2950	
				19.7	2500	765

30 to 100 deg C/s depending on thickness; time across the quenching unit less than 1 min; all points of the plate being quenched from an initial temperature within a 50 deg C interval).

"Directed" rolling has replaced "controlled" rolling. Controlled and, later, directed, accelerated cooling will take over and may be the dominant topic in a future presentation of our work.

REFERENCES

1. C. Rossard, P. Blain, Rev. Mét. 1962, vol. 59, pp. 223-236.
2. C. Rossard, Rev. Mét., 1968, vol. 65, pp. 181-195.
3. A. LeBon, J. Rofes-Vernis, C. Vossard, Mém. Scient. Rev. Mét., 1973, vol. 70, pp. 577-588.
4. A. LeBon, J. Rofes-Vernis, C. Rossard, Metal Science, 1975, (9), pp. 36-40.
5. A. LeBon, L. de Saint-Martin, Proceedings, Micro-alloying '75, 1976, Union Carbide Corp., New York, p. 90.
6. M. LaFrance, F. Caron, G. Lamant, J. LeClerc, ibid. p. 367 .
7. G. Fritsch, G. Haralamb, J. C. Illaire, J. P. Schiavon, J. Bouvard, Rev. Mét., 1973, vol. 70, pp. 213-223.

DISCUSSION

P. R. Slimmon (Bethlehem Steel): In the computer controlled rolling schedule, how do you determine slab and plate temperature? Does this information feed back into the computer program to adjust drafting practice?

J. Bouvard: The rolling schedule is calculated off-line once for all. It takes into account the estimated temperature of the slab as it exits the preheating furnace, the characteristics of the rolling mill, the dimensions of the slab, the final dimensions of the plate and the other rolling parameters. The rolling schedule also considers the expected temperature at each pass (surface and average bulk temperature). Surface temperatures can be checked with pyrometers, and in actual fact the difference between calculated and true temperatures is of the order of only ± 10°C. This is because of the regularity of the rolling process where all steps are closely monitored in time (by means of a stop watch). The computer program also ensures proper gauge in successive passes by taking into account small variations in metal plasticity as detected by variations in specific rolling forces.

P. R. Slimmon: Where are slabs kept during the hold period? On by-pass tables?

J. Bouvard: While being cooled, the slabs are either laid on a slab lifter or they are maintained on rocker rolls in line with the rolling stand(s), depending on the rolling schedule and type of mill.

C. A. Parrini (Italsider): Do you have automatic computer rolling in your plate mill?

J. Bouvard: The finishing stand of the Longwy Works is equipped with a process computer which actually controls the whole of the rolling operations in real time. The stand of the Dunkerque Works is operated manually.

C. A. Parrini: Do you have any problem of plate rejection, such as rejecting four to seven slabs together if something goes wrong?

J. Bouvard: If a problem occurs during rolling, there is a high probability that part or all of the slabs will be rejected. However, it is often possible to resume the rolling operations after diverting only one or two slabs.

J. L. Mihelich (Climax Molybdenum): How is the rate of production effected by the various controlled rolling procedures, e.g. Multiphi, vs standard controlled rolling?

J. Bouvard: Rolling under temperature control leads to a decrease in productivity which may reach 50% in the particular case of a single rolling stand without a slab lifter. However, in the case where two four-high mills are operated with a slab lifter, the productivity of a temperature-controlled rolling process is roughly similar to that of a rolling process without precise temperature control.

B. Rothwell (Noranda Research): The three stage rolling envisaged by the authors finishes immediately before the onset of the austenite-ferrite transformation. Three-stage processes advocated by some Japanese sources finish in the two-phase region, while the British Steel Corporation is actively considering rolling in the fully ferritic condition. What are the authors' feelings as to the relative merits of these approaches, both as regards the production aspects and the metallurgical characteristics of the product?

I should also like to comment on plate mill design. When a second mill stand is added to a large plate mill, generally for reasons of productivity, provided sufficient distance is available between the two stands, conventional two-stage controlled rolling becomes extremely straightforward and productive. Do you feel that similar benefits could accrue, by the addition of a third stand, in the case of three stage rolling, and if so, could such an investment be economically justified?

J. Bouvard: Rolling in the two-phase region is currently being studied and the decision to implement it or not will depend on our experimental results. With regard to the proposed expansion of the Dunkerque Works, the addition of a second stand is not only geared to increasing productivity but it is destined also to give us a more powerful tool which would allow us to roll at even lower temperatures.

It is obvious that the addition of a third stand would facilitate three-phase rolling; such an approach, however, could not justify the capital investment.

M. R. Krishnadev (Laval University): The possibility of predicting commercial rolling practice by means of a hot torsion machine is very interesting. However, the limitations of the hot torsion machine should be recognized -- i) small specimen size, hence making it impossible to have a direct relation between processing parameters and toughness and ii) stress history is more complex in rolling than in torsion. Would you like to comment on the possibilities of overcoming these limitations?

J. Bouvard: The hot torsion test is only one approach for studying what happens during rolling, but the grain size data that it generates allow a close estimate of the rolling conditions required to produce the desired yield strength and impact transition temperature of the product. It must also be pointed out that some adjustments of the mill itself may be necessary.

E. Kranz (Mannesmannrorhen-Werke): If you calculate the yield strength with the Hall-Petch formula for the hot torsion test samples from the grain size of the structure, how does this system work for acicular ferrite steels, with special regard to strain hardening behaviour, and if the system does not work, what will you do then?

J. Bouvard: For a pure acicular structure it is not possible to use the Hall-Petch relation. For a partially acicular structure the measurement of grain size plus Hall-Petch relation gives an upper limit of the yield strength of the plate. From knowledge of the strain-hardening of this kind of steel, we can predict that the pipe is very well approximated by that upper limit. By applying a severe controlled rolling schedule (MULTIPHI) on that kind of steel, we have almost a pure ferritic structure, so there is no problem of predicting the yield strength.

NEW MANUFACTURING PROCESSES AND PROPERTIES OF ARCTIC GRADE LINE-PIPE

H. Matsubara, B. Sakai, and T. Itaoka
Nippon Kokan K.K.
Tokyo, Japan

We have developed several new manufacturing processes to meet the stringent requirements on the quality of Arctic grade line pipe materials. De-sulfurization has been effective in the achievement of a high transverse shelf energy in the Charpy test. To improve the low temperature toughness of the base plate, a modified rolling sequence was adopted in controlled rolling, and a modified multistage quenching and tempering process also proved beneficial to the heat-treated low-nickel steel. A new straight seam welding process, high current MIG arc welding, and quenching and tempering processes for pipes have been developed to obtain the excellent toughness properties in not only base metal but also the weld and heat affected zone.

By combining an optimal chemical composition and these new processes, it is possible to manufacture every type of Arctic grade line pipe. It has also been demonstrated that the line pipe manufactured by these processes gives excellent performance in practice.

INTRODUCTION

The steels for gas transmission line pipe used in the Arctic region must meet specific quality requirements such as high strength, low-temperature notch toughness, notch ductility and good weldability so as to prevent brittle fracture and unstable ductile fracture in service resulting from high operating pressures and low operating temperatures (1). To meet these requirements the line pipe must possess such mechanical properties as high absorbed impact energy and excellent drop weight tear test (DWTT) characteristics at service temperature. The carbon-equivalent of the steel should also be low. As these properties are required in the weld metal and heat affected zone as well as in the base metal of line pipe, efforts are being made to develop a new technology to manufacture steel plate and pipe of desired properties.

In the manufacturing processes of line pipe, the UOE process is especially advantageous in the manufacture of high quality line pipe in that the forming method is optimized to facilitate the production of heavy walled line pipe, and the expansion process is conducive to increasing the strength of the material and relaxing most of the internal residual stresses resulting from pipe forming. It has been demonstrated by a series of experiments that high quality line pipe which gives excellent performance can be produced by the UOE process from lower carbon-equivalent steels.

The pipes for use in the Arctic are broadly divisible into two kinds according to design temperature: line pipe for natural gas transmission service at -25°C or higher temperature, and pipe which is exposed to a temperature below -40°C in compressor and cooling stations or as auxiliary piping on a natural gas transmission line.

We have developed some new techniques for manufacture of such high quality pipes, as summarized in Table 1. Line pipe giving excellent performance at various design temperatures can be made by the UOE process employing these new techniques.

Table. I Developed Manufacturing Processes for the Arctic Grade Pipes

Manufacturing Process	Improvement Items
1 Steel Making Desulfurization Sulfide Shape Control	} Absorbed Energy of Charpy Test
2. Plate Production New Controlled Rolling Modified Quenching and Tempering	DWTT Characteristics Toughness of Base Metal
3. Pipe Production New Welding Materials High Current MIG Arc Process Heat Treatment of Pipe	Toughness of Weld Metal } Toughness of Weld Metal and HAZ

IMPROVEMENT OF SHELF ENERGY

Desulfurization

It is well understood that the most important factor affecting the Charpy shelf energy in the direction transverse to the pipe axis is the presence of elongated sulfide inclusions. The reduction of manganese sulfide by decreasing the sulfur content below 0.007% results in a drastic increase in the shelf energy.

Recently we have introduced a new method of desulfurization which consists in the stirring of molten iron in the ladle with the addition of calcium carbide. The characteristics of this mechanical desulfurizing method are shown in Table 2. The sulfur content of molten iron obtained after desulfurization depends very little on the sulfur content of molten iron before desulfurization and consequently the sulfur content of the steel stabilizes at the lower level.

Rare Earth Metal

Rare earth metal (REM) treatment can also be applied to desulfurized steel to provide a high Charpy absorbed energy in the transverse direction. The favourable effect of REM treatment on the transverse shelf energy has often been reported for steels with sulfur content over 0.005% (2,3). However, our latest test result (Figure 1) shows that REM treatment also improves the transverse shelf energy in steels with extra low sulfur content. This test was performed by adding REM to 30 t of molten steel. The effect of REM was clearly shown throughout the ingot and the contamination by concentrated inclusions at the bottom of the ingot, which had been reported by many investigators, was absent.

Table 2 Desulfurization Equipment of Molten Iron

Type of Equipment	Mechanical Stirring
Desulfurization Agent	CaC_2
Quantity of CaC_2	Aiming (S) in Steel: ≤ 0.007 % — CaC_2 3.0 Kg/Ton; ≤ 0.006 % — 4.5; ≤ 0.005 % — 6.0
Desulfurization Time	9 ~ 13 min.
Hot Metal Ladle Capacity	200 Ton
Capacity	30 ladles / day

Aiming (S) in Steel	CaC_2 Kg/Ton
≤ 0.007 %	3.0
≤ 0.006 %	4.5
≤ 0.005 %	6.0

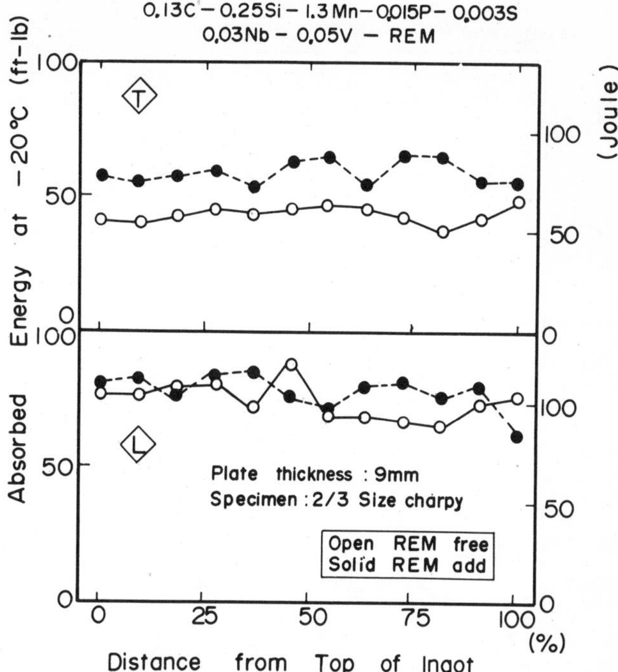

Figure 1: Effect of rare earth metal (REM) treatment on shelf energy of extra-low sulfur steel (0.003%S).

IMPROVEMENT OF LOW TEMPERATURE TOUGHNESS

Controlled Rolling

The controlled rolling technique for making very tough plates "as rolled" has made remarkable progress in recent years. The controlled rolling technique which was developed mainly for Nb (Cb) steels, combines the retardation of recrystallization of austenite and the refining of ferrite grain size by Nb with the procedure for rolling temperature control (4,5). The notch toughness obtained by controlled rolling depends on the degree of total reduction below a certain temperature. It was understood that the refined ferrite structure produced by controlled rolling was due primarily to an unrecrystallized elongated austenitic structure. This necessitated the high reduction in rolling of steel at a suitable temperature to obtain the required impact transition temperature. Recently, however, line pipe plate has been made heavy-walled and requires a still lower transition temperature, so that the conventional concept of controlled rolling finds no more use in practical applications.

To solve this problem, a new technique was developed which controls more strictly the whole rolling process, from the slab reheating temperature to deformation below the recrystallization temperature of austenite. This technique enhances the formation of a fine recrystallized austenitic structure in the high temperature rolling stage and the deformation of austenite below its recrystallization temperature. As shown in Figure 2 (6), the recrystallization of austenite depends upon the rolling temperature and the reduction. Consequently, the rate of reduction should be increased with decreasing temperature to obtain fine recrystallized austenite grains. Furthermore, the finer the austenite grain size before rolling, the smaller the reduction required for recrystallization and the smaller the grain size after recrystallization, as shown in Figure 3 (6).

On the basis of these findings, a new rolling sequence shown in Figure 4 has been established at the Fukuyama Works of NKK, for the purpose of pro-

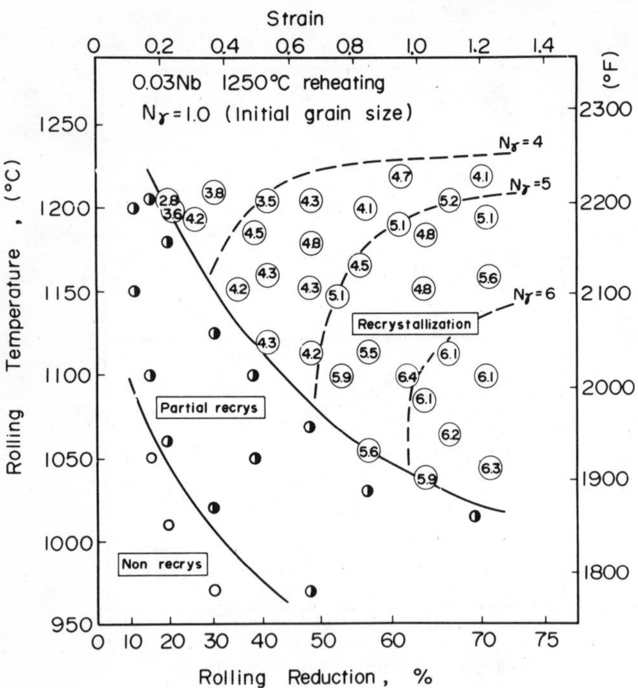

Figure 2: Austenitic recrystallization and resulting grain size in Nb(Cb)-steel

duction of Arctic grade X70 plates (7,8).

Types A and B (Figure 4) are the preliminary sequence and the 85% SATT of DWTT tested on plates ranges from -10°C to -30°C. The hatched zone in Figure 4 represents an improvement on the rolling sequence. The reheating temperature of slabs is 1,200°C, and the two control points are set during controlled rolling, i.e. when the rolling thickness is reduced to 100 mm or 70 mm, the material temperature is controlled at 870°C or 830°C, respectively, and the finishing temperature is controlled above 700°C in the final reduction pass. This modification of the rolling sequence has resulted in excellent DWTT characteristics.

Modified Quenching and Tempering

It is difficult to manufacture heavy-walled

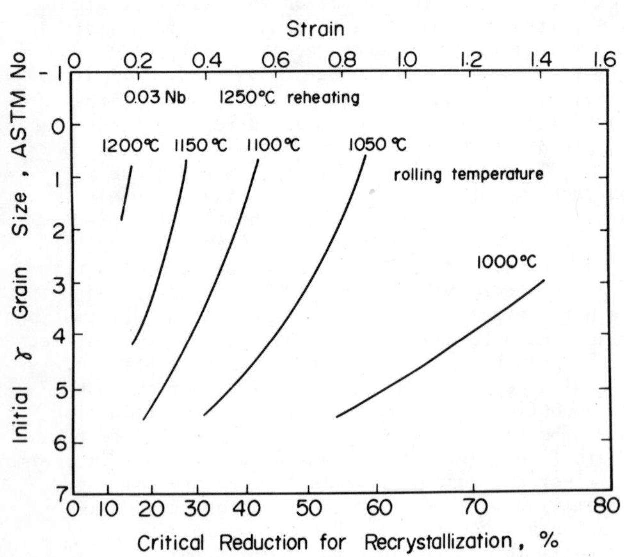

Figure 3: Effect of initial grain size on critical rolling reduction for austenitic recrystallization

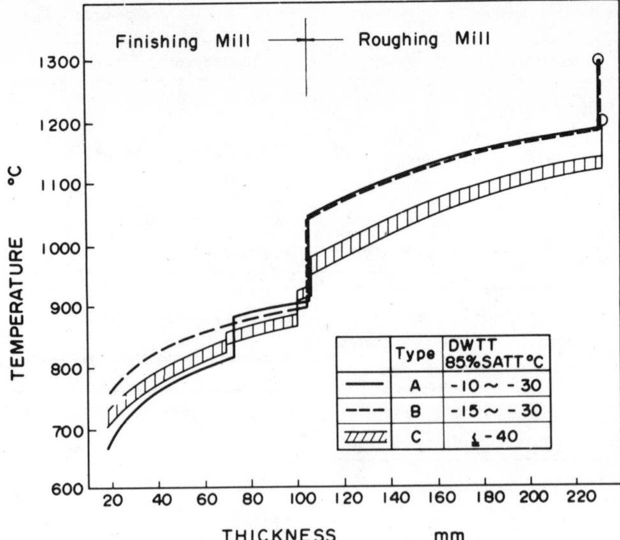

Figure 4: Schematic diagram of controlled rolling sequence

tough line pipe for use at service temperature, for example -60°C, from plate obtained by controlled rolling or conventional quench-and-temper. To solve this problem, a modification of the conventional quench-and-temper process, called "Q-Q'-T" or the multi-stage heat treatment process, has been developed for manufacture of desired plates from low-nickel steel (9).

The new heat treatment process is shown schematically in Figure 5. According to this process, the plate is quenched from a temperature of about 900°C (Q process) and a second quenching (Q' process) is accomplished from a temperature of A_1 + 30 deg.C before tempering.

The low-temperature toughness of the resulting material is remarkably improved over the steel obtained by the conventional Q-T process, as shown in Figure 6. The effect of the nickel content of the steel takes the form of an increase in strength of about 4 ksi per 1% of nickel added, no matter whether the conventional Q-T process or the Q-Q'-T process is employed. The addition of nickel, however, produces a better effect on the low-temperature toughness of steel when the Q-Q'-T process is employed.

The following three factors may explain the

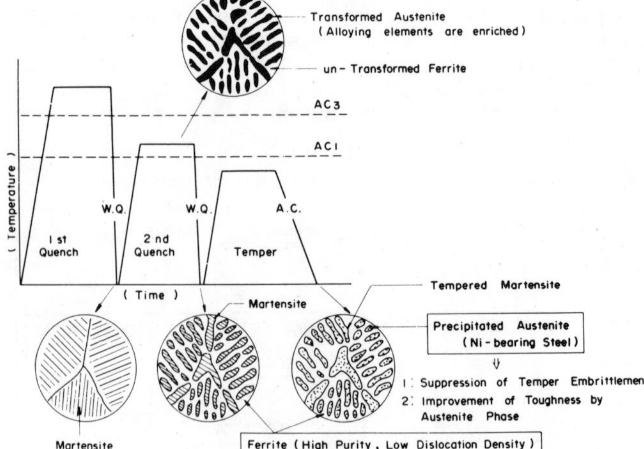

Figure 5: Schematic diagram of heat treatment and mechanism of toughness improvement by Q-Q'-T process

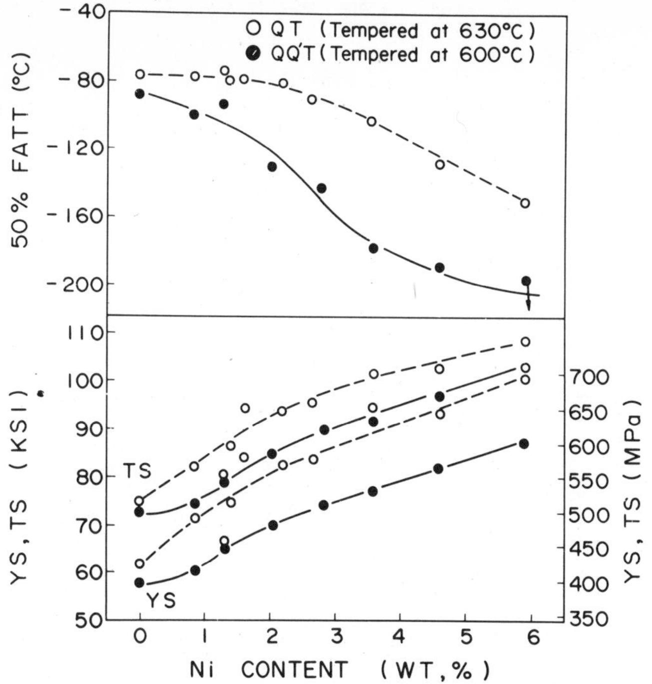

Figure 6: Effect of Ni content on mechanical properties (0.06C-1.5Mn-0.15Mo-xNi)

favourable effect of the Q-Q'-T process on the low-temperature toughness of steel:

(1) making fine structure
(2) improvement in the toughness of the ferrite matrix
(3) precipitation of austenite

The action of these factors is illustrated in Figure 5. Assuming that the DWTT shear area of a line pipe of 1.00 in. (25.4 mm) wall thickness should not be less than 85% at -40° or -60°C, the steel obtained by the conventional Q-T process must contain 4.0% or 5.5% nickel, respectively, to meet this requirement. On the other hand, the nickel contents may be reduced to only 1.5% or 2.5% if the Q-Q'-T process is employed.

Table. 3 Comparison of Characteristics of Some Welding Methods

	High Current MIG	Conv MIG	Tandem SAW
Wire dia. (mm)	4.0	1.2 ~ 1.6	4.0
Number of Electrode	Tandem	Single	Tandem
Number of Molten Pool	2	1	1
Welding Current	High	Low	Higher
Arc Voltage (V)	Low	Low	High
Welding Speed	Middle	Slow	Fast
Depth of Penetration	Higher	High	Middle
Number of Pass	Each Side One Pass	Multi - Pass	Each Side One Pass
Welding Efficiency	High	Lower	Higher

IMPROVEMENT OF WELD TOUGHNESS

High Current MIG Arc Welding

When submerged-arc welding (SAW) is employed in the manufacture of heavy-walled, super-tough line pipe, the welded portion, especially the heat affected zone, is less tough than the base metal. The Charpy absorbed energy in the HAZ produced by SAW varied with a continuous change of microstructure from fusion line to original base metal. To overcome this problem, we have developed a new straightseam welding process named "high current MIG arc welding".

The high current MIG process consists of inert-gas shielded tandem arc welding, but differs from conventional MIG arc welding in that welding is made in a relatively large current range (from 600 to 1,000 A), using welding wires 3.2 to 4.0 mm diameter. This new process permits only one MIG run on each side, no matter how thick the pipe may be, with much the same efficiency as that obtained by the conventional submerged arc welding process. Table 3 compares the results obtained by the three processes, i.e. high current MIG, conventional MIG, and conventional SAW. Figure 7 shows the welding head arrangement of high-current MIG.

Figure 8 relates the heat input required with the pipe wall thickness, for the different welding processes. When compared with the SAW process, the high current MIG process requires less heat input for the same wall thickness. Since the actual heat input of the high current MIG process is smaller than the sum of the heat input of two electrodes, its heat input requirement is estimated to be very close to that of the conventional multi-pass MIG process.

The toughness and maximum hardness of the HAZ of 3.5% nickel steel welded by high current MIG and other processes are compared schematically in Figure 9. Even if the same heat input is used for both the high current MIG and conventional SAW processes, the Charpy absorbed energy in the HAZ is increased remarkably in the welds made by the high current MIG process. The improvement in Charpy absorbed energy in the HAZ seems to be attributable to the tempering effect and less heat input mostly because of the two molten pools. The maximum hardness

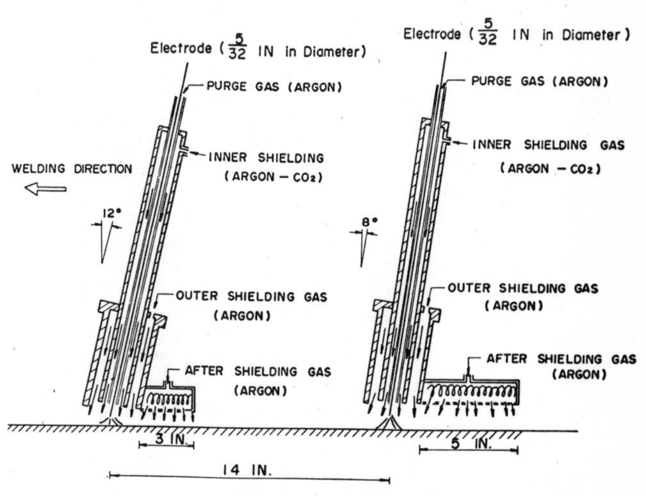

Figure 7: Types of Welding Head

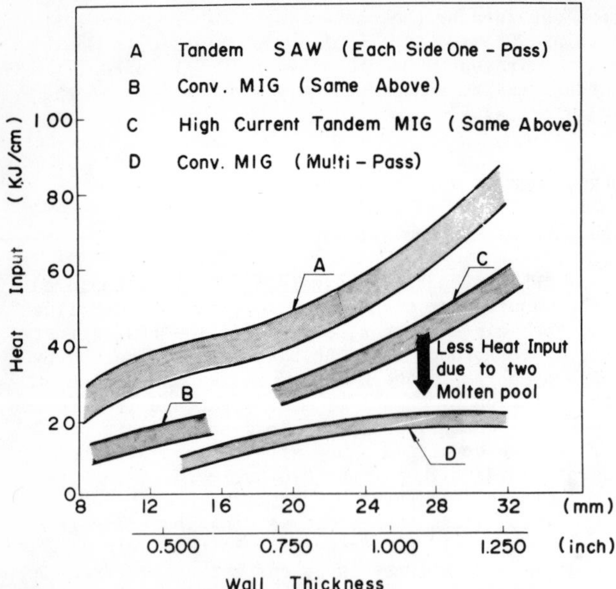

Figure 8: Relationship between wall thickness and heat input

of the HAZ can also be reduced to a considerable extent by the selection of a proper chemical composition for the base steel.

Figure 10 shows the result obtained by this process in a 3.5% Ni steel. The low-temperature toughness of both weld and HAZ is as good as that of the base metal. Figure 11 shows the macrostructure of such a welded joint.

Quench-and-Temper of Pipe

We have also developed a new heat treatment process for pipe so as to obtain excellent properties of the weld metal and heat affected zone.

The simplest method for providing a uniform quality for all parts of the pipe, including the welded portion, is the quenching and tempering obtained from the UOE + SAW process. The major advantages of this process are an improvement in toughness of the welded portion, the elimination of the HAZ hardness peak, and a decrease in susceptibility to HAZ hydrogen cracking. Other benefits include the elimination of the adverse effect on toughness of cold forming during pipe forming and an increase in the upper limit of wall thickness and of strength grade of pipes made in a given UOE mill facility.

We have also developed pipe Q-T equipment and procedures based on our original concept. The principal considerations were the prevention of distortion during quenching and the uniformity of temperature in the longitudinal and circumferential directions during heating and cooling. The pipe is heated by an electric induction coil and quenched by mist jet from its inner surface and by laminar flow from its outer surface. The quench rate is equal to that used in "roller quenching" which is generally employed in the production of Q-T plates. This equipment produces pipe which is identical in properties to Q-T plate.

The toughness and the macrostructure of the welded portion of a 3.5% Ni steel pipe produced by this equipment is shown in Figures 12 and 13. The results indicate that the properties are uniform throughout the pipe, including the welded portion.

PROPERTIES OF THE ARCTIC GRADE PIPE

Chemical Composition and Physical Properties

The chemical composition and physical properties of the line pipes manufactured by the processes described above are shown in Tables 4-7. Table 4 shows the test results of X70 pipe produced from controlled-rolled plates of low-alloy steels. Tables 5, 6 and 7 show the test results of X65 pipe produced from Q-Q'-T plates and the pipe Q-T process for low-nickel steels.

Field Weldability

The under bead cracking test was performed on line pipe plates according to the method of Battelle Memorial Institute so as to evaluate their field weldability. Welds were made with cellulosic electrodes at a heat input of 600 J/mm. As shown in Figure 14, the extent of under bead cracking was always less than 50%, but the rate of under bead cracking improved with decreasing carbon-equivalent. When inclusion shape was controlled by the rare earth metal addition, the steel showed a very low susceptibility to cracking.

Susceptibility to Lamellar Tearing

When "hot tapping" the pipe line fillet welds, which have considerable constraints, are usually made and lamellar tearing may result. It is said that the steel susceptibility to lamellar tearing has a linear relationship with the reduction in area in through-thickness tensile tests.

As shown in Figure 15, the reduction in area in the through-thickness direction depends largely on the sulfur content of the steel. It shows a remarkable improvement when the sulfur content is reduced to less than 0.007%. Lamellar tearing, however, does not easily occur in Arctic grade line pipe, because the sulfur content is controlled.

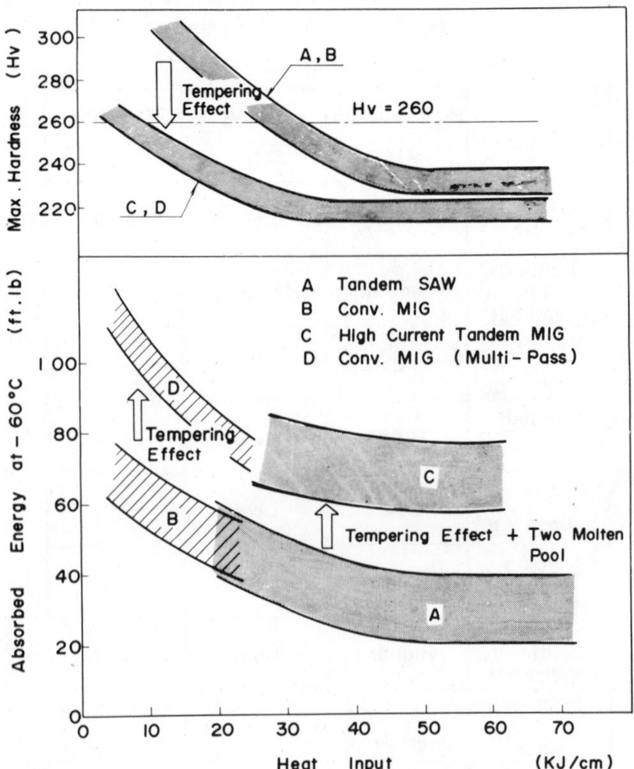

Figure 9: Effect of welding heat input on impact energy and maximum hardness of HAZ

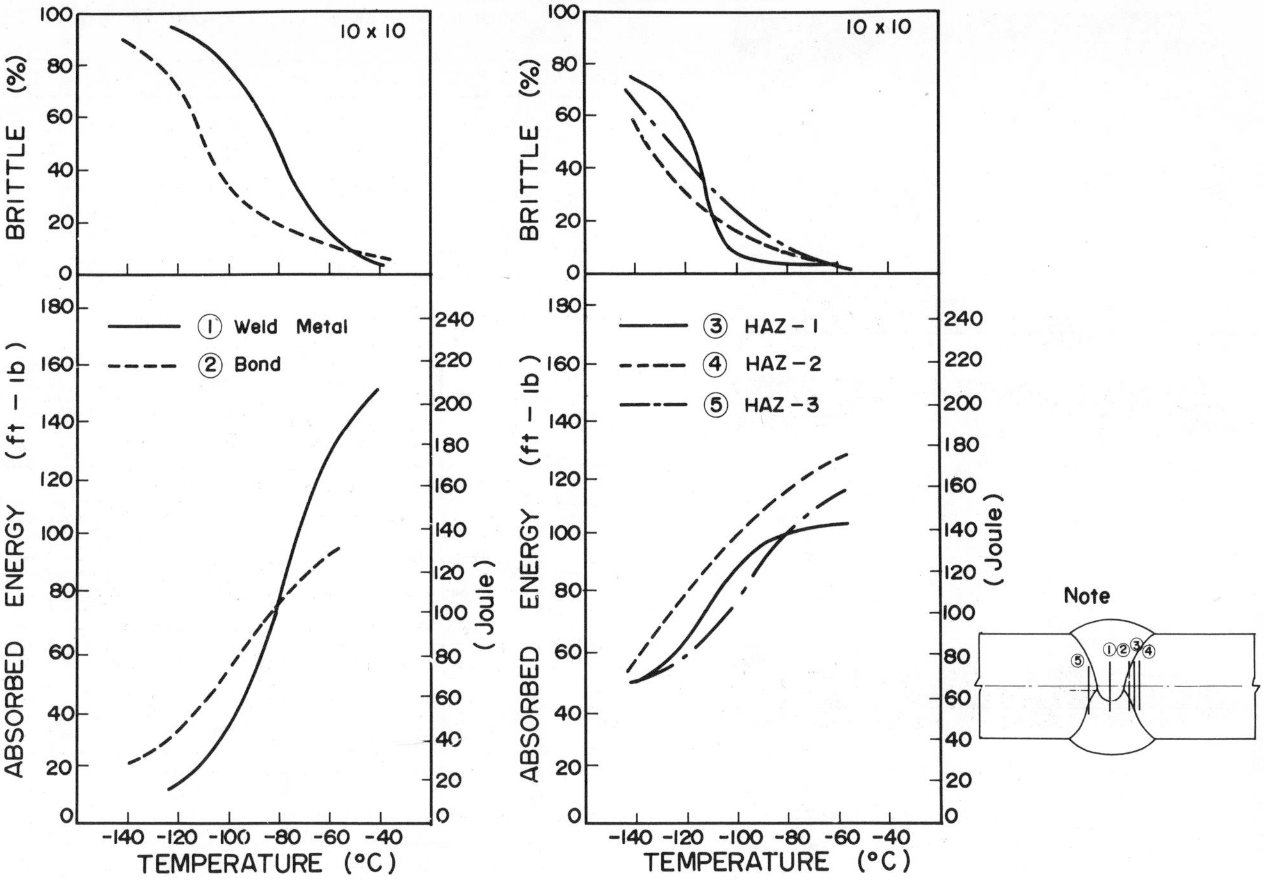

10 x 10
BRITTLE (%)
① Weld Metal
② Bond
③ HAZ - 1
④ HAZ - 2
⑤ HAZ - 3
ABSORBED ENERGY (ft - lb)
(Joule)
TEMPERATURE (°C)
Note
⑤ ①②③④

Figure 10: Charpy energy curves of weld and HAZ, welded by high current MIG process (3.5% Ni steel)

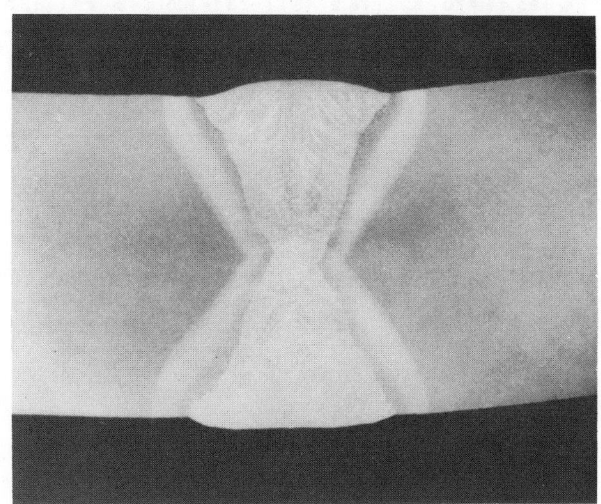

Figure 11: Macrostructure of High Current MIG weld in 48 in. (1220 mm) x 1.0 in.(254 mm) pipe of M steel (3.5% Ni)

10 x 10
BRITTLE (%)
= Body
= Weld
= HAZ
ABSORBED ENERGY (ft - lb)
(Joule)
TEST TEMPERATURE (°C)

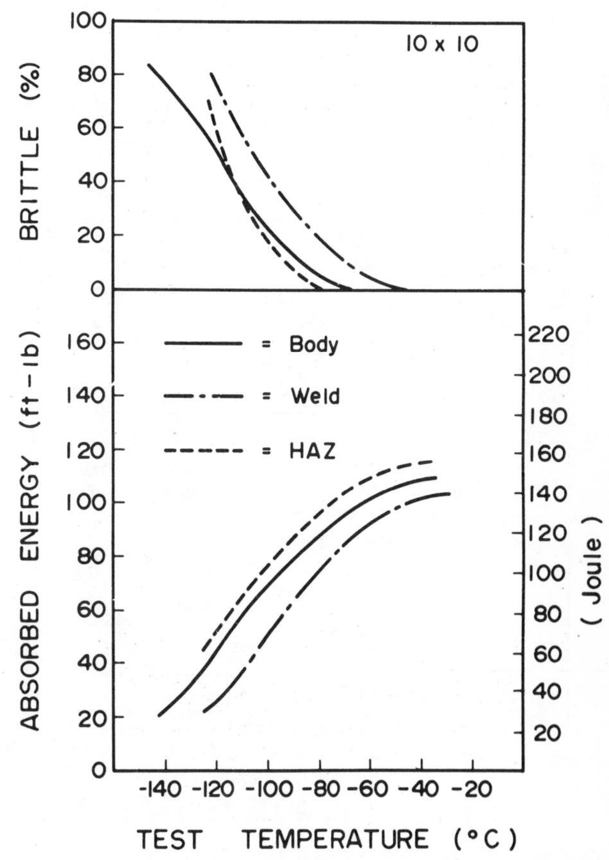

Figure 12: Charpy energy curves of quenched and tempered pipe (3.5% Ni steel)

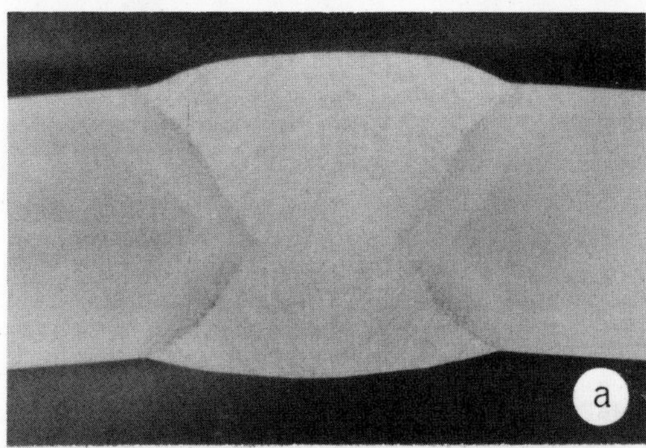

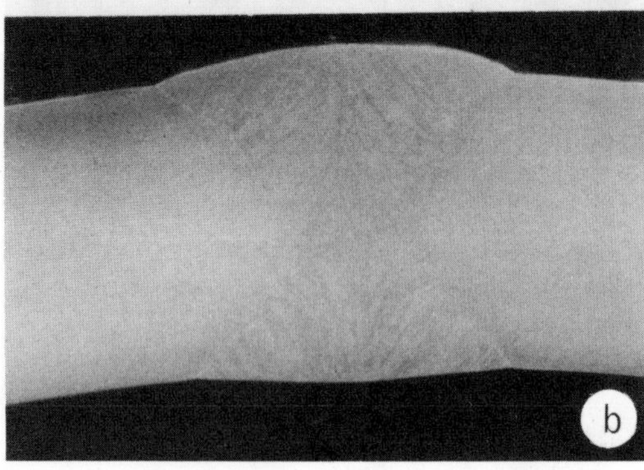

Figure 13: Macrostructure of Welds made (a) before and (b) after QT in 24 in.(610 mm) x 1.000 in.(25.4 mm) J1.4 Nisteel

Table.4 Chemical Composition and Mechanical Properties of Low Alloy X70 Pipes

(1) chemical composition

Steel	C	Si	Mn	P	S	Cu	Ni	Mo	Nb	V	Ceq*
A	0.07	0.30	1.46	0.013	0.005	0.01	0.25	0.14	0.04	0.09	0.38
B	0.06	0.30	1.45	0.013	0.005	0.01	0.25	0.15	0.04	0.09	0.36
C	0.08	0.29	1.58	0.013	0.004	0.21	0.25	—	0.04	0.10	0.39
D	0.07	0.28	1.61	0.012	0.004	0.21	0.25	—	0.04	0.09	0.39

$$* \quad Ceq = C + \frac{Mn}{6} + \frac{Cr + Mo + V}{5} + \frac{Cu + Ni}{15}$$

(2) mechanical properties

Steel	wall thickness mm	Transverse Tensile Test of Body				Charpy Absorbed Energy at -25°C			DWTT
		YS (MPa)	TS (MPa)	YR (%)	El (%)	Body (Joule)	Weld (Joule)	HAZ (Joule)	-25°C shear (%)
A	18.3	548	651	84	36.5	129	91	129	100
B	20.3	510	632	81	41.0	161	107	90	100
C	18.3	538	664	81	34.5	145	83	82	99
D	20.3	566	666	85	35.0	109	62	56	100

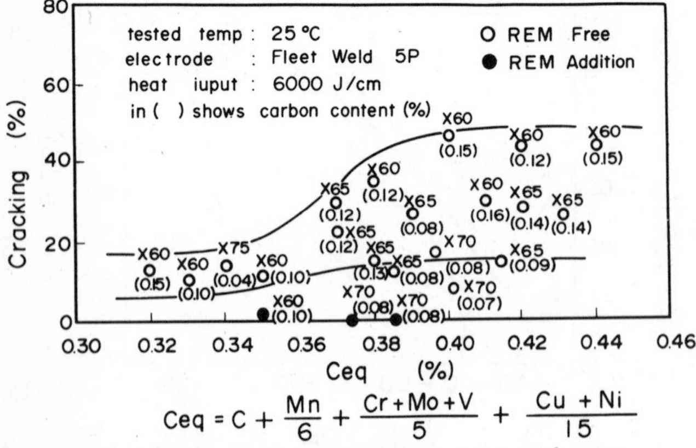

$$Ceq = C + \frac{Mn}{6} + \frac{Cr + Mo + V}{5} + \frac{Cu + Ni}{15}$$

Figure 14: Effect of carbon equivalent and rare earth metal (REM) treatment on under-bead cracking

Table5 Chemical Composition of Low Ni X65 Pipes

Steel	C	Si	Mn	P	S	Ni	Mo	Cr
I	0.09	0.35	1.29	0.011	0.005	0.72	0.17	—
J	0.09	0.25	1.17	0.014	0.007	1.41	0.17	—
K	0.06	0.28	1.44	0.012	0.006	2.10	0.16	—
L	0.06	0.27	1.36	0.012	0.008	2.85	0.26	0.50
M	0.06	0.30	0.72	0.013	0.006	3.52	0.06	0.28

Table.6 Properties of Heavy Wall Line Pipes Manufactured from Q−Q′−T Plate

Steel	W.T. (mm)		Tension				DWTT	Charpy 10x10			
							85%	Body		Weld	HAZ
			YS/MPa	TS/MPa	YR/%	El/%	SATT/°C	FATT/°C	vE/Joule	vE/Joule	vE/Joule
I 0.7Ni	25.4	Plate	457	602	75.8	53.9	−42	−107	204*	—	—
		Pipe	469	594	78.9	51.3	−32	−91	185*	76*	64*
J 1.4 Ni	25.4	Plate	508	628	81.0	49.0	−50	−112	173*	—	—
		Pipe	517	627	82.4	49.5	−36	−94	174*	110*	72*
K 2.1Ni	16.5	Plate	460	569	80.8	46.6	−85	−127	173**	—	—
		Pipe	450	581	77.6	44.6	−68	−114	168**	160**	69**
L 2.8 Ni	25.4	Plate	523	657	79.5	45.7	−91	−140	115**	—	—
		Pipe	529	666	79.4	43.7	−75	−139	90**	86**	66**

* Tested at −40°C ** Tested at −60°C

Table.7 Properties of Pipe QT.

Steel	W.T. (mm)	Tension				DWTT	Charpy 10x10			
						85%	Body		Weld	HAZ
		YS/MPa	TS/MPa	YR/%	El/%	SATT/°C	FATT/°C	vE*/Joule	vE*/Joule	vE*/Joule
M 3.5Ni	15.9	505	644	77.5	37.7	−83	−120	141	131	153
J 1.4Ni	25.4	470	622	76.2	46.1	−53	−105	149	141	127
	15.9	499	699	71.4	34.4	−61	−97	110	116	115

* Tested at − 60°C

The effect of a separation phenomenon, which generally appears on the fracture surface in heavily controlled-rolled steel, on lamellar tearing was investigated in a simulated "hot tapping" test (10) as shown in Figure 16. Tests were conducted on four pipes produced from controlled rolled and quenched-and-tempered plate. Sleeves were welded by fillet welding with both high cellulosic and low hydrogen wire at about 10°C.

The test results are shown in Table 8. (Here,

$$\text{"crack ratio"} = 1/n.\sum_i \ell_i/25 \times 100\%,$$

where ℓ_i are measured crack lengths and n is the number of specimens.) Hydrogen-induced delayed cracking, although slight, appeared in the high-cellulose welded portion, but lamellar tearing did not appear in any steel. It can be concluded that lamellar tearing is not affected by the separation phenomenon.

Crack-Opening-Displacement

The fracture initiation property of line pipes can be evaluated by the crack-opening displace-

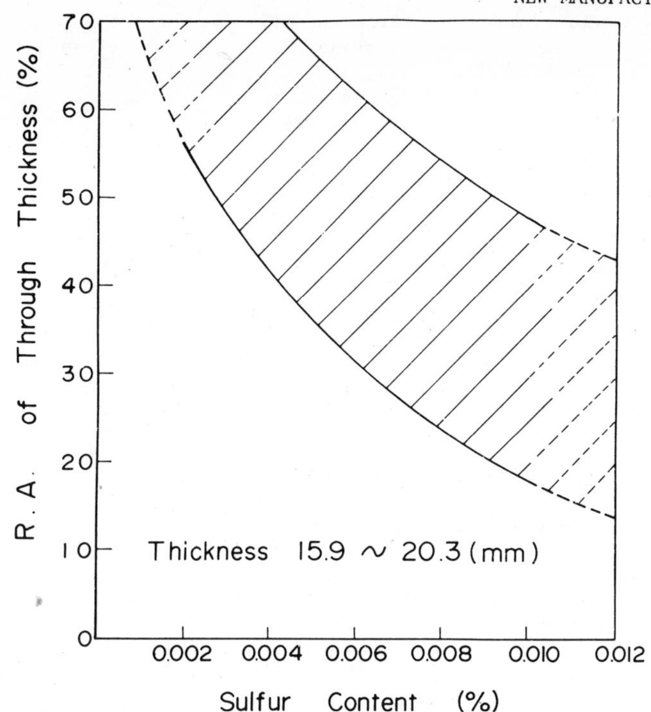

Figure 15: Effect of sulfur content on through-thickness properties

ment (COD) test. This property acquires special importance for line pipe which is used at a low design temperature, e.g. in cooling and pumping stations. The COD characteristics of submerged-arc welded and quenched-and-tempered pipes are shown in Figure 17. The base metals of both pipes show excellent COD values, but there is a remarkable difference between

Table 8 Test Results of Hot Tapping

Size		1219.2 mm O.D. x 20.3 mm W.T.						1219.2mm O.D.x25.4mm W.T.	
Material	Process	CR		CR		Soft CR		Plate QT	
	Ceq.	0.39		0.39		0.40		0.42	
Separation		normal		few		less		nothing	
Electrode		High Cellulose	Low Hydrogen	High Cellulose	Low Hydrogen	High Cellulose	Low Hydrogen	High Cellulose	Low Hydrogen
Crack Ratio	Underbead Cracking	1.5	none	1.2	none	2.6	none	3.1	none
	Lamellar - tear	none	none	none	none	none	none	none	none

$$\text{Crack Ratio} \equiv \frac{1}{n}\left(\sum_{1} \frac{\ell_1}{25}\right) \times 100$$

where, ℓ : crack length n : number of specimens

COD values in the HAZ of the two pipes, the quenched-and-tempered being superior.

SUMMARY

To meet the specific requirements for Arctic gas transmission line pipe, we have developed several new manufacturing processes. By judicious combination of these processes it is possible to manufacture all kinds of line pipe. The Q-Q'-T process, high current MIG process and pipe Q-T process, among others, have made it possible to manufacture heavy-walled line pipe for use at extremely low temperatures.

Figure 18 shows an optimum manufacturing process for line pipe which must not only meet the requirements of wall thickness and service temperature but also be uniform in quality throughout, including the weld metal and heat affected zones.

It has also been demonstrated that the line pipe manufactured by the processes described give excellent performance as Arctic grade line pipe.

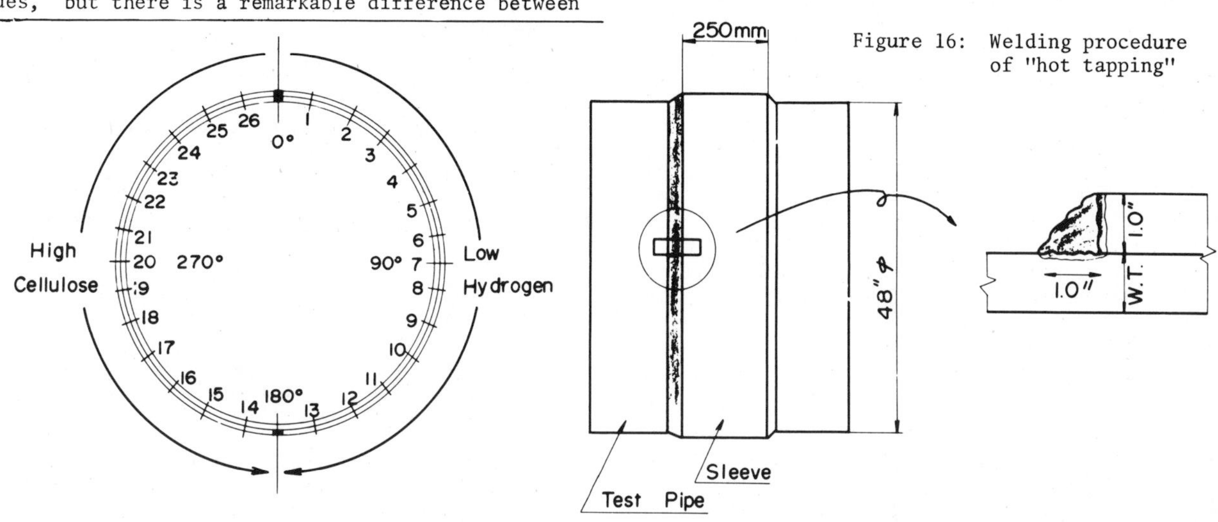

Figure 16: Welding procedure of "hot tapping"

Note a) Heat Input ; 20 KJ/in.

b) Leg Length for Welding ; 1.0" (25.4 mm)

c) Welding Method ; Vertical Down Welding

d) Welding Temperature ; Room Temp. (no preheating)

e) Welding Condition ; 100A 25V 19 cm/min.

f) Layer and Pass ; 6 Layers and 22 Passes

g) Metallographic Research ; at Position 1 ~ 26

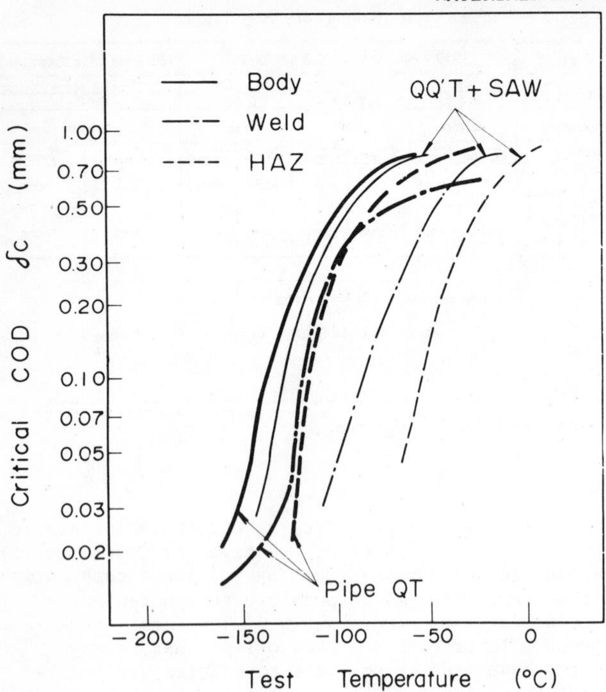

Figure 17: Results of COD test on pipes produced by pipe Q-T process and Q-Q'-T-SAW process (1.4% Ni steel, 25.4 mm thick)

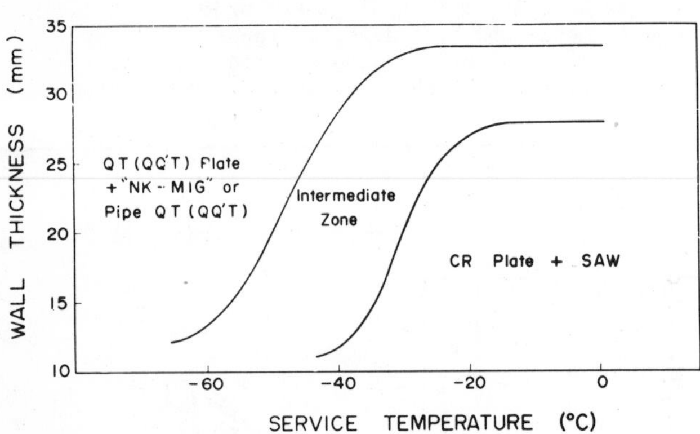

Figure 18: Scope of Pipe Production Process for Low Temperature Service (Required toughness in service: Body > 80 ft lbf (108 J); SA(DWTT) > 85%; Weld HAZ > 60 ft lbf (81 J))

REFERENCES

1. R. J. Eiber, Symposium on Line Pipe Research AGA L 30000, (1965), p. 83.
2. L. Luycky, J. R. Bell, A. McLean, and M. Korchynsky, Met. Trans., 1970, vol. 1, p. 3341.
3. H. Gondoh, S. Sugimura and S. Yamamoto, AWRA Symposium on "Development in Gas Pipeline Technology" May 1973.
4. J. J. Irani, D. Burton, J. D. Jones and A. B. Rothwell, ISI Publication 1967, vol. 104, p. 110.
5. J. D. Jones and A. B. Rothwell, ISI Publication 1968, vol. 108, p. 78.
6. I. Kozasu, C. Ouchi, T. Sampei and T. Okita, Proceedings, Microalloying '75. 1976, Union Carbide Corporation, New York, p. 120.
7. H. Matsubara, S. Matsumoto and A. Tanaka, Rev. Met., 1975, vol. 71, p. 359.
8. T. Yamaguchi, T. Osuka, T. Taira, and N. Iwasaki, Proceedings, Microalloying '75, 1976, Union Carbide Corporation, New York, p. 415.
9. T. Yamaguchi, K. Tsukada, J. Tanaka and T. Osuka, TetsutoHagane, 1975, vol. 12, p. S524.
10. T. Yamaguchi, T. Taira and K. Hirabayashi, Nippon Kokan Technical Report-Overseas, 41, Dec. 1974.

DISCUSSION

P. R. Slimmon (Bethlehem Steel): The production of plate for Arctic linepipe requires optimization of the steelmaker's facilities right from initial melting of the steel to the final processing of the plate into pipe. The authors are to be complimented for combining a number of these considerations into a single paper. In your discussion of REM additions, were the rare earths added as a ladle-addition or an ingot addition? How many pounds of rare earth were added per ton? Did the rare earth addition have any effect on plate surface quality?

H. Matsubara: Ingot addition at 220 g/t, for 0.004%S steel. We have no problems with plate surface quality.

P. R. Slimmon: In your controlled rolling procedure is there any special consideration with regard to slab reheating temperature and temperature distribution through the thickness of the slab?

H. Matsubara: Lower soaking temperature needs longer soaking time controlled to have uniform temperature distribution through the slab thickness. Usually the temperature of the preheating zone is set 50 deg C higher than the soaking zone for a controlled rolled slab.

P. R. Slimmon: Does your pipe contain a titanium addition for improving HAZ properties for high heat input welding techniques? Is the material ingot cast or strand cast?

H. Matsubara: In this case, Ti was not added and usually we do not use Ti for pipe. But we do make a high strength, high welding heat-input steel plate, containing Ti, for shipbuilding. Strand casting is better than ingot casting for Ti-containing steel.

P. R. Slimmon: Do you have the capability to produce large tonnages of quenched and tempered pipe?

H. Matsubara: The capacity is thousands of tons per month (depending on the pipe size).

E. Kranz (Mannesmannrohren-Werke): In the manufacturing of QT pipe how do you control the temperature during heating before quenching?

H. Matsubara: An infrared pyrometer is used. The temperature is controlled through the velocity of the pipe and electric power input.

E. Kranz: Do you use cold expansion after pipe QT, and how is the geometry of the QT pipe?

H. Matsubara: Cold expansion after QT is not applied. The geometrical condition of the QT pipe is satisfactory without sizing.

E. Kranz: Regarding the QT-pipe: what frequency do you use for induction heating?

H. Matsubara: 100 to 150 Hz.

E. Kranz: Using the induction heating system starting at room temperature, (that means far below the Curie-temperature) how is the heating curve due to the skin effect and how does that influence your temperature gradient through the wall?

H. Matsubara: I have no heating curve available here, but I am sure that the skin effect or temperature gradient through the wall thickness is very small, because of the uniform microstructure and hardness through the thickness.

E. Kranz: How do you manage the internal quenching, with special regard to getting no prequench in your heating zone before reaching the required temperature?

H. Matsubara: Pipe axis and the direction of nozzles for the cooling jet provide some gradient to prevent the water from flowing back to the heating zone.

G. D. Uttrachi (Union Carbide, Linde Div.): The high DC welding current used for the 2-wire MIG system will create inevitable arc blow problems, especially on the inside of the pipe. What have you done to overcome this problem?

H. Matsubara: Welding direction and direction of supplying DC current can be designed to protect against this problem.

C. A. Parrini(Italsider): What is the possible effect of vanadium in a low C, Mn, Mo, Nb(Cb) steel with very low nitrogen?

H. Matsubara: The yield strength of a pipe, measured with flattened specimens is lower than the plate yield strength on the material, as shown on Table 4.

C. A. Parrini: Was the limit of a maximum 25 mm plate thickness in controlled rolling due to rolling mill stand limits or to other considerations?

H. Matsubara: Rolling mill stand load limit.

F. G. Bourdillon (Usinor): In the improved controlled rolling diagram (Figure 4) the second stage of deformation is very small, corresponding to one or two passes at about 900°C. Is this small reduction stage determined by production considerations or is it a metallurgical problem? If it is a metallurgical problem, could you be more explicit?

H. Matsubara: The distance between roughing and finishing mill is approximately 70 m. Before entering the finishing mill the plate has thin scale on the surface. The actual surface temperature for controlled rolling is measured after one pass reduction to remove the thin scale. The operator of the finishing mill and the process computer confirm the temperature and then the third stage of rolling is started.

A. B. Rothwell (Noranda Research): How would you assess the relative economic and metallurgical benefits of two-head, high heat input MIG welding as opposed to four-head, low heat-input processes as already experimented with in Japan?

H. Matsubara: The shape of the weld bead (outside view and macrostructure) welded by the high current, two-head MIG, looks the same as an SAW bead. In the pipe mill, it is important to inspect carefully the welded portion with existing automatic NDT systems and techniques. Productivity of the high-current MIG is better.

J. E. Hood (Steel Company of Canada): Would you please comment on the need for pipe sizing after pipe quenching and tempering, especially at the ends of the pipe.

H. Matsubara: Usually the pipe sizing after pipe QT is not applied in our mill. The following items are controlled: 1) The precise analysis and estimation of the geometrical changes due to metallurgical phase transformation during heat treatment. 2) The pipe (before the heat treatment) is made to shape suited to the change and has no big residual stress. 3) The QT facilities were designed on a uniform heating and cooling basis. 4) The shorter the length of the heated zone of a pipe the better.

P. E. Bedford-Jones (Steel Company of Canada): The graph of weld process comparison showed that tandem MIG welding resulted in a slower welding speed than tandem submerged arc welding. What factors do you consider are significant in choosing the tandem MIG process over the submerged arc welding method?

H. Matsubara: The impact value of the weld metal and HAZ is much better with high current MIG than with SAW and the productivity is not so different. Heat input of the MIG is less than SAW (cf. Figure 8). For making the same deposit of weld metal, the MIG saves the additional heat input to melt flux in the SAW process. The oxygen content of weld metal with the MIG is less than SAW.

M. R. Krishnadev (Laval University): Your paper is timely and very interesting. Have you looked at the possibility of copper additions to your basic composition? We have developed HSLA steels with about 2% Cu, 1.5% Ni, and 0.1% Cb which have strength levels in the range X-100 to X-120, with remarkable toughness. (M. R. Krishnadev and A. Galibois, Proceedings, IV Interamerican Conference on Materials Technology, Caracas, Venezuela, 1975, CRDAT, Mexico, pp. 369-375.)

H. Matsubara: Thank you for your valued information. We have some possiblity of Cu additions, if we have no maximum limitation of Cu content in the specifications. Some new weld materials suited for such high Cu-Ni steels will be developed.

D. Fleckenstein (Union Carbide): Were all the data in this paper on rare earth metal treated steel?

H. Matsubara: The steels shown on Table 4 and Figure 1 are REM treated steels. The other steels are not REM treated. Usually we do not use REM steels.

D. Fleckenstein: Does the Q-Q'-T process also work for low alloy as it does for the low-Ni steels?

H. Matsubara: Only for low-Ni steels.

D. Fleckenstein: Was the whole pipe or just the weld zone subjected to the Q-T Process? Was it heated from the inside and out or just the outside?

H. Matsubara: The whole pipe is heat-treated. Pipe is heated from the outside.

L. Luyckx (Reactive Metals and Alloys): Congratulations to the authors for the tremendous amount of development work conducted to optimize line pipe quality at minimum cost and to Hiroyoshi Matsubara for a lively and clear presentation. My questions concern the use of rare earth metals (REM) in your steels, although I noted that you are referring only to experimental quantities of REM-treated steel. Does the improvement of transverse shelf energy introduced by REM in a 0.003%S steel justify the commercial use of REM?

H. Matsubara: Frankly speaking, I think it is difficult to justify the commercial use of REM to improve only the transverse Charpy value. But the improvements of through-thickness properties and under-bead cracking will justify the commercial use of REM in future.

L. Luyckx: Is the mechanism of impact toughness improvement as shown in Figure 1 still exclusively sulfide shape control or are there other effects?

H. Matsubara: Just sulfide shape control, I think.

L. Luyckx: Did your mould practice involve bottom pouring or top pouring? What kind of protection?

H. Matsubara: Bottom pouring. Argon gas is used for protection.

L. Luyckx: What is the maximum sulfur level at which REM additions produce acceptable inclusion contamination and segregation?

H. Matsubara: I think 0.007% S.

L. Luyckx: Would you be confident in using REM in slab casting, if so, at what sulfur level?

H. Matsubara: We do not use REM in slab casting yet.

L. Luyckx: Can calcium do the same job as REM in this application?

H. Matsubara: We are now trying to use calcium for thick plates (3 in. (76 mm) and over) and also the controlled rolled plates (1 in. (25 mm) and less in thickness).

HIGH-STRENGTH STEELS FOR ARCTIC PIPELINES

J. D. Boyd
Physical Metallurgy Research Laboratories
Canada Centre for Mineral and
Energy Technology (CANMET)
568 Booth St.
Ottawa, Canada K1A 0G1

There are strong incentives for increasing the yield strength of linepipe steel beyond the current level for Arctic pipelines, which is approximately 480 MPa (70 ksi). Direct quenched and tempered low-alloy steel offers the best possibility for producing such high-strength linepipe, from the points of view of both metallurgy and production. Experimental results indicate that the required strength and impact toughness can be obtained in direct quenched and tempered 13 mm (0.5 in.) plate of a low-carbon manganese molybdenum niobium (columbium) steel. The excellent strength/toughness combination is attributed to utilizing the maximum benefit of ferrite grain refinement such that only a small part of the total yield strength is provided by precipitation hardening or dislocation substructural strengthening.

INTRODUCTION

There are strong incentives for increasing the yield strength of linepipe steel beyond the current level for Arctic pipelines, which is approximately 480 MPa (70 ksi). The ratio of gas transmission rate to the weight of steel could be increased by increasing operating pressure, and there is a growing demand for pipe for high stress applications such as offshore pipelines (3). Significant advantages could also be realized with the present operating parameters by using high-strength linepipe having reduced wall thickness. This paper discusses the motivation for, and the possibility of producing 690 MPa (100 ksi) yield strength linepipe steel with the necessary toughness and weldability for Arctic pipelines. Results of pertinent laboratory experiments on three high-strength low-alloy (HSLA) steels are presented.

MICROSTRUCTURE AND MECHANICAL PROPERTIES OF LINEPIPE STEEL

The important property requirements, for HSLA steels in general, and linepipe steels in particular are (4):

1. high yield strength
2. high resistance to brittle cleavage and low-energy ductile fractures, as well as a low transition temperature
3. good weldability
4. good cold formability
5. low cost

These properties are attained in current "Arctic" grades of linepipe steel due to development in two major areas; composition and hot rolling. Generally, the steel is low carbon, low sulphur, fully deoxidized, rare-earth treated, and contains microalloy additions of elements such as Nb, V or Ti. The skelp is produced by controlled rolling followed by air cooling, although controlled cooling is sometimes employed. The principal metallurgical effect of controlled rolling is the refinement of the ferrite grain size (d), which has the powerful effect of simultaneously increasing the yield strength (YS) and decreasing the impact transition temperature (ITT). Both properties exhibit a linear variation with $d^{-1/2}$, such that typically the YS increases 15-20 MPa (2-3 ksi) and the ITT decreases 10-15 deg C for a unit increase in $d^{-1/2}$ ($mm^{-1/2}$) (1,2).

For a ferrite grain size of 5 μm, which is representative of the finest grain size available in current linepipe steels, the data in Figure 1 indicate that approximately 300 MPa (43 ksi) of the total yield strength is attributable to grain refinement. This calculation is not rigorous for two reasons. First, the experimental YS versus $d^{-1/2}$ relations in Figure 1 inevitably include effects of other strengthening components, such as precipitation and substructure, which change unavoidably as the grain size is varied. Secondly, it is not valid to assume that the various strengthening components are linearly additive, except in the special case where glide dislocations encounter a few strong obstacles interspersed among many weak ones (7). However, for the purpose of estimating the relative magnitudes of the different strengthening mechanisms, these two inaccuracies can be ignored. Thus, for a 480 MPa (70 ksi) YS linepipe steel with a 5 μm ferrite grain size, approximately 180 MPa (26 ksi) of the total YS is attributable to the combined effect of mechanisms such as the intrinsic strength of the ferrite lattice, solid solution elements, precipitation and substructure (both subgrains and unrecovered dislocation arrays). The latter two mechanisms are especially important because of the almost universal use of microalloy elements, Nb, V, or Ti, and low finish-rolling temperatures in order to obtain the required ferrite grain size. As a consequence of these practices, the final microstructure contains precipitates of alloy carbide or nitride (or carbonitride), and a substructure.

The conclusion to be drawn from this is that a remarkable advance in the technology of controlled-rolled HSLA steel would be required to be able to produce a microstructure having a ferrite grain size

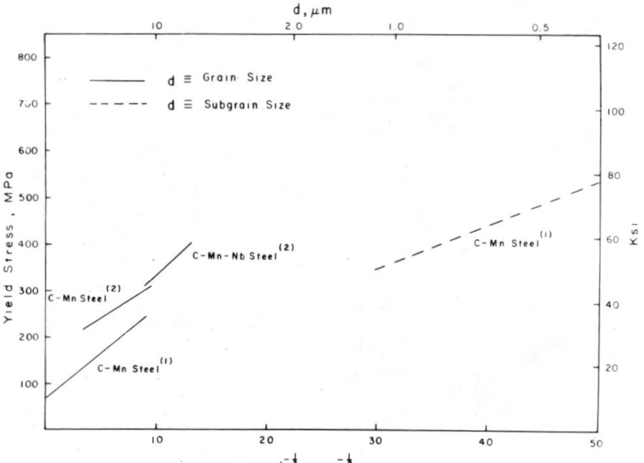

Figure 1: The variation in yield strength with ferrite grain size and subgrain size for C-Mn and C-Mn-Nb(Cb) steel

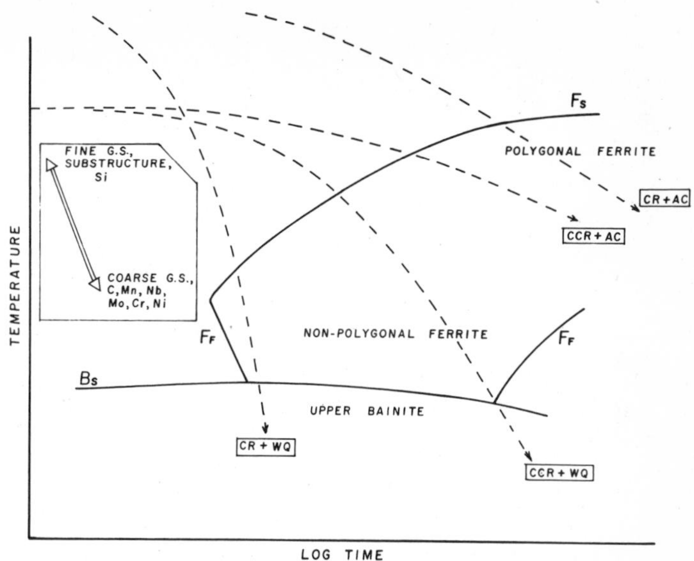

Figure 2: Schematic continuous-cooling-transformation diagram for low-carbon steels, (solid lines). Broken lines indicate transformation paths for different rolling schedules and cooling rates

corresponding to a 690 MPa (100 ksi) YS, i.e. 1-2 μm. Failing that, the development of higher-strength steels will depend upon utilizing the strengthening effects of precipitates and unrecovered dislocation arrays. Unfortunately, strengthening due to subgrains, precipitates or dislocations does not include the unequivocal decrease in the ITT that accompanies grain refinement. The data in Figure 1 on the variation in YS with subgrain size indicates a maximum strength increment of approximately 150 MPa (22 ksi) due to this mechanism for a subgrain size of 0.5 μm. Decreasing the subgrain size has little effect on the ITT (1,2). Current evidence would suggest that the unit cleavage process is more closely related to the ferrite grain size or bainite packet size, rather than to the size of individual subgrains or laths (8-10). It is well established that precipitation hardening increases the ITT, a figure of 0.3-0.5 deg C for each 1 MPa increase in yield stress being generally accepted for hardening by NbC(CbC) or VC (2). However the suggestion has been made that this problem could be alleviated by ensuring that the precipitate size distribution is such that glide dislocations cannot shear the particles (11), and there is some supporting experimental evidence (12). The specific effect of an unrecovered dislocation array on the ITT has not been precisely determined, but it has been estimated that the ITT increases approximately 0.2 deg C for every 1 MPa increase in YS due to this strengthening mechanism (2).

The various microstructural constituents referred to above and their relation to the processing variables can be illustrated with reference to the schematic continuous-cooling-transformation (CCT) diagram shown in Figure 2. In this diagram the F_S and F_F curves refer to the start and finish of the austenite-ferrite transformation, and the B_S line represents the start of the austenite-upper bainite transformation. (Note that the F_F lines do not necessarily indicate 100% transformation). At the higher transformation temperatures, the final microstructure is a mixture of pearlite and polygonal ferrite (Figure 3a). Transmission electron microscopy (TEM) shows that the ferrite typically consists of recrystallized grains, subgrains having a very low dislocation density, and small (∿ 100 Å) intragranular

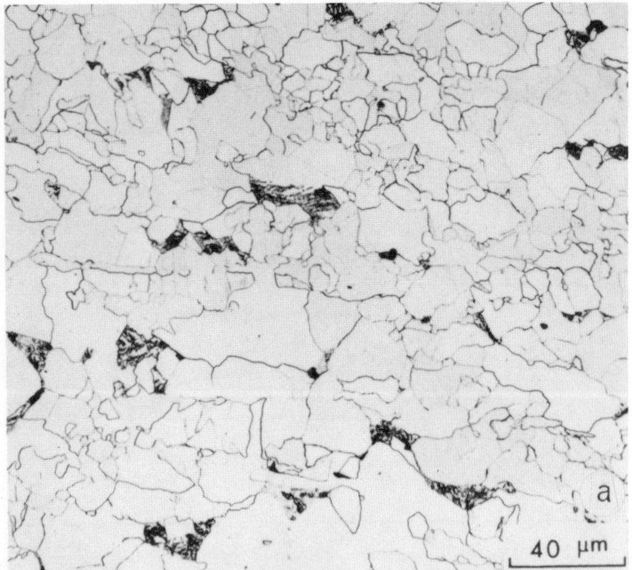

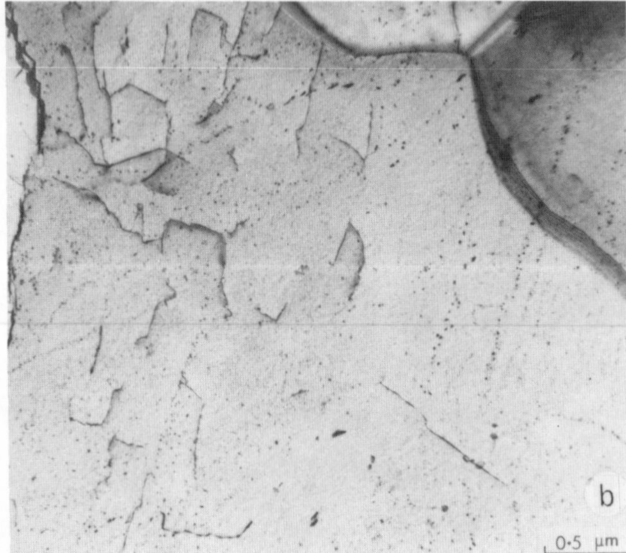

Figure 3: Typical polygonal ferrite microstructure. (a) optical (b) TEM

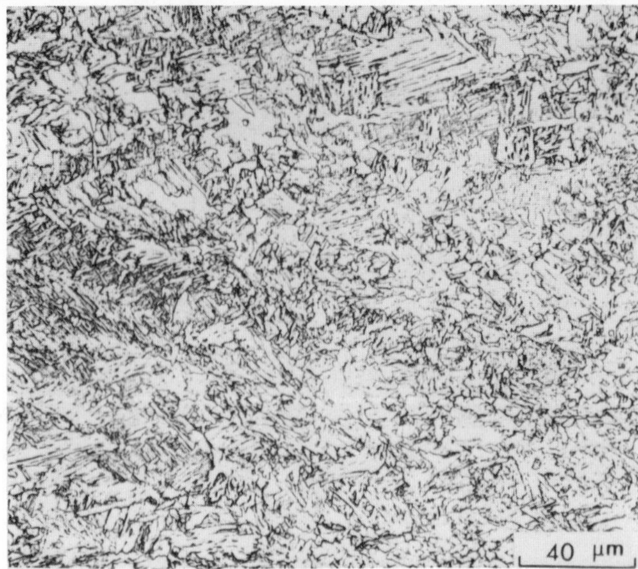

Figure 4: Typical acicular ferrite microstructure (optical).

precipitates (Figure 3b). With decreasing transformation temperature, the nucleation rate of ferrite grains increases and the migration rate of low energy interfaces decreases. Consequently, the ferrite grain size is reduced, and the grain morphology becomes more acicular (Figure 4). This characterization of the microstructure as polygonal or acicular represents the limit of resolution of optical microscopy. TEM is required for a more detailed analysis. For example, microstructures which cannot be distinguished optically from that shown in Figure 4 can be classified by TEM into two main types: 1) Nonpolygonal ferrite, which consists of a mixture of small, equiaxed and elongated ferrite subgrains, containing a dislocation density varying from medium to high (Figure 5a); 2) Upper bainite, which consists of packets of parallel ferrite laths containing a very high dislocation density, with layers of cementite, and possibly retained austenite, at the lath boundaries (Figure 5b). The transformation mechanism for the acicular microstructures is not precisely understood. There is a point of view that the variation in microstructure from equiaxed ferrite subgrains, through

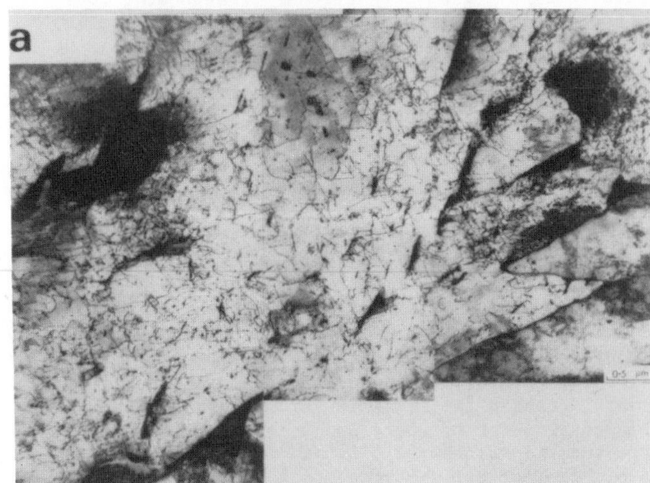

Figure 5: Representative microstructures (TEM) showing (a) non-polygonal ferrite, (b) upper bainite

elongated subgrains to upper bainite is indicative of a continuous variation in transformation mechanism, as opposed to a sharp demarcation between a diffusion-controlled and a shear transformation. However, the fact that: 1) the microstructures can be distinguished by TEM, (upper bainite is distinguished from elongated subgrains of nonpolygonal ferrite since the former has a much higher aspect ratio and higher dislocation density than the latter); 2) there is a measurable change in the thermal expansion which is represented as a sharp line between nonpolygonal ferrite and upper bainite on the CCT diagram (Figure 2) (13), and 3) the ITT for structures containing upper bainite is generally higher than for nonpolygonal ferrite (4,14,15), suggests that the distinction between these two microstructures is real and ought to be maintained.

In practice, a fine ferrite grain size is obtained by a combination of two techniques: 1) by means of grain-refining additions, such as Nb, (Cb) and controlled rolling, it is ensured that the austenite grain size is as small as possible prior to the austenite-ferrite transformation, and 2) the transformation path (Figure 2) is controlled to give the optimum microstructure. It has been determined for controlled-rolled air-cooled plate that the best combination of strength, toughness, weldability and economy is obtained by having most of the transformation occur low in the nonpolygonal ferrite region of the CCT diagram, but avoiding upper bainite as much as possible. The location of the ferrite transformation curves is a sensitive function of the austenite condition immediately prior to transformation, which is defined by its composition, grain size, dislocation substructure and precipitate distribution. (The effect of each of these parameters on the curves is indicated by the arrows in the upper left of Figure 2). Therefore for a fixed cooling rate, (air-cooled plate, for example) the desired transformation path is obtained by controlling the austenite condition, i.e., by manipulating the composition and the rolling schedule.

THE CASE FOR QUENCHED AND TEMPERED STEEL

Clearly, the ability to control the final microstructure, and hence the mechanical properties,

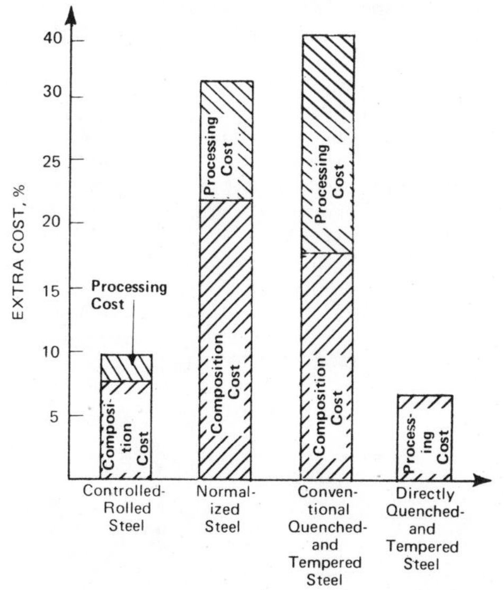

Figure 6: Extra composition and processing costs for producing specially treated plates compared to the production of carbon-manganese steels of the same quality and size (from ref. 6)

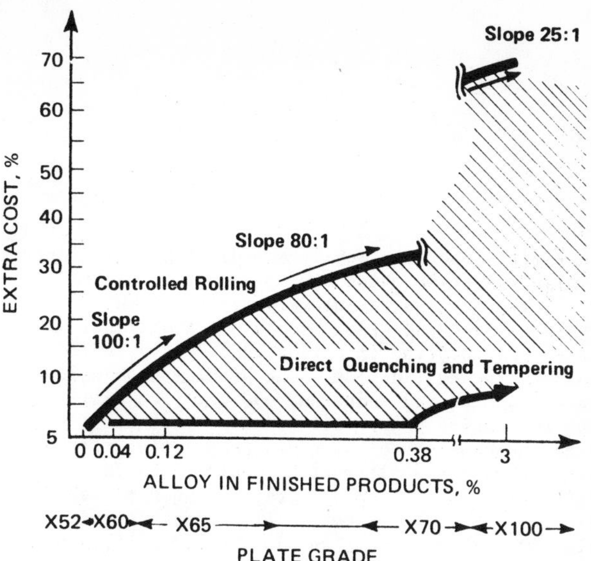

Figure 7: Extra cost of alloying as a function of grade of steel for controlled rolling, and direct quenching and tempering (from ref. 6)

is greatly enhanced by the facility to increase the cooling rate after the final rolling pass (i.e. direct quenching), and subsequently to heat treat the plate (tempering). Figure 2 shows that by direct quenching it is possible to achieve a finer ferrite microstructure, and hence a better strength/toughness ratio for a given steel composition than by controlled rolling alone, i.e., there would be no increase in alloy mix costs, and on the basis of composition, there should be no significant change in weldability. Another way of looking at it is that by direct quenching and tempering, the maximum benefit of ferrite grain refinement can be achieved at the lowest alloy content. This minimizes the proportion of the total YS that must be provided by the less desirable mechanisms (in terms of effect on the ITT), of precipitation, subgrain and dislocation strengthening in order to reach the 690 MPa (100 ksi) strength level.

At present, the quench and temper process appears to be the most practical way to produce high-strength linepipe steels (3,6,16), and there is an increasing amount of research and development work in this area. Parrini et al (6) have considered in detail the relative costs of producing high-strength plate by various methods. Figure 6 shows their data on relative alloy costs and processing costs for producing 20 mm (0.79 in.) plate having a 441 MPa (64 ksi) YS and a Charpy impact energy at -20°C of 45 J (33 ft lbf). In Figure 7, the extra cost of alloying is shown as a function of both the grade of steel and the total amount of alloy added. These data indicate that the direct quench and temper process is more or less competitive with controlled rolling for grade X-65. Since controlled rolling is invariably used for linepipe steel at this strength level, there must be overriding production advantages for this method. For example, although it has required an upgrading of the rolling facilities for most producers, the resulting increases in production rates have been very high. The introduction of direct quenching would require additional capital investment, and would reduce the overall production rate. However, Figure 7 indicates that the alloy costs for controlled rolling increase very sharply between grades X-70 and X-100, and this provides a strong incentive for utilizing direct quenching and tempering. There are also anticipated production problems associated with controlled rolling higher-strength steels, viz.,

Table 1

Chemical Analyses of Experimental Steels, Wt Pct

C	Mn	Ni	Mo	Cr	Cu	Nb (Cb)	V	Al	Si	P	S	Ce	La
.06	1.43	.075	.010	.030	.010	.070	-	.070	.11	.010	<.005	-	-
.046	1.88	.083	.27	.055	.002	.072	-	.065	.20	.014	<.005	115*	48*
.11	1.15	.083	.26	-	-	.020	.060	.058	.34	.011	<.005	570*	268*

* Parts per million by weight

higher mill loads, extremely stringent process control, and high rejection rates.

The data represented in Figures 6 and 7 pertain to the production of plate. Additional factors are involved in estimating comparative costs of manufacturing linepipe. One problem with using direct quenched and tempered, 690 MPa (100 ksi) YS plate for making heavy-wall linepipe is that it would exceed the capacity of many of the existing pipe mills. A possible alternative would be to form the pipe from the as-quenched plate, and then to heat treat the pipe. For example, if the as-quenched plate has a YS of less than 550 MPa (80 ksi), heavy-wall pipe could be formed from this material on existing equipment. The final properties would have to be developed by tempering the pipe, which would also act as a post-weld heat treatment. The principal disadvantage of this approach is that a large proportion of the total YS (approx. 20%) would have to be provided by precipitation hardening.

A different processing sequence, which has been developed by some European and Japanese companies for grade X-70 linepipe, is to form the pipe from as-rolled plate, and then re-austenitize, quench and temper the pipe. This results in extremely good impact toughness, but is doubtful if a yield strength much in excess of 550 MPa (80 ksi) could be reached by this technique. The general experience has been that the best combination of strength and toughness at higher strength levels is obtained by direct quenching (6,17). However, there may be some production advantages to quenching and tempering the pipe. One company is experimenting with induction heating (5), which may permit a high austenitizing temperature with little grain coarsening, but details of the heating cycles have not been reported.

MECHANICAL PROPERTIES OF QUENCHED AND TEMPERED HIGH STRENGTH LOW-ALLOY STEELS

Figure 8. View of laboratory rolling mill, with the water-spray quench apparatus in the foreground

Experimental

Experimental HSLA steels have been processed at the CANMET laboratories to simulate the hot rolling, direct quenching and tempering of plate. The three compositions which have been investigated to date are given in Table 1. Slabs of each steel, weighing approximately 20 kg (44 lb), were hot rolled to 13 mm (0.5 in.) plate on a 450 x 450 mm (18 x 18 in.) two-high reversing mill. The rolling schedule consisted of two roughing passes immediately after the slab was removed from the soaking furnace, a hold in air to approximately 900°C, and a final series of passes finishing at approximately 800°C. At least 50 per cent of the total reduction was done below 900°C, and the reduction per pass for the final 2 passes was approximately 25 per cent. After the final rolling pass, the plate was directly quenched to room temperature by means of a quench facility located at the end of the runout table (Figure 8). The cooling rate at the mid-thickness of the plate was 70 to 90 deg C/s, which is comparable to that for a commercial roller quench facility. Tensile and Charpy impact tests were made using specimens from plate in the as-quenched condition, and from plate which had been tempered at 600°C. More details on the processing and testing of this material have been reported elsewhere (14).

Results

Complete stress-strain curves for each of the steels and conditions tested are shown in Figure 9, and the corresponding full-Charpy impact transition curves are shown in Figure 10. The important tensile and impact properties and processing data for each steel are summarized in Table 2.

All three steels exhibited continuous yielding behaviour (rounded stress-strain curves) in the as-quenched condition. This is consistent with the results reported by other laboratories (16), and is attributed to the high mobile dislocation density in the acicular ferrite structures (Figure 5). After tempering, the hardening rate was sharply decreased in all cases, and there was evidence of discontinuous yielding. The magnitude of the yield drop and the Lüders strain decreased in the order of increasing yield stress for the three experimental steels. The strength increment due to tempering was in all cases relatively small (23 to 48 MPa). This is attributed to the combined effects of softening due to recovery of the as-quenched substructure (Figure 11), and hardening due to a limited amount of alloy carbonitride precipitation.

The Charpy curves show a general decrease in shelf energy with increasing YS for both the as-quenched and tempered conditions. Since a definite shelf energy is not shown in each case, the impact energies associated with ductile fracture are quantitatively compared in Table 2 by considering the Charpy energy values at 0°C. The 55 J impact transition temperatures show significant differences among the three experimental steels. The two steels with the lowest carbon contents had ITT's less than -70°C, whereas the 0.11C steel had an unacceptably high

Table 2

Mechanical Properties of Direct Quenched and Tempered 13 mm Plate (transverse specimens)

		As-Quenched				As-Tempered (600°C)			
Steel	Finishing Temp., °C	Quench Rate deg C/sec	Cv at 0°C J (ft lbf)	ITT (55J) °C	YS MPa (ksi)	Tempering Treatment	Cv at 0°C J (ft lbf)	ITT (55J) °C	YS MPa (ksi)
.06C-1.4Mn-.07Nb	825	70	190 (140)	-70	552* (80.0)	6 h	151 (111)	-71	575** (83.3)
.05-1.9Mn-.3Mo-.07 .07Nb	805	90	130 (96)	-78	689* (99.8)	10 h	134 (99)	-91	737** (106.8)
.11C-1.2Mn-.3Mo-.02Nb-.06V	780	70	56 (41)	0	729* (105.7)	10 h	33 (24)		776* (112.5)

* 0.2% offset yield stress; ** lower yield stress

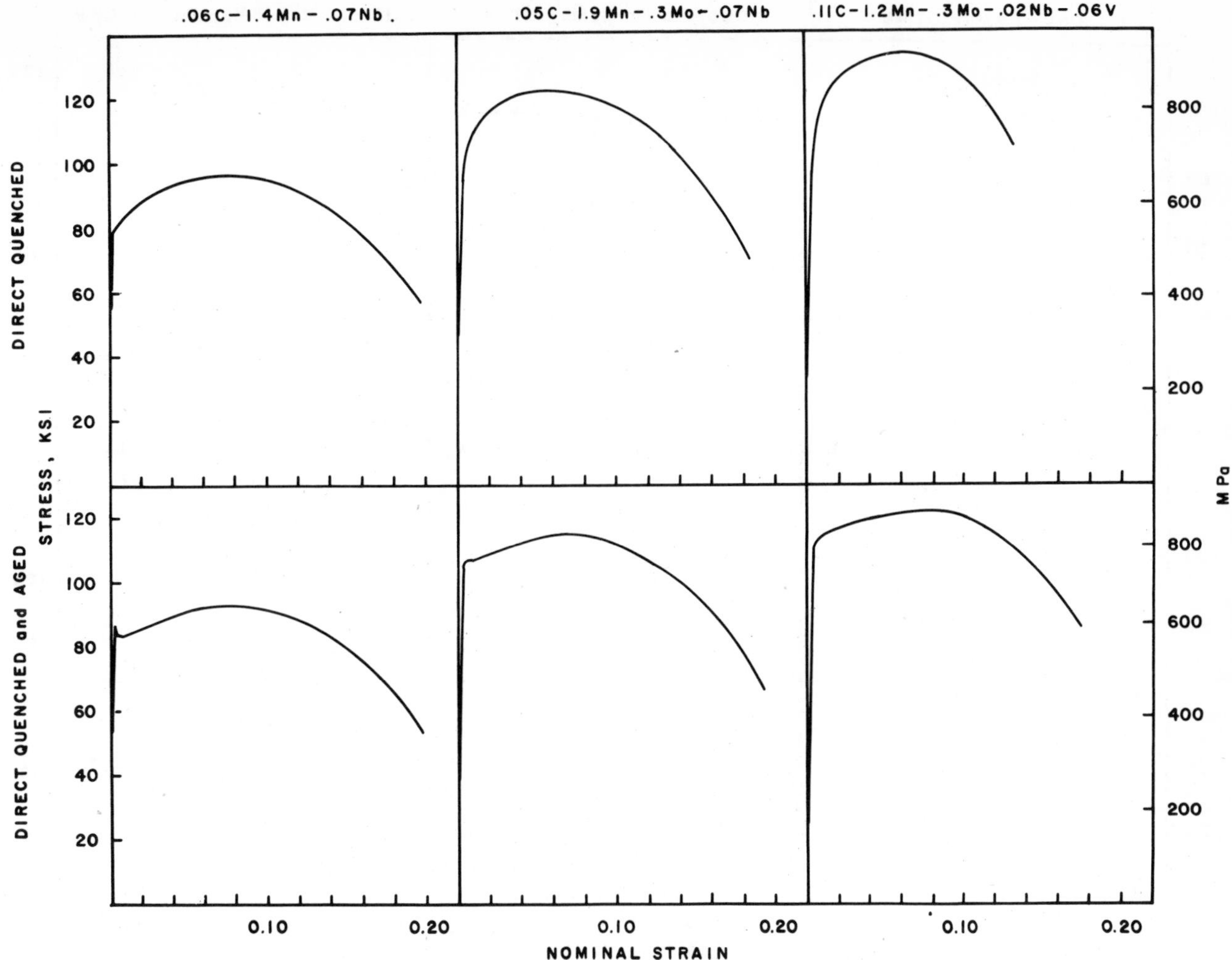

Figure 9. Stress-strain curves for direct quenched and tempered 13 mm plate

ITT and extremely low impact energies. Furthermore, the ITT for both of the lowest carbon steels decreased upon tempering. The largest positive effect of heat treatment on impact toughness was exhibited by the Mn-Mo-Nb(Cb) steel which had a 55 J ITT of -91°C and a shelf energy of 150 J in the tempered condition.

DISCUSSION

The best combination of strength and toughness was obtained in the Mn-Mo-Nb(Cb) steel in the direct-quenched and tempered condition. The reason for the simultaneous increase in strength and toughness during tempering has not been investigated in detail. One possibility is that the decrease in the free-nitrogen concentration in the ferrite lattice due to niobium (columbium) carbonitride precipitation during tempering and the recovery of the dislocation sub-structure produce a decrease in the ITT which exceeds any embrittling effect of the precipitates themselves. It is also probably significant that precipitation hardening and substructural strengthening account for a small fraction of the total YS. Thus, in accord with the principle expounded above, optimum toughness has been achieved by maximum utilization of ferrite grain refinement as a strengthening mechanism. The microstructure of all three steels consisted of a mixture of non-polygonal ferrite (Figure 5a) and upper bainite (Figure 5b). The optical microstructure in all cases was fine-grained acicular ferrite similar to Figure 4.

Although the strength and toughness of the Mn-Mo-Nb(Cb) steel in the as-quenched condition are not as good as in the tempered condition, the YS is still close to 690 MPa and the 55 J ITT of -78°C is quite acceptable for Arctic linepipe. Furthermore significant advantages in pipe manufacture are claimed for steels which have a continuous yielding, rapid work hardening stress-strain behaviour (21). Therefore, consideration should also be given to using the Mn-Mo-Nb(Cb) steel in the as-quenched condition for high-strength linepipe.

For the purpose of comparison with these results, a summary of published data on direct quenched and tempered HSLA steels is given in Table 3. The data illustrate the generally high impact energies and low ITT's which can be obtained at strength levels in the range 550 to 690 MPa (80 to 100 ksi), for very low alloy steels. However, the properties obtained with the Mn-Mo-Nb(Cb) steel in the present work are superior to all of the steels listed in Table 3. One important factor is the quench rate, which with one exception, was higher than that for all the previous investigations. It is particularly noteworthy to compare the present results with those for the Mn-Mo-Nb(Cb) steel studied by Morrow (16). The composition and finish-rolling temperatures are similar in the two investigations, but the as-quenched YS reported by Morrow (499 MPa) is much less than that found in the present work (689 MPa). This is attributed to the large difference in the quench rates for the two cases. Note also that in Morrow's case there

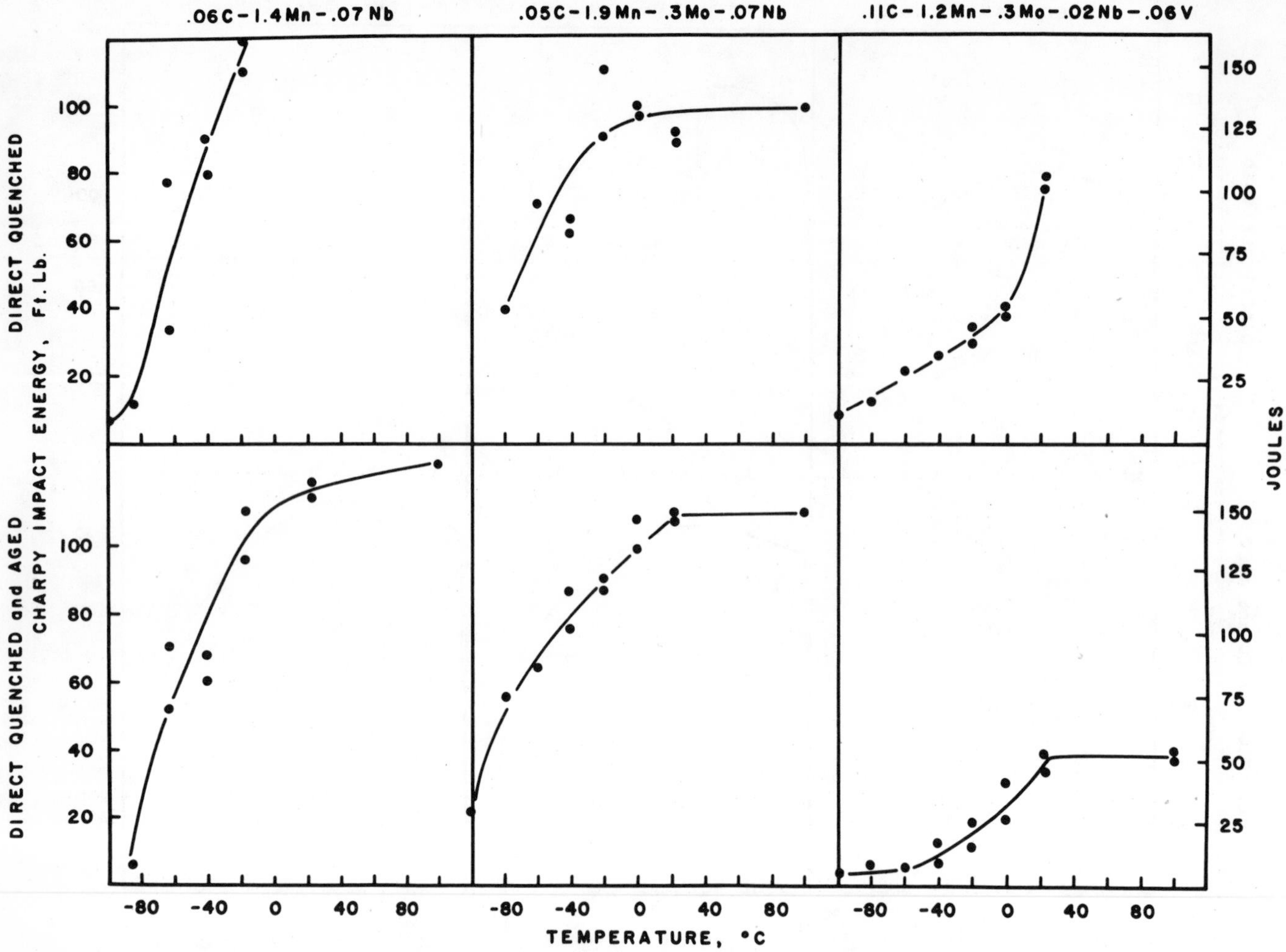

Figure 10. Charpy impact transition curves for direct quenched and tempered 13 mm plate

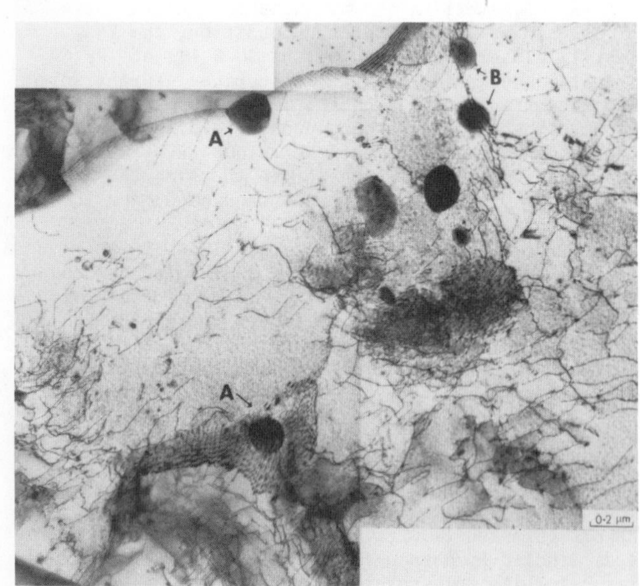

Figure 11. 0.06C-1.4Mn-0.07Nb(Cb) steel, solution treated 1 h at 950°C, quenched and aged 100 h at 600°C

was a large (120 MPa) strength increment during tempering, and a corresponding increase in the ITT, which indicates an embrittling effect due to precipitation. The published data for re-austenitized, quenched and tempered steels (Table 4) show excellent values of impact toughness, but the YS values are consistently less than for equivalent compositions given a direct quench and temper treatment. These data also indicate that extra alloying would be required to achieve a YS of 690 MPa in a re-austenitized, quenched and tempered steel.

In addition to the strength, yielding behaviour and impact toughness of the quenched and tempered steels, two other properties pertinent to linepipe should also be investigated; namely weldability and environmental cracking susceptibility. There is concern that the microstructure of a quenched and tempered steel, which is the result of a fairly complex thermo-mechanical cycle, will anneal rapidly even in the low-temperature region of the weld heat-affected zone (HAZ), resulting in a loss of strength and toughness. Parrini et al (6) have reported results of testing specimens of direct quenched and tempered steels which were given simulated welding thermal cycles (Gleeble). These results indicate a general decrease in strength and crack-initiation toughness (COD test) for the simulated HAZ material. Another microstructural effect in micro-alloyed steels which is pertinent to weld HAZ's is the observation that large cementite particles form during tempering, due to their much faster coarsening rate compared

Table 3

Data on Quenched and Tempered HSLA Steels
(Direct Quench and Temper)

Composition, Wt. Pct.										As-Quenched			As-Tempered			
C	Mn	Ni	Mo	V	Nb (Cb)	N	Thickness, mm(in.)	Finishing Temp. °C	Quench Rate deg C/sec	Cv at 0°C J (ft lbf)	ITT (55J) °C	YS MPa (ksi)	Cv at 0°C J (ft lbf)	ITT (55J) °C	YS MPa (ksi)	Ref.
.05	1.74	-	-	-	.05	-	19 (.75)	845	8	298 (220)	-112†	430 (62.4)	317 (234)	-79†	540 (78.3)	16
.07	1.43	-	-	-	.085	-	13 (.50)	840	100				140*** (109)	-110	561 (81.3)	18
.07	1.43	-	-	-	.085	-	13 (.50)	850	50				223*** (165)	-95	571 (82.8)	18
.05	1.52	-	-	-	.08	-	25 (.98)	950	22				164* (121)	-70	650 (94.2)	17
.07	1.60	-	-	-	.07	-	12 (.47)	900	40				170*** (125)	-60†	677 (98.1)	6
.09	1.31	.43		-	.03	-	19 (.75)	915					228** (168)		512 (74.3)	5
.05	1.75	-	.32	-	.05	-	19 (.75)	845	8	271 (200)	-112†	499 (72.4)	263 (194)	-79†	619 (89.8)	16
.07	1.25	-	-	.15	-	-	12 (.47)	900	40					-80†	589 (85.3)	6
.08	1.40	-	-	.14	-	-	25 (.98)	950	22				49* (36)	-25	770 (112)	17
.08	1.54	-	-	.15	-	.02	25 (.98)	950	16				64* (47)	-45	660 (95.7)	17
.07	1.25	-	-	.15	-	.015	12 (.47)	900	55				160*** (118)	-70†	677 (98.1)	6

* at -40°C; ** at -100°C; *** shelf energy ; † 28J

with the alloy carbonitrides (14). The large spheroidal precipitates in Figure 11, (e.g., at "A" and "B") are examples of such particles which resulted from a long (100 h) tempering treatment. It is expected that cementite particles would coarsen rapidly in the weld HAZ and contribute to the reduced toughness. It has been suggested by Pickering (4) that this particular difficulty could be alleviated by lowering the carbon and nitrogen contents of the steel to the alloy carbide stoichiometric composition. Clearly, more detailed study of the weldability of quenched and tempered HSLA steels is needed. Environmental cracking is a potential problem with high-strength linepipe because it exceeds Rc 22, which is conventionally taken to be the threshold hardness for hydrogen stress cracking.

CONCLUSIONS

1. To produce 690 MPa (100 ksi) YS linepipe steel by controlled rolling alone would require a large increase in total alloy content, and would incur the disadvantages of high cost, in addition to reduced impact toughness and weldability.

2. The best combination of strength, impact toughness and weldability at the lowest alloy content is obtained by the direct quench and temper process. The pipe could be formed from quenched and tempered plate, or from as-quenched plate, which would necessitate tempering the pipe.

3. The re-austenitize, quench and temper process, applied to either plate or pipe, produces extremely high impact toughness, but it is not suitable for strength levels above 550 MPa (80 ksi).

4. The results of laboratory experiments indicate that the required strength and impact toughness can be obtained in direct quenched and tempered 13 mm. (0.5 in.) plate of a low carbon Mn-Mo-Nb(Cb) steel. The excellent strength/toughness combination is attributed to utilizing the maximum benefit of ferrite grain refinement, such that only a small proportion of the total yield strength is provided by precipitation hardening or dislocation substructural strengthening.

5. A need for further study of the weldability and environmental cracking susceptibility of quenched and tempered linepipe steels is indicated.

Table 4

Data on Quenched and Tempered HSLA Steels
(Reheat, Quench and Temper)

Composition, Wt. Pct.									Thickness mm(in.)	Finishing Temp. °C	Austenitize Temp. °C	As-Quenched			As-Aged			Ref.
C	Mn	Cr	Ni	Mo	Cu	V	Nb	N				Cv at 20°C J (ft lbf)	ITT (68J) °C	YS MPa (ksi)	Cv at 20°C J (ft lbf)	ITT (68J) °C	YS MPa (ksi)	
.07	1.60	-	-	-	-	-	.07	-	12 (.47)	900	910				250** (184)	-155†	451 (65.4)	6
.07	1.43	-	-	-	-	-	.085	-	13 (.50)	840	950				268** (198)	-100	460 (66.7)	18
.10	1.30	-	.45	-	-	-	.03	-	15 (.59)	915					293* (216)		563 (81.7)	5
.05	1.79	-	-	.31	-	-	.10	-	14 (.56)	865	925	127 (94)	-45	541 (78.4)	161 (119)	-75	569 (82.4)	19
.05	1.98	-	.11	.32	.18	-	.08	-	16 (.63)		927				>163 (>120)	<-115	573 (86)	20
.07	1.25	-	-	-	-	.15	-	.015	12 (.47)	900	910					-100†	589 (85.3)	6
.035	.44	.68	.89	.21	1.16	-	.045	-	19 (.75)		899	>163 (>120)	-134	476 (69)	>163 (>120)	-101	614 (89)	20

* at -23°C; ** shelf energy ; † 28J

REFERENCES

1. B. L. Bramfitt and A. R. Marder: "Processing and Properties of Low Carbon Steel", p. 191, M. J. Gray, ed., TMS-AIME, New York, 1973.
2. T. Gladman, D. Dulieu, and I. D. McIvor: Proceedings, 'Microalloying 75', 1976, Union Carbide Corp.,New York, p. 32.
3. F. S. Somerville: ibid., p. 354.
4. F. B. Pickering: ibid., p. 9.
5. H. Gondoh et al: ibid., p. 435.
6. C. Parrini, N. Pizzimenti and A. Pozzi: ibid., p. 288.
7. A. J. E. Forman and M. J. Makin: Can. J. Phys., 1975, vol. 45, pp. 511-517.
8. K. Cooper and J. D. Embury: Can. Met. Quarterly, 1975, vol. 14, pp. 69-83.
9. S. Matsuda, T. Inoue, H. Nimura and Y. Okumura: "Toward Improved Ductility and Toughness", p. 45, Climax Molybdenum Dev. Co. (Japan), 1971.
10. J. Tanaka, S. Tani and C. Ouchi: Trans. Iron Steel Inst. of Japan, 1975, vol. 15, pp. 19-26.
11. R. B. Nicholson: "Effect of Second-Phase Particles on the Mechanical Properties of Steels"; p. 1, Iron and Steel Inst., London, Spec. Rep. No. 145, 1971.
12. M. Fukuda, T. Hashimoto and K. Kunishige: The Sumitomo Search, 1973, vol. 9, pp. 8-23.
13. Y. E. Smith and C. A. Siebert: Met. Trans., 1971, vol. 2, pp. 1711-1725.
14. J. D. Boyd: Met Trans. 1976, vol. 7A, pp. 1577-1586, 1604-1609.
15. J. J. Irani, D. Burton and F. Keyworth: J. Iron Steel Inst., 1966, vol. 204, pp. 702-710.
16. J. W. Morrow: Climax Molybdenum Co., Rept. No. L-176-154, Ann Arbor, 1975.
17. G. Tither, J. Kewell and M. G. Frost: "Effect of Second Phase Particles on the Mechanical Properties of Steel", p. 157, Iron and Steel Inst.,London, Spec. Rep. No. 145, 1971.
18. R. F. Dewsnap and M. G. Frost: Report No. MG/36/72, British Steel Corp., London, 1972.
19. R. L. Cryderman: Report No. ISJ-677, Climax Molybdenum Co., Ann Arbor, 1972.
20. R. J. Jesseman and R. C. Smith: Publn. No. 74-Pet-9, ASME, New York, 1974.
21. G. Tither and M. Lavite: J. Metals, 1975, vol. 27, pp. 15-23.

DISCUSSION

C. A. Parrini (Italsider): It is a pleasure for me to lead the discussion on this paper because I am spending, and will continue to spend, a considerable amount of time on the problem of direct quenching (DQ). In the next two years we will invest over $700,000 for fundamental research in this field. I agree with all considerations you have made in this work and will add only that DQ is opening a very wide new metallurgical field that needs to be carefully analyzed for two reasons: 1) It offers metallurgists excellent opportunities for achieving HSNA (high strength non-alloyed) steels. 2) It is the only way to escape the situation of the "elephant controlled by the mosquito" or the too strong dependence of steel properties on very small but too expensive amounts of alloying additions. Why did you choose Grade X-100 for your tests?

J. D. Boyd: The 100 ksi (690 MPa) strength level was selected as a reasonable increase over current strength levels that could still be achieved by processing and heat treating of low-carbon, low-alloy steels.

C. A. Parrini: Why 10 h of ageing time?

J. D. Boyd: The 10 h ageing times were adopted in order to maximize the age-hardening effect. I realize that such a period may not be appropriate in actual production, and is probably unnecessary in practice.

C. A. Parrini: Could you comment on the effects of deformed versus non-deformed austenite on final properties.

J. D. Boyd: The austenite condition is very important due to its effect on the transformation kinetics. Our experience indicates that deformed, unrecrystallized austenite is preferable.

C. A. Parrini: What are you going to do in this field in the future?

J. D. Boyd: Our future studies will include weldability and environmental cracking considerations.

T. Kunitake (Sumitomo Metal Industries): In your first slide, you showed the CCT diagram of austenite. If you talk about the transformation behaviour of austenite subjected to direct quenching, the CCT diagram must be the one of deformed austenite. Did you measure the transformation of deformed austenite? If so, how did you do that?

J. D. Boyd: The schematic CCT diagram shown is based on published results of quench dilatometry of deformed specimens. These results agree well with our observation of microstructures of controlled-rolled, direct quenched plate.

A. Sage (Highveld Steel and Vanadium): Why were these particular steels used in this study? Would it not be more useful to start with proven compositions which are made as strip, the production of which is made under similar conditions to direct quenching and ageing. The V-N and V-Cb compositions used in strip production have the advantage that they are made with low carbon contents which gives good weldability and the total alloy content is low, which keeps costs low.

J. D. Boyd: We were emphasizing the microstructural effects and so started by looking at those compositions which showed the greatest effects. There was no prejudice against the use of vanadium steels.

A. B. Rothwell (Noranda Research): The principles of quenching immediately from the rolls, and the benefits to be gained thereby, have been known for some years, but only now are major steelmakers seriously considering the capital investments which would be required. The main question mark is the flexibility of the process. The quenching fixture cannot be sited so that it interferes with the normal operation of the mill, and some delay and temperature inhomogeneity appears inevitable. We have been carrying out some work on the design of alloys which are relatively insensitive to these factors, and the results to date are available to anyone who is interested. Incidentally, Dr. Sage will be pleased to know that if you can get the steel into the quench press quickly enough, vanadium will give you higher strength for your money than will columbium. Columbium steels seem less sensitive to delays before quenching, however.

I should also like to question the assertion that gain in strength is due primarily to grain refinement rather than to precipitation effects. The main advantage of quenching directly rather than after intermediate reheating is the ability to combine grain refinement (through controlled rolling) with substantial precipitation hardening. In low carbon steels, in fact, the peak hardness on tempering may be higher than the as-quenched value, indicating a marked precipitation hardening response.

J. D. Boyd: The principal contribution of the present work is that our spray quench facility permits work on 0.5 in. (13 mm) plate with mid-thickness cooling rates of 70-80 deg C/s. Also, I think we are advancing the understanding of microstructure/strength/toughness relationships primarily by transmission electron microscopy (TEM). Our experience indicates that the low-carbon low-alloy compositions are quite flexible in terms of delay time between final pass and quench and uniformity of properties throughout the thickness of the plate. Our experience with niobium (columbium) steels has been that the precipitate hardening response is very small. Very rough calculations indicate that 60-70% of the total (100 ksi) YS in the DQ condition is due to grain refinement. It is not clear what proportion of the YS is due to precipitation hardening, but the volume fraction of precipitate observed by TEM is very low. There is some Nb(C,N) precipitation during ageing at 600°C, but there is also some recovery of the dislocation substructure. The nett result is a minimal increase in yield strength (∿5 ksi or 34 MPa). The principle of combining grain refinement with precipitation hardening by DQ and tempering may work better in vanadium-bearing steels, but we have not investigated that (yet).

C. Sargent (University of Saskatchewan): Why does the addition of nickel increase the toughness of steel?

J. D. Boyd: The only significant observation on the effect of nickel is the fact that the slip mode at low temperatures in ferrite is wavy in Ni-bearing steels, whereas the slip bands are planar in plain C-Mn steels. The proposed mechanism is a decrease in the local stress concentrations (e.g. at carbide particles) with the wavy slip mode.

E. Kranz (Mannesmanrohren-Werke): In your paper you made a statement that the only suitable way to fabricate a high-strength pipe with high toughness is the direct quenching technique. We cannot agree with this. Mannesmann has done some work in quenching of linepipe and from our experience this is a very valid method of producing pipes, even up to Grade X-100. These pipes have uniformity, including weld and HAZ. So Mannesmann decided to build production equipment for QT pipes which will go into service in the near future.

J. D. Boyd: It is probably an overstatement to say that direct quench (DQ) is the only way to produce high strength linepipe. However, based on published data available at the time of writing the paper, the DQ technique is the best technique for 100 ksi (690 MPa) YS steel. All of the work on reheat, quench and temper treatments, including quenching linepipe, show excellent toughness values up to approximately 80 ksi (550 MPa) YS, but there were no results for higher strength steels. This is the first I have heard of the Mannesmann results for X-100 quenched and tempered linepipe.

B. E. Boardman (John Deere): Both Matsubara and Boyd have alluded to higher strength plate steels but have not specifically mentioned grades (i.e. strengths). Based on past plate and strip mill history these grades will be named X75, X80, X85 etc. I contend that this narrow spread is a disservice to the design engineer because there is not a statistical difference between grades.

Whenever you mention "higher strength" in the future please do not report mean value and stop. Also report the variance and other related statistical information.

THE CONTROL OF FRACTURE TOUGHNESS IN STRUCTURAL STEEL WELDMENTS

A. G. Glover, J. T. McGrath and N. F. Eaton
Canadian Welding Development Institute
Toronto, Ontario
Canada

The achievement of adequate fracture toughness in a weldment is essential to the prevention of fracture in steel structures operating in a low temperature environment. Some effects of microstructure and weld process variables on submerged arc weld metal fracture toughness are presented. A fine bainitic structure and a low volume fraction of inclusion particles are conducive to high fracture toughness. Increased flux basicity can act to refine the bainitic microstructure as well as lower the inclusion volume fraction.

INTRODUCTION

One of the prime requirements of engineering structures for operation in an Arctic environment is that they have adequate resistance against brittle failure. The fracture toughness of the welded joint is of interest because of the many factors which can influence its magnitude. While one must consider the fracture toughness of the heat-affected-zone as well as the weld metal, this paper will be concerned primarily with weld metal toughness.

In defining a fracture toughness criterion, data associated with crack initiation are preferable. It has been found that cracks which initiate in weld metal, generally deflect into the base metal where they are either arrested or continue to propagate (1,2). Thus, depending upon the amount of plastic deformation that can take place at the tip of a defect, a fracture mechanics approach can be used to measure weld metal fracture toughness. The more empirical Charpy impact test, which measures the impact energy required to initiate and propagate a crack, is useful primarily in quality control by providing a comparison of various weld metals.

Historically, the fracture toughness of weld metal in structural steel weldments has been shown to have a wide variation. This variation in toughness may be due to the variation in weld metal structure which can occur, depending upon the welding procedure. The microstructural features which determine weld metal fracture toughness are

a) amount and distribution of the transformation products, i.e., proeutectoid ferrite, coarse and fine bainite and martensite; and

b) type and distribution of second phase constituents, i.e., carbides, nitrides and non-metallic inclusions.

It has been shown that cleavage cracks can readily initiate if the microstructure contains a large amount of coarse bainite and martensite (3,4). The presence of fine bainite, however, promotes fracture toughness in weld metal (5,6). The resistance to ductile failure in weld metal is directly related to the volume fraction of inclusions. Because inclusions are mainly oxygen-containing oxides and silicates, many investigations have related Charpy shelf energy with oxygen content of the weld metal (7,8). Taylor and Farrar (9) have compiled data on this relationship and indicated that the greatest decrease in shelf energy takes place when the oxygen content of the weld metal is increased from 300 to 600 ppm. The microstructure of weld metal depends upon (a) weld composition, and (b) cooling rate. These factors are controlled by a range of weld process variables, including wire and flux composition, heat input, preheat and postheat temperatures, and number of welding passes.

It is the purpose of this paper to (1) define the microstructural features that contribute to weld metal fracture toughness; and (2) clarify the role that weld process variables play in controlling weld metal microstructure.

EXPERIMENTAL PROCEDURE

Weld Preparation

A series of butt welds were prepared by the submerged arc process. The welds were made in structural steels A515 and A36, the composition and mechanical properties of which are listed in Table 1. The welding consumables were Wire A (C 0.10, Mn 1.5, Si 0.03, Mo 0.5) and Flux F and Flux E. The basicity of Flux F was 0.5, while that of Flux E was 2.0. (The concept of flux basicity will be discussed later). Welding parameters were 32 V,

Table 1

Base Material Data

Base Metal	C	Mn	Si	Y.S. MPa	U.T.S. MPa
A 36	0.29 max.	0.8-1.2	0.15-0.30	250 min.	480
A515	0.31 max.	0.9 max.	0.15-0.30	260 min.	530

Table 2

Material and Welding Conditions

Weld	Base Material	Wire	Flux Code	Flux Basicity	Energy Input kJ/mm	No. of Passes
1	A515	A	E	2.0	2.3	22
2	A515	A	F	0.5	2.3	20
3	A 36	A	F	0.5	2.3	16
4*	A 36	A[a]	E	2.0	2.3	23
5**	X70 Pipe Steel	B	E[b]	2.0	2.3 4.3	1 (one wire) 1 (two wire)

* Supplied by Ontario Hydro; ** An experimental Steel supplied by Steel Company of Canada

a-Slight chemical alteration; b-Pipe line variety

525 A, with a welding speed of 432 mm/min, yielding an energy input of 2.3 kJ/mm. Approximately 20 passes were laid down with preheat of 80°C and an interpass temperature of 150°C.

The materials and welding conditions are summarized in Table 2. Welds 1 to 3 were prepared in this investigation, while welds 4 and 5 were obtained from outside sources as indicated. Weld 5 was made in a HSLA X70 grade pipe steel. The analyses of the weld metals are contained in Table 3.

Characterization of Microstructure

Quantitative optical metallography was employed to measure the amounts of the microconstituents, i.e., transformation products, and the volume fraction of inclusion particles in the weld metals.

The percentage of microconstituents was determined by etching with 2% nital and using a point counting technique that had previously been calibrated on a known volume fraction. A total of 1000 counts were made in 40 areas at a magnification of 820X for each weld specimen. The volume fraction of the inclusion particles was obtained by examining specimens in the as-polished condition.

Fracture Testing

Evaluation of the fracture toughness of the weld metals was done by the Charpy impact test and the fracture mechanics, J-integral test (10).

The Charpy transition curves were used as a means of comparing the fracture resistance of the various weld metals. The Charpy specimens were taken from the centre of the weld metal with the line of the notch perpendicular to the plate surfaces. Care was taken to ensure that the notch sampled both the as-deposited and refined regions in the multi-pass welds.

Fracture toughness related to crack initiation was measured by the J-integral test (10). The J integral test has been devised to measure the fracture toughness of materials exhibiting general yield behaviour prior to the initiation of unstable fracture. Unlike the COD test, which is concerned with events at the crack tip, the J-integral provides an average measure of the elastic-plastic stress/strain field around the crack and can be used as a fracture criterion. The fracture toughness parameter associated with crack initiation is termed J_{Ic}. The specimens for the J-integral test were bend specimens, 10 mm x 20 mm x 120 mm long. A fatigue precrack, a, was introduced such that the ratio a/W = 0.6, where W is the width of the specimen.

Table 3

Weld Metal Analyses

Weld No.	C	Mn	Si	Ni	Cr	Mo	Cu	S	P	Cb	Mn/Si
1	0.13	1.1	0.22	n.d.	n.d.	0.43	0.16	0.014	0.010	-	5.00
2	0.12	1.4	0.46	n.d.	n.d.	0.41	0.19	0.021	0.008	-	3.04
3	0.07	1.4	0.53	n.d.	n.d.	0.41	0.23	0.021	0.011	-	2.64
5	0.045	1.74	0.27	0.35	0.078	0.41	0.09	0.003	0.005	0.035	6.44

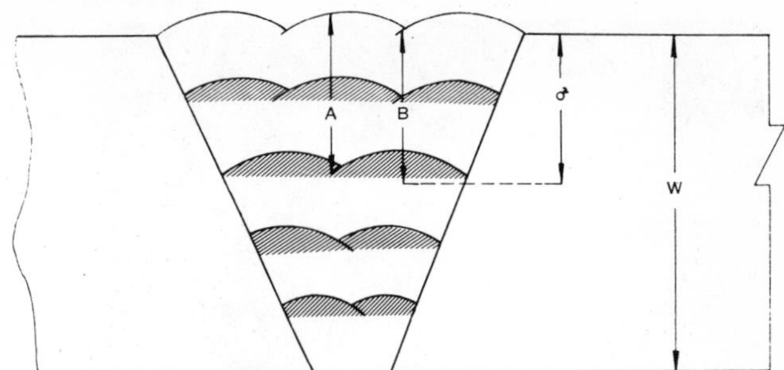

Figure 1: Position of Fatigue Crack in (A) Refined Region, and (B) As-deposited Region

A limited number of these tests were carried out, principally on weld 2. The purpose of the tests was to distinguish between the fracture toughness of the as-deposited and refined regions of the multi-pass weld. To accomplish this, the tip of the fatigue crack had to be positioned within these regions as illustrated in Figure 1. A third set of J-integral test specimens was prepared with a through-thickness notch sampling both weld metal structures, not unlike the Charpy specimens.

RESULTS

Metallography of the Weld Metals

The macroscopic structures of typical multipass welds are shown in Figures 2 and 3. It is apparent that when using the basic Flux E, a greater degree of refinement is obtained in the weld metal. For the welds illustrated, in base A515, weld 1 has 60% as-deposited and 40% refined, whereas weld 2 has 75% as-deposited and 25% refined.

Microscopically, all weld metals showed an inclusion size distribution from a maximum of 3μm to submicron. The majority of the non-metallic inclusions were in the 1 to 2 μm range, and the inclusion volume fractions of the welds are given in Table 4. All the weld metals contained a considerable proportion of inclusions in the sub-micron

Table 4

Microstructural Analysis

Weld	Microconstituents: Proeutectoid Ferrite %	Fine Bainite %	Upper Bainite %	Others %	Volume Fraction of Inclusions %
1	13	76	10	1	0.23
2	1	5	91	3	0.33
3	4	-	96	-	0.32
4	38	43	15	4	0.30
5	1	98	1	1	0.16

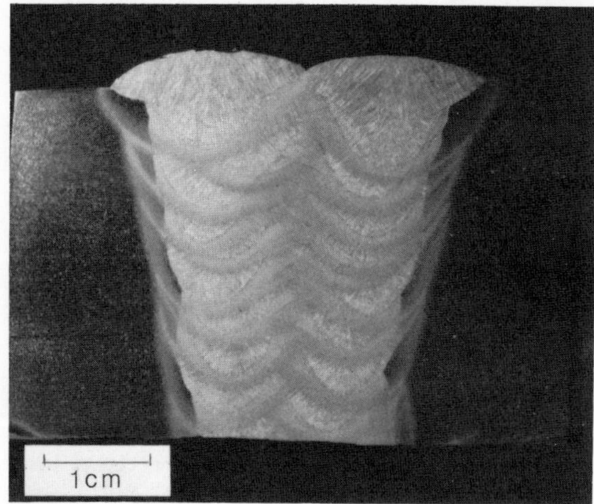

Figure 2: Macrostructure of Weld 1

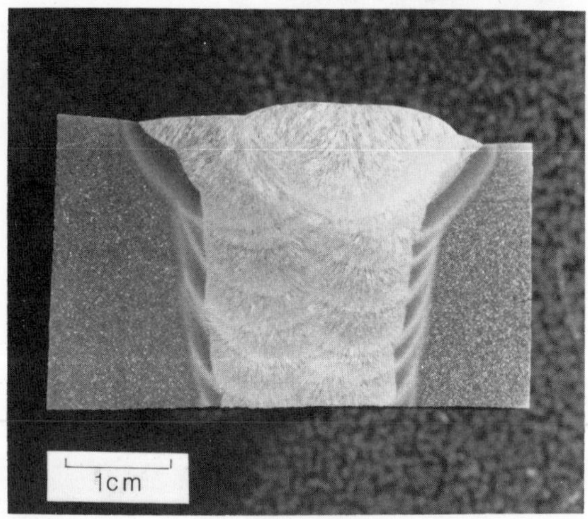

Figure 3: Macrostructure of Weld 2

Figure 4: Non-Metallic Inclusions in Weld 1, Volume Fraction 0.23%. As-Polished

range with the exception of weld 5, which was relatively free of them. A typical inclusion content is shown in Figure 4.

All the welds, with the exception of weld 5, were deposited with the same wire but different fluxes and therefore exhibited a range of microstructures when etched in 2% nital. The results

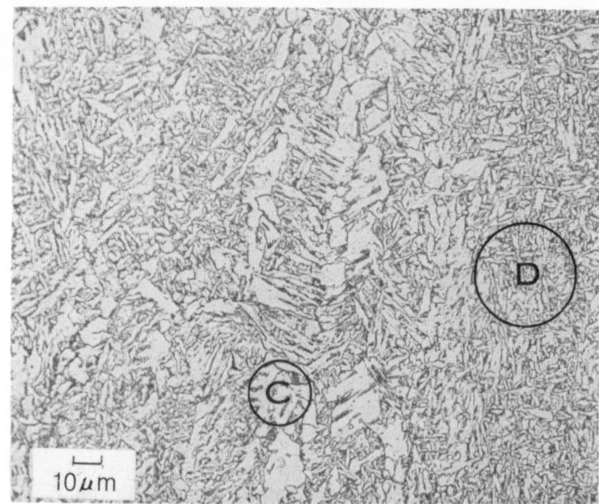

Figure 5: Microstructure of Weld 4, showing pro-eutectoid Ferrite (C) and Fine Bainite (D). 2% Nital etch

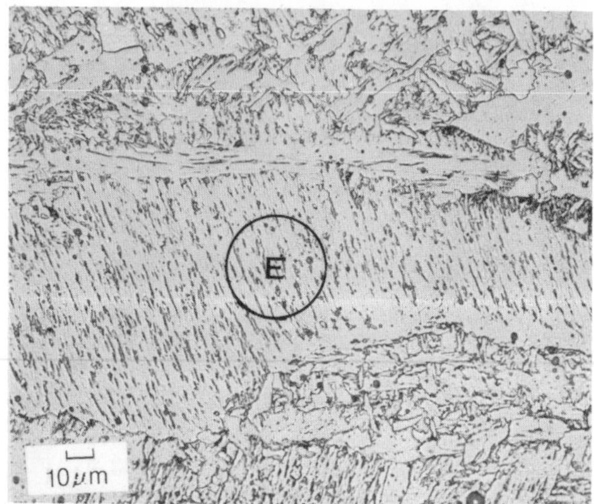

Figure 6: Microstructure of Weld 3, showing Coarse Bainite (E). 2% Nital etch

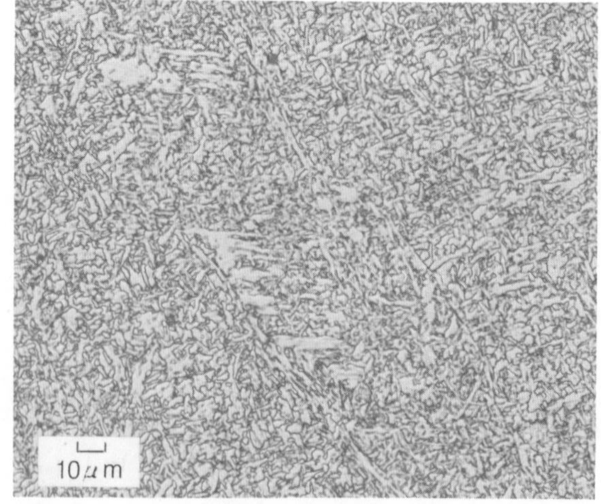

Figure 7: Microstructure of the Line Pipe Weld, showing very fine Bainitic structure. 2% Nital etch

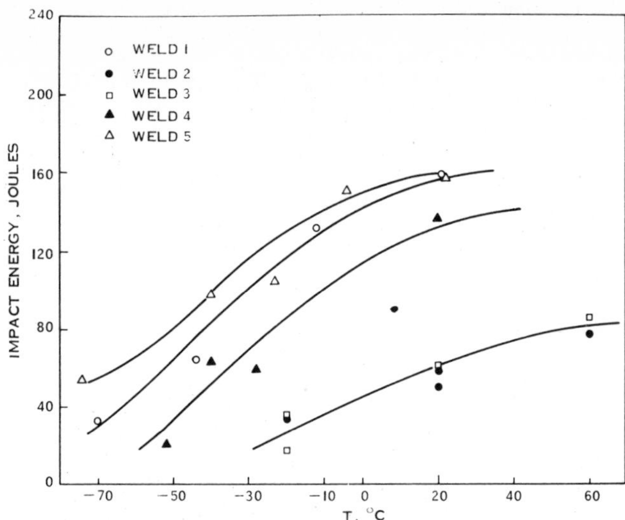

Figure 8: Charpy V-notch impact curves for the series of SA welds

of the microstructural analysis of the as-deposited region are shown in Table 4. The coarse columnar grains were delineated by narrow ribbons of pro-eutectoid ferrite, about 5 µm in thickness. However, weld 4 contained large areas of this component (Figure 5). Depending on the flux/wire combination, the interior of the columnar grains consisted either of coarse bainite (Figure 6) or fine bainite (Figure 5). The microstructure of the line pipe weld was almost entirely fine bainite (Figure 7).

In the multi-pass welds the cast structure of an as-deposited region was partially modified during the deposition of a subsequent weld pass. These reheated regions were approximately 1.5 to 2 mm wide and contained an ill-defined mixture of proeutectoid ferrite, fine equiaxed ferrite and bainite with precipitates decorating the grain boundaries. These precipitates were not identified. However, in view of the composition of the weld metal these are assumed to be molybdenum carbide.

Fracture Toughness of the Weld Metals

The impact data obtained from the Charpy V-notch tests at various temperatures is shown on the transition curves of the various weld metals in Figure 8. There was little difference between welds 2 and 3, and they are plotted as one curve, with an upper shelf energy of 82 J. The remaining welds showed a considerable improvement in upper shelf energies, varying from 140 to 160 J. Welds 2 and 3 failed in a fully brittle mode at temperatures below -10°C, whereas the other welds exhibited complete brittle failure at temperatures of -50°C and lower with a marked difference in lower shelf energies, varying from 20 J to 50 J. The range of transition temperatures at 68 J (50 ft lbf) was from -58°C to +30°C.

The results of the J integral tests on the three areas -- average, as-deposited and refined -- of weld 2 are shown in Figure 9, which gives J_{Ic} in the range of (0.82 to 0.96) x 10^5 m.N/m² This range, however, covers the experimental scatter and thus one can conclude that the J_{Ic} for the three regions is essentially the same, i.e. (0.89 ± 0.07) x 10^5 m.N/m². The value of σ_{flow} was calculated from the mid-value of σ_{YS} and σ_{UTS}.

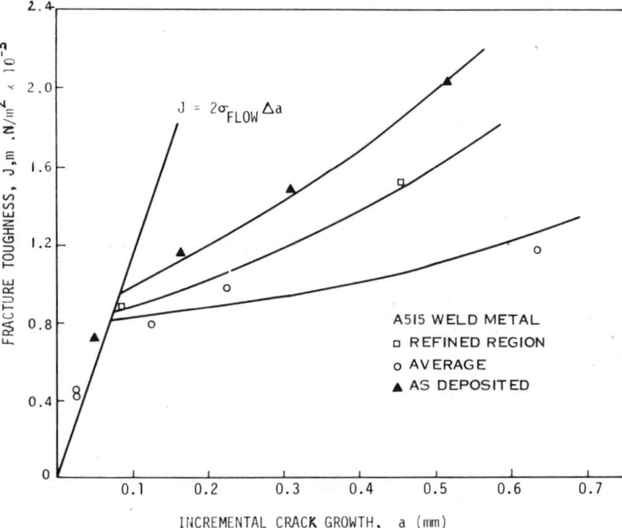

Figure 9: J-integral test results for the various regions in Weld 2

DISCUSSION

The Charpy impact data for the welds investigated can be related to the amount of microconstituent in the as-deposited region. Since the as-deposited region occupies at least 75% of the weld (with the exception of weld 1), it is assumed that the microstructure within this region has the greatest effect on impact resistance. A decrease in Charpy transition temperature is associated with an increase in the amount of fine bainite or a decrease in coarse upper bainite. The refined bainite is resistant to cleavage fracture for two reasons -- (a) carbide particles are very fine and well distributed; and (b) the colony size of the ferrite laths is small and effective in retarding crack propagation. On the other hand, cleavage cracks can initiate and propagate at the site of carbide films along the ferrite boundaries of coarse bainite.

Let us examine the factors that control weld metal microstructure. These are, primarily, weld composition and cooling rate. Welds 1 and 2 have been subjected to the same thermal conditions and therefore the difference in microstructure of the as-deposited regions must be due to weld composition. It is suggested that the fine bainitic microstructure of weld 1 compared to weld 2 is due to the higher Mn/Si ratio. Manganese is effective in lowering the austenite-to-ferrite transformation temperature and the bainite-start temperature, (3,11) thus promoting finer transformation products.

On the other hand, increasing silicon raises the austenite-to-ferrite transformation temperature (3), resulting in a coarser transformation product (12). While a fine bainite microstructure in the as-deposited region contributes to the superior toughness of weld 1, a further factor in promoting high toughness is the higher percentage of refined region in the multi-pass weld. The use of the basic Flux E leads to changes in the weld bead profile. The effective decrease in applied arc voltage means that a flatter weld bead is produced, leading to a higher proportion of refined region in the weldment as illustrated in Figure 2 and 3.

There is insufficient data to comment on the factors that produced the fine bainitic structure in weld 5. However, the microstructural analysis of this weld provides additional evidence that a fine bainitic microstructure does result in a low Charpy transition temperature.

The beneficial effect of a fine microstructure can be counteracted by an extremely high volume

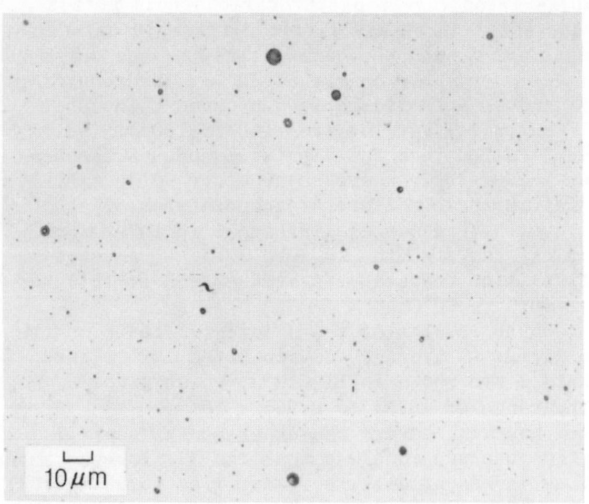

Figure 10: Non-Metallic inclusions in a weld with a volume fraction of 0.6%. As-polished.

fraction of inclusions. The weld shown in Figure 10 had a microstructure with 50% fine bainite. However, the volume fraction of non-metallic inclusions was 0.6. This depressed the whole impact energy curve and gave an upper shelf energy of 55 J.

The difference in the inclusion contents of the weld metals was almost certainly due to the low basicity index Flux F, containing a substantial proportion of silica. This is apparent from the analysis of weld metals 1 and 2, which contain respectively 0.22% and 0.46% Si and the initial wire only 0.03% Si. The higher basicity Flux E contains only 20-25% silica as compared to 40% for Flux F. The globular non-metallic inclusions, which are products of oxidation-deoxidation reactions, are known to affect ductile fracture energy by a microvoid coalescence mechanism (13). Welds 1 and 5, made with the most basic flux, contain the lowest volume fraction of inclusions and have the highest upper shelf energies.

The other correlation that exists between inclusion volume fraction and impact energy is also illustrated by welds 1 and 5. The two welds have nominally similar impact energy curves, except for the lower shelf values. The energy required to produce brittle fracture in weld 1 was 30 J and 54 J for weld 5. This type of fracture mode would almost certainly be influenced by the non-metallic inclusion contents, particularly the mean free path available between the inclusions. The degree of contamination by non-metallic inclusions would depend upon the level of oxidation-deoxidation reactions and the reaction products, which are usually some form of manganese silicates. It is therefore reasonable to assume that the non-metallic distribution would depend upon the manganese and silicon present in a weld metal. Indeed, recent work (14) has shown that the inclusion population in a weld metal is a function of the Mn/Si ratio and the weld metal cleanliness improves with increasing Mn/Si ratio. Weld 5 has a Mn/Si ratio of 6.4 compared with 5.0 in weld 1, which is consistent with a higher proportion of fine, submicron size inclusions in this latter weld, and this has produced more favourable conditions for cleavage cracks to propagate, resulting in the lower brittle fracture energy.

The J integral tests indicated that there was no difference in the magnitude of the fracture toughness parameter J_{Ic} for the as-deposited, refined and average regions of weld 2. One can comment that the J_{Ic} value of 0.9×10^5 m.N/m^2 is indicative of a fairly brittle weld metal. The reason that a higher toughness value was not obtained, particularly when the tip of the fatigue crack was in the refined region, can be related to the fact that the tough refined region is a small area which is under restraint from the larger brittle as-deposited region. The restraint forces act to limit the amount of plastic deformation that can take place within the refined region. Because of this action it is impossible to distinguish between the fracture toughness of the as-deposited and refined regions of the weld metal. Whether this holds true for other multi-pass welds remains to be investigated.

CONCLUSIONS

The influence of weld metal microstructure and weld process variables on fracture toughness has been studied in a series of multi-pass and two-pass submerged arc welds and has led to the following conclusions:

(a) The as-deposited regions of the submerged arc weld contained a range of microstructures varying from a high fine bainite content to a very high coarse upper bainite content.

(b) Weld metals containing a high percentage of fine bainite, together with a low volume fraction of non-metallic inclusions, exhibit the best toughness. A coarse upper bainite structure results in poor fracture toughness.

(c) An increasing manganese/silicon ratio promotes a finer transformation product in the as-deposited weld metal.

(d) The upper shelf energy is controlled by the volume fraction of non-metallic inclusions which affect ductile fracture energy by a microvoid coalescence mechanism.

(e) The lower shelf energy is controlled by the spacing of the submicron non-metallic inclusions. A high volume fraction leads to easier cleavage crack propagation and low shelf energies.

(f) A high manganese/silicon ratio in the weld metal is conducive to producing low volume fractions of non-metallic inclusions.

(g) The value of the fracture toughness parameter J_{Ic} associated with crack initiation was unchanged for the as-deposited, refined and average regions of a multi-pass weld.

Acknowledgements

The authors wish to acknowledge the assistance of Mr. I. D. Montgomery in all phases of the experimental program, and Mr. D. Carpenter, who conducted the fracture mechanics test program. They also wish to thank Union Carbide Canada Limited for preparing the weldments, and Ontario Hydro and The Steel Company of Canada Limited for supplying weld samples. The use of Ontario Hydro research facilities was greatly appreciated.

REFERENCES

1. W. H. Munse, "Fracture", ed., H. Liebowitz, Academic Press, 1969, vol. 4, p. 371.
2. H. Kihara, T. Yoshida and H. Oba, IIW Document X-217-59, 1959.
3. R. W. K. Honeycombe and F. B. Pickering, Met. Trans. 1972, vol. 3, p. 1099.
4. L. J. Habraken and M. Economopoulos, Symp. Transformation and Hardenability in Steels, Climax Molybdenum Corporation, 1967.

5. J. G. Garland and P. R. Kirkwood, Met. Const., 1975, vol. 7, p. 275, 320.
6. J. M. Sawhill, Climax Molybdenum Corporation, Rept. L-176-115, 1973.
7. S. S. Tuliani, T. Boniszewski and N. F. Eaton, Welding and Met. Fab., August 1969, vol. 37, p. 327.
8. P. C. Hughes, Aust. Weld. J., August 1968, vol. 12, p. 29.
9. L. G. Taylor and R. A. Farrar, Welding and Met. Fab., 1975, vol. 43, p. 305.
10. J. D. Landes and J. A. Begley, Fracture Analysis Part II, ASTM STP 560, 1973, p. 170.
11. K. E. Dorschu and R. D. Stout, Welding J., Research Supp. 1961, vol. 40, p. 97-s.
12. V. E. Lazko, V. G. Lazko and Y. L. Yarovinskii, Weld. Prod. 1970, vol. 6, p. 29.
13. L. L. J. Chin, Welding J., Research Supp. 1969, vol. 48, p. 290-s.
14. D. J. Widgery, Weld. Res. Inter. 1974, vol. 4, (2), p. 54.

DISCUSSION

J. N. Cordea (Armco Steel): I compliment the authors on their efforts to measure the quantities of the various types of microstructures in the weld metal and relate the data to fracture toughness. It is a difficult but meaningful approach to controlling weld metal toughness. I noted that the fine bainite optical microstructure appears very similar to the acicular ferrite in low C alloy steels. Can you comment on the differences between these two apparently similar microstructures?

J. T. McGrath: The main difference between acicular ferrite and fine bainite is that the latter structure would have a fine dispersion of carbides within the ferrite grains. There does seem to be some confusion however, as to at what transformation temperature it is possible to obtain acicular ferrite in low carbon HSLA steels. It has been suggested that fine acicular ferrite can be obtained at temperatures above the transformation to a coarse upper bainite structure. There is clearly a need to resolve this situation.

P. E. Bedford-Jones (Steel Company of Canada): The hardenability of the weld deposit will be important in achieving high weld toughness under fixed welding conditions. Hardenability is a factor in achieving the best structure and toughness. Flux selection is most critical. High silica fluxes are to be avoided since the silica has a high oxygen potential, and will generally decompose under normal operating conditions, causing both oxygen and silicon to be picked up in the weld deposit.

J. T. McGrath: We agree.

B. E. Boardman (John Deere): In the previous paper, Boyd went to great lengths to discuss the differences between two low temperature non-polygonal ferrite structures obtained by a direct quench of plate. You, though, did not mention different structures. Was this because you only observed one of the structures and if so which one?

J. T. McGrath: The two low temperature transformation products (non-polygonal) that we observed in the weld metals were coarse and fine bainite. Another type of non-polygonal product reported in low carbon HSLA steel is acicular ferrite. It is very much like fine bainite insofar as the microstructure is composed of fine needles of ferrite. The main difference between acicular ferrite and fine bainite is that the latter structure would contain a dispersion of fine carbide particles within the ferrite grains.

A. B. Rothwell (Noranda Research): The analysis of toughness was based on Charpy tests. Was there any significant difference between the strength of the different weld metals, and if so, was this taken into account (as regards both transition temperature and shelf energy?)

J. T. McGrath: For the multi-pass welds 1 to 4 inclusive, on C-Mn base plate, the all weld metal yield and tensile strengths were all essentially the same (within a scatter of 10%). Weld 5 was a typical two-pass SA weld for line pipe (X70 grade) and also had yield and tensile strengths within the same scatter band as welds 1 to 4.

C. P. Hoogensen (R. M. Hardy and Associates): How did you quantitatively determine the constitutents of the weld metal?

J. T. McGrath: The quantitative determination of weld metal micro-constituents was carried out using a point counting technique in which over 40 fields of view were examined in the transverse section of the weld. The point counting technique was calibrated using an Al-Cu eutectic system with known percentages of constituents.

C. P. Hoogensen: The crack front propagation of the fatigue crack in a COD test is often irregular for "as welded" specimens. Did you experience such problems and if so how did you correct them?

J. T. McGrath: In the specimens used for J-integral tests the fatigue crack front was linear. These as-welded specimens were 10 mm x 20 mm in cross section and had been machined down from larger weldments, hence some residual stresses were relaxed and also, generally for small specimens, the shape of the fatigue crack front is less influenced by the residual stresses. If a bowed crack front is obtained, however, this can be overcome by the design of the machined notch and also by using an initial compressive stress cycle in fatigue pre-cracking.

A. B. Rothwell (Noranda Research): In the J-integral test, was equal crack length/ligament depth maintained when comparing as-deposited with refined regions?

J. T. McGrath: For the J-integral tests, the "a" value (i.e. the machined and fatigue crack length) was maintained at constant length for all tests, resulting in a/w = 0.6.

R. J. Cooke (National Energy Board): Do you expect an effect on notch toughness results when the notch or fatigue crack tip is moved away from the weld centre line and the symmetry of the plastic zone is influenced by non-uniform constraint imposed by the fusion line and HAZ?

J. T. McGrath: Research studies reported by the British Welding Institute (R. E. Dolby, Met. Const. and Brit. Weld. J. 1974, vol. 6, p. 228) on HAZ toughness does suggest that if the plastic zone size of a crack tip in the coarse grain region extends into the weld region, the weld metal toughness can have an effect on HAZ toughness.

STEEL AND WELD MATERIAL REQUIREMENTS FOR THE PREVENTION OF WELD CRACKING IN HEAVY WALL PIPE

T. Bada, T. Yatake, N. Yurioka and T. Kikuno
Nippon Steel Corporation
Fuchinobe, Sagamihara Kanagawa
229 Japan

Root cracking in V-groove girth welding using vertical down cellulosic electrodes is a type of hydrogen induced cold cracking at the heat affected zone of the base metal. This cold cracking of steel is better evaluated by the cold cracking susceptibility index, P_{cm} than by the carbon equivalent. Longer incubation periods for cold cracking are expected for steels less susceptible to cold cracking. Root cracking can be prevented by depositing a hot pass within the incubation time.

If pipe wall thickness is increased, micro-cracking of weld metal is more likely to occur when cellulose electrodes are used. The critical preheating and interpass temperatures necessary to prevent micro--cracking become as high as 200°C when 32 mm thick pipe is welded by cellulosic electrodes. To prevent cracking and to permit faster welding operations, it is recommended that the root and hot passes be welded by cellulosic electrodes following with filler and cover passes using low-hydrogen electrodes for the welding of heavy wall pipe in pumping stations.

INTRODUCTION

A significant increase in energy demand in recent years has made it necessary to exploit energy resources in the Arctic. Pipelines are constructed in the frigid area to transport oil and natural gas. High strength steels are used for these pipelines because of the high pressure transmission involved.

A pipeline is constructed by field or shop welding unit lengths of pipe. The safety of an Arctic pipeline must be ensured by the use of steels with high toughness at low temperatures, and also by sound welding of joints. Accordingly, the most important task is to prevent weld defects, particularly cold cracking, since a cold crack with very sharp tip radius might become the initiation point of brittle fracture.

Cold cracking of steel is enhanced by hydrogen. Most pipeline welding is carried out using cellulosic electrodes because they permit faster welding and provide economy as well as good inside bead shape. However, the weld metal produced by cellulosic electrodes contains a large amount of diffusible hydrogen. Cold cracking is also more likely to occur with an increase in pipe wall thickness and steel strength level. Heavy wall pipe is used in pumping and cooling stations.

MATERIALS USED FOR WELD CRACKING TESTS

Steels

Four types of API 5LX X65 steels were employed for the weld cracking tests conducted by manual arc welding of heavy wall station pipes. Table 1 shows the chemical composition of the steels used in the tests and Table 2 shows the mechanical properties of the steels. The steels A and B are Nippon Steel WELTEN 62 which are quenched-and-tempered weldable structural steels of 62 kgf/mm^2 (608 MPa) tensile strength and are used for oil storage tanks, for example. WELTEN 62 was selected for the tests in order to investigate the effect of chemical composition of steel on cold cracking. Steel C and D are also quenched-and-tempered heavy wall pipe steels with improved low temperature toughness. The thickness of all plates was 32 mm except steel A, which was 38 mm.

C_{eq} and P_{cm} (1) in Table 1 represent the cold

Table 1 Chemical composition of steel

Steel		Thick (mm)	Chemical composition (%)										Ceq	Pcm
Symbol	Name		C	Si	Mn	P	S	Ni	Cr	Mo	Nb	V		
A	WT62	38	0.14	0.32	1.18	0.011	0.005	—	0.19	—	—	0.05	0.385	0.226
B	WT62	32	0.13	0.25	1.36	0.023	0.006	—	0.01	—	—	0.05	0.369	0.212
C	WT62M	32	0.10	0.24	1.35	0.010	0.006	0.39	—	0.11	0.04	—	0.373	0.193
D	2.5Ni	32	0.06	0.13	0.84	0.008	0.003	2.72	—	0.20	0.01	0.03	0.426	0.169

Table 2 Mechanical properties of steel

Steel		Thick mm	Y.P. kgf/mm² (Mpa)	T.S. kgf/mm² (Mpa)	EL %	vTrs ℃	vE (T direction)	
Symbol	Name						−25℃ kgf-m (J)	−45℃ kgf-m (J)
A	WT62	38	56.3(553)	65.2(640)	31	−36	12.1(118)	6.3(62)
B	WT62	32	56.2(552)	68.3(671)	46	−38	12.3(121)	8.6(85)
C	WT62M	32	57.8(568)	62.7(616)	50	−72	14.7(144)	12.3(121)
D	2.5Ni	32	50.3(494)	62.8(617)	57	−120	27.3(268)	27.2(267)

cracking susceptibility of steel and they are calculated from the chemical composition of steel, using the following equations:

$$C_{eq} = C + Mn/6 + (Cr + Mo + V)/5 + (Ni + Cu)/15 \quad (1)$$

$$P_{cm} = C + Mn/20 + Si/30 + Cu/20 + Ni/60 + Cr/20 + Mo/15 + V/10 + 5B \quad (2)$$

Equation (1) is widely used and Equation (2) is often used in Japan to evaluate the susceptibility of steel to cold cracking. Weldability of steel has been significantly improved in the last few decades, mainly by reduction of carbon content. It was noticed that C_{eq} could not indicate accurately the susceptibility to cold cracking for a recently-developed weldable steel, though it correlates with the hardness of the heat affected zone very well. In 1971, Japanese steelmakers and fabricators made a number of weld cracking tests using relatively low carbon steels and recognized that P_{cm} is a more appropriate measure of cold cracking susceptibility.

Welding Materials

The welding materials used in the cracking tests were developed by Nippon Steel Welding Products and Engineering Co. as electrodes for the vertical down welding of linepipe steel for Arctic use. CGP A is a low-hydrogen type, while CHN A and CHN B are cellulosic types. The diffusible hydrogen contents of weld metal deposited by these electrodes are shown in Table 3. The hydrogen content of cellulose electrodes is as high as 30 ml/100 g. The hydrogen contents were measured by the JIS (Japanese Industrial Standard) method, and is shown schematically in Table 3.

Table 4 shows the chemical composition and mechanical properties of the all-weld metal from CGP A, CHN A and CHN B electrodes. Table 5 shows the properties of joints made by these electrodes in steel C (WELTEN 62M) under the welding conditions shown in Table 6. The strength of the weld metal made from CHN A is lower than that from the other electrodes, but satisfies the API 5LX X65 strength level.

Table 3 Diffusible hydrogen of electrode

Electrode	Diffusible hydrogen (ml/100gr)
CGP A	3.2
CHN A	31.8
CHN B	36.9

JIS method for diffusible hydrogen: specimen 12 × 20 × 130; 4 mm dia. electrode, 170 A, 25 V, 15 CPM → Water quench → Collecting hydrogen in glycerine bath at 45℃ for 48hrs

Table 4 Properties of all weld metal

Electrode			Chemical composition (%)							Mechanical properties		
Name	Type	Dia (mm)	C	Si	Mn	P	S	Ni	Mo	Y.P. kgf/mm² (Mpa)	T.S. kgf/mm² (Mpa)	vE(−45℃) kgf-m (J)
CGP A	Low H	4.0	0.09	0.61	0.89	0.020	0.011	2.68	—	55.9(548)	62.7(614)	7.7(75)
CHN A	Cellulose	4.0	0.08	0.28	0.60	0.016	0.017	2.91	—	50.5(495)	56.9(558)	8.1(79)
CHN B	Cellulose	4.0	0.11	0.26	0.68	0.013	0.010	2.36	0.16	52.7(516)	62.1(609)	7.3(72)

Table 5 Properties of weld metal of joints

Material		Chemical composition (%)							Mechanical properties		
Steel	Electrode	C	Si	Mn	P	S	Ni	Mo	Y.P. kgf/mm² (mpa)	T.S. kgf/mm² (mpa)	vE(−45℃) kgf-m (J)
WT62M	CGP A	0.10	0.52	0.88	0.019	0.014	2.67	0.01	62.1(609)	68.4(670)	8.3(81)
	CHN A	0.08	0.25	0.75	0.015	0.016	2.87	0.01	55.3(542)	62.9(616)	8.7(85)
	CHN B	0.09	0.21	0.72	0.013	0.011	2.30	0.12	58.9(577)	66.9(656)	8.6(85)

Table 6 Conditions for down hill welding at 2 o'clock position

Electrode	Pass	Dia (mm)	Current (A)	Voltage (V)	speed (mm/min)	heat input (kJ/mm)
Low hydrogen CGP A	Root	3.2	130	25	180	1.08
	Hot	4.0	200	26	330	0.95
	Filler	4.0	180−210	25−28	300−350	0.8−1.1
Cellulose CHN A CHN B	Root	3.2	130	25	290	0.67
	Hot	4.0	180	28	350	0.87
	Filler	4.0	170−200	27−30	300−370	0.7−1.1

EXPERIMENTAL RESULTS AND DISCUSSION

y-Groove Restraint Cracking Test

y-groove restraint cracking tests are very often conducted in Japan to evaluate the cold cracking susceptibility of steels. The shape and dimensions of the cracking test are shown in Figure 1. The Japanese Industrial Standard stipulates that the welding for this test should be conducted with a 4 mm diameter electrode, flat position, at 170A, 25V, 150 mm/min and 1.7 kJ/mm heat input.

The y-groove restraint cracking tests for steel A were conducted varying the diffusible hydrogen content by changing the content of hydroxide mineral of the flux-covered NSW L60 electrodes. The cracking tests for steels B, C and D were conducted using low hydrogen CGP A and high hydrogen CHN B, both of which have almost the same strength levels.

The results of the cracking tests are shown in Figure 2 in which the critical preheating temperature necessary for the prevention of root cracking

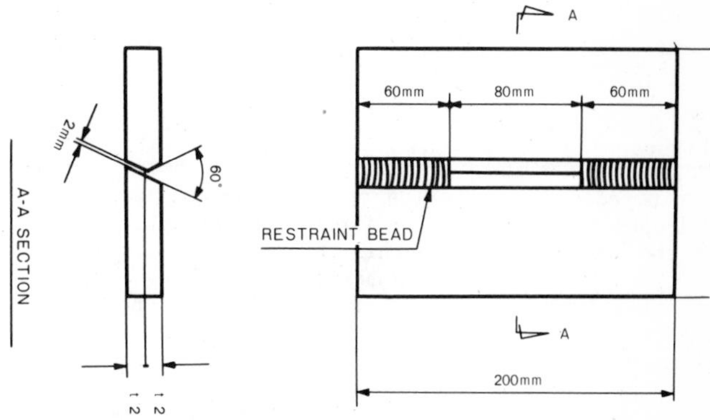

Figure 1: Shape and dimensions of y-groove restraint cracking test

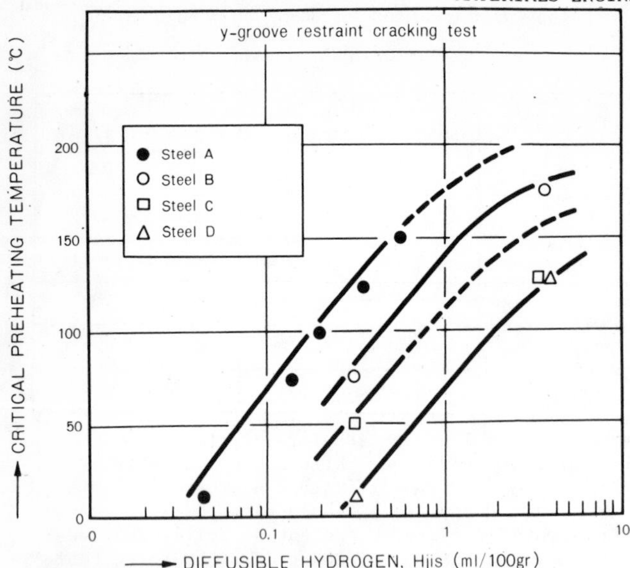

Figure 2: Relationship between critical preheat temperature and diffusible hydrogen content

Figure 3: Root crack in Y-groove restraint cracking test (38 mm thick WELTEN 62, low hydrogen electrode L60)

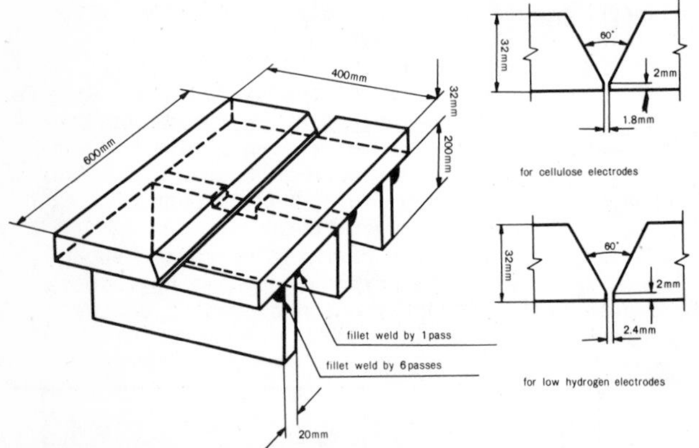

Figure 4: Dimensions of V-groove cracking test

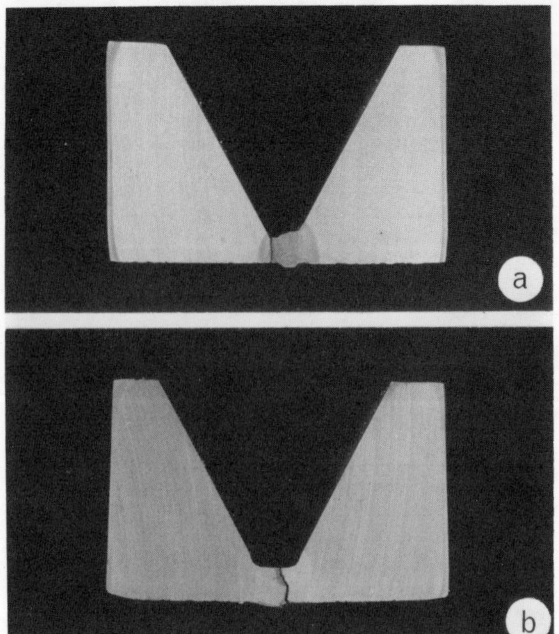

Figure 5: Root crack in V-groove (32 mm thick WELTEN 62, cellulose electrode CHN B) (a) root pass cracking test, and (b) root and hot pass cracking test

is plotted against the logarithm of the diffusible hydrogen content (Hjis). A macro-photographic example of the root cracking in this test is shown in Figure 3.

It is seen from a series of cracking tests of steel A that a linear relationship holds between the critical preheating temperature and log (Hjis), when (Hjis) is less than 10 ml/100 g. The results shown in Figure 2 imply that the root cracking susceptibility of steels may be more precisely evaluated by P_{cm} than by C_{eq}. For instance, steel D with the highest C_{eq} but the lowest P_{cm} value requires the lowest preheat temperature. The critical preheating temperature differs by 50 deg C between steels A and B. This difference can be related to the higher P_{cm} value and greater thickness of steel A.

V-Groove Root Cracking Test

Cold cracking in steel welds includes root cracking, toe cracking, under-bead cracking and weld-metal micro-cracking. Of these, root cracking is most commonly observed since the root part of the weld always contains sharp notches. Once a root crack is initiated in a higher strength steel weld, there is a risk of a root crack propagating to a through-thickness crack.

Root bead cracking tests were conducted using test specimens with the same groove and almost the same restraint as those for actual pipeline welding, as shown in F gure 4. The steels used in this test were 32 mm thick steel B, C and D. The preheating of test specimens was carried out by electrical strip heaters. Two types of root cracking test were conducted, one being root pass cracking and the other root-and-hot-pass cracking. The objective of the latter test was to determine the effect of hot pass deposition on the occurrence of root cracking. The hot pass was deposited 30 min after the completion of root pass welding. Cracking inspection was made by macrographs of the beads sectioned 48 h after weld completion. Macrophotographs of typical root cracks in a root- pass test and in a root-and-hot-pass test are shown in Figure 5. These bead macro-sections were made on steel B with the cellulosic electrode CHN B, without preheat and at an ambient temperature of approximately 10°C. In most cases, the root cracks initiated in the HAZ and then propagated into the weld metal deposited by the hot pass.

Table 7 shows the critical preheat temperature for preventing root cracking in the V-groove tests. In the root pass cracking tests, root cracking did not occur even without preheating when the low hydrogen electrodes were used, but all the steels sustained

Table 7 Critical preheating temperature for preventing root cracking

Type of steel	Type of Electrode	Root pass	Root + Hot pass *
WT 62 (B)	CGP A	≦10℃	≦10℃
	CHN B	50℃	50℃
WT 62M (C)	CGP A	≦10℃	≦10℃
	CHN B	50℃	≦10℃
2.5 Ni (D)	CGP A	≦10℃	≦10℃
	CHN B	50℃	≦10℃

* The interval between root and hot pass is 30 mins.

root cracking when cellulosic electrodes were used. This root cracking occurrence was completely prevented, irrespective of the type of steel, by preheating to 50°C. In the root-and-hot-pass cracking tests where hot pass was deposited 30 minutes after root pass, a favourable effect of hot pass on root cracking prevention was recognized in steels C and D. However, for steel B (with higher P_{cm} level) it was necessary to preheat specimens to 50°C in order to prevent cracking in root-and-hot-pass tests.

The critical preheating temperature for preventing root cracking in the V-groove cracking test is up to 100 degC lower than that in the y-groove restraint cracking test. This difference can be explained by a shape effect of the grooves. Satoh et al., (2) investigated the effect of groove shape on the occurrence of root cracking using HT 80 (80 kgf/mm^2 or 780 MPa TS) steel. The results of this investigation are shown in Figure 6.

In the welding of a V-groove, such as the X-C groove shown in Figure 6, a bending compressive stress is exerted by the microscopic bending deformation due to the combined effect of joint restraint and thermal stress. The restraint tensile stress caused by shrinkage of weld metal is then compensated by the compressive stress, so that the root cracking susceptibility in V-groove welding can be significant y reduced.

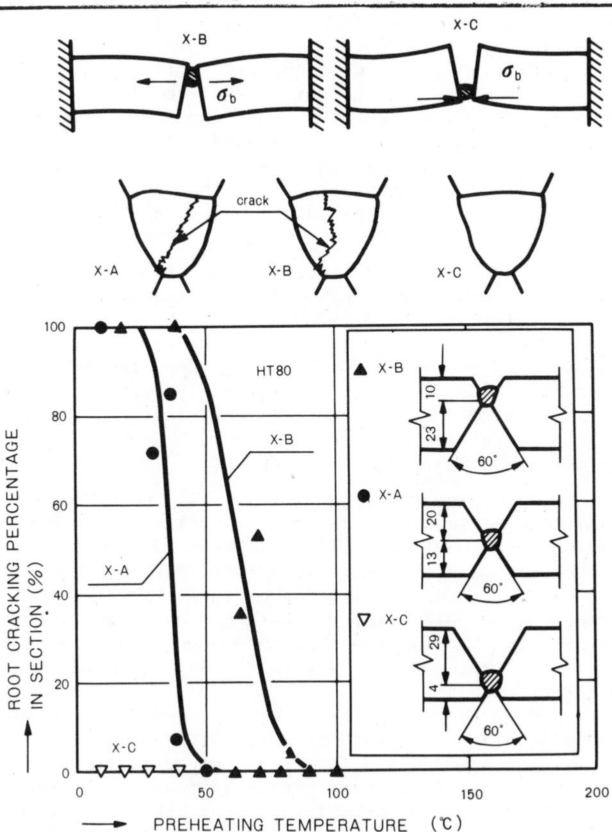

Figure 6: Effect of groove shape on critical preheating temperature

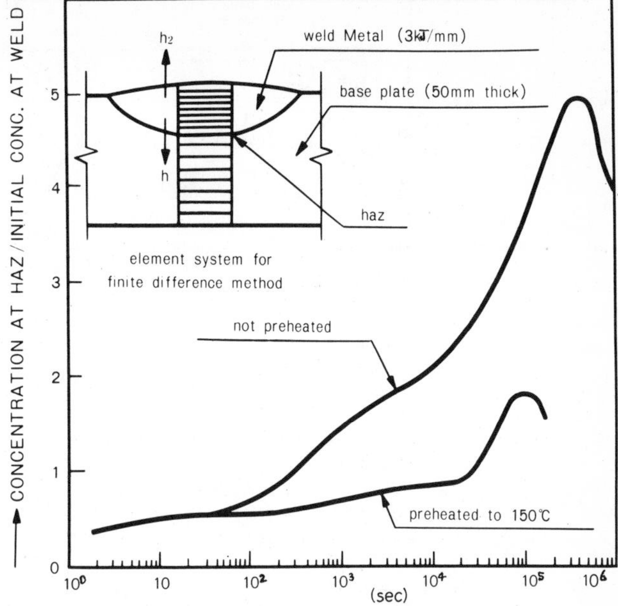

Figure 7: Computation of hydrogen accummulation at heat affected zone

Incubation Period for Root Cracking

It is important to know the incubation period of root cracking, since the maximum allowable interval between root pass and hot pass must be determined in the welding fabrication procedure. To understand the incubation period for cold cracking, the role of hydrogen must be determined.

Some authors have solved the unsteady diffusion problem of hydrogen accummulation in the heat affected zone by the finite difference method, employing the assumption that the HAZ is subject to plastic deformation by thermal stresses and that the activity of hydrogen decreases at the HAZ while increasing the potential for hydrogen occlusion (3). The result of numerical analysis on the effect of preheating treatment on the accummulation of hydrogen in the heat affected zone of a base plate is shown in Figure 7.

If cold cracking occurs when the content of hydrogen accummulating at the hydrogen trapping site exceeds the critical level, it is clear from Figure 7 that it takes some time for hydrogen cracking to occur. This time is supposed to be the incubation period for cold cracking. The hydrogen accummulation curves in Figure 7 show that preheating the steel to 150°C reduces the maximum level of hydrogen accummulation below the critical level so that cold cracking does not occur. The incubation period also becomes longer as the preheat temperature is raised.

In order to experimentally determine the incubation time, acoustic emission caused by the initiation of cracking was measured. The apparatus for measuring acoustic emission consists of a Dunegan* D750 sensor, a Dunegan* 801P preamplifier (40 dB gain, 10 kHz to

* Dunegan Endevco, San Juan Capistrano, Calif. 92675

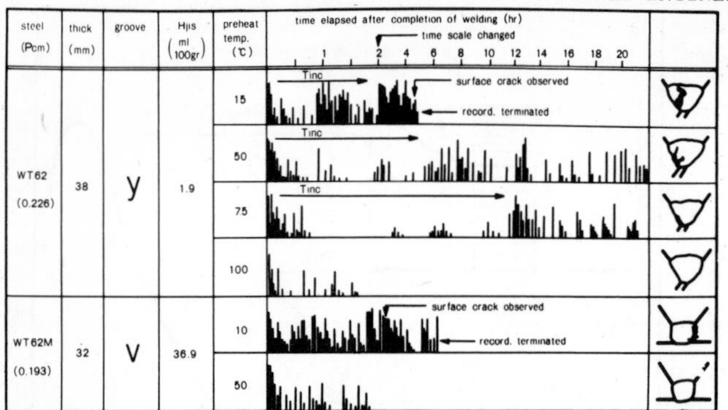

Figure 8: Acoustic emission signals due to occurrence of cold cracking

2 MHz) and a main amplifier with 18 dB gain. A sensor was attached to a cracking test piece 20 mm from the groove, using high temperature grease as couplant. Some examples of recorded output are shown in Figure 8. Although the acoustic emission measured after the test specimen completely cools down is believed to correspond with the occurrence of cold cracking, emission measured shortly after the completion of welding might include that due to shrinkage of the test piece. Therefore, it is difficult to make an accurate determination of the incubation period from the acoustic emission record. Rough estimates of incubation period are shown by "Tinc" in Figure 8.

It is seen from Figure 8 that the incubation period for root cracking in Y-groove restraint cracking tests increases as preheating temperature is increased. This experimental result agrees with the effect of preheating temperature on incubation period estimated from the theoretical calculation, shown in Figure 7.

Measurement of acoustic emission was also made for the V-groove root cracking tests. However, the incubation period could not be estimated from the records of acoustic emission since it was impossible to distinguish the acoustic emission due to cracking from that due to thermal shrinkage. The incubation period of cold cracking in V-grooves by cellulose electrodes is relatively short. As already shown in Table 7, root cracking was observed in steel B, but not in steels C and D, when hot pass was deposited 30 min after the root pass using cellulose electrodes without preheating. This suggests that the incubation time for root cracking in steel B is less than 30 min and that for steels C and D is more.

It is concluded from the theoretical calculation and the experimental results that the incubation period for root cracking becomes longer with a decrease in P_{cm}, with a decrease in hydrogen content in weld metal and with an increase in preheat temperature.

Test of Micro-Cracking in Weld Metal

Root cracking can be prevented by depositing the hot pass within the incubation period of cracking of the root bead, as described above. However, micro-cracking in weld metal deposited by cellulosic electrodes might not be prevented unless preheating is carried out to a sufficiently high temperature. Multi-pass weld cracking tests were conducted to investigate the preheat and inter-pass temperatures for preventing hydrogen-induced micro-cracking in weld metal in joints of 32 mm wall-thickness pipe.

The steel C was welded with low-hydrogen electrode CGP A and cellulosic electrodes CHN A and CHN B. The shape of the test piece and the groove were the same as for the root cracking tests. Multi-pass welding was conducted using the vertical down technique at the 2 o'clock position and the welding conditions

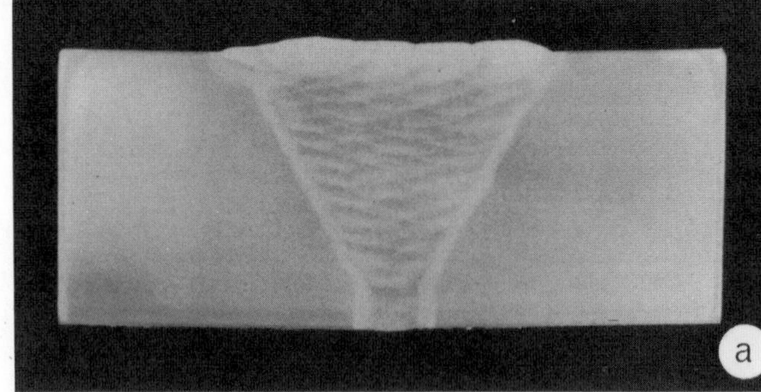

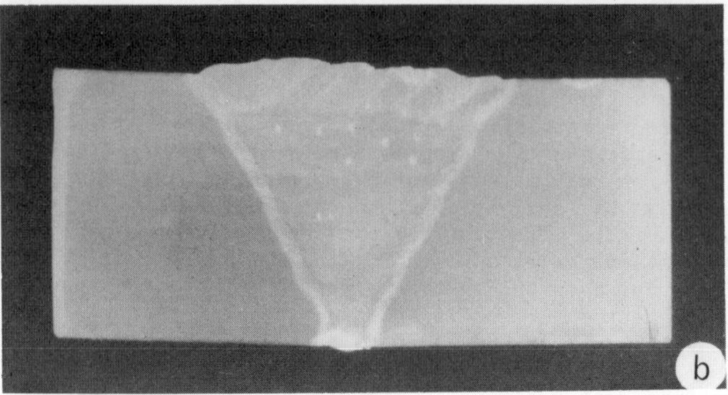

Figure 9: Macrograph of V-groove multi-pass weld, 32 mm thick WELTEN 62 M, interpass temperature of 100°C, (a) low-hydrogen electrode CGP A, (b) cellulosic electrode CHN B

given in Table 6. The cracking was inspected by sectioning test pieces 48 h after the completion of welding. Macro-photographs of joints made by low-hydrogen electrode CGP A and cellulosic electrode CHN B are shown in Figure 9.

Figure 9(b) shows a number of micro-cracks in the weld metal made by cellulosic electrodes. The micro-cracks are about 0.5 mm long and located between the penultimate and the middle layers at about half the pipe wall thickness. All welded joints were inspected by a radiographic method before being sectioned. However, the radiographic inspection method completely failed to detect these micro-cracks.

Figure 10 shows the relationship between the average number of micro-cracks longer than 0.2 mm and the inter-pass temperatures. No micro-cracks were observed in the sections of welds made by the low-hydrogen electrodes with an interpass temperature as low as 50°C. In order to completely prevent micro-cracking in weld metal made from cellulosic electrodes, the inter-pass temperature must be kept above 175°C for CHN A and above 200°C for CHN B.

According to Okumura et al. (4), occurrence of micro-cracking in weld metal is influenced by both the strength level and diffusible hydrogen content of the weld metal. Using a constant interpass temperature of 100°C, they observed a critical relationship between HT 80 weld metal strength and hydrogen content (Figure 11). It is seen that the occurrence of micro-cracking is related linearly to the logarithm of hydrogen content.

To prevent occurrence of micro-cracks in high-strength weld metal, such as HT80, it is necessary to keep pre-heating and interpass temperatures sufficiently high or to conduct post-heat treatment directly after the completion of welding, even when welding is performed with low-hydrogen electrodes. Micro-cracks are not initiated in the weld metal in joints of heavy X65 steel if low-hydrogen electrodes are

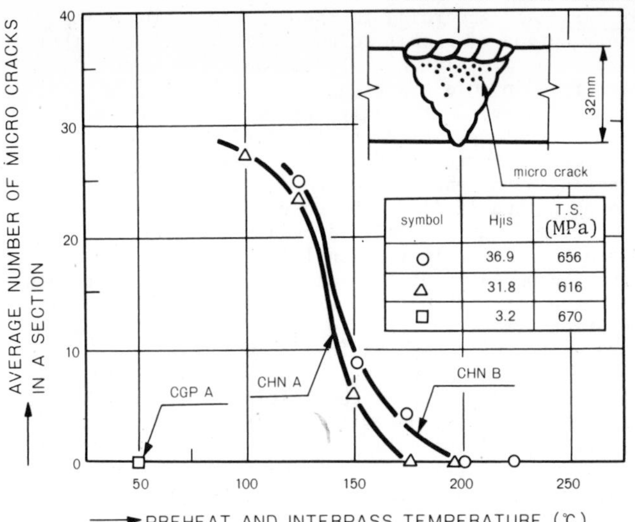

symbol	Hjis	T.S. (MPa)
○	36.9	656
△	31.8	616
□	3.2	670

Figure 10: Relationship between occurrence of micro-cracking in weld metal and preheat and inter-pass temperature

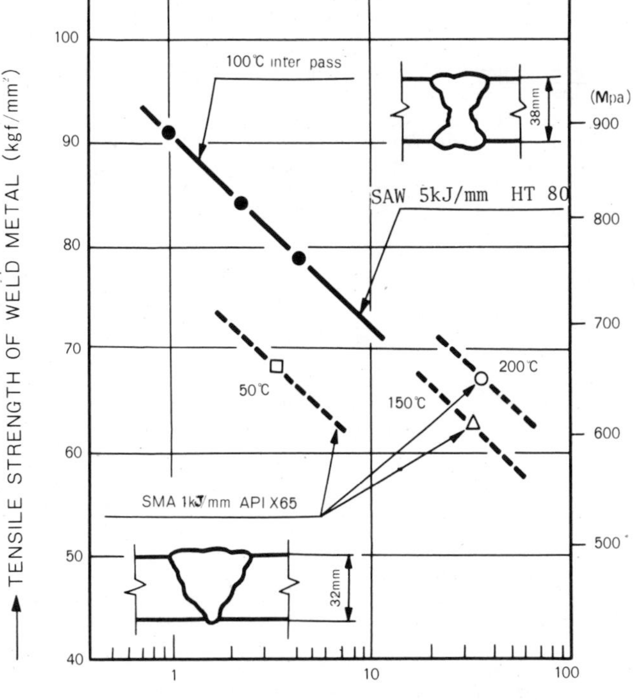

Figure 11: Effect of diffusible hydrogen content on tensile strength of weld metal

used, since the strength level of this steel is much lower than that of HT80 steel. However, micro-cracking is likely to occur in weld metal of X65 steel when cellulosic electrodes are used, as can be seen in Figure 11 by the extrapolation of Okumura's empirical line to a high hydrogen region. The critical preheat and interpass temperatures are estimated from the empirical line in Figure 11 to be 100°C, assuming that the weld metal strength is 64 kgf/mm^2 (627 MPa) and that diffusible hydrogen content is 35 ml/100 g.

In the welding of heavy wall X65 pipe steel using cellulosic electrodes, to prevent micro-cracking in weld metal it is necessary to keep the interpass temperature above 175°C. The large difference between the estimated interpass temperature and that obtained from experiment can be attributed to the difference in the welding heat input for the HT80 and X65 experiments. HT80 steel was welded by 5.0 kJ/mm submerged arc welding and the present experiment was carried out by vertical down manual arc welding with heat input as low as 1.0 kJ/mm. Sufficient effusion of hydrogen from the bead surface every welding pass cannot be expected due to the higher cooling rate of a weld when lower heat-input welding is performed.

It was shown that 200°C was required to prevent micro-cracking in 32 mm thick welds made by cellulosic electrode CHN B. However, micro-cracks in weld metal were not observed when 18.2 mm wall thickness API 5LX X70 pipes were welded by CHN B, even while keeping the interpass temperature to as low as 100°C. Rabensteiner et al. (5) observed that no cracking occurred in 16.3 mm wall thickness X60 and X70 pipe joints welded by cellulosic electrodes with the interpass temperature kept at 100°C. It follows that the occurrence of micro-cracking is influenced not only by the strength of weld metal and hydrogen content but also by the pipe wall thickness.

The interpass temperature must be kept above 200°C to prevent the occurence of micro-cracking in weld metal of heavy wall pipe if cellulosic electrodes are used. It is desirable to use low-hydrogen electrodes for filler and capping passes in welding of heavy wall line pipe.

Cracking in Heat Affected Zone of Base Metal

All the API 5LX X65 steels used in the present experiments were quenched-and-tempered steels. Root cracks at the HAZ of the base steel were observed in the V-groove cracking tests when root beads were made by cellulosic electrodes without preheating treatment. However, the incubation period for root cracking was more than 30 min when the cold cracking susceptibility index, P_{cm}, was less than 0.20. The root cracking is easily prevented by depositing the hot pass within 30 min of the root pass. Despite the experimental fact that a number of micro-cracks were observed in weld metal deposited by cellulosic electrodes, no hydrogen-induced cracks were observed in the heat affected zones of the base plates used in the cracking tests. This must be attributed to the lower cold-cracking susceptibility of the steels.

Heavy wall pipelines at pumping and cooling stations might have joints other than V-groove circumferential ones. As shown in Figure 6, root cracking is more likely to occur in X- or K-grooves. It is recommended that steels less susceptible to cold cracking be used for heavy wall pipe for Arctic use, and that cold-cracking susceptibility be evaluated using P_{cm} rather than carbon equivalent, particularly for relatively low carbon steels.

CONCLUSIONS

A number of cold cracking tests were conducted to investigate root cracking and multi-pass weld cracking. Steels used in the tests were 32 mm thick API 5LX X65 quenched and tempered steels, some of which possess high toughness at low temperatures for Arctic use. The welding for cold cracking tests was carried out by cellulosic electrodes and low-hydrogen electrodes which were developed for use in vertical down welding of line pipe. The results of the cracking tests are as follows:

1) The susceptibility of low carbon steels to cold cracking can be evaluated more accurately by the cold cracking susceptibility index, P_{cm}, than by the carbon equivalent, C_{eq}.

2) The incubation period for cold cracking

is longer for steels less susceptible to cold cracking. The incubation period for root cracking in the HAZ is more than 30 min for steels with P_{cm} less than 0.20, when welding is carried out with cellulosic electrodes without preheat. Root cracking is prevented by depositing the hot pass within the incubation period of root pass cracking.

3) The occurrence of micro-cracking in weld metal is governed by the strength level of the weld metal, diffusible hydrogen content and wall thickness of pipe. The critical preheating and interpass temperatures in preventing occurrence of micro-cracks in weld metal are as high as 200°C when 32 mm wall thickness pipe is welded by cellulosic electrodes. On the other hand, no micro-cracks are observed, even with a low interpass temperature, if low-hydrogen electrodes are used.

For the prevention of cracking and achievement of faster welding fabrication, heavy wall pipe should be welded using cellulosic electrodes for root and hot passes and low-hydrogen electrodes for filler and capping passes.

REFERENCES

1. K. Satoh, S. Matsui, K. Horikawa, K. Bessyo, T. Okumura, International Institute Welding Document, IX-834-73, 1973.
2. K. Satoh and S. Matsui, Japan Welding Society, Report No. WDA-9-73, 1973.
3. K. Kohira, T. Yatake, N. Yurioka, International Institute Welding Document, IX-941-76, 1976.
4. T. Okumura and K. Horikawa, 1st International Symposium of Cracking, Japan Welding Society, Kyoto, Japan, 1971, vol. 1, IA7.1-7.17.
5. G. Rabensteiner, H. Schabereiter and H. Königshofer, Z. Schweisstechnik, 1975, vol. 66 (2), pp. 37-48.

DISCUSSION

B. A. Graville (Dominion Bridge): Your excellent paper gives further confirmation of the need to use alternative estimates of weldability like P_{cm} rather than the conventional CE for lower carbon materials. I would only add that under rapid cooling conditions nickel appears to be less detrimental than either the CE or P_{cm} suggest (it may be slightly beneficial) and this is supported by your results on steel D.

You make the assumption that the delay in root cracking is caused by the time for hydrogen diffusion to the HAZ. This may be an oversimplification There are several reasons for delay which may operate all at once. First, the cooling period, since hydrogen embrittlement does not occur at elevated temperatures. Secondly, gross diffusion of hydrogen, as you suggest. Thirdly, the development of reaction stress which may take several hours. Fourth, the delay characteristic of hydrogen embrittlement related to local diffusion.

I'll stop here!

A final question - do you think the microcracks are significant? Would you not be happy to leave them in the weld metal?

N. Yurioka: According to the P_{cm} expression, the contribution of nickel to cold cracking is 1/60 that of carbon. I think nickel does not play a significant role in cold cracking. The high cracking resistance of steel D is mainly due to low carbon martensitic structures which greatly differ from medium or high carbon martensitic ones. We assumed that cold cracking occurrence is governed by concentration of hydrogen locally diffusing to the HAZ, not by gross diffusion. In my local hydrogen accumulation theory, based on the chemical potential of hydrogen, hydrogen never accumulates at the locally strained region such as notch tip portions, at elevated temperatures. The reaction stress in welds is caused when the temperature of the weld becomes less than about 600°C. The level of reaction stress does not change so much on further cooling to room temperature. However, hydrogen cracking occurs at below 100°C. The reaction stress cannot explain the delayed cracking phenomenon, although the reaction stress is one of the causes for cracking. Our assumption may be oversimplified but it can explain delayed phenomena pretty well.

The critical COD values of the weld metals of the tested covered electrodes (CGPA, CHNA, CHNB) exceeded 0.15 mm at -40°C. A crack of a few mm length is acceptable, based on COD theory. Therefore, microcracks are not significant. However, I would not be happy to leave them in weld metal.

B. Fruck (Imperial Oil): Low-hydrogen electrodes are commonly selected to control hydrogen-induced cracking. What is not common is a downhand low-hydrogen electrode for pipeline welding.

Is the electrode's fluidity combatted by a specific design feature in the rod, by welder specialty, by welding procedure design, or by a combination of all of them?

N. Yurioka: The fluidity of low-hydrogen vertical-down electrodes was controlled by the design feature in the rod alone. To cope with a dripping problem of molten slag when using low-hydrogen rods in downhill welding, the melting point and viscosity of the slag were appropriately increased over those used in conventional low-hydrogen electrodes.

C. A. Parrini (Italsider): Did you analyse the effect of room temperature during welding on hydrogen cold cracks?

N. Yurioka: Yes we did. There are many tests evaluating the weldability of steel. They are Lehigh tests, y-groove cracking tests and implant tests. In these tests, a single pass weld is made and then a specimen is cooled down to the ambient temperature. The occurrence of cold cracking is greatly influenced by the ambient temperature. Our results in y-groove cracking tests showed that cracking is more likely to occur as the ambient temperature decreases, although the crack growth rate is quite slow at low temperatures. However, in actual welding, multi-pass techniques are usual; in these circumstances, as long as the interpass temperature is maintained, the ambient temperature does not effect hydrogen cracking, even when it is sub-zero.

SESSION SUMMARY

A. B. Rothwell and J. D. Embury

At the end of these sessions one perceives a degree of optimism, in that the pipeline companies are convinced that they have the knowledge to build a safe system and the steel industry had demonstrated its confidence in its ability to supply pipes to the required levels of quality on a regular basis - provided the price is economically viable! However, there was considerable debate as to the relative merits of different approaches to such questions as the provision of adequate resistance to ductile crack propagation, but the general impression is that there is a fair degree of confidence in the industry's ability to deal with these problems in practice.

Against this generally positive picture, some areas of ignorance remain which are troublesome both from the fundamental viewpoint and from the viewpoint of the basis for Arctic design. Many of the steels proposed for these applications are based on the relatively novel concept of manipulating initial yield and strain-hardening behaviour rather than absolute yield strength level at the plate stage, in order to satisfy flattened strap yield strength requirements. (It is interesting to speculate, in fact, whether these steels would have become so popular if ring-expansion yield strength had been specified, particularly in the case of UOE pipe which casts real doubt on the method of establishing criteria and specifications for these materials.) While the behaviour of the type of microstructure involved (typically, hard islands of martensite/retained austenite in a softer matrix) is quite well documented for uniaxial tension, the much more complex, and variable, strain path in actual pipe mill operations is extremely difficult to deal with. It is encouraging that efforts to clarify this area are being actively pursued in Canada at this time, particularly in the light of the upsurge of interest in similar structures in thin strip for automotive applications, where even more complex forming operations may be involved.

Turning to the question of toughness, two areas of uncertainty still exist. In the first place, it is apparent that the various empirical correlations for the arrest toughness of the pipe body only work reliably within the range of conditions already studied: as with most empirical correlations, interpolation is usually safe, but extrapolation is extremely hazardous! This means that, in the present state of more fundamental knowledge, (lack of a universally applicable theoretical model which can be correlated with QC tests), advances in operating parameters can only be made by carrying out a sufficient number of extremely expensive full-scale tests. Failing this, a crack arrestor technique must be adopted, with its attendant expense and hazards. It is thus clear that the fundamental work going on in this area is vitally important.

The initiation toughness of weld zones is also of great interest and again, while much is known on the subject, the quantitative relationship between toughness, microstructure and welding parameters, in both weld metal and heat-affected zone, is only just being established. In the case of the HAZ, while valid toughness measurements probably can be made in the research laboratory, as was pointed out in the discussion, it is difficult to see how a useful quality control test could be specified at the present time.

As regards field-welding, it seems clear that the technical knowledge needed to ensure high quality joints is available. As some recent experiences with pipeline construction have indicated, the principal problems may be administrative and managerial rather than technical.

Finally, it is worthwhile to mention the various new techniques which have been discussed for the production of even higher-strength materials. It seems clear that we now stand close to the borderline of what can be done with existing technology, and that further advances will rely on processing routes which will necessitate considerable capital investment. While the plant involved could obviously be used for the production of existing quality levels, it seems likely that the investment can only be justified by a significant increase in the mechanical properties exploitable by the pipeline companies. Yield strengths around the 100 ksi (700 MPa) level and high toughness in heavy-walled pipe down to extremely low temperatures have been mentioned. It is important for future progress that the pipeline companies be capable of assessing the economic implications of these developments, and that the regulatory bodies be able to satisfy themselves as to the validity of the resulting system designs. Some form of coordinated programme would appear to be necessary to meet these requirements.

FRACTURE - SAFE DESIGN

INTRODUCTION

G. T. Hahn

Arctic engineers can draw on two fracture safe design practices. The conventional practice is to select a material at least as tough as one that has given satisfactory performance in service in a similar design. This approach can employ the Charpy energy, a transition temperature, or some other measure of toughness, and is widely used, as evidenced by the papers by Schwartzbart, Gondoh, et al. and Eiber and Maxey. We now recognize that fractures can be caused by isolated crack-like defects after these have become enlarged by prolonged fatigue or environmental cracking. For this reason, extensive and long-term service experience is a prerequisite. The practice cannot be applied to radically new designs, or to designs with new materials or new fabrication methods for which there is no record of service performance. The Comet aircraft failures are the classic example. Here, the inability of the conventional practice to assure the safety of a new design cost the U.K. supremacy in commercial aviation.

In the last 20 years an analytical method of fracture safe design has evolved. This new approach is based on an analysis of the mechanics of crack extension (fracture mechanics) and contains the following elements:

(i) Expressions of the fundamental resistance to crack extension under monotonic, cyclic and sustained loading, and practical methods of measuring these quantities.

(ii) Fracture mechanics analyses for calculating the crack extension driving force for different crack sizes, component geometries and loading conditions.

(iii) Nondestructive inspection methods for detecting cracks and measuring their size and shape.

Taken together, these three elements make it possible to predict the failure of a component without further experimentation or service experience. They also provide a basis for devising a fracture control plan: a design, toughness specification, and inspection strategy for assuring against fracture during the service life of a component.

The new fracture mechanics approach for safe design has obvious attractions for Arctic engineering, but it is no panacea. The methodology is currently well developed only for stationary and slowly extending cracks in heavy sections and for relatively low toughness values. The problem of crack arrest in pipes has not been fully analysed. For this reason, the papers on crack arrest in pipes by Shoemaker et al. and by Eiber and Maxey reflect the old, full scale service experience approach. The application of fracture mechanics requires a large investment in fracture toughness and cyclic- and sustained-load crack approach rate tests for both base metal and welds. Such work has only recently begun for the steels used in ship, bridge, rail and nuclear pressure vessel construction. Cracking problems are touched on by Ogle but this paper does not emphasize the massive data collection task involved. A large investment in flaw detection is also required. The virtues of the acoustic emission methods of detection are discussed in the papers of Hay and Bassim and by Nagumo and Watanabe. The special problem of flaws resulting from field damage that may occur after installation and inspection is examined by Jeglic. It seems clear the designers of Arctic structures will make good use of both the conventional and the new fracture safe design practices. They will draw on service experience when available, and on fracture mechanics principles whenever innovations in design and materials are called for and when unusual service conditions are encountered.

DETECTION OF INCIPIENT BRITTLE FRACTURE BY ACOUSTIC EMISSION

D. Robert Hay and M. Nabil Bassim
Centre de Développement Technologique
Ecole Polytechnique
C.P. 6079, Station A
Montreal, Canada

Acoustic emission is a powerful new supplementary nondestructive testing technique. This paper reviews the basic technical aspects and application of acoustic emission and describes recent laboratory and field observations. The fracture mechanics basis for the detection of "active" flaws in the subcritical region is outlined. The general features of acoustic emission and procedures for its application are described. Approaches to inspection via conventional nondestructive testing and acoustic emission are compared. Theoretical and experimental correlations between acoustic emission and fracture mechanics developed by the authors, as well as examples of its application in their field work, are described.

INTRODUCTION

Achieving reliable performance of load-bearing engineering structures involves a complex interaction of the philosophy of design, of materials technology, of inspection methodology, and of engineering economics. Much of the interest in materials technology for northern applications focusses on the brittle fracture problem in ferrous construction materials arising from low service temperatures and the costs of structural failure in terms of the direct and indirect costs to the structural system and to the delicate northern ecology. Those load bearing structures which preoccupy the northern engineering community and which involve reliability on a large scale include pipelines and LNG tankers. While design of structures on a strength-basis is founded on well-established engineering principles, fracture-based design philosophy is an area under active development at present. In addition, current fracture control philosophy involves not only sound fracture-based design criteria but also a follow-up inspection plan for pre-service and in-service inspection.

Acoustic emission (AE) testing is a relatively new nondestructive testing technique for evaluating the integrity of load-bearing stuctures (1). It is different from conventional NDT methods in that it involves a passive, remote inspection philosophy rather than active probing of the entire area of interest. Thus, in general, acoustic emission offers the potential of an increased efficiency of inspection over conventional nondestructive testing as well as a higher sensitivity to defects which are likely to lead to failure.

Since acoustic emission involves a relatively recent technology, this paper reviews the technique itself and then proceeds to show how this method, unique among NDT procedures, interacts closely with the developing concepts of fracture control and materials technology, and why it is likely to play an important role in assuring the reliability of structural materials used in the North.

FRACTURE CONTROL PHILOSOPHY

The problem of brittle fracture of structural materials has occupied the attention of designers and users of structural and mechanical components throughout our industrialized age. The scope of the problem ranges from down-time and repair inconveniences in operating equipment to the full scale, dramatic failures of large structures. It is not necessary to go to the far North to obtain examples of the latter catastrophes since the well-documented "Liberty" ship experience and the failure of the Three Rivers (Duplessis) Bridge occurred at latitudes in which we in Canada normally inhabit.

The philosophy developed to prevent failure by fracture recognizes a basic fact that materials contain flaws. It then proceeds to specify the size of a crack which is tolerable in the structure under the conditions for which it is designed. This is done in several ways ranging from the closed-form analytical solutions of fracture mechanics to the graphical representations of the accumulated experience derived from the analysis of a large body of data on actual service failures. Linear elastic fracture mechanics provides a relationship for brittle metals:

$$Q\sigma^2\pi C_C = (K_{Ic})^2 \qquad (1)$$

where σ is the stress on the component, C_C is the size of crack which is unstable under the stress σ, Q is a geometrical factor which depends upon the

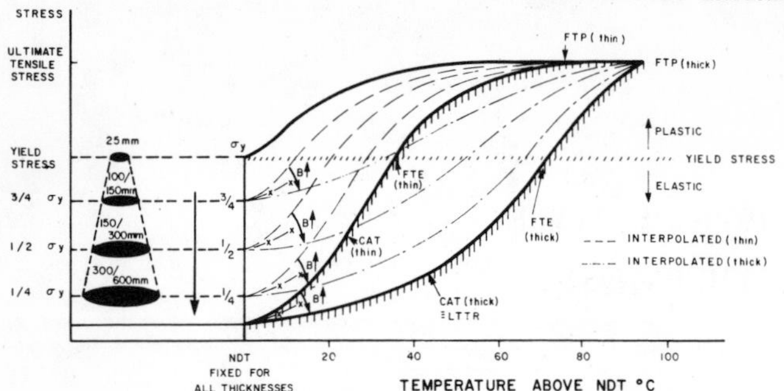

Figure 1: Fracture Analysis Diagram (after ref 2)

geometry of the crack and the component, and K_{Ic} is the plane-strain fracture toughness, a property of the metal. For more ductile materials, the Fracture Analysis Diagram (Figure 1) provides a similar relationship for ductile materials (2). Regardless of the approach, the objective of the analysis is to provide a quantitative relationship between the size at which a flaw becomes unstable and propagates catastrophically and the stress to which the structure is submitted. The general form of such a relationship is shown schematically in Figure 2. An inspection component is required in a fracture control plan to insure that the material contains no flaws of the critical size or greater.

CHARACTERISTICS OF ACOUSTIC EMISSION

Acoustic emission, also known as "stress-wave emission" is a transient elastic wave generated by the rapid release of energy within a material. It is a phenomenon belonging to the same group of seismic effects which accompany earthquakes and the crackling sounds from wooden structures which occur prior to and during failure. The "cry" of tin as it is bent is another phenomenon in this category. However, in addition to these examples where the stress-wave emission is converted into audible sounds, emissions are also present in many other materials at much higher frequencies and much lower amplitudes as well. Advances in electronic instrumentation have made it possible to use this phenomenon for the engineering evaluation of the mechanical integrity of materials and structures as well as for materials research.

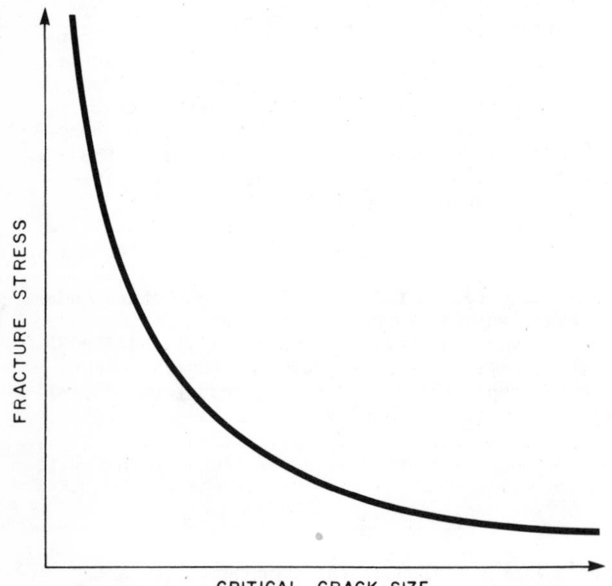

Figure 2: Stress versus critical crack length

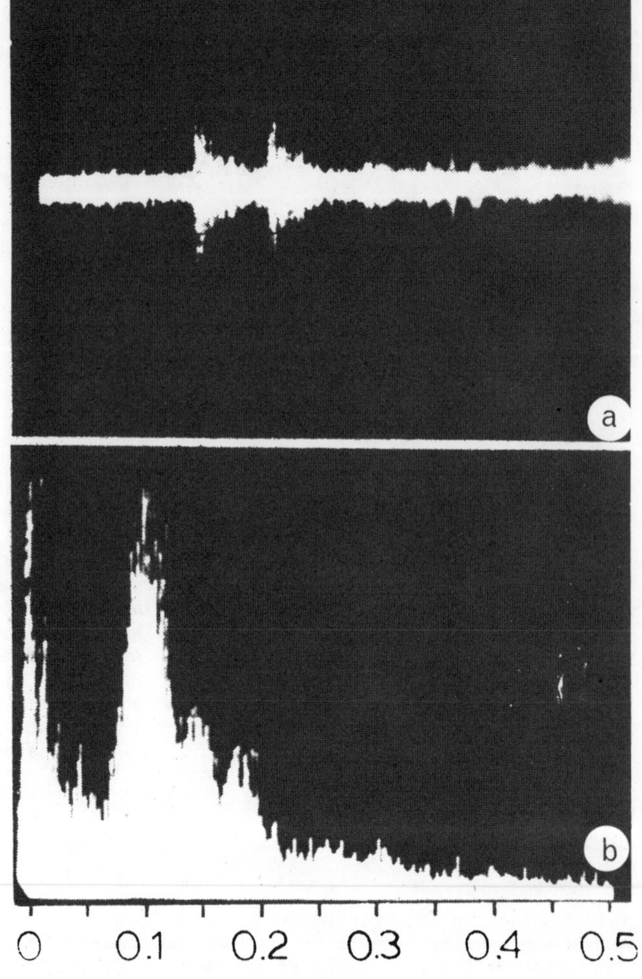

Figure 3: (a) Typical acoustic emission signal from a mild steel; (b) its frequency spectrum

There are various mechanisms in solids which are potential sources of acoustic emission. Foremost among these are plastic deformation by dislocation motion and crack nucleation and propagation. Other possible sources include twinning, martensite phase transformation, and movement of magnetic domain walls.

The individual acoustic emission is a short-time event, typically of a duration between 10^{-7} and 10^{-3} sec. Such a short-duration pulse contains a broad spectrum of information in the frequency domain. While the amplitude of the pulse is higher at low frequencies, the fact that the pulse does contain frequency components up to a few MHz provides a certain flexibility in designing acoustic emission systems for particular applications.

The displacements involved can be as low as 10^{-12} in. (10^{-11} mm). With conventional transducers, amplifications of 10^3 to 10^7 are required.

A typical emission from a 1015 steel is shown in Figure 3a. It is characterized by a rapid initial rise-time followed by a decay over a period of the order of milliseconds. Also shown (Figure 3b) is a frequency spectrum taken from such a pulse, which illustrates the broad band of information contained in the frequency domain. It is convenient to regard the pulse as a damped sinusoid for purposes of analysis. The structure of the pulse is a complex function of the nature of the source itself, the internal reflections and other modifications of the emission wave as it propagates to the transducer. Subsequently, the transducer imposes its own characteristics on the pulse.

ACOUSTIC EMISSION SYSTEMS

Generally, there are three basic AE system categories. There are general purpose or special application single-channel systems, dual-channel systems developed for monitoring one-dimensional systems such as welding processes, and multi-channel systems used for structural evaluations and for surveillance. Typical data presentations include the total number of emission events or the rate at which events occur as a function of a test parameter such as load, pressure or time; the number of transducer oscillations (ring-downs)or rate of transducer oscillations as a function of a test parameter; computational data for location of the position of the sources of emission.

An acoustic emission system (Figure 4) includes the material and structure to be evaluated, the transducer, the signal conditioning section, the analysis section, the display section, and the material/transducer interfaces. The nature of the material and of the overall structure of which it is a part, the mode of deformation, the nature and positions of the transducers and the material/transducer interfaces all act to determine the type of electrical signal obtained at the output of the transducer. The variables which largely determine the type of signal to be processed are found at the front (transducer) end of the system. Further back, the usual system comprises electronics designed for such features as high-gain, low-noise amplification, advanced signal conditioning operations, and rapid data processing and presentation.

The conditioned signals are transmitted to the computer for source location analysis, event counting and other analyses. Cathode ray tube displays include source position and other data, such as accumulated events as a function of a test parameter, and source position data printouts.

The system is calibrated using a pulser or other device for putting a signal into the structure, both for establishing gain and threshold settings and for calibrating the triangulation instrumentation. Generally, these data are recorded on tape so that the information can be replayed into the acoustic emission system for further analysis. Both the ASME and ASTM are actively working on the development of codes for applying acoustic emission to the inspection of structures.

COMPARISON OF INSPECTION PHILOSOPHIES

Conventional NonDestructive Testing

Conventional nondestructive tests require that the critical areas of a structure be traversed point by point with a probing medium such as dyes, magnetic particles, and/or ultrasonics, x-ray, or electromagnetic (eddy current) radiation. Perturbations of the probing medium due to defects are then observed and interpreted by experienced personnel as to their severity. Interpretation is referenced either to the operator's experience in less than critical situations or, in critical structures such as nuclear reactors, to extensive reference codes. The attempt is made today to quantitatively evaluate flaw significance by comparing the measured flaw size with critical flaw sizes calculated using fracture mechanics. In addition, the calculation of critical flaw sizes provides the inspector with an indication of the sensitivity required in the NDT method used.

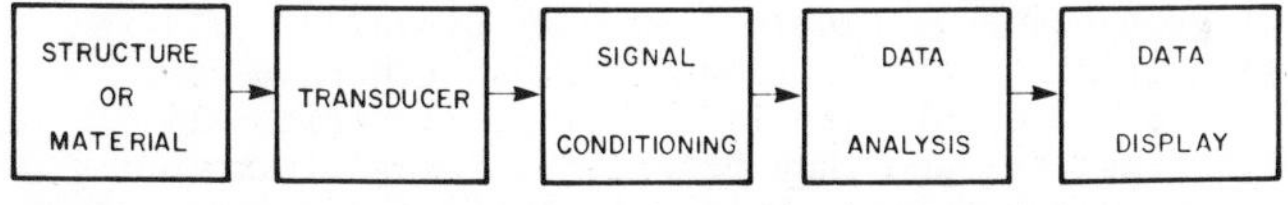

Figure 4: Components of an acoustic emission system

Acoustic Emission Testing

Most metallic engineering structures are designed in materials which exhibit some ductility. In such materials, crack growth proceeds incrementally before reaching the critical size and is accompanied by plastic deformation in the crack-tip zone. Acoustic emission depends on such subcritical crack activity and upon general or localized yielding for release of stress waves which are detected at the transducers. Thus, only the flaws which are active under loading are detected. By testing under monotonically increasing load, only the larger flaws are detected at the low loads as they are the first to approach criticality (Figure 2). When the load increases, the sensitivity increases as smaller flaws approach criticality. The sensitivity of acoustic emission is not, therefore, determined by inherent characteristics of a probing medium, but rather by the strength of the source, the detection capability of the instrumentation, and the background noise of the environment in which the structure is located.

While acoustic emission offers an efficiency of inspection due to its remote monitoring capability, it also offers an additional efficiency in searching only for those flaws which are "active" under actual or simulated loading conditions.

ACOUSTIC EMISSION DISCRIMINATION TECHNIQUES

Because the sentitivity with which acoustic emission testing can detect flaw activity depends on the level of the signal available for data processing and the signal-to-noise ratio, various techniques have been developed to distinguish acoustic emission signals and to extract them from ambient noise. Basic discrimination is usually carried out by accepting only those signals which exceed a voltage threshold set just above the ambient noise level. Since the acoustic emission signal comprises a wide band of information (Figure 3) including frequencies into the low MHz region, it is possible to eliminate low frequency noise by filtering. Usually the low-pass limit is set at a minimum of 100 kHz. In addition,discrimination based upon pulse rise-time is carried out by recognizing only those data whose rise-time exceeds a pre-set value. This is accomplished by closing the system down for a pre-determined period when a low rise-time signal is detected or by allowing the threshold to float up on the low rise-time signal (Figure 5). In multi-channel systems, discrimination can be effected by only accepting signals from selected areas of the structure. This is illustrated in Figure 6 for the master/slave technique. In large triangulation arrays more elaborate spatial acceptance criteria may be established.

In addition to the time-domain techniques, techniques are being developed in the frequency domain, to discriminate between acoustic emission signals and noise, and to identify sources.

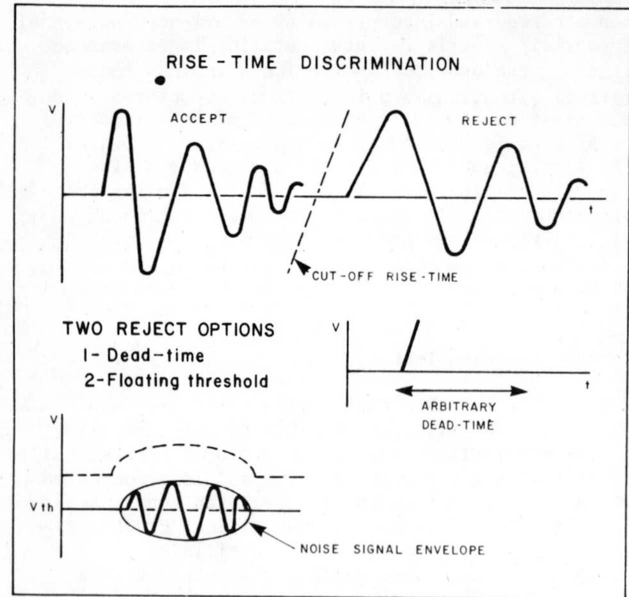

Figure 5: Noise discrimination by control of the threshold level.

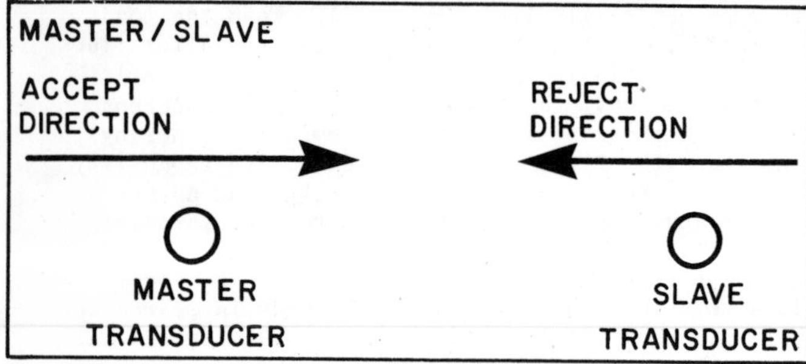

Figure 6: The master/slave principle for spatial noise discrimination

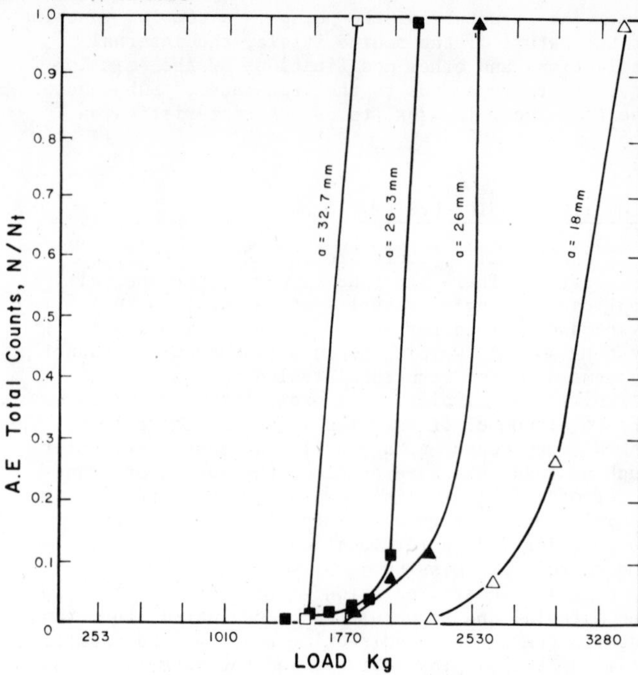

Figure 7: Effect of applied load on total emission counts for specimens with different crack length.

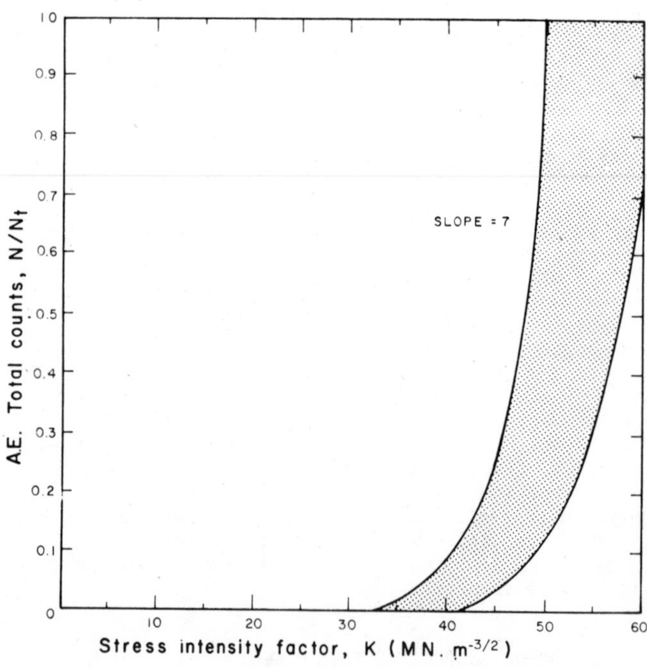

Figure 8: Total counts versus stress intensity factor for a ductile steel.

RELATION BETWEEN ACOUSTIC EMISSION AND FRACTURE MECHANICS

Fracture mechanics concepts are primarily concerned with brittle fracture which occurs well before yielding of the material. Through the use of the plane strain fracture toughness K_{Ic}, it is possible to compute the critical flaw size under a given load. Acoustic emission has been correlated to the stress intensity factor K by Dunegan et al. (3) with an equation of the form,

$$N = A K^n \quad (2)$$

where N is the cumulative acoustic emission counts and A is a constant. The exponent n has a theoretical value of 4 for plane strain but experimental measurements vary between 4 and 8. Equation 2 is applicable also for materials exhibiting elastic-plastic behaviour (4). In this case, the plastic behaviour admits exponents greater than 4. In general, it was found that acoustic emission becomes noticeable when the crack becomes active and starts to propagate. Figure 7 shows acoustic emission cumulative count as a function of the applied load for fracture mechanics specimens containing cracks of different lengths. It is noticed that there is a relatively quiet period at low load levels followed by a rapid increase in activity, which corresponds to activation of the crack and ends in fracture of the specimen. Figure 8 gives N as a function of K. The exponent n for this particular material was found to be 7.

Criteria for fracture using acoustic emission have been proposed including, for example, the use of a stress intensity factor parameter K_{IAE}, the value of the factor at which noticeable acoustic emission occurs. Figure 9 summarizes values of K_{IAE} for a group of steel alloys (5). In general, for a large number of materials K_{IAE} is significantly lower than K_{Ic} and thus provides warning of impending failure. For more ductile materials, the J-integral provides a more appropriate reference parameter for

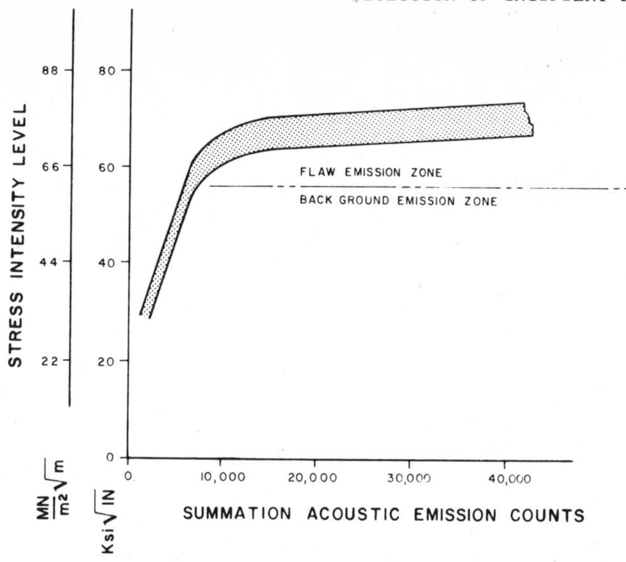

Figure 9: The total count versus K_{Ic} for pressure vessel steels.

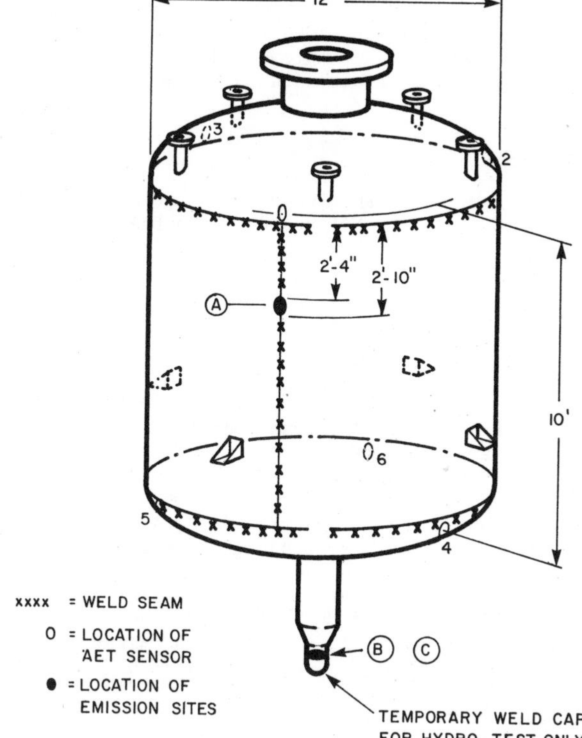

Figure 10: A typical transducer array on a pressure vessel

elastic/ plastic materials and provides better phenomenological consistency as both quantities are related to the energy dissipated in advancing a crack.

EXAMPLES OF APPLICATION OF ACOUSTIC EMISSION

Monitoring Structural Integrity

Acoustic emission has been applied extensively for monitoring the structural integrity of pressure vessels and of nuclear components during proof testing and in service (6). Using the method of triangulation, it is possible to locate and position active flaws and to determine their severity. Figure 10

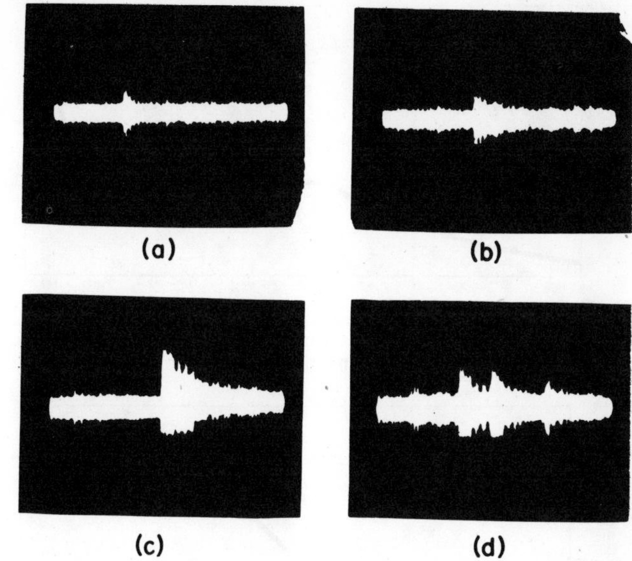

Figure 11: A sequence of acoustic emission signals in a cracked specimen to fracture

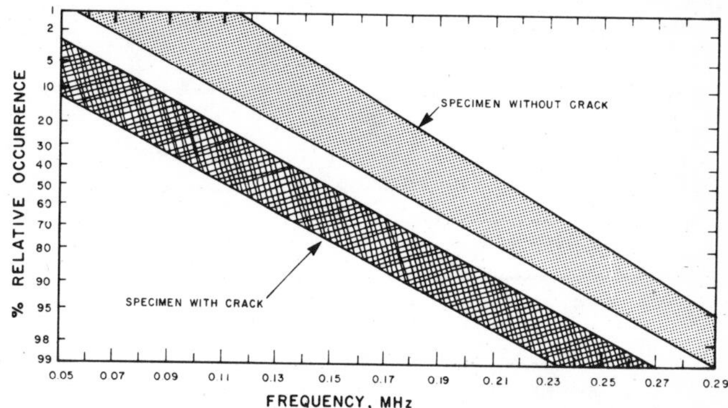

Figure 12: Statistical plot of the frequency distribution from a flawed and unflawed specimen of a mild steel

shows a typical transducer array installed on a pressure vessel (7), while Figure 11 illustrates the development of the acoustic signals as a function of time to fracture. It is seen that the acoustic signals have a lower energy at the point of instability and that the signals grow in amplitude and pulse width with increasing load to fracture. Figure 11(d), taken just prior to fracture, exhibits an overlapping of signals which is typical of continuous emission. It has been observed that a specimen with a flaw usually emits acoustic signals with a lower frequency content than a similar unflawed material, as shown in Figure 12, which gives the relative occurrence as a function of frequency (8). The count rate also increases towards fracture, as shown in Figure 13. These examples clearly demonstrate the potential of acoustic emission in predicting failure in structural components well before it happens.

Monitoring in adverse environment

Acoustic emission was used to monitor a steam reformer furnace component in a petrochemical plant (9). This particular structure is subjected to high skin temperature, about 1300°F (700°C), and considerable background (hydraulic) noise. The acoustic emission transducers were mounted on wave-guides which were then welded to the structure. Constant load springs were used to secure the bonding of the transducers to the structure. Event count of the

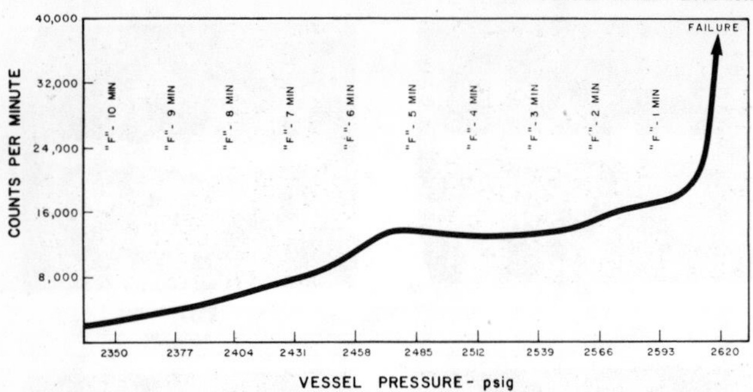

Figure 13: Count rate versus hydrostatic pressure during testing of a pressure vessel

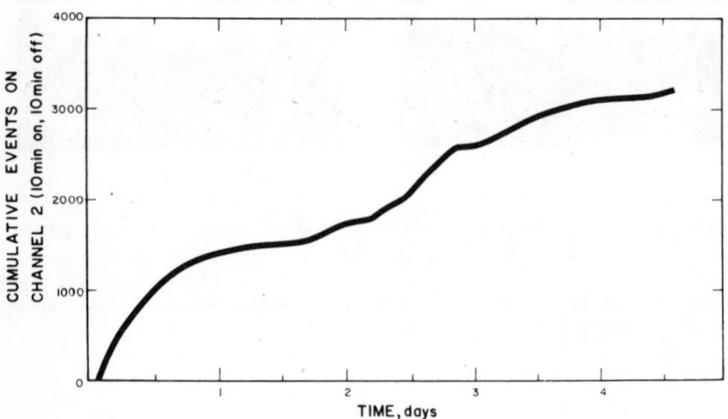

Figure 14: Cumulative events in a steam methane reformer furnace

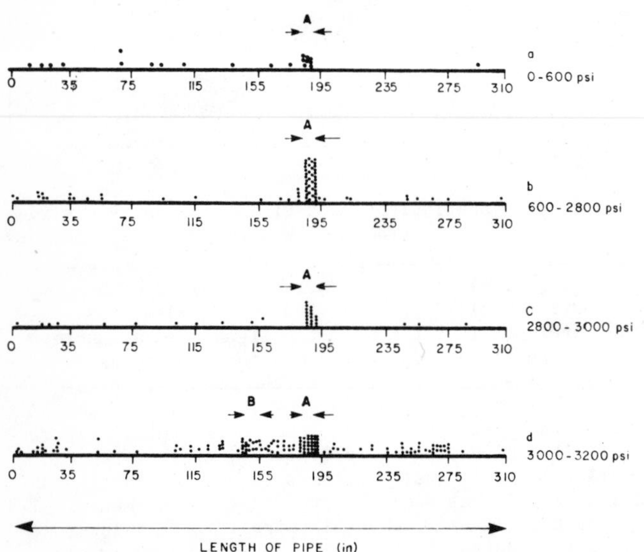

Figure 15: The acoustic emission activity along a linepipe, 48 in. (1220 mm) diameter and 310 in. (7.9 m) long, as a function of hydrostatic pressure

acoustic emission versus time for a period encompassing start-up of the unit and steady state operation is shown in Figure 14. Features of the cumulative event curve were correlated with variations in the operating conditions such as the pressure and rate of flow of the gases in the vessel and to the cracking of refractory during the curing cycle. The results obtained demonstrate that acoustic emission can be applied to complex structures in such adverse environment.

DETECTION OF STRUCTURAL YIELDING

Acoustic emission has been used by the authors to detect structural yielding during burst testing of a line pipe. Figure 15 shows a sequence of the distribution of acoustic emission activity along the pipe as a function of applied pressure. Close to yielding and slightly into the plastic region (Figure 15d) the acoustic emission activity is distributed along the pipe and is more intense in the region marked B. The pipe subsequently bulged and then burst in this region, thereby demonstrating the ability of the technique to detect general and localized structural yielding in large structures.

SUMMARY

Acoustic emision is evolving rapidly from a laboratory technique to an industrial inspection method. The examples provided from the authors' experience show that with contemporary state-of-the-art instrumentation it is quite feasible to exploit the efficiency and sensitivity of acoustic emission even in adverse environments. In the Arctic, where for reasons of the economic and ecological impacts of brittle failure of major engineering installations, it will be essential to consider the use of new nondestructive testing techniques. Among the new novel techniques, acoustic emission is one of the most likely to be implemented for evaluating the integrity of materials used in the North.

Acknowledgment

The authors acknowledge the National Research Council of Canada, the Defence Research Board and the Steel Company of Canada for support of this work.

REFERENCES

1. R. F. Drouillard; American Society for Testing and Materials, ASTM STP 571, 1975, pp. 241-284.
2. J. F. Knott: "Fundamentals of Fracture Mechanics", J. Wiley, New York, 1973.
3. H. L. Dunegan, D. O. Harris and C. A. Tatro, Engineering Fracture Mechanics, 1968, vol. 1, p. 105.
4. J. Masounave, J. Lanteigne, M. N. Bassim and D. R. Hay, Engineering Fracture Mechanics, in press.
5. R. R. Corle and J. A. Schliessmann, Materials Evaluation, 1973, vol. 31, pp. 115-120.
6. D. O. Harris and H. L. Dunegan, ASTM STP 515, 1972, pp. 158-170.
7. N. O. Cross, L. L. Loushin and J. L. Thompson, ASTM STP 505, 1972, pp. 270-296.
8. M. N. Bassim, D. R. Hay and J. Lanteigne, Materials Evaluation, 1976, vol. 34, pp. 106-113.
9. D. R. Hay, M. N. Bassim and D. Dunbar, Materials Evaluation, 1976, vol. 34, pp. 20-24.

DISCUSSION

J. F. Clayton (Gulf Oil Canada): The discrimination possible by AE is fascinating and offers intriguing possibilities. But how do you know magnetic domain walls are moving? I find the use of the terms "remote" and "passive" to describe AE misleading for such a powerful technique which I am sure offers great possibilities in Arctic operations. To assure 100% testing of a pressure vessel prior to shipping to the Arctic is a major advance. I felt it was not obvious from the paper that flaws cannot only be detected but also assigned a magnitude and an exact location. Even in Arctic service cost is a factor and I would like you to comment on this.

D. R. Hay: Discrimination techniques are used to distinguish between acoustic emission signals and background noise signals. This type of discrimination is now routinely available in commercial equipment. My inclusion of magnetic domain wall motion detection was probably misleading. But AE is used for this when the sample and conditions are well-defined. AE techniques cannot readily discriminate between magnetic effects and deformation effects in a general situation. The ability to distinguish between the types of sources of acoustic emission is a subject currently under investigation in several laboratories. For the latter type of discrimination, most of the research effort is directed toward frequency domain analyses such as spectral analysis.

Source location is carried out in systems with two or more channels of instrumentation and either a minicomputer or, for two-channel systems, a handwired analysis module. The difference in time of arrival of the AE signal at the transducers is used to calculate the position of the source. Source location is possible to within a few inches in the typical pipe segments we have tested. After detecting a source, other NDT methods must be used to check out the defects. Source intensity is measured by counting the number of emissions produced at a particular point.

At present, acoustic emission is still relatively expensive. Costs for AE testing services on a daily basis may be 2 to 3 times that for conventional NDT. However, the efficiency of testing and the sensitivity of the technique have to be weighed against these costs.

A. Glover (Canadian Welding Development Institute): Would you comment on the spacing of the transducers for on-line monitoring of a pipeline in, typically, 5 mile (8 km) lengths?

D. R. Hay: This problem requires some further definition. There are some data in the literature which suggest that distances up to 1000 ft (300 m) can be used. I would prefer to test with transducers spaced at 200 ft (60 m).

J. T. McGrath (Canadian Welding Development Institute): If a pipe system is to be constructed from the Arctic islands there must be a high standard of structural integrity, particularly in those sections under water. How useful could the acoustic emission technique be in monitoring these under-sea sections?

D. R. Hay: The problem of extracting the signals from the transducer would have to be considered, as would the problem of protecting the instrumentation which would have to be placed under water.

B. W. Jackson (National Energy Board): Can AE be applied to continuous pipeline monitoring? Does the presence of flowing oil have an effect on acoustic emission detection? If so, would this problem disqualify it for use on oil pipeline monitoring? Can the detector spacings be increased to 1 - 2 mile (2 - 3 km)?

D. R. Hay: I believe that AE can indeed be applied to continuous pipeline monitoring and that flowing oil noise can be discriminated. However, at present it looks like transducer spacings of up to 1000 ft (300 m) are most appropriate with present-day technology.

B. A. Graville (Dominion Bridge): A crack or defect exists in a structure which is loaded. If the crack tip yields and becomes blunt that is a good thing. If the crack extends -- that is a bad thing. How do you distinguish between good and bad events in acoustic emission?

D. R. Hay: If the crack tip stress intensity is such as to induce blunting, it is well to know that there is a crack of this magnitude present and it should probably be checked out just as is the extending crack. Good and bad sources are graded according to the number of events associated with each source. Laboratory research programs are underway in several organizations to develop other techniques for source identification.

D. L. Cheever (John Deere): Noise and the need for sophisticated interpretation have limited the use of acoustic emission as an on-line monitor to detect crack growth during the service life of a complex structure. Are you familiar with any recent successful applications on a large complex structure, such as a dragline boom or a bridge? Most field applications appear to be limited to pressure vessels during hydrotest.

D. R. Hay: Other applications include such structures as bridges during periodic proof tests. For example we have used AE to detect reversible slipping at rivets in a bridge with AE. General purpose commercial equipment is not really amenable to continuous monitoring of a specific complex system. Generally, it is necessary to characterize the potential failure modes of the structure as well as its environmental conditions. Appropriate discrimination modes can then be designed into a specific system at reasonable cost.

ACOUSTIC EMISSION TECHNIQUE FOR STEEL QUALITY AND CONSTRUCTION INSPECTION

M. Nagumo and T. Watanabe
Nippon Steel Corporation
Kawasaki-City, Japan

The present status of acoustic emission (AE) inspection techniques on commonly-used weldable constructional steels, i.e. a plain carbon steel and two HSLA steels, is described. Burst type AE signals are shown to be effective for flaw inspection of fabricated structures, and that the pre-yield stages of deformation can be readily detected at -78°C. At room temperature, AE signals are quite weak, except at high deformation rates for plain carbon steel with a tensile strength of 41 kgf/mm^2 (400 MPa). The presence of notches can suppress AE because of the formation of a plastic zone at the notch root. A fatigue crack might be overlooked by AE during a hydrostatic test, since the plastic zone ahead of the crack cannot produce AE because of the Kaiser Effect.

Detection and location of flaws in an actual pressure tank at the time of hydrostatic test can be satisfactorily performed. Criteria for ranking the severity of flaws are proposed based on the degree of AE source concentration, the dependence of emission on pressure, and the acoustic wave amplitude. The results of AE measurements correspond fairly well with the results of ultrasonic inspection.

INTRODUCTION

Acoustic emission (AE) or stress wave emission (SWE), which is generated when a material releases elastic energy in the course of deformation, fracture or phase transformation, has recently been suggested as a tool for the nondestructive testing of material and constructions. It has been successfully applied for flaw detection during the hydrostatic testing of pressure tanks (1,2,3), and for performance examination of nuclear reactor vessels (4,5), bridges (6) and gas piplines (7).

When compared with other traditional nondestructive testing methods, AE inspection may be regarded as a dynamic method since it picks up detrimental flaws which induce localized deformation or fracture under stress during service. Even a small hair-line crack, which is apt to be overlooked by X-ray methods, can be detected by AE if it grows on the application of stress. On the contrary, a large defect which is readily detectable by ultrasonic testing cannot be detected by AE if it is stationary under loading. It is also an advantage of AE that the surveillance of inaccessible large areas is possible at any time and without much interruption of operations.

Many problems of AE inspection standardization still remain, however, and the feasibility of AE is not established for all materials. The most important problem may be the evaluation of AE information, i.e. the judgement of the engineering significance of an emission source.

Both the acoustic wave characteristics and the stages of deformation or fracture at which AE is produced are dependent on many variables, such as the materials, their geometry, deformation rate, testing temperature. Furthermore, AE characteristics are modified when acoustic waves propagate through the material, due to multiple reflection, attenuation and velocity dispersion. This poses problems for the definitive identification of AE sources. Instrumentation coupled with data handling systems must then be established.

Therefore, the instrumentation for acoustic wave detection and the analysis of correspondence between AE information and originating flaws or physical processes are still pre-requisite procedures for practical application of the AE inspection technique, particularly in novel situations like engineering in the Arctic.

The procedures for an AE investigation should include: 1) accumulation of basic AE data under various test conditions, and identification of the corresponding physical processes, such as plastic deformation and cracking; 2) instrumentation of the flaw detection system and grading of detected flaws in terms of AE patterns.

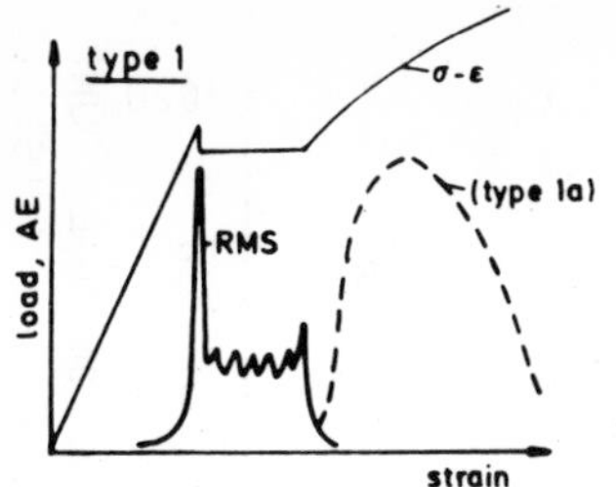

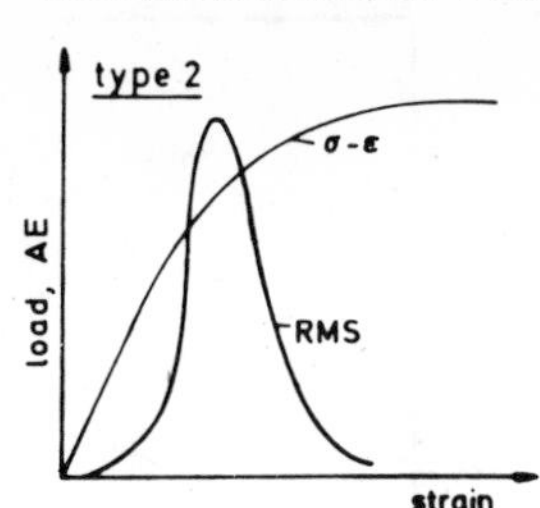

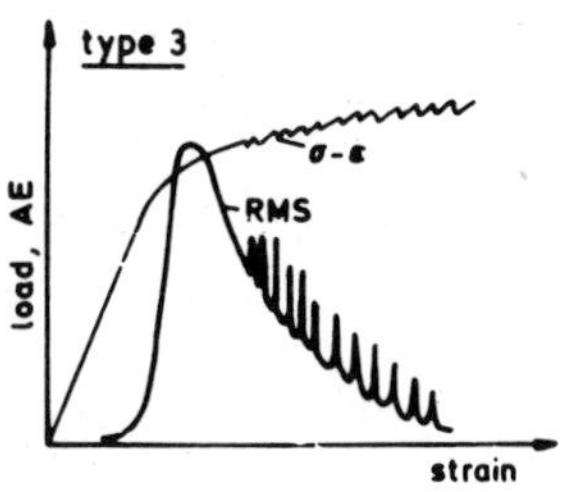

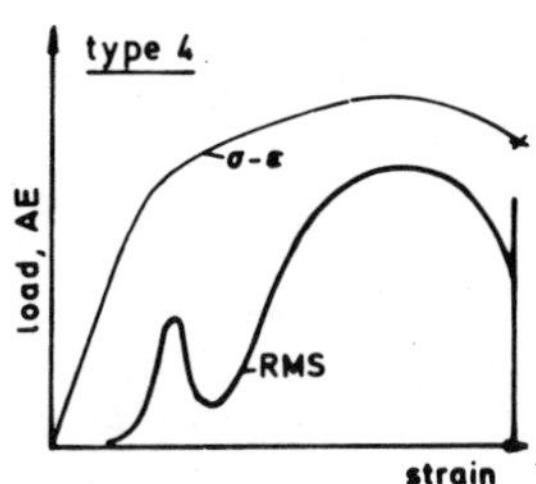

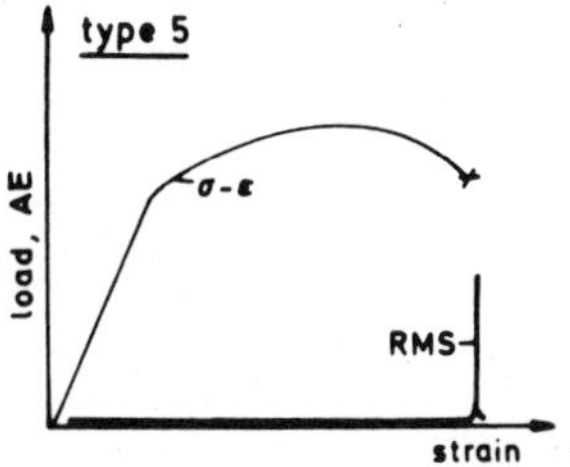

Figure 1: Types of Continuous AE Pattern from the Plastic Deformation of Metals (after ref. 8)

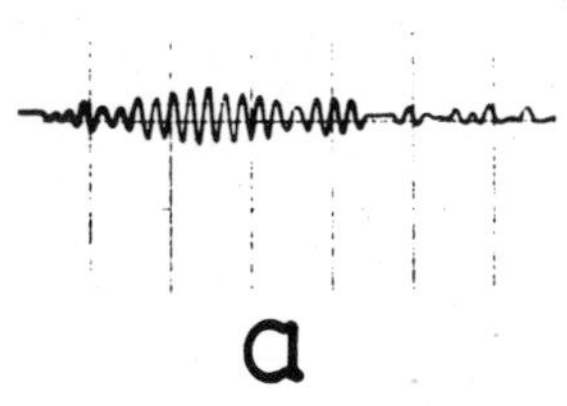

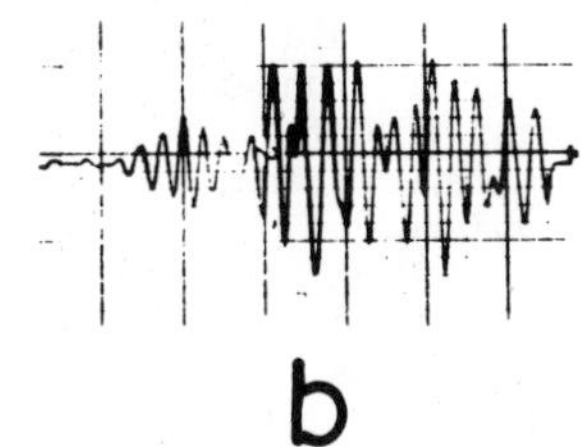

Figure 2: Acoustic Wave Form due to (a) Plastic Deformation and (b) Cracking at Delayed Fracture of an HSLA Steel

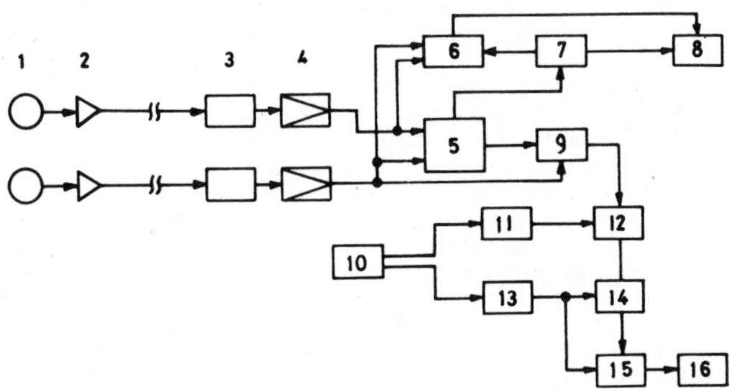

Figure 3: Block Diagram of Laboratory AE Apparatus

BASIC EMISSION PATTERNS OF CONSTRUCTION STEELS

It is necessary to know at what stage a material in service produces detectable AE patterns. AE patterns obtained during tensile testing were classified by Eisenbläter and Jax (8) into five types, as shown in Figure 1. The classification is made in terms of the root mean square (rms) voltage, i.e. the average AE energy.

Figure 1 concerns continuous-type AE signals, but continuous signals can be regarded essentially as profuse generations of burst-type signals. For the purpose of flaw inspection of a structure, burst-type AE signals having sufficient spacing are useful.

It has been shown (9) that AE due to plastic deformation is distinguishable from that due to cracking at delayed failure of high strength steels by observation of the wave form. Typical examples are shown in Figure 2, (a) for plastic deformation and (b) for crack propagation. These acoustic waves were obtained from an HSLA steel of tensile strength 140 kgf/mm^2 (1370 MPa) during a delayed fracture test in 0.1N HCl. The testing machine was of the cantilever type, using a specimen of geometry 10 x 10 x 160 mm, with a 45° notch 2 mm deep and 0.1 mm root radius. The sensor was a PZT-5 (Dunegan Model K-140B) with a resonant frequency at 225 kHz, coupled with an electronic filter with a 100∿300 kHz range.

That the AE pattern in Figure 2(a) is due to plastic deformation was confirmed by examining AE patterns during tensile testing of the same material at various test conditions including stress relaxation, unloading and reloading. The AE signals as shown in Figure 2 were monochromatic. The frequency of AE is dependent both on the frequency characteristics of the sensor and the nature of the AE source. A sensor actually has some peaks within its frequency band and AE which activates one of these peaks is detected.

Basic AE patterns of standard construction steels will now be presented, with particular emphasis on application to engineering problems.

Instrumentation

A key to the analysis of AE is an ability to discriminate signal from noise. There are several devices for noise elimination. One which is useful in the field is based on data handling. For example, an acoustic wave source may be located by the periodic subtraction of a background from accumulated counts due to all probable source positions (10). Other types employ multi-transducers and are useful for material testing.

A block diagram of the laboratory apparatus is shown in Figure 3. The components are: 1) AE sensor, typically PZT with max resonance 225 kHz; 2) pre-amplifier, 40 db gain, band width 100 kHz∿2MHz; 3) filter group, consisting of a high-pass over 100 kHz, 100 kHz∿300 kHz, 300 kHz∿1 MHz and 1∿2 MHz filters 4) main amplifier, max gain 60 db; 5) coincidence circuit; 6) transient recorder; 7) wave memory and output control; 8,16) chart recorders; 9) slicer; 10) time-base oscillator; 11) counter control; 12) counters; 13) count output control; 14) shift register; 15) D/A switching circuit.

A dual transducer system constitutes a delayed coincidence gate circuit, by which signals from only a given area can be picked up. In this way, uncertainty of the data due to mechanical and electrical noise can be eliminated. Amplification of 100 db is thus possible with a peak noise level of 7 μV. Pulses above pre-set thresholds are counted for each threshold. The numbers of threshold levels can be

Table 1

Chemical Analysis of Tested Steels (wt %)

	C	Si	Mn	Cr	Mo	Cu	V	B	P	S
SM-41	0.18	0.20	0.75	----	----	----	----	-----	0.002	0.005
WELTEN-62	0.12	0.25	1.20	0.15	----	----	0.03	-----	0.002	0.005
WELTEN-80C	0.13	0.30	0.90	0.75	0.40	0.25	0.04	0.002	0.002	0.005

increased to eight. This device is suitable for determining the distribution of signal magnitudes and also for separation of superposed events. The acoustic wave form is monitored by means of a high speed transient recorder coupled with a chart recorder, magnetic tape or another larger computer.

The proper choice of transducers and specimen coupling is essential for AE measurement. For use at temperatures as low as -80°C, a PZT-5 transducer with a grease interface posed no problems.

Materials and Specimens

Standard construction steels with nominal tensile strengths of 41 kgf/mm^2 or 400 MPa (SM-41), 62 kgf/mm^2 or 610 MPa (WELTEN-62) and 80 kgf/mm^2 or 780 MPa (WELTEN-80C) were examined. The chemical analyses are shown in Table 1. SM-41 is an as-rolled plain carbon steel, a commonly used structural steel with a ferrite/ pearlite structure, while WELTEN-62 and WELTEN-80C are HSLA steels with tempered martensite structures.

Specimen geometries are shown in Figure 4 and were designed to simulate flaws in actual constructions and also to produce AE at definite regions in order to reduce noise. The coincidence gates were adjusted to detect signals originating at a central region about 30 mm long. For experiments at low temperatures, the placement of two transducers allowed the rejection of simultaneously detected signals, such as those of electrical origin. A fatigue notch was introduced into the second specimen.

AE Emission Pattern during Tensile Testing

It has been established that for most metals acoustic waves are most profusely generated during initial yielding. Qualitatively this is also true

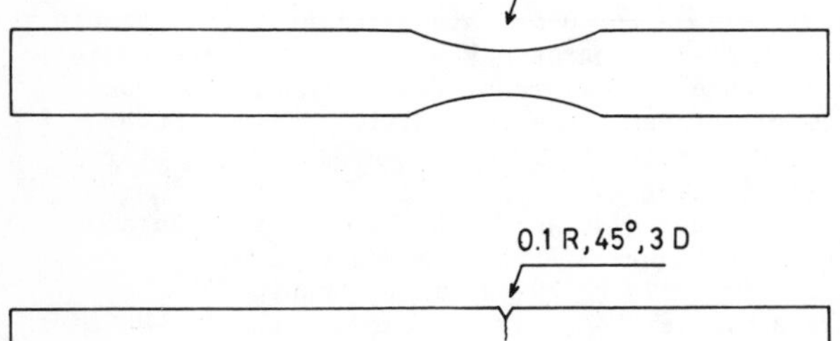

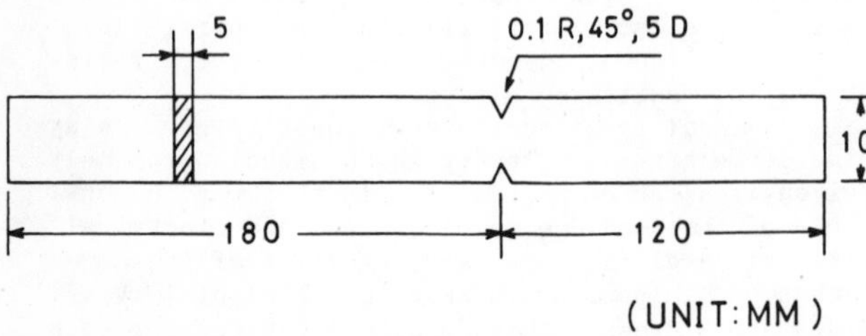

Figure 4: Specimen Geometries

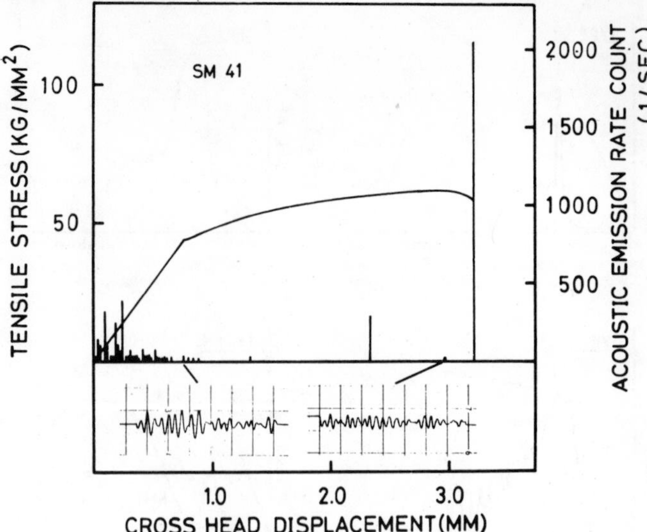

Figure 5: AE Pattern of SM-41 Steel during Tensile Deformation of 1 mm/min at -78°C. Notched specimen, 0.1 mm root radius

for the present steels. However, AE patterns vary with the type of steel and with test conditions.

At room temperature, the SM-41 steel produced very little AE, except at deformation rates above 5 mm/min. At low temperatures, emission was activated at all deformation rates. An emission pattern as illustrated in Figure 5 may belong to Type 2 (Figure 1), i.e. peak emissions occurring close to yielding, with a few in the work-hardening regime. Note that significant ductility remained at -78°C.

From a practical point of view, detectability of plastic deformation prior to failure by means of acoustic emission is expected to be very difficult at room temperature in this type of steel. This has been shown to be the case. On the other hand, it can be said that low temperatures provide a beneficial environment for AE inspection and the early stages of deformation can be detected. From wave form information, the AE origins could not be distinguished.

High-strength steels also produced few acoustic emissions at room temperature and at low deformation rates. Dependence of the frequency of emission events upon deformation rate is shown in Figure 6. Increase in emission at low temperatures is similar to that of steel SM-41. The example shown in Figure 7 from WELTEN-80C is characterized by considerable AE during work hardening and greater amplitude signals than from SM-41. It can be related to Type 2 of Figure 1. WELTEN-62 showed an intermediate behaviour.

It should be noted that fatigue-notched specimens produced no AE at the incipient stage of tensile testing at room temperature. This is probably due to an effect discovered by Kaiser (11), wherein AE are not generated at re-loading until the applied stress exceeds the prior stress level, a condition at the notch root where a plastic region had been formed at the time of introduction of the fatigue notch. This suggests that fatigue cracks might be overlooked by AE during hydrostatic testing of a structure.

In the present experiments, the number of detected AE events is much less than reported previously (12). This may be due to the use of a coincidence gate system to detect signals originating only at the central area of the specimens. This system is considered to be better for flaw location in engineering structures, since multi-transducer arrays are used. There may also be an effect of specimen geometry. It is well known that AE, par-

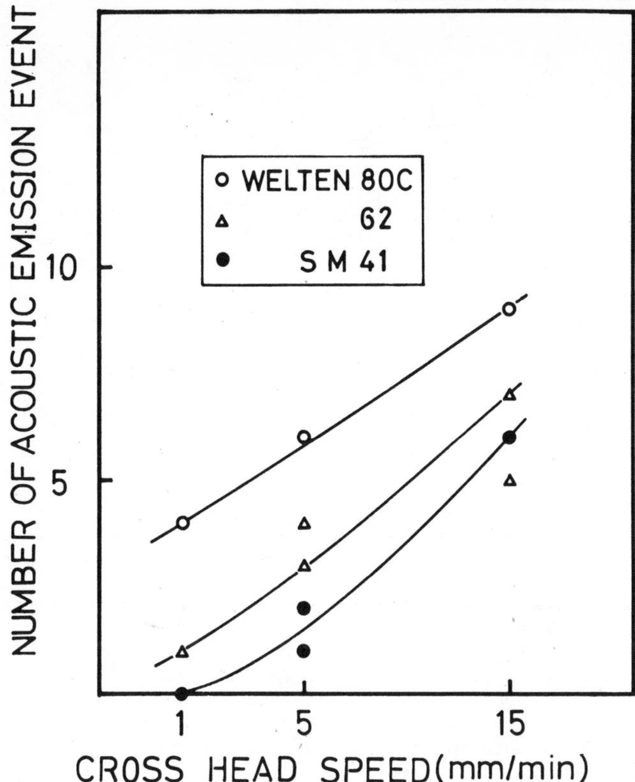

Figure 6: Relationship between AE Events and Tensile Deformation Rate at Room Temperature

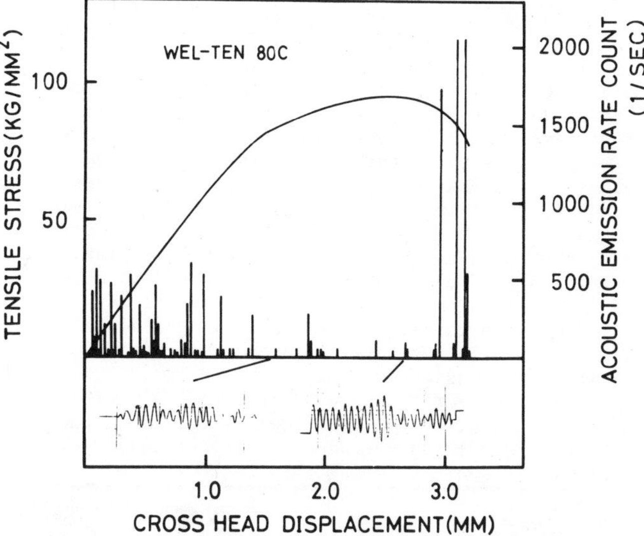

Figure 7: AE Pattern of WELTEN-80C Steel during Tensile Deformation (1 mm/min at -78°C) Notched specimen, 0.1 mm root radius

ticularly the burst-type is produced by discontinuous movements of dislocations, as in Lüder's band formation. The tensile curves of the present specimens hardly show sharp yield drops or yield elongation. Hence, the gradual formation of plastic regions ahead of a notch can reduce generation of burst-type AE, particularly in mild steels. In other words, an AE event indicates the onset of heterogeneous and discontinuous plastic deformation induced by a release of stress concentrators or by cracking.

Acoustic emission is generally enhanced in higher strength steels, partly due to the higher dislocation velocities in these materials. Increases in AE at low temperatures may be due to other mechanisms, such as formation of straighter slip bands and discontinuities of deformation by interaction between dislocation and interstitial atoms such as carbon or nitrogen, and it does not always mean that the material is brittle.

FLAW DETECTION IN STRUCTURES

Flaw Location System

The earliest application of the AE technique for a surveillance device was made in 1963 for detection of flaw growth during hydrostatic testing of missile engine casings (13). Since then, many systems have been developed, principally for flaw location in pressure vessels. The principle of flaw location is the determination of the distances from multi-transducers placed on the structure from the differences in arrival time of an acoustic wave at each transducer.

There are several variations of flaw location systems distinguished mainly by the transducer array network and the method of computation of AE source location.

In a non-modular array system, transducers are placed in convenient but defined positions on the structure to be inspected. Source location is obtained from measurement of the relative arrival times of an acoustic wave at three transducers in the network, i.e. from the intersection of two hyperbolas which are defined as the loci of a point for which the distance difference from the transducers is given. This system enables a high degree of precision of source location, although it does require some lengthy computation time. This disadvantage is alleviated by the application of high-speed computers.

In a modular array system, transducers are positioned at the apexes of a set of triangles, as shown in Figure 8(a), for example. The whole area of the construction is thus divided into many sectors which are subdivided into finer zones (Figure 8(b)). The sector in which AE is generated is determined by the number and arrival orders of the first three activated transducers. In the seven-sensor module of Figure 8, the sectors are shown for which AE activates the central transducer, 5, first. Each zone of Sector 3 (Figure 8(b)) is then characterized by the relative arrival times at transducers 5, 6 and 2. The AE source is assigned to a definite zone when the set of the arrival time data matches with a prepared table for each zone, which gives the boundary limits of arrival time. The computation for source location is quite fast, but it needs a rather large memory capacity for the conversion table and the location precision is limited.

The block diagram of a 28 and 32 channel system developed by Nippon Steel (N.A.I.S.-28,-32) is shown in Figure 9, as an example. Its components are: 1) PZT AE sensors, max resonance 400 kHz, 2) pre-amplifier, 37 db gain, band width 50 kHz∿2 MHz; 3) filter system (4 low-pass and 4 high-pass filters); 4) main amplifier, max gain 46 db; 5) slicer; 6) counter; 7) counter control; 8) interface; 9) computer for location; 10) CRT display; 11) typewriter; 12) paper tape puncher; 13) terminal box; 14) totalizer; 15) XY recorder; 16) audio-monitor; 17) data recorder; 18) transient recorder; 19) pressure measuring channel. The system is a modified non-modular array system.

Figure 10 shows a development map for a cylindrical pressure tank with the whole surface divided into rhombus and triangles. The use of a rhombic instead of triangular array reduces considerably the procedure for location computation. The map

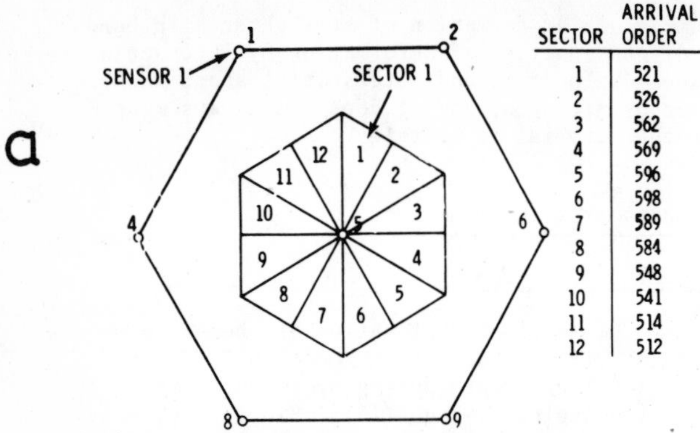

AREA DEFINED BY ACOUSTIC BURST SIGNALS ARRIVING FIRST AT SENSOR 5. THE TABLE LISTS THE ORDER OF ARRIVAL FOR ACOUSTIC BURST SIGNALS IN EACH OF THE 12 SECTORS AROUND SENSOR 5.

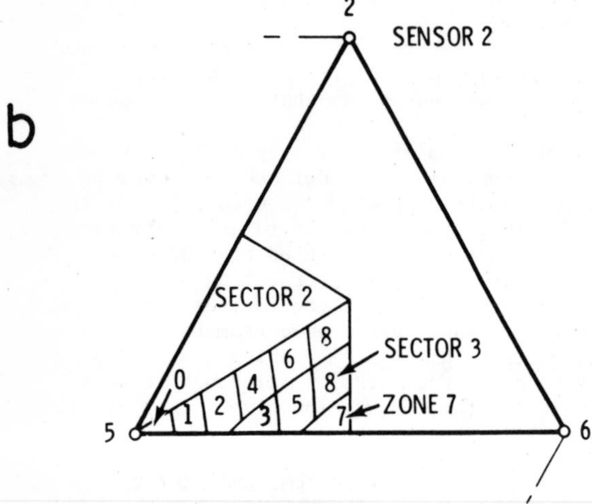

Figure 8: (a) A Seven-Sensor Module. (b) Part of Sensor Module showing Division of Section 3 into 10 Zones (after ref. 10)

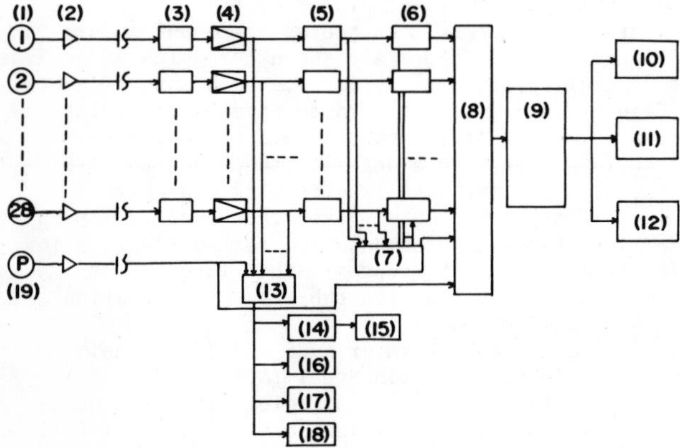

Figure 9: Block Diagram of N.A.I.S. 28 AE Source Location System

is displayed on a cathode ray tube screen, and the sources are shown in it as bright spots in real time.

The rhombus in which the AE source is located is identified by the numbers and orders of the transducers which the AE has activated. The location computation is then done with that rhombus as the intersection of two orthogonal hyperbolas, the origin of which is the center of the rhombus. In this way, the source position is expressed by Cartesian coordinates, the X- and Y-axis of which are the diagonals of the rhombus.

In the N.A.I.S.-32 system, a mini-computer

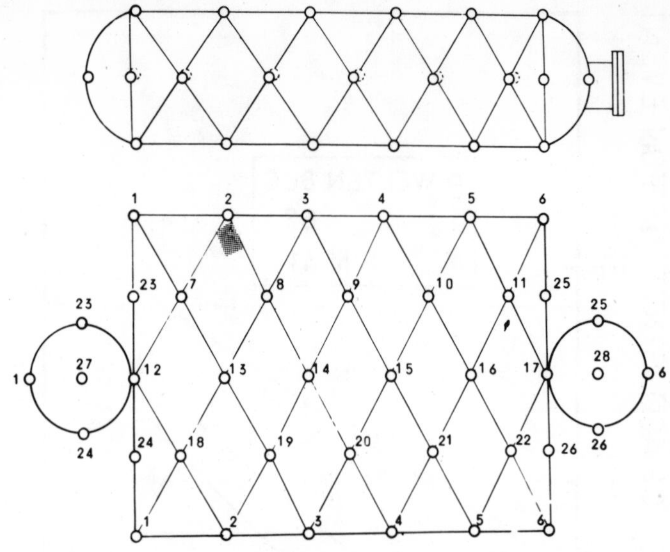

Figure 10: A Development Map for a Cylindrical Pressure Vessel

HP-2100 is employed. A location computation is completed about 10 ms after the first arrival of an acoustic wave at a transducer, and the result is stored in memory cores and displayed on the CRT in a further 18 ms. It is simultaneously printed out with other information, such as time of generation and pressure.

Field Tests and Grading of Emission Signals

In 1973, an inspection using the N.A.I.S.-28 system was conducted during the hydrostatic test of a liquid butane spherical storage tank. The inner diameter of the tank was 17.85 m and the wall thickness was 25 mm. The spherical surface was divided into twelve rhombus as shown in Figure 11, and transducers were placed at the apexes and centre of each rhombus. To avoid installation of the transducers at manholes, landings, supports etc., it was devised so that one of the symmetry axes of the transducer arrangement made an angle of 22.5° to the vertical. Sensitivities of each channel were adjusted to detect burst-type AE. Combinations of PZT transducers, amplifiers with gains of up to 83 db and band-pass filters of 50∿750 kHz were employed. Maximum resonance frequency was at 400 kHz.

The pressurization was performed to a final pressure of 0.162 kgf/mm² (1.6 MPa) in 43 h, including five pressure holding periods. The total number of located AE sources during this test was 786.

Figure 11: Hard Copy of CRT Display of Development Map for a Spherical Tank, showing Grouping of Located AE Sources (* indicates support position)

Table 2

Flaw Ranking by AE Pattern

AE generation pattern with respect to changes in pressure	Degree of concentration of located AE generating points: High	Medium	Low
I Frequent during whole process	a	a	b
II Increased at high pressure	a	b	b
III Frequent at low and middle pressure, but decreased at high pressure	b	c	d
IV Frequent at low and middle pressure, but stopped at high pressure	c	d	e
V Sporadic during whole process	c	e	e
VI Partially sporadic	c	e	e

Rank of Flaw	Stability	Severity of Flaw
a	Very unstable	Critical flaw Special attention required
b	Unstable	Major flaw attention required
c	Somewhat stable	Medium flaw slight attention required
d	Stable	Slight minor flaw
e	Not detected	Harmless minor flaw

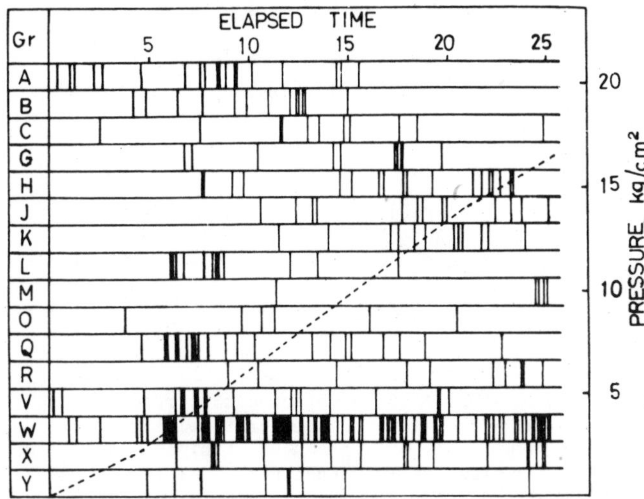

Figure 12: AE Generation Pattern for the Groups of Figure 11, as a function of Pressure

Taking into account the distribution of these sources, they were divided into 26 groups and another random 315 spots. Figure 11 shows the locations of these groups together with the positions of weld lines.

For each of 26 groups, the severity was estimated with respect to the emission frequency dependence on pressure change and the degree of source concentration. Table 2 shows tentative flaw ranks classified according to those criteria. The basic idea of this classification is that AE occurring in a localized area with strong pressure dependence indicates an instability of the original flaw. The emission pattern of each group is summarized in Figure 12, and wave forms, presumably corresponding to both plastic deformation and fracture, were obtained as shown in Figure 13.

After the test, ultrasonic flaw inspection was carried out in those 16 areas where sources were concentrated, and flaws were detected in 14 areas. Most of these flaws were small weld defects of Class-1 (Japanese NDIS-71 standard), but some Class-4 flaws and non-metallic inclusions were found in the base metal. The correspondence of flaw ranking by AE to the ultrasonic inspection is shown in Table 3. Except for Group X, the correspondence is fairly good.

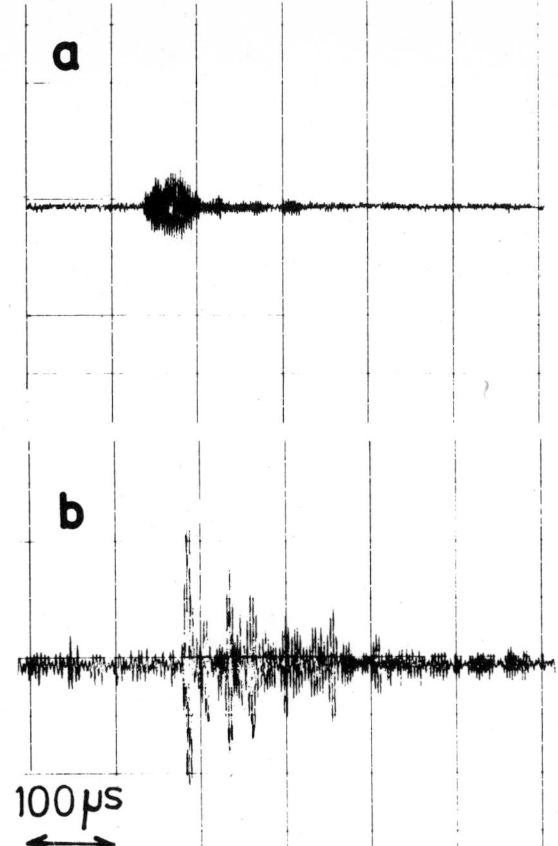

Figure 13: Acoustic Wave Forms During Hydrostatic Test, presumably due to (a) Plastic Deformation and (b) Cracking

The ranking standardization is now being improved by taking into account information from acoustic wave amplitude. An attempt has been made on another hydrostatic test of a pressure tank on which various artificial weld defects were introduced (14). Large amplitude signals originated in general at defects which underwent significant extension by pressurization.

Another hydrostatic test was conducted with a cylindrical vessel made of mild steel. The diameter and length were 1.0 m and 1.2 m respectively, and wall thickness was 6 mm. From an X-ray transmission inspection conducted before the hydrostatic test, many defects such as blow holes and lack of fusion were observed at all weld lines. It was anticipated that fracture would be initiated at these defects on pressurization of the vessel above the design value of 0.01 kgf/mm^2 (0.10 MPa).

The AE surveillance was done with the N.A.I.S.-32 system. During pressurization, a remarkable swelling of the tank body occurred above 0.4 kgf/mm^2 (3.9 MPa) without any irregular deformation along weld lines. AE was observed from only a few of the weld defects, but most generated no AE. The final failure of the vessel took place at the central part of the body in the base plate at 0.455 kgf/mm^2 (4.5 MPa). A fractograph indicated a typical ductile fracture mode, which is reasonable since the estimated

Table 3

Comparison of AE Flaw Ranks with Ultrasonic Test Results

Group	AE Generation Pattern High Pressure	Medium Pressure	Low Pressure	Degree of concentration	Flaw Rank (see Table 2)	Results of Ultrasonic Flaw Detection
A	8	10	0	High	(c)	Three Class 1 flaws in Base metal
B	4	10	0	High	(c)	Four Class 1 flaws in weld zone
D	2	7	3	Medium	(c)	Many inclusions in base metal
G	2	3	5	Medium	(e)	Three Class 1 flaws in weld zone
H	2	4	12	High	(a)	One Class 4 flaw in weld zone
J	0	4	9	Low	(b)	One Class 4 flaw and One Class 1 flaw in weld zone
K	0	3	9	Low	(b)	Three Class 1 flaws in weld zone
L	5	5	1	Medium	(d)	Five Class 1 flaws in weld zone
M	0	1	4	Medium	(e)	One Class 1 flaw in weld zone
O	2	4	1	Low	(e)	Two Class 2 flaws in weld zone
Q	10	8	3	High	(b)	Two Class 1 flaws in weld zone
R	0	3	7	Low	(b)	Five Class 1 flaws in weld zone
V	10	7	3	Medium	(c)	One Class 1 flaw in weld zone
W	17	42	37	Low	(b)	Four Class 4 flaws, Two Class 2 flaws and 19 Class 1 flaws in weld zone
X	3	5	10	Medium	(b)	No flaw
Y	3	5	1	Low	(e)	No flaw

applied tensile stress exceeded the plate strength.

However, one could not forecast the failure from that part by AE, since no significant signals were generated there. That the ductile deformation of mild steel does not produce AE is consistent with a preliminary test result described earlier. A laboratory test is thus useful in determining the effectiveness of an AE inspection.

The weld defects were again examined by X-ray transmission after the test, and no remarkable changes of profiles were observed. The AE pattern from a few of the defects was of a type highly dependent on pressure. Such defects would extend on further pressurization if the strength of the plate were not exceeded.

CONCLUSIONS

The present status of AE inspection techniques has been described with commonly-used weldable construction steels, i.e. a plain carbon steel and two HSLA steels. Low temperature testing is appropriate for AE measurement providing the steels are still sufficiently ductile. By means of burst-type AE signals, which are effective for flaw inspection, a pre-yield stage of deformation can be readily detected at -78°C. At room temperature, significant AE signals are only produced at high deformation rates for a plain carbon steel with tensile strength level of 41 kgf/mm^2 (400 MPa). The presence of notches can suppress AE because of gradual formation of a plastic zone at the notch root, particularly in a mild steel. A fatigue crack might also be overlooked by AE during a hydrostatic test, since the plastic zone ahead of the crack produces no acoustic emission.

Detection and location of flaws in an actual pressure tank during hydrostatic test can be satisfactorily performed. Criteria for flaw ranking (i.e. judgment of the relative severity of flaws) are proposed, based on the degree of AE source concentration, on the pressure dependence of emission, and also on acoustic wave amplitude. The criteria correspond fairly well with results of ultrasonic inspection.

For the advancement of AE inspection techniques, the following further studies are recommended: 1) collation of experience with different materials and types of construction under environmental conditions such as those prevailing in the Arctic. For this purpose, laboratory tests with controlled testing conditions are useful for revealing the physical processes producing acoustic emission; 2) increasing the sensitivity of the apparatus, including both improvement of transducers and the data handling system to eliminate noise; 3) development of systems to monitor structures during operation.

REFERENCES

1. N. O. Cross, L. L. Loushin and J. L. Thompson, ASTM Report STP-5050, 1972.
2. P. G. Bentley, E. J. Burton, A. Cowan, D. G. Dawson and T. Ingham, 2nd International Conference on Pressure Vessel Technology, 1973, ASME, New York, p.643.
3. N. Chretien, P. Bernard and B. Barrichin, ibid., p. 655.
4. J. Eisenblatter, W. Heide, P. Jax, H. Jost and R. Klat, Conference on Periodic Inspection of Pressurized Components, London, 1974, p. 168.
5. Southwest Research Institute, SWRI Project 17-2440 Bi-annual Progress Report Report No. 17, 1972.
6. A. A. Pollock and B. Smith, Non-Destructive Testing, 1972, vol. 5, p. 348.
7. E. A. Lehman, Pipe Line Industry, June 1974, p. 28.
8. J. Eisenblätter and P. Jax, 2nd Acoustic Emission Symposium, Tokyo 1974, HPI and NDI, Tokyo, p. 149.
9. M. Nagumo and Y. Monden, Report of Delayed Fracture Study Group, Japan Iron Steel Inst. 1976, p. 149.
10. P. H. Hutton, W. D. Jolly and J. B. Vetrans, U.S.-Japan Joint Symposium on AE, 1972, HPI and NDI Tokyo, p. 53.
11. J. Kaiser, Arch. Eisenhutt, 1953, vol. 24, p. 43.
12. T. Suzuki, Japan Joint Symposium on AE, 1972, HPI and NDI, Tokyo.
13. R. K. Steele, A. T. Green and C. S. Lockman, Modern Plastics, 1964, vol. 41, p. 137.
14. T. Watanabe, S. Hashirizaki and H. Arita, NDT International (formerly Non-Destructive Testing), 1976, vol. 9, pp. 227-232.

DISCUSSION

J. F. Clayton (Gulf Oil Canada): It appears this was a sophisticated system that represents a significant advance in the application of AE. I think the Kaiser effect should be mentioned and it be explained that AE is a one-shot effect. To get an additional signal the applied stress must be increased above the original value. It is a pity that stainless steel does not exhibit AE -- particularly in view of potential pressure vessel design savings. Also common structural steels generate little AE at room temperature. Lower temperature and high strain rates solve this problem usually. Again, I would like to ask about cost.

N. Yurioka (on behalf of the authors): Your comment was very much appreciated. We have considerable experience in conducting AE inspection for spherical tanks in Japan by NAIS (Nippon Steel Acoustic Emission Inspection System). The inspection cost was approximately $20,000 for a 20 m dia. tank and $60,000 for a 35 m dia. tank. This cost includes all inspection expenses.

D. R. Hay (Ecole Polytechnique): At present in the U.S. it costs $800/diem for a service group applying AE in the field.

A. G. Glover (Canadian Welding Development Institute): A comment on the previous question about the much-abused Kaiser effect. There is considerable controversy over the Kaiser effect. However, it can be used to great effect when, for example, a proof test is carried out. If subsequent to the test there is a material alteration, i.e. crack growth, then AE will be detected when the stress is reapplied. Similarly in fatigue, early plastic deformation can be detected, then when the fatigue crack is initiated, further AE signals will be detected at the peak of each cycle.

N. Yurioka: I agree with your comment. AE signals will be generated whenever the reloading exceeds the prior load level. In a fatigue test, AE signals will be detected as long as the fatigue crack grows. However, fatigue cracks which are already contained in a structure might be overlooked by AE measurement during hydrostatic testing, since no AE signal is generated due to the Kaiser effect until the hydrostatic testing stress exceeds the stress at which the fatigue crack was made.

ALUMINUM ALLOYS FOR ARCTIC SERVICE

J. G. Kaufman
Aluminum Company of America
Alcoa Laboratories
Alcoa Center, Pa.
USA

The properties which make aluminum alloys ideal for Arctic applications include high toughness, the absence of any ductile to brittle transition, and also strength, ductility and fatigue resistance as high as, or higher than, at room temperature. Light weight, corrosion resistance, weldability, and availability in varied forms complete the combinations that make such alloys so economically attractive. Recent and extensive design data on the strength, fracture toughness and fatigue crack growth resistance of Al-Mg alloy 5083 illustrate why this type of alloy has been widely used in the most critical low temperature applications. The combinations of strength and toughness of other alloys are also discussed.

INTRODUCTION

Aluminum alloys represent natural selections for structural applications in Arctic environments, since there is an absence of any ductile to brittle transitions (1,2) and full advantage can be taken of their high reliability at even the severest of weather conditions anticipated. In addition, the high strength-to-weight ratios, availability in many product forms, and superior corrosion resistance make them economical choices, particularly when maintenance costs are included.

A wide variety of aluminum alloys and tempers are available and many provide specific combinations of strength, formability, toughness, and corrosion resistance that make them desirable for critical applications. In this paper, special emphasis will be placed on new data for those alloys which have been most widely used in low temperature applications, notably the 5000 (Al-Mg) series, which satisfy the most severe requirements of liquefied fuel storage and transportation at temperatures as low as -452°F (-269°C). Although the severest of weather conditions anticipated in Arctic environments would seldom involve temperatures below -65°F (-59°C) it is appropriate to include data for lower temperatures to illustrate that a considerable margin of safety is provided by the use of these materials.

Aluminum wrought alloys can be classified in several ways, the most general being related to the strengthening mechanism. Some alloys are strengthened primarily by strain hardening, while others are strengthened by solution heat treatment and precipitation aging. These are generally referred to as strain-hardenable and heat-treatable alloys, respectively.

The principal alloying element indicated by the first digit of the alloy designation leads to a second system of classification (4). Pure aluminum (1XXX), and alloys containing manganese (3XXX) and magnesium (5XXX) as the principal alloying element are strain-hardenable. Those containing principally copper (2XXX), magnesium and silicon (6XXX) and zinc (7XXX) are heat-treatable. Most, but not all, of those alloys containing silicon (4XXX) are non-heat-treatable.

Another method of classifying aluminum alloys, important for cryogenic considerations, is by degree of weldability. Most subzero applications call for welded construction to provide economy and pressure-tightness.

ALLOY CHARACTERISTICS

There are certain characteristics of aluminum alloys -- regardless of strengthening mechanism, principal alloying elements, and weldability --which make all these alloys of interest for low-temperature applications.

Strength

The strengths of aluminum alloys, like those of most metals, are higher at cryogenic temperatures than at room temperature. They increase with decreasing temperature, at least to -423°F (-253°C) where they tend to level off (5). This is illustrated by the typical tensile properties of a number of alloys and tempers shown in Table 1, and by the typical tensile strengths of welds shown in Table 2. These tables are based on data from a large number of tests of each alloy and temper. The typical properties in Table 1 also illustrate the increased ductility of aluminum alloys at low temperatures.

The moduli of elasticity under axial and shear loadings increase with decrease in temperature (6), as shown in Figure 1. The increase is essentially linear, so that at -65°F (-54°C) and -320°F (-195°C), the values are approximately 4% and 12%, respectively, above the room temperature values. It follows that

Table 1

Tensile Properties of Typical Aluminum Alloys

Temperature °F (°C)	Alloy and Temper	TS ksi(MPa)	0.2% offset Y.S. ksi(MPa)	Elongation in 4D %
	1100-0			
Room		13(90)	5 (34)	40
-112(-80)		15(103)	5.5(38)	43
-320(-195)		25(172)	6 (41)	55
-452(-269)		46(317)	8.4(58)	37
	2219-T81			
Room		66(455)	50 (345)	10
-112(-80)		71(490)	54 (372)	10
-320(195)		83(572)	61 (421)	12
-423(-252)		99(683)	68 (469)	15
	3003-0			
Room		16(110)	6 (41)	40
-112(-80)		19(131)	6.5(45)	44
-320(-195)		32(221)	8.5(59)	46
-423(-252)		55(379)	10 (69)	48
	5083-0			
Room		42(290)	21 (145)	22
-112(-80)		43(297)	21 (145)	27
-320(-195)		59(407)	23 (159)	34
-452(-269)		79(545)	27 (186)	30
	5083-H321			
Room		46(317)	33 (228)	16
-112(-80)		47(324)	33 (228)	21
-320(-195)		64(441)	39 (269)	27
-452(-269)		83(572)	40 (276)	31
	5454-0			
Room		36(248)	17 (117)	25
-112(-80)		38(262)	17 (117)	31
-320(-195)		55(379)	20 (138)	38
-452(-269)		74(510)	24 (166)	34
	5454-H34			
Room		44(403)	35 (241)	16
-112(-80)		46(317)	36 (248)	20
-320(-195)		63(434)	41 (283)	30
-423(-252)		90(621)	43 (297)	36
	6061-T6			
Room		45(310)	40 (276)	17
-112(-80)		49(338)	42 (290)	19
-320(-195)		58(400)	46 (317)	23
-452(-269)		74(510)	53 (365)	27
	7075-T73			
Room		73(503)	63 (434)	13
-112(-80)		81(559)	69 (476)	13
-320(-195)		93(641)	77 (531)	14
-452(-269)		107(738)	85 (586)	13

the value of Poisson's ratio remains constant at about 1/3 over the whole temperature range.

Fracture Characteristics

Since aluminum alloys have no ductile-to-brittle transition and the ductility of the most versatile cryogenic alloys is greater at subzero temperatures than at room temperature, Charpy and Izod impact tests are not required by ASTM or ASME specifications and are seldom used in testing aluminum alloys. There are ample data illustrating this po-

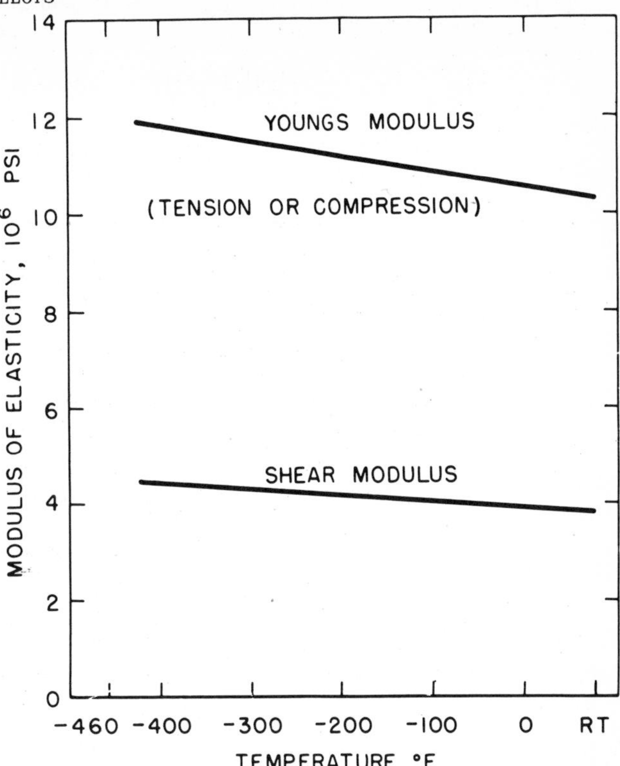

Figure 1: Modulus of elasticity of alloy 5083 at low temperatures

sition. For example, tensile impact, notch-tensile impact and Charpy impact data for 5083-H321 alloy plate and 5183 alloy weldments were obtained by Olleman and Wolfer (7). The data show that regardless of direction of stressing, type of loading, or location of specimen within the part (plate, weld, or heat-affected zone), there was no indication of any transition.

Evaluation of loading-rate effects is generally obtained from tensile tests, which provide data that may be more readily translated into engineering information. Data obtained at Alcoa Laboratories and those in the literature (8), show that almost all aluminum alloys are insensitive to strain rates between about 10^{-5}/s and 1.0/s at room and low temperatures. At higher rates, both strength and elongation are generally higher than at conventional rates.

At high strain rates, the total energy to fracture also is as high, or higher, than at conventional rates. This is supported by the results of falling-weight impact tests of 5083 alloy plate (Table 3). These measurements were obtained from impact tests with a freely-falling 257 lb (116 kg) tup on a 16 in. (406 mm) octagonal plate supported on a 12 in. (305 mm) circle.

Additional indications of the fracture characteristics have been gained from investigations of the notch toughness, tear resistance and fracture toughness of the alloys (1).

Notch toughness may be defined as the ability of a material to exhibit plastic deformation at severe stress raisers, and thereby avoid cracking which might lead to fracture. This is usually evaluated by tensile tests of notched specimens, and a comparison of the net-section fracture strengths with the tensile properties of the material.

Specifically, the ratio of the tensile strength of a severely notched specimen to the tensile-yield strength of the material (the notch-yield ratio) has been found to be the most reliable indicator of relative notch toughness. The notch tensile

Table 2

Typical Tensile Strengths of Welds in some Aluminum Alloys

Alloy			Typical Tensile Strength, ksi (MPa)				
Parent	Filler	Condition	Room Temp.	-112°F (-80°C)	-320°F (-195°C)	-423°F (-252°C)	-452°F (-269°C)
2219	2319	AW*	35(241)	36(248)	50(345)	54(372)	--
		HTA†	45(310)	49(338)	59(407)	60(414)	60(414)
3003	1100	AW	16(110)	19(131)	32(221)	49(338)	51(352)
5083	5183	AW	42(290)	43(297)	59(407)	63(434)	64(441)
5454	5554	AW	36(248)	39(269)	54(372)	63(434)	64(441)
6061	4043	AW*	27(186)	30(207)	40(276)	--	--
		HTA†	43(297)	47(324)	53(365)	55(379)	56(386)

* As-welded; aged 30 days at room temperature

† Heat-treated and aged (For 2219, T62 temper. For 6061, T6 temper)

strength is related to the stress at which appreciable plastic deformation occurs. The higher the notch-yield ratio, the greater the amount of plastic deformation which precedes fracture (9). As illustrated in Figure 2, 5083 alloy, in two tempers and also welded with 5183 filler alloy, has excellent notch toughness. Over the entire range from room temperature to -452°F (-263°C), the notch toughness of the welds, as well as the parent materials, remains high, with notch-yield ratios of 1.6 or higher.

Tear resistance is the resistance to crack growth in a nonuniform stress field. It is usually evaluated by determining the energy required to initiate and propagate a crack, in a specimen of the design depicted in Figure 3, by measurement of appropriate areas under autographic load-deformation curves. The test itself generally involves slow tearing. But it has been shown in tests of alloys to which fracture-mechanics analysis can be applied that unit propagation energy is directly related to resistance to stable crack growth, as measured by the critical stress-intensity factor from fracture toughness tests.

As shown in Figure 4, the tear resistance, like the notch toughness of 5083 and of welds in 5083 at subzero temperatures, is as high as or higher than at room temperature (10). Further, the unit-propagation energy values are exceptionally high, indicative of a great resistance to unstable crack growth and a great tolerance for design discontinuities. Data for all three compatible filler alloys -- 5183, 5356 and 5556 -- suggest a consistently high level of tear resistance. Of the three, 5183 probably offers the best combination of strength and toughness with 5083 parent alloy.

Fracture toughness is a measure of the resistance of a material to unstable crack growth in elastically stressed material. All fracture-mechanics concepts

Table 3

Results of Falling Weight Impact Tests of Some Aluminum Alloys

Alloy and Temper	Thickness in. (mm)	Plain Plate				Welded Panel*			
		Room Temperature		-280°F(-173°C)		Room Temperature		-280°F(173°C)	
		Critical Height of Drop in.(mm)	Permanent Deformation in.(mm)	Critical Height of Drop in.(mm)	Permanent Deformation in.(mm)	Critical Height of Drop in.(mm)	Permanent Deformation in.(mm)	Critical Height of Drop in.(mm)	Permanent Deformation in.(mm)
5083-0	0.25(6.35)	31(787)	1.0(25)	33(838)	1.0(25)	33(838)	1.0(25)	34(864)	0.9(23)
	0.375(9.53)	63(1600)	1.2(30)	80(2032)	1.2(30)	81(2060)	1.3(33)	93(2362)	1.2(30)
	0.50(12.7)	110(2790)	1.2(30)	134(3400)	1.2(30)	123(3120)	1.2(30)	129(3280)	1.1(28)
5083-H321	0.25(6.35)	17(432)	0.6(15)	25(635)	0.7(18)	18(457)	0.5(13)	24(610)	0.6(15)
	0.375(9.53)	31(487)	0.6(15)	45(1143)	0.7(18)	49(1245)	0.8(20)	54(1370)	0.8(20)
	0.50(12.7)	75(1905)	0.8(20)	87(2210)	0.7(18)	85(2150)	0.8(20)	97(2460)	0.8(20)

* Welded panel contained T weld, as indicated:

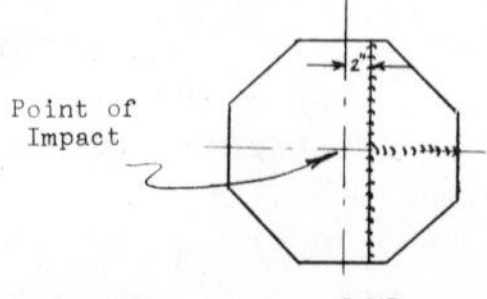

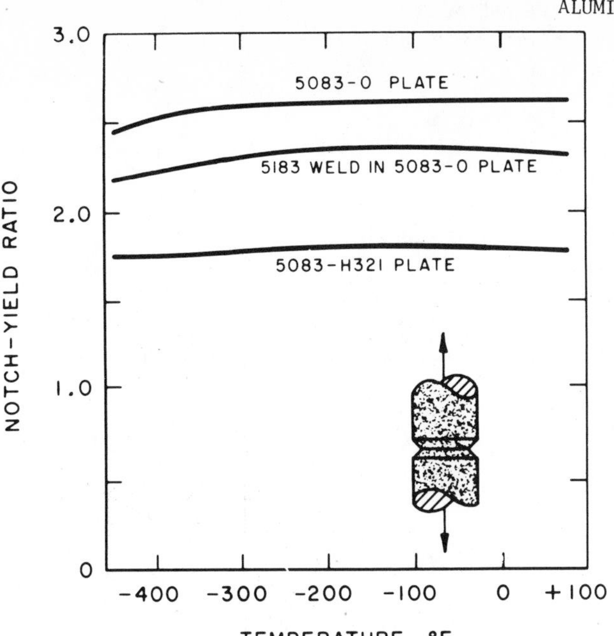

Figure 2: Notch toughness of 5083 plate and 5183 welds at very low temperatures

Tear strength, psi = $\frac{P}{A} + \frac{MC}{I} = \frac{P}{bt} + \frac{3P}{bt} = \frac{4P}{bt}$

Unit propagation energy, in.-lb per sq in. = $\frac{\text{energy to propagate a crack}}{bt}$

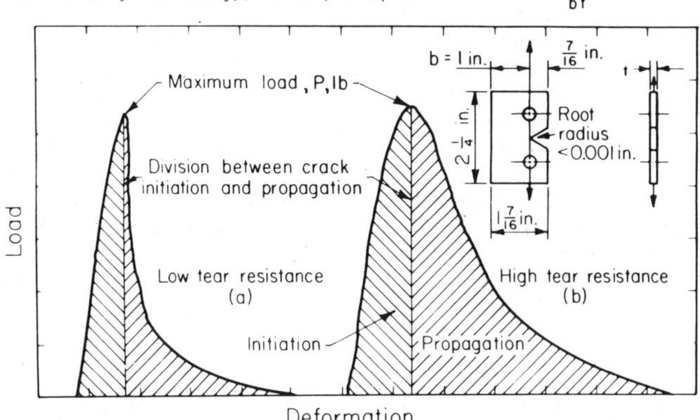

Figure 3: Tear test specimen and representative tear-test curves

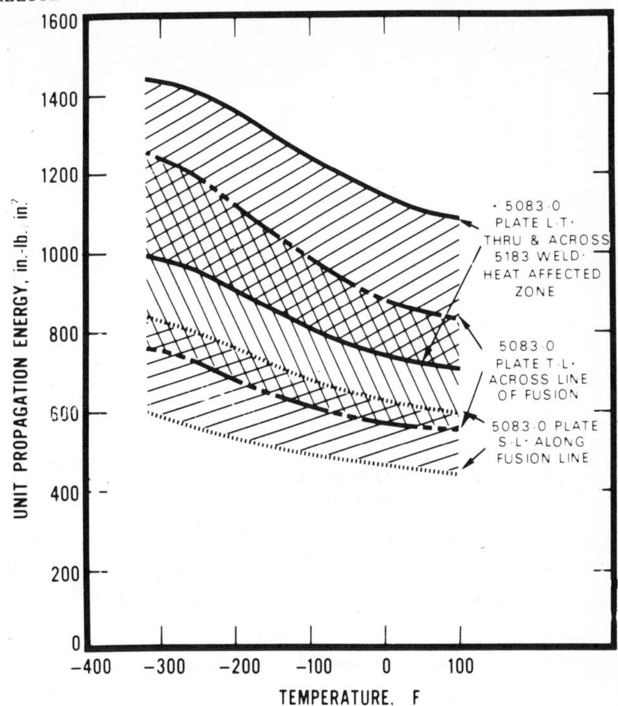

Figure 4: Unit propagation energies in thick 5083-0 plate and 5183 welds

and equations used in developing fracture-toughness data assume rapid crack growth with fracture taking place at elastic stresses (i.e., without any plastic deformation). The critical stress-intensity factor, K_c, developed in fracture toughness tests provides a relationship between stress and the size of discontinuity that will cause unstable crack growth at elastic stresses.

However, tough aluminum alloys, such as 5083, particularly in the annealed conditon, do not normally exhibit elastic, unstable crack growth, either in test panels or in real structures. In very large-scale fracture toughness tests that have been made of 5083-0 plate and 5183 weldments at room temperature, -260°F (-160°C) and -320°F (-195°C), a ductile tearing type of fracture has been observed with no evidence of any instability (10). Alloy 5083-0 plate and weldments are so tough that even large 7.7 in. (190 mm) notch-bend specimens are not thick enough to force plane strain fracture on these materials. In fact, it is estimated that specimens greater than 12 in. (305 mm) in thickness and 24 in. (610 mm) wide would be required to do so. Ductile fracture is also exhibited under plane stress conditions; 2 in. (51 mm) or 4 in. (100 mm) thick, 44 in. (1120 mm) square edge-notched fracture toughness panels of 5083-0 plate fractured by ductile tearing. If and when cracks do develop in 5083-structures, it is by ductile tearing and they are quickly arrested unless the energy source is not limited.

Thus, estimates of the fracture-toughness parameters must be made on the basis of correlations developed in tests of materials to which the elastic-fracture mechanics analysis is applicable (1).

All of the available data from the literature (1,3,6,11) and, in particular, those from Kaufman et al. (10), have been used to develop a fracture toughness composite for 5083-0 and 5183 weldments, (Figure 5). This is applicable to the LT, TL, LS and TS orientations of the plate and the through-crack or cross-weld crack at any location in the weld (12). Based upon tests that have been made of material up to 4 in. (100 mm) thick, the K_c trend line has been established and is projected out to the estimated K_{Ic} value at a thickness of 12 in. (305 mm), the minimum thickness for which the available estimates of K_{Ic} would suggest the plane-strain condition might be expected to prevail. In reviewing this summary, it is appropriate to note that no fracture instabilities have been obtained in any of the referenced tests. Thus the data can be considered to represent conservative estimates, since there is a general tendency for data from specimens which are under-sized in plan dimensions to provide values below the true fracture instability values.

Figure 5 shows that for thin 5083-0 plate K_c exceeds 100 ksi$\sqrt{\text{in}}$ (110 MN/m$^{3/2}$). Therefore, the critical crack length for stresses equal to the yield strength of parent plate or of welds at -320°F (-195°C) is greater than 10 in. (250 mm) for large panels. Since it is inconceivable that a crack would be allowed to grow to such a dimension in a tank or other structure, the problem of unstable crack growth is not likely to be encountered in this material.

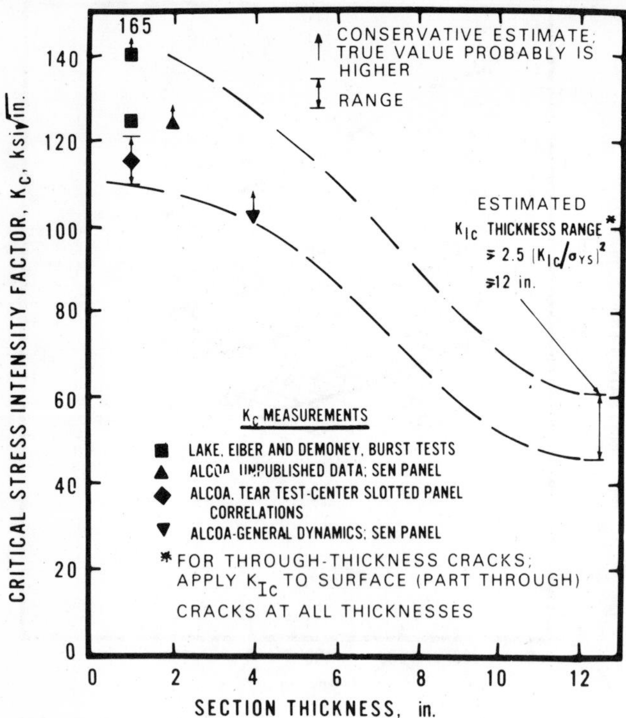

Figure 5: K_c as a function of thickness for 5083-0 plate and 5183 welds in 5083 plate

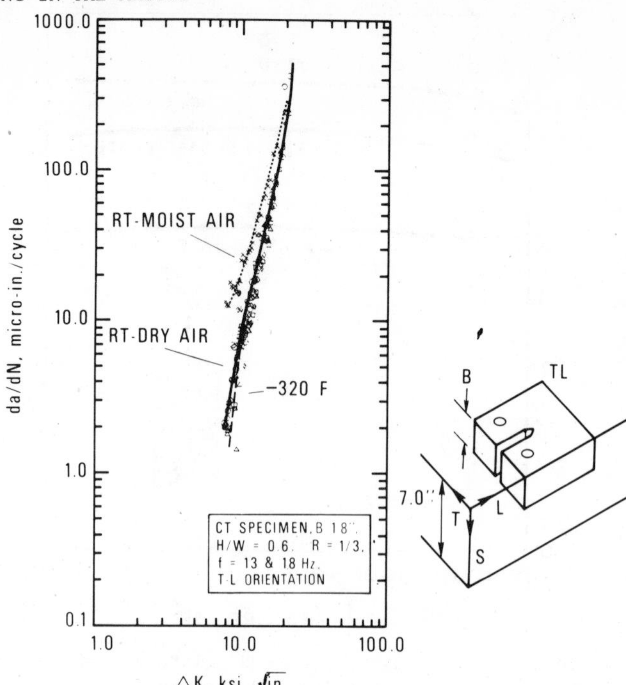

Figure 7: Effect of temperature, humidity and salt water on fatigue crack growth in 7.0 in. (180 mm) 5083-0 plate.

Fatigue Characteristics

Ample data demonstrate the higher fatigue strengths of aluminum alloys at low temperatures (13). For example, the axial stress fatigue strengths of alloy 5083-H113 (H321), and of welds made with compatible filler alloys 5556 (Figure 6), are, on average, about 20% higher at -320°F (-195°C) than at room temperature. With notched (K_t > 12) specimens, the percentage difference is even greater, indicating the lack of notch sensitivity of this alloy under fatigue loading at low temperatures.

Schwartzberg et al. (14) have demonstrated that even at -423°F (-253°C) the fatigue strengths of aluminum alloys are greater than at -320°F (-195°C). Designing against fatigue at low temperatures should introduce no new problems for the designer.

Fatigue crack propagation data are used to predict the rate at which a crack will grow and when the crack will reach its critical length for unstable fracture (12). Figure 7 shows that at low stress intensities the rate at which a crack will grow in alloy 5083-0 plate at -320°F (-195°C) is slightly less than the rate in dry air at room temperature,

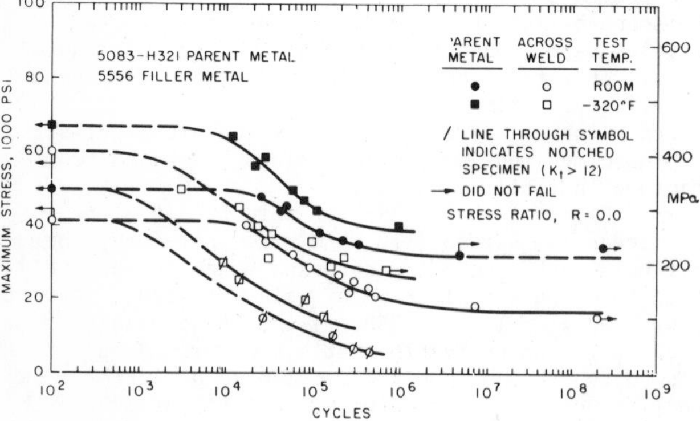

Figure 6: Axial-stress fatigue curves for 0.86 in. (22 mm) thick groove-welded 5083 plate (0.3 in./8 mm cylindrical specimens)

and considerably less than the rate in moist air at room temperature. At higher stress intensities, crack growth rate is relatively unaffected by these variations in humidity and temperature. The data also illustrate that if NDT procedures and designs can be established so that the ΔK level is below about 5 ksi (28 MPa), no significant fatigue crack growth would be expected. This approach has been used successfully in liquid natural gas transport barges.

Joining

The alloys which have found wide use in cryogenic applications are readily weldable by conventional MIG or TIG procedures. When strain-hardened or solution-heat-treated alloys are welded, the heat-affected zone (HAZ) represents a region of reduced strength. The reduction in strength may be noted by a comparison of the typical tensile strengths of welds in Table 2 with those of parent alloys and tempers in Table 1. In strain-hardened alloys, the strengths of welds are essentially the same as those of the annealed parent alloy at temperatures down to -320°F (-195°C), and slightly less than those of the annealed parent alloy at lower temperatures. For all alloys, weld strength efficiencies are constant over much of the range of subzero temperatures, as illustrated in Figure 8. In heat-treatable alloys, welding reduces the strength but not to the level of the annealed parent alloy. This is the result of the mild re-solution heat treatment and quench gained from the welding and subsequent air cooling. Various techniques are used to minimize strength reductions, ranging from use of local thickening (lands) to special welding techniques which limit temperature rise and provide rapid chill.

In the design of welded joints in a strain-hardened alloy, the weld-qualification requirement and the allowable stress value are usually based on the specified properties of the annealed parent alloy. For a heat-treated alloy, these quantities

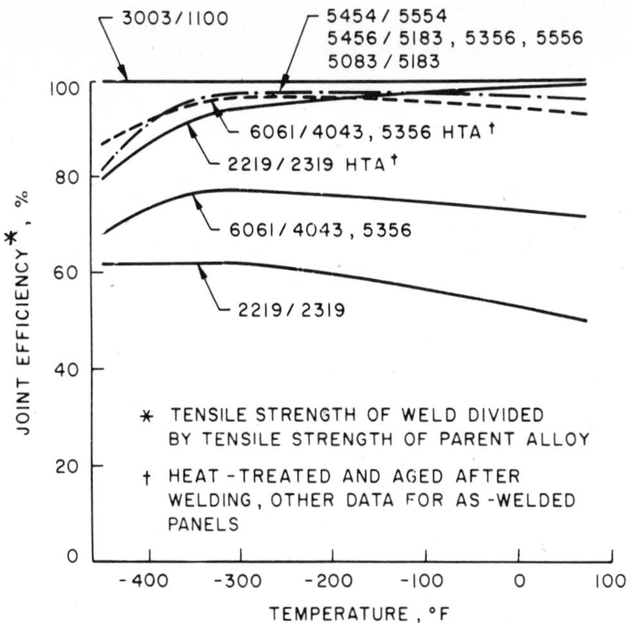

Figure 8: Weld joint strength efficiencies for aluminum alloys at low temperatures.

are developed from a statistical analysis of test data from actual welds.

The fracture chracteristics of the welds are at least as good as those of the alloy in the strain-hardened or heat-treated temper (15). Both the notch-yield ratio and unit-propagation energy of the welds are in the same range as, or above, those of alloy 5083-H321. To maintain a uniform level of strength and toughness in a structure, it is not uncommon to design it entirely of annealed material.

The greater variation in fracture data for welds is due to the irregular fracture paths developed because of the irregularities of the weld beads. Also, poor welding procedures, which result in unsatisfactory structures in the weld (hot-short cracks, large cells, lack of fusion, etc.), will adversely affect the strength and fracture characteristics of the weld. Weld quality-control tests should avoid these.

ALLOYS

Some specific comments regarding the characteristics of the various series of commercial aluminum alloys indicate the many applications for which they are suited.

1XXX Series (Unalloyed, Strain-Hardenable)

These comprise commercially pure aluminum, alloy 1100, and variations having higher purity, relatively low strength and high elongation in all tempers. Their use is limited to applications where formability, ductility and resistance to corrosion are more important than strength. They are weldable, but since the welding heat reduces strength, the properties of the fully annealed temper must be used in establishing design stresses.

2XXX Series (Al-Cu, Heat-Treatable)

Considerable experience has been gained with alloys 2014 and 2219 in cryogenic applications, mainly in the aerospace field. Alloy 2014 is very strong, yet it possesses a useful level of toughness at very low temperatures. Special welding techniques have been employed by the aerospace industry to obtain reliable welds. Post-weld thermal treatments can be used to increase weld strength but these reduce joint toughness. Alloy 2219 has less strength than alloy 2014, but it is tougher and much more readily weldable. The weld strengths are about 75% of that of the parent material, and can be increased to 100% by post-weld thermal treatments.

Other alloys of the 2000 series are not readily weldable and so are limited in their cryogenic applications.

3XXX Series (Al-Mn, Strain-Hardenable)

Of the few commercial 3000 series alloys, alloy 3003 has been used most widely in low-temperature applications. It is used principally in situations where brazing is involved, and for piping. It has relatively low strength but very good notch toughness, has good ductility and formability, and is easily welded.

5XXX Series (Al-Mg, Strain-Hardenable)

The broadest application of aluminum alloys in cryogenic situations has involved the 5000 series, notably alloy 5083. These alloys, with more than about 2.5% magnesium, have reasonably high strengths and excellent toughness. Of the group, alloy 5083 offers about the best overall combination of these properties, many of which have been illustrated previously. The notch toughness and tear resistance of alloy 5083 and of welds in 5083 are exceptionally high at low temperatures. Because welding results in a reduced-strength zone, design is usually based on the properties of the annealed parent alloy.

Other alloys of the 5000 series have interesting cryogenic properties. Alloy 5456 has the highest-strength of the series with a procedure qualification requirement (ASME) of 42 ksi (290 MPa).

6XXX Series (Al-Mg-Si Heat-Treatable)

The 6000 series alloys, like the 5000 series, have high toughness at subzero temperatures. Alloys 6061, 6063 and higher strength alloy 6066 are readily welded and formed and have high resistance to stress-corrosion cracking. Weld strengths are about 60% of parent alloy (T6 temper) strengths, but may be increased to nearly 100% by post-weld thermal treatment.

7XXX Series (Al-Zn-Mg, Heat-Treatable)

The copper-free alloys of the 7000 series have attracted considerable attention for cryogenic applications because of their weldability and toughness. Of the group, 7005 has about the best combination of strength and toughness. It displays little or no decrease in toughness with decrease in temperature (13), whereas some of the stronger alloys show significant, if gradual, decreases.

The copper-bearing, high-strength 7XXX series are not considered weldable by normal procedures. This and their lower toughness at cryogenic temperatures make them less useful for low-temperature service.

APPLICATIONS

Aluminum alloys are economically used in the construction of a wide variety of equipment designed for the processing, storage and transport of fuels and cryogens, and of structures exposed to low temperatures. Aluminum is compatible with all known cryogens.

Process and Storage

Aluminum alloys have played a part in low-temperature processing and storage for many years. Early air-separation plants were built of 3003 alloy because it could be easily joined and was approved by the ASME Boiler and Pressure Vessel Code. Applications for 3003 included reversing exchangers, piping, and tanks.

The higher-strength 5XXX alloys, 5083 and 5456, found use in towers, reboilers, pressure vessels and tanks for liquid oxygen, nitrogen, hydrogen and helium at temperatures as low as -452°F (-269°C).

Aluminum alloys are also widely used for cryogenic storage tanks, both pressurized and atmospheric and in spherical or cylindrical shapes. Such storage equipment almost always involves double-wall design, in which the inner, or cold, container is aluminum. The outer container is aluminum or carbon steel and the annular space is filled with insulation. For vertical field-erected tanks, tapered plate is usually selected. Welding costs are frequently reduced because the average metal thickness is less.

Probably the largest aluminum cryogenic tanks are found in the burgeoning liquefied-natural-gas (LNG) industry. Large LNG tanks (175,000 bbl and 225,000 bbl) utilize 5083-0 alloy plate. Spherical shells of 5083 alloy are used when the inner shell must withstand pressures exceeding atmospheric. Heat gain is minimized by the low surface-to-volume ratio of this configuration.

Aluminum alloy tubes (3003-0) and shells (5083-0) are used in wound heat exchangers. Primary applications of this type of construction have been in helium and methane liquefaction plants. Such exchangers can use hundreds of miles of small tube wound around a core.

Transportation

In many cases, aluminum is specified for both inner and outer shells of transport tankage for increased payload within highway weight limitations. For example, a 4000 USgal (15,000 ℓ) unit for liquid oxygen built of 5083 alloy is 11,000 lbs (5,000 kg) lighter and provides 40% more load capacity than that of a similar unit built of steel.

Railroad tank cars are similarly built, but usually use steel external tanks.

Marine transport of LNG at about -260°F (-160°C) has been growing rapidly since the practicality of this transport method was demonstrated in 1959 by the Methane Pioneer (13). This ship was fitted with five tanks of 5XXX series aluminum alloy having a total capacity of nearly 35,000 bbl. Two larger ships were subsequently built, each having nine 5083 alloy aluminum tanks -- scale ups of the Methane Pioneer type. Four ships with aluminum cargo tanks were built to transport LNG from Libya to Italy and Spain (13). Each ship holds 250,000 bbl, equivalent to about 750 million ft^3 (20 million m^3) of gas. Most recent ships employ the Kvaerner Brug spherical tank design for maximum material economy.

Aluminum tanks, piping and heat exchangers are also found in the dockside liquefaction plant in Algeria and in the receiving facilities in England.

REFERENCES

1. J. G. Kaufman and M. Holt, Technical Paper No. 18, 1965, Aluminum Company of America, Alcoa Center, Pa.
2. Aluminum, 1967, vol. 2, ASM, Metals Park, Ohio.
3. J. G. Kaufman and E. T. Wanderer, Machine Design, 1965, vol. 37, pp. 199-205.
4. Aluminum Standards and Data, 1976. The Aluminum Association, New York.
5. J. G. Kaufman, K. O. Bogardus, and E. T. Wanderer, Adv. Cryogenic Engineering, 1968, vol. 13, pp. 294-308.
6. J. G. Kaufman and E. W. Johnson, ibid., 1960, vol. 6, pp. 637-649.
7. R. D. Olleman and G. C. Wolfer, ibid., 1959, vol. 5, pp. 430-438.
8. A. L. Austin and R. F. Streidel, Proceedings, ASTM, 1959, vol. 59.
9. J. G. Kaufman and E. W. Johnson, ibid., 1963, vol. 62, pp. 778-793.
10. J. G. Kaufman, F. G. Nelson and R. H. Wygonik, ASTM Special Technical Publication 556, 1974, pp. 125-158, ASTM, Philadelphia.
11. R. L. Lake, F. W. DeMoney and R. J. Eiber, Adv. Cryogenic Engineering, 1968, vol. 13, pp. 278-293.
12. J. G. Kaufman and R. A. Kelsey, ASTM Special Tech. Publn. 579, 1975, pp. 138-158, ASTM, Philadelphia.
13. J. G. Kaufman and F. G. Nelson, Space/Aeronautics, 1962, vol. 38, pp. 91-93 and 96.
14. F. R. Schwartzberg, R. D. Keys and S. H. Osgood, Cryogenic Materials Data Handbook, Supplement No. 4, 1962, U.S. Department of Commerce, PB 171809-4.
15. F. G. Nelson, J. G. Kaufman and M. Holt, Welding J., 1966, vol. 45, (7), pp. 321s-329s.

DISCUSSION

D. J. Burns (University of Waterloo): One aspect which you have not dealt with in the specifications for LNG tanks is the weld defects which are allowed, in view of the very high fracture toughness of the alloys themselves.

J. G. Kaufman: Any defect, other than a solid copper inclusion, up to 0.25 in. (6 mm) in any dimension, a 0.75 in. (19 mm) long defect, fully embedded, if it is not more than 0.063 in. (1.6 mm) wide, or surface crack no more than 0.25 in. (6 mm) long and 0.063 in. (1.6 mm) deep are permitted. These limits are based on stress intensity calculations together with code interpretations. As for multiple defects, they are to be treated individually, unless they are closer than 4x(maximum dimension) when they are treated as a combined defect. Due to the high fracture toughness of these alloys, of course, much larger defects could be tolerated. But we believe it is not appropriate to encourage sloppy welding practice by relaxing the defect requirements.

A. Hurlich (General Dynamics): I think you are being much too kind to the boiler code committee. We have been working for quite some years to get them to set more rational standards for allowable defect conditions particularly in the 5083 alloy. Before you did the heavy plate tests, we took your data on 0.75 in. (19 mm) tear tests and estimated critical crack lengths of 40 in. (1020 mm) at room temperature and 60 in. (1520 mm) at LNG temperatures, which are gratifyingly close to the results you obtained in actual tests.

B. E. Boardman (John Deere): You indicate a K_t value of 12 for welded 5083 alloy and show that fatigue strengths increase with decreasing temperature. At what life was that fatigue strength determined? Was that fatigue strength from S-N type data or was it from strain controlled data? Did you determine the fatigue strength reduction factor, K_f, as a function of temperature?

J. G. Kaufman: All data were obtained in conventional constant deflection S-N testing. The increase in fatigue life was independent of life; percentage increases were largest at the fatigue limit (i.e. > 10^6 cycles). The value of K_f remained essentially constant with change in temperature. The data which permit that conclusion are included in the paper.

A. B. Rothwell (Noranda Research): In view of the fact that you have referred to design stresses of 10 ksi (70 MPa), while previous discussions at this conference have considered operation at 80% of SMYS, which in steels may be in excess of 70 ksi (480 MPa), the contention that aluminum alloys may be beneficial in any application where weight reduction is important appears dubious.

J. G. Kaufman: A value of 10 ksi (70 MPa) was used in this particular application for 5083-0/5183 because of the combined bending and tensile stresses involved and the ASME requirements for that situation. Where higher strengths are required, other aluminum alloys such as 2014-T641, 2219-T851 or 7005-T16351 could be used, and readily match constructional steels on a strength/weight ratio.

M. R. Krishnadev (Laval University): In what specific areas of Arctic applications do you recommend the aluminum alloys in preference to steels, and why?

J. G. Kaufman: The properties of aluminium alloys make them candidates for all applications in Arctic environments, and economics will control which ones are selected. It is important to consider maintenance and handling costs in figuring the economics, as the superior corrosion resistance and light weight are critical factors in dealing with overall costs.

M. R. Krishnadev: One of the limitations of aluminum alloys is their lower strength levels compared to steels. What do you think would be realistic values of maximum strength achievable in the near future in Al-alloys having the potential for Arctic usage?

J. G. Kaufman: On a strength/weight basis, aluminium alloys do compare favourably to steels right now. Even in an absolute comparison, many alloys, such as 2014-T6 and 7075-T7351 with yield strengths around 60 ksi (410 MPa), are equal or superior in strength to many common structural steels. These are not the alloys we would select for applications requiring very high toughness. For these cases, alloys like 2219-T851 and 7005-T5351 with yield strengths around 45 ksi (310 MPa) are the best available now. For super critical applications (e.g. LNG tankers), it seems possible that yield strengths up to 30 ksi (210 MPa) will be available in aluminium alloys within 5 years.

MATERIALS OF CONSTRUCTION FOR ARCTIC VALVES

H. Schwartzbart
Rockwell International
400, North Lexington Ave.
Pittsburgh, Pa. 15208
USA

Three classes of material are important in the construction of valves to be used in the pipeline transportation of oil and gas in the Arctic. These are metals, elastomers and sealants. The principal metallurgical challenge is how to provide, most cost-effectively, the required toughness at Arctic temperatures, especially in the choice of material for the valve body. Valve sealing may be accomplished by use of suitable elastomers and sealants which retain their sealing capability at sufficiently low temperatures. Thus, for a large pipeline ball valve carrying gas or oil to provide long-lasting reliable and safe service requires proper materials selection, as well as optimum fabrication procedures.

This paper presents the results of an extensive study of materials, both metallic and elastomeric, and welding practices used in trunnion-mounted ball valves for Arctic service. The principal conclusions relative to the choice of cast body materials are:
1) For service at -20°F (-30°C), ASTM A352 Grade LCC, welded with Linde 44 filler wire or equivalent, is a reasonable choice, provided the sulfur and phosphorus contents are restricted. 2) For service at -80°F (-62°C), ASTM A352 Grade LC2.1, modified to reduce the tensile and yield strengths (to 80 and 50 ksi [550 and 345 MPa], respectively) welded with Linde 110 filler wire or equivalent, without post-weld stress relief, is the best overall choice.

Fluorosilicone is the superior low temperature elastomer for dynamic seals, based upon its superior mechanical behaviour and chemical resistance to hydrocarbons.

INTRODUCTION

The pipeline transmission of oil and gas from Alaska and Northern Canada presents unique challenges to materials and fabrication engineers, especially in the selection of the most cost-effective steels and fabrication procedures, while not compromising safety and environmental considerations. Furthermore, elastomers and sealants must be chosen that will retain their sealing capability at Arctic temperatures.

The questions of which gas pipelines are to be built have not been resolved as of this writing. More importantly, the particular specifications governing the construction have not been finalized. It is not the intent of this paper to provide a critique of specifications, but rather to present the results of a study of material properties, which in the metallurgical area was concentrated on the Charpy V-notch impact strength of weldments in a number of candidate steels.

The sealants will not be discussed because of their highly proprietary nature, except to note that they have been especially formulated to operate over the required temperature range, and to be compatible with the hydrocarbon line fluids. Metals will be discussed relative to one particular set of specifications as a frame of reference, and in terms of operation at temperatures of -20°F (-30°C) and -80°F (-62°C). A minimum of experimental details will be presented since these have appeared elsewhere (1,2).

METALS

The Rockwell Arctic trunnion-mounted (TM) ball valve is shown in Figure 1. It is a special version of the standard Rockwell TM ball valve, responsive to the specifications discussed below. The valve is an assembly of cast steel shell components joined together by submerged arc welding.

The specifications used as a frame of reference were prepared in 1971-1972 by Northern Engineering Services, Ltd. for the Canadian Arctic Gas Study, Ltd. These specifications preclude the use of ordinary carbon steels for the pressure-containing envelopes,

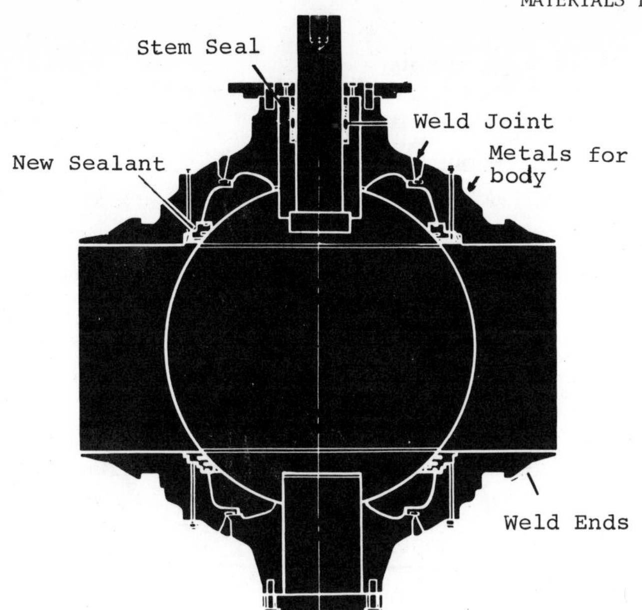

Figure 1: Rockwell Arctic Trunnion Mounted Ball Valve

not only because of the extremes in low temperature (as low as -80°F [-62°C]) expected but also because rather high levels of absorbed energy are demanded in the Charpy V-notch impact properties of candidate steels and the filler metals needed for weld fabrication and repairs.

Table 1 is taken from the Canadian-Arctic specification for pipeline and compressor station valves 16 in. (400 mm) and larger and illustrates the approach taken with respect to relating the strength of a given steel to its toughness at specified design temperatures of -20°F (-30°C) and -80°F (-62°C). These requirements apply not only to the base metal but also to the weld metal and heat-affected-zone (HAZ). A further stipulation is that no component, weld or HAZ is to exceed Rc 24 (KHN 272). With

Table 1

Canadian-Arctic Impact Energy Specifications

Tensile Strength ksi (MPa)	Charpy V-notch Impact Minimum Acceptable Energy, ft lbf (J)	
	Alternate 1	Alternate 2
	3 spec. avg.	3 spec. avg.
65 (450) and under	15 (20)	25 (34)
65 (450) to 80 (550)	20 (27)	35 (47)
80 (550) to 95 (660)	25 (34)	40 (54)
95 (660) to 110 (760)	30 (41)	50 (68)
over 100 (760)	Subject to negotiation	

Notes: (1) Alternate 1 applies to components that are either not welded or if welded, are to be thermally stress-relieved. Alternate 2 applies to components that will be used in the as-welded condition. (2) Except at the 15 ft lbf (20 J) and 50 ft lbf (68 J) average levels, which permit one specimen of a set to be as low as 12 and 40 ft lbf (16 and 54 J), respectively, the minimum value permitted for a single specimen at all other levels is 5 ft lbf (7 J) less than the required average.

these specifications in mind, a program was conducted to evaluate the most likely steel casting grades to be selected for Arctic service in combination with appropriate submerged-arc welding wires. Since the Canadian Arctic specifications, for example, require that the HAZ meet the same Charpy impact values specified for the base metals, an important objective of the program was to determine the toughness characteristics of the heat-affected zones. Studies were conducted on 1 in. (25 mm) and 3 in. (76 mm) thick welded cast steel plates meeting the chemical composition requirements of ASTM A352 Grades LCC, LC2, LC2.1, and LC3, and on welding filler metals manufactured by Linde under the numerical designations 44, 100, and 110.

MATERIALS AND WELDING

Table 2 lists the composition and tensile properties of the steels used in this investigation. These materials were cast by ESCO Corporation, Portland, Oregon, and Birdsboro Corporation, Birdsboro, Pennsylvania, in the above-mentioned grades to ASTM Specification A352 and heat treated by the foundries according to the footnotes to Table 2. The 3 in. (76 mm) thick ESCO plates were cast as 12 in. (305 mm) squares and the 1 in. (25 mm) thick plates were cast in a 6 in. (152 mm) by 12 in. (305 mm) size. The Birdsboro plates, which were obtained in the 3 in. (76 mm) thickness only, of Grade LC2 material, were also 12 in. (305 mm) square.

The welding materials and the base material to which they were applied are listed in Table 3. These materials were selected on the basis of their published impact properties plus their reasonably close matching of composition and other properties. The Linde 0091 flux is a basic flux designed especially to produce good impact properties with a wide variety of filler metals.

Although the plate preparation, welding and testing procedures are not detailed here, the experiments were conducted so as to most closely simulate the actual valve fabrication. To study the effect of stress relief, both as-received and welded plates of each thickness were stress-relieved at 1100°F (590°C) by a commercial heat treater who followed the procedures in Paragraph UCS-56 of Section VIII, Division I, of the ASME Boiler and Pressure Vessel Code.

RESULTS AND DISCUSSION

Tensile results are given in Table 4 as averages of triplicate tests. Except for the tests on the as-received base metal, all the data are from specimens which were oriented transverse to the weld centerline. Because specimens of this type are composite in nature and do not generally extend uniformly, elongation data for these tests were not recorded. However, the reduction of area values were recorded as valid ductility measurements. In general, the reductions of area reported for the specimens from the 1 in. (25 mm) plate represent the ductility of base metal, whereas the data for specimens from the 3 in. (76 mm) plate represent the ductility of the weld metal. The reason for this behaviour is that the entire reduced section in the three-inch plate was weld metal, whereas in the one-inch plate only the center of the reduced section was weld metal. With a slightly stronger weld metal, the point of failure in the specimens from the one-inch plate was therefore forced into the base metal.

As can be seen from the data in Table 4, except for the tensile and yield strength values of the LC2.1 material, values exceed the minimum required properties specified for the base materials in ASTM

Table 2

Chemical Composition (wt %) and Tensile Properties of the Cast Steel Plates

Steel	Heat No.	Data Source	C	Mn	Si	S	P	Ni	Cr	Mo	Heat Treatment (see below)	TS ksi (MPa)	YS ksi (MPa)	Reduction of Area %	Elong. in 2in (51 mm) %
LCC	64630	ESCO	0.18	1.09	0.27	.007	.012	---	---	---	A	80 (550)	58 (400)	60	29
		R1[b]	0.18	1.20	0.35	.009	.015	---	---	---					
		ASTM A352	0.25[a] max.	1.20[a] max.	0.60 max.	0.045 max.	0.04 max.	---	---	---		70 (480) min.	40 (280) min.	35 min.	22 min.
LC2	63609	ESCO	.034	0.47	0.34	.003	.012	2.49	---	---	A	77 (530)	63 (430)	58	28
		R1[b]	.053	0.66	0.44	.013	.011	2.06	---	---					
	E6158	Birdsboro	.142	0.69	0.46	.011	.013	2.80	.27	.05	C	77 (530)	56 (390)	56	30
											D	80 (550)	62 (430)	57	30
		R1[b]	.15	0.66	0.50	.011	.010	2.55	---	---					
		ASTM A352	0.25 max.	0.50-0.80	0.60 max.	0.045 max.	0.04 max.	2.0-3.0	---	---		70 (480) min.	40 (280) min.	35 min.	24 min.
		RMC 90036	0.12 max.	0.50-0.80	0.60 max.	0.025 max.	0.025 max.	2.0-3.0	---	---		65 (450) min.	40 (280) min.	35 min.	24 min.
LC2	65527	ESCO	.07	0.49	0.49	.012	.017	2.58	1.53	0.44	B	99 (680)	82 (570)	72	27
		R1[b]	.097	0.51	0.33	.010	.019	2.45	1.44	0.45					
		ASTM A352	0.22 max.	0.55-.75	0.50 max.	0.045 max.	0.04 max.	2.5-3.5	1.35-1.85	.30-.60		105 (720) min.	80 (550) min.	30 min.	18 min.
		RMC 90036	0.12 max.	0.55-.75	0.50 max.	0.025 max.	0.025 max.	2.5-3.5	1.35-1.85	.30-.60		80 (550) min.	50 (350) min.	40 min.	22 min.
LC3	63608	ESCO	.065	0.51	0.43	.009	.012	3.50	---	---	A	93 (640)	74 (510)	43	24
		R1[b]	.086	0.56	0.45	.007	.013	3.05	---	---					
		ASTM A352	0.15 max.	0.50-.80	0.60 max.	0.045 max.	0.04 max.	3.0-4.0	---	---		70 (480) min.	40 (280) min.	35 min.	24 min.

a. For each reduction of 0.01%C below the max. specified, an increase of 0.04%Mn above the max. specified is permitted, to a max. of 1.40%Mn.

b. These are Rockwell check analyses made on the test plates.

Heat Treatments: (A): 1800°F (980°C) (5 h) AC, 1650°F (900°C) (3 h) WQ, 1250°F (680°C) (4 h) WQ.

(B): 1950°F (1070°C) (5 h) AC to 400°F (200°C) max. 1250°F (680°C) (4 h) AC, reheat 1850°F (1010°C) (4 h) AC to 400°F (200°C), reheat 1700°F (930°C) (3 h) WQ, 1230°F (670°C) (4 h) WQ.

(C): 1650°F (900°C) AC, 1600°F (870°C) AC, 1180°F (640°C) AC.

(D): 1650°F (900°C) AC, 1600°F (870°C) WQ, 1180°F (640°C) AC.

A352-72 (Table 2). However, in ordering the LC2.1 steel, the requirements were modified to meet 80 ksi (550 MPa) min. tensile strength and 50 ksi (345 MPa) min. yield strength. This low-carbon modification was designed specifically to improve the impact strength and as a result there was, as expected, some loss in tensile and yield strength.

Microhardness traverses are given in Figures 2 to 5. These traverses were all taken at the T/4 point from the top surface of the weld. In the case of Figures 4b and 5b, the width of the HAZ in the as-welded specimen was different than in the stress-relieved specimen; in all other cases, the width was identical for the two conditions.

As can be seen in Figure 2, the LCC-Linde 44 combination produced joints with acceptable hardnesses in the stress-relieved condition, but in the as-welded condition the HAZ of the 1 in. (25 mm) material reached a hardness of KHN 292 (Rc 28) which is above the acceptable level of KHN 272 (Rc 24). These results indicate that stress-relief is necessary for this material in the smaller sections to ensure a hardness below the specified maximum. The lower hardness values in the 3 in. (76 mm) section reflect the difference in the amount of metal and/or the number of weld passes above the T/4 point in the thicker material. These welding conditions would give a greater degree of heat treatment and a lower hardness in the thicker material.

Figure 3 shows the hardness traverses for the LC2-Linde 100 tests. For both the 1 in. (25 mm) and 3 in. (76 mm) thicknesses, in the as-welded condition the weld metal hardnesses are approximately KHN 290 (Rc 27-28), which is in excess of the specified KHN 272 (Rc 24) max. Stress relief reduced the weld metal hardness in both cases to a satisfactory level of approximately KHN 260 (Rc 22).

For the LC2.1-Linde 100 tests, the hardness traverses are shown in Figure 4. The weld metal hardness, in both thicknesses, is above the specified maximum hardness level, even after stress relief. However, the HAZ's, which were also above KHN 272 (Rc 24) in the as-welded condition, have been reduced to acceptable levels of hardness by stress relief. Because the weld metal used for both the LC2 and LC2.1 casting was the same, it is apparent that the Linde 100 weld metal is sensitive to slight variations in welding procedures or heat treatment to produce the different results observed when conditions were maintained as constant as possible. The results were not caused by dilution, because dilution effects are not long range enough to affect the entire cross-section of welds as large as those in this investigation.

Table 3

Composition and Tensile Properties of Welding Materials

Material and Use	Size in. (mm)	Flux	Data Source	Composition - wt% C	Mn	Si	S	P	Mo	Ni	V	Cr	Cu	TS ksi (MPa)	YS ksi (MPa)	Reduction of Area %	Elong. in 2 in. (51 mm) %
Linde 44 for LCC	3/32 (2.38)	0091	Linde R1[b]	.13 .20	2.25 1.40	.10 .33	.02 .007	.02 .014	.40 .36	.55 .60	--- ---	---- ----	--- ---	107 (740)	87 (600)	61	23[c]
Linde 100[a] for LC2,LC2.1	3/32 (2.38)	0091	Linde R1[b]	.15 .09	2.00 1.42	.10 .38	.008 .008	.007 .013	.53 .47	2.6 2.6	.02 .003	.33 .27	.30 .43	115 (790)	105 (720)	50	18
Linde 110 for LC3	3/32 (2.38)	0091	Linde R1[b]	.05 .042	1.30 .84	.20 .43	.005 .007	.005 .012	.33 .30	3.1 2.87	.02 .005	.10 .068	.15 .15	95 (660)	80 (550)	65	23

a. This welding wire was used on both the ESCO and Birdsboro LC2 steels. b. These are Rockwell check analyses made of the submerged-arc weld. c. Elongation in 1.4 in. (35.6 mm).

LC3	63608	ESCO R1[b]	.065 .086	0.51 0.56	0.43 0.45	.009 .007	.012 .013	3.50 3.05	--- ---	--- ---	A	93 (640)	74 (511)	43	24
		ASTM A352	0.15 max.	0.50-.80	0.60 max.	0.045 max.	0.04 max.	3.0-4.0	---	---		70 (483) min.	40 (276) min.	35 min.	24 min.

a. For each reduction of 0.01 %C below the max. specified, an increase of 0.04% Mn above the max. specified is permitted to a max. of 1.40% Mn

b. These are Rockwell check analyses made on the test plates

Heat Treatments: (A): 1800°F (980°C) (5 h) AC, 1650°F (900°C) (3 h) WQ, 1250°F (680°C)(4 h) WQ

(B): 1950°F (1070°C) (5h) AC to 400°F (200°C) max. 1250°F (680°C) (4 h) AC, reheat 1850°F (1010°C) (4 h) AC to 400°F (200°C), reheat 1700°F (930°C) (3 h) WQ, 1230°F (670°C) (4 h) WQ

(C): 1650°F (900°C) AC, 1600°F (870°C) AC, 1180°F (640°C) AC

(D): 1650°F (900°C) AC, 1600°F (870°C) WQ, 1180°F (640°C) AC

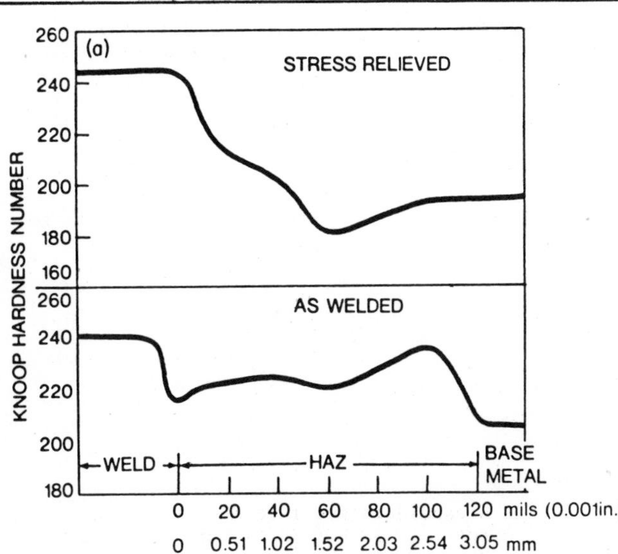

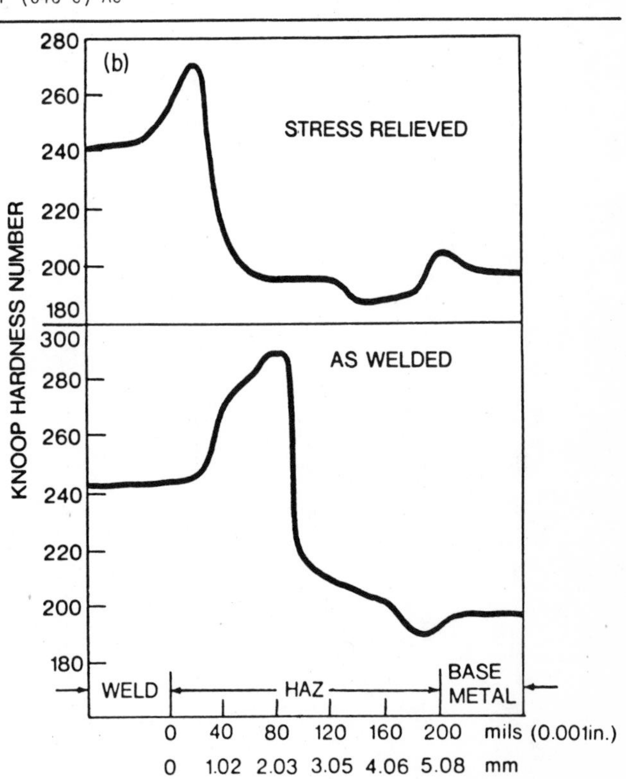

Figure 2: Microhardness Traverse of Welds in LCC Welded with Linde 100 Wire; (a) 3 in. (76 mm), (b) 1 in. (25 mm) plate

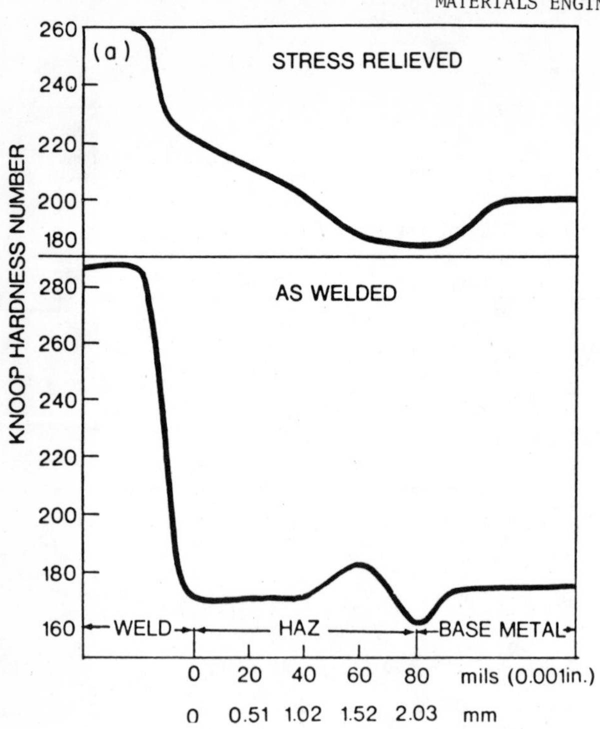

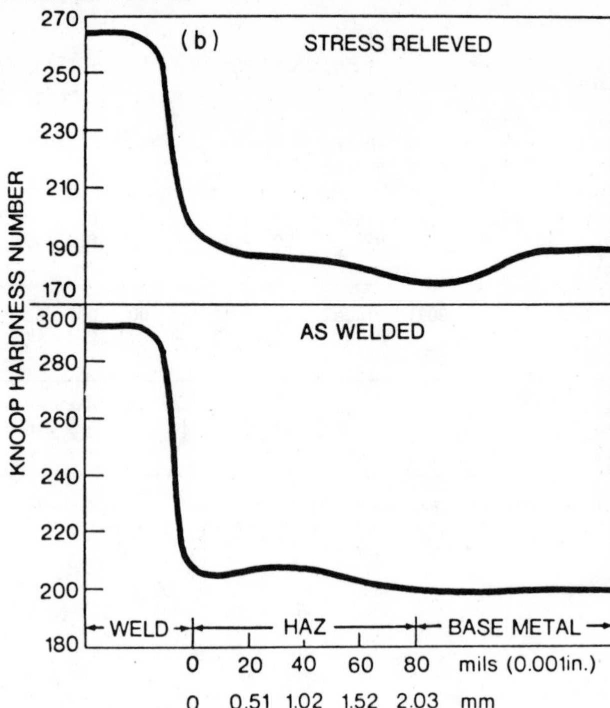

Figure 3: Microhardness Traverse of Welds in LC2 welded with Linde 100 wire; (a) 3 in. (76 mm), (b) 1 in. (25 mm) plate

Table 4

Tensile Properties of Base Metal and Welded Joints

Steel	Thickness in. (mm)	TS ksi (MPa)	YS (0.2% offset) ksi (MPa)	Reduction of Area, %	Elongation in 2 in. (50 mm)
		Base Metal (As-Received)			
LCC	3 (76)	80 (550)	59 (410)	63	25
		Transverse to Weld (As-Welded)			
LCC	1 (25)	85 (590)	64 (440)	41	--
	3 (76)	93 (640)	77 (530)	64	--
		Transverse to Weld (Stress-Relieved)			
LCC	1 (25)	83 (570)	62 (430)	53	--
	3 (76)	95 (655)	84 (580)	69	--
		Base Metal (As-Received)			
LC2	3 (76)	79 (540)	63 (430)	72	28
		Transverse to Weld (As-Welded)			
LC2	1 (25)	77 (530)	60 (420)	70	--
	3 (76)	79 (550)	62 (430)	71	--
		Transverse to Weld (Stress-Relieved)			
LC2	1 (25)	75 (520)	58 (400)	61	--
	3 (76)	98 (680)	81 (560)	63	--
LC2*	3 (76)	102 (710)	93 (640)	51	--
		Base Metal (As-Received)			
LC2.1	3 (76)	92 (630)	75 (520)	60	23
		Transverse to Weld (As-Welded)			
LC2.1	1 (25)	98 (670)	73 (500)	58	--
	3 (76)	112 (770)	80 (550)	48	--
		Transverse to Weld (Stress-Relieved)			
LC2.1	1 (25)	86 (590)	68 (470)	68	--
	3 (76)	111 (770)	90 (620)	62	--
		Base Metal (As-Received)			
LC3	3 (76)	88 (600)	68 (470)	69	25
		Transverse to Weld (As-Welded)			
LC3	1 (25)	94 (650)	74 (510)	60	--
	3 (26)	90 (620)	72 (500)	71	--
		Transverse to Weld (Stress-Relieved)			
LC3	1 (25)	92 (630)	71 (490)	68	--
	3 (76)	89 (610)	75 (520)	71	--

* Birdsboro castings, all other material was from ESCO

The data for LC3-Linde 110 tests are plotted in Figure 5. For the 3 in. (76 mm) thick material, the results for the stress-relieved material appear to be the reverse of what would be expected, but careful checking has verified these data. There must have been some variation in the original heat treatment of these plates to cause this difference, because they were all from the same heat and the slight variations in chemical composition which might occur from plate to plate could not account for this behaviour. The primary significance is that the maximum hardness in the HAZ (KHN 280 or Rc 25-26) after stress relieving exceeded the specified maximum of KHN 272 (Rc 24). The 1 in. (25 mm) thick LC3-Linde 110 tests did not exhibit any unusual behaviour and, as shown in Figure 5(b), hardnesses throughout the joint were below the specified maximum after stress relief.

Most of the Charpy-V impact data are presented in Figures 6 to 9. Two plots for each material are presented, viz. in the as-welded and stress-relieved conditions. The data points indicate the location of the notch (i.e. whether in the weld deposit, HAZ or base material), and the plate thickness. In all cases, the Charpy bars were taken from the T/4 position, oriented with the long axis of the bar transverse to the weld.

LCC STEEL

LCC is a candidate steel to meet the specification requirements at -20°F (-30°C) but not at -80°F (-62°C). As the target lines in Figure 6 show, for the strength level into which the heat of steel falls (80 ksi [550 MPa] to 95 ksi [655 MPa], the minimum acceptable average impact energy is 40 ft lbf (54 J) as-welded, and 25 ft lbf (34 J) as stress-relieved. At -20°F (-30°C), two of the values were lower than the target minimum in the as-welded condition, and three values fell below the target minimum in the stress-relieved condition. It is the author's judgment that LCC welded with Linde 44 wire, with post-weld stress relief, is a good choice for service

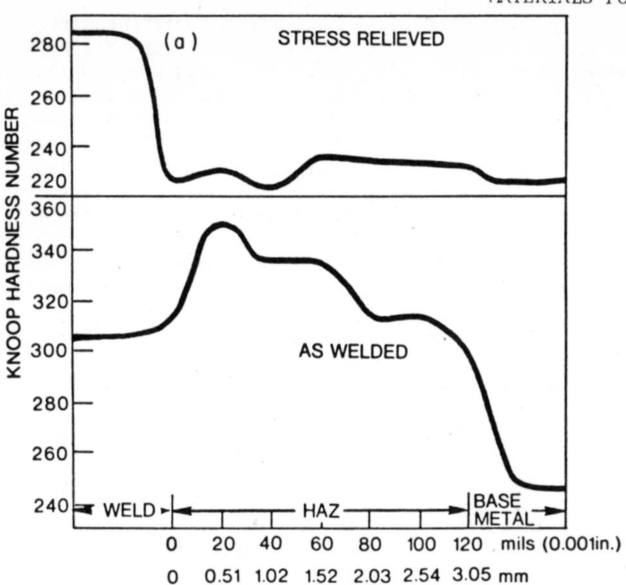

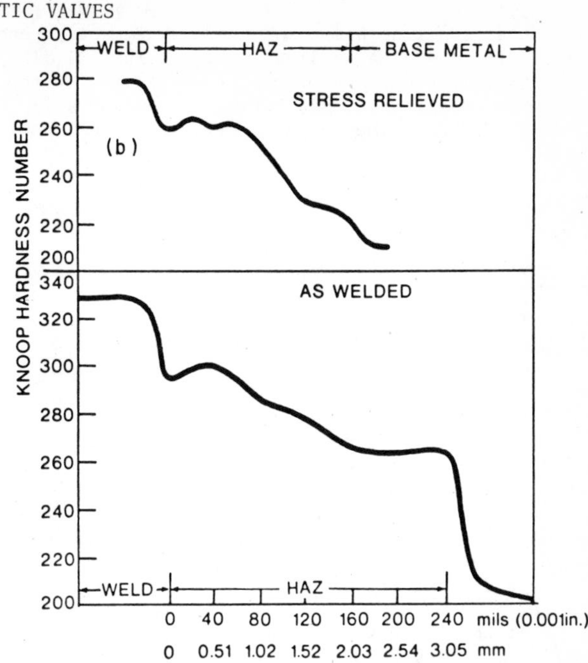

Figure 4: Microhardness Traverse of Welds in LC2.1 welded with Linde 100 Wire; (a) 3 in. (76 mm), (b) 1 in. (25 mm) plate

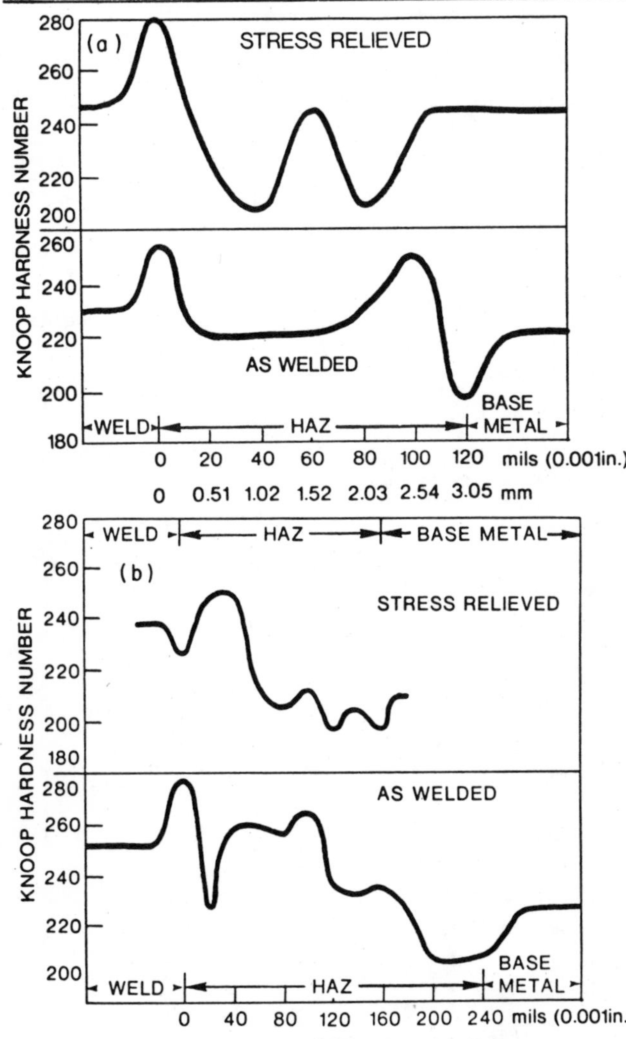

Figure 5: Microhardness Traverse of Welds in LC3 Welded with Linde 110 Wire; (a) 3 in. (76 mm), (b) 1 in. (25 mm) plate

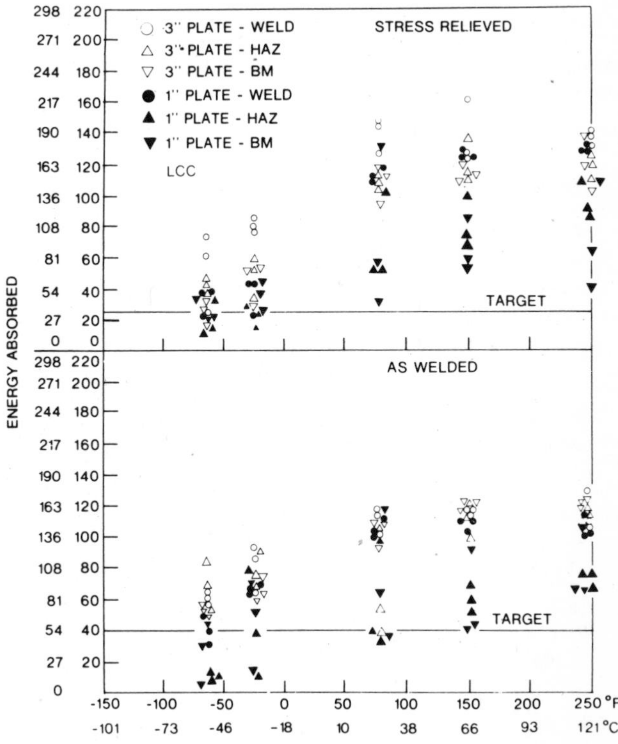

Figure 6: Charpy V-Notch Impact Behaviour of LCC Welded with Linde 44 Wire

at -20°F (-30°C) although there is some possibility of meeting the target minimum without stress relief.

A further margin of safety can be obtained if the specified tensile strength range of the LCC is modified downward. The average tensile strength of this heat of LCC was 80.3 ksi (554 MPa), which barely placed it in the 80 to 95 ksi (550 to 655

MPa) range requiring a minimum Charpy-V impact strength of 40 ft lbf (54 J) as-welded and 25 ft lbf (34 J) as stress-relieved. If the specified tensile strength range were modified to fall between 65 and 80 ksi (448 and 552 MPa), the target minima from the Canadian Arctic specification would have been 35 and 20 ft lbf (47 and 27 J) instead of 40 and 25 ft lbf (54 and 34 J), giving a greater margin of safety.

LC2 STEEL

The Charpy data for the ESCO LC2 steel welded with Linde 100 wire are presented in Figure 7. This steel, along with LC2.1 and LC3, is a candidate for use at -80°F (-62°C).

Figure 7 shows that in the as-welded condition the toughness is marginal relative to the target minimum. Recalling Figure 3, the Knoop hardness in the weld exceeded KHN 290. Stress-relieving lowered the hardness of the weld, and in some cases raised the toughness, which, together with the reduction in target minimum from 35 to 20 ft lbf (47 to 27J), yielded results exceeding target in all cases but one.

It should be noted that the carbon content (.03/.05%) of the ESCO LC2 steel is rather low in comparison with steels normally made to ASTM A352 Grade LC2 (.25 max.). In view of this atypical composition of the ESCO heat, the results from the quenched and tempered 3 in. (76 mm) thick Birdsboro plate with an 0.14/0.15% carbon content are of particular interest. The Birdsboro data, which were confined to the stress-relieved condition, exhibited no discernable difference in toughness at -80°F (-62°C) from the ESCO data, but did show appreciably lower shelf-energy levels.

LC2.1 STEEL

The Charpy data for LC2.1 steel welded with Linde 100 wire are presented in Figure 8. At -80°F (-62°C) this material has excellent impact properties in the as-received base metal (BM in Figure 8), but after stress relieving these properties drop considerably, the 3 in. (76 mm) material exhibiting values that are below specification at -80°F (-62°C) and markedly lower than those of the 1 in. (25 mm) material. One explanation for the poor behaviour of the 3 in. (76 mm) material is that its lower solidification rate could have maximized the opportunity for those residual elements known to contribute to temper embrittlement in alloy steels (As, Sb, Sn, P) to segregate in the grain boundaries and to be responsive to the stress-relieving treatment.

The heat affected zones in the LC2.1 material also showed a drop in impact properties as a result of stress-relief. For the 3 in. (76 mm) material, this loss was not large enough to make the material unacceptable at -80°F (-62°C); however, for the 1 in. (25 mm) material, stress relief resulted in an energy absorption of only 10 ft lbf (14 J) or less at -80°F (-62°C).

In contrast to its satisfactory impact properties when used to join the LC2 plates, the Linde 100 weld metal in both the 1 in. and 3 in. (25 mm and 76 mm) LC2.1 material exhibited relatively low (about 50% lower than in the LC2 welds) impact properties in the as-welded condition. At the energy levels shown at -80°F (-62°C) (about 20 ft lbf [27 J]), the toughness of this particular weld metal would not meet the specified minima required for the range of tensile strength into which this metal fell. However, after stress-relief, this weld metal was considerably improved.

LC3 STEEL

The data for LC3 steel welded with the Linde 110 wire are given in Figure 9. At -80°F (-62°C), the target minimum values were not met in all cases. In the as-welded condition, the problem was mainly in the 3 in. (76 mm) base metal plate; in the stress-relieved condition, it was mainly in the HAZ of welds

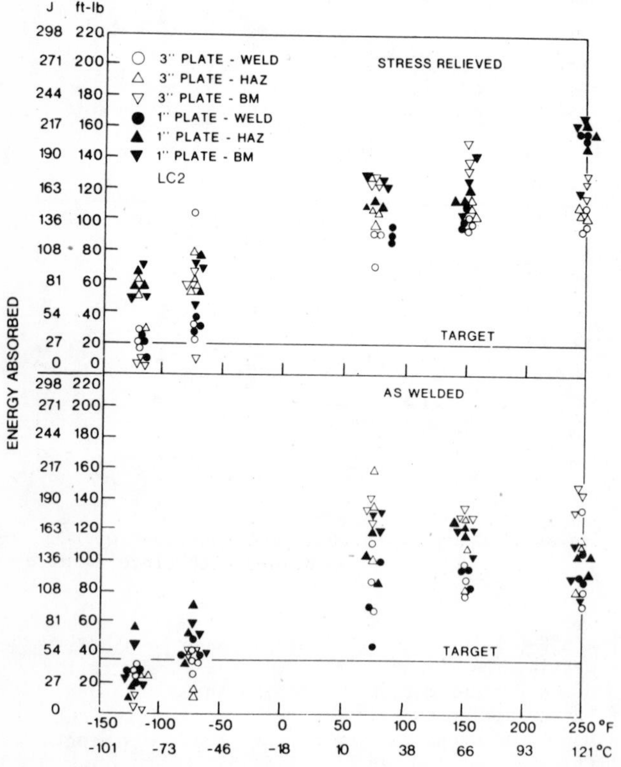

Figure 7: Charpy V-Notch Impact Behaviour of LC2 Welded with Linde 100 Wire

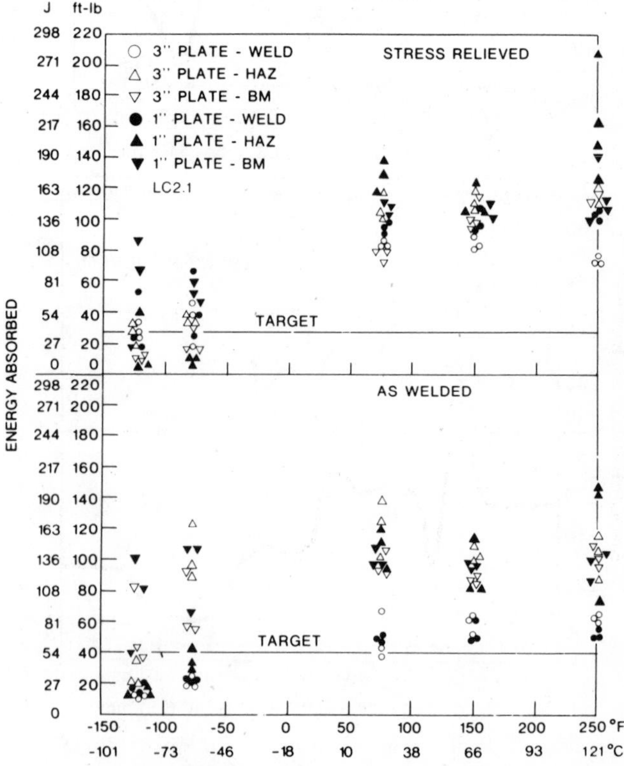

Figure 8: Charpy V-Notch Impact Behaviour of LC2.1 Welded with Linde 100 Wire

in the 1 in.(25 mm) plate. As in the case of LC2.1, stress relieving had a generally degrading effect on toughness at -80°F (-62°C).

RELATIVE TOUGHNESS OF WELDED STEELS AT -80°F (-62°C)

In comparing the performance of LC2, LC2.1 and LC3 weldments at -80°F (-62°C), two frames of reference are possible, one relative to the Canadian Arctic specification and the other on an independent basis. On both these bases it is the judgment of the author that the most effective choice is LC2.1 welded with Linde 110 wire or equivalent, without post-weld stress relief. Examination of Figures 7, 8 and 9 shows the impact strength of the LC2.1 as-welded to be generally the highest at -80°F (-62°C) of all the materials and conditions examined. Furthermore, from Figure 8, of the eight points which fell below the target minimum in the as-welded condition, six of them were for weld metal (Linde 100 wire). It is the author's position that the Linde 110 wire, containing more nickel than Linde 100 wire, would yield a higher toughness, as was indeed demonstrated in the work on LC3 (Figure 9). Thus the toughness of welds made in LC2.1 with Linde 110 wire, without post-weld stress relief, would have been superior to the results with any of the three plate compositions, in either the as-welded or stress relieved conditions. This choice is made notwithstanding the fact that there will be regions of the welded joints which exceed the specified maximum hardness. It is interesting to note the precedent for the use of welded LC2.1 (or HY 80), not stress-relieved, in the construction of submarine hulls.

The Charpy-V toughness results show no systematic effect of the two plate thicknesses studied. The data plotted in Figures 6 to 9 demonstrate a co-mingling of points, so that, in general, one can consider that they came from the same data population.

TOUGHNESS OF COMMERCIAL HEATS OF GRADE LCC AND LC2.1

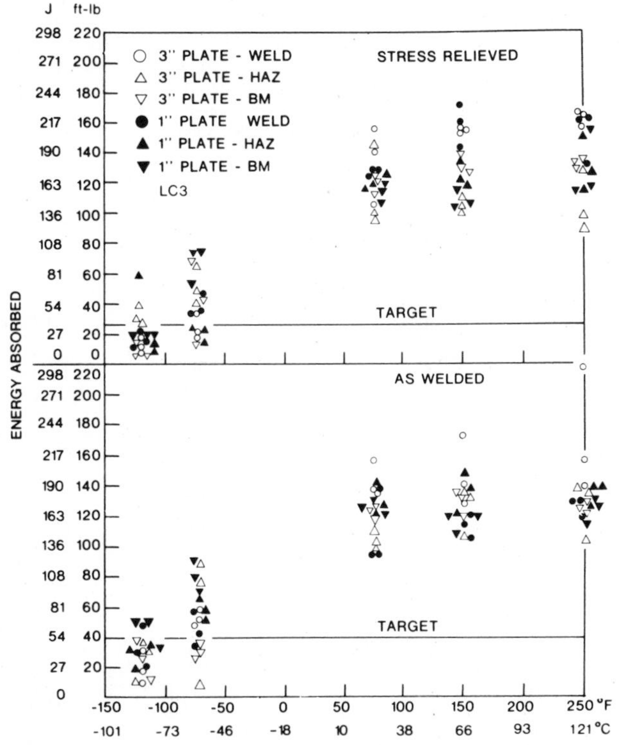

Figure 9: Charpy V-Notch Impact Behaviour of LC3 Welded with Linde 110 Wire

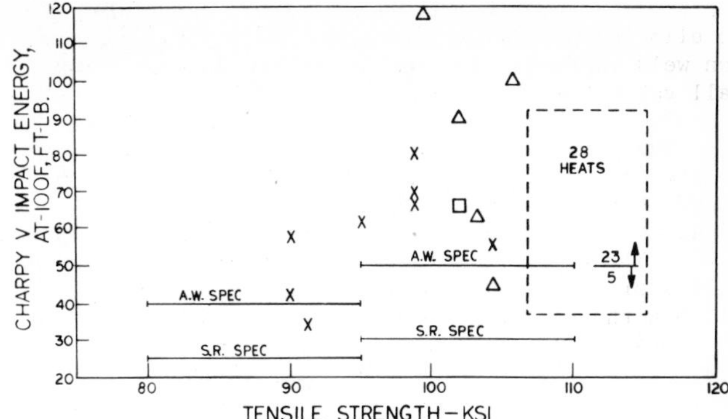

Figure 11: Charpy-V Impact Energy at -100°F (-73°C) vs Tensile Strength for 36 Commercial Heats of Quenched and Tempered LC2.1 Steel in Thicknesses up to 16 in. (410 mm)

Having studied the toughness of a very limited number of heats of steel, it is appropriate to examine a larger data population, especially of the two compositions of interest, viz. LCC for -20°F (-30°C) service and LC2.1 for -80°F (-62°C) service.

Figure 10 shows Charpy V-notch toughness at -20°F (-30°C) as a function of tensile strength for 20 commercial heats of quenched and tempered LCC steels in various thicknesses. Also shown are the Canadian Arctic target specifications. It can be seen that only one heat in one condition (the highest strength level of all) fell below the specified as-stress-relieved toughness. Relative to the specified as-welded toughness, about as many fell below the target as above, the distribution being more unfavourable at higher strength levels.

Similar data are given for 36 commercial heats of LC2.1 steels in Figure 11. Note that the testing temperature is -100°F (-70°C) and the data are presented for section thicknesses up to 16 in. (410 mm). Of all the data plotted, no values fall below the as-stress-relieved specification, and seven values fall below the as-welded specification.

BODY WELD JOINTS

Much attention, both analytical and experimental, has been devoted to the valve body welds, including the issue of joint design. It is not unconventional to utilize partial penetration welds in the manufacture of pressure vessels, including valve

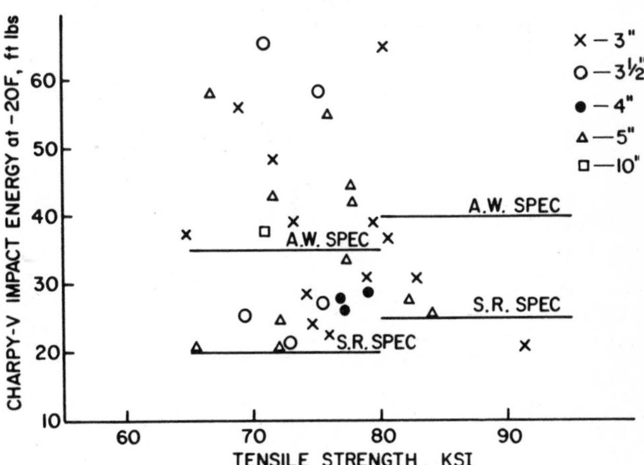

Figure 10: Charpy-V Impact Energy at -20°F (-30°C) vs Tensile Strength for 20 Commercial Heats of Quenched and Tempered LCC Steel in Various Thicknesses at T/4 Position

bodies. However, it was deemed highly desirable to eliminate the notch inherent in a partial penetration weld in the Arctic version of the Rockwell TM ball valve.

The design finally adopted is shown in Figure 12. The protuberance shown near the bottom of the weld aids the assembly of the shell components during manufacture; yet the actual joint geometry is a straight butt and results in a full-penetration weld.

Three-point bend tests were performed on welded plates of LCC at -20°F (-30°C) and LC3 at -80°F (-62°C) to show the relationship between joint design and toughness. The results are presented in Table 5. Three different joint designs were tested. First, a partial-penetration weld in which the residual crack was perpendicular to the outer fiber tensile stress; secondly, a partial-penetration weld in which the residual crack was parallel to the outer fiber tensile stress; and thirdly, a full-penetration weld. Table 5 shows that static toughness, as measured by the area under the load-deflection plot (in triplicate tests), is highest for the full penetration weld and lowest for the residual crack perpendicular to the direction of outer fiber tensile stress.

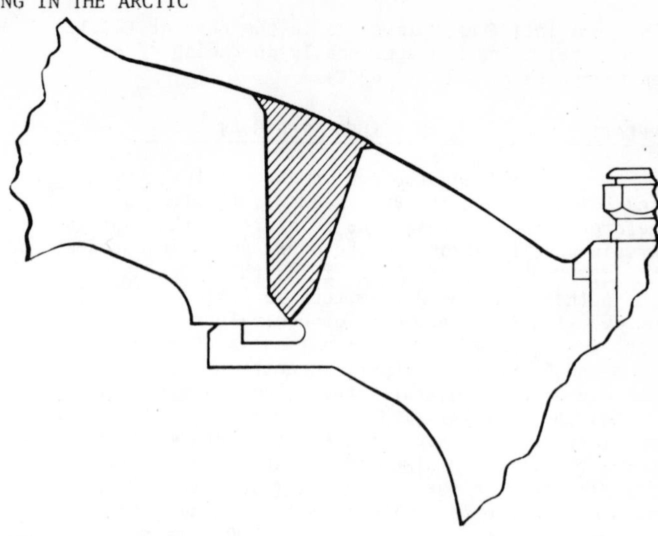

Figure 12: Weld Joint Design for Arctic Ball Valve

ELASTOMERS

There are two approaches to providing the required dynamic seals in the trunnion and seat regions of the ball valve. One utilizes an elastomeric member made of a material with sufficient resistance to hydrocarbons and capable of retaining its elastomeric capability to sufficiently low temperatures. The other approach is to utilize a basically non-elastomeric material, e.g. Teflon, in a suitable seal design. In both approaches, a suitable sealant is used in conjunction with the main sealing member.

There is no intent here to compare the relative functional and economic merits of these two approaches, but only to present the results of mechanical tests of candidate elastomers.

The classes of elastomeric materials is well in excess of ten, and the number of individual formulations certainly ranges in the hundreds. Based upon the two main technical requirements, -- resistance to hydrocarbons and retention of elastomeric capability to low temperatures -- exploratory literature searching and screening tests indicated that attention should be confined to only the following classes of elastomers: buna-N, special low-temperature buna-N, Hydrin and fluorosilicone.

(The elastomers described represent only a few of the many materials screened for the present applications. They are: Buckeye Rubber Company (PARCO) Compound #4329-70, a copolymer of butadiene and acrylonitrile commonly known as nitrile rubber or buna-N; B. F. Goodrich's Hydrin 56-72, a low-temperature version of Hydrin 200 which is a copolymer of epichlorohydrin with ethylene oxide - a polyether; Dow Corning's Silastic LS-2380, a modified fluorinated copolymer of various proprietary siloxane-forming monomers; and Minnesota Rubber Company's Compound #523-EU, a buna-N elastomer modified with a proprietary system of additives to improve the low temperature properties of the material.)

Tensile bars and buttons of several formulations were obtained from vendors and tests conducted over a temperature range from 80°F (30°C) to -100°F (-70°C). Measurements were made of ultimate tensile strength, elongation at failure of the tensile specimen, and hardness taken on a button which had been held at the subject temperature. Tensile strengths and elongation values were obtained from 0.5 in. (12 mm) wide Standard Die A specimens as described in ASTM D412. Tensile testing was done at a crosshead speed of 20 in./min (510 mm/min).

Table 5

Static Toughness of Welded Joints in Three-Point Bending

Weld Configuration	Steel (Test Temp.)	Static Toughness: in.lbf/in.^{3} (kJ/m^3)			
		Test 1	Test 2	Test 3	Mean
0.125 in. (3.18 mm) land	LCC (-20°F/-30°C)	1.0	1.5	2.8	1.8 (12)
	LC3 (-80°F/-60°C)	0.8	0.95	1.1	0.95 (6.5)
0.063 in. (1.59 mm) land	LCC (-20°F/-30°C)	1.3	1.6	1.9	1.6 (11)
	LC3 (-80°F/-60°C)	3.4	3.5	3.8	3.6 (25)
0.031 in. (0.79 mm) land	LCC (-20°F/-30°C)	3.7	4.7	4.9	4.4 (31)
	LC3 (-80°F/-60°C)	3.5	3.2	8.7	5.1 (35)

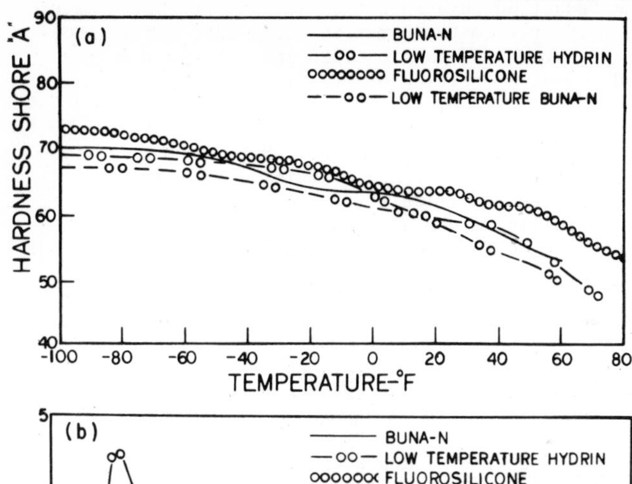

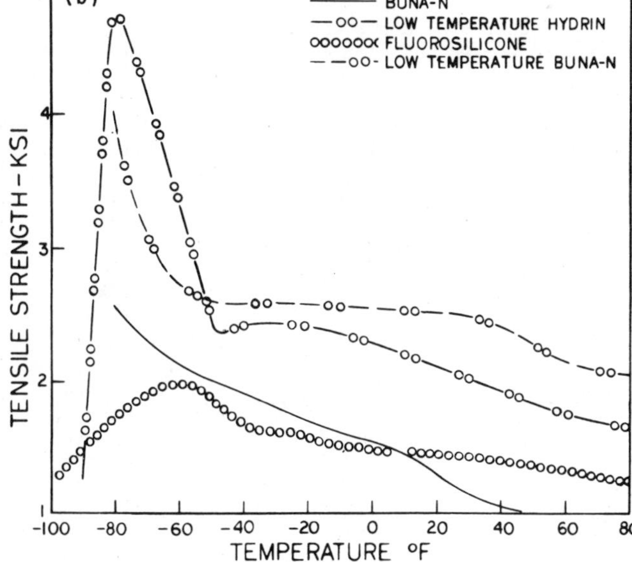

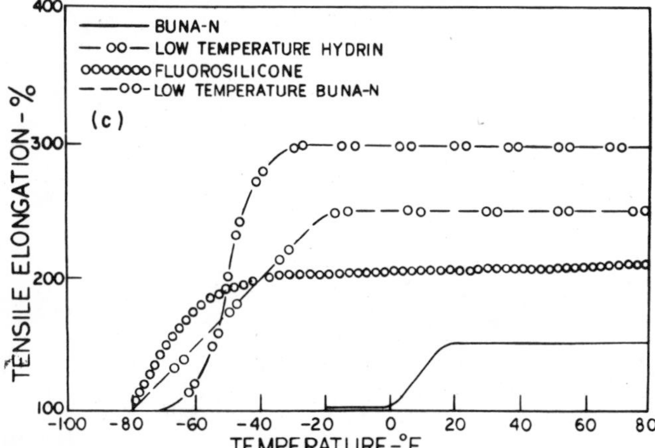

Figure 13: Effect of Temperature on (a) hardness, (b) tensile strength, and (c) tensile elongation of selected elastomers

The results are plotted in Figure 13 for only four of the formulations tested, these being the most illustrative. While data points are not shown on the graphs, it should be noted that each curve was developed from at least 50 individual tests. The data presented demonstrate that different types of elastomers react to changing temperature in different ways. While there are definite trends in the changes in the mechanical properties which are shared by all elastomers tested in this program, there exist differences peculiar to specific materials. The trends which are shared by all elastomers tested are: increase in hardness, increase in tensile strength and decrease in elongation with decrease in temperature. Certain peculiarities exist in some elastomers and are represented by test results contrary to these generalizations.

In evaluating any elastomer for low temperature use, the generalization which can be universally applied in our experience is that the low temperature dynamic use limit can be no lower a temperature than that at which the elongation of the elastomer is 100%, as measured by ASTM D-412. From experience with all kinds of elastomers, including natural and synthetic rubbers, polyurethane, silicones and fluorosilicones, we have found that with an elongation below 100%, a material is not resilient enough to effect seals or rebound after deflection. In some cases, an elastomer may be considered unsuitable for use even though the elongation is greater than 100%, based on interpretation of other test results or additional information about the material.

Two or more polymers are often blended, resulting in a rubber with a combination of properties at low temperatures different from those of the components. Therefore, each elastomer must be considered individually when being evaluated for low temperature applications.

Two observations can be made from the data presented in Figure 13. First, note the peak in the tensile strength of the special low temperature Hydrin. The sharp rise in tensile strength as temperature is lowered, which is also exhibited by some buna-N formulations, is believed to be due to partial crystallization. This is believed to be a reversible phenomenon so that it cannot be avoided by a pre-refrigeration treatment. The other point worth noting is the limited low temperature elongation of regular buna-N. Not only is the absolute elongation considerably lower than the other materials, but it begins to lose its elongation capability at 20°F (-7°C) and the value drops below 100% at -20°F (-30°C).

Our judgment is that fluorosilicone is the superior low temperature elastomer for dynamic seals, based upon its superior mechanical behaviour and chemical resistance to hydrocarbons. Certain low temperature buna-N formulations are the next choice.

CONCLUSIONS

The principal conclusions relative to the choice of body materials are:

1. For service at -20°F (-30°C), ASTM A352 Grade LCC,welded with Linde 44 filler wire or equivalent, is a reasonable choice. Its chemical analysis should be controlled to restrict the sulfur and phosphorus contents to much lower maximums than A352 presently permits. In the post-weld stress-relieved condition, the impact strengths of weld metal, heat-affected zone and base metal generally exceeded the target minimum value of 25 ft lbf (34 J). Microhardness traverses across the welded joints yielded no values exceeding the specified maximum of KHN 272 (Rc 24). The results indicate the desirability of specifying the tensile strength of LCC steel to fall in the range of from 65 to 80 ksi (450 to 550 MPa).
2. For service at -80°F (-62°C), ASTM A352 Grade LC2.1 steel, modified in its chemical analysis to reduce the tensile and yield strengths (to 80 and 50 ksi [550 and 350 MPa], respectively) welded with Linde 110 filler wire or equivalent, without post-weld stress relief, is the best overall choice. Stress-

relieving generally decreases the impact strength, although it can bring the hardness into the specification range.
3. No discernible effect of plate thickness (1 in. or 3 in. [25 mm or 76 mm]) on toughness was noted.
4. For dynamic seals, fluorosilicone is the superior low temperature elastomer, based upon its superior mechanical behaviour and chemical resistance to hydrocarbons.

Acknowledgments

Many individuals collaborated to generate the data reported in this paper. The efforts of W. C. Banks, C. W. Hartle, R. A. Douty, K. F. Skidmore, R. Frankovich and M. Davis are particularly acknowledged.

REFERENCES

1. W. C. Banks, K. F. Skidmore and H. Schwartzbart, Trans. ASME, Pressure Vessel Tech., 1974, vol. 96, Series J (2), pp. 73-80.
2. R. A. Douty, W. C. Banks and H. Schwartzbart, Welding J., 1976, vol. 55, (8), pp. 661-671.

DISCUSSION

D. Kenny (Dominion Foundries and Steel): My first question pertains to the fact that section size was found to have no systematic effect on the Charpy V-notch toughness results. This is to be expected in steels of high hardenability, but it is somewhat surprising that this would occur in less highly alloyed steels. Work which we have done at Dofasco showed a marked effect of section size in carbon steels. For example, an increase in thickness from 1 in. (25 mm) to 4 in. (100 mm) in a normalized, quenched and tempered 0.15%C and 0.40% Mn steel resulted in a decrease in impact energy from 30 ft lbf (40 J) to 10 ft lbf (14 J) at 0°F (-18°C). Do you feel there is a particular reason for the lack of section size effect in the carbon steels that you examined?

H. Schwartzbart: I have no explanation. Whatever section size effect existed in the 3 in. (76 mm) to 1 in. (25 mm) plates, it was not great enough to be disclosed in the normal scatter band associated with Charpy testing.

D. Kenny: In your paper you commend using LCC grade steel with a post-weld stress relief for applications at -20°F (-29°C). As an alternative would you consider increasing the alloy content with the view to improving toughness?

H. Schwartzbart: That would be an acceptable technical alternative. Relative economics and the particular specifications that come out will dictate the best overall alternative. If, as seems possible from some of the discussions here this week, the specifications are relaxed a little, we may not have to stress relieve at all.

J. N. Cordea (Armco Steel): It seems unusual to have a post-weld stress relief recommended for -20°F (-29°C) service while it is not recommended for -80°F (-62°C) service. What specific composition changes do you recommend for the LC2.1 steel to attain the -80°F (-62°C) service properties?

H. Schwartzbart: The LCC joints were not degraded by the stress relief treatment; the LC2.1 were. The reduction in carbon from 0.22 max to 0.12 max, in sulphur from 0.045 max to 0.025 max, and in phosphorus from 0.04 max to 0.025 max will provide for -80°F (-62°C) service of LC2.1.

J. N. Cordea: How do you rationalize the use of the high nickel content of the -80°F (62°C) service LC2.1 steel in sour (H_2S containing) oil and gas atmospheres? Sulfide stress corrosion cracking is a possibility especially in the vicinity of the welds where the heat-affected-zone hardnesses exceed 24 R_c.

H. Schwartzbart: The gas for the subject pipeline is sweet.

D. Kenny: Could you explain the reason for choosing the rather complex heat treatment used for the LC2.1 material?

H. Schwartzbart: I don't know. I believe the treatments were worked out with our vendors, but I am not certain.

T. Kunitake (Sumitomo Metal Industries): As for the effect of stress relief treatment, I believe both the effects on the toughness and on the residual stress have to be evaluated. Did you evaluate the effect of stress relief treatment on the residual stress?

H. Schwartzbart: We did not measure residual stresses at all. I believe that within the context of this paper they are not significant.

L. Luyckx (Reactive Metals and Alloys): I noticed during your presentation of this excellent paper that, in LC2.1, the stress relieving operation needed to comply with an antiquated hardness specification had such a negative effect upon the Charpy V-notch impact values at -80°F (62°C) that these fell below specification. Your tentative explanation was that residual elements would tend to segregate to as cast grain boundaries in the weld metal which the stress relieving operation would help to reveal. Even if the LC2.1 problem has been solved by going to a better welding wire chemistry, I wonder whether a REM treated wire would not in general be useful in boosting weld toughness by accomplishing the double function of 1) neutralizing the residuals, even those that cannot be eliminated easily (Sn, As, Pb, S, O, H_2), and 2) refining the grain size of the weld and minimizing segregation, which is a known REM effect.

G. D. Uttrachi (Union Carbide, Linde Division): In fact Harry's paper showed with one of the wires used, Linde 100, the weld metal toughness improved with a stress relieving heat treatment. It was the base plate HAZ which was degraded. The welding wire/flux cannot be of any help for the HAZ properties. If rare earth additions are to be effective they would have to be added to the base plate. The addition of rare earth metals has been evaluated in welding wire for other reasons than those mentioned. In fact, they will not transfer across the arc to be effective in the weld metal.

J. L. Gerlitz (Shell Canada): Will steps be taken to monitor and upgrade casting quality, regarding defect type and severity level in valves requiring low temperature toughness? What type of monitoring methods and quality levels are and will be used?

H. Schwartzbart: For the entire range of valve types, including nuclear valves, many NDT methods are used to assure the meeting of customer and code requirements. These include X-ray, magnetic particle, liquid penetrant and ultrasonics. The specific monitoring methods and quality levels for any specific valve application are dictated by the customer's specifications.

J. P. Tralmer (Shell Oil): Could you explain the use of a maximum hardness limit of 272 KHN for valves which are expected to be used in sweet service?

H. Schwartzbart: I suspect this may have been an oversight on the part of the specification writers.

B. Warr (Hawker Siddeley Canada): What do you define as restricted sulphur and phosphorus levels for LCC? What generally is your deoxidation practice for LC2.1?

H. Schwartzbart: See the RMC specification in Table 2. Victor Behal can probably answer the second question.

V. G. Behal (Dominion Foundries and Steel): For deoxidation, we usually use 0.30 to 0.50% Si with 2 lb/t aluminium.

H. C. Cotton (British Petroleum): Degradation of Charpy-V properties after post heat treatment in the stress relieving range of temperature are often attributable to temper embrittlement effects. Increasing the cooling rate after stress relieving to, say, 100 deg C/h is usually highly beneficial. Post heat treatment is usually so advantageous in its tempering and averaging effects that it would be wrong to fail to take advantage of it for insufficient reason. What was the cooling rate of the 3 in. (76 mm) section to which you refer and what was the effect of measuring it?

H. Schwartzbart: I do not know the cooling rate of the stress relief treatment which was done by a commercial heat treater. We did not study the effect of change in cooling rate.

V. G. Behal: While at this point of this week's discussion I would not wish to guess as to the validity of present requirements for mechanical properties of Arctic service cast steel valves, we believe the ASTM Heavy Section Task Group established that A352-LC2 grade varied in NDTT between -40°F and 0°F (-40°C and -18°C) in sections from 2 in. (51 mm) to 5 in. (127 mm) and it is questionable if a material of NDTT -40°F (-40°C) should be used at -20°F (-29°C). Also, there are requirements for sections heavier than the 3 in. (76 mm) discussed in your paper, where no submerged arc welding is required. We feel that LLC modified with 1.75% Ni and 0.20% Mo offering an NDTT of -90°F (-68°C) in a 3 in. (76 mm) section, is a far more suitable product for service at -20°F (-29°C).

Also, we feel that A352 LC2.1 chemistry, quenched and tempered to the modified requirement of 90 ksi (620 MPa) tensile and 65 ksi (450 MPa) yield, offers a very acceptable solution for cast steel valves for service at -80°F (-62°C), as a sample from a 3 in. (76 mm) section offers an NDTT of -150°F (-100°C) and as much as -90°F (-68°C) in 5 in. (127 mm) sections, while meeting all requirements of the Arctic specifications in the weld metal, parent metal and HAZ, using an appropriate welding rod, for manual arc welding, followed by stress relieving or even requenching and tempering.

It might be of interest that both of the above grades will be included in forthcoming ASTM and ISO specifications for cast steels for low temperature service application.

PRODUCTION & PIPELINE VALVES FOR ARCTIC SERVICE

Donald S. Burns
Cameron Iron Works, Inc.
Houston, Texas
USA

Many steels which are resistant to shock loading at average temperatures become brittle in the subfreezing temperatures of the Arctic. Specially heat-treated low-carbon steels of modified specification are suitable for sustained use at temperatures to -67°F (-55°C). Normalized low-alloy steels which have been subsequently quenched and tempered are acceptable for use at temperatures to -75°F (-59°C). IN-787, a low-alloy nickel steel demonstrates excellent impact properties at -100°F (-73°C).

Experimental evidence suggests the feasibility of varying the chemistry of special grades of stainless steel to provide corrosion resistance as well as the low temperature impact properties required for the Arctic.

INTRODUCTION

Changes in the strength, ductility, and toughness of steel reflect changes in the steel microstructure - control of the microstructure is control over the physical properties. Changes in the microstructure of steel are the result of varying two primary factors: i.e. chemistry and heat treatment.

Martensite is the hardest of the austenite transformation products, but it is also usually the most brittle. However, further heat treating of martensite, specifically tempering, will produce optimum strength and toughness with a very favourable ductility. The normalizing process produces the fine grain size important for strength and toughness and makes the steel product more suitable for further heat treatment.

Cameron writes its own metallurgical specifications for the carbon steel used to make valves for Arctic projects. Heat treatment, designed with valve size in mind, ensures a fine-grained microstructure and provides maximum low temperature ductility. Cameron is also experimenting with stainless steels for use in corrosive well conditions at Arctic temperatures.

THE ARCTIC PROJECTS

Three major international concerns have written specifications for equipment used for developing and transporting the vast oil and gas reserves of the Arctic: The Alyeska Pipelines Service Company (formerly Trans Alaska Pipeline Company), the Canadian Arctic Gas Study, Ltd., and the U.S.S.R. government's development program for its northern section.

The specifications written for these Arctic projects, in effect, tell the manufacturers which materials are acceptable for equipment construction and which materials are not.

The Trans Alaska Pipeline project will transport oil from Prudhoe Bay to the ice-free port of Valdez. The original Trans Alaska Pipeline specifications were written in early 1969. The first valves were produced according to these specifications in late 1969 and early 1970, in anticipation of the beginning of construction of the pipeline.

The Trans Alaska specifications and the Alyeska revisions establish requirements for steels used for the construction of mainline valves for the Trans Alaska Pipeline. These valves are made for use in temperatures to -50°F (-46°C). The extensions and operators to these valves are designed to function at temperatures to -80°F (-62°C). The metallurgical portion of these specifications requires impact tests for each heat of steel -- an average of three specimens must absorb a minimum 25 ft lbf (37 J) impact energy at -50°F (-46°C).

Complete weld tests are required for each heat of steel used in welding fabricated valves. Weld tests are performed per the ASME Boiler and Pressure Vessel Code, Section 9. The weld metal, base metal and heat-affected zone must all meet the minimum requirements of the specifications. Since American Welding Society (AWS) specifications do not include values for these extreme temperatures it is necessary to qualify each electrode by trade name. Figure 1 shows the welding qualification tests that were run to meet Alyeska requirements.

The second major project, a study by the Canadian Arctic Gas Study, Ltd., is known as the Mackenzie Valley Line. This pipeline, which will be approximately 2700 miles (4300 km) long, runs from Prudhoe Bay through the Mackenzie Valley to the northern sections of the United States. It will tap the vast natural gas supplies of the Arctic and bring them into Canada and the United States.

The Canadian Arctic Gas Study material specifications are similar to the Alyeska specifications. Originally, the mainline valves were specified for use at temperatures to -50°F (-46°C), with extensions and operators specified for use at temperatures to -80°F (-62°C). Revised specifications are somewhat less stringent with mainline valves specified for use at temperatures to -20°F (-29°C).

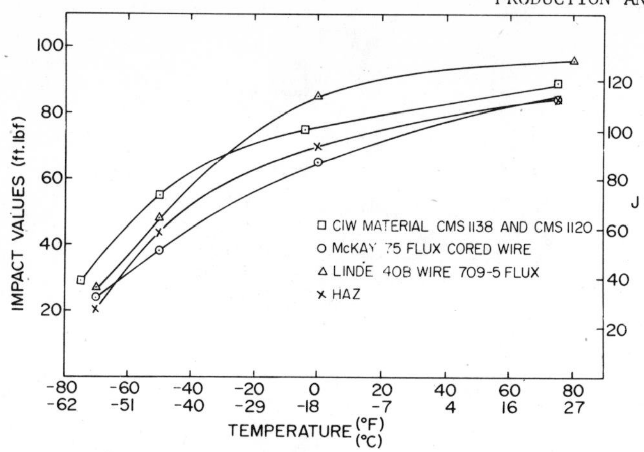

Figure 1: Typical Impact Energy Curves of Low-Carbon Steels for Pipeline Valves and Welding Qualifications

The Canadian Arctic Gas metallurgical specifications are also similar to Alyeska specifications, the one exception being the notch toughness requirement, which is based on the actual tensile strength of the steel used. Table 1 gives some examples of Trans Alaska, Alyeska and Canadian Arctic Gas Study Ltd. specifications.

The third major arctic project is the Soviet Union effort for the development of the oil and gas supplies of its northern section, primarily Siberia. The Soviet Union is far ahead of the United States and Canada in developing the vast Arctic reserves. They have ordered and accepted delivery of more than one hundred million dollars worth of valves. The U.S.S.R. valves are specified for use at temperatures to -67°F (-55°C). Valve bore sizes are as large as 65 in. (1420 mm). Working pressures reach 1100 psi (7580 kPa).

It is interesting to note that the Soviet Union specifications, unlike the Alyeska and Canadian specifications, are primarily based on mechanical acceptance limits. The manufacturer must determine the types of steel used for the construction of valves for Soviet Arctic projects. The acceptance test requirements are detailed for each valve size. For example, it is necessary to test each size valve prototype at temperatures to -67°F (-55°C) under full pressure differential for a minimum 1000 cycles. This is a severe test which will pinpoint most design or material weaknesses.

PRODUCTION AND PIPELINE VALVE MATERIALS

Table 1

Examples of Requirements for Arctic Conditions

Specification	Tensile Strength	Impact Energy Average of 3 ft lbf (J)		Minimum Value ft lbf (J)		Percent Shear
		a(Alt.1)	b(Alt.2)	a(Alt.1)	b(Alt.2)	
Canadian Arctic Gas Study Ltd. No. 2950-6-1 Rev. 5 January 2, 1973	65ksi(450MPa) and under	15(20)	25(34)	12(16)	20(27)	
	65 to 80 ksi (550 MPa)	20(27)	35(48)	15(20)	30(41)	
	80 to 95 ksi (660 MPa)	25(34)	40(54)	20(27)	35*(48)	
	95 to 110 ksi(760 MPa)	38*(41)	50*(68)	25*(34)	40*(54)	
	Over 110 ksi (760 MPa)	(Subject to Negotiations)		(Subject to Negotiations)		
Trans Alska Pipeline System No. 14-3-1 May 6, 1969	Up to 65 ksi (450 MPa)	15(20)		12(16)		
	Over 65 ksi (450 MPa)	25(34)		15(20)		
Alyeska Pipeline Service Company No. 14-3-5 July 10, 1973	Up to 65 ksi (450 MPa)	15(20)		12(16)		50
	Over 65 ksi (450 MPa)	25(34)		15(20)		50

* Subject to negotiation if maximum thickness exceeds 2 in. (51 mm)
(a) Alternate 1 shall apply to components which are not welded. If welded, components shall be thermally stress relieved after all welding is completed.
(b) Alternate 2 shall apply to material which will be used in the "as welded condition".

Table 2

Chemistry Requirements of Typical Arctic Materials

	*CMS 1138	*CMS 1120	*ZCMS 66	+IN 787
Carbon	0.22 Max.	0.22 Max.	0.20/0.26	0.04/0.06
Manganese	0.85/1.2	0.85/1.20	0.90/1.2	0.28/0.40
Chromium			0.25/0.35	0.60/0.70
Nickel			0.20/0.30	0.85/0.95
Molybdenum			0.17/0.23	0.15/0.20
Silicon	0.15/0.30	0.15/0.30	0.20/0.35	0.20/0.30
Phosphorus	0.035 Max.	0.30 Max.	0.03 Max.	
Sulfur	0.035 Max.	0.035 Max.	0.03 Max.	
Vanadium			0.05/0.10	
Aluminum			0.025 Residual	
Copper				1.15/1.30
Columbium				0.02/0.04
Grain Size	ASTM 5 or Finer		Manufactured to Fine Grain Melting Practice	
TS ksi (MPa)	70(480)Min.	65(450)Min.	90(620)Min.	87 ksi
YS ksi (MPa)	40(280)Min.	36(250)Min.	60(410)Min.	85 ksi
Elongation	22% Min.	24% Min.	18% Min.	28%
Area Reduction	30% Min.		35% Min.	76%

* Cameron Material Specification; + International Nickel

Carbon Steel

Perhaps surprisingly, carbon steels satisfy the material requirements of all three major Arctic projects. These are carbon steels made according to very rigid metallurgical specifications, and with special heat treating, but carbon steels nonetheless.

ASTM and AISI specifications for carbon steels do not give all the chemistry controls necessary to meet the metallurgical requirements of equipment used in the extreme temperatures of the Arctic. Therefore, Cameron Iron writes its own metallurgical specifications for carbon steels used in the construction of wrought valves furnished to the Alyeska group and to the U.S.S.R. operations. These chemistry controls are listed in Table 2.

Fine grained, normalized, low carbon, manganese steels which have been quenched and tempered are also acceptable for low temperature service. Figure 1 includes typical transition curves for two Cameron-produced low-carbon steels. Each point on the curve is an average of 21 different heats of steel.

Low-Alloy Nickel Steel

Table 2 refers to a steel designated IN-787--a low-alloy nickel steel developed by the International Nickel Company and manufactured by Armco Steel. IN-787 has excellent impact properties at temperatures below -100°F (-73°C) and has excellent welding characteristics. There has been considerable interest in this steel for use in valves which operate at temperatures to -85°F (-65°C). These extremely low temperatures are beyond the mechanical capabilities of controlled low-carbon grades of steel. The Canadian Arctic Gas Study, Ltd. specifications included valves as large as 24 in. (610 mm) diameter bore for use at temperatures to -85°F (-65°C). Figure 2 shows an experimental 24 in. (610 mm) ANSI 600 lb. class valve built of IN-787, which has successfully com-

Figure 2: Experimental 24 in. (610 mm) ANSI 600 lb. Class Valve Built of IN-787 steel

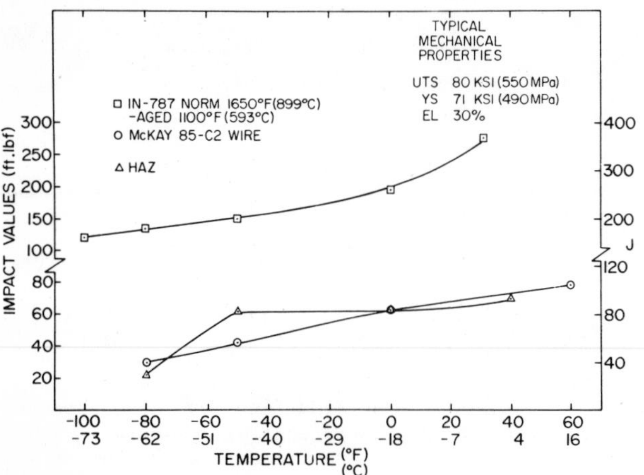

Figure 3: Typical Impact Values for Normalized and Aged IN-787 steel

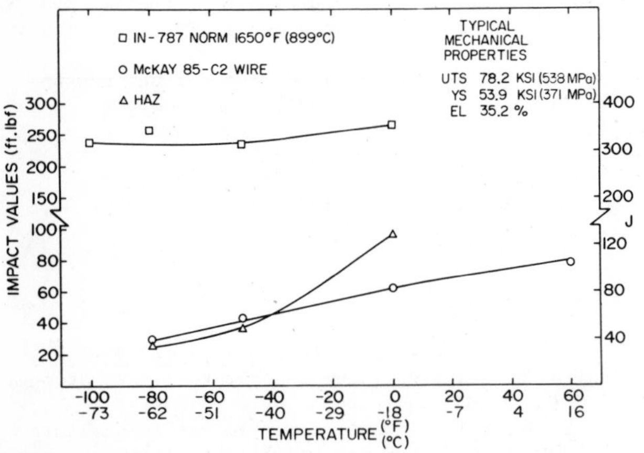

Figure 4: Typical Impact Values for Normalized IN-787 steel

pleted tests at temperatures to -90°F (-68°C).

Figures 3 and 4 give the data from two different heat-treat conditions of IN-787 at -100°F (-73°C). The most promising data are from tests conducted with normalized IN-787.

Figure 5 shows the consequences of a series of bend tests conducted on an IN-787 weldment at -80°F (-62°C). This test is performed by submerging

Figure 5: IN-787 Bend Test Samples

the machined side bend specimens in an alcohol solution and stabilizing the specimens at -80°F (-62°C). The specimens are removed from the alcohol solution, placed in a side bend fixture, and bent within 30 s of removal from the solution. In this way, the ductility of steel specimens at extremely low temperatures is demonstrated. The results of this test for material not qualified for low temperature service are often quite spectacular.

Figure 6 shows a 56 in. (1420 mm) pipeline valve in a cold box, which has just completed a series of 1000 cycles at -67°F (-55°C). The proof of a product is the result of the final product prototype testing under the most severe environmental conditions in which one would expect the product to be used.

WELLHEAD AND TREE PRODUCTION

Wellhead and tree production represent another phase of metallurgical planning in the Arctic. Wellheads are usually exposed to Arctic conditions with little or no protection. They must, therefore, meet the most stringent requirements for operating at temperatures to -75°F (-59°C).

The majority of Cameron's pressure-containing components are manufactured from API Type 2 steel, specifically Cameron's ZCMS-66 which is described in Table 2 and in Figures 7 and 8. This material is low-carbon manganese steel with controlled amounts of molybdenum, chromium, nickel and vanadium. This steel, which is normalized and then quenched and tempered, has good impact properties at temperatures to -75°F (-60°C). Figure 9 shows a typical installation being used in the Arctic.

Figure 6: 56 in. (1420 mm) Pipeline Valve After Cold Box Testing at -67°F (-55°C) for 1000 Cycles

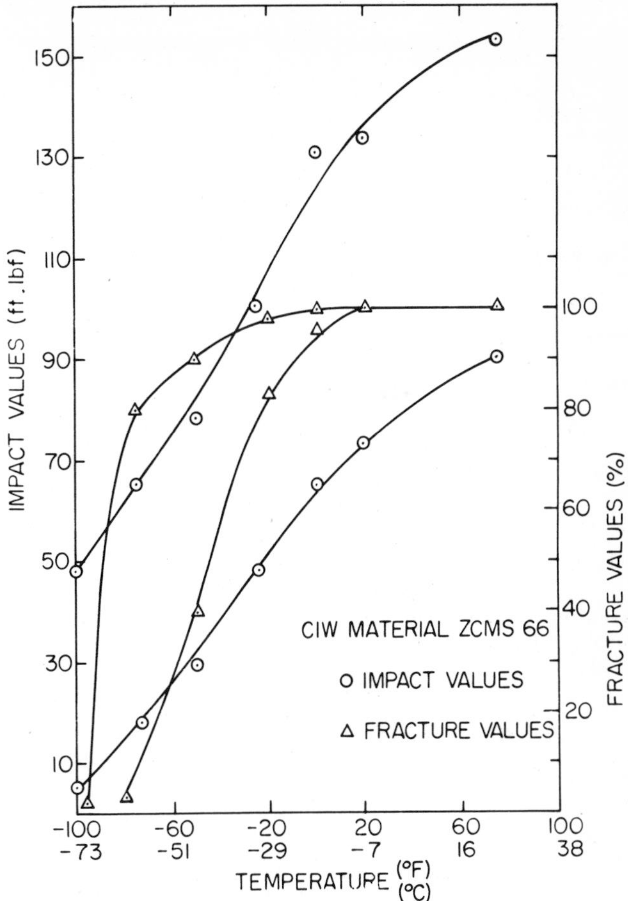

Figure 8: Impact Energy and Percent Shear Curves for ZCMS-66 alloy

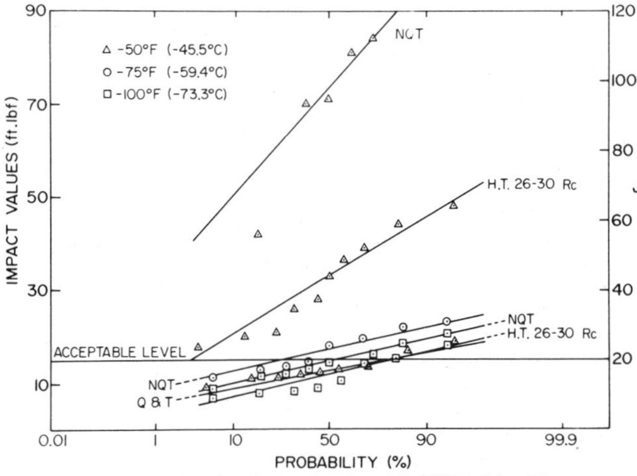

Figure 7: Statistical Analysis of ZCMS-66 alloy

The majority of wells drilled in the Canadian and Alaskan Arctic environments are "sweet" (non-corrosive) wells, and alloy steels are acceptable in these conditions. If corrosive environments are present, they are often controlled with an inhibition system.

In more temperate climates, 410 stainless steel or ASTM A-351, grade CA-15 -- the cast version of 410 stainless steel -- are used for corrosive well conditions. CA-15 grade steel has good corrosion resistance and good mechanical properties (i.e. good tensile strength, yield strength and elongation properties). However, it has a 15 ft lbf (20 J) transition value at approximately 0°F (-18°C). Arctic

Figure 9: Typical Arctic Tree Installation

Table 3

Chemistry of ASTM A-351 Grade CA-6NM and AISI 410

Element	CA-6NM	AISI 410
Carbon	0.06 Max.	0.15 Max.
Manganese	1.00 Max.	1.00 Max.
Phosphorus	0.03 Max.	0.04 Max.
Sulfur	0.03 Max.	0.03 Max.
Silicon	0.20/0.35	1.00 Max.
Chromium	11.50/14.00	11.50/13.50
Nickel	3.50/4.50	
Molybdenum	0.40/1.00	
Copper	0.50 Max.	
Aluminum	0.05 Max.	

specifications for wellhead equipment are generally based on a temperature of -75°F (-59°C). This makes the 410 stainless steel unacceptable for Arctic service.

We are investigating several grades of exotic steels which appear capable of meeting the tensile and impact requirements for Arctic service. Unfortunately, most steels with mechanical properties capable of meeting Arctic service requirements are cost prohibitive.

One relatively new stainless steel that does show promise is ASTM A-351, Grade CA-6NM. The ASTM chemistry requirements for this steel are listed in Table 3 and compared with 410 stainless steel. This steel was developed for, and has been used primarily in, cast products. Initial work on this steel has been done on forged-down cast keel blocks furnished by the casting industry. Since all data looked promising, a chemistry more tailored toward wrought products was developed. One experimental heat of steel was cast and made into forging billets. From these billets, 3 in. (76 mm) and 4 in. (102 mm) forged gatevalve bodies, commonly used on wellhead equipment, were made and heat treated to develop a hardness of 22 Rc maximum and to meet the API Type 2 requirements of 60 ksi (410 MPa) minimum yield and 90 ksi (620 MPa) minimum tensile strength. The heat treatment used and physical properties obtained are shown in Table 4. Charpy impact transition curves were developed on this grade of steel, and the data are shown in Figure 10. The 15 ft lbf (20 J) transition temperature is below -300°F (-180°C), and the 50% shear transition temperature is below -100°F (-73°C).

These data are encouraging and have prompted

Table 4

Typical Properties of ASTM A-351, Grade CA-6NM

Area	Orientation	UTS ksi(MPa)	YS ksi(MPa)	Elong. (%)	R.A. (%)	Hardness (Brinell)
Flange	Radial	116.4(802)	73.2(505)	23.1	68.5	241
Flange	Tangential	116.0(800)	69.2(477)	22.8	68.8	241
Body	Longitudinal	119.6(824)	79.3(547)	22.4	73.4	241
Body	Transverse	119.4(823)	79.3(547)	21.4	66.4	241

Chemistry	C	Mn	P	S	Si	Cr	Ni	Mo	V	Cu	Al	Ti	Co
	0.045	0.61	0.017	0.015	0.30	11.94	3.99	0.67	0.025	0.10	0.028	0.01	0.07

Heat Treatment	
	1850°F (1010°C) - Air Cool
	1250°F (680°C) - Air Cool
	1125°F (610°C) - Air Cool

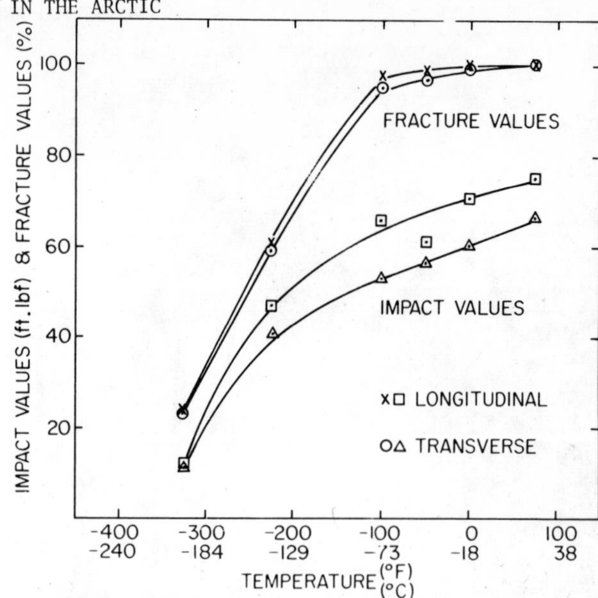

Figure 10: Typical Impact and Percent Shear Curves for ASTM A-351, Grade CA-6NM alloy, modified for Forging Application

further development of this steel to meet the 22 Rc maximum hardness requirement as imposed by NACE Specification MR-01-75 when a hydrogen sulfide environment is expected. Figure 11 displays the results of a series of tests in hydrogen sulfide environments showing its relative resistance to corrosion, compared to a typical 410 stainless steel. The CA-6NM alloy performed considerably better than the 410 stainless steel.

NACE Specification MR-01-75 allows the use of 410 stainless steel in the quenched and double-tempered condition. This series of tests suggests that the CA-6NM in the quenched and double-tempered condition is superior to the 410 stainless steel.

Two small induction heats of modified CA-6NM with lower carbon and molybdenum contents were made to evaluate the effects of the carbon and molybdenum on the hardness of this steel. The results of these tests are shown in Figure 12. Subsequently, three additional laboratory heats of CA-6NM were poured to confirm the encouraging effect of the lower carbon on the hardness of this steel. The results of these tests are shown in Table 5.

We conclude from these data that with appropriate chemistry restrictions this steel can meet the API Type 2 steel requirements and be below the

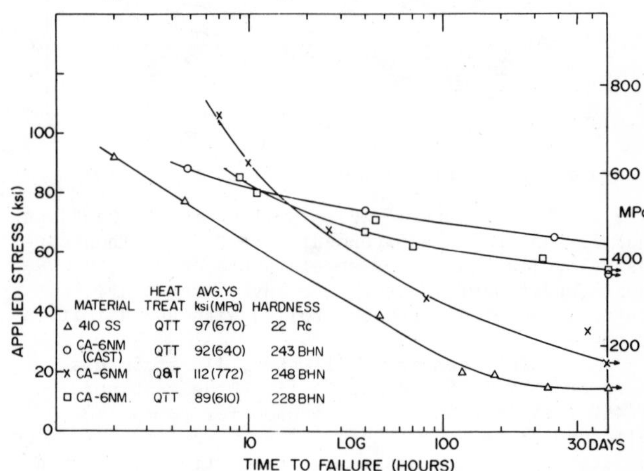

Figure 11: Relative Resistance of Stainless Steels to Failure in H_2S Environment

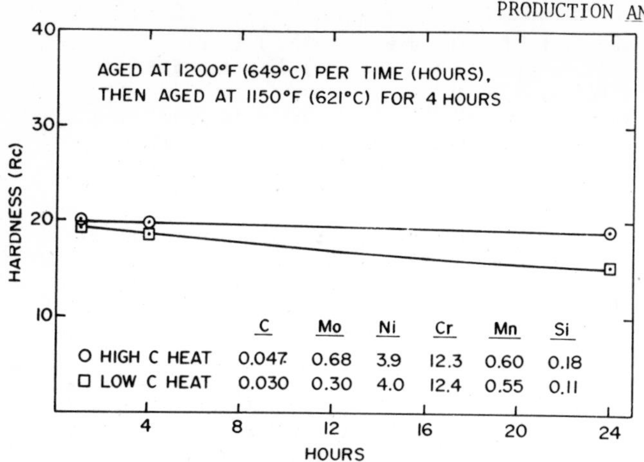

Figure 12: Effect of Chemistry Modification on CA-6NM alloy

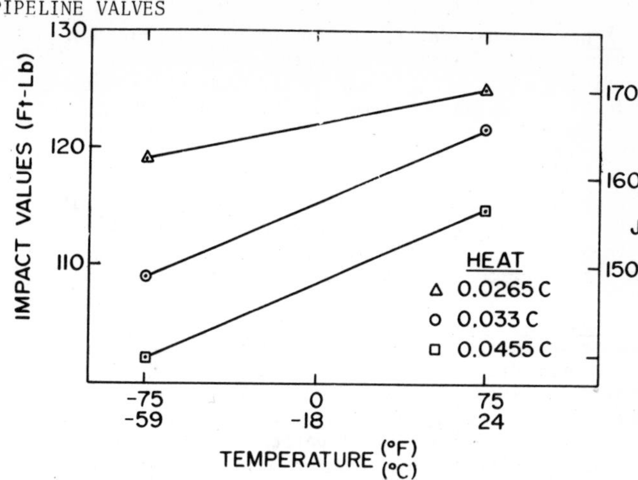

Figure 13: Impact Energies of Three Heats of Modified ASTM A-351, Grade CA-6NM Alloy

Table 5

Hardness Variation of Modified ASTM A-351, Grade CA-6NM

Heat Treatment	Chemical Composition C	Mn	Cr	Ni	Mo	Si	Hardness (Brinell)
4 Hrs. @ 1250°F (680°C)Air Cool	0.0455	0.585	11.60	4.105	<0.01	0.14	217
10 Hrs. @ 1250°F (680°C)Air Cool	0.0265	0.635	11.82	4.00	<0.01	0.15	207-212
20 Hrs. @ 1100°F (590°C)Air Cool	0.033	0.56	9.935	4.015	<0.01	0.11	207

Table 6

Chemistry Specifications for ASTM A-351, Grade CA-6NM

Element	Specification	Aim
Carbon	0.04 Max.	LAP
Manganese	0.50/0.90	0.70
Silicon	0.15/0.35	0.15
Sulfur	0.025 Max.	LAP
Phosphorus	0.015 Max.	LAP
Chromium	11.00/12.00	11.5
Nickel	3.50/4.00	3.75
Molybdenum	0.25 Max.	LAP
Copper	0.50 Max.	LAP
Aluminum	0.06 Max.	LAP

22 Rc maximum requirements of the NACE Specification MR-01-75. Any chemistry specification must have a broad range so it can be expanded into a chemistry range for the melt shop. From the experimental heats of steel investigated, we have proposed that a steel specification containing the chemistry range listed in Table 6 be considered as a substitute for the more common 410 or CA-15 type grades of steel for use in Arctic temperatures (LAP signifies "low as possible").

Figure 13 represents the composite data of the impact testing done on the last three experimental heats of CA-6NM. This indicates that the notch toughness of the material has been maintained and that there was no loss of notch toughness due to modifications of the ASTM A-351, Grade CA-6NM chemistry range.

SUMMARY

These data are presented with the intention of advising industry of the work done by one manufacturer in the area of metallurgy for the Arctic climate. In summary:

1. For pipeline valve construction, carbon steels properly made and properly specified are completely acceptable for materials in environments as cold as -67°F (-55°C).

2. For very low (80°F, -62°C) temperature conditions pipeline valve construction materials are available to meet the demanding environmental conditions.

3. Low alloy steels, specially controlled in chemistry and used in the normalized, quenched and tempered condition, are completely acceptable for temperatures down to -75°F (-59°C).

4. When special grades of stainless steel are needed to combat corrosion as well as Arctic climate conditions, it is possible to vary the chemistries of existing steels to comply with the requirements of corrosion and low temperature impact properties.

DISCUSSION

D. Kenny (Dominion Foundries and Steel): You have mentioned that carbon steels are suitable for the three major Arctic projects. Could you comment on the comparison between your work and that of the previous author (H. Schwartzbart) who claims a more highly alloyed steel is needed to satisfy the -80°F (-62°C) portion of the specification?

D. S. Burns: Forged low-carbon fine-grain steels are completely acceptable for temperatures down to -50°F (-46°C). I hope I did not say that carbon steels are acceptable down to -80°F (-62°C). The paper suggests IN787 for use to -80°F (-62°C). This is a low-alloy steel and would be in line with the type of alloy mentioned by Schwartzbart.

D. Kenny: You have stated that changes in microstructure are primarily produced by varying the chemistry and heat treatment. No mentioned has been made of the effect of section size. Was section size found to have any effect?

D. S. Burns: The modified CA6N, (Cameron specification ZCMS 303) has been looked at for section size effects. The largest section we have tested was 6 in. (154 mm). We did have good uniform results on this particular part.

T. Kunitake (Sumitomo Metal Industries): Pipeline flanges might be as important as valves. We have been conducting research and development work on pipeline flanges for Arctic use. We agree that IN-787 has excellent toughness at low temperatures. However, in the course of our investigations we developed a vanadium-nitrogen alloy which also has some very attractive properties. The chemical compositions of steels investigated for use in Arctic pipeline flanges are shown in Table 1. Carbon contents of all steels are kept very low to obtain low carbon-equivalent for superior weldability. Steel A was intended for use at -29°C (-20°F). Steels B, C and D were intended for use at -62°C (-80°F).

Table 1 Chemical Compositions of Flanges

	Chemical Compositions										Ceq
	C	Si	Mn	P	S	Ni	Cr	Mo	V	N	
A Mn-V	0.09	0.29	1.42	0.011	0.008	0.12	0.14	0.11	0.03	—	0.40
B Mn-Ni-Cr-Mo	0.07	0.18	1.34	0.012	0.013	0.47	0.84	0.12	—	—	0.52
C 3.5Ni-Cr-Mo	0.06	0.25	0.66	0.007	0.009	3.57	0.39	0.12	—	—	0.38
D Ni-V-N	0.06	0.25	1.62	0.006	0.007	1.03	0.02	0.01	0.07	0.009	0.37

$$Ceq = C + \frac{Si}{24} + \frac{Mn}{6} + \frac{Ni}{40} + \frac{Cr}{5} + \frac{Mo}{4} + \frac{V}{14}$$

Table 2 Mechanical Properties of Flanges

	Flange Size	Base Flange						Welded Zone (40,000 J/cm)				
								Welded Joint			V Notch Charpy Value at Bond	
	(inch)	σ_y (kg/mm²)	σ_b (kg/mm²)	El (%)	RA (%)	vE-20°F (kg-m)	vE-80°F (kg-m)	σ_y (kg/mm²)	σ_b (kg/mm²)	El (%)	vE-20°F (kg-m)	vE-80°F (kg-m)
A	24	45.3	55.2	32	76	30 (SA:100)	—	46.7	58.6	16	17 (SA:100)	—
A	48	48.3	57.8	28	72	28 (SA:100)	—	—	—	—	—	—
B	24	45.7	56.1	33	72	—	27 (SA:100)	43.7	54.8	15	—	22* (SA:100)
C	24	46.9	57.2	31	76	—	30 (SA:100)	46.2	58.7	15	—	15* (SA:100)
D	24	40.2	54.5	37	80	—	29 (SA:100)	39.2	52.9	16	—	—

* V groove

Table 3 Characteristics of the Flanges

Steel	Characteristics	Service Temperature
A	1. Most economical 2. For less severe use	-20°F (-29°C)
B	1. Economical	-80°F (-62°C)
C	1. Expensive 2. More reliable	
D	1. Economical 2. VN precipitation hardening 3. Superior weldability	

The 24 in. (610 mm) diameter flanges (steels A, B, C and D) were manufactured by die-forging and ring-rolling processes followed by a Wagner-type finish rolling, while the 48 in. (1220 mm) flange (steel A) was manufactured by ring forging with a hydraulic press. Flanges were subjected to quenching and tempering heat-treatment. The mechanical properties of the flanges are shown in Table 2. The flange of Steel A showed excellent Charpy V-notch toughness with 100% shear fracture at -29°C (-20°F). Steels B, C and D show excellent toughness at -62°C (-80°F). All flanges satisfied the strength requirements as X-65 and X-70 linepipe flanges, which are defined as 80% of the strength of matching pipe. Table 2 also includes the properties of the welded joint made by submerged arc welding. The strength of the welded joints exceed the requirements for X-65 and X-70.

As a summary, characteristics of the flanges made from the various steels are shown in Table 3. Steel D is characterized by the unique chemical composition which utilizes VN precipitation hardening. This steel is attractive from both economics and weldability.

D. S. Burns: We have not looked at the V-N system. Thank you for the information.

L. Luycx (Reactive Metals and Alloys): Referring to your latest CA-6NM steel developed for Arctic corrosion resistance on well head forgings, I noticed your tendency to lower the carbon content of this steel (to 0.0265%). This will pay off. From my experience with "Ebrite" (26 Cr/1Mo steel) for pitting corrosion resistance, I wonder if you have looked into your nitrogen content. In Ebrite, the corrosion resistance requirements were extremely severe but so were the carbon and nitrogen maximum specifications (each at 100 ppm max.). I do not think that you have to go that low in nitrogen but I suggest that it may be useful to monitor your heat-to-heat nitrogen variability to possibly help explain corrosion resistance variability, as well as weld toughness. Zirconium or rare earths might help neutralize some of the deleterious effects of residuals.

D. S. Burns: We have not looked into nitrogen content effects. I will mention this to our melt shop and ask that they monitor for nitrogen variability.

G. L. Archer (The Welding Institute): What is the nominal design stress level in your valves?

D. S. Burns: The nominal design stress is 0.25 x UTS.

G. L. Archer: Did you put any flaws or notches in your full size tests?

D. S. Burns: No notches were intentionally placed in the full size test valves. All welds were non-destructively tested before pressure and low temperature testing. Any flaws present would have been small.

M. R. Krishnadev (Laval University): I congratulate you on an excellent presentation and for having the courage to use the copper-nickel steel, IN-787, which people tend to consider expensive in spite of its excellent properties.

I agree with your assessment of IN-787 as a suitable candidate for Arctic valve applications and in this connection I would like to bring to your attention the work that we are doing to develop copper-bearing steels for low-temperature applications.

We have developed compositions with yield strengths of over 130 ksi (900 MPa) in strip material and 100 ksi (690 MPa) in 0.75 in. (19 mm) thick plates. (A Canadian patent has been granted for these compositions). Although these compositions have higher alloy content than IN-787, one can obtain higher strength levels coupled with good toughness without resorting to a separate normalizing treatment. We are now carrying out experiments aimed at increasing the sectional capability to 1 in. (25 mm) and over.

Have you evaluated the acicular ferrite steels for valve applications?

D. S. Burns: We have not looked into acicular ferrite steels for low temperature applications.

M. R. Krishnadev: Why do you use such low stress levels for designing valves? Is it not more realistic to use higher strength levels and thinner plates?

D. S. Burns: The design stress levels are spelled out by the ASME codes which apply to these products. The codes spell out the materials and their minimum strength levels. Flanges are all designed to these strength levels. The added tensile strength of the IN-787 cannot be used because of the fixed dimensions. We also need rigidity in our parts. Reducing the wall sections would cause rigidity problems which we could not tolerate.

J. N. Cordea (Armco Steel): I would like to add to Mr. Burns' excellent presentation that the IN-787 steel he refers to is covered by ASTM specification A707, "Flanges, Forged, Carbon and Alloy Steel for Low Temperature Service", (Grade L5), and A710, "Low Carbon, Age-hardening Ni-Cu-Cr-Mo-Cb Alloy Steel", (Grade A). Because of its low carbon content, the steel is very weldable and by either normalizing and ageing or quenching and ageing it can develop excellent strength-toughness properties to temperatures -80°F (-62°C) and, in some cases, lower.

MECHANICAL DAMAGE AND ITS EFFECTS ON FRACTURE INITIATION IN LINE-PIPE

F. S. Jeglic
CANMET, Department of Energy, Mines and Resources
568 Booth St., Ottawa
Canada

Field damage inflicted upon a line-pipe by construction equipment was simulated in specially-designed normal and tangential impact tests. Microstructural changes were noted in the surface layer of the damaged region. The damaged surface layer consists of two sublayers: a white deposited layer and a deformed layer. Chemical composition and hardness of the deposited layer corresponds to the composition and hardness of the tool which inflicted the damage. When stressed, the surface layer cracks at the yield strength of the parent material. The initiated cracks grow through the underlying parent material and cause failure. Gouged tensile samples failed at a maximum cyclic stress which is greater than the yield stress, whereas dented and gouged pipe specimens failed at maximum cyclic stresses below the yield stress of the parent material.

INTRODUCTION

Different forms of mechanical damage inflicted upon a pipeline have been systematically investigated by McClure et al (1). Mechanical damage in the form of stress concentrators (milled V-notch, weld crack and gouge), plain dents and combinations of plain dents with concentrators, were examined with respect to the failure pressure. The investigation showed (Figure 1) that standard pipeline steel API 5LX-52 is not notch sensitive over the temperature range from -30°C to 55°C. The introduced stress concentrators merely reduce the wall thickness of the pipe; reduction of the wall causes a proportional decrease of the failure pressure. Plain dents, from 5.6 to 8.6% of the pipe diameter deep, introduce high localized axial and circumferential stresses and cause yielding well below the nominal yield pressure of the perfect pipe. Plain dents, however, have no effect on failure pressure of the pipe over the temperature range from -31°C to 32°C.

The Battelle investigation (1) showed that the combination of dent and milled V-notch stress concentrator is the type of defect which reduces the failure pressure substantially. In this case, the failure pressure is temperature-sensitive. For example, a notch 10% of the wall thickness deep reduces the failure pressure by 30%, whereas a notch of 25% of the wall thickness reduces the failure pressure by 70%. The reduction of failure pressure

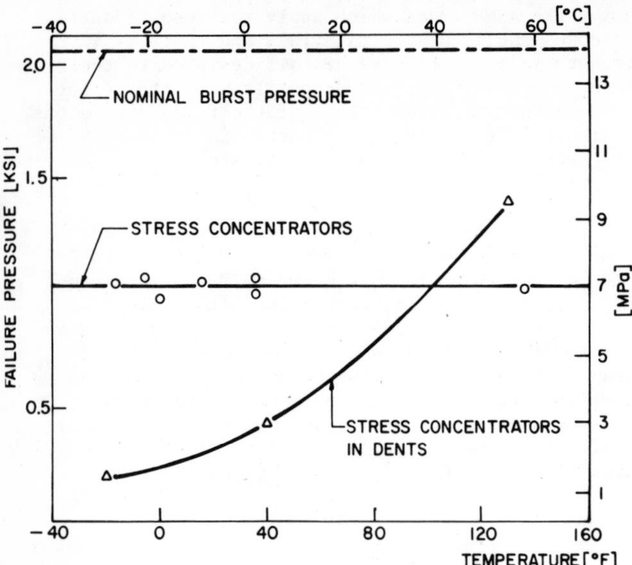

Figure 1: Comparison of 50% stress concentrators with dent and without dent with respect to failure pressure [after ref. 1] (API 5LX-62, 760 mm dia, 9.53 mm wall, 20 mm dent).

with temperature for a pipe containing a notch of 50% of the wall thickness situated in a dent 2.6% of the diameter deep is shown in Figure 1. At -30°C the failure pressure of the damaged pipe is only 10% of the nominal bursting pressure. The Charpy V-notch energy lies at this temperature on the lower energy plateau.

A statistical survey (2) indicates that mechanical damage is inflicted upon pipelines frequently. Heavy equipment can produce gouges as well as dents on the surface of a pipe. A gouge neither represents a stress concentrator nor reduces the wall thickness significantly. A shallow dent (2% of the pipe diameter or smaller) associated with the gouge might even not be noticeable by visual observation. Such a defect is not considered potentially dangerous to the integrity of the pipeline in CSA Z184.

In the present investigation the effect of such a defect on the failure pressure was examined. The first objective was a study of formation and laboratory reproducibility of mechanical damage. The second objective was a study of fracture initiation in the damaged region.

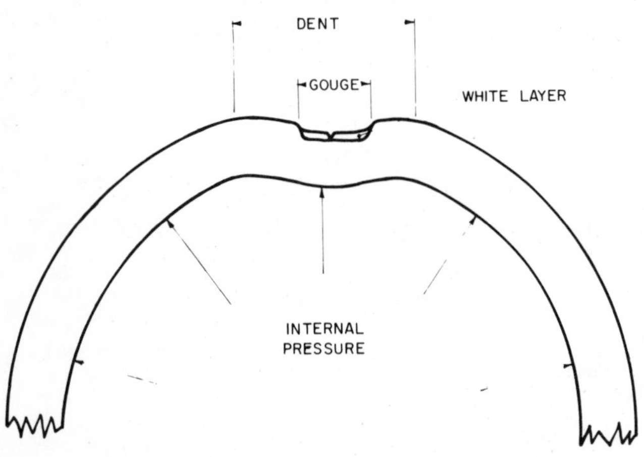

Figure 2: Schematic presentation of failure initiation

A FAILURE INITIATION MODEL

Under typical field circumstances a pipeline may be damaged in an impact which leaves behind a shallow gouge in a dented area (Figure 2). Such damage will most probably be inflicted by the blade or teeth of earth-moving equipment. The relatively sharp and hard teeth of the equipment will not only inflict the gouge and dent, but they will also severely deform, or possibly transform, the pipe surface layer. If deformation and transformation occurs, a thin layer of hardened material is formed on the surface.

If the dented and gouged pipe is internally pressurized the stresses in the dented region are intensified. In this intensified stress field lies a hard surface layer of low static ductility. The underlying parent material of high static ductility will reach its yield stress at relatively low internal pressure. Under this local stress condition a crack can develop in the hard layer. This crack will grow radially into the pipe wall. It will be arrested if it encounters parent material of high ductility or will propagate if the parent material is of low ductility. The ductility is generally reduced by decrease of temperature and by an increase of the deformation rate. However, if the crack arrests in the parent material it represents a stress concentrator and a potential initiation site for any slow growth mechanism. This sharp crack will grow in a low-cycle fatigue manner if the pipe is repeatedly pressurized to the pressure level which caused the crack to develop.

Results of studies of crack initiation and low-cycle fatigue crack propagation at room temperature and -12°C are reported here.

MECHANICAL DAMAGE

Examination of a Field Failure

A field fracture of a 324 mm x 5.4 mm API 5LX-60 steel line pipe, originating in a mechanically damaged area was examined in the laboratory (3). The failure pressure was 12.4 MPa, corresponding to 90% of the specified minimum yield strength. The estimated temperature at the time of fracture was about 5°C. At this temperature the drop-weight-tear-test absorbed energy of this material lies well on the upper energy plateau.

The square fracture profile in the central section of this 1.2 m long rupture (Figure 3) indicates radial crack growth through the wall. The rest of the rupture length has a slant fracture profile, which indicates longitudinal fracture propagation. On the surface of the square fracture section a 0.45 mm deep gouge (8.5% of the wall thickness) and a scrape were observed. Even after bulging accompanying the rupture, a 1.65 mm deep dent was detected (0.5% of the diameter). Numerous longitudinally-oriented cracks were observed on the surface of the scrape. Measurements of the wall thickness in the vicinity of the fracture reveals a substantial wall-thickness reduction at the slant fracture sections and no wall reduction at the square fracture sections. Microscopic observation of sections of the damaged areas (Figure 4) revealed two surface layers in the scraped area: a white-etching, hard (54 Rc) layer and a deformed layer (30 Rc). The surface hardness of the parent metal was 20 Rc. The thickness of the white layer was 0.040 mm. Electron microprobe analysis (Table 1) of the white layer and the underlying parent metal showed the two regions to be of very different composition. The cracks observed in the cross-section of the

a)

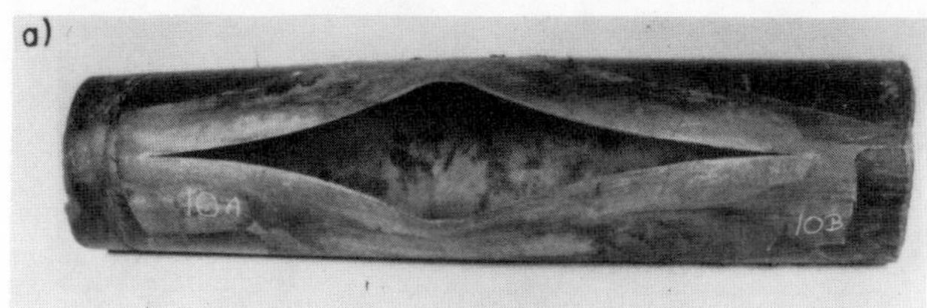

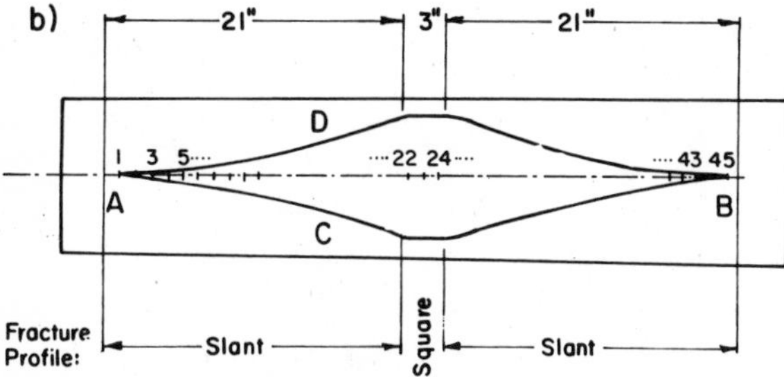

Figure 3: Field fracture of 324 mm diameter pipe; a) general view; b) basic dimensions (in.)

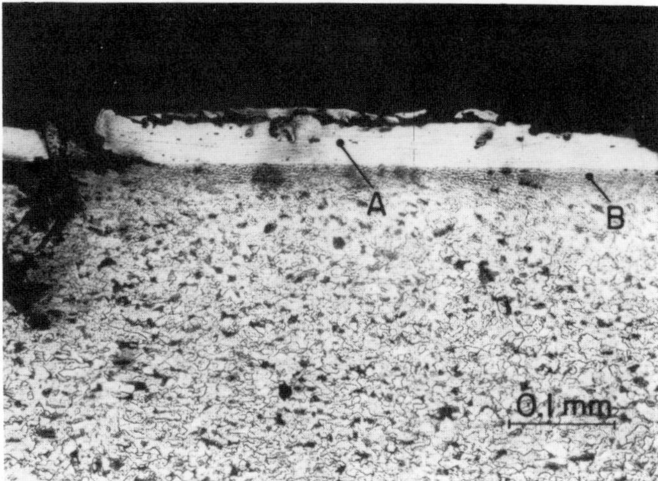

Figure 4: White (A) and deformed (B) layers in the scraped area of the 324 mm diameter pipe.

scraped area extended through both layers. They were all of approximately the same depth, averaging 0.25 mm.

These observations reveal that the pipe was dented, gouged and scraped, and two hard layers were formed on the surface. Cracks did initiate in the scraped and dented area. By further pressurization, one of the cracks grew through the wall and caused failure below the pressure corresponding to the specified minimum yield strength.

Table 1

Microprobe Analyses of Layers in Field Failure

Material	Composition, wt %			
	Si	Cr	Ni	Mn
Parent Metal Steel API-5LX60	0.0 ± 0.016	0.04 ± 0.02	0.05 ± 0.03	1.25
White layer	0.6 ± 0.016	2.5 ± 0.02	0.03 ± 0.03	0.95

Table 2

Composition and Yield Strength of Materials Used

Material Description	Composition in Wt.%									Yield Strength	
	C	Mn	P	Si	Ni	Cr	Mo	V	W	MPa	ksi
Pipe API 5LX 60 (Field Failure)	0.16	1.40	0.01	0.02	-	-	-	-	-	398	57.8
Impact Test Sample Plate API 5LX 65	0.17	1.32	0.01	0.02	0.10	0.08	-	0.21	-	515	74.8
Chisel, AISI 4135 (Normal Tests)	0.34	0.65	0.02	0.30	0.06	0.58	0.365	-	-		
Chisel, Tool Steel (Tangential Tests)	1.40	0.50	0.09	0.63	0.23	4.0	0.92	1.0	5.7		
Pipe, SCH 40 (Pressurization Tests)	0.18	0.73	0.01	0.2	0.04	0.09	0.01	-	-	386	56.0

Table 3

Charpy Impact Test Results for Line-Pipe Steel API 5LX65

(after ref. 7) (Transverse Specimen)

	Full Size							
	Shelf Energy		Transition Temperature					
			% Shear				20 ft lbf (27 J)	
			75		50			
	J	ft lbf	°C	°F	°C	°F	°C	°F
Average	101	74.8	1	34	-16	3	-54	-65
Lowest Data	88	65	-17	2	-29	-20	-61	-78
	2/3 Size							
							15 ft lbf (20 J)	
Average	60	44	-122	10	-25	-13	-54	-65
Lowest Data	53	39	-47	-52	-50	-58	-66	-86

Laboratory Investigation of Mechanical Damage

Mechanical damage, especially the formation of hard surface layers, was investigated in the laboratory using flat samples. Standard line-pipe steel API 5LX-65 (for composition see Table 2, for fracture toughness, Table 3) was impacted in a normal and a tangential direction by a tool-steel chisel (composition given in Table 2).

The impact energies used in the laboratory experiments ranged from 23.4 J/mm (438 ft lbf/in.) to 609 J/mm (11,500 ft lbf/in.). This energy range covers the energies with which construction equipment may impact a pipeline. If, for example, a 40 ton tractor with a 4.85 m wide bulldozer strikes a pipe over a contact width of 76 mm at a speed of 2 km/h, the impact energy per unit length of damage is 80 J/mm; or if a hydraulic excavator drops a 1.5 ton hoe dipper from 305 mm and strikes the pipeline with one 76 mm wide tooth, the unit length energy will amount to 53 J/mm. The parameters used for calculation of energy in these two examples lie at the lower limit of equipment capacity. Therefore unit energies of this magnitude and larger can be expected in the field.

In the normal impact test (Figure 5) a weight was dropped on the chisel which indented the sample perpendicularly to the surface (4). The wedge action and the normal force brought the sample and the chisel into a close sliding frictional contact. In the tangential impact test (Figure 6) the chisel was attached to a massive pendulum. When the pendulum swung over the sample, the chisel gouged the surface of the sample tangentially. A frictional sliding contact was also achieved in the tangential impact tests.

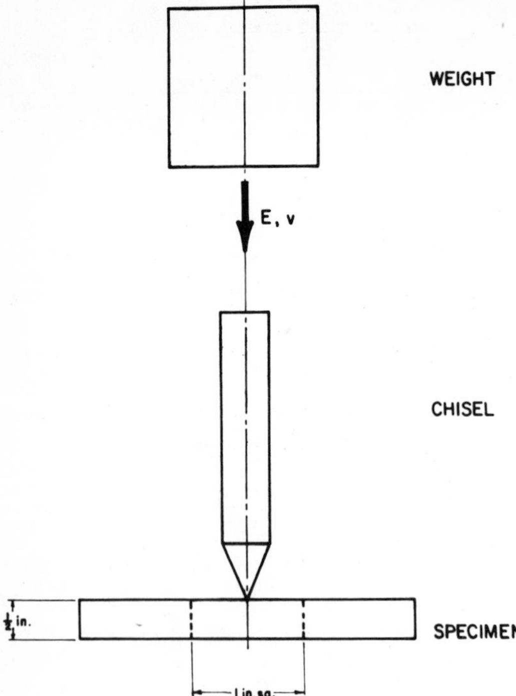

Figure 5: Schematic of the normal impact test.

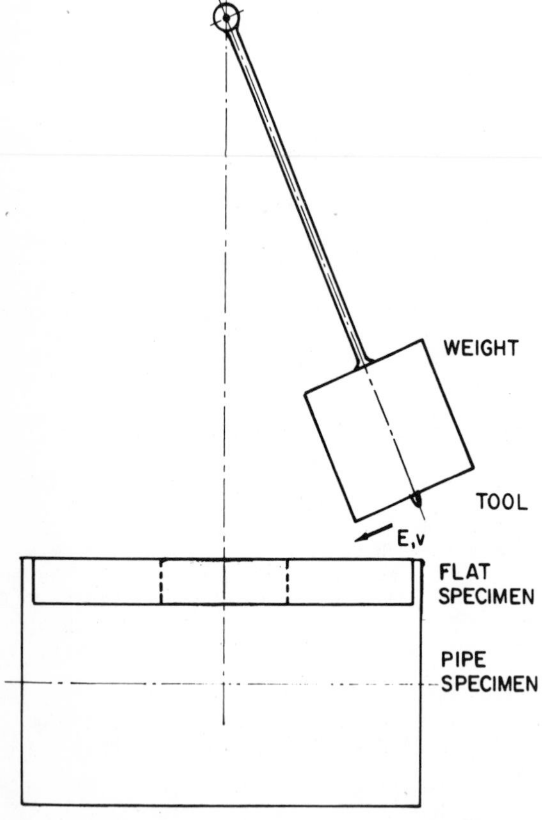

Figure 6: Schematic of the tangential impact test.

In the normal impact tests, two distinct interface layers were observed between the indented chisel and the sample material, as shown in Figure 7. Microprobe analysis of the layers showed that the layer closest to the chisel had the composition of the chisel, whereas the layer closest to the sample had the composition of the line-pipe material. The

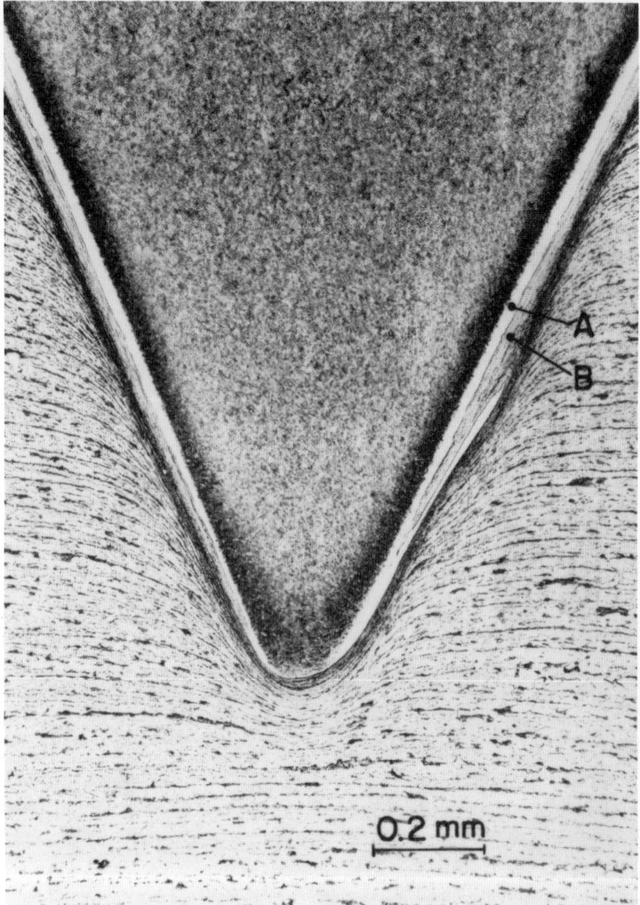

Figure 7: Imbedded chisel in normal impact test ["A"-white layer; "B"-deformed layer]

layer with the composition of the chisel was resistant to conventional etches. It remained white and featureless. The layer with the composition of the pipe was severely deformed material. Microhardness traverses over the interface showed that the hardness of the white layer (65 Rc) exceeded the hardness of the chisel (60 Rc). The hardness of the deformed layer (45 Rc) exceeded the hardness of the parent material (24 Rc). Thicknesses of both layers were measured and correlated with the impact energy. The maximum thickness of the white layer ranged from 10 μm to 70 μm. The thickness of the deformed layer was almost constant for all normal impact tests, with a mean value of 28 μm. The maximum thickness of the white layer increased linearly with impact energy. Correlation of the maximum thickness of the white layer and deformed layer versus the impact energy is shown in Figure 8, for tests made at room temperature.

Tests conducted at lower temperatures, to -56°C, suggest that temperature has no noticeable effect on the appearance or the thickness of the interface layers.

In the tangential test (5), the chisel does not remain in permanent contact with the damaged surface. The impact energy is only partially absorbed in the damage process. The thickness of the surface layers depends on the absorbed energy. Again, two distinct layers were observed (Figure 9), viz. a white-etching outer layer and a deformed layer beneath it. The microprobe analyses (6) of these two layers has shown that the composition of the white etching surface layer was the same as the composition of the chisel, and the composition of the deformed layer

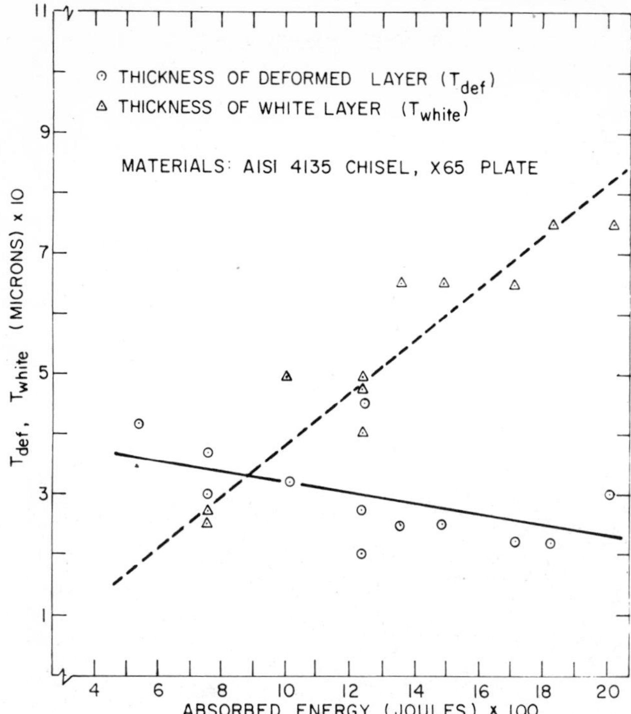

Figure 8: Thickness of the interface layers for normal impact tests as a function of impact energy

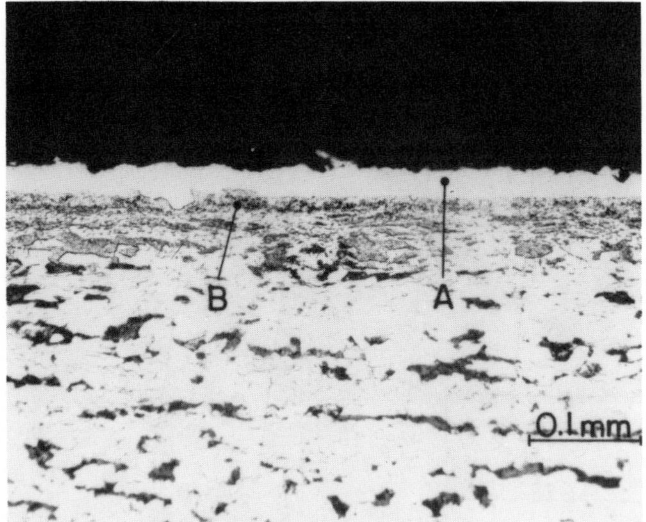

Figure 9: Cross-section of the sample produced in the tangential impact test ["A"-deposited layer; "B"-deformed layer]

Table 4

Microprobe Analysis of White Layer from Tangential Impact Test

Composition, wt %										
Fe	C	Mn	Si	Ni	Cr	Co	Mo	V	W	Se
80.9	1.5	0.61	0.27	0.16	5.0	--	0.23	0.93	11.08	--

was the same as the composition of the sample material (Table 4). It can be concluded that the chisel deposits some of its material on the surface of the sample. The white layer will, therefore, be referred to as the deposited layer. The thickness of the deposited and deformed layers were measured in the mid cross-section of the gouge. Linear correlations of the average thicknesses of the deposited and deformed layers and the absorbed energy are possible, as shown in Figures 10 and 11. The average thickness of the deposited layer ranged in these tests from 2.3 μm to 11.1 μm. The thickness of the deformed layer ranged from 7.6 μm to 30.5 μm. From microhardness measurements performed on the cross-section, the average hardness of the deposited layer was 57.5 Rc, and of the deformed layer, between 30 Rc and 40 Rc, whereas the hardness of the parent material was 24 Rc. The average hardness of the chisel material was 63.5 Rc. The hardness of the deposited layer thus approached the hardness of the chisel. In the tangential impact tests, a deposited and deformed layer also formed at -54°C, the average thicknesses being within the scatter band of the room temperature data.

Laterally unrestrained convex coupons were tested tangentially at room temperature (5). As expected, the values of absorbed energies are higher than those of flat specimens. In Figures 10 and 11, the data from tests on convex samples lay below the line estimated for flat samples. The increase of energy absorption is attributed to the energy required for elastic and plastic deflection of the convex sample.

FRACTURE INITIATION DUE TO MECHANICAL DAMAGE

Uniaxial Tests

Large-size tensile specimens (gauge cross-section 17 mm x 13 mm) with a transverse gouge in the gauge length were tested in uniaxial monotonic tensile tests at room temperature. Reduction of the specimen thickness due to the gouge was 4.8%. No significant difference in yield strength, ultimate tensile strength, and elongation in 50 mm was observed, when comparing data obtained on gouged samples with those of smooth samples (Table 5). Visible transverse cracks (Figure 12) developed at the load level of general yielding, although the final fracture occurred in a typical tensile manner.

Similar uniaxial tests were carried out in low-cycle fatigue at 1 Hz. Specimens of the same size as used in monotonic tests were cycled between a small tensile load and a load corresponding to 115% of the yield stress. As summarized in Table 5, a smooth specimen failed in 1480 cycles, whereas two transversely-gouged specimens failed in 476 (wall thickness reduction 3.9%) and 50 cycles (wall thickness reduction 4.2%) when cycled between the same stress limits. The gouges reduced the fatigue life by 60% and 96.6% respectively. Transverse cracks developed in the gouge at an early stage of the fatigue tests. In the smooth specimen a visible surface crack developed at 95% of the fatigue life. The inflicted gouges thus considerably shorten the initiation stage of surface crack formation.

Biaxial Tests

Two 170 mm outer diameter mild steel (SCH 40) end-capped pipe samples were dented and longitudinally gouged. They were subjected, at 22°C, to cyclic internal pressurization at 0.1 Hz. The longitudinal gouges placed within the dented area had

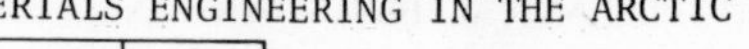

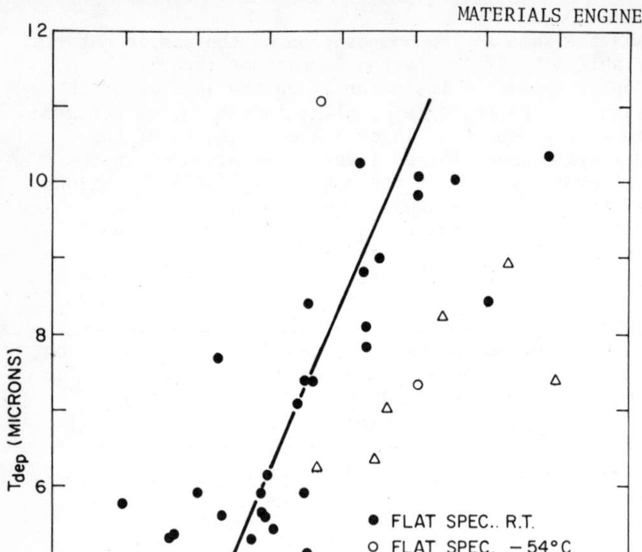

Figure 10: Thickness of deposited layer for tangential tests as a function of absorbed energy

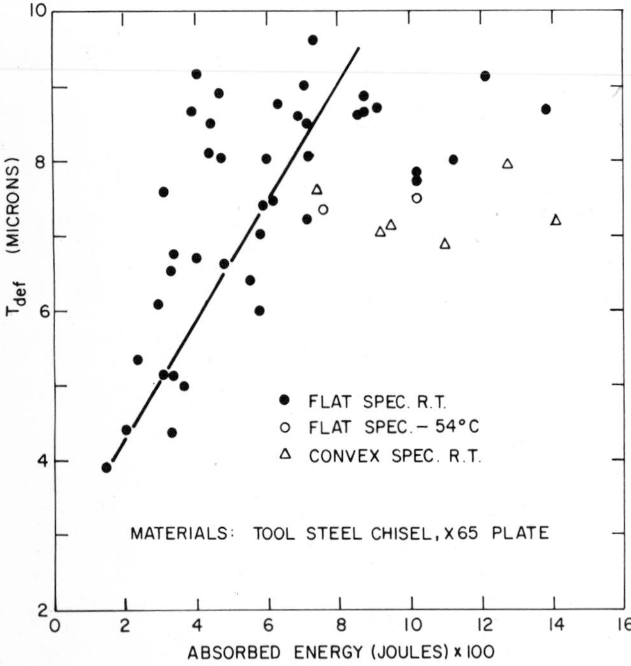

Figure 11: Thickness of deformed layer for tangential tests as a function of absorbed energy

depths of 1% and 21% of the 7.11 mm pipe wall thickness. The depths of the dents were 1% and 2% of the pipe diameter. Composition of the pipe material is given in Table 2.

The pipe with the dent of 2% of the diameter and gouge depth of 21% of the wall thickness fractured at a maximum stress corresponding to 88% of the nominal yield stress in 7 pressure cycles. Visible longitudinal cracks developed when the gouged cross-section approached the yield strain. Cracks penetrated the deposited layer but were arrested in the parent material. Under repeated pressurization a crack propagated in the radial direction. In the last pressure cycle a bulge developed while the overloaded cross-section under the crack was stretching to failure. The through-wall fracture of square fracture profile was 50 mm long. It propagated longitudinally symmetrically in both directions to a total length of 160 mm.

Fracture initiation in the hard layer is caused by intensified stresses in the dent. Elastic strain in the dented area was measured by

Table 5

Monotonic and Cyclic Tensile Test Data

MONOTONIC TESTS

Gouge Depth	Impact Energy		Absorbed Energy		Yield Strength		UTS		Elong % in 2 in.
mm	J/mm	ft lbf/in.	J/mm	ft lbf/in.	MPa	ksi	MPa	ksi	%
no gouge					516	74.9	609	88.4	20
0.61	356	6685	35	657	513	74.5	609	88.4	20

CYCLIC TESTS (1 Hz)

Gouge Depth	Impact Energy		Absorbed Energy		Min Stress		Max Stress		Cycles to Failure	Elong % in 2 in.
mm	J/mm	ft lbf/in.	J/mm	ft lbf/in.	MPa	ksi	MPa	ksi		%
no gouge					4.65	0.675	592	86.0	1480	27
0.55	371	7010	22.6	426	4.65	0.675	592	86.0	465	23
0.56	352	6651	27.1	512	4.65	0.675	592	86.0	50	21

Figure 12: Cracked surface layers tested in monotonic tension

Table 6

Strain Measurement Adjacent to Gouge in a 0.40 mm deep Dent

Internal Pressure		Hoop Stress		Circumferential Strain		
				Undented Pipe Surface		Dent
				Calculated	Measured	Measured
MPa	ksi	MPa	ksi	Strain ($\times 10^{-6}$)		
6.9	1.00	81.6	11.83	335	340	406
13.8	2.00	163.1	23.66	670	660	764
20.7	3.00	244.7	35.49	1005	975	1096
24.1	3.50	285.5	41.41	1173	1162	1220
27.6	4.00	326.2	47.32	1340	1366	Drop

resistance strain gauge. The strain measured in the dent was compared to the strain in the undented area. The strain difference between strain in dented and undented areas was largest at low pressures. This strain difference decreased as the pressure approached the yield strain of the dented areas, as shown in Table 6 .

Cyclic pressurization of a third 170 mm diameter pipe specimen was undertaken at -12°C. This specimen failed in 37 cycles. The maximum pressure corresponded to 92% of the nominal yield stress. The gouge depth on this specimen was 12.5% of wall thickness and the depth of the dent was 2% of the diameter. The fracture mechanism in this test was very similar to that observed at room temperature. Cracks initiated in the hardened layer, were arrested in the parent metal, and then one propagated through the wall under repeated pressurization.

Data for all pressurization tests are tabulated in Table 7. Only one part of the proposed failure initiation model was proven experimentally with the internal pressurization tests. Dented and gouged pipe with a maximum deposited layer thickness of 11 um developed cracks in the deposited layer at a pressure corresponding to 90% of the yield strength. These cracks propagated through the wall in low-cycle fatigue. The failure mechanism in which the parent material possesses sufficiently high ductility to arrest the initiated cracks was operative for this material at room temperature and at -12°C.

The second part of the proposed failure model is expected to occur at lower temperatures. Low-temperature internal pressurization tests are now in progress.

SUMMARY

In this investigation, it was shown experimentally that:

1) two hard layers are formed on the surface of the line-pipe steel in normal and tangential impact tests;
2) the thickness of the white layer is proportional to the absorbed impact energy;

Table 7

Internal Pressurization Tests on 1 m lengths of capped 168 mm x 7 mm Pipe

Test Temp	Depth of Gouge	Depth of Dent	Minimum Cyclic Pressure		Maximum Cyclic Pressure		Cycles to Failure	Impact Energy		Absorbed Energy	
°C	mm	mm	MPa	ksi	MPa	ksi		J/mm	ft lbf/in.	J/mm	ft lbf/in.
22	1.52	3.5	1.4	0.20	27.6	0.20	7	276	5213	97.1	1832
22	0.40	2.0	1.4	0.20	28.9	4.20	454	234	4420	32.0	604
-12	0.89	3.8	1.4	0.20	31.7	4.60	37	230	4344	43.7	826

3) the formation of the hard layers is not changed by temperatures down to -54°C;
4) mechanical damage does not affect the monotonic tensile properties, but substantially reduces low-cycle fatigue life at room temperature;
5) gouged and dented pipe fails in low-cycle fatigue at a maximum internal pressure corresponding to 90% of the nominal yield stress at room temperature.

Acknowledgement

The author is indebted to A. J. Williams and L. P. Trudeau for their interest in the project and E. D. Smith and H. Nelson for technical assistance.

REFERENCES

1. G. M. McClure, R. J. Eiber, G. T. Hahn, F. W. Boulger and K. Masubuchi, in "Research on the Properties of Line-pipe", American Gas Association, 1962, pp. 33-44.
2. R. B. Smith, 5th Symposium on Line-Pipe Research, 1975, Houston, p. F3.
3. F. S. Jeglic, Internal Report PM-R-74-17, CANMET, Physical Metallurgy Research Laboratories, 1974.
4. F. S. Jeglic, Internal Report ERP/PMRL-75-1(R), CANMET, Physical Metallurgy Research Laboratories, 1975.
5. F. S. Jeglic, Internal Report ERP/PMRL-75-25(R), CANMET, Physical Metallurgy Research Laboratories, 1975.
6. F. S. Jeglic and R. H. Packwood, Internal Report ERP/ PMRL-75-36(J), CANMET, Physical Metallurgy Research Laboratories, 1975.
7. D. R. Bell, Internal Report PM-R-72-12, CANMET, Physical Metallurgy Research Laboratories, 1974, p. 7.

DISCUSSION

W. A. Maxey (Battelle Columbus Laboratory): I do not believe Battelle has solved all the problems with the dent and gouge. They have not really done very much work in this area. Some of the work you have referred to was done in the mid-1950's. You attack a problem that seems to be always present, not only for pipelines but other structures as well and that is the problem of external damage. The Battelle research you have referred to appeared to indicate a shift in the initiation transition temperature of the deformed base metal so that the static transition temperature locally is as high as the dynamic transition temperature of the non-deformed base metal. Did you observe a shift in transition temperature and will any future work examine this particular aspect?

F. S. Jeglic: The static transition temperature in mild steel is approximately 170 deg C lower than the dynamic transition temperature. The Battelle research indicates that a combination of stress concentrators and dents increases static transition temperature. It is believed that in the present tests the brittle failure of the white layer produces a dynamic component to the static loading of the underlying base metal, and thus increases the apparent static transition temperature. Low-temperature pressurization tests are in progress to elucidate this point.

P. E. Bedford-Jones (Steel Company of Canada): The condition of the white alloy layer of material on the gouged surface defect accurately describes the condition of the initiation portion of two service failures in 36 in. (910 mm) x 0.375 in. (9.53 mm) linepipe of X65 alloy in 1968. At that time, the technical experts were unable to explain why the surface layer, about 0.008 to 0.010 in. (0.20 to 0.25 mm) thick had a very high Cr and Mn content, much above the base chemistry of the pipe. Until now, this is the first reference I have come across which confirms this "pickup" phenomenon. These were large longitudinal defects of 17 to 20 in. (430 to 500 mm) which failed in service. In the pipe were short transverse notches from rough handling, about 0.5 in. (12 mm) or less, that ruptured under high pressure hydrotesting, but the severe defects did not. Perhaps you might comment on this.

F. S. Jeglic: The question compares a short (12 mm) stress concentrator to a long (430-500 mm) gouge probably containing a white deposited layer, with respect to the failure pressure. Generally, the depth of a defect affects the failure pressure more than its length. During hydrostatic testing the failure pressure of the transverse stress concentrator was obviously reached. This stress concentrator was probably deeper than the longitudinal gouge. The deposited white layer in the gouge probably cracked during the hydrostatic testing and consequently propagated under any of the slow crack growth mechanisms. The long gouge thus caused failure in service at lower internal pressure than that applied during hydrostatic testing.

B. E. Boardman (John Deere): Did you consider the effect of the residual stresses in the dent which were introduced by the formation of the dent? Specifically, the formation of the dent would leave residual surface tensile stresses which when cycled would result in positive R values.

F. S. Jeglic: The residual stress field of the external surface of a dent containing a gouge is complex. Residual stresses are caused by the surrounding area of the dent which is stressed but does not yield. Residual stresses are a function of the shape and depth of the dent. They also vary with the direction and location in the dent. In an experimental study (S. P. Belonos and R. S. Ryan, Oil and Gas J., 1958, Nov., pp. 155-161) of residual stresses in a localized, sharp dent, compressive residual stresses were measured on the exterior surface in axial and circumferential directions. Our measurements of the circumferential strain in a shallow dent during internal pressurization showed that deformation in the dent is intensified (see Table 6). Since residual stresses and applied stresses are additive, the R-value of the circumferential stress cycle might be initially negative and become positive after the dented area changes shape.

J. L. Gerlitz (Shell Canada) Does the length of the concentrators cause the burst pressure to become temperature dependent?

F. S. Jeglic: Figure 1 shows a diagram of test temperature versus burst pressure. Burst pressures of stress concentrators on the undented pipe are independent of test temperature in the temperature range from -30°C to 55°C. Burst pressures of the pipes with stress concentrators in the dents show distinct temperature dependence within the same temperature range. This change in temperature dependence is attributed to the change of the stress field in the vicinity of the stress concentrator and increased freedom of movement of the edges of the concentrators. The length of the stress concentrators was assumed to be constant throughout the test program although this was not specifically mentioned in reference (1). It was observed in our work that a longer gouge did not necessarily result in a longer through-the-wall fracture opening. The effect of the length of the axial defect was not investigated in this project.

K. N. Street (R. M. Hardy and Associates): White layers or abraded materials have been seen in the past and have been generally called "martensitic" layers due to their extremely high hardnesses. Would you reject the possibility that the basic material transfer mechanism from chisel to pipe in your case may involve highly localized melting?

F. S. Jeglic: Although it is known that metal adhesion can occur in the solid state, it is believed that localized melting takes place in this kind of impact test. It is also believed that the melting takes place at the tip of the tool because it is in frictional contact with the pipe surface all the time during the gouging process, whereas each location of the gouge is only instantaneously in contact with the tool tip. Furthermore, thermal conductivity of the tool steel is less than that of the linepipe steel. The pipe configuration represents a more efficient heat sink than that of the tool. Surface discolouration of the tool tip observed after the test corresponds to about 400°C, but this does not exclude the possibility that deposited material from the tool tip reached a much higher temperature.

K. N. Street: Did you attempt to produce such hard layers by impacting your pipe with a softer (not too soft) object or with a variety of impacter alloys? Such data could be useful in selecting materials for backhoe teeth, etc.

F. S. Jeglic: Two different steels were used for striking tools. They differed in composition and in surface hardness, (51 Rc and 63 Rc). The difference in hardness did not have any observable effect on the formation or thickness of the white and deformed layers. If it is assumed that the tool tip reaches melting temperature, then it is really temperature-softened tool material deposited on the harder pipe steel in the moment of contact. Further investigation in this direction, i.e. using different steels for the striking tool, might produce useful data for development of steels used in production of teeth and blades for excavation and earth-moving equipment, but such a study is not included in the present program.

K. N. Street: Hydrostatic pressurization produces maximum stresses at the internal pipe surface and this probably explains well why more service failures have not been seen. It would appear that the shape and nature of the dent or gouge would be very important in determining the residual stress state around the "white" layer.

F. S. Jeglic: Circumferential stress in the pipe wall subjected to internal pressure is maximum at the internal pipe surface. The difference between the circumferential stresses at the internal and external pipe surfaces increases with the wall thickness. In the dented area residual stresses are superimposed on the intensified applied stresses. The magnitude of residual stresses and the intensification factor are dependent on the shape and depth of the dent. In the present work, gouges represented a minimum wall reduction and stress concentration. The dents were shallow, only 2.5% of the pipe diameter. Most defects in the work were within the

CSA acceptance limits. Moreover, the configuration and dimensions of defects were kept as constant as possible. Therefore, the effects of the depth and the shape of the dent on failure pressure cannot be obtained from the data acquired to date.

B. Hawbolt (University of British Columbia): I would think that both the denting and the gouging would introduce high (additive) compressive stresses in the outer damaged work hardened surface (the parent metal beneath the white layer). On pressure testing, these residual stresses would have to be overcome to introduce tensile yielding and subsequent failure. Hence the effect of the damage might not be seen unless compressive yielding is examined. This would be an added safety factor for external flaws and their potential relationship to pipe failure (cracking) initiating at these flaws.

F. S. Jeglic: In the field, denting and gouging occur simultaneously as the result of a single accidental impact. In the laboratory, the pipe was first dented and then gouged. The gouging resulted in a reduction of the residual compressive stresses in the surface of the dent. Compressive yielding does take place, hence the resulting permanent deformation, i.e. dent. Residual stresses are mainly caused by the region adjacent to the dent which was stressed but did not yield. In the gouge itself localized heating takes place which also alters the stress distribution in the white layer and the deformed layer. If the resultant residual stress field in the dent is exposed to the effects of internal pressurization of the pipe, the tensile stress component in the circumferential direction fractures the white layer before the yield strength is reached in the pipe wall outside the dented region.

P. Chollet (Noranda Research): With reference to the white layer, did you encounter cases where the nature of the interface with the substrate pipe material (diffusion bond versus partial diffusion or decohesion) would or could affect the propagation of cracks formed in the white layer as a result of pipe expansion?

F. S. Jeglic: Numerous gouged and dented samples were sectioned and examined after failure. Although decohesion of the deposited white layer in the dent was expected, none was observed. To illustrate crack initiation in the white layer and its growth into the base metal, three micrographs of the sectioned gouge after fracture are shown in Figure 13. All three micrographs show white deposited surface layers and cracks which were up to 100 mm long in the axial direction. They all opened under circumferential tensile stress. There is no evidence of decohesion between the white layer and base metal. In all pressurization tests it was observed that the tensile stress component in the circumferential direction overcomes the cohesive force within the white layer before the shear stress component could overcome the adhesion force between the white layer and deformed layer. This behaviour of the white layer is facilitated by the transitional nature of the mechanical properties of the deformed layer between the base metal which is soft and ductile and the hard and brittle white layer. After the white layer is cracked, all the stresses in the external surface layer are released. Consequent deformation occurs at the tips of the axial cracks (growth or blunting).

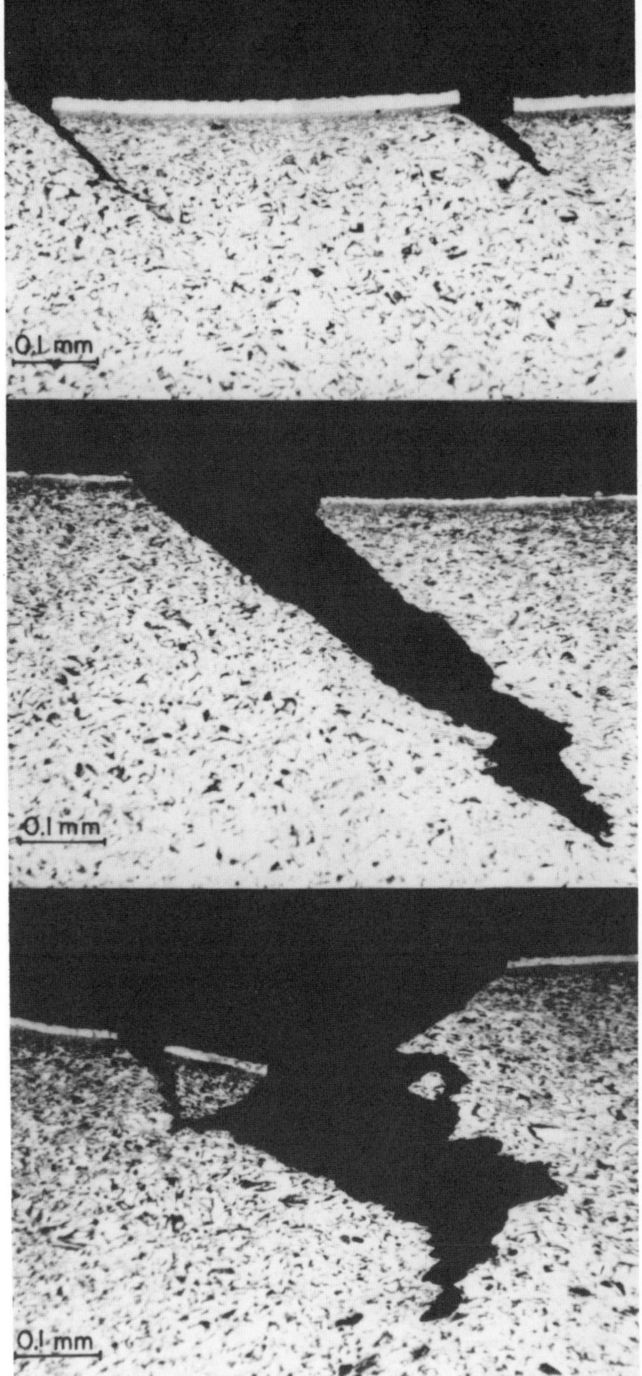

Figure 13: Cross-sections showing cracks in the dented and gouged area adjacent to the fracture on the 168 mm OD pipe-specimen which was tested in cyclic pressurization (454 cycles to failure) at room temperature

SULPHIDE STRESS CRACKING IN LINE-PIPE HEAT AFFECTED ZONE MICROSTRUCTURES

I. C. G. Ogle
CANMET, Department of Energy, Mines
and Resources, Ottawa
Canada

Techniques have been developed to simulate and evaluate the sulphide stress cracking (SSC) susceptibility of the range of microstructures occurring within the longitudinal seam weld heat-affected zone (HAZ) of a controlled rolled line-pipe steel typical of the type proposed for Arctic service. Specimens containing stress raisers were loaded by 2-point bending with a following load to strains which were predetermined by strain gauge calibrations. All SSC tests were performed in highly hydrogen embrittling, acidified saline solutions saturated with hydrogen sulphide.

Effects of microstructure and hardness on the critical stress for initiation of SSC and on fracture mechanism as indicated by scanning electron microscopy were determined. Test results were projected to pipeline operating conditions by comparing the critical stress (σ_c) for each microstructure studied with the pipeline operating stress (σ_a).

In one microstructure of hardness 24 Rc SSC initiation occurred at stresses below yield. The fracture path was clearly transgranular and of the quasi-cleavage type usually associated with hydrogen embrittlement. However, because the yield strength of this simulated HAZ microstructure was relatively high, the ratio σ_c/σ_a was significantly greater than 1.0. Specimens consisting of microstructures which were representative of other locations in the seam weld HAZ of the steel tested, exhibited SSC initiation at stresses above their respective yield strengths. The lower yield strength microstructures indicated a tendency towards a mixed transgranular/ intergranular mode of fracture. From the results to date, little danger of SSC in the seam weld HAZ is expected under pipeline operating conditions in the Arctic.

INTRODUCTION

In 1971, the Canadian Department of Energy, Mines and Resources initiated a comprehensive program to investigate a number of commercially available line pipes such as might be used for the transmission of natural gas from the Mackenzie Delta. These pipes were of diameter 30 to 48 in. (760 to 1220 mm) and of yield strength 67 to 84 ksi (460 to 580 MPa).

Although environmental cracking (EC) was not considered to be a major failure mechanism, Biefer (1) developed a simple screening test by which he could identify, for each line pipe, that location amongst parent metal, weld metal and HAZ, exhibiting the lowest resistance to sulphide stress cracking (SSC). Under the rather severe test conditions, he showed that the seam weld HAZ was generally the location most susceptible to SSC. This concurs with a statement by Carter (2) that welding of a steel generally lowers its resistance to SSC.

Original material property specifications for acceptability of a carbon steel in sour service were based on a maximum hardness of 22 Rc (3). This specification has been adopted in Canadian standards (4,5) governing steel line pipe for sour service, natural gas transmission and applies to parent metal, weld metal and HAZ. Its validity has been established by field experience with traditional line pipe steels. However, cause for concern exists on consideration of the present trend towards development and use of higher strength controlled-rolled line-pipe steels in both sour and sweet service.

It is generally accepted that the metallurgical structure of a steel can influence its susceptibility to SSC at a particular strength level. Recent commercial controlled-rolled line-pipe steels are considerably more complex, metallurgically, than their traditional counterparts. Since the lack of field experience has not permitted validation of the 22 Rc criterion for acceptability of controlled-rolled line-pipe steels in sour service and since the SSC screening tests of such steels (1) have indicated a tendency for SSC initiation in HAZ locations, the present study was undertaken in an attempt to quantify the risk of SSC initiation in HAZ microstructures in these line-pipes.

Although Mackenzie Delta and Arctic Island gas fields can be defined as "sweet" by Canadian Standards (4), recent analyses indicated the presence of finite concentrations of hydrogen sulphide. These sulphide levels may constitute a danger to line-pipe integrity for steels of yield strength 80 to 100 ksi (550 to 690 MPa). Laboratory studies and field tests have suggested that the occurrence of SSC is a distinct possibility at hydrogen sulphide partial pressures as low as 0.001 atm (6-8). A continuation of the work reported herein is underway to investigate the SSC susceptibility of developmental line-pipe steels in environments presently defined as "sweet" but containing small amounts of hydrogen sulphide.

For the present study, it was considered advantageous to test specimens consisting of simulated HAZ microstructures rather than as-welded specimens. The particular simulation technique employed was believed to be more suitable than that employed in other studies of microstructural effects on hydrogen embrittlement of welds (9-12). The line pipe steel selected for investigation was one which exhibited SSC initiation only in the seam weld HAZ during laboratory screening tests (1) and is a relatively low yield strength controlled-rolled steel.

EXPERIMENTAL

Materials

The starting material for weld simulation consisted of strips, 1.75 x 0.25 x 0.040 in. (44.5 x 6.35 x 1.02 mm) thickness, machined from line pipe "F" parent material. Steel "F" composition is shown in Table 1. The longitudinal direction of each strip was transverse to the pipe axis; strip thickness direction coincided with that of the wall thickness. Weld deposit specimens were cut from inner and outer line pipe surfaces in the same orientation as described above. The weld deposit was centred with respect to specimen length. All specimens were ground to a 12 μ in. (0.305 mm) surface finish (centre-line average).

HAZ Simulation

Weld simulation techniques utilize the fact that, for a given steel, HAZ microstructures can be defined in terms of the peak temperature attained and the time-temperature relationship during cooling. In the present research on steel "F", four peak temperatures, 1300°C, 1100°C, 900°C, and 700°C were chosen to ensure adequate representation of the range of microstructures occurring in the longitudinal seam weld HAZ of the line pipe manufactured from this steel. The form of each of these thermal cyclces was established by an empirical technique (13) employing a "Gleeble", an instrument which can be programmed to impose, reproducibly, any pre-selected thermal cycle on a specimen.

The technique focussed on successful simulation by the 1300°C peak temperature cycle of the near-fusion line HAZ microstructure resulting from the outside pass of a 2-pass submerged-arc seam weld. To achieve this simulation, an iterative procedure was used,

Table 1

Chemical Composition of Line-Pipe "F"

Element, %		Element, %	
C	0.18	Mo	0.01
Mn	1.32	V	0.05
Si	0.38	Ti	>0.004
Al	0.025	Cb	0.036
S	0.009	Zr	0.050
P	0.008	Ce	0.015
Ni	0.01	La	0.005
Cr	0.05		

which was based on the relationship between specimen cooling rate at 425°C and hardness following application of a thermal cycle. Success of simulation was judged by hardness and microstructural comparisons of simulated specimens with the actual line pipe HAZ. All reported hardnesses are averages of 10 readings as measured by a Tukon micro-hardness tester (500 g load) and subsequently converted to equivalent Rc hardness values.

Forms of each of the 1100°C, 900°C and 700°C peak temperature thermal cycles were approximated on the basis of the form of the 1300°C peak temperature thermal cycle; all are depicted in Figure 1. Corresponding simulated microstructures are compared with seam-weld HAZ microstructures in Figure 2. Hardnesses of the near-fusion line HAZ and simulated microstructures are given on these figures.

Mechanical properties of the four simulated microstructures were obtained from specially designed 0.250 in. (6.35 mm) gauge length Hounsfield cylindrical tensile specimens. These data are presented in Table 2 together with mechanical properties of line-pipe steel "F" parent metal.

Environmental Cracking Tests

In the SSC tests, parent metal and HAZ-simulation specimens were provided with stress raisers consisting of two holes, 0.028 in. (0.70 mm) in diameter, drilled 0.125 in. (3.18 mm) apart at specimen mid-length. Specimens were stressed in 2-point bending by a modified Uhlig Tester which is illustrated in

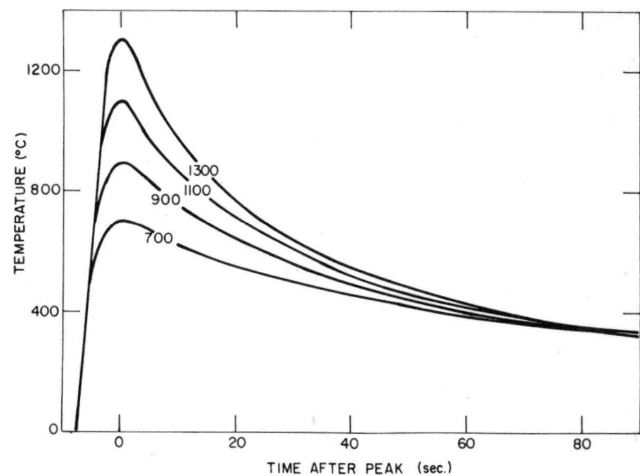

Figure 1: Weld simulation thermal cycles

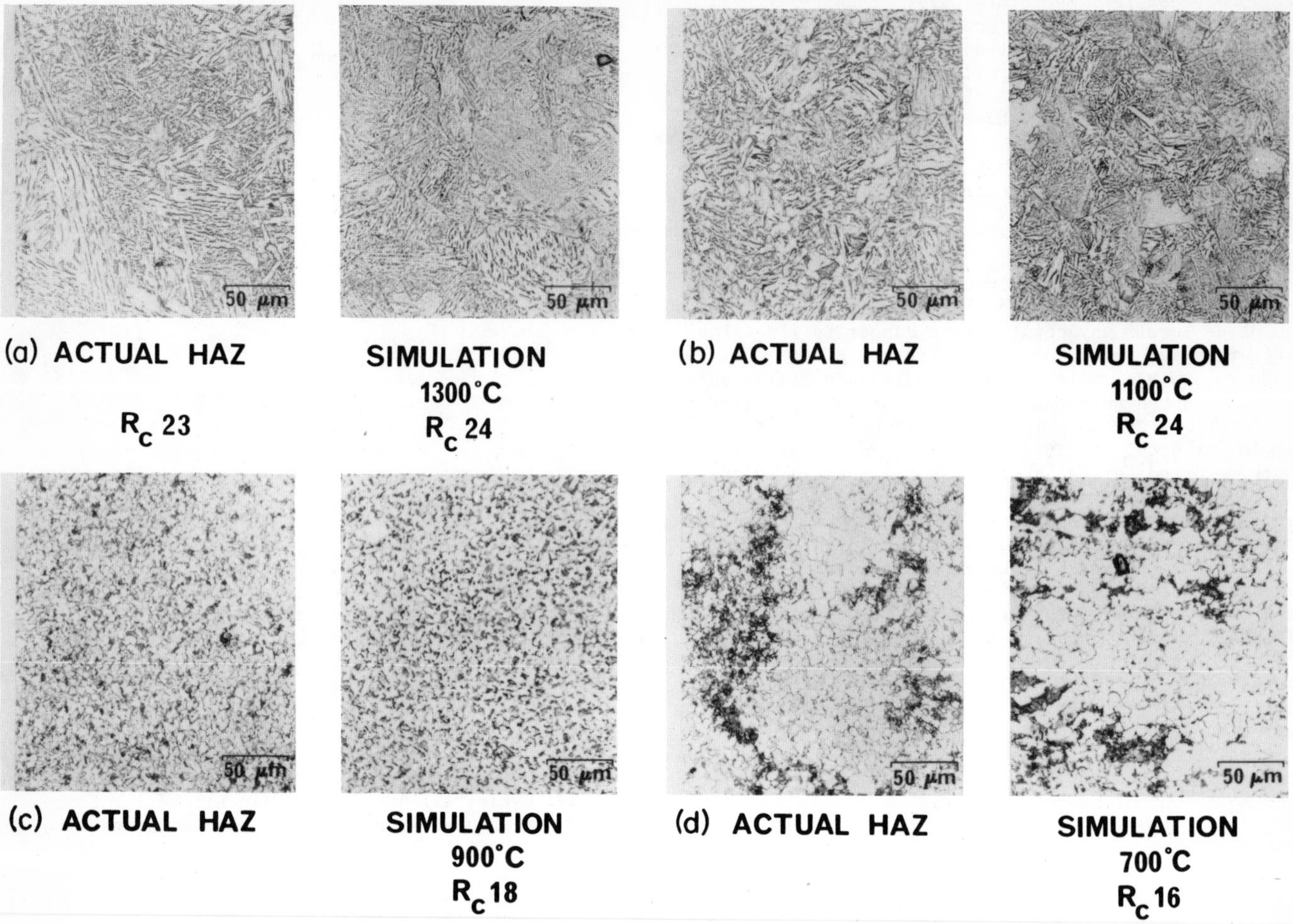

(a) ACTUAL HAZ R_c 23 — SIMULATION 1300°C R_c 24

(b) ACTUAL HAZ — SIMULATION 1100°C R_c 24

(c) ACTUAL HAZ — SIMULATION 900°C R_c 18

(d) ACTUAL HAZ — SIMULATION 700°C R_c 16

Figure 2: Comparison of actual heat-affected-zone (HAZ) microstructures with those simulated by the various peak temperature thermal cycles

Figure 3. The spring loading mechanism incorporated in the test rig applies a following load subsequent to crack initiation, thus ensuring failure and facilitating automatic measurement of time to crack initiation.

A calibration procedure was undertaken to relate bending strain, recorded by strain gauges, to mid-point deflection, as measured by a dilatometer gauge to 0.0001 in. (0.003 mm). This was performed for specimens representing the parent metal and each of the four simulation conditions. The method of strain-gauge monitoring of bending stress was selected because critical stresses were expected to be, at least in part, beyond the linear elastic region where the calculation of theoretical bending stress for 2-point loading is not applicable. In this case, equivalent stresses were obtained by referral to the stress-strain behaviour of the Hounsfield tensile specimens.

The test solution was identical to that used for the earlier U-bend screening tests (1), viz: 3.5% NaCl, 0.5% acetic acid in distilled water (initial pH 2.8). Prior to tests, solutions were purged with nitrogen to minimize the oxygen content. Upon specimen immersion, the flow of hydrogen sulphide was started. Zero time with respect to time to failure data corresponded to 5 min after commencement of flow.

Times to failure were recorded for each type of specimen as a function of the mid-point deflection for strains ranging in small increments from about 1.0% down to about 0.2%. The strain below which no cracking was encountered before the 200 h termination time was defined as the critical strain. Times to failure were also recorded for each of parent metal,

Table 2

"F" Mechanical Properties of Simulated and Parent Material

Simulation Peak Temp.	Hardness Rc	Yield Strength, 0.2% Offset		UTS	
		ksi	MPa	ksi	MPa
1300°C	24	103.8	716	118.9	820
1100°C	24	96.1	663	112.0	772
900°C	18	64.9	447	102.3	705
700°C	16	74.8	516	93.1	642
Parent	14	64.2	443	91.9	634

Figure 3: Stress Corrosion cracking test rig

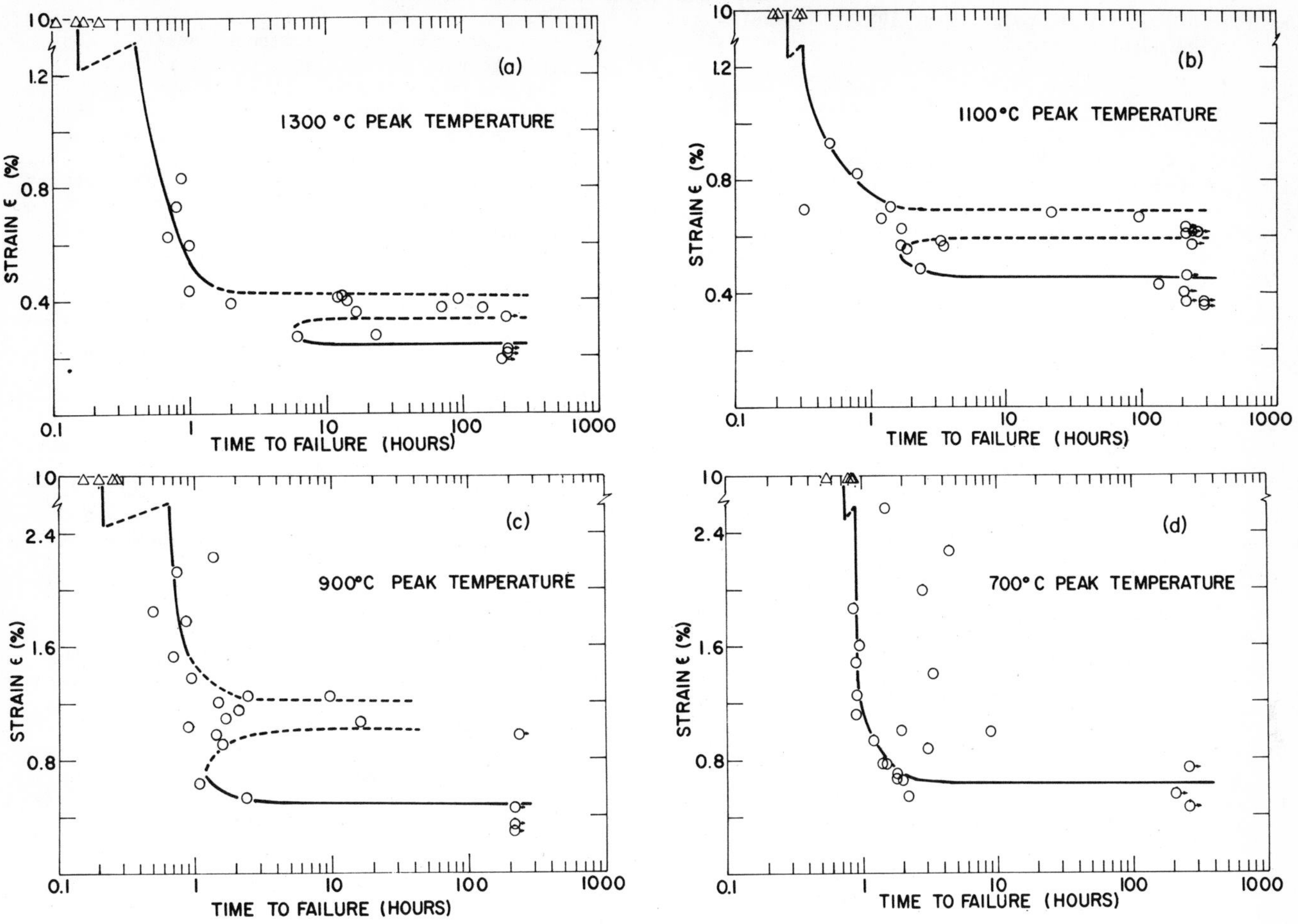

Figure 4: Sulphide stress cracking behaviour of the HAZ simulation specimens

HAZ-simulation and weld deposit specimen types at a deformation for which the chord length was 1.44 in. (36.6 mm), equivalent to a strain of approximately 10%.

In an effort to characterize the fractography of SSC fractures, fracture surfaces of some specimens were examined by scanning electron microscopy.

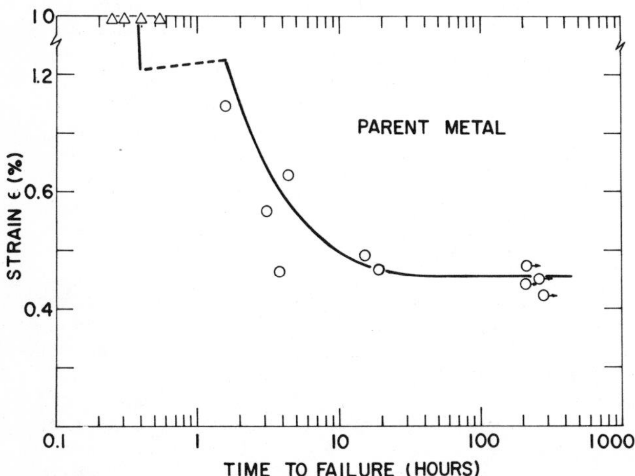

Figure 5: Sulphide stress cracking behaviour of parent metal

RESULTS AND DISCUSSION

Effect of Applied Stress on Time to Failure

Results of the bent-strip SSC tests are summarized in Figure 4 which depicts time to failure as a function of strain for specimens given weld simulation thermal cycles at peak temperatures of 1300°C, 1100°C, 900°C, and 700°C. These specimens will henceforth be identified by the peak temperature of the thermal cycle to which they were subjected. Results obtained with parent metal specimens (not given a thermal cycle) are shown in Figure 5. In addition to providing critical strains below which no failures were encountered within the 200 h test period, these curves show two interesting features.

Figure 4 (a,b,c) representing the 1300°C, 1100°C and 900°C specimens, show an apparent recession in cracking tendency or, alternatively, a range of strain above the critical strain at which delayed or no crack initiation was observed. Similar behaviour, reported by Sandoz (14), was shown not to have been caused by the lack of plane-strain conditions. The implication of such behaviour during bent beam SSC tests is that unless critical strains are determined precisely, relatively high "pseudo-critical" strains could be quoted in place of true critical strains.

The other feature shown in these figures is the existence of two regimes of strain dependence of time to failure (t_f). From the critical strain to about 0.8%, t_f is very strain-dependent while at strains from about 0.8% to at least 10%, t_f is relatively independent of strain.

Effect of Stress Raisers

Since the specimen geometry and stressing method adopted in this study do not provide plane-strain conditions, valid stress intensities cannot be calculated. Instead, nominal strains are employed as the critical parameter descriptive of susceptibility to SSC. The stress raisers utilized in the test technique are considered to be only one factor among many that constitute an accelerated corrosion test and allow a margin of safety in the interpretation of test results.

In the standard tests, two through-thickness holes were drilled at specimen mid-length to act as stress raisers since they were suitable for thin beams and proved successful in causing crack initiation at specimen mid-length, thus providing reproducible results. The maximum stress concentration factor resulting from this configuration of stress raisers is approximately 1.5 (15), occurring at the edge of a hole.

The strains shown in Figures 4 and 5 correspond to those recorded by a 0.125 in. (3.2 mm) long and 0.062 in. (1.6 mm) wide strain gauge, centred between the holes. The values recorded are averages of the strain over this area, which extends along the specimen length beyond the more heavily-strained region between the holes. Measurements made using 0.015 in. (0.4 mm) long by 0.020 in. (0.5 mm) wide gauges were employed to correct for the strain averaging effect obtained from the larger-sized strain gauges. The nominal strain, defined as the strain after discounting effects of the stress raisers, was then calculated by considering the amount of stress intensification registered by the smaller gauges as a result of their proximity to the stress raisers (16).

Susceptibility of HAZ Structures to SSC

The laboratory-determined critical strains for each of the structures investigated are listed as nominal strains in Table 3. Also given are other parameters which relate to the projected susceptibility to SSC of the seam-weld HAZ and parent metal of line pipe "F" under normal operating stresses. Among the parameters shown in Table 3 for each specimen group are: time to failure (t_{f-10}) for mid-length deformations of about 10% strain; critical stress (σ_c) as determined from Hounsfield stress-strain curves, given the critical strain (ε_c); yield strength (YS); and the applied operating stress (σ_a), which is made equal to 0.8 x YS of the parent material.

Table 3

Critical Strain and Critical Stress for

Simulated HAZ Microstructures and Parent Metal

Peak Temperature (°C)	ε_c Critical Strain (%)	t_{f-10}, Time to Failure (h)	σ_c, Critical Stress (ksi/MPa)	Ratio σ_c/YS	Ratio σ_c/σ_a*
1300	0.25	0.15	74.8/516	0.72	1.46
1100	0.47	0.24	97.0/669	1.01	1.89
900	0.50	0.21	65.5/452	1.01	1.27
700	0.65	0.74	76.3/526	1.02	1.48
Parent	0.53	0.38	64.2/442	>1.00	1.25
Weld	-	0.39	-	-	-

* σ_a = 51.8 ksi (357 MPa)

On examination of the results shown in Table 3, it is evident that the specimens inherently most susceptible to SSC, as indicated by their low σ_c/YS ratio, and the only ones to fail at an applied stress below their yield strength were the 1300°C specimens which simulated the microstructure and properties of the near-fusion line HAZ adjacent to the mill weld. However, if one examines the ratio of critical stress to applied operating stress (σ_c/σ_a) computed for each specimen type, it appears that all microstructures have acceptable resistance to SSC under operating stresses.

Another method of quantifying acceptability of steels for sour service is by the use of a parameter, $S_c = \varepsilon_c.E/10^4$, which has become widely recognized in this capacity through the development of oil-field tubular goods. Related field experience has suggested that steels for which S_c > 12 psi (83 kPa) have acceptable resistance to SSC (17). It should be noted that this acceptance level is based on a less-demanding test than that employed in this study. The test technique (18) involved 3-point loading of a beam containing two holes, for which the maximum stress concentration can be calculated to be 1.2 (15). Of the specimens tested in the present study, only those simulating the near-fusion line HAZ microstructure were unacceptable using the S_c criterion (S_c = 7.5 psi = 52 kPa). Since, in this study, the test technique was associated with relatively severe SSC condition, and since the yield strengths of the different groups of specimens varied considerably relative to the projected line-pipe operating stress, the ratio σ_c/σ_a is considered to be a more useful criterion than is S_c for evaluation of acceptability for sour service.

Hardness Limitations Imposed on Line Pipe in Sour Service

In relation to the generally-accepted 22 Rc maximum hardness criterion for the use of steels in sour service (3), two of the microstructures tested (those typical of the 1300°C and 1100°C specimens) exceeded this hardness, although only marginally. However, this study has indicated that both microstructures would likely be resistant to SSC under operating conditions.

This can rationalized on two bases. The operating stress of a pipeline is determined by the specified minimum yield strength of the parent metal and thus is theoretically constant. It follows, then, that the higher the yield strength of an area within the HAZ, the lower will be the ratio of the operating stress to the yield strength for that area, and consequently, the less severe will be the conditions affecting SSC. In addition, the inherent resistance to SSC of this generation of line-pipe steel might be expected to be relatively high because of the low sulphur and phosphorus contents (19).

Effect of Microstructure

Although this study was not designed to isolate the effects of microstructure on the inherent susceptibility to SSC of HAZ microstructures, one such effect is apparent. In Table 3, an anomaly in the trend of increasing susceptibility to SSC (decreasing ε_c) with increasing yield strength is exhibited by the 700°C specimens. It can be seen in Table 2, that the 700°C specimens possessed a high yield strength to tensile strength ratio relative to the other microstructures. This is thought to have been caused by ageing and the resulting presence of vanadium and columbium carbides and nitrides. This particular

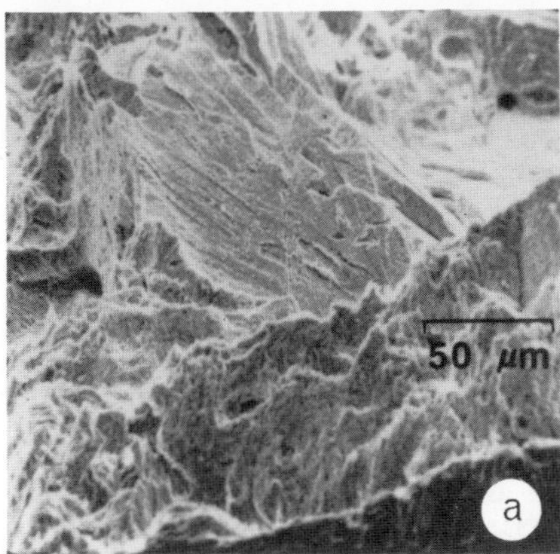

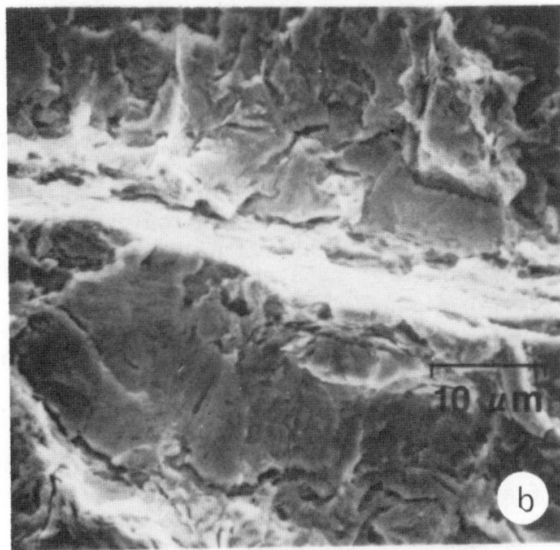

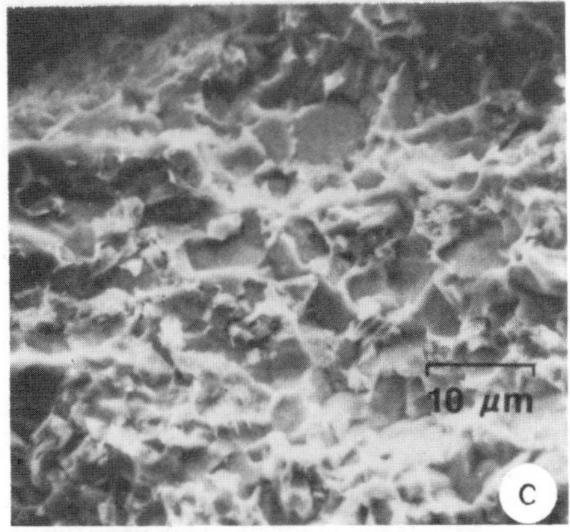

Figure 6: Scanning electron fractographs of (a) transgranular fracture, near-fusion line microstructure; (b) transgranular fracture, near-parent microstructure; (c) intergranular fracture, near-parent microstructure.

case indicates that microstructure plays a role in determining the SSC resistance of a material, and that hardness is not the only criterion to be considered.

Relationship between Bent-strip and U-bend Tests

The results of the bent-strip testing program which are herein reported and which involved individual parent, mill-weld deposit, and simulated HAZ specimens are in excellent agreement with the test results obtained by Biefer (1) utilizing composite U-bend specimens as cut from mill-welded line pipe fabricated from steel "F".

The bent-strip testing program has shown that the time to failure for any one specimen group, strained to greater than about 0.8%, was relatively insensitive to increased strain to, at least, 10% strain. However, the t_{f-10} data in Table 3, which represent the average times to failure for specimens bent to about 10% strain at mid-length, indicate that for each specimen type, there existed a unique t_{f-10} value. It is of consequence that the greater was the SSC susceptibility amongst parent and simulated HAZ specimens, or the lower was the ε_c value for a specimen, the lower was the corresponding t_{f-10} value. Assuming that this inverse relationship between SSC susceptibility and t_{f-10} can also be applied to the mill-weld-deposit specimens tested, it is apparent that the mill-weld deposit was at least as resistant to SSC as the parent metal.

Thus, on the basis of the determinations of ε_c and t_{f-10}, this study indicates that the structure most susceptible to SSC amongst parent, simulated HAZ structures and weld metal of steel "F" was that simulating the near-fusion line, mill weld, HAZ. Although not specific as to locations within the HAZ, Biefer (1) also concluded from screening tests of composite U-bends that the HAZ of steel "F" was the location most susceptible to SSC.

Fractography of SSC Failures

U-bend fracture surfaces of steel "F" exhibited what has been described as intergranular and transgranular crack paths (1). In the present study, a detailed examination by scanning electron microscopy of parent and simulated HAZ bent-strip SSC fracture surfaces indicated that although for the most part fracture was transgranular, intergranular fracture was evident under certain conditions.

Specimens possessing a large prior austenite grain size (near-fusion line microstructures) exhibited fracture surfaces similar to that illustrated in Figure 6(a). The mode of fracture of specimens possessing a fine-grain size was more difficult to characterize because of the greater masking effect of corrosion subsequent to crack propagation. However, on examination of fracture surfaces of bent-strip specimens which had been retrieved immediately from the test solution upon failure, it was evident that parent and 900°C specimens failed by both transgranular (Figure 6(b)) and intergranular fracture (Figure 6(c)).

The fractography of SSC failures of steels has recently been described (20) as being transgranular for yield strengths of 75 to 94 ksi (520 to 650 MPa) and intergranular for yield strengths of 103 to 157 ksi (710 to 1080 MPa). The findings of this study, viz. transgranular fracture for yield strengths of 75 to 104 psi (520 to 720 MPa) and mixed transgranular and intergranular fracture for a yield strength of about 65 ksi (450 MPa), are essentially in agreement.

CONCLUSIONS

Weld simulation methods combined with EC tests on bent-strip specimens containing a stress raiser, although time consuming, have provided quantitative information regarding the susceptibility to SSC of seam-weld HAZ microstructures in line pipe steel "F".

Steel "F" line pipe was previously shown by U-bend laboratory tests (1) to have contained a seam-weld HAZ of low relative resistance to SSC. Insofar as the bent-strip test results obtained in this study can be applied to the much more complex line pipe operating conditions, little danger of SSC in the

HAZ is expected. The microstructure inherently most susceptible to SSC, and the only specimen group to fail at an applied stress less than the respective yield strength, was that simulating the near-fusion line HAZ structure. However, although specimens of this microstructure failed in the elastic region and exhibited a hardness marginally greater than that generally considered to be a guideline for acceptability for sour service, the critical stress for SSC initiation was significantly higher than the maximum operating stress.

Fractography of SSC failure surfaces of bent-strip specimens of the selected steel revealed a transgranular failure mode for the higher yield strength, near-fusion line microstructures and a mixed transgranular/intergranular mode for the lower yield strength, near-parent microstructures.

Acknowledgments

This study was conducted under the general supervision of G. J. Biefer. The experimental work was performed by D. Linkletter.

REFERENCES

1. G. J. Biefer, Report ERP/PMRL-75-4(R), Physical Metallurgy Research Laboratories, Ottawa, February, 1975.
2. C. S. Carter, M. V. Hyatt, Proc. Int. Conference on Stress-Corrosion Cracking and Hydrogen Embrittlement of Iron-Base Alloys, Firminy, France, 1973.
3. "Materials for Valves for Resistance to Sulfide Stress Cracking in Production and Pipeline Service", NACE Standard MR-01-75, Materials Performance 1975, vol. 14, (4).
4. CSA Standard Z184-1973, "Gas Transmission and Distribution Piping Systems".
5. CSA Standard Z145.2-1974, "High-Strength Steel Line Pipe, 18 Inches and Larger in Diameter".
6. F. E. Blount, B. C. Arnwine, R. J. Chandler, Materials Protection, 1962, vol. 1 (12), pp. 24-26.
7. C. M. Hudgins, R. L. McGlasson, P. Mehdizadeh, W. M. Rosborough, Corrosion, 1966, vol. 22, pp. 238-251.
8. R. S. Treseder, T. M. Swanson, Corrosion, 1968, vol. 24, pp. 31-37.
9. F. Watkinson, R. G. Baker, H. F. Tremlett, British Welding J. 1963, vol. 10, pp. 54-62.
10. T. Bonizewski, F. Watkinson, R. G. Baker, H. F. Tremlett, British Welding J. 1965, vol. 12, pp. 14-36.
11. T. Bonizewski, R. G. Baker, British Welding J. 1965, vol. 12, pp. 349-362.
12. F. Watkinson, Welding J. Research Supp. 1969, vol. 48, pp. 417s-424s.
13. I. C. G. Ogle, Report PM-R-74-23, Phys. Met. Research Laboratories, Ottawa, December 1974.
14. G. Sandoz, Memorandum Report 2454, Naval Research Laboratory, Washington, D.C., February 1972.
15. R. E. Peterson, "Stress Concentration Factors", J. Wiley and Sons, 1974, p. 145.
16. S. P. Timoshenko, J. N. Goodier, "Theory of Elasticity", 3rd edition, 1970, p. 90, McGraw-Hill.
17. T. M. Swanson, J. D. Tralmer, Paper No. 101, Corrosion '75, NACE, Toronto, 1975.
18. J. D. Fraser, G. C. Eldridge, R. S. Treseder, Corrosion, 1958, vol. 14, pp. 517t-523t.
19. E. Snape, Corrosion, 1968, vol. 24, pp. 261-282.
20. M. Watkins, M. F. Bluem and J. B. Greer, Paper No. 98, Corrosion/75, NACE, Toronto, 1975.

DISCUSSION

R. P. Culbertson (Brown and Root): You indicate in the paper that microstructure plays a determining role in SSC resistance. Would you please explain this comment?

I. C. G. Ogle: This statement was based on the SSC behaviour of the group of specimens thermally cycled to 700°C compared to that of the parent metal. Mechanical properties of this specimen group indicated both higher yield strength and higher hardness than those of the parent metal. Since these cycled specimens underwent, effectively, only a subcritical heat treatment, one would expect only minor microstructural changes such as those associated with ageing. Yet their SSC resistance was significantly higher than that of the lower strength parent material. I think the point to recognize is that hardness alone is not sufficient to describe a material's resistance to SSC. This is, of course, not a novel idea, and has been studied in some detail.

R. P. Culbertson: The penetration of hydrogen into the microstructure has been a problem for many years. The Japanese have performed some work on the effect of minor additions of copper to low sulphur steel to provide resistance to hydrogen penetration. However, the mechanism of penetration is still undefined. Do you care to discuss this problem and are you planning a program to evaluate this problem, for if we understand how it occurs then we can provide a solution.

I. C. G. Ogle: The effect of hydrogen penetration to which you refer is hydrogen-induced step-wise cracking. This form of hydrogen damage results in ductile fractures in contrast to the brittle fractures typical of SSC. Some work by the Arabian American Oil Company conducted since the Japanese work has supported the beneficial effects of copper at the 0.25% level. Delamination frequency was related to the presence of elongated Type II MnS inclusions, usually associated with fully-killed steels. The mechanisms by which copper mitigates this form of damage are thought to be two-fold in that (i) the rate of the cathodic hydrogen evolution reaction is reduced and (ii) the presence of copper affects the ease of hydrogen adsorption. Since this latest study utilized Mr. Cotton's "BP Test", perhaps he would like to comment.

In answer to your last question, I am presently investigating this form of hydrogen damage in pressure vessel steels and hope to extend the test program so as to include some linepipe steels.

H. C. Cotton (British Petroleum): The test referred to as having been used by Aramco to examine delamination effects in wet H_2S environments is in fact the BP Test which we began some years ago. A large number of samples have been tested. The test was not designed to examine the sulfide stress cracking effect which BP is presently examining by K_{1scc} methods. I caution against hasty conclusions that the harder or stronger HAZ zones mentioned by the speaker are immune. In fact there seems to be evidence to the contrary. Neither is it true that girth welds and their HAZ's are not susceptible. Meanwhile increasing strength above X70 for sour gas service is not recommended in the absence of clear evidence that it is safe to do so.

F. S. Somerville (Canadian Arctic Gas Study): Could you comment on the effect of residual stress as it would affect performance of HAZ's, particularly in light of your comments that the high strength portion of the HAZ microstructure which failed in the elastic range was at a stress level less than the nominal operating stress level for the pipeline.

I. C. G. Ogle: Stu, I'm afraid your question is based on a misunderstanding. Nevertheless, it is interesting to consider the effect of surface residual stress on SSC in linepipe. Actually, the high strength portion of the HAZ exhibited a threshold stress for SSC initiation of 72% of Y.S., or about 75 ksi (520 MPa) compared to an operating stress of 52 ksi (360 MPa).

From results I have seen, a figure of 20 ksi (140 MPa) tensile residual stress is reasonable at the fusion line in cold expanded linepipe. So the total additive applied stress, viz. 72 ksi (500 MPa), is still slightly below the threshold stress as measured by a test involving a rather severe environment.

R. J. Cooke (National Energy Board): Could you comment on the possibility of sulfide stress cracking occurring at the inside toes of submerged arc welds in cold expanded pipe, considering the potentially severe local strain history in the HAZ microstructure that could result from cold expansion.

I. C. G. Ogle: I can, at best, hypothesize since I did not investigate the effects of prior cold deformation. It is generally accepted that prior cold work is detrimental to a material's resistance to SSC. In the case of inside weld toes one would also have to consider the stress intensification brought about by the surface topography at these locations. In one case of failure initiating at inside toes of a long seam weld, with which you are familiar, SSC probably played a role. However, in this particular case, excessive strain hardening occurred during cold expansion because of prior misalignment of outside and inside passes. One point to consider is that there is generally less hardness variation across weldments in HSLA linepipe than in conventional higher carbon linepipe. This tendency should contribute to a less severe strain distribution following cold expansion of HSLA steels.

I agree with the implications of your question in that cold expansion may further decrease the SSC resistance of a linepipe location which is inherently the most susceptible to SSC.

C. A. Parrini (Italsider): I agree that whatever is the amount of H_2S in the gas, even if low, the potential risk of SSC in the long term must be considered. I would like your opinion on the effect of inclusions in the HAZ's as initiators for SSC.

I. C. G. Ogle: Most examples of brittle SSC field failures that I have seen have shown, characteristically, crack initiation at the root of a corrosion pit. It is possible, however, that the presence of inclusions was instrumental in the formation of pits. In laboratory tests, specimens contained stress raisers which would tend to mask the effect of inclusions as locations for crack initiation. If one considers internal inclusions and hydrogen-induced step-wise cracking or delamination at these inclusions, I suspect that if delamination occurred, the yield strength of the surrounding metal would be low enough that brittle SSC propagation would not be a problem.

B. Rothwell (Noranda Research): Judging from the diagrams shown, the thermal cycles used on the X65 material were considerable faster than those which would be experienced in a typical Arctic pipeline seam weld, welded with a heat input of ∿ 4 kJ/mm (a typical value); a typical cooling time from 800°C to 500°C for the latter would be approximately 70 s. This, coupled with a moderately high carbon content, leads to a considerably higher hardness than would be expected in a typical Arctic X70 pipe.

Has any investigation been made of specimens cycled with peak temperatures in the inter-critical zone? It would seem that enrichment of the regions which were austenitic at the peak temperature could lead to very high local hardness and enhanced susceptibility to sulphide stress cracking.

I. C. G. Ogle: In establishing the thermal cycles to be used as a basis for simulation of the actual HAZ microstructures, the cooling rate at 425°C was used as the parameter characterizing the thermal cycle curves, rather than cooling time from 800-500°C, which I know you prefer. This probably accounts for the conclusion you have reached regarding the relative energy inputs of simulation thermal cycles used in this work and typical energy inputs for Arctic X70 linepipe. In passing, the same thermal cycles used in this work have been applied to simulation of HAZ microstructures of Arctic X70 pipe, in an extension of the work described here, with excellent agreement between maximum hardnesses of actual and simulated HAZ microstructures.

With regard to the effect on hardness of a thermal cycle to a peak temperature in the inter-critical region, I have not measured any unusually high hardnesses in the near parent region of an X65 mill weld HAZ. I suspect that, although there may be some carbon enrichment, the cooling rate at this distance from the fusion line is low enough that no siginificant hardening results in these relatively low carbon steels.

G. D. Uttrachi (Union Carbide, Linde Division): Are you familiar with the work of Kotecki and Howden which showed the weld metal, not the heat affected zone, was responsible for hydrogen sulphide cracking? This work was done on actual welds, not with a Gleeble which exaggerates the HAZ area. Kotecki showed that welds made with active fluxes, those which add Mn or Si to the weld metal, create microscopic high hardness areas near the weld surface, which are the initiation sites for cracks.

Do you know if the flux used for the welds in your work was an active alloy adding flux?

I. C. G. Ogle: Yes, I am aware of the work by Kotecki and Howden and I believe that they were concerned primarily with weld metal cracking, not HAZ cracking. My only comment is that in the work I have described, I also tested specimens containing actual weld metal cut from the pipe. Since they showed essentially the same resistance to SSC as did the parent metal, weld metal would have to be described as non-susceptible to SSC.

I do not have any information regarding the type of flux used for the X65 pipe which I tested.

J. F. Clayton (Gulf Oil Canada): Gulf's immediate problems are much more concerned with wet CO_2 in the Arctic though there may be small amounts of H_2S, and these cannot be ignored. However, the current NACE H_2S test is much too severe for the purpose.

In support of the concept of the danger of low H_2S, we had a case of a failed 7075-T6351 Al turbo-expanded wheel, where the allowable stress was reduced 15-25% in sales gas containing less than 2 ppm H_2S and only a few grains of water.

I. C. G. Ogle: It is interesting to hear your concerns and I agree that the NACE SSC is too severe, since it is designed to test susceptibility to cracking and not pitting type corrosion.

H. Schwartzbart (Rockwell International): I question the appropriateness of the "Gleeble philosophy" in this case. This philosophy implies that one can learn something useful about the performance of graded structures (i.e. a heat-affected zone) by duplicating in bulk the structure existing at a plane. There is a strong possibility that what one learns is not relevant to the real case, because one of the unique things about the structure at a plane in the heat-affected zone is that it is surrounded by unlike neighbouring material, which is in itself unique. I feel that real welds should be studied in the NACE tension test, allowing the crack to initiate and grow in its region of choice (most susceptible), then using scanning electron microscopy and Auger electron spectroscopy to study the fracture face.

I. C. G. Ogle: I think the question to consider is: How successfully can one quantify the susceptibility to SSC of a HAZ? In the NACE tensile test, using cylindrical specimens containing the actual weld and HAZ, once the applied load causes yielding in the parent metal adjacent to the weldment there is no easy way to characterize the stress applied to the HAZ areas of higher yield strength than the parent. These areas are, of course, those which, on the basis of single YS vs. SSC susceptibility relations, one would expect to be the most susceptible and hopefully those for which the test is designed. Generally speaking, this argument applied to any laboratory SSC test utilizing as-welded specimens, in that threshold stresses for those areas which are usually the most susceptible cannot easily be determined because of non-uniform yielding. The Gleeble allows one to circumvent this problem.

While I disagree with your views on the applicability of the "Gleeble philosophy", I do agree with your suggested use of careful fractographic techniques.

ENVIRONMENTAL ACCELERATION OF CRACK GROWTH IN AN X-65 LINE-PIPE STEEL UNDER CYCLIC LOADING

O. Vosikovsky
CANMET, Department of Energy, Mines and Resources
568 Booth St.
Ottawa K1A 0G1
Canada

The effect of 3.5% salt water, distilled water, and sour crude oil environments on fatigue crack growth in X65 steel has been investigated over a wide range of stress intensities and cyclic frequencies. Also, the effect of electro-chemical potential has been evaluated in salt water.

The maximum environmental acceleration of crack growth occurs in the intermediate range of stress intensities, and increases with decreasing frequency and cathodic potential, or in crude oil, with increasing hydrogen sulphide content. The maximum increase in growth rate (40 times higher than in air) has been found in salt water under cathodic potential at $\Delta K=25\ MPa\sqrt{m}$ and at the lowest frequency tested, 0.01 Hz.

At low stress intensities close to the threshold limit, the growth-rate curves in all environments converge to the growth rate in air.

At the free-corrosion potential, the growth rates in salt and distilled water are the same. Crude oil without added sulphide reduces the crack growth rate compared to air. In crude oil saturated with H_2S, a substantial acceleration of crack growth appears, even at high frequencies, and persists up to high stress intensities, whereas in other media the growth rate under these conditions approaches the growth rate in air.

INTRODUCTION

Subcritical growth of a crack from an initial defect under fluctuating pressure, enhanced by an aggressive environment, constitutes a potential mode of pipeline failure which has not been much explored. Considering the stringent requirements on safety of large-diameter Arctic pipelines, it has been recognized that a knowledge of the effects of the environments encountered in pipeline service on fatigue crack growth is essential. To this end, the effects of 3.5% salt and distilled water environments under different electrochemical potentials, and crude oil with two levels of hydrogen sulphide, on crack growth in an X65 steel were evaluated over a wide range of low frequencies.

Several recent studies (1-6) have shown that environments with the ability to produce hydrogen can significantly increase the rate of fatigue crack growth, even in steels not considered to be susceptible to stress-corrosion cracking or when the maximum stress intensity is below K_{Iscc}. This enhancement of growth rate depends primarily on the aggressiveness of the environment, the stress intensity range, the frequency and the shape of the loading wave.

EXPERIMENTAL PROCEDURE

The X65 steel commercially manufactured to API 5LX Specification used in this study came from 12.7 mm thick plate. The chemical composition and mechanical properties (in the T-L orientation used for all tests) were as follows: C 0.16%, Mn 1.34%, Si 0.33%, P 0.006%, S 0.009%, V 0.046%, Nb (Cb) 0.031%, σ_{LYS} = 459 MPa, σ_{UTS} = 570 MPa. The average ferrite grain diameter was 18 μm.

Fatigue crack growth specimens were of the pin-loaded, single-edge notch type 12.7 mm thick, 76.2 mm wide, and 580 mm long. The sharp notch was 9.5 mm deep and 1.6 mm wide. Prior to acquisition of growth rate data, the specimens were pre-cracked in air to a distance of 2.5 mm from the notch tip. The load range during pre-cracking was gradually lowered until the ΔK was reached at which the subsequent test started.

Tests were conducted on an MTS servo-controlled, closed-loop hydraulic testing system at room temperature, using a triangular load wave shape. The stress ratio, R = K min/K max, was held constant at 0.2. The crack length in air and in salt water, was measured on both sides of the specimen using two travelling microscopes. In crude oil and in salt water under anodic potential, the electrical potential drop method (7) was used. The accuracy of both methods was better than ±0.05 mm. To obtain compatible results by both methods, the crack lengths measured by microscope were corrected for crack front curvature, using direct measurements made after fracture. The growth rates were calculated from subsequent crack length measurements (by dividing the crack increments Δa by the numbers of elapsed cycles ΔN) with ΔK computed for the midlength of every crack increment from a standard calibration equation (8). The average crack length increment was 0.5 mm.

The reference data were gathered in laboratory air of constant humidity (39 ± 1% R.H.). For tests in aqueous and crude-oil environments a "Plexiglas" chamber containing about 2 ℓ of liquid was mounted over the notch. The 3.5% salt water or distilled water was periodically replaced so that the pH of the solution varied from 6.5 to 7.5. A cathodic potential of -1.05 ± 0.01 V (vs. saturated calomel electrode, SCE) was achieved by coupling the specimen to two Zn anodes. For the lower cathodic potential of -1.43 ± 0.08 V(SCE), either Mg anodes or a constant current supply source connected to two Pt anodes was used. In this case the pH of the solution varied from 6.5 to 9. The free-corrosion potential varied within -0.68 ± 0.03 V(SCE). Platinum anodes were used to apply an anodic potential of -0.5 ± 0.05 V(SCE).

The blend of sour crude oil contained 0.65% S and less than 0.3% water. The H_2S content during the tests with a sealed chamber was approximately 1 ppm. In a second series of tests, the crude oil was saturated with H_2S by bubbling the gas through during the test. The H_2S content after saturation was 4700 ppm.

RESULTS

Crack growth rates per cycle Δa/ΔN versus stress intensity factor range, ΔK, are plotted in the usual log-log diagrams. The main variable, apart from environment conditions, is the frequency, which varied from 0.01 to 15 Hz.

The reference fatigue crack growth rates in laboratory air at a frequency of 15 Hz are shown in Figure 1. The data were acquired on four specimens and they fall within a ±25% scatter-band. Over a wide range of ΔK, from 6 MPa√m to 70 MPa√m the growth rates can be approximated by a straight line with a slope n = 2.82. Below this range, the growth rate

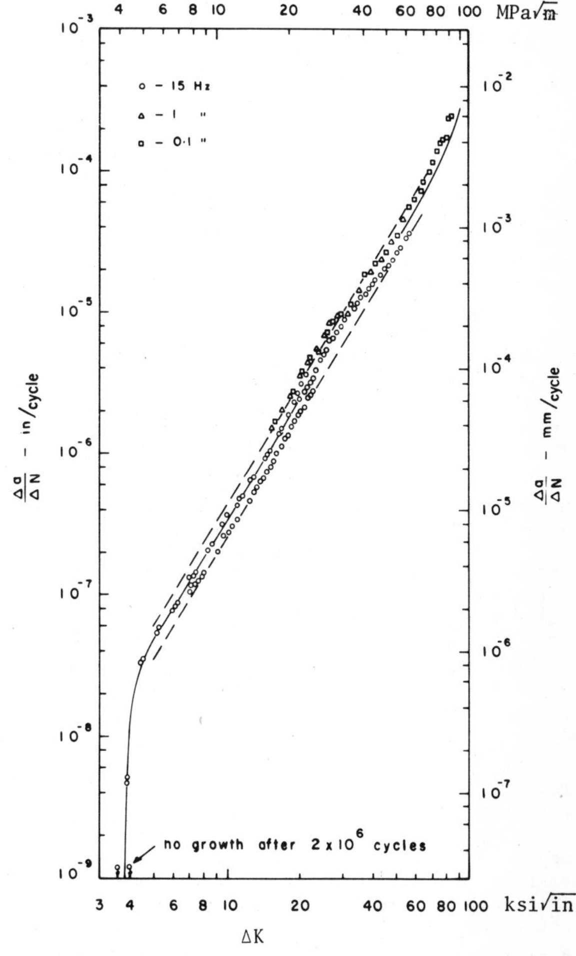

Figure 1: Fatigue crack growth rates in laboratory air at three frequencies, with scatter-band for 15 Hz.

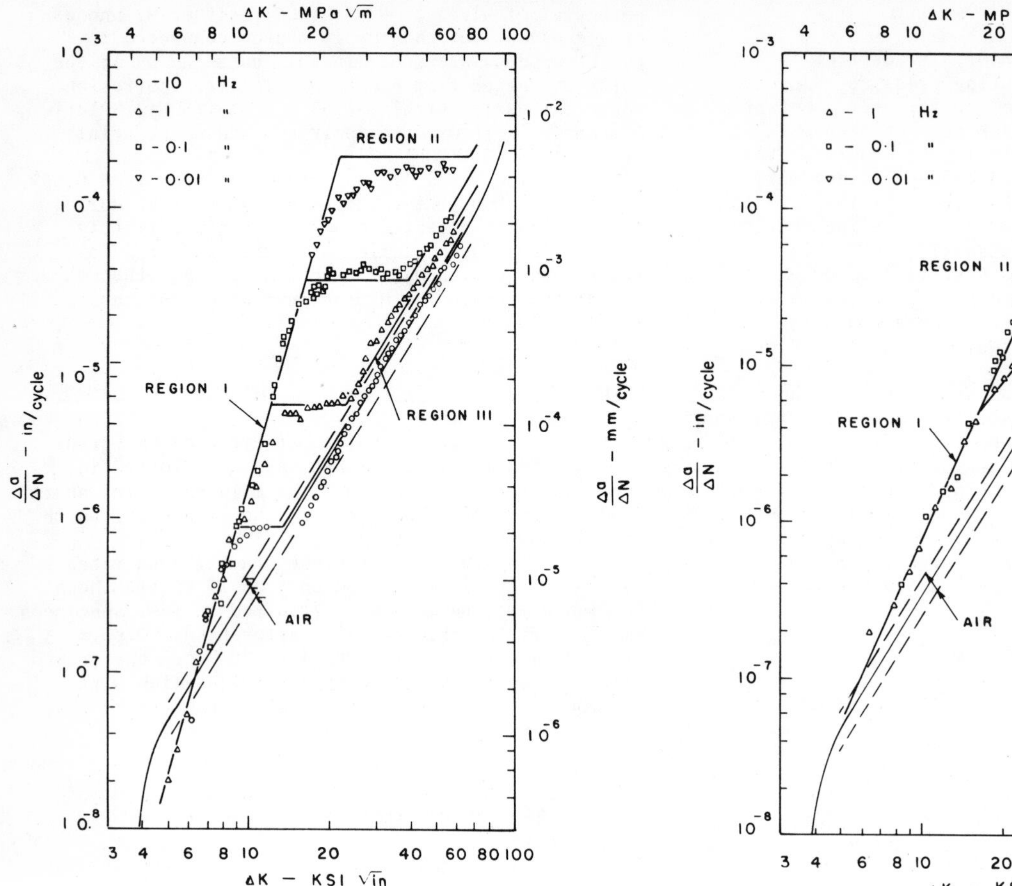

Figure 2: Fatigue crack growth rates in 3.5% salt water at -1.04 V(SCE) and four frequencies.

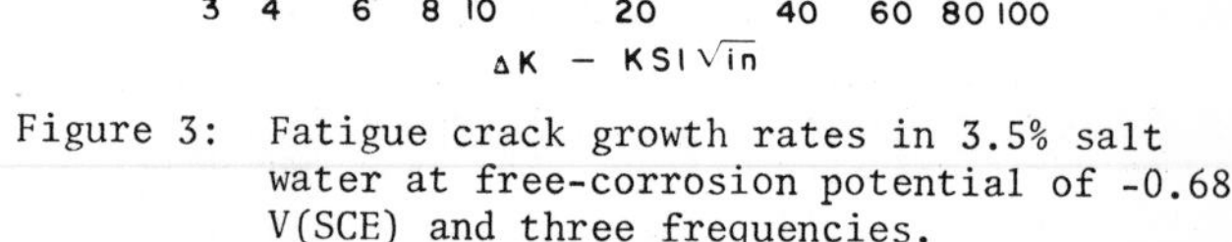

Figure 3: Fatigue crack growth rates in 3.5% salt water at free-corrosion potential of -0.68 V(SCE) and three frequencies.

falls abruptly to an apparent threshold at ΔK = 4.4 MPa√m. Above this range, the growth rate increases faster as the plane stress condition is approached. The data for lower frequencies follow the upper limit of the scatter-band, and there appears to be no significant effect of frequency in air.

The crack growth rates in 3.5% NaCℓ solution are presented in Figures 2 to 4, together with reference data from air. The effect of frequency is shown in Figures 2 and 3 at the Zn cathodic potential (-1.04 V) and under free corrosion (-0.68 V(SCE) respectively. In both cases, in the lower ΔK range, designated region I, the data for all frequencies fall on common straight lines converging to the threshold in air. A complex frequency effect appears at higher ΔK. At certain growth rates, which are the same for both potentials, the curves for single frequencies deviate from the common lines and start to converge on the air growth-rate curve -- region II. As a result, the maximum environmental acceleration of crack growth occurs at a mid-range ΔK, and shifts to higher ΔK with decreasing frequency. Maximum increases in growth rates for the Zn potential compared to those in air are 40x, 15x, 6x, and 3x for 0.01, 0.1, 1 and 10 Hz respectively. For free corrosion the corresponding increases are, on the average, about one-third these rates.

The rate of convergence to the air data in region II is much faster for the Zn potential. Under this condition, the growth rates remain practically constant up to a point slightly above the air growth rates, and past this they follow the air data -- region III. For free corrosion, the rate of convergence increases with decreasing frequency.

The effect of electrochemical potential on growth rates at 0.1 Hz is presented in Figure 4. The results show that the occurrence of a plateau in region II is typical only of the Zn potential. At the lower Mg potential of -1.43 V(SCE), the growth rates in region I coincide with those for the Zn potential. In region II they converge toward the free-corrosion growth rates. An anodic potential of -0.5 V(SCE) produced the same growth rates as free corrosion.

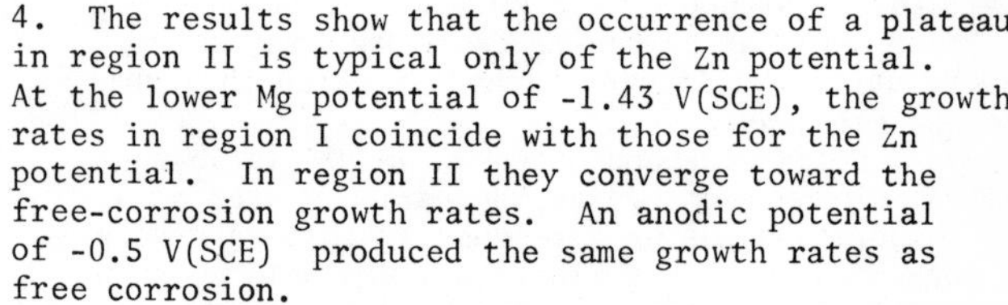

To investigate the effect of water without sodium chloride, one test was run in distilled water at a frequency of 0.1 Hz and at the free-corrosion potential. The results are plotted in Figure 5, together with the curve for salt water at the same frequency and the air scatter-band. It can be seen that the growth rates with and without chloride are identical.

The crack growth rates in sour crude oil with low (∿ 1 ppm) and high (4,700 ppm) H_2S content are presented in Figure 6. The results show a predominant effect of hydrogen sulphide. In crude oil with low H_2S content, the growth rates in the low ΔK range are lower than in air. This indicates that crude oil alone inhibits the crack growth at low ΔK and shifts the threshold to a higher ΔK value. Frequency affects growth rate in a similar way to salt water at free corrosion, but to much less a degree. Compared to air, maximum acceleration of growth rate in low H_2S crude oil is only half of that in salt water under free corrosion at the same frequency (0.1 Hz).

In crude oil saturated with H_2S, contrary to the results in other environments, the high acceleration of growth rate persists up to high ΔK and is affected by frequency only at high stress

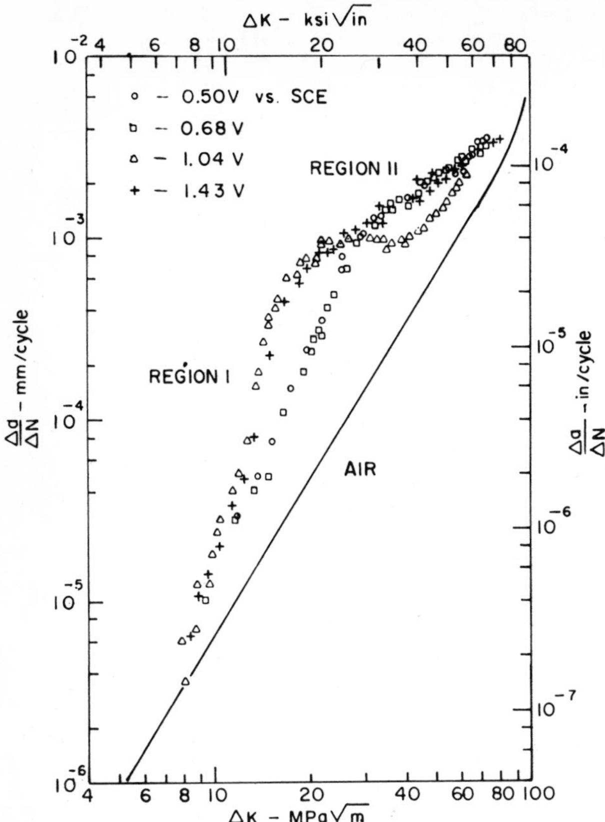

Figure 4: Fatigue crack growth rates in 3.5% salt water at 0.1 Hz and four electrochemical potentials.

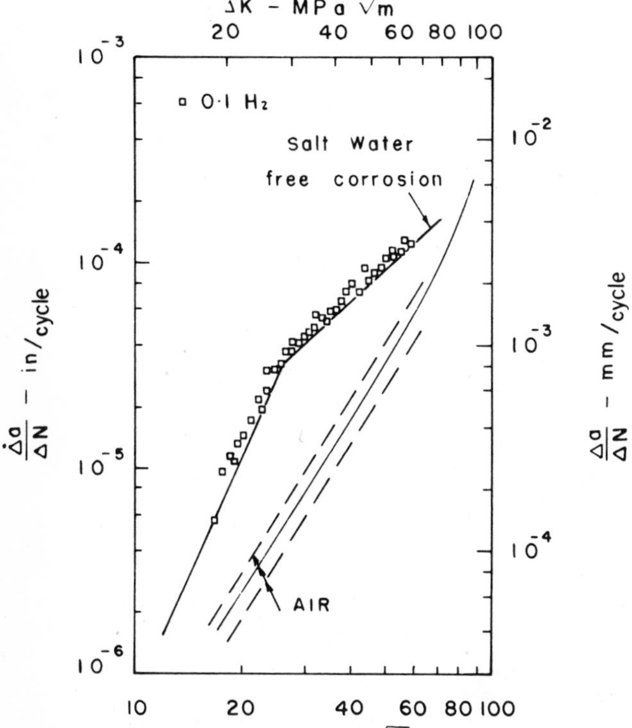

Figure 5: Fatigue crack growth rate in distilled water at free-corrosion and frequency 0.1 Hz. [The solid line for 3.5% salt water at free corrosion is redrawn from Figure 3].

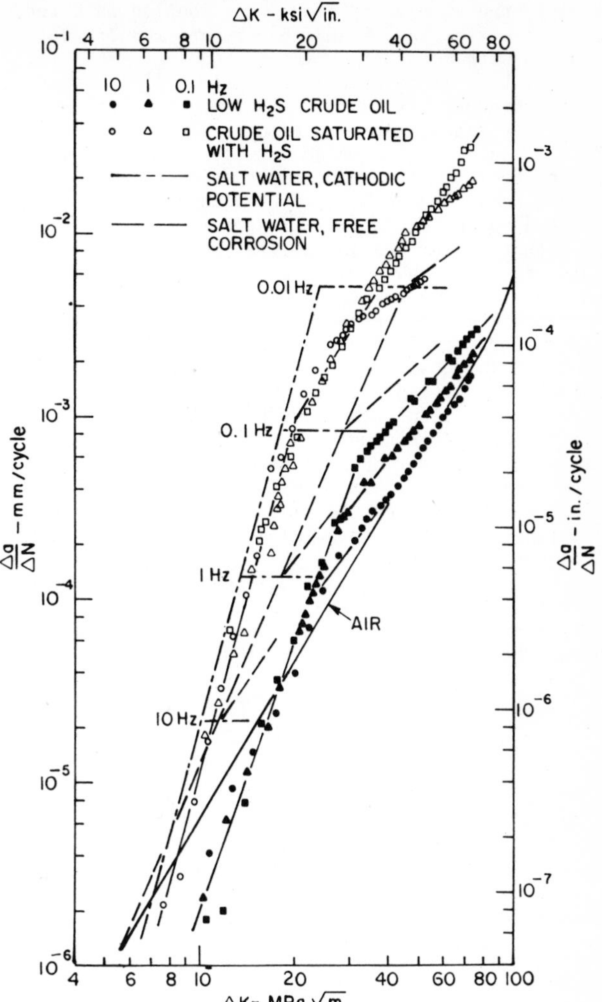

Figure 6: Fatigue crack growth rates in crude oil with two levels of H_2S content at three frequencies.

intensities. The growth rate curve exhibits a frequency independent decrease in slope at a growth rate of 10^{-3} mm/c. From this value and above, the curve is parallel to the air data, and the crack grows 20 times faster than in air.

DISCUSSION

These results show that under cyclic loading the enhancement of subcritical crack growth by conventional environments can be substantial, even in a low yield strength steel like Grade X65. In sour crude oil with a high content of hydrogen sulphide, or in salt water under cathodic potential at low frequency, the increase in growth rates, compared to air, is more than one order of magnitude. Judging from the identical growth rates in distilled and salt water under free corrosion, various ground waters can be expected to accelerate crack growth in a similar way.

These observations indicate that environmental enhancement of subcritical crack growth should be taken into consideration during design and inspection, as it is in the case of high- strength steels. For example, by applying the growth rates in H_2S-saturated crude oil (Figure 6) to an 860 mm diameter pipeline of 7.1 mm wall thickness, a 1 mm deep initial crack can be expected to grow to the critical size for failure after about 400 full pressure cycles.

However, the stress amplitude distribution in a real pipeline may be random and the present results were acquired with constant amplitude loading. So, in order to be able to make a realistic prediction of cycle-dependent crack growth in a pipeline, either the growth rates under representative random load spectra would have to be acquired or a correlation between growth rates under constant amplitude and random loading would have to be found. Barsom (9) reported for bridge steels identical growth rates for both types of loading if, in the case of random amplitude, the growth rates were plotted against the root mean square of the ΔK population.

The crack growth rates in salt water under Zn and free-corrosion potentials, as shown in Figures 2 and 3, can be approximated by region I and II segments of straight lines, or mathematically as power-law functions of ΔK and frequency (10). The only frequency-dependent plateau in the growth rate curves appears, for unknown reasons, only at the Zn potential. At lower cathodic potentials, Figure 4, the curve exhibits the same shape as at the free-corrosion or anodic potential, and this shape seems to be typical.

If the deviations at high frequencies are neglected in Figure 6, the growth rate curve in crude oil saturated with H_2S consists of two segments, and can be described by the following equations:

$$\Delta a/\Delta N = 9 \times 10^{-12} (\Delta K)^{6.2} \text{ for } \Delta K < 20 \text{ MPa}\sqrt{m}$$

and

$$\Delta a/\Delta N = 2 \times 10^{-7} (\Delta K)^{2.8} \text{ for } \Delta K > 20 \text{ MPa}\sqrt{m}$$

In crude oil with a low sulphide content, the growth-rate curves exhibit the typical ΔK and frequency dependence, but the increase in growth rates is not too significant.

A comparison of crack growth rates in both media is made in Figure 6, where the essential parts of the curves for salt water at Zn and free-corrosion potentials from Figures 2 and 3 are redrawn. The comparison demonstrates the complex effects of environment and frequency. The general feature shown by all curves is the frequency-dependent change of slope, or region I and II behaviour. The only exception is the growth-rate curve in sulphide-saturated crude oil. There, the frequency dependent change of slope appears only at high growth rates and is preceded by another frequency-independent change of slope in region I. The region I growth rates in sulphide-saturated crude oil are only slightly lower than those in salt water under the Zn potential. The difference can be attributed to the inhibitive effect of plain crude oil.

Examination of fractures in both environments (10-11) revealed cleavage-like transgranular cracking through favourably oriented grains, and distinct brittle striations with a wider spacing than the corresponding macroscopic growth rate. In air, or in cases where the environmental acceleration of growth was small, ductile striations predominated.

Fractographic findings, together with the fact that the highest increases in growth rates were measured under conditions promoting charging by hydrogen (cathodic potential or high H_2S content), indicate that hydrogen embrittlement is responsible for the growth rate enhancement. Considerable increases in fatigue crack growth rates can be found also in pure hydrogen gas, as reported by Nelson (6) and Clark (5) for low- and medium-strength steels. In media with a high hydrogen charging ability, such as crude oil saturated with H_2S, substantial acceleration of crack growth persists, even at high frequencies. In media with a lower hydrogen charging propensity like salt water, the embrittlement process is far more time or frequency dependent, and a high growth rate enhancement is achieved only at low cyclic frequencies. The convergence of the growth rate curves to the threshold in air indicates that a certain amount of plastic strain at the crack tip is required for hydrogen to interfere with the fracture process.

CONCLUSIONS

The following conclusions have been drawn from this study of the effects of conventional environments and cyclic frequency on fatigue crack growth in X65 line-pipe steel.

Environments like 3.5% salt water, water, or sour crude oil containing hydrogen sulphide, considerably increase the rate of crack growth under cyclic loading. Maximum enhancement of growth rates occurs at intermediate and high stress intensity ranges, but close to the threshold in air the environmental effects are almost negligible.

Crack growth rates in salt water are strongly affected by cyclic frequency and electrochemical potential. The highest increase in growth rate (40 times that in air) was measured at a cathodic potential and at the lowest frequency used, 0.01 Hz.

In crude oil saturated with H_2S the maximum increase in growth rate has been slightly lower (20 times that in air), but persisted over a wide range of stress intensity ranges and frequencies. The results in crude oil with a low H_2S content have indicated that in a low ΔK range plain crude oil has an inhibitive effect on crack growth.

The fatigue crack growth-rate curves in all environments tested exhibit a general pattern in shape and can be described by simple power-law equations as a function of ΔK and frequency.

Acknowledgement

The author is grateful to L. P. Trudeau for helpful consultations during the course of this work and for comments on the manuscript.

REFERENCES

1. J. P. Gallagher and R. P. Wei, Proceedings, International Conference on Corrosion Fatigue, NACE, 1972, pp. 409-423.
2. T. W. Crooker and E. A. Lange, Welding J. Res. Suppl., 1967, vol. 46, pp. 322-328.
3. J. P. Gallagher, J. Materials, 1971, vol. 6, (4), pp. 941-964.
4. J. M. Barsom, J. Eng. Fracture Mechanics, 1971, vol. 3, (1), pp. 15-25.
5. W. G. Clark, Jr., "The Effect of Hydrogen Gas on the Fatigue Crack Growth Rate Behaviour of HY-80 and HY-130 Steels", ASM/CMU Conf. on Hydrogen in Metals, Champion, Pennsylvania, Sept. 1973.
6. H. G. Nelson, "Hydrogen-Induced Slow Crack Growth of a Plain Carbon Pipeline Steel Under Conditions of Cyclic Loading", Conf. on the "Effect of Hydrogen on Behaviour of Materials", AIME, Jackson, Wyoming, 1975.
7. O. Vosikovsky, "Determination of Fatigue Crack Growth Rate by the Potential Drop Method: Set-up and Calibration", Dept. Energy, Mines and Resources,

CANMET, Report ERP/PMRL-75-15(R), 1975.

8. W. F. Brown and J. E. Srawley, "Plane Strain Crack Toughness Testing of High-Strength Metallic Materials", ASTM STP410, 1966.
9. J. M. Barsom, "Fatigue-Crack Growth under Variable-Amplitude Loading in Various Bridge Steels", Symposium on Fatigue Crack Growth under Spectrum Loads, ASTM, Montreal 1975.
10. O. Vosikovsky, J. Eng. Materials and Technology, Trans. ASME 1975, vol. 97, pp. 298-304.
11. O. Vosikovsky, Corrosion, 1976, vol. 32, pp. 472-475.

DISCUSSION

E. C. Hamre (Interprovincial Steel and Pipe): It is interesting to note the combined effect of two factors which individually may not present any particular problems but in combination may be very significant. Would it be possible to relate the data presented in the paper to real operating pipelines; specifically with various depth defects? What would be the effect of very slow cycling, since the greatest difference was observed at 0.01 Hz?

O. Vosikovsky: An example of the number of cycles required to grow a long, constant depth, inside axial crack of different initial depths, a_i, to failure is given in Table 1 for four cyclic hoop stress ranges, $\Delta\sigma$. The analysis was made for a 34 in. (860 mm) x 0.281 in. (7.1 mm) pipeline made of X52 steel, using the growth rates in H_2S-saturated crude oil (Figure 6) under the assumption that crack growth rates in X52 and X65 steels are identical. The critical crack depth for failure was chosen to be 4 mm. Minimum initial crack lengths for which the cyclic lines are given correspond to ΔK of approximately 5 $MPa\sqrt{m}$, a value slightly above the threshold in air. For example, it requires 734 cyclces from zero to operational pressure, to extend a 1 mm initial crack to the critical size of 4 mm. For X65 steel under the same conditions only about 400 cycles are required.

As X65 steel is immune to stress corrosion under static load in salt water, the environmental attack has to peak at a certain low frequency and then drop. Gallagher (3) found for HY80 steel, some indication that environmental attack levels off at a frequency of 0.01 Hz.

Table 1

Cycles to Failure of an X52 Pipeline for Various Stress ranges and Initial crack depths

a_i (mm)	$\Delta\sigma$ = 0.1 SMYS*	$\Delta\sigma$ = 0.2 SMYS	$\Delta\sigma$ = 0.4 SMYS	$\Delta\sigma$ = 0.72 SMYS
0.1				114,970
0.2				28,970
0.3			645,930	12,070
0.4			300,930	6,370
0.5			177,930	3,862
0.6			111,930	2,524
0.7			70,930	1,743
0.8			45,330	1,243
0.9			29,430	930
1.0		1,490,810	19,720	734
1.2		690,810	9,720	514
1.4		333,810	4,720	382
1.6		166,810	2,520	282
1.8		83,810	1,440	208
2.0		41,810	907	153
2.2	1,647,500	21,210	640	112
2.4	831,500	10,710	473	82
2.6	423,500	5,410	335	59
2.8	206,500	2,630	242	41
3.0	101,500	1,200	172	28

* SMYS = 52 ksi (360 MPa)

H. C. Cotton (British Petroleum): I overheard a gentleman over here ask, "How many cycles are there in a pipeline, anyway?" Well, I would estimate that a well-run pipeline which never comes off stream would experience about 200 stress cycles in a 30-year period. I am not sure, therefore, that you are simulating a real-life situation. Of course, if you happen to have an anode nearby which is as big as your pipeline and 3% sodium chloride is poured over it at regular intervals you may have a problem. I believe your conditions of testing are unduly severe.

R. J. Cooke (National Energy Board): Mr. Cotton's concern about the feasibility of corrosion fatigue crack propagation ever occurring in a crude oil pipeline appeared to be specifically related to the Alyeska pipeline and the low number of significant pressure fluctuations this particular pipeline is estimated to experience in service. While such an argument is very likely valid for this case, in view of its fixed operating conditions and constant throughput, some reservation should be expressed about more conventional crude oil lines presently operating in North America. A large diameter crude oil pipeline in Canada has experienced three service and one re-test failure in recent years, after five years of operation. The failures were attributed to the initiation and propagation of corrosion fatigue cracks at the inside toe of the longitudinal weld. This pipeline, unlike the Alyeska pipeline, transports a number of different crude types in batches (including ones containing significant amounts of H_2S) and supplies a large number of refineries whose demands may change. In addition, it is subject to hydraulic effects related to its looped configuration and may experience automatic control variability. All of these factors make such a pipeline subject to a significant number of pressure fluctuations.

D. J. Burns (University of Waterloo): How can you be sure that your failures are due to corrosion fatigue, and not just corrosion?

O. Vosikovsky: The fracture surfaces on X65 showed very clear striations.

WIDE-FLANGE BEAMS FOR LOW TEMPERATURE SERVICE

H. Gondoh, N. Eguchi, S. Ishimori
and T. Haze
Nippon Steel Corporation
Kimitsu-City, Chiba 299-11
Japan

The application of controlled rolling has recently made it possible to economically produce wide-flange beams for use in Arctic conditions as members of pipelines, buildings, bridges, storage tanks, etc. The wide-flange beams reviewed here are mainly of junior size, made of high-tensile steel, with a yield point which exceeds 345 MPa on account of the precipitation hardening and grain refinement due to V and Nb (Cb), and excellent low temperature toughness with 50% FATT in the range -60°C to -120°C. Low temperature brittle fracture bend tests on full-scale welded beams revealed a good agreement between the brittle fracture behaviour and theoretical design curves.

INTRODUCTION

In recent years, many energy development projects have been initiated in frigid climatic regions. These projects require construction of long pipelines, bridges, buildings, liquified gas storage tanks and their accessory structures, for which large tonnages of wide-flange beams are required. Wide-flange beams for these applications should be of high-strength steels having good weldability and high toughness at low temperature. Conventional wide-flange beams do not satisfy these requirements, so new products specially designed for low-temperature applications must be developed.

Wide-flange beams for low-temperature service can be produced by three methods: 1) normalizing hot-rolled wide-flange beams to develop uniform fine-grained structure; 2) fabricating high-strength steel plate with good weldability and high toughness at low temperature; 3) controlled rolling.

The first two methods are complex and uneconomical. The controlled rolling method is a recently-developed process for the manufacture of high-strength steel plate with good notch toughness. This process is extensively applied to the manufacture of plate for pipes, tanks and similar items, but it has not yet been applied to the production of wide-flange beams because the rolling procedures are complex and require precise temperature control.

Based on extensive experience in research on the manufacture of high-strength steels, we have established an economical process for the manufacture of wide-flange beams for low-temperature use, with controlled rolling on a new continuous rolling mill.

The influence of heating and rolling temperatures was investigated on several types of high-strength low-alloy steels containing precipitation hardening elements. Product properties were analyzed from the standpoint of rolling and metallurgical engineering. A full-size beam was also subjected to a low-temperature brittle fracture test.

Recently many studies have been made on the brittle fracture behaviour of high-strength steels. The following parameters have been used to describe the dynamic condition at crack tips: 1) stress intensity factor; 2) crack opening displacement (C.O.D.); 3) tensile plastic zone size; 4) J-integral. Of these, the stress intensity factor is limited to fracture by small-scale yielding and the others are applicable to large-scale yielding. For these studies the C.O.D. has been adopted, since it seemed most directly related to practice.

TEST SPECIMENS

The wide-flange beams tested came in (mm) sizes of (H 250 x 125 x 6/9), (H 400 x 200 x 8/13)*, (H 400 x 400 x 13/21), and (H 400 x 400 x 20/35), of which sizes (H 400 x 200) and smaller were rolled at the Nippon Steel Kimitsu Works, and the heavy sizes of (H 400 x 400) were rolled on the wide-flange mills at the Hirohata Works.

The chemical analysis of the test steels is shown in Table 1. Steel A is semi-killed; steels B and J are Al-killed commercial grades; the other test steels are 1.25 to 1.5% Mn-Al-killed (trace of Ni and Cu) low-temperature service steels in which V and Nb(Cb) are added singly or in combination. In all of these, the carbon equivalent is invariably 0.4% or less.

(H 250 x 125 x 6/9) C1 to H (excepting D and G) steels and the (H 400 x 400) steel K were subjected to controlled rolling for precipitation hardening and grain refining. Some of the steels were normalized at 900°C for 30 min. The (H 400 x 200 x 8/13) beam was prepared for a full-scale low-

* See Figure 11 for an example of this dimension terminology.

Table 1 Chemical composition of test steels* (Wt%)

Test steels	C	Si	Mn	Nb	V	Ni	Cu	Other alloys	Al	Ceq.**
A	0.27	0.04	0.36	--	--	--	--	--	--	0.33
B	0.11	0.27	1.23	--	--	--	--	--	0.022	0.33
C1	0.12	0.27	1.23	--	0.06	--	--	--	0.026	0.34
C2	0.13	0.24	1.38	--	0.05	0.24	0.23	--	0.024	0.38
D	0.12	0.27	1.24	0.05	--	--	--	--	0.028	0.34
E	0.11	0.23	1.39	0.05	0.05	0.24	--	--	0.031	0.36
F	0.08	0.26	1.56	0.05	0.06	0.22	--	--	0.032	0.36
G	0.06	0.26	1.56	0.05	0.04	--	--	--	0.034	0.34
H	0.06	0.26	1.57	0.05	--	--	--	--	0.028	0.33
I	0.06	0.25	1.52	0.05	--	--	--	0.17	0.030	0.37
J	0.08	0.26	1.32	--	--	--	--	--	0.011	0.31
K	0.12	0.25	1.40	--	0.06	0.21	0.17	0.20	0.026	0.41

* Total of P, S: Less than 0.04%

** Ceq.(%) = C(%) + Mn/6(%) + Si/24(%) + Ni/40(%) + Cr/5(%) + Mo/4(%) + V/14(%)

temperature bend test.

TENSILE PROPERTIES

For tensile tests, specimens of 200 mm gauge length were taken from the locations shown in Figure 1. Tables 2 and 3 show the tensile properties of as-rolled and normalized test steels. All steels, except A, B and J satisfied the ASTM-A 441-74 specifications (YS: min. 345 MPa; TS: min. 485 MPa; elongation: min. 18%). They also met the provisions of ASTM-A 537-74a and A633-72 (normalized steel) which specify similar mechanical properties. The yield point and tensile strength of (H 250 x 125 x 6/9) controlled-rolled beams were clearly increased by the addition of V and Nb(Cb). A yield point rise was particularly notable in the Nb(Cb)-added steels. Steels E, F and G, with combinations of Nb(Cb) and V, exhibited the highest yield ratios.

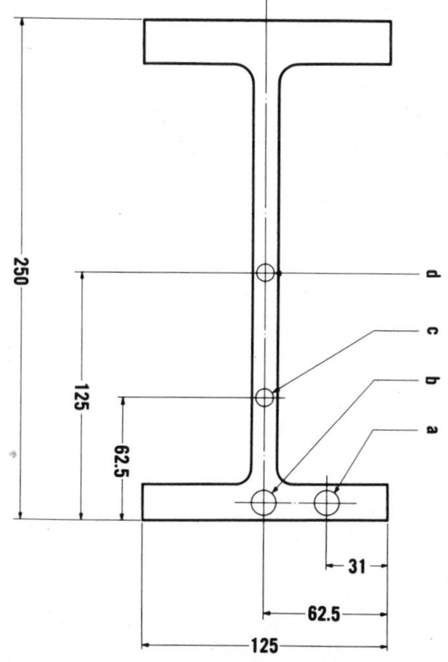

Figure 1: Sampling positions for tensile and Charpy V-notch impact tests (dimensions in mm).

Wide-flange beams have somewhat different mechanical properties depending on their cross sections. Generally, the web is stronger than the flange because the web is finished at comparatively lower temperatures during hot rolling.

MICROSTRUCTURE

Figure 2 shows the microstructures of longitudinal sections taken from the mid-point of the flange thickness. With every specimen, the pearlitic structure is seen stretched in the rolling direction in a fibrous pattern. With the addition of V, the ferritic grains are somewhat refined, and by the combination of Nb(Cb) addition and controlled rolling, they are further refined to ASTM grain size 11 or 12. In Ni-bearing steels E and F, the pearlitic structure is more extensively dispersed than in the other steels.

WELDABILITY

y-Groove Cracking Test

200 x 150 mm specimens were taken from C2 and E steel flanges for y-groove cracking tests (JIS Z 3158-(1966), the so-called "TEKKEN" type y-groove cracking test). Welding conditions were: "L-60" (JIS D 5816, corresponding to AWS E-8016-G), a 4 mm coated electrode wire for high-tensile steel; 170 A; 24 V; 150 mm/min. The welding was conducted at both 15°C and 50°C.

The welding produced neither root cracks nor surface cracks. In y-groove cracking tests the crack sensitivity of the base metal is critically evaluated, to such an extent that under normal welding conditions weld cracks are unlikely with this newly-developed steel.

Maximum Hardness in Weld HAZ

Specimens were cut from the flange of each steel beam in sizes 200 x 75 mm and tested for maximum hardness in the weld heat-affected zone (JIS Z 3101 [1972]). Welding was done at 170 A; 24 V;

Table 2 Tensile Properties and 50% FATT of Test Steels

Steel	Dimension (mm)	Sampling position	As rolled						Normalized				
			Rolling method*	Yield strength MPa	Tensile strength MPa	Elongation %	Yield ratio %	50% FATT °C	Yield strength MPa	Tensile strength MPa	Elongation %	Yield ratio %	50% FATT °C
A	H 250 x 125 x 6/9	a	OR	274	437	26	62	+20					
		c		322	428	28	75	-20					
B		a	CR	308	458	30	67	-60	307	432	28	71	-80
		b						-55					
		c		336	449	27	75	-70					
		d						-70					
C1		a	CR	360	487	29	74	-75					
		c						-90					
C2		a	CR	371	517	27	72	-60	355	493	26	72	-90
		c		442	507	28	87	-100					
D		a	OR	437	525	26	82	-80					
		c		430	517	25	83	-100					
E		a	CR	505	578	25	88	-95	418	518	26	81	-130
		b						-70					
		c		522	604	23	87	-90					
		d						-70					
F	H 250 x 125 x 6/9	a	CR	511	578	23	89	-90	415	505	26	82	-140
		c		546	615	22	89	-90					
G		a	OR	458	516	25	89	-110					
		c		490	544	25	90	-120					
H		a	CR	454	520	26	87	-120					
		c		454	510	26	89	-120					
C2	H 400 x 200 x 8/13	a	OR	416	533	29	78	-35					
		c		450	550	25	82	-45					
G		a	OR	453	544	25	83	-55					
		c		495	552	25	90	-60					
I		a	OR	392	556	25	71	-10					
		c		396	569	25	70	-40					
J	H 400 x 400 x 20/35	a	OR	260	414	38	63	-45	283	414	33	68	-75
		b		253	423	42	60	-35					
		c		273	412	35	66	-45					
K		a	OR	377	514	33	73	-35	350	506	35	69	-70
		b		355	524	37	60	-30					
		c		378	520	27	73	-35					

*CR = controlled rolling; OR = ordinary rolling

and 150 mm/min using "N-11", a coated electrode wire (low hydrogen type) for high-tensile steel (corresponding to AWS F 7016-G), and Vickers hardness was measured across the weld section. Under the same conditions, Al-killed 1% Mn steel was welded using "G-200", a coated electrode (ilmenite type), and post-welding hardness was compared with the newly-developed steels. The test results shown in Figure 3 reveal that with the increase in Ceq and thickness of flange, the maximum hardness level increases. The maximum hardness of C2 steel (with the highest Ceq) was Hv 270. The maximum hardness depends on both the size of the wide-flange beams and welding conditions.

Table 3 Tensile properties and 50% FATT of heavy beams

Steel	Dimension mm	Sampling position	50% FATT °C	Yield strength MPa	Tensile strength MPa	Elongation %
J	H 400 x 400 x 13/21	a	-65	303	430	34
		b	-50	275	422	44
		c	-45	345	440	32
K		a	-65	400	510	30
		b	-60	385	530	38
		c	-70	410	530	26

Charpy V-notch Energy

At position "a" (Figure 1), a groove of the AWS TC-L4a type was prepared and welding was then performed at 175 A; 24 V; 150 mm/min, with 4 passes and 2,000 J/mm heat input using "N-11", a 4 mm electrode wire (drying temperature: 375°C; drying time: 1 h). Next, 7.5 x 10 x 55 mm Charpy V-notch impact test pieces were taken longitudinally from the HAZ and the weld metal and were tested at -46°C. The results are summarized in Figure 4. In addition, Figure 5 presents impact transition curves for each weld location in steel F.

These results indicate that the Charpy V-notch energy of each test steel is higher in the HAZ than in the base metal, which is consistent with the concept of heating-induced normalizing as revealed in the hardness distribution in Figure 6.

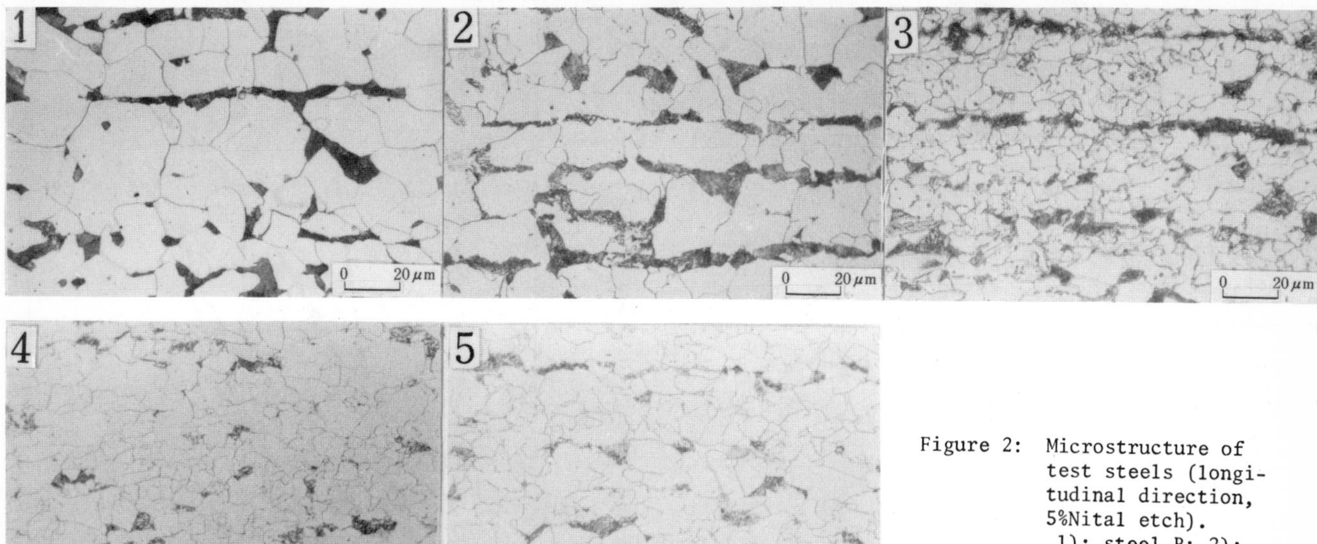

Figure 2: Microstructure of test steels (longitudinal direction, 5%Nital etch).
1): steel B; 2): steel C2; 3): steel E; 4) steel F; 5): steel G

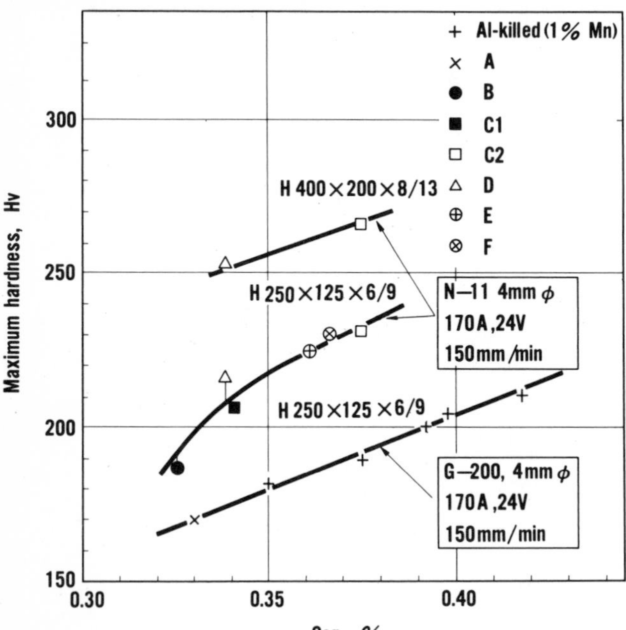

Figure 3: Maximum hardness in weld heat-affected zone

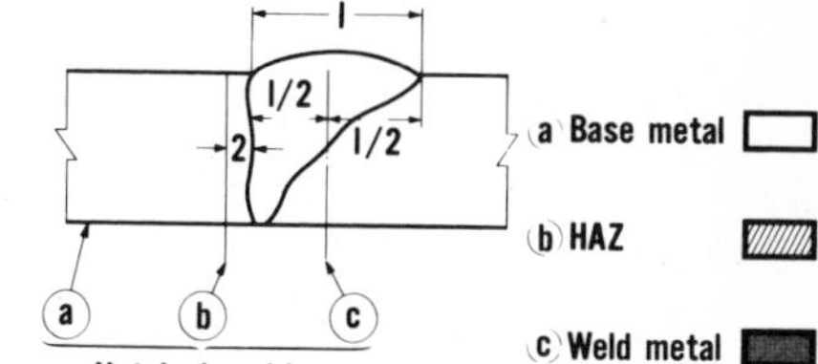

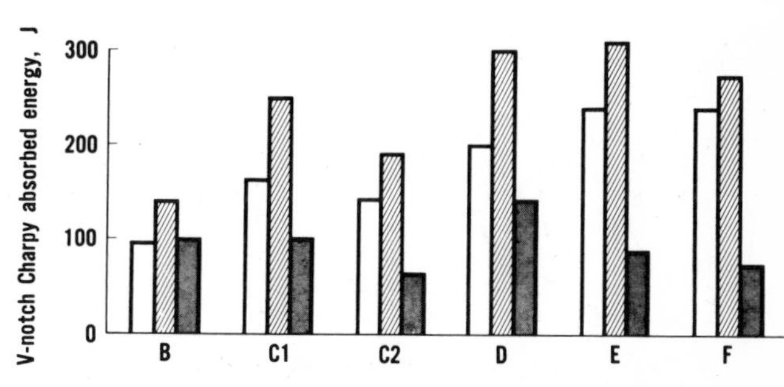

Figure 4: Charpy V-notch energy in base metal, HAZ and weld metal (specimens, 7.5 x 10 x 55 mm).

LOW TEMPERATURE CHARACTERISTICS

Charpy V-Notch Impact Test

Charpy impact test pieces were sampled longitudinally from each of the locations shown in Figure 1 in sizes of 10 x 10 x 55 mm (2 mm V-notch) or (7.5, 5.0) x 10 x 55 mm (2 mm V-notch). Figure 7 gives the Charpy V-notch impact transition curves for each of the controlled-rolled H250 x 125 x 6/9 steel beams; Table 2 gives 50% fracture appearance transition temperatures (FATT). Compared with Al-killed steel B, increasing improvements in properties were notable in V-added steel C2, Nb(Cb)-added steel D, and V-Nb(Cb)-added steels E and F, in that order. Low C, high Mn-Nb(Cb) or Nb(Cb)-V type steels G and H exhibited particularly outstanding property improvement. Shelf energies increased appreciably when the carbon content of steels was 0.10% or less.

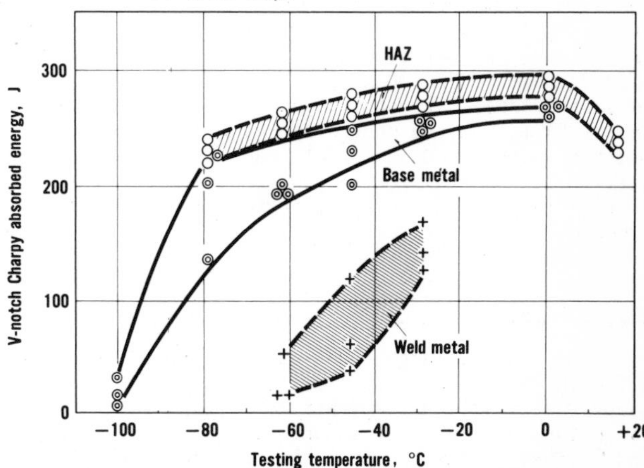

Figure 5: Charpy V-notch transition curves of welds in Steel F (Specimens 7.5 x 10 x 55 mm).

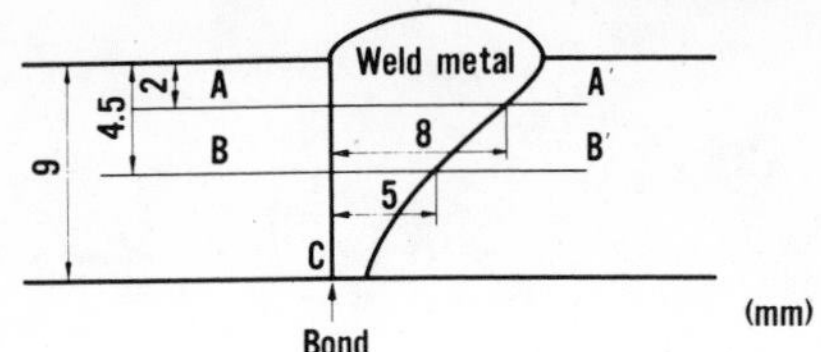

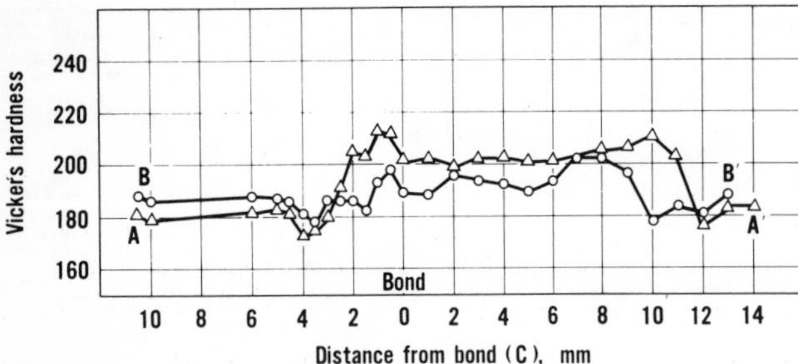

Figure 6: Vickers hardness transverses across weld in steel F.

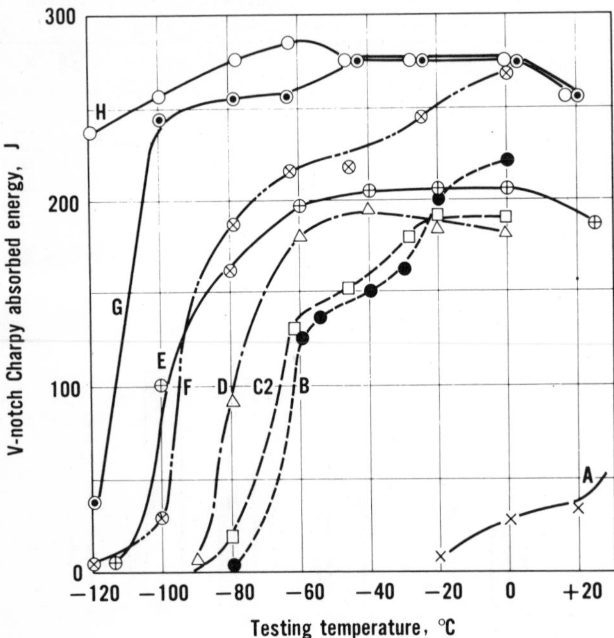

Figure 7: Charpy V-notch transition curves of test steels (H 250 x 125 x 6/9, Specimens 7.5 x 10 x 55 mm).

Figure 8 shows the results of the Charpy impact tests on as-rolled and normalized test pieces, taken from (H 400 x 400 x 20/35) beams. Table 2 provides 50% FATT at each of the sectional positions. The 50% FATT from the controlled rolling of specimens from the (H 400 x 400 x 13/21) beams is included in Table 3. Generally, the low temperature toughness of wide-flange beams varies with the flange thickness as shown in Figure 9.

Low Temperature Bend Test

Wide-flange beams of steels I, C2, G in the (H 400 x 200 x 8/13) size and with different Charpy-V transition temperatures (Figure 10) were bead-welded transversely on the tension side. The bonds (lines of fusion) were then notched with 40 mm long notches (tip radius 0.1 mm) as shown in Figure 11. They were then bent to fracture at test temperatures of 0°C, -46°C, -62°C and -79°C.

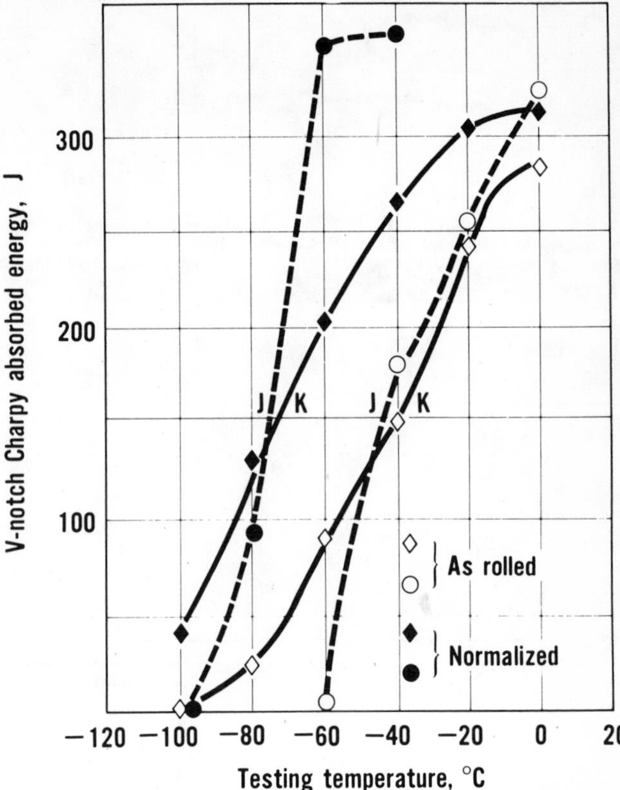

Figure 8: Charpy V-notch transition curves of Steels J and K (H 400 x 400 x 20/35, Specimens 10 x 10] 55 mm).

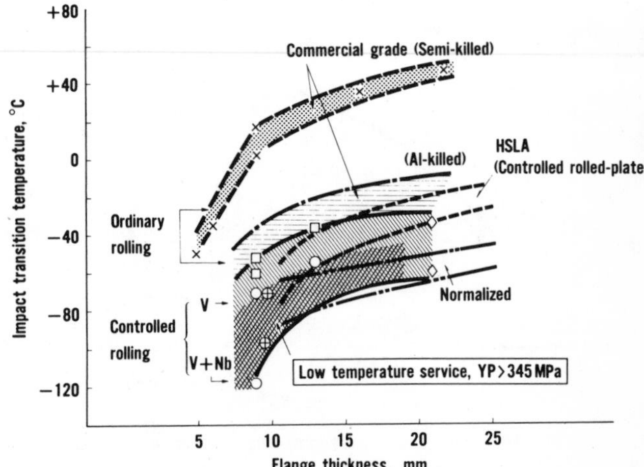

Figure 9: Relationships between Charpy V-notch transition temperature and flange thickness

In the bend tests, the opening displacements at the notch tips were measured by a clip gauge. The tension flange center surfaces at the points of loading and the notch surface were also measured for surface strain and deflection using a wire strain gauge and a dial gauge. Figure 12 shows deflection and displacement curves. As these curves indicate, every test steel exhibits ductile fracture at test temperatures of 0°C and -46°C, but fractures at -62°C and -79°C are mostly brittle.

Examples of fractures occurring in steel C2 at the test temperature of -46°C are shown in Figure 13. Evidently, the fractures initiate at the notch and propagate several millimeters from the weld metal.

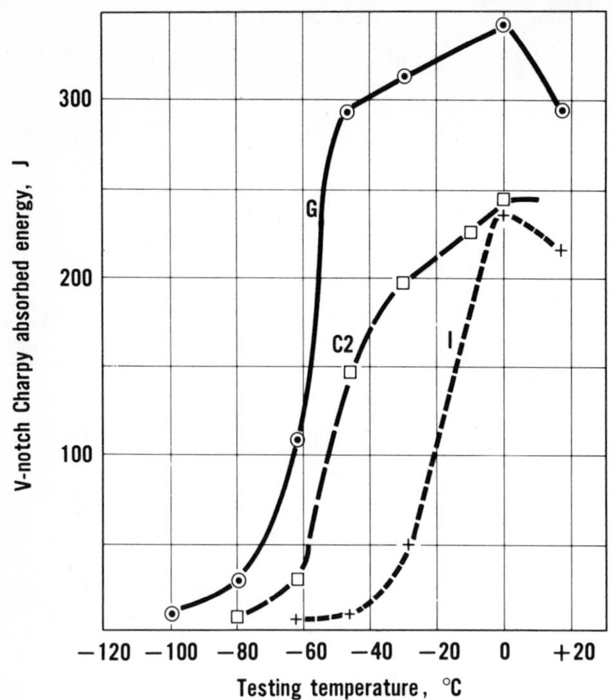

Figure 10: Charpy V-notch transition temperature curves of Steels G, C2 and I (H 400 x 200 x 8/13, Specimens 10 x 10 x 55 mm)

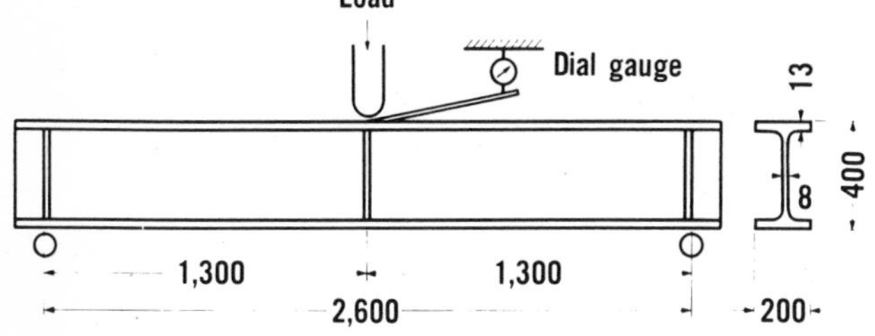

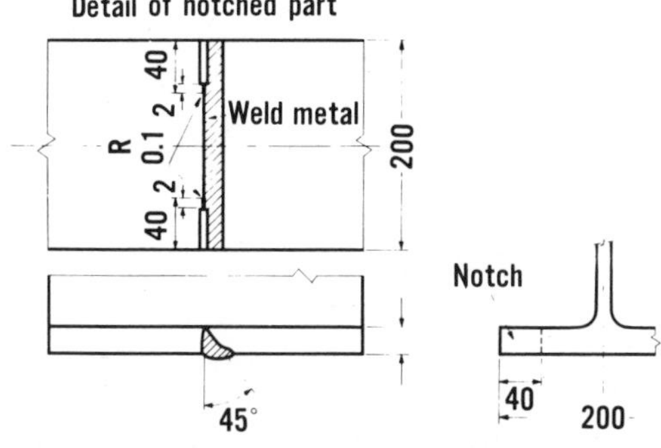

Figure 11: Geometry of low temperature bend specimens

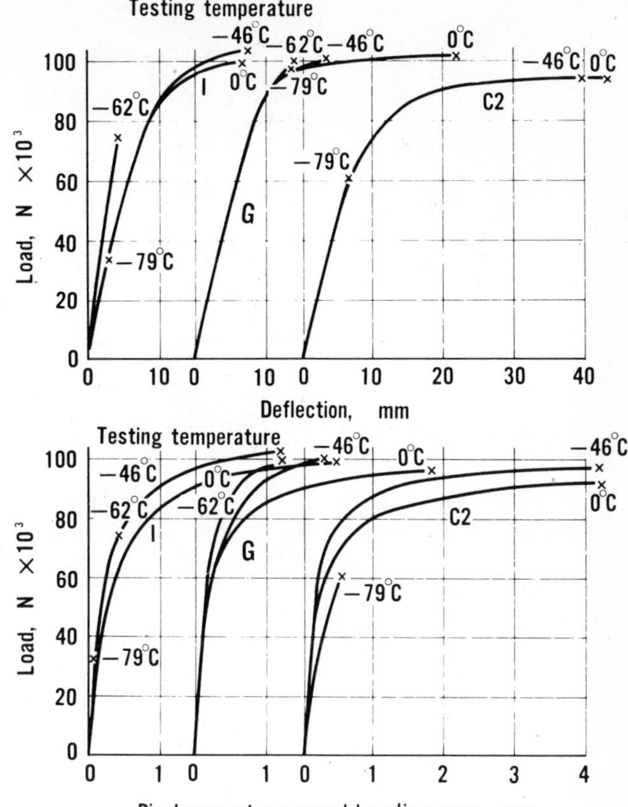

Figure 12: Load-deflection and displacement curves during low-temperature bend test. "x" = fracture

DISCUSSION

Effects of Composition and Rolling Conditions

Figure 14 shows the relationships between yield strength and Charpy-V transition temperature of high-strength low-alloy steels made by controlled rolling, reported by Irvine et al (1,2). The data include 0.05% and 0.17% carbon steels containing between 0.5% and 1.5% manganese, with some containing niobium (columbium).

When the present results are plotted on the same axes, ordinary rolled steels D, E and F fall in the 0.05% C and 1.5% Mn-Nb(Cb) steel region. Aluminum-killed steel B and the Nb(Cb)-free steel, C2, exhibit lower strength-ductility balances than the steels D, E and F. Controlled-rolling steels B and C2 moves their points in the direction of the dotted arrows, indicating improved strength-ductility balance. This improvement is thought to be the result of grain refinement by controlled rolling. A very good relationship exists between ferrite grain size and 50% FATT.

Criteria of Brittle Fracture

Relationships between non-dimensional crack opening displacement (COD) and strains, e/e_y, for every test steel were calculated from the COD values obtained in the full-scale bending tests, and are plotted in Figure 15, where e_y = YS/E, and (a) is the half-crack length (mm). A design curve proposed by Burdekin (3) is also shown in the Figure. The present test results are in good agreement with this design curve, with the exception of the 0°C and -46°C values where ductile fracture occurred.

Critical COD levels rise with temperature until a certain temperature level is exceeded. Then thumb-nail shaped cracks start at the notch root and develop into ductile fractures. The temperatures at which these cracks initiate (Ti) can be accurately evaluated from 50% FATT. Also, the COD values at which ductile cracks initiate (δi) are relatively independent of the measuring conditions, and are proportional to the yield point.

Values of Ti and δi were calculated as follows in a recent study (4):

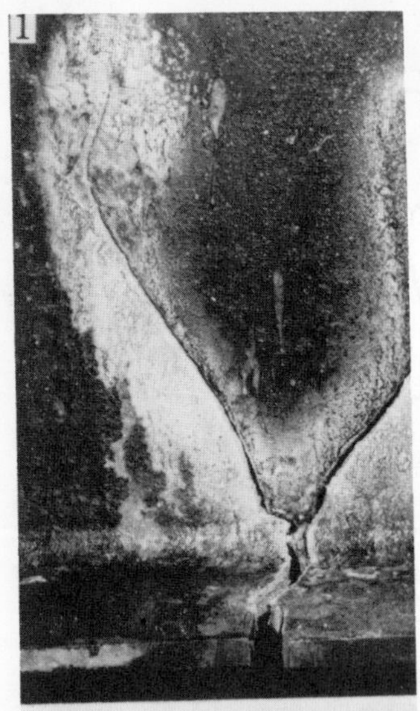

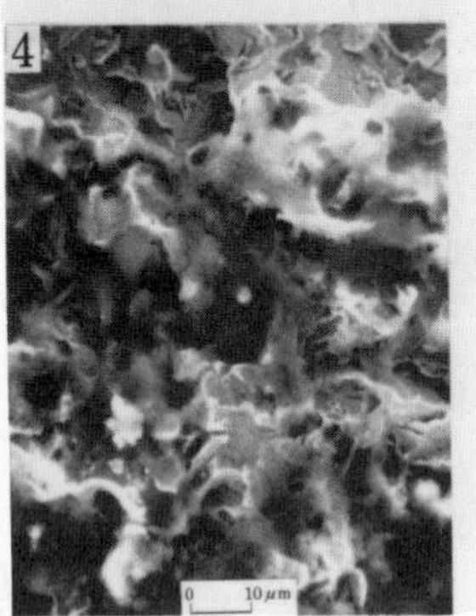

Figure 13:

Fracture of low temperature bend test piece (Steel C2, tested at -46°C). 1 and 2) Fracture appearance on beam tension side; 3) Fracture, showing initiation point at notch tip; 4) SEM fractograph

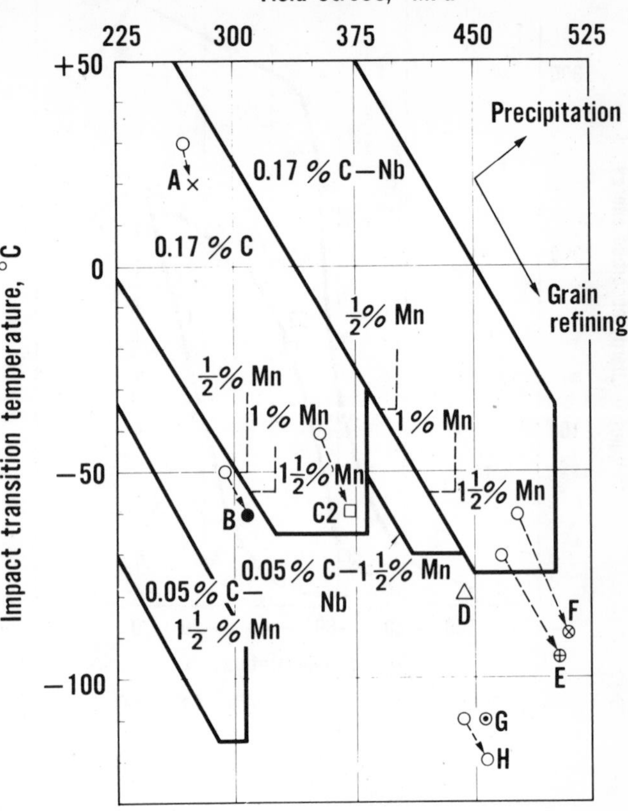

Figure 14: Effects of controlled-rolling and composition on yield stress and Charpy-V transition temperature (o = ordinary rolling; dotted arrow = effect of controlled rolling) (after refs 1 and 2)

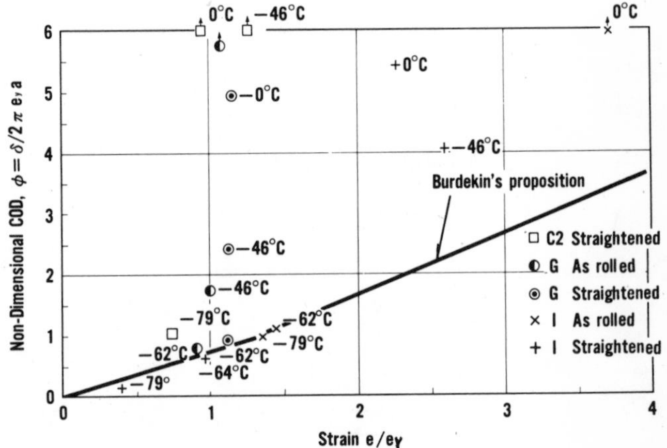

Figure 15: Relationship between COD and strain

Steel	Observed 50% FATT(°C)	Observed Ti(°C)	Calculated Ti(°C)	Calculated δi(mm)
C2	-30	-62	-78	0.33
G	-45	-79	-89	0.31
I	-10	-62	-62	0.34

The 50% FATT shown above are the values actually measured in the bond area. The observed temperatures are somewhat higher than the calculated ones, possibly due to the influence of the residual stresses resulting from welding and rolling.

SUMMARY

Wide-flange beams for low temperature service in Arctic conditions were studied for their mechanical properties and low temperature characteristics. The results are summarized as follows:

Regular Beams

a) When low C, high Mn, Al-killed steels with V and Nb(Cb) singly or in combination are controlled rolled, wide-flange beams with excellent low temperature toughness (345 MPa yield; -60°C, 50% FATT) can be economically produced. With suitable modified composition, steels for beams at much lower temperature service can be produced.

b) Weldability is excellent, Ceq being low.

c) On full-scale bending, the low temperature brittle fracture behaviour can be analysed by COD theory. The observed values were in good agreement with Burdekin's design curve.

Heavy Beams

a) Mechanical properties and low temperature toughness of heavy beams depend on flange thickness.

b) For 345 MPa yield wide-flange beams 50% FATT occurs at approximately -30°C on ordinary rolling, -60°C after controlled rolling, and -70°C after normalizing.

REFERENCES

1. F. B. Pickering, Proceedings, Microalloying '75, Union Carbide Corp.,New York, 1976, p. 9.
2. K. J. Irvine, Iron and Steel, 1971, vol. 44, p. 31; J. Iron Steel Inst. 1970, vol. 208, p. 717.
3. F. M. Burdekin and M. G. Daws, Proceedings, "Practical Application of Fracture Mechanics to Pressure Vessel Technology", p. 28, Inst. Mech. Engrs., 1971.
4. T. Kanazawa et al, Proceedings, International Conference on Prospects of Fracture Mechanics, Japan Welding Society, 1974, p. 547.

DISCUSSION

P. R. Slimmon (Bethlehem Steel): Controlled rolling of structural shapes marks another improvement in the processing of material. Nippon Steel Corporation is fortunate to have mills capable of this type of processing. What are the typical phosphorus and sulphur levels in your steels? Was inclusion shape control used?

N. Yurioka (on behalf of the authors): Typical levels of phosphorus and sulphur are 0.015% and 0.007% respectively.

P. R. Slimmon: In the paper it is mentioned that there is a wide variation in temperature between the web and flange during rolling of a shape. What part of the section is used as a control point for your aim finishing temperature?

N. Yurioka: The temperature difference between the web and flange is approximately 120 deg C at the finishing stage. A temperature control point is at the flange, which is the higher temperature part of a section.

P. R. Slimmon: Can you define the controlled-rolling practice more specifically in terms of heating and reduction below intermediate holding temperatures?

N. Yurioka: The intermediate holding time and temperature are tens of seconds and 950°C. After intermediate holding, average reduction of section is approximately 60%. The finishing temperature of control-rolled beams is less than 920°C, while that of conventional rolling is 980°C.

P. R. Slimmon: Did you control roll sections and then normalize them? Does this type of processing give improvements in toughness over conventionally rolled and normalized material?

N. Yurioka: The property of normalized steel shown in the presentation was obtained from conventionally rolled and then normalized beams. There is no significant difference between microstructures of conconventionally rolled steel and controlled-rolled steel once they are normalized.

MECHANICAL CRACK-ARRESTOR CONCEPTS FOR LINE-PIPE APPLICATIONS *

A. K. Shoemaker, R. F. McCartney
and K. D. Ives
U. S. Steel Corporation
Monroeville, Pennsylvania, 15146
USA

Analysis of full-scale tests of running-shear fractures in gas-transmission line pipe has shown the strain, deformation, and pressure distributions associated with a propagating shear crack. An understanding of this behaviour suggests several different means by which a propagating shear crack can be arrested by mechanical means rather than by providing sufficient ductility or toughness in the steel of the pipe itself. This paper summarizes these mechanical crack-arrestor concepts and describes tests which document their effectiveness.

A mechanical crack arrestor was fabricated by loosely thread wrapping two layers of hot-rolled rod on a 42 in. (1070 mm) diameter by 0.75 in. (19 mm) wall X-65 pipe. A second means of arresting a longitudinal propagating shear crack in a gas-transmission line is to develop a circumferential crack in the path of the longitudinal crack. In many full-scale tests, strain concentrations caused by girth welds and changes in pipe-wall thickness have initiated circumferential cracks.

Propagating ductile cracks can also be arrested by alteration of the time-dependent mechanical processes taking place at the crack tip. Results are presented from a test in which a crack was arrested on encountering a sudden change in pipe wall mass.

INTRODUCTION

With the discovery of large quantities of gas and oil in Arctic areas, the pipeline industry has been faced with the need for significant technological advances. One of these is that of designing against long running shear fractures in gas transmission line pipe. Many investigations (1) have examined the different aspects of the problem which have included analytical analysis, full-scale testing, and small scale laboratory testing for measuring material properties. These investigations have not lead to analytical solutions which can be used to predict the material properties necessary to arrest running shear fractures. However, with the aid of empirical correlations between full-scale tests and Charpy V-notch measurements these analyses and empirical correlations can be used to estimate the minimum toughness required to arrest a running shear fracture under various test conditions (2). For example, for buried test pipe at 50°F (10°C) made from steels which do not exhibit separations, the Charpy V-notch toughness necessary to arrest a running shear fracture is given by the condition,

$$CVN > 0.016\ \sigma^{1.5}\ D^{0.5}$$

where CVN = 2/3-size Charpy toughness in full shear (ft lbf); σ = design hoop stress (ksi); and D = pipe diameter (in.). Unfortunately, the predictions of other investigations (1,3) are not consistent with the AISI investigation (2) or with one another in predicting the significance of different design variables. Furthermore, none of the existing predictive equations can be used to predict behaviour of pipe steels that exhibit separations in a full-scale running shear fracture test. Separations, or "splitting", (i.e., multiple cracks on the fracture surface, normal to the primary running crack and parallel to the pipe surface) occur in many steels that have been control-rolled to below the upper transformation temperature (Ar_3) (4). In addition, the current predictive equations cannot be used when the gas is a two-phase (gas and liquid) mixture.

A full-scale testing program has led to a much clearer understanding of the pressures, strains, and

* It is understood that the material in this paper is intended for general information only and should not be used in relation to any specific application without independent examination and verification of its applicability and suitability by professionally qualified personnel. Those making use thereof or relying thereon assume all risk and liability arising from such use or reliance.

deformation which occur during a running shear fracture (5,6). An understanding of the mechanics of the running shear fracture suggests several means by which a crack can be arrested other than by providing sufficient ductility (toughness) in the pipe wall.

PIPE BEHAVIOUR DURING RUNNING SHEAR FRACTURE

Before detailing means of mechanically arresting cracks in pipelines, it is necessary to review the mechanics of the pipe behaviour for a propagating shear crack (5). During a running fracture, the shape of the pipe in advance of the crack tip becomes oval, due to the flap opening behind the crack tip. The crack is driven by the pressure acting on these flaps. The analysis is best illustrated by considering the four stages or locations relative to the crack tip, shown in Figure 1. Stage 1 is the area well in advance of the crack tip. Stage 2 is the area approximately two pipe diameters in advance of the crack tip. The area at the crack tip is stage 3, and stage 4 involves the flap opening behind the crack tip and the pressure acting on the flap.

At stage 1, a position well in advance of the crack tip, the first event that occurs after fracture has initiated is a reduction in the hoop strain due to pipe flexural waves which are generated at the initiation point. These flexural waves travel down the pipe at speeds of 2000 to 4000 ft/s (600 to 1200 m/s). The reduction in the hoop strain caused by these waves at the top of the pipe was observed to be as much as 25% of the original elastic-strain value. The next event which occurs at location 1 is a slow pressure decay due to the gas decompression. The gas-decompression front travels down the pipe at a speed of between 1100 and 1400 ft/s (335 and 425 m/s) depending on the gas density.

As the crack approaches the region of stage 2, the longitudinal tensile strain in a 1 ft wide (0.3 m) band on the top of the pipe continuously increases to a maximum value at about the time the crack is two pipe-diameters from the point. The longitudinal tensile strain in this "tongue" is at least 1 to 2% and causes a force which lifts the pipe ahead of the running fracture.

The major event occurring in stage 2 is the change in pipe shape from circular to an oval with the major axis horizontal. This ovality is caused by the flaps opening behind the crack and the pressure acting on the flaps. The reaction of the escaping gas behind the crack drives the pipe downward and the sidewalls of the pipe outward and forces the pipe to become oval. As mentioned earlier, the longitudinal strain in the tongue on the top of the pipe has reached a plateau or a maximum strain about two pipe diameters ahead of the crack tip, and the hoop strain on the top of the pipe changes from membrane tension to bending, with the average strain (average between the ID and OD value) becoming zero, or even compressive.

In stage 3, near the crack tip, the circumferential bending strains on the top of the pipe are reversed as the top of the pipe wall is subjected again to hoop membrane tensile strains. During this part of the fracture event the tensile strains cause a thinning and fracture of the pipe wall.

In stage 4, behind the crack tip, the flaps are opened outward. The pressure is distributed on the flaps over a distance of one to two pipe diameters behind the crack tip. The pressure is therefore a force acting on the mass of the pipe wall which causes an acceleration of the flap. This force acts both normal to the crack surface as a crack-opening force and as a radial force driving the flaps outward. The pressure on the flaps drives the pipe downward and the sides of the pipe outward, causing the oval shape in advance of the crack.

MECHANICAL MEANS OF ARRESTING RUNNING SHEAR FRACTURES

Constraint of Flaps

The running-shear fracture is driven by the pressure acting on the flaps behind the crack tip, which forces the flaps outward and subsequently tears the pipe apart. Constraint of the flap displacement by mechanical means should reduce the force driving the crack and cause the crack to stop. Backfill offers such a constraint but hot-rolled rod, high-strength wire strapping around the pipe, or providing a sleeve around the pipe should provide effective constraints. A rod-wrapped arrestor (loosely wrapped on the pipe) appeared attractive because it would require a minimum amount of relatively low cost material added to the pipe (because of the strength of the rod available) and would provide a structure which is over-constrained (multiple strands versus a single member as a pipe sleeve would be).

A full-scale test was conducted with 42 in. (1070 mm) diameter by 0.75 in. (19 mm) wall X-65 pipe, presurized with air to 1670 psig (11,500 kPa) or to 72% of the specified minimum yield strength (SMYS), i. e. 47 ksi (320 MPa). The test pipe length was about 300 ft (90 m) and the pipe was tested above ground with no backfill. The west half (approximately 17 ft or 5.2 m) of pipe 1508 (see Figure 2) was thread-wrapped loosely by hand over a 19 ft (5.8 m) length with two layers of 0.220 in. (5.6 mm) diameter hot-

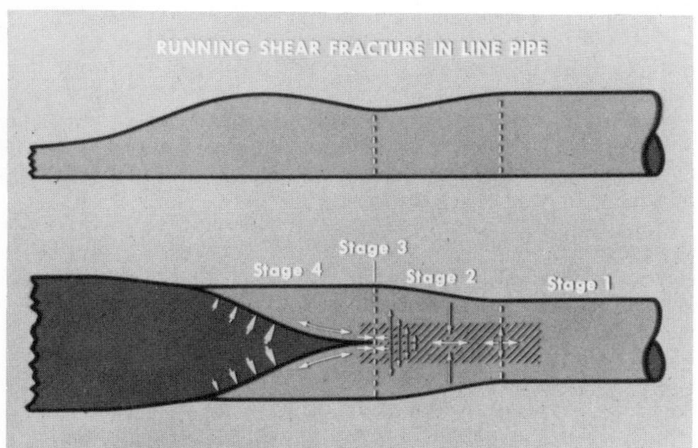

Figure 1: Running shear fracture in linepipe

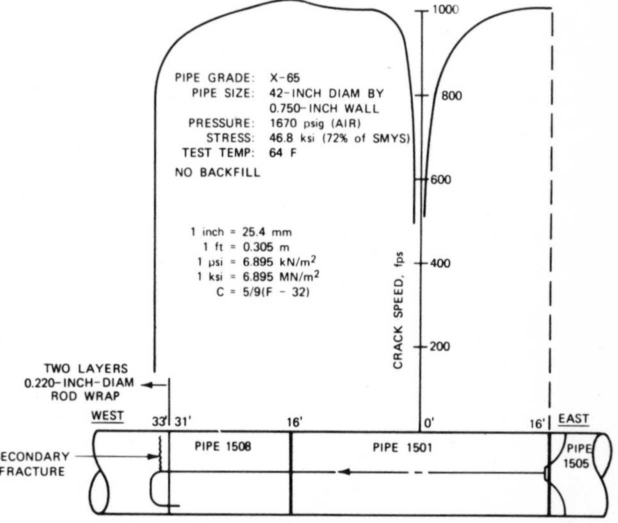

Figure 2: Crack speeds for El Paso test 2

Figure 3: Rod wrapped arrestor

Figure 4: Crack arrest in rod arrestor

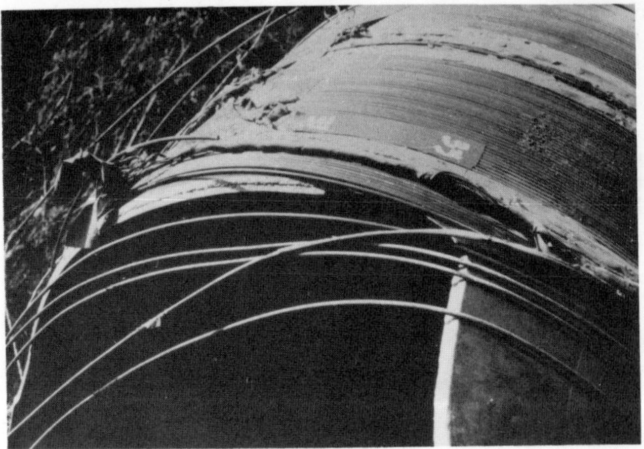

Figure 5: Crack arrest under rod wrap

rolled rod, as shown in Figure 3. The east half of the test is not described because the crack arrested at the girth weld prior to reaching the east-end crack arrestor. The rod had a yield strength of 83.8 ksi (578 MPa), a tensile strength of 139.1 ksi (959 MPa), an elongation of 6.2% (in 10 in. or 250 mm) and 46% reduction in area. The chemical compositions of the rod and pipe are given in Table 1. The X-65 test pipe exhibited 100% shear fracture in the drop-weight-tear-test (DWTT) and 21 ft lbf (28.5 J) energy in 2/3 size Charpy V-notch (CVN) specimens tested at the test temperature of 64°F (18°C).

After the pipe was pressurized to 1670 psig (11,500 kPa), the crack was initiated by remotely failing a part-through-wall notch at the center of pipe 1501, (Figure 2). To the east, the crack accelerated to a speed of 1000 ft/s (300 m/s) but the girth weld between pipe 1501 and 1505 opened before the

Table 1

Chemical Composition of Rod and Test Pipe (%)

	Rod	Pipe
C	0.67	0.15
Mn	0.55	1.35
P	0.011	0.010
S	0.033	0.007
Si	0.14	0.48
Cb	ND	0.030
V	ND	0.058
Al	0.037	ND

(ND = not detected)

longitudinal fracture arrived and the longitudinally running fracture was arrested when it reached the circumferential crack. To the west, the crack accelerated to over 1000 ft/s (300 m/s) then decelerated to about 950 ft/s (290 m/s) and ran under the rod (Figures 4 and 5). After the crack had passed under the first 2 ft (0.6 m) of rod wrapping, it turned to the south (see Figure 2), and ran an additional 7 in. (180 mm). The crack then continued to propagate by tearing an additional 11 in. (210 mm) and then tore back toward the initiation notch. A secondary tensile fracture occurred on the flap behind the crack tip.

The arrest of the crack 2 ft (0.6 m) under the rod wrap in an uncovered pipe with only 21 ft lbf (28.5 J) of Charpy toughness, and pressurized to 72% SMYS clearly demonstrates the effectiveness of this type of arrestor. About 50 broken hoops of rod were found on the ground at the location where the crack ran under the rod-wrapped arrestor. This means that the flaps had broken the rod for a distance of a little more than 6 in. (150 mm) into the arrestor, even though the crack ran much farther.

The ends of the failed rod showed the classical ductile cup-cone fracture. The diameters of several of the broken rod hoops were measured to determine the pattern of straining. Ten in. (254 mm) back from the failed end of the rod, the diameter was thinned by an amount equal to that measured as the maximum uniform strain in a tension test of the same rod. Thus, the strain in the rod was not localized at the top of the pipe near the crack path. Close-up high-speed motion pictures (1000 frame/s) of the crack arrest in the rod arrestor (Figure 6) showed several

Figure 6(a): Crack reaches leading edge of arrestor

Figure 6(b): Crack arrests 2 ft (0.6 m) into arrestor

Figure 6(c): Rods fail due to flap opening

rods broken at locations other than at the top of the pipe (this observation was deduced from the length of the rods shown in Figure 6(c)). The reduction in area for the maximum uniform strain (10%) and at fracture (46%) was the same in both the full-scale test and in a static test run in the laboratory. Therefore, it is concluded that the high loading rate developed during the full-scale test had little

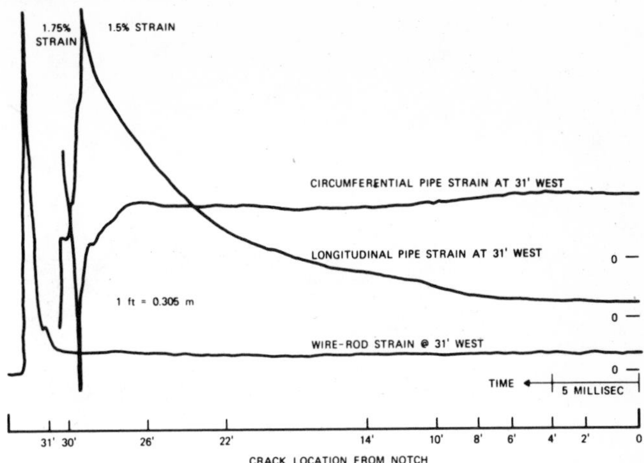

Figure 7: Outputs for strain gauges located at the beginning of the rod arrestor

effect on the ductility of the rod.

The ability of the rod to plastically strain over a long length is important because during the time that the rod is plastically straining the resisting force of the rod is being maintained on the flaps behind the crack tip. The delayed failure of the rods, after the crack passed under them, was documented by superimposing the records from three strain gauges located at the start of the arrestor, 31 ft (9.5 m) west of the initiating notch. A circumferential and a longitudinal gauge were located on the top of the pipe just ahead of the first rod wrap, and a third gauge was located on the top of the first wrap. Figure 7 shows a plot of the outputs from the gauges with respect to the location of the crack tip (from the timing-wire circuits) with time after crack initiation. The circumferential strain in the pipe decreased (because of the ovaling of the pipe) and then increased as the crack approached the 31 ft (9.4 m) rod location in the same manner as previously shown (5). The longitudinal tensile strain in the pipe increased continuously to 1.5% prior to the arrival of the crack tip. Both of these gauges failed when the crack was within about a foot (300 mm) of the arrestors. However, the gauge on the rod showed a peak strain of 1.75% that occurred after the crack had passed the rod on which it was located.

Arresting by Longitudinal Strain Development

Because of the flap opening behind the crack tip during the propagating shear fracture, the longitudinal tensile strain on the top of the pipe, well in advance of the crack tip, continually increases until it reaches a maximum level about two pipe diameters ahead of the crack tip. Many full-scale propagating-shear-fracture tests have terminated when the longitudinal strain ahead of the propagating crack caused circumferential cracking in the girth welds prior to the arrival of the longitudinally running fracture. The longitudinally running fracture was arrested at the previously-formed circumferential crack, as seen in Figure 8.

The longitudinally-developed strain might be used advantageously for mechanical crack arrestors. Although the longitudinal strain levels measured during full-scale tests were only 1 to 2%, strain concentrations can increase the local strain to a level sufficient to cause circumferential cracking, at, for example, the toe of a girth weld.

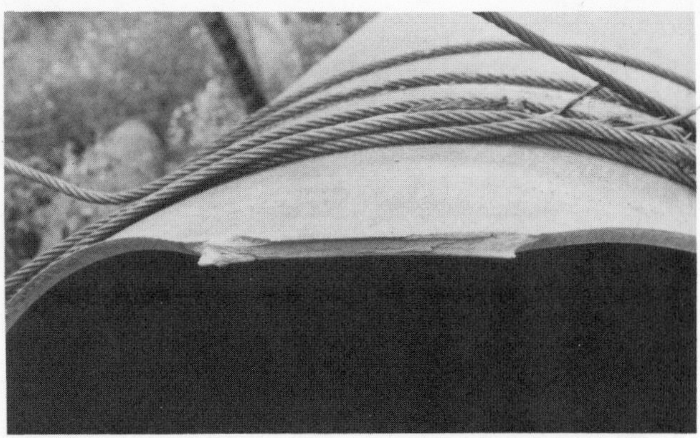

Figure 8: Girth weld failure

Addition of Mass to the Pipe Wall

Although the acceleration (displacement) of the flaps can be reduced by reducing the pressure or increasing the restraining force, an alternate means of reducing the flap acceleration is to provide a larger mass to be acted upon by the residual flap pressure.

A test was conducted with 42 in. (1070 mm) diameter by 0.375 in. (9.5 mm) wall X-65 pipe having a 2/3-size CVN toughness of about 40 ft lbf or 54 J (100% shear fracture). A series of lead weights, each 1 x 6 x 10 in. (25 x 150 x 250 mm), were secured to the top of the pipe 70 ft (21 m) from the crack initiation point (Figure 9). These weights were spaced about 1 in. (25 mm) apart and covered an area 30 in. (760 mm) wide by 10 ft (3 m) long along the top of the pipe. Each weight was secured to the pipe with two bolts threaded through the pipe wall. By adding pieces of lead, the effect of the weights on the stiffness of the pipewall was minimized and, the weights provided only additional mass to be accelerated with the pipe wall.

Figure 9: Pipe with lead weights attached

The pipe was not backfilled and pressurized to 80% SMYS (52 ksi or 360 MPa). The crack, after travelling through 70 ft (21 m) of pipe, had a constant speed of 800 ft/s (240 m/s). After passing 3 in. (76 mm) beyond the leading edge of the first row of lead weights, the crack turned and started to spiral. Thus, the crack arrested after passing into the first row of lead weights.

Mechanical Crack Arrestor Design

Three separate mechanisms have been described as means of arresting running shear fractures: (1) constraint of flap displacement, (2) initiation of circumferential cracks ahead of the longitudinally running crack by taking advantage of the high longitudinal strain in advance of the crack and (3) provide a larger mass in the pipe wall which, when encountered by the running crack, must be accelerated with the flaps.

As the first example of a mechanical crack arrestor, consider the rod-wrapped arrestor used for the El Paso test described above. This type of arrestor primarily limits the flap displacement behind the crack tip. This design has the advantage of using very low cost product which has a high strength and, therefore, requires a minimum amount of material. The amount of rod needed can be estimated by comparing the tensile breaking load of the arrestor with an estimate of the residual pressure force on the flaps behind the crack tip. Because of the size and stiffness of the rod, the rod would not be an effective means of providing additional mass or in resisting pipe ovaling ahead of the crack tip. Also, the longitudinal strain on the top of the pipe would not be affected. On the other hand, this type of arrestor provides over-constraint in that even if several rods fail due to mechanical damage the arrestor would still be effective. Susceptibility of a rod-wrapped arrestor to stress and crevice corrosion should be considered. However, five year service tests of wire-wrapped pipe in an aggressive environment have demonstrated several different coating systems that are effective in preventing corrosion problems (7).

Another arrestor system would be a ring sleeve slipped over the pipe. This system would be effective in constraining the flaps and also in stiffening of the pipe and resisting ovaling ahead of the running fracture. However, if the ring sleeve was fillet welded to the pipe, or if a heavy-wall short pipe length was used, both of these systems could also be effective as concentrators of the longitudinal strain at the toe of fillet or girth welds (because of the increased cross section and the weld geometry). A heavy-wall pipe will have a reduced hoop stress which will also resist crack arrest. Disadvantages of these systems would be the costs of making such rings or sleeves and the costs of the additional field welding.

In addition to the above, many standard construction practices for transmission lines may be effective means for mechanically arresting cracks. For example, concrete anchor blocks will provide a significant mass requiring acceleration, provided the concrete is prevented from spalling off the pipe during ovaling in advance of the fracture. Valves, tees, and similar massive pieces should be equally effective. Also, field bends of conventional pipe may cause propagating cracks to arrest. For example, if a crack propagates down the top of a bent pipe, the flap formation behind the crack tip would be asymmetric. The asymmetric displacement of the flaps should cause the crack to spiral, which could then lead to crack arrest.

Finally, two conditions must be satisfied when designing a mechanical crack-arrestor system. First, the arrestor should be an integral part of the pipe and not attached to the ground. Because significant lifting forces are developed in the pipe ahead of the running fracture, any constrained member wrapped over the pipe and fixed to the ground could fail before the crack arrives and therefore fail to arrest it. Secondly, the arrestor should be flexible enough or be sufficiently well attached to the pipe such that it will not spall off during pipe ovaling in advance of the fracture.

The criteria for determining which mechanical crack arrestor is "the best" must be based upon both the technical aspects of the probability that such an arrestor will arrest the crack and the economics of the arrestor. Therefore, depending upon many engineering considerations not dealing directly with the arrestor effectiveness, such as method and location of the installation of the arrestor, a certain type of arrestor may be suitable for one service application but not for another.

The exact levels of the transient pressures, strains and deformations which occur during a running shear fracture for different design conditions are not known. Therefore, full-scale-tests should be conducted to prove the effectiveness of any proposed mechanical crack arrestor system. Mathematical analyses are being developed (8,9) which may be of assistance in designing future systems. Finally, consideration must also be given to the transient forces present in the vicinity of an arrested crack due to inertial forces and residual gas venting from the failed pipe. Even after a crack has stopped a second fracture may initiate beyond the arrestor and continue to run along the pipe.

SUMMARY

The results of full-scale tests document the different means by which a ductile fracture propagating in line pipe can be arrested. Although a propagating crack may, in some instances, be arrested by providing adequate pipe wall ductility, mechanical crack arrestor systems may offer a more positive and reliable safety assurance. Full-scale test results have shown that the following concepts provide effective means for arresting propagating shear cracks:

1. Constraint of the flaps behind the propagating crack tip by the use of wire, straps, or rings around the pipe.

2. Development of circumferential cracks ahead of the propagating crack due to high longitudinal strain levels at stress concentrations such as girth welds.

3. Provide periodic large masses along the pipe length which must be accelerated by the pressure acting on the flaps behind the propagating crack.

Practical mechanical crack arrestor systems may employ one or more of these concepts. Until proper analytical models are available, arrestor designs should be documented with full-scale tests.

Acknowledgment

The full-scale tests which developed the model of the running shear fracture were sponsored by the American Iron and Steel Institute. The authors are also grateful for the permission of El Paso Natural Gas Co., to publish the results of the rod-wrapped arrestor test.

REFERENCES

1. "Symposium on Crack Propagation in Pipelines", 1974, Institute of Gas Engineers, Newcastle-Upon-Tyne, England, unpublished proceedings.
2. "Running Shear Fractures in Line Pipe", American Iron and Steel Institute, 1974, New York.
3. W. A. Maxey, 5th Symposium on Linepipe Research, American Gas Association, Catalogue No. L30174, 1974, pp. J-1 to J-30.
4. D. S. Dabkowski, P. J. Konkol, and M. F. Baldy, Metals Engin. Quart.,1976, (2), pp. 22-32.
5. K. D. Ives, A. K. Shoemaker, R. F. McCartney, J. Engineering Materials and Technology, 1974, vol. 96, pp. 309-317
6. A. K. Shoemaker and R. F. McCartney, ibid, pp. 318-322.
7. U. S. Steel Corporation, unpublished data.
8. L. B. Freund, D. M. Parks, and J. R. Rive, "Running Ductile Fracture in a Pressurized Linepipe", 1974, Eighth National Symposium on Fracture Mechanics, Providence, Rhode Island.
9. M. F. Kanninen, S. G. Sampath, and C. Popelar, "Steady-State Crack Propagation in Pressurized Pipelines Without Backfill", 1975, unpublished paper, Second National congress on Pressure Vessels and Piping, San Francisco.

DISCUSSION

G. T. Hahn (Battelle Columbus Laboratories): This is a subject near and dear to me, and I would like to tell you how impressed I am by the visual evidence of what is going on. I think you can sit in a laboratory and speculate, but the impact of actually seeing the phenomena in progress is certainly no substitute for all the speculation. So I think the observations that you have made on the dynamics of pipes will prove to be very useful. They have been useful to you already as is evident from your presentation. For some years I have argued with my colleague Mel Kanninen, who has been working to develop computation techniques for analysing the dynamic axial crack problem, about where the driving force is situated for the running crack. It is clearly not situated at any one particular point, but there is driving force coming from a region, some of it in advance of the crack, some of it near the crack front, some of it behind, and I speculated some years back that a good bit of it was coming from behind, from the flaps, and you mentioned also the role of the flaps. We thought of them at the time as sails. The pressure in the line was blowing on them and this was driving the crack forward. From your presentation, it looked as if, for the wire arrestor, that the crack entered the wire configuration only a few inches and already the driving force must have decreased very greatly, because it stopped. And then you mentioned also in the case of the lead weights that the crack entered the arrangement of lead weights only a short distance and again turned and arrested. It seems to me that the largest part of the driving force must be in the region rather close to the tip of the crack, maybe a few inches on either side. I wonder what you think about that?

A. K. Shoemaker: My own feeling is also that it is within a few inches. I think that what is hard to realize though is, again even within the few inches, how much displacement there is of the flap. The displacement is significant, and I feel it is still behind the crack. There was really no way that the wire could alter the stress field ahead of the crack tip, because it was basically loose and we monitored that also. There was not any strain to start with and it was not till after the fact that you saw the strength. So, I feel that the dominant driving force is very close to the tip, but primarily behind it.

G. T. Hahn: The other point that you made at the very end is that designs for crack arrestors would have to be proven experimentally and that you had little hope that an analytical capability could be devised in short order. I certainly agree with you that any designs that are developed on the basis of analyses should be checked experimentally, but I think an analytical capability would be very helpful to the designer and that he could then weigh the various parts of the design and get an optimum design for the price. I would also agree with you that I do not think we are at the stage now where we have such an analytical capability, but judging from the theoretical work that has been done at Battelle on the problem of the running crack, I think things certainly could be done -- computations can be done which would aid in the design process, if not designing it completely. We are gradually coming to a point where it will be possible to analyze dynamic events along the lines that we have been analyzing initiation and static events. Ultimately this will help those who are trying to design crack arrestors. It will certainly be possible to give some insight to the designer on how the driving force of the crack depends on the general configuration of the pipe as it is opening and this would then help in the design of arrestors.

F. S. Somerville (Canadian Arctic Gas Study): The work you have done is basic to our understanding and I think unique. Could you comment on the need for flexibility in the design of mechanical crack arrestors? Compare, for example, wire or rod wrap with sleeve crack arrestors.

A. K. Shoemaker: I would view a sleeve crack arrestor as being flexible in terms of its ability to deform during the pipe ovalizing ahead of the running crack tip. Systems which would spall-off the pipe or crack during ovalizing would be inadequate as arrestors.

F. S. Somerville: For buried pipelines, could you compare re-initiation as it may relate to geometry at an arrest occurring normally in the pipe body with arrest at a crack arrestor, including consideration that the latter may be of the"ring-off" type (e.g. girth weld). Such a failure could perhaps be "neater" and less dangerous than a pipe with a big lip on one side.

A. K. Shoemaker: Our experience has been that cracks which arrest and ring the pipe have the highest probability of kicking the pipe a significant distance and hence reinitiating. If the failed pipe is continuous, it will help to resist the reactive forces during the gas venting after arrest.

F. S. Somerville: Would you comment on the utility of the CV100 concept for ductile fracture arrest design in Arctic pipelines?

A. K. Shoemaker: Using the design philosophy of a mechanical crack arrestor to limit a propagating ductile fracture, the importance of ductile toughness level is only to establish the critical flaw size for crack initiation. I am not aware of any experimental data which indicates that the intercept values as opposed to the energy at operating temperature have a significant effect upon the critical flaw size. This behaviour is primarily flow stress, and not toughness, dependent.

J. M. Wallbridge (Foothills Pipe Lines): You mentioned the problem of stress corrosion of the wire or rod crack arrestors. In your paper you indicate that you have a number of coating systems which will solve the corrosion problems. Could you give us some details of these systems? Do you have enough experience for a long enough time at a sufficient number of locations to be confident that stress corrosion of the wrap can be prevented? This question is raised because of the experience of Alberta Gas Trunk Line with a high strength wrap which suffered extreme stress corrosion when installed in a very mild environment with a good coating. Failure took place at or before the hydrotest.

A. K. Shoemaker: I am not familiar with the details of the failure of the AGTL line. However, our experience with coating systems for this type of application stems from five years of service tests of pressurized wrapped pipe in an aggressive service environment. U. S. Steel would be happy to discuss these test results, in detail, with interested parties.

E. Shelton (Alberta Gas Trunk Line): The use of high-strength wrap could result in environmental cracking problems and consequent loss of effectiveness when used in actual construction where coating defects are inevitable. The use of high-strength coated wrap at Alberta Gas Trunk Line has been somewhat disappointing. Do your evaluation tests of high-strength wrap include tests with simulated coating defects?

A. K. Shoemaker: The tests do not include simulated coating defects. However, during the periodic inspection of the tests it is possible to identify defects which occurred. Some of the coating systems with cathodic protection appear to be performing satisfactorily even with these defects. The rod used in our tests was not high-strength -- it was only a hot-drawn rod product, with no cold work, and therefore no residual stresses.

J. M. Wallbridge: You indicated that there was a significant time delay between the arrival of a fracture and the time when the pipe is thrown from the ditch in the event of a girth weld failure. If this is the case under test conditions, is not the ejected pipe in many cases subject to a lower pressure force due to the return of the reflected wave from the end of the test section?

If a project is designed using crack arrestors it is likely that a lower toughness pipe will be specified and probably purchased than if the pipeline is designed for fracture control using pipe toughness. Will this lower pipe toughness not result in higher fracture velocities and therefore higher pressures at the crack tip, again increasing the available energy to throw the pipe from the ditch in the event of girth weld failure?

Does the combination of these two effects not mean that there has been insufficient testing to demonstrate that multiple sequential girth weld failures are not a failure mode for pipelines employing crack arrestors?

A. K. Shoemaker: The return of the reflected wave would certainly alter the pressure decay. However, depending upon the location of the arrest relative to the end of the test pipe length there is a significant period of time (fractions of a second are significant) for acceleration of the pipe at pressures not effected by the reflected wave.

Of course the first question to raise concerning crack arrestors instead of toughness for design is whether or not both designs will arrest the crack in the first place. Full-scale test data have shown that there are certain design situations where toughness alone will not arrest the running ductile crack. In these situations the crack arrestor design concept is necessary. I agree that the pipe toughness will affect the crack speed when using crack arrestors. However, it may be that properly designed crack arrestors and consideration of the mode of crack arrest may be used to offset the somewhat higher crack speeds and local pressures associated with the lower toughness pipe. A full-scale test of the "system" would, hopefully, demonstrate this behaviour.

Data to date does suggest that girth weld failures may have a higher probability of causing reinitiation. Perhaps this is due to the crack "ringing" the pipe resulting in a free end of the pipe at a high residual pressure. I feel there are more "foolproof" methods for mechanically arresting cracks than by using girth welds of low dynamic toughness.

C. A. Parrini (Italsider): I am grateful to the AISI group, and particularly to you, John Timmers and Mike Healy for the cooperation we had from you in order to be successful with our tests in Sardegna. From our results we have found 30% reduction of CVA (from 70 to 50 ft lbf or 95 to 68 J) with a reduction of only 12% in hoop stress, from an increase of 10 to 15% in pipe thickness. What do you think about using this approach in order to have a pipe with higher wall thickness, to act at lower hoop stress, as crack arrestors, also with acceptable low Charpy-V energies?

A. K. Shoemaker: As long as we are not concerned with special design circumstances such as two-phase gas flow, such a section of pipe with a suitable length for the required crack decelleration and arrest should be an adequate crack arrestor. I would be concerned about strain concentrations at the regions where change in pipe thickness occurs.

J. T. McGrath (Canadian Welding Development Institute): If the girth weld is a potential crack arrestor, do you see the possibility of specifying a level of fracture toughness of the girth weld that will allow crack initiation and propagation in the weld in advance of the running crack?

A. K. Shoemaker: The difficulty in stopping a crack by specifying a girth weld toughness is that the probability of arrest must be established. This would require estimates and significant testing to verify the expected results. It is a statistical situation. The mechanical system is a much more positive system which requires much less testing for verification.

J. T. McGrath: Would you comment on the use of a metal laminate construction as a possible method of crack arrest in pipelines?

A. K. Shoemaker: The wire rod wrap, sleeve on pipe, or wire rope arrestor are all forms of a laminated construction, in my view. The point is that they do not have to carry any of the normal design load during normal operation. If they do, then the reduced hoop stress in the pipe may be viewed simply as an additional factor for assisting in the arrest of the crack.

M. R. Krishnadev (Laval University): I think that much more experimental data are needed before one goes ahead with the use of mechanical arrestors. My view is that the use of inherently tougher and cleaner steel is still our best bet. Arrestors may be used only for additional safety. Do you agree?

A. K. Shoemaker: I totally disagree. I believe the next paper, by Eiber and Maxey, plus our own data on uncovered pipe unquestionably shows that toughness alone will not assure arrest for some design situations.

M. R. Krishnadev: Have you carried out any tests on buried pipes and in low temperature environments? I think such tests would be of more relevance to actual service conditions.

A. K. Shoemaker: No low temperature tests were conducted by U.S. Steel.

M. R. Krishnadev: What will be the additional cost ($/mile) involved in using the crack-arrestors?

A. K. Shoemaker: The economics of such a system will depend upon the system used. The details of alternatives needs to be evaluated by the pipeline user.

M. R. Krishnadev: You have used a wire rope with a very high carbon content (0.67%) and I think that it will be of not much use as a constraint at low temperatures.

A. K. Shoemaker: As indicated in the paper, the wire rod behaved in a very ductile manner during the test. I have no reason to believe that a reduction in temperature from 75°F (24°C) to -10°F (-23°C) would have any significant effect on the dynamic ductility of this product.

M. R. Krishnadev: Did you observe any difference in the fracture behaviour of spirally welded and longitudinally welded pipes?

A. K. Shoemaker: We have not tested spiral pipe.

R. J. Cooke (National Energy Board): Could you comment on the role that backfill type and configuration may have on the possibility of re-initiation ahead of an arresting crack.

A. K. Shoemaker: Anything which can be done to oppose the forces developed by the pressure inside the pipe should assist in arresting and retarding re-initiation of a crack. Thus backfill should be very significant. The added mass of the backfill and attendant reduction in pipe wall acceleration will also increase the time allowed for gas venting and corresponding pressure decay. But the next paper provides more hard data on the effects of backfill.

FULL-SCALE EXPERIMENTAL INVESTIGATION OF DUCTILE FRACTURE BEHAVIOR IN SIMULATED ARCTIC PIPELINE

R. J. Eiber and W. A. Maxey
Battelle Columbus Laboratories
Columbus, Ohio
USA

Analyses of three full-scale experiments conducted under simulated Arctic conditions of temperature (-4° C to -12°C), and pressure (1680 psig/11.6 MPa) and employing a modified gas composition (high concentration of heavy hydrocarbons) on 48in.(1220 mm) diameter by 0.720 in. (18 mm) wall thickness Grade X-70 line pipe indicate that the fracture behaviour is not as expected, based on the empirical formulation developed for prior X-52 through X-65 materials that were not controlled-rolled to temperatures below Ar_3. Several factors in these experiments are different from past experience, viz., rich gas composition, frozen backfill, high pressure, large diameter pipe and high-strength steel. Any or all of these factors could be crucial to the final understanding of the shear fracture behaviour observed. The results indicate that reliable fracture control for the conditions investigated can be obtained through the use of mechanical crack-arrestor devices.

INTRODUCTION

Three full-scale experiments were conducted on 48 in. (1220 mm) by 0.720 in. (18 mm) X-70 line pipe, completely pressurized with natural gas of a composition similar to that expected during the service of the proposed pipeline from the Mackenzie Delta and Prudhoe Bay to the U.S.-Canadian Border. The pipe and gas temperatures in the experiments were 10°F to 24°F (-4°C to -12°C) and the natural gas pressure corresponded to a pipe hoop stress of 80% SMYS (specified minimum yield strength).

The primary objective of the first two experiments was to determine the toughness properties of longitudinally-welded pipe necessary to arrest a propagating ductile fracture under simulated operating conditions. The second and third experiments had the objective of examining the effectiveness of a split sleeve and a section of wire-wrapped pipe as a means of arresting propagating ductile fractures. A section of spirally-welded pipe was also employed in the third experiment to determine if there was any substantial difference from straight-seam pipe, insofar as fracture arrest is concerned.

EXPERIMENTAL FACILITY

The experiments were conducted using a test facility consisting of 580 ft (177 m) of pipe, with 800 ft (240 m) of 12 in. (305 mm) diameter pipe connecting the two ends of the 48 in. (1220 mm) pipe. Figure 1 shows the facility layout and the location of the major components, which are as follows: gas compressor -- maximum pressure rating 2500 psig (17 MPa); charcoal stripper vessel for removing heavy ends from the incoming natural gas; control buildings for instrumentation and monitoring test progress; heat exchanger and gas circulating fans, (the heat exchanger is connected to a 100 t refrigeration unit which is the cooling source for the test loop); various remotely-operated valves to control the gas flow.

The main 580 ft (117 m) of 48 in. (1220 mm) diameter pipe has two 4 ft x 10 ft x 20 ft (0.9 m x 3.0 m x 6.1 m) concrete anchors on each end of the test pipe to anchor the pipe in place.

The experiments were conducted by welding into the center of the test line the specific pipe lengths of interest. All girth welding on the test lengths of pipe in the first two experiments used a special welding technique that employed small-diameter low hydrogen electrodes welded in the downhill position. The purpose of these special welds was to achieve a low transition temperature for the weld deposit.

After the test line was welded together for each experiment, it was hydrostatically tested to 100% SMYS (2100 psig/4.5 MPa). After the hydrostatic test, the pipe was dried and gas was introduced into the test section to a pressure of approximately 100 psig (690 kPa) following which the necessary hydrocarbons, consisting primarily of C_2 through C_6, were added. The pipe was then pressurized with available pipeline gas and the cooling started. Additional gas was added until the desired test conditions were achieved, viz. temperature, pressure, and depth of frozen backfill.

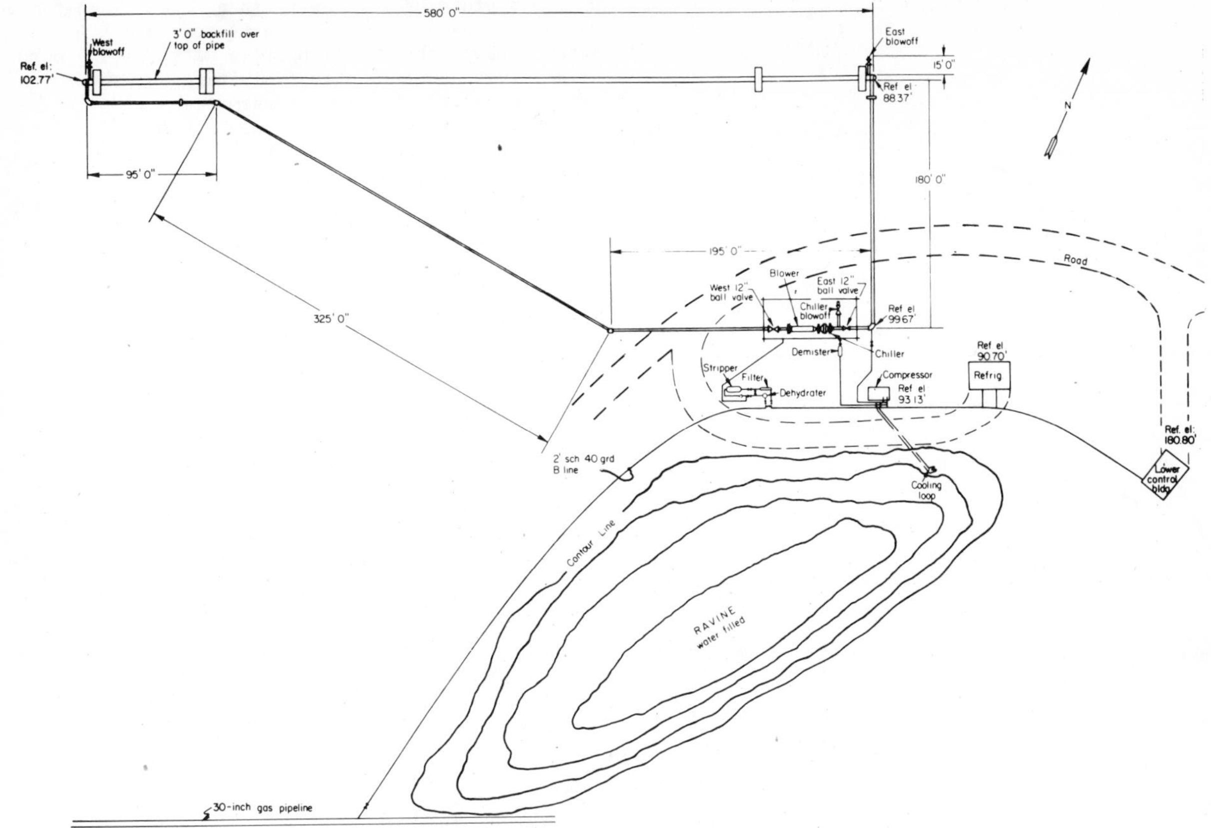

Figure 1: Plan of Athens test site

CHARACTERISTICS OF MATERIALS EXAMINED

The pipe materials examined in this program were produced as small orders and therefore tend to have less uniformity than if made as part of a large order. They are controlled-rolled steels and have a low transition temperature and a high Charpy plateau energy. The pipe was purchased to meet all requirements of CSA Z245.2 Grade 70, API 5LX-70 and 5LS-70, and, in addition, to supplemental drop weight tear test (DWTT) and Charpy impact energy requirements. The DWTT requirements were 85% shear area transition temperature (SATT) at -10°F (-23°C). The Charpy energy levels were specified as CV100 (see NOMENCLATURE, p.316) and covered a range of 100 ft lbf (136 J) to provide a range for examination in the full-scale experiments.

The controlled-rolled materials for Arctic application are rolled at finishing temperatures below the upper critical transformation temperature (Ar_3) and therefore exhibit fracture appearances that have splits or separations. Dabkowski et al (1) found that for steels that exhibited separations there was little correlation between this type of fracture irregularity and steel composition, melting practice, or casting practice. The only obvious correlation was with finishing temperature on the plate mill. In general, the lower the finishing temperature (particularly below Ar_3) the greater the tendency to produce separations. Separations are beneficial in that they occur just prior to the main fracture and effectively reduce the transition temperature, because the material separates into a number of thin platelets prior to the main fracture, which reduces the through-thickness restraint. Static through-thickness tensile tests on materials of this type generally indicate yield and tensile strengths similar to those obtained in the transverse direction of the plate. The through-thickness elongation is generally lower than the normal transverse value. Thus, this phenomenon represents a metallurgical development that makes it possible to obtain significantly lower transition temperatures in high toughness, relatively thick, controlled-rolled materials than has been possible in the past.

On small notched specimens, such as those employed in the DWTT, the standard 0.625 in. (16 mm) dynamic tear (DT), and the Charpy V-notch tests, the results of testing the specimens between the lowest temperature for 100% shear appearance and the shelf energy region are summarized in the following:

1) as the temperature is lowered from the upper plateau, separations appear and their number generally increases.

2) the energy absorbed in breaking specimens decreases from the upper plateau energy and continues to drop as the temperature is decreased, even though the main fracture surface has an appearance of 100% shear.

3) separations disappear as the shear area on the specimen decreases and are generally absent at shear areas of 50% and less.

To illustrate the above phenomena, the plotted Charpy data for one of the pipe lengths examined is shown in Figure 2. Because of the difference in the shape of the Charpy energy curve for these controlled-rolled materials, several new terms have been defined to more fully describe the variable energy levels of the 100% shear area specimens. These new terms are shown in Figure 2 at their appropriate energy levels. The term CV100 in this instance is 52 ft lbf (70 J). The CV100 energy level is a conservative measure of the upper plateau toughness of the material in the region of 100% shear fracture. Another measure of the toughness of the pipe material in the region of 100% shear has been defined as the intercept energy or CVI. CVI is obtained as shown in the bottom half of Figure 2

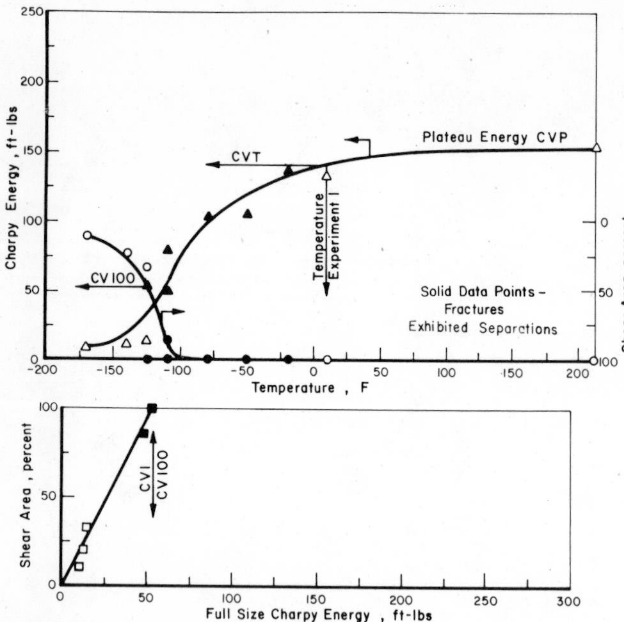

Figure 2: Example of Charpy V-notch data from a controlled-rolled line pipe material

by cross plotting the Charpy shear area against the Charpy energy data at a given temperature. A line drawn through the partly brittle data, giving more weight to the energy data exhibiting 50% shear or more, intercepts the 100% shear area at the CVI energy. For materials which are not controlled-rolled below Ar_3, CVI and CV100 are essentially equal to the upper shelf plateau energy, CVP. It has been observed that for controlled-rolled materials, CVI and CV100 are generally below CVP. In this investigation, the CV100 energy has been examined to determine if it predicts the toughness of the pipe material when used in the temperature range below the upper plateau but above the 100% shear transition temperature.

EXPERIMENTAL RESULTS

The primary objective of Experiment 1 was to determine the pipe toughness of longitudinally-welded pipe necessary to arrest a propagating ductile fracture. Table 1 presents the pipe layout for this experiment along with a summary of pipe properties determined before, and in some lengths after, the experiment. The center six lengths of pipe, A18 through A23, were considered to be the test section for this experiment. The three pipe lengths to the west of the origin were arranged such that the fracture would encounter pipe lengths with increasing toughness. The Charpy CV100 values to the west of

Table 1

Experiment 1 - Pipe Toughness Properties

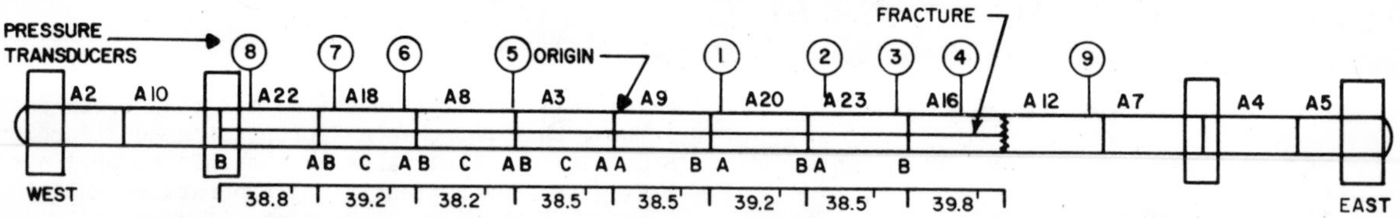

PRESSURE TRANSDUCERS — 8, 7, 6, 5, 1, 2, 3, 4, 9
ORIGIN — FRACTURE
WEST: A2, A10, A22, A18, A8, A3, A9, A20, A23, A16, A12, A7, A4, A5 :EAST
B | AB C | AB C | AB C | AA | BA | BA | B
38.8' | 39.2' | 38.2' | 38.5' | 38.5' | 39.2' | 38.5' | 39.8'

Approx. Sample Position	A22		A18		A8			A3		A9		A20	A23		A16
	B	A	C	A	C	A	B	C	A	A	B	A	A	B	A
Charpy-V Energy[ft lbf/J]															
CV100	70/ 95	70/ 95	66/ 89	60/ 81	43/ 58	59/ 80		45/ 61	58/ 79	50/ 68		104/ 141	120/ 163		
CVI		60/ 81	47/ 64	52/ 71	40/ 54	42/ 57		41/ 56	30/ 41	39/ 53		75/ 102	56/ 76		
CVT		164/ 221	88/ 119	133/ 180	56/ 76	86/ 117		53/ 72	78/ 106	140/ 190		152/ 206	150/ 203		
CVP		164/ 221	130/ 176	152/ 206	78/ 106	96/ 130		69/ 94	78/ 106	140/ 190		152/ 206	150/ 203		
Dynamic Tear Energy [ft lbf/J]															
Energy at Test(10°F/-12°C)		930/ 1260	740/ 1000	820/ 1110	580/ 790	670/ 910				770/ 1040		900/ 1220	830/ 1130		
Upper Shelf Energy		1120/ 1520	940/ 1270	1100/ 1490	680/ 920	720/ 980				1040/ 1410		1120/ 1520	1050/ 1520		
Mill Tensile Data															
YS [ksi/MPa]	71.5/ 493			72.2/ 498		72.0/ 496	80.4/ 554				77.7/ 535	74.1/ 511		75.0/ 517	76.2/ 525
UTS [ksi/MPa]	88.9/ 613			91.3/ 629		91.8/ 633	96.0/ 662				95.0/ 655	90.0/ 621		90.5/ 624	91.5/ 631
% elongation in 2 in.	43			40		39	36				38	42		43	40
Measured Fracture Speed [ft/s / m/s]				750/ 230		750/ 230			1000/ 305	950/ 290		550/ 170	450/ 140		
Required CV, calculated per Hypothesis (Appendix) Backfill [ft lbf/J]				32/ 43		32/ 43			22/ 30	23/ 31		52/ 71	67/ 91		
No backfill [ft lbf/J]				55/ 75		55/ 75			38/ 52	39/ 53		67/ 91	112/ 151		

the origin range from 43 to 70 ft lbf (58 to 95 J) and the Charpy energy at the test temperature ranged from 53 to 64 ft lbf (72 to 87 J). Similarly, to the east of the fracture origin, the Charpy CV100 values ranged from 50 to 120 ft lbf (68 to 163 J) and the Charpy energy at temperature was 140 to 152 ft lbf (190 to 205 J). All Charpy values reported are for full-size transverse Charpy specimens with the notch oriented through the thickness and have been determined on specimens removed from the pipe without flattening.

The fracture was initiated at a pressure of 1680 psig (11.5 MPa) and a pipe temperature and gas temperature of 10°F (-12°C). (Pipe and gas temperatures varied from 9.5°F to 11.5°F). All the pipe had been insulated with a 1 in. (25 mm) thickness of urethane insulation (2 lb/ft^3 or 32 kg/m^3 density) between the pipe and the soil, but after the experiment approximately 6 in. (150 mm) of frozen soil was found around the pipe. The fracture was initiated by cutting a 24 in. (610 mm) long axial flaw in the pipe with an explosive linear cutter. As shown in Table 1, eight lengths of pipe fractured in a ductile mode for a total of 311 ft (95 m).

The fracture speeds are measured using wires that encircle the pipe at various distances along the pipe and are electrically insulated from the pipe surface. The breaking of the wires is recorded on a tape recorder and the fracture speed calculated from the time-distance data. To the west of the fracture origin, the fracture propagated at from 1000 ft/s (305 m/s) down to 750 ft/s (229 m/s) as it entered the final length, A22, through which it propagated. The fracture on this end arrested at a concrete anchor and steel anchor forging. To the east of the origin the fracture started at a speed of 950 ft/s (290 m/s) and decreased to 450 ft/s (137 m/s) in the last instrumented length, A23. The fracture continued into the next length, A16, and arrested by fracturing the girth weld between A16 and A12, which was not of the low-hydrogen type employed in the remaining weld of the test section.

The gas employed for this experiment consisted of the available pipe line natural gas which had been modified by the addition of approximately 10,000 lb (4,500 kg) of hydrocarbons ranging from C_2 to C_5. The additional hydrocarbon significantly altered the gas behaviour as it expanded from the pipe in the fracture process.

Difficulties were encountered with the pressure transducers in this experiment. After the pressure decompressed to approximately 1150 psi (7.5 kPa) an extreme amount of electrical noise was picked up on the transducers, rendering them inoperative. This pressure corresponds to the estimated pressure at the point where the gas would be expected to decompress below the hydrocarbon dew point, forming liquid particles in the decompressing gas. The formation of liquid particles during decompression slows up the decompression and maintains a constant pressure for a short period of time before further pressure decay. This discontinuity in the decay produces a higher driving force for the crack and thus makes it more difficult to arrest the fracture under the conditions examined.

Figure 3 shows the pipe fracture following the experiment. It can be seen that the fracture propagated axially along the top of the pipe with a considerable elongation at the fracture edge, producing the radial rippling evident in the photograph. The reductions in thickness at the fracture edge ranged from 15 to 27%, roughly ordered in accordance with the Charpy CV100 energy shown in Table 1. These thickness reductions extended out for a distance of 6 to 9 in. (150 to 230 mm) from the fracture edge. Figure 4 shows the fracture surface appearance of pipe lengths A9, A20, and A23. The other fracture surfaces were similar, each exhibiting a separated appearance.

Figure 3: Fractured pipe in Experiment 1

The primary objective of Experiment 2 was the same as Experiment 1, namely to determine the pipe toughness properties of longitudinally welded pipe necessary to arrest a propagating ductile fracture. The secondary objectives were (1) to further examine the gas decompression behaviour, (2) to evaluate the effect of the insulation around the pipe as used in the first experiment, and (3) to evaluate the effectiveness of sleeves and wire-wrapped pipe as arrestors. Table 2 (p. 312) shows the pipe layout for this experiment, along with a summary of the pipe properties. The center nine lengths of pipe, S1 through the second piece of A15, were considered to be the test section for this experiment. Crack arrestors were applied on lengths S1, A11, and the most easterly section of A15. It was desired that the fracture propagate until it either arrested in the pipe or at a crack arrestor, so in this experiment all girth welds were also of the low-hydrogen type. The gas composition was modified slightly from that of Experiment 1 in that approximately 4700 lb (2100 kg) of C_2 and C_6 hydrocarbons were added to the available natural gas. This addition caused a discontinuity in the pressure decay to occur at a slightly higher level than experienced in the first experiment.

Experiment 2 was conducted at a pressure of 1685 psig (11.5 MPa) and an average gas temperature of 24°F (-4°C). Less than 2 in. (51 mm) of frozen soil was formed around the pipe at the time of the experiment, due to the higher overall temperatures. Five lengths of pipe fractured as shown in Table 2 and two more partly fractured, for a total length of 186 ft (57 m). The arrest to the east was accomplished by a split-sleeve crack arrestor. This arrestor was a 4 ft (1.2 m) long sleeve made from

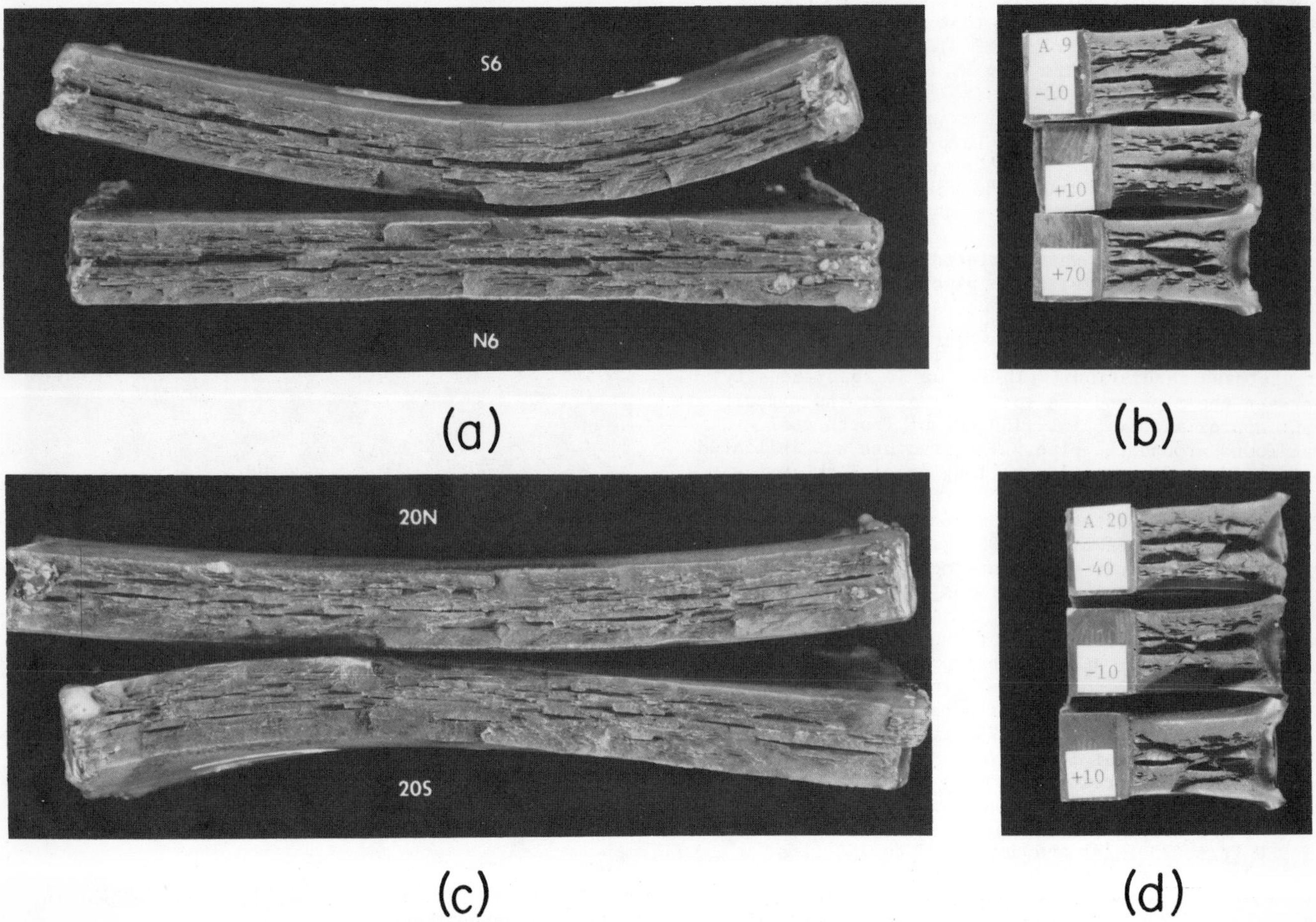

(a) (b)

(c) (d)

Figure 4: Fracture surfaces in pipe lengths A9, A20, and A23 from Experiment 1, and dynamic tear test laboratory specimens

sections of the 48 in. (1220 mm) x 0.72 in. (18 mm) pipe. The fracture extended approximately 6 in. (150 mm) beneath the sleeve before it turned and reversed its direction, extending back to the edge of the sleeve. To the west of the fracture origin, the fracture propagated through two full lengths of pipe and then after propagating approximately 10 ft (3 m) into length B6 the fracture turned into the helical direction, propagated around the pipe and arrested. In this experiment, the fracture propagated at speeds to the east of the origin ranging from 900 to 350 ft/s (275 to 110 m/s) and to the west from the origin at speeds ranging from 800 ft/s

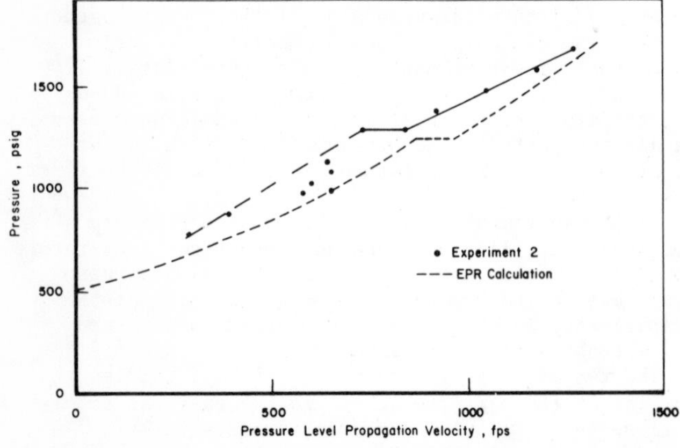

Figure 5: Gas decompression behaviour in Experiment 2

(240 m/s) down to zero.

One half of pipe length B5 (the half away from the origin) had been insulated with the 1 in. (25 mm) thick urethane insulation used in Experiment 1, to evaluate the effect of the insulation on fracture speed. (Note: The soil temperature outside the insulation on this pipe length was 44°F / 7°C). The fracture speeds in B5 in the non-insulated section were 390 ft/s (119 m/s) and in the insulated section ranged from 290 to 400 ft/s (88 to 121 m/s) with some scatter evident. The results do not indicate that the fracture increased in speed in the insulated section and therefore it can be concluded that the insulation did not have a significant effect on fracture speed in Experiment 1. Figure 5 shows the measured decompression obtained from the pressure transducers in Experiment 2. Despite the considerable scatter in the data due to the noise in the pressure transducer signal, a distinct discontinuity was observed in the pressure decay, as expected for a gas which crosses the hydrocarbon dew point boundary during decompression.

Thickness reductions obtained in this experiment ranged from 13 to 18%, typical of those observed in the first experiment. Also, all fracture surfaces exhibited separated fracture appearances, with the exception of pipe length B6, which is shown in Figure 6 along with the fracture surface in pipe length B5 which is typical of that observed in all other pipe lengths. We have no explanation for the lack of separations in the fracture appearance in pipe length B6. [Note that the dynamic tear fracture

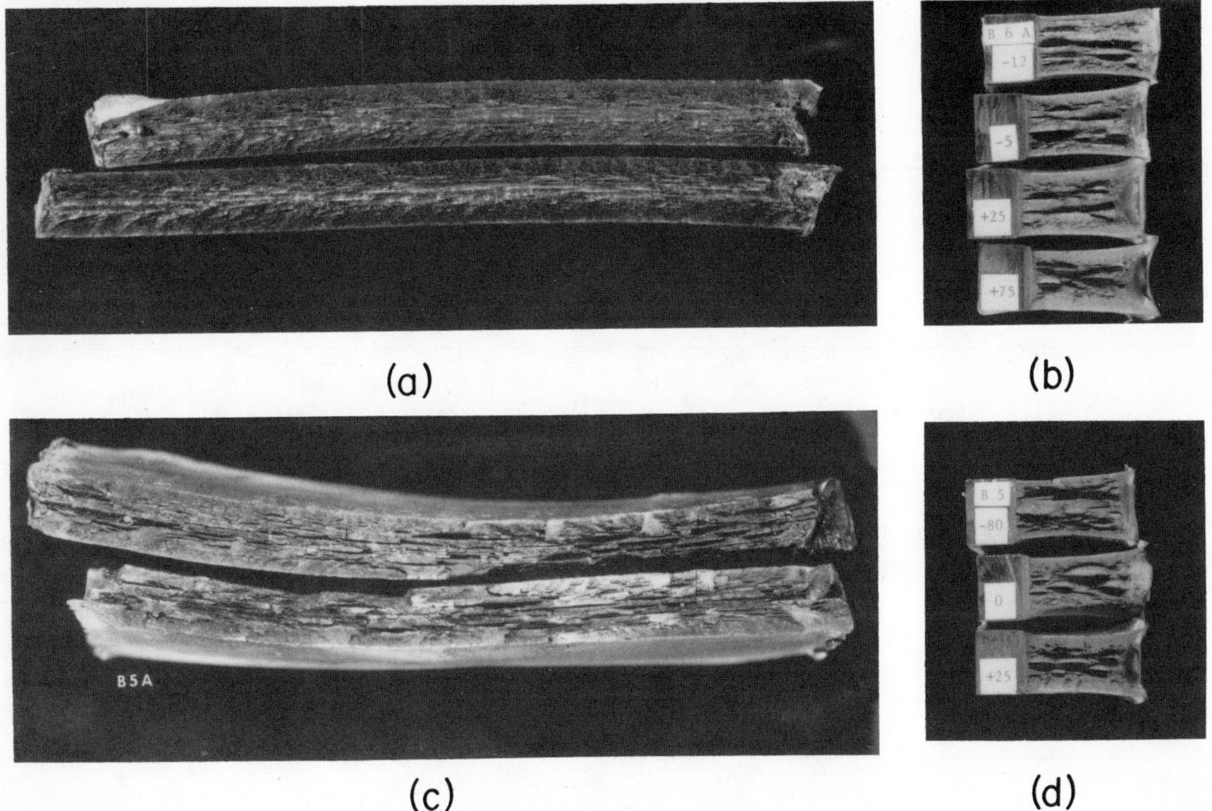

Figure 6; Fracture surface of pipe lengths B6 and B5 from Experiment 2, and dynamic tear test laboratory specimens

surface exhibited a separated fracture appearance not typical of that observed in pipe length B6 in the experiment.]

The purpose of Experiment 3 was to determine the fracture arrest characteristics of split-sleeve crack arrestors and to examine the fracture arrest characteristics of spirally-welded pipe. In this experiment, the girth welds in the test section were modified to be more typical of those expected in construction of the pipeline. All girth welds were made with AWS E-8010 electrodes. No insulation was used in this experiment. The gas composition for this experiment was modified by the addition of approximately 11,300 lb (4,100 kg) of hydrocarbons ranging from C_2 through C_6.

Table 3 shows the pipe layout for Experiment 3 along with the pipe properties. The center seven lengths of pipe, C9 through D5, were considered to be the test section. The "C" sections were spiral weld pipe; the remainder was longitudinally welded. The split-sleeve crack arrestors were placed on pipe lengths D2 and C6.

Experiment 3 was conducted at a pressure of 1680 psig (11.5 MPa) and an average gas temperature of 13°F (-10.5°C). Fifteen to 18 in. (380 to 460 mm) of frozen soil around the pipe existed at the time of the experiment. The fracture pattern is shown in Figure 7. Only the two origin lengths fractured in the primary fracture in this experiment. The girth welds on the ends of the origin lengths fractured before the propagating fractured arrived and arrested the fractures. The momentum of the fractured pipe is believed to be responsible for the extension of the fractures in pipe length D2 from D3. A buckle occurred at the girth weld between D2 and D5 and a fracture reintitiated from the buckle and ran another 21 ft (6.4 m) to the east. The arrest on the east end occurred just before a 4 ft long sleeve on length D7. The three pipe lengths that had propagating shear fractures all had highly separated fracture surfaces. Figure 8 (p. 314) shows fractographs from pipe lengths C1 and D3.

DISCUSSION

The objective of this study was to define the toughness level required of the pipe material to arrest a propagating ductile fracture. In general, the experiments produced more extensive fracture and higher velocity fractures than had been anticipated. A fracture arrest in the middle of a pipe length was achieved only once out of a possible 6 arrests. The reason for this arrest is not understood at this time. The fracture properties of the arrest sections, such as measured by the Charpy V-notch and Dynamic Tear Test, were not distinguishable from pipe lengths through which fractures propagated. The arrest sections did show fewer and smaller sep-

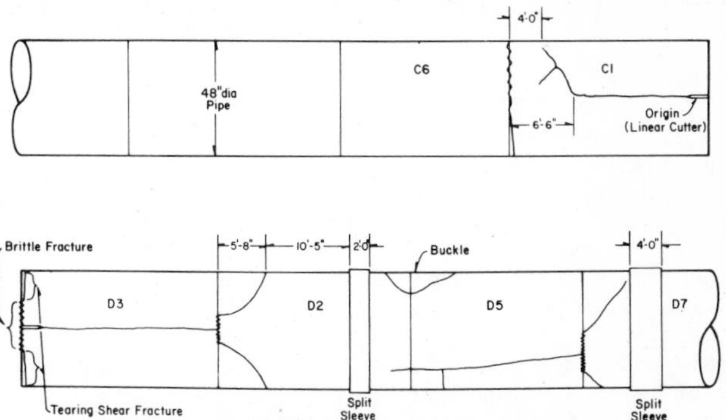

Figure 7: Fracture pattern in Experiment 3

Table 2

Experiment 2 - Pipe Toughness Properties

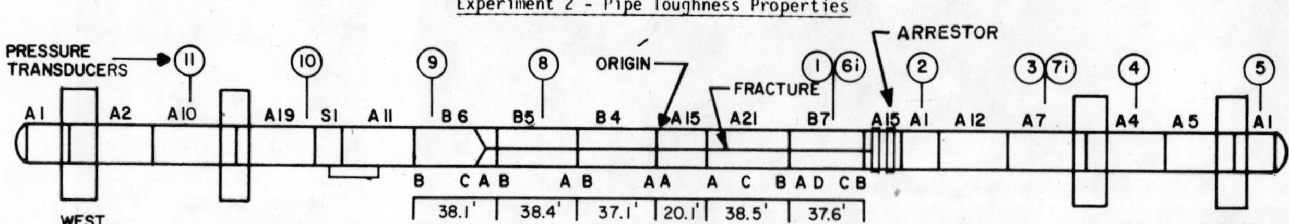

Approx. Sample Position	B6 B	B6 C	B6 A	B5 B	B5 A	B4 A	A15 A	A21 A	A21 C	A21 B	B7 A	B7 D	B7 C	B7 B
Charpy V-Energy [ft lbf/J]														
CV100		79/ 107	53/ 72		64/ 87	46/ 62	57/ 77	57/ 77	68/ 92		81/ 110	95/ 129	46/ 62	
CVI		65/ 88	35/ 47		52/ 71	43/ 58	57/ 77	54/ 73	60/ 81		63/ 85	75/ 102	45/ 61	
CVT		132/ 179	127/ 172		146/ 192	142/ 192	152/ 206	161/ 218	135/ 182		147/ 199	147/ 199	102/ 138	
CVP		136/ 184	132/ 179		155/ 210	142/ 192	152/ 206	161/ 218	138/ 187		156/ 210	160/ 217	130/ 176	
Dynamic Tear Energy [ft lbf/J]														
Energy at test (24°F/-4°C)		835/ 1130	910/ 1230		920/ 1250	870/ 1180	NA	870/ 1180	730/ 990		840/ 1140	870/ 1180	850/ 1150	
Upper Shelf Energy		1015/ 1380	980/ 1330		1040/ 1410	1050/ 1420	NA	1130/ 1530	1000/ 1360		1070/ 1450	1040/ 1410	1030/ 1400	
Mill Tensile Data														
YS [ksi/MPa]	71.3/ 491			71.9/ 496		71.0/ 490	74.5/ 514			73.1/ 504				71.5/ 493
UTS [ksi/MPa]	90.5/ 624			90.3/ 623		88.8/ 612	90.4/ 623			90.5/ 624				89.6/ 618
% elongation in 2 in.	40			40		41	41			42				43
Measured Fracture Speed [ft/s / m/s]			0/0 to 200/ 61		350/ 110	800/ 240 to 500/ 150	900/ 270 to 600/ 180	350/ 110			500/ 150		700/ 210	
Required CV, calculated per hypothesis (appendix)														
Backfill [ft lbf/J]			162/ 220		92/ 125	58/ 79		92/ 125			55/ 75		33/ 45	
No backfill [ft lbf/J]			207/ 280		147/ 199	98/ 133		147/ 199			87/ 118		55/ 75	

arations on the fracture surface tnan did other pipes, but this does not seem to be predictable from the property tests that were made. In Figures 4, 6, and 8, the separations evident on the fracture surface from the pipe experiments are all of the same intensity as the DT laboratory test specimen with the exception of pipe B6 in Experiment 2, where the fracture surface of the pipe exhibited substantially fewer and smaller separations than the DT specimens.

Differences from Earlier Experiments

Several parameters were different in these experiments to those of previous full-scale experiments and with so many variables in these parameters it is only possible to speculate on the effect of each. The pressure level of 1680 psig (11.6 MPa) producing a stress level of 56 ksi (390 MPa) in the 48 in. (1220 mm) OD by 0.720 in. (18 mm) wall thickness pipe is at the extreme limit of previous full-scale experiments, in terms of pressure and stress level, and is beyond the limit of previous data in terms of wall thickness. The temperature is below that for previous all-ductile experiments. Prior ductile fracture experiments have not been insulated and did not have frozen ground formed around the pipe.

The decompression behaviour of the gas in these experiments is considerably different from that in prior experiments in that a constant pressure level propagates in the pipe ahead of, or with, the fracture front in a certain speed range. It appears that, because the decompressed pressure level is quite different for two-phase gas flow through the propagating opening as opposed to single phase all-gas outflow, the driving force on the fracture is increased and could account for the longer and higher-velocity fractures of these experiments.

The fracture speed behavour in the origin pipe length was different in Experiment 2 from those observed in Experiments 1 and 3. In Experiment 2 the fracture speed peaked at a high velocity close to the origin and then dropped to a lower velocity just before entering the adjacent pipe length. This is the generally-observed behaviour of past full-scale experiments with all-vapor gas decompression. In Experiments 1 and 3 the fracture speeds in the origin lengths were high and constant throughout the complete pipe length, similar to the peak velocity obtained

Table 3

Experiment 3 - Pipe Toughness Properties

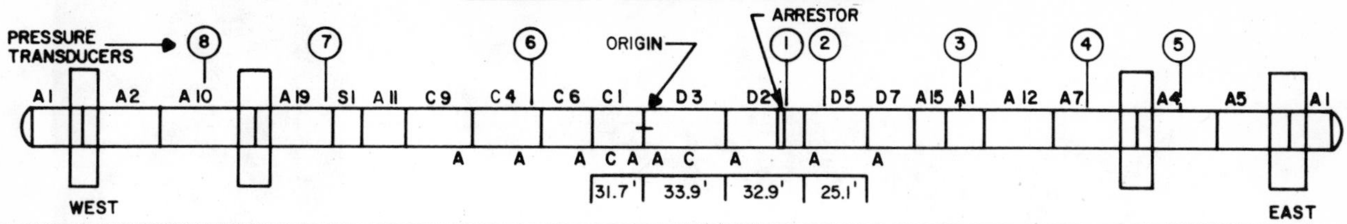

PRESSURE TRANSDUCERS ⑧ ⑦ ⑥ ORIGIN ARRESTOR ① ② ③ ④ ⑤

A1 A2 A10 A19 S1 A11 C9 C4 C6 C1 D3 D2 D5 D7 A15 A1 A12 A7 A4 A5 A1

A A A C A A C A A A

31.7' 33.9' 32.9' 25.1'

WEST EAST

Approx. Sample Position	C9		C4		C6		C1		D3		D2		D5		D7	
	B	A	B	A	B	A	B	A	A	B	A	B	A	C	A	B
Charpy-V Energy [ft lbf/J]																
CV100		74/ 100		87/ 118		66/ 89		42/ 57	45/ 61		70/ 95		70/ 95		52/ 71	
CVI		54/ 73		50/ 68		47/ 64		42/ 57	47/ 64		53/ 72		65/ 88		52/ 71	
CVT		110/ 149		100/ 136		75/ 102		135/ 184	139/ 188		110/ 149		137/ 186		128/ 173	
CVP		132/ 179		135/ 184		75/ 102		140/ 190	139/ 188		124/ 168		137/ 186		128/ 173	
Dynamic Tear Energy [ft lbf/J]																
Energy at Test (13°F/-10.5°C)		600/ 814		680/ 922		630/ 854		680/ 922	810/ 1100		790/ 1070	790/	870/ 1180		690/ 935	
Upper Shelf Energy		NA		NA		900/ 1220		NA	100/ 1360		875/ 1190		935/ 1270		820/ 1120	
Mill Tensile Data																
YS [ksi/MPa]	85.1/ 587		82.7/ 570		84.2/ 581		79.8/ 550			74.3/ 512		75.2/ 518		78.5/ 541		75.8/ 523
UTS [ksi/MPa]	114.6/ 790		112.7/ 760		110.0/ 758		108.3/ 746			89.2/ 615		89.4/ 616		93.0/ 641		97.6/ 673
% elongation in 2 in.	35		33		35		38			42		42		36		34
Measured Fracture Speed [ft/s / m/s]								870/ 265	700/ 213							
Required CV, calculated per hypothesis(appendix)																
Backfill [ft lbf/J]								25/ 34	35/ 48							
No backfill [ft lbf/J]								45/ 61	60/ 81							

in Experiment 2. These peak speeds have not been included in the correlations used to develop the AGA-BCL ductile fracture (2) hypothesis. The peak speeds produced in the origin lengths are generally, but not always, more closely predicted by assuming non-backfilled conditions and full initial pressure at the crack tip on the assumption that insufficient time existed for decompression to occur. There are two possible explanations for this behaviour, viz. the warmer temperature and minimal frozen ground in Experiment 2, and the decompressed pressure level and the velocities of the constant pressure level on the decompression curve being higher in Experiment 2 than in Experiments 1 and 3. To explain the differences, one can only be speculative at this time. As an example, the greater thickness of frozen backfill may have modified the decompression behaviour behind the crack tip on the fracture flaps, or the frozen backfill in Experiments 1 and 3 may have reduced the "effective" inertial mass of the moving pipe in the vicinity of the crack tip.

Fracture Behaviour and the Ductile Fracture Hypothesis

Tables 1 to 3 summarize the Charpy-V energies calculated from the AGA-BCL hypothesis (see Appendix) as "required" Charpy energies for the fracture speeds measured in the pipe experiments. These calculations are based on both backfill and no-backfill conditions. Figures 9 and 10 present plots of these "required" Charpy energies at the measured fracture speeds versus the measured Charpy energies of the pipe lengths involved in the experiments. In each figure, the measured Charpy energy at the test temperature, CVT, and the measured minimum Charpy energy at the 100% shear area, CV100, are presented. It should be noted that, in general, there is a considerable range between the CV100 energy and the CVT energy for most pipe lengths. This range reflects the amount of increase in shelf energy that occurs between the point of 100% shear and the point where the energy begins to remain constant. In general, the CVT energies are very close to the Charpy energies on the upper plateau, CVP.

In Figure 9, it can be observed that most of the values of CV100 lie above the one-to-one agreement line, which indicates that the measured fracture speed was higher than would be predicted using the measured Charpy energy of that pipe length. The required Charpy energies based on backfill conditions are, in general, significantly lower than the measured

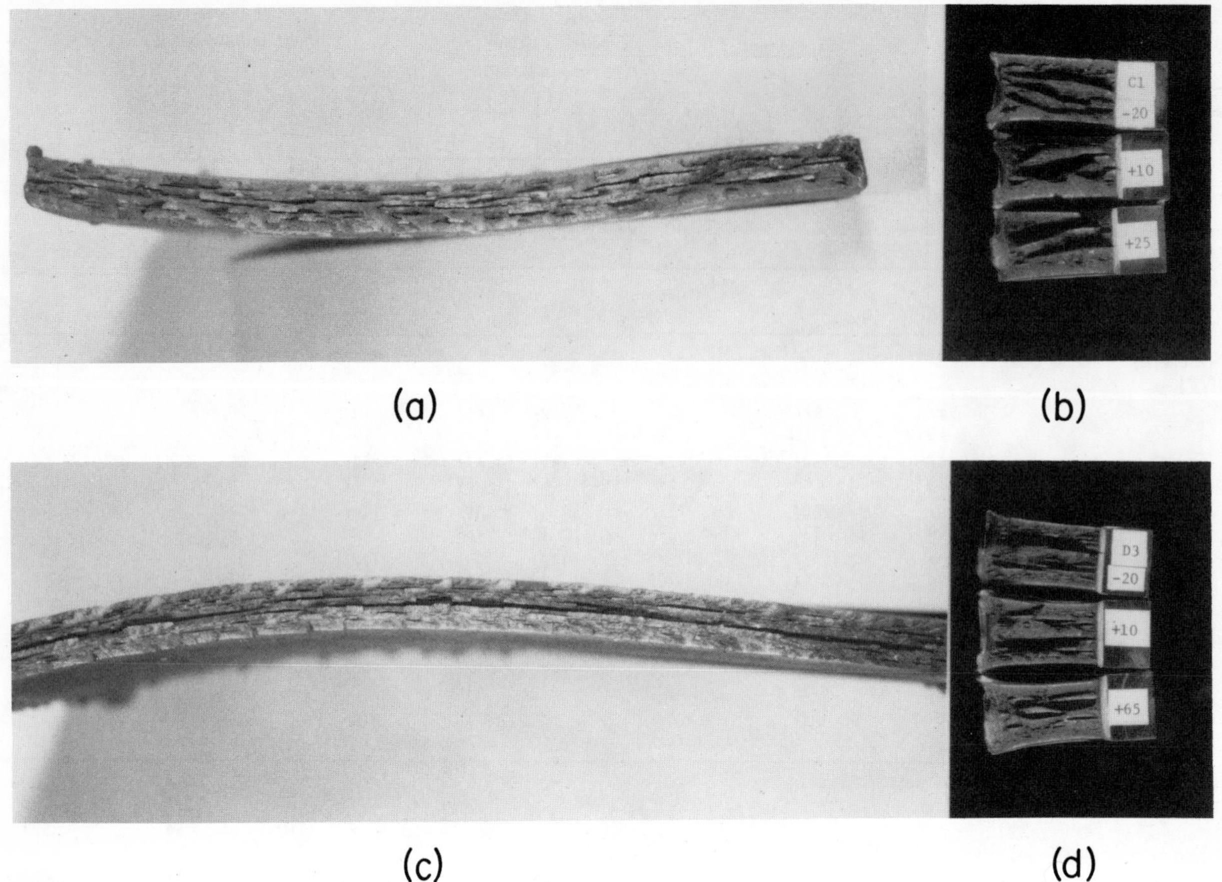

Figure 8: Fracture surfaces in pipe lengths C1 and D3 from Experiment 3 and dynamic tear test laboratory specimens

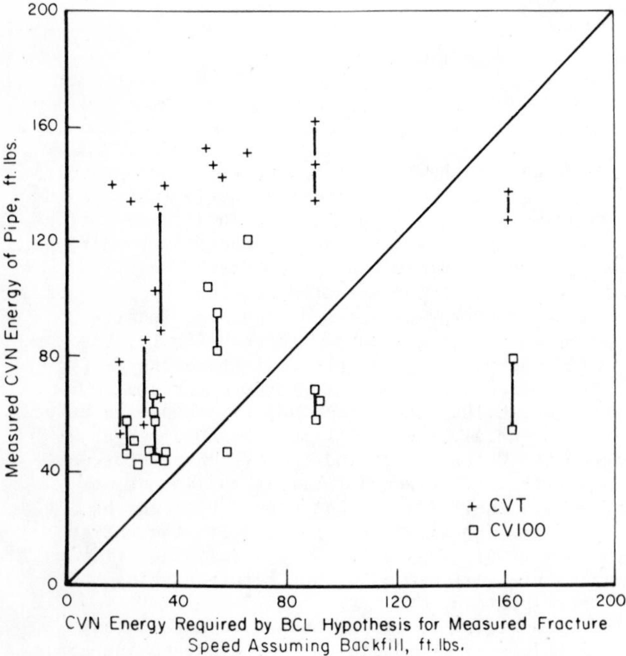

Figure 9: Comparison of Charpy energy prediction based on BCL-hypothesis with measured Charpy energies, assuming backfill

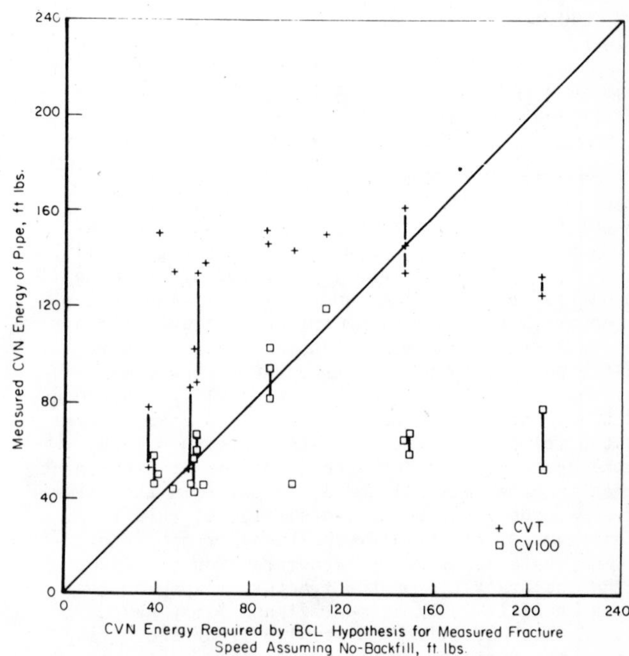

Figure 10: Comparison of Charpy energy prediction based on BCL-hypothesis with measured Charpy energies, assuming no backfill

energies of the pipe lengths.

Figure 10 is similar to Figure 9, except it is based on no-backfill conditions. In this figure, the required Charpy energies are in reasonable agreement with the CV100 energies measured on the pipe lengths. The one major exception is pipe length B6 which has a required no-backfill Charpy energy of 207 ft lbf (280 J). For this pipe length, the measured energies, even the Charpy plateau energies, are significantly below the energy required by the BCL hypothesis. Furthermore, the one-to-one agreement line either crosses close to the CV100 energy or between the CV100 energy and the CVT energy, which indicates that some of the pipe lengths are exhibiting greater toughness than the minimum CV100 energy.

Figure 11 shows the DTT energy at the test temperature plotted against measured fracture velocity for the experiments. Fracture velocities from arrest to 700 ft/s (210 m/s) occur at energy levels of about 850 ft lbf (1150 J). This indicates that the DTT energy does not correlate consistently with behaviour in this instance. The data was also examined to evaluate whether the lowest energy at 100% shear in the DT test provided a better correlation. It is concluded that most of the DTT energy values are close to the DT energy at the lowest temperature for 100% shear, and thus the correlation would not be improved.

Arrest at Mechanical Arrestors

Two other types of arrest have occurred in these experiments. One of these is arrest of a fracture by the circumferential fracture of a girth weld before the propagating fracture arrives at the weld. The other type of arrest was caused by a split sleeve placed on the pipe during construction. The arrest of a fracture at a girth weld has been observed in a number of past full-scale experiments. In this instance, weld metal has a dynamic transition temperature above the test temperature and a static transition temperature below it. In this situation, under normal loading conditions the weld will behave in a ductile manner, but under the influence of the large plastic zone propagating ahead of a fracture, the girth weld fails in a brittle manner due to the high strain rate associated with dynamic loading.

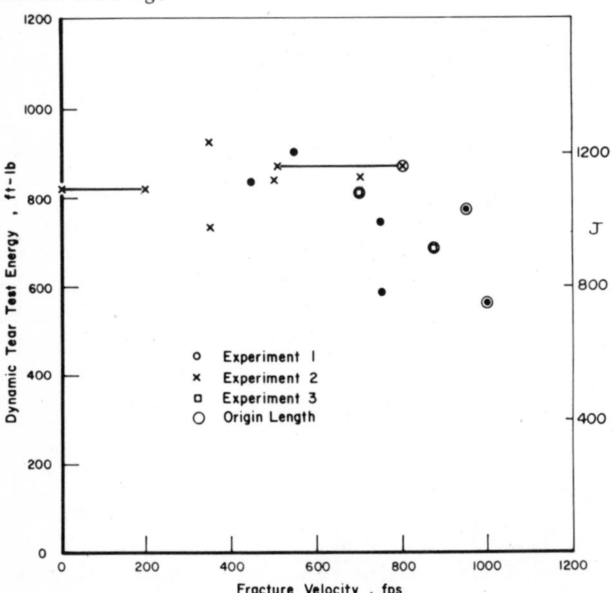

Figure 11: Dynamic tear test energy as a function of fracture velocity

The arrests caused by split sleeves are believed to be due to a two-fold mechanism: 1) the sleeve carried part of the pressure load so that the crack running beneath the sleeve suddenly sees a reduced stress level, and 2) the additional stress concentration due to bulging at the crack tip is reduced by the presence of the sleeve.

The experiment 2 data seem to be more widely scattered and only generally exhibit the expected trend of low energy associated with high fracture velocity. The one pipe length in which the fracture arrested (length B6) in Experiment 2 would not be expected to arrest based on the CV100 energy value. The full-scale fracture appearance of this pipe length did not show large deep separations like the other fracture surfaces, suggesting that the behaviour probably should be represented by the Charpy plateau energy. Even if the plateau energy (CVP) of pipe length B6 (132 ft lbf/177 J) is used, arrest would not be predicted using the backfill condition.

The sudden configurational change in Experiment 2 may influence the arrest, in that the last 18 ft (5.5 m) of the fracture propagation before entering pipe length B6 went through a section of pipe length B5, insulated with 1 in. (25 mm) thick urethane which had a 44°F (7°C) soil temperature outside the insulation. There were, however, no fracture velocity changes in pipe length B5 in travelling from the non-insulated to the insulated section, which suggests that the insulation did not influence the fracture behaviour. If the arrest in pipe length B6 is strictly due to the toughness of the pipe material, then a further study is necessary to explain why the B6 fracture surface showed fewer separations than the other pipe sections.

CONCLUSIONS

The fracture lengths and fracture velocities produced in these experiments suggest that under the imposed conditions of frozen soil, high pressure, low temperature, and proposed gas composition, unstable ductile fracture can occur in the materials examined. Fracture velocities are generally greater than predicted using CV100 Charpy energy levels or the Charpy energy at temperature. The measured fracture velocities in these experiments were generally higher than those predicted using the AGA-BCL ductile fracture hypothesis. The reason for the discrepancy is not understood at this time. These experiments have shown that crack arrestors are a reliable method of controlling ductile fracture propagation.

Acknowledgment

The authors are indebted to Canadian Arctic Gas Study Group for their support in conducting this research and permission to publish the results. In addition they want to thank F. S. Somerville, T. C. Slimmon, E. L. Von Rosenberg and A. W. Stanzel for their assistance. They are also indebted to the Battelle field staff of J. W. Garrabrant, R. H. Wright and G. A. Rue for their perseverance in conducting these experiments.

APPENDIX

AGA-BCL Ductile Fracture Hypothesis

A key part of this paper, and other papers in this conference, involves a comparison of the

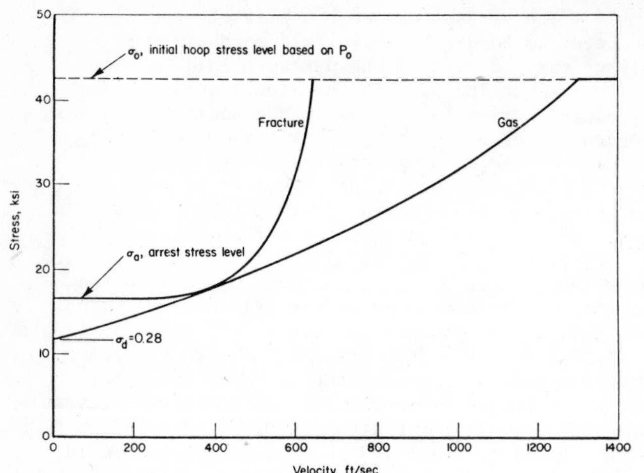

Figure A-1: Stress-velocity relationship for fracture arrest

fracture results of experiments on line pipe with the prediction of the fracture behaviour using an empirical model developed by the Battelle Columbus Laboratories for the American Gas Association. The hypothesis consists of an empirical model for predicting the fracture behaviour, i.e., fracture speed as a function of the decompressed stress or pressure at the crack tip. Arrest or propagation can be predicted by comparing the fracture behaviour curve with that calculated for the gas decompression behaviour, as shown in Figure A-1. If the curves intersect, then the fracture would be expected to propagate, if the curves are just tangent or if the fracture curve lies above the gas decompression curve, then the fracture would be expected to arrest.

There are two basic assumptions involved in this formulation of the fracture problem. The first is that the fracture arrest toughness is the same as the fracture initiation toughness. The basis is that both are quasi-static processes and thus the toughness should be similar. The second assumption is that a propagating crack in a pipeline after it has propagated some distance reaches a steady state condition and thus has an "effective" crack length which is independent of the total crack length from the origin of the fracture.

The hypothesis includes the contribution of pressure behind the crack tip through a maximum effective bulging stress concentration factor, M_T, and a maximum effective half crack length, c (in.), that is propagating with a fracture. These maximum effective values were defined through correlations with full-scale results to be M_T = 3.33 and $c/\sqrt{Rt}$ = 3.0. The following formula (2) relates the ductile fracture arrest stress, σ_a (ksi), with the Charpy plateau energy level CVP (ft lbf) or CV100 (ft lbf).

$$12\ CVP/A_c\bar{\sigma}^2\sqrt{Rt} = 24/\pi\ .\ \ell n\ \sec\ [\pi/2.(3.33\sigma_a/\bar{\sigma})] \quad \text{(A-1)}$$

The fracture velocity is given by

$$V_f = 47.8\ [\bar{\sigma}\ /\ \sqrt{R_{max}}]\ [(\sigma_d/\sigma_a)-1]^{1/6} \quad \text{(A-2)}$$

where the ductile fracture arrest stress σ_a is obtained from equation (A-1). Equation (A-2) is in terms of R_{max} (ft lbf) for a full-size Charpy specimen and the constant 47.8 is for the fracture of backfilled pipe. For nonbackfilled pipe, the constant is 70.2, as determined from experimental data.

The gas decompression relationship for gas that decompresses in the vapor phase is given by

NOMENCLATURE

A_c	Fracture area of CVN specimens
c	one-half the total notch length
CVN	Charpy V-notch impact test specimen
CVP	Charpy plateau (shelf) energy
CVT	Charpy energy at the temperature of the full-scale pipe experiment
CV100	Minimum Charpy energy of the lowest temperature specimen exhibiting 100% shear area
CVI	Energy at 100% shear on a plot of energy versus shear area
M	Stress concentration due to bulging around an axial crack in a cylinder; [M times the nominal hoop stress in the cylinder represents the equivalent gross stress applied to the same crack in an infinitely large flat plate]
M_T	The "Folias Correction" (4), M for through-wall axial cracks in cylinders; for $0 < c\sqrt{RT} < 3.0$, a close fit to Folias' accurate theory is given by $M_T = [1 + 1.255\ c^2/Rt\ \ 0.0135\ (c^4/R^2t^2)]^{0.5}$
P_o	Initial pressure
P_d	Decompressed pressure level
R	Pipe radius
R	Transverse energy required to advance the crack front based on a full-size Charpy specimen
R_{max}	The energy required to advance a 100% ductile crack equivalent to transverse Charpy plateau energy, based on a full-size specimen
t	Pipe wall thickness
V_a	Acoustic velocity of gas at initial conditions
V_d	Propagation velocity at decompressed pressure level (P_d)
V_f	Fracture velocity
Y	Transverse yield strength of pipe material
σ_o	Initial circumferential or hoop stress, $\sigma_o = PR/t$
σ_a	Arrest hoop stress
σ_d	Decompressed stress level
$\bar{\sigma}$	Flow stress, $\bar{\sigma}$ = Y + 10

$$P_d/P_o = \sigma_d/\sigma_o = [V_d/6V_a + 5/6] \quad \text{(A-3)}$$

For other types of decompression, such as experienced in the experiments described in this paper, sophisticated computer analyses are necessary to predict the gas decompression behaviour.

REFERENCES

1. D. S. Dabkowski, P. J. Konkol and M. F. Baldy, Metals Engin. Quarterly, 1976 (2), pp. 22-32.
2. W. A. Maxey, 5th Symposium on Line Pipe Research, American Gas Association, Catalog No. L30174, 1974, pp. J-1 to J-30.
3. W. A. Maxey, J. F. Kiefner, R. J. Eiber and A. R. Duffy, "Experimental Investigation of Ductile Fractures in Piping", 12th World Gas Conference, Nice, France, 1973.
4. E. S. Folias, Int. J. Fract. Mech., 1965, vol. 1, p. 20.

DISCUSSION

K. R. Perun (Brown and Root): Since a primary objective of the experiments was to determine the pipe toughness properties necessary to arrest a propagating ductile fracture, and a fracture arrest in the pipe material was achieved only once, would you conclude that mechanical crack arrestors are much more feasible than arresting a propagating ductile fracture by increasing the Charpy-V shelf energy of the pipe material?

W. A. Maxey: In this specific instance, mechanical arrestors are a feasible means of arresting a propagating ductile fracture. One of the pipe lengths in these experiments had a CV100 of 120 ft lbf (160 J), which is very high, but it still supported a fracture which propagated at 450 ft/s (140 m/s). In other applications, it may be just as feasible to increase the shelf energy of the pipe material to control fracture propagation in all pipe lengths.

K. R. Perun: As noted, the arrest of a propagating ductile fracture at a girth weld was due to a high strain rate associated with dynamic loading. It appears that an improvement in notch toughness of the weld and heat affected zone is needed to be compatible with the pipe material and raise the weld efficiency. Do you agree?

W. A. Maxey: We do not agree that the notch toughness of the weld and HAZ of the girth welds need be compatible with the dynamic fracture toughness of the pipe material. We see no need for the girth weld to have notch toughness properties sufficient to withstand a propagating ductile fracture. The normal design considerations for girth welds are static, with the only dynamic loading being an earthquake loading which has a strain rate of 10^{-3}/s, which is essentially static. The notch toughness properties of the girth welds in the first and second experiments were not equal to those of the pipe but still did not fracture in the experiments.

J. M. Wallbridge (Foothills Pipe Lines): Your data show a very large difference between CVI and CV100 energy. This indicates to me that insufficient Charpy specimens were tested and too few test temperatures were used and as a result the CV100 energy obtained is too high. Would you agree, and if so would you also agree that this may be the explanation for the higher than expected fracture velocity?

W. A. Maxey: The basic difference between the CVI values and CV100 energy values reported is that the CVI values were determined on the low energy side of the scatterband and the CV100 energy values were picked for the average of the data. We do not believe that additional Charpy specimens would indicate appreciably lower CV100 energy values.

J. M. Wallbridge: You indicated that there was a significant time delay between the arrival of a fracture and time when the pipe is thrown from the ditch in the event of a girth weld failure. If this is the case under test conditions, is not the ejected pipe in many cases subject to a lower pressure force due to the return of the reflected wave from the end of the test section?

If a project is designed using crack arrestors it is likely that a lower toughness pipe will be specified and probably purchased than if the pipeline is designed for fracture control using pipe toughness. Will this lower pipe toughness not result in higher fracture velocities and therefore higher pressures at the crack tip, again increasing the available energy to throw the pipe from the ditch in the event of girth weld failures?

Does the combination of these two effects not mean that there has been insufficient adequate testing to demonstrate that multiple sequential girth weld failures are not a failure mode for pipelines employing crack arrestors?

W. A. Maxey: In the third experiment conducted in the series described in this paper, the fracture arrested at the girth weld at approximately 0.05 s. The major pipe movement occurred sometime between 0.250 and 0.400 s, which occurred before the reflected wave arrived at the girth weld location. Thus in this specific instance the pressure acting on the girth weld is the same pressure level that would have been experienced in a long pipeline. Data from Experiment 3 indicate that the pressure level acting on the fractured girth weld at the time the pipe length started to lift from the ditch was approximately 600 psi (410 kPa).

The pressure acting on the pipe at a girth weld arrest location is not dependent upon the speed of the fracture approaching that point, but only upon the pressure for a zero velocity crack. Thus the toughness of the linepipe does not control the pressure at a girth weld arrest location. The second point is that whether a pipe lifts from the ditch as a result of a girth weld arrest is a function of the configuration of the fractured end of the pipe. If the pipe fracture configuration is a complete circular severance, there is no unbalanced force due to the pressure acting on the end of the pipe to lift the pipe from the ditch. In the experiments that have been conducted the fractures at the girth welds have not been complete circular severances, but have been nonsymmetrical which provided an unbalanced force and caused the pipe to lift from the ditch.

Finally, the key factor in controlling whether a girth weld will fracture ahead of a propagating ductile fracture and thereby arrest the propagating ductile fracture is a function of the fracture properties, toughness and transition temperature of the girth weld and the number of defects contained in the girth weld. Since both of these factors will be controlled in an actual pipeline, we do not believe that pipe toughness level contributes to the potential for girth weld failures or fracture arrests.

E. Shelton (Alberta Gas Trunk Line): One of the most significant and reassuring results of both the AISI and Battelle tests is the difficulty in getting fractures to propagate, particularly in the high toughness materials currently being specified for pipe. As Shoemaker pointed out, there have been only two shear fractures in actual service (sic) and in pipe of considerably lower toughness than generally used. Does a significant difference relate to the idealized type of flaw which is initiated in the full scale tests (i.e. top of pipe, axial orientation) which would not generally occur in actual initiation situations?

W. A. Maxey: The observation that a number of ductile propagating fractures have occurred in service is an indication that fractures can be initiated in service. I would think that the initiation site and type used in our tests would, however, represent a "worst case" situation.

T. C. Slimmon (Northern Engineering Services): I would like to comment on the number of long shear fractures that have occurred. I think Shoemaker said that the two long shear fractures in the late 1960's started the research work, not that there have only been two fractures, as claimed by Shelton in his discussion. We are aware of seven or eight long shear fractures (over 300 ft or 90 m) that have occurred in Canada and the U.S.

Please comment on the effect of the crack arrestor in the third experiment on the reinitiation of the fracture. Did it have any effect?

W. A. Maxey: The crack arrestor in the third experiment had no effect on the reinitiation of the fracture. The fracture reinitiated because the pipe section containing the crack arrestor lifted up in the air, causing a buckle in the pipe and the fracture reinitiated from the buckle. The observation that the buckle did not form at the crack arrestor is an indication that the crack arrestor did not adversely affect the behaviour of the pipe.

D. J. Burns (University of Waterloo): If a crack arrestor comprises a wire wrap which is stiff relative to the pipe, it will produce very high longitudinal bending stresses in the pipe, and one could then expect the fracture to turn. Is this the basic philosophy of the design of these crack arrestors, rather than stopping a lip from flying up?

W. A. Maxey: I do not believe the design of crack arrestors is as yet that well understood, or optimized.

M. R. Krishnadev (Laval University): Do you think that the use of mechanical arrestors should be made compulsory and be included in the specifications for large diameter pipelines?

W. A. Maxey: We do not believe that mechanical arrestors should be made compulsory on large diameter pipelines. The need for mechanical arrestors depends upon the ability to control the fracture with the inherent fracture toughness properties of the material. It is our opinion that each pipeline should be designed to control the fracture in the best manner, technically and economically.

M. R. Krishnadev: What type of materials, in terms of composition, strength and toughness, would you advocate? What should be their size and spacing?

W. A. Maxey: The types of materials, composition, size and spacing of crack arrestors is a subject that has not been optimized at the present time. In the specific study described, half-diameter length sleeves were found to arrest propagating ductile fractures and in other studies wire wrap has been shown to arrest propagating ductile fractures. There are other combinations that should work equally well but have not been investigated.

F. S. Somerville (Canadian Arctic Gas Study): If it is necessary to use the artificial CV100 energy together with the non-backfilled condition to enable the Battelle hypothesis to fit an Arctic burst test, do we in fact have a valid method for the design of Arctic pipelines?

W. A. Maxey: We believe that the Battelle hypothesis which has been developed provides a preliminary design tool for looking at the fracture toughness requirements for Arctic pipelines. At the present stage of development of the hypothesis we do not believe that it can be applied to the design of an Arctic pipeline without experimentally verifying the results from the hypothesis.

F. S. Somerville: Would Kent Shoemaker care to comment on the utility of the CV100 concept for ductile fracture arrest?

A. K. Shoemaker (United States Steel): I think the point has been made that the concept, as far as the Arctic pipe is concerned, simply does not work out. I agree with that.

E. Kranz (Mannesmannrohren-Werke): What would you expect from a so-called "backfill" of about 200 ft (60 m) of water in an underwater pipeline?

W. A. Maxey: We do not know the effect of water as a backfill on a pipeline. We would speculate that it would behave the same as if it were backfilled with dirt, but do not have any data to substantiate this speculation.

C. A. Parrini (Italsider): I would like to have your and Kent Shoemaker's comments on possible behaviour of quenched and tempered steels for each of initiation, propagation and arrest of fracture.

W. A. Maxey: The initiation toughness data that we have developed for quenched and tempered materials follows the same relationship and behaviour pattern as as-rolled or control-rolled materials. We do not have any full-scale information on the propagation behaviour of quenched and tempered materials, except for some relatively old data on experimental quenched and tempered materials with very low toughness levels. This old data is of limited value because the material had such low toughness levels and such a non-uniform structure.

A. K. Shoemaker: In about the second test we ever ran, we looked at 48 in. (1220 mm) quenched and tempered pipe, of about 90 ksi (620 MPa) yield and approximately, as I recall, 58 ft lbf (79 J) Charpy-V energy. It behaved in accordance with the predictions being only a very marginal situation, based on toughness. It is primarily a matter of toughness. However, those early tests had problems, and should not be relied upon.

W. M. Drope (Northern Engineering Services): Over the years, I have experienced many gas line operating failures, two of which were "high frequency" with the accompanying sine wave brittle tearing. (This is a far worse type of running failure than we have been discussing here). I am reminded that at least three of the four termination points were in heavy wall cased crossings. It would appear that maybe we have had crack arrestors since Day 1 of our industry; just not properly spaced.

Would it not be possible for those who keep such records to see how many running failures have run through cased crossings? This could add to our knowledge.

R. J. Cooke (National Energy Board): During the course of this conference, considerable attention has been devoted to methods of designing gas pipelines such that unstable ductile crack propagation can be arrested. Papers by Somerville and Wallbridge have indicated something of the design approach adopted by two proposed northern projects, through the selection of theoretically self-arresting pipe or by the use of mechanical crack arrestors. The paper by Eiber and Maxey has indicated that self-arrest through notch toughness selection may not always be possible and, along with Parrini and Shoemaker, has discussed the effectiveness of mechanical crack arrestor designs. However, little attention has been given to the design philosophy behind adopting this approach in the first place.

In order to place this design approach in perspective, one should first assess the probable need for fracture arrest. The northern pipelines, for which crack arrest designs might be considered will likely employ the toughest and most completely inspected pipe that is commercially available in North America. This toughness and testing, the remote location and the proposed use of sophisticated on-line inspection make the probability of fracture initiation very low, particularly in relation to a conventional pipeline. Even if initiation does occur, the low historical incidence of long ductile failures and the known function of random high toughness pipe joints, circumferential welds, weights, anchors and bends as built-in crack arrestors, suggests that most such failures will be relatively short and within some length where the repair time (or relationship to overall reliability) is independent of length. From this it can be concluded that the possibility of a long failure of unpredictable length is remote even in the absence of design measures for crack arrest. However, the possibility is not entirely negligible. Therefore, the need for designing for crack arrest must be decided on whether the implications of unpredictable long fractures are such that increased or absolute reliability, safety and security of gas supply must be provided. Such a need can be visualized in an area of heavy population density where safety is the predominant consideration, or in an unlooped, remote pipeline having a large or total market dependence. The presently proposed northern pipelines may fall into the latter category although the short term use of conventional supplies as an emergency alternative and the longer term possibility of looping should be considered.

Assuming that need for absolute or predictable reliability can be established, it is of interest to discuss the potential that current approaches to crack arrest have in achieving this. The results of Eiber and Maxey suggest that designing self-arresting northern pipelines through toughness selection will not provide this assurance. Revisions to the currently proposed relationships along with additional full scale testing of candidate 42 in. (1070 mm) or 48 in. (1220 mm) diameter pipe materials is necessary before this approach meets the design requirement. On the other hand, a variety of mechanical crack arrestor designs have been demonstrated, but the full scale testing has also shown that re-initiation or by-passing of such devices cannot be discounted.

In conclusion, it appears that the current approaches to fracture arrest only serve to diminish an already remote possibility of very long fractures. While the use of these approaches may be entirely justified on this basis when relative cost is assessed, they do not provide absolute and predictable reliability within the pipeline itself. If absolute security of supply is required, this may be best obtained independently of any single pipeline. For the case of northern pipeline projects, the development of storage facilities either in Alberta or closer to markets may better provide the desired security.

SESSION SUMMARY

D. J. Burns

These sessions have considered papers on the fracture-safe design of valves, pipelines and structural elements for the Arctic.

The papers on valves concentrate on the design of materials, metallic and non-metallic. They provide some guidance on the pragmatic choice of body materials for impact strength and corrosion resistance and of seal materials for strength and chemical resistance to hydrocarbons.

Three of the five papers on line-pipe steels, all from CANMET, Ottawa, were concerned with the origins of damage to a pipeline and by implication, possible effects on fracture initiation. One paper considered field damage inflicted by construction equipment whereas two others concentrated on sulphide stress cracking, and the environmental acceleration of crack growth by cyclic loading. In the discussions of the latter two papers, some argued that the test conditions were not representative of service conditions, and therefore, the results could be misleading.

Two papers discuss the use of acoustic emission for the detection of flaws in components intended for Arctic service. Both papers provide only an introduction to the problems of applying the technique in the field. Those who wish to obtain a broader picture should read ASTM Special Technical Publication 571, 1975, entitled "Monitoring Structural Integrity by Acoustic Emission".

Two papers in these sessions considered the choice of materials for support structures, buildings, bridges, and storage tanks. The paper from Nippon Steel illustrates the advantages of one particular steel with low temperature, brittle fracture, bend-tests on full-scale welded beam. Kaufman provides an introduction to aluminum alloys for Arctic applications. It should be read in conjunction with the paper by Tenge and Solli (p. 125) on the application of fracture mechanics for the design and construction of liquid natural gas tanks in ships. These two papers illustrate how fracture mechanics has been used in the quality control of these very large structures. Information on other materials used for such tanks, e.g., 9% nickel and 5% nickel steels can be found in ASTM Special Technical Publication 579, 1975, "Properties of Materials for Liquid Natural Gas Tankage".

The papers by Shoemaker et al. and by Eiber and Maxey presenting the results of full-scale studies of running fractures in pipelines, along with the paper by Parrini et al. (p. 166) presented earlier, are particularly interesting because they illustrate the use of mechanical crack arrestors and discuss the influence of frozen backfill and pipe mass on crack arrest. They also serve to emphasize Hahn's caution in his introduction to the sessions (p. 224) that the problem of crack arrest in pipes is not fully understood.

SOME FINAL REFLECTIONS

J. Convey

When one begins to look at the arguments pro and con as to what materials we're going to use in Arctic development there remains many unanswered questions. But it is in conferences such as this where we manage to get together and discuss the state of the art and the depth of our knowledge with respect to what is needed if we're going to open up the Arctic resources. It was mentioned in one of the papers that quite a lot of people went into northern Canada, for a short while then they would leave things for the eskimos to sort out. I remember my first visit into the Arctic, up in the northwestern part of Ungarva. We landed at the airport and were met by eskimos individually driving jeeps and dressed in G.I. uniforms. Now the town of Chimo in 1948 was a Canadian airport but it had been a United States airport during World War II and was the refuelling base for the bombers that were being delivered to Russia. When the war ended the USA withdrew from Chimo and the eskimos in the area took over most of the living quarters and they made full use of a mountain of gasoline in drums. It was no longer fit for aviation, but it was interesting to see the eskimos riding around in the bay with outboard motors. Their only use for native kyaks was to put on a demonstration for visitors such as us. But there they were and it came under the control of one man and he carefully rationed out that gasoline. They still have some, it was mentioned that it ran out in 1963, but it has not run out, they still have some. In addition, their families were living in homes in which they had frigidaires and what caught my eye was the ladies wearing their mukluks and furs, but they had beautiful cotton print dresses over the top of them. And this in a sense gives you some idea of the awakening of the Arctic, the people themselves. They are expecting a fair share of what is going on in our Northern Development. We expect to open up the Arctic but in opening it up, we have recognized during the discussions this week the problems that are ahead of us, not only in Canada but in other Arctic areas, and I can assure you the quality of the papers which you have given and discussed is the sort of working atmosphere, the sort of information which is being looked for. Alone we cannot do it, collectively we can and in this way I sincerely hope that this Conference will be succeeded within a few years, at which time we will be able to discuss not a test five-mile pipeline, but how a 1500 mile 48 in. pipeline has succeeded. And to you, gentlemen, we say thank you for coming here and giving us of your time, your talents and your knowhow. Thank you.

AUTHOR INDEX

Page numbers underlined refer to major contributions.

SUBJECT INDEX

G

H

Q

R

S